TEXTBOOK OF CYTOLOGY

TEXTBOOK OF Cytology

SECOND EDITION

WALTER V. BROWN

Department of Botany
University of Texas
Austin, Texas

ELDRIDGE M. BERTKE

Department of Zoology
Arizona State University
Tempe, Arizona

with 470 *illustrations*

THE C. V. MOSBY COMPANY

SAINT LOUIS 1974

SECOND EDITION

Printed in the United States of America

Distributed in Great Britain by Henry Kimpton, London

Library of Congress Cataloging in Publication Data

Brown, Walter Varian, 1913-
Textbook of cytology.

Includes bibliographies.
1. Cytology. I. Bertke, Eldridge Melvin, 1920- joint author. II. Title.
[DNLM: 1. Cytology. QH581 B88lt 1974]
QH581.2.B76 1974 574.8′7 73-14625
ISBN 0-8016-0831-7

CB/CB/B 9 8 7 6 5 4 3 2 1

PREFACE

Since the publication of the first edition of this book in 1969, cytology in the broad sense, which includes much of cell biology, has continued to advance, slowly in some areas but rapidly in others. In virology, knowledge of chemical and structural variability of the pseudoorganisms, assembly, relations to membranes, and host relations has progressed rapidly. New techniques for staining the heterochromatins of chromosomes and their uses in cytogenetics, especially human cytogenetics, is a new and fast-moving field of cytology. Knowledge of peroxysomes as a class of cytoplasmic organelles, under various names, has expanded considerably. The Kranz syndrome of certain green plants, which includes a new and specialized (although variable) photosynthetic pathway, is also a new and dynamic field of interrelated biochemistry, cytology, and anatomy. The study of microfilaments has taken on new significance in protoplasmic movements of all kinds. The discovery of "reverse transcriptase" has redirected some thinking in the field of replication-transcription-translation models. These are merely samples of recent cytological progress included in this second edition.

As discussed more fully in the preface to the first edition, emphasis continues on the broad and general treatment and the structural aspects of cytology, although the amount of biochemistry has generally been increased. The topics of history and nature of cytology, cell chemistry, and differentiation have been eliminated as specific discussions, and the glossary has not been included. Furthermore, the topics of cytogenetics and reproductive cells have been reduced and combined into one chapter. On the other hand, a new chapter on viruses and Prokaryota has been added, and such topics as ribosomes, mitochondria, microtubules, peroxysomes, and microfilaments have been considerably expanded. All chapters have been brought up-to-date, which required sometimes much and sometimes little modification of the first edition, depending on the amount of recent progress in the specific field.

Again we acknowledge our debt to all the scientists who have built cytology into the biologically fundamental and dynamic field that it is and to all the others, including those who have constructively criticized the first edition. We are especially indebted to our wives, who have aided one way or another in bringing this second edition to completion.

Walter V. Brown
Eldridge M. Bertke

CONTENTS

CHAPTER 1

Cytological techniques

Cells and tissues must be prepared properly for the study of their morphological and chemical organizations. Most often, for a particular type of study to be undertaken, special techniques and procedures are needed to produce the proper results. In fact, knowledge of the chemistry of fixation is most important in the preparation of tissue for cytological studies. This is particularly true for histochemistry, both histochemistry per se and enzyme histochemistry. One must be certain in the case of enzyme histochemical studies that the fixatives used do not appreciably destroy or remove the enzyme activity or mask the reactive sites. Similarly, the proper preparation is equally important for the demonstration as well as identification of various chemical components within the cell.

Generally two avenues of approach can be used for cytological studies: living cells or tissues can be used, or the cells can be killed by chemical fixation.

The study of living cells can be best accomplished by the use of phase-contrast microscopy. At times the light microscope can be used, particularly if vital stains such as trypan blue, Janus green B, neutral red, etc., are used. These stains not only make the cells discernible, but many of the vital stains presently available will also selectively stain specific structures.

Killing the cells by chemical fixation preserves the morphology. After fixation, various specific staining procedures can be used.

FIXATION

Although fresh cells or tissues can be studied by phase-contrast microscopy, living tissues deteriorate rapidly, and permanency cannot be maintained for future reference. In addition, many cytoplasmic and nuclear structures may be ill defined in the living cell, but they can be studied more precisely when stained to produce better definition and contrast. As a result, the tissues used for cytological and histological studies are prepared to overcome some of the disadvantages of living tissues. Preparation of tissue also allows for some degree of permanency.

The most important single step in the preparation of tissues is fixation. Without proper precaution at this stage, alterations in cytological structure can render the tissue unsuitable for subsequent study. Fixation should accomplish the following things:

1. It should kill the cells rapidly so that at the time of microscopic examination it should be reasonably similar to the tissue at the time of killing.
2. It should alter the refractive indices so that the cell organelles and cellular inclusions can be readily seen.
3. It should harden the tissue somewhat so that after embedding the tissue can be cut readily.

At the present time there are numerous kinds of fixatives that can be used. The choice will depend on the nature of the study. For convenience, fixation can be divided into chemical and physical fixation.

Chemical fixation

Chemical fixation is the most commonly used method for the preparation of tissue for cytological as well as histological study. One of the prerequisites of chemical fixatives is that they must rapidly penetrate the tissue to produce the fixation of proteins and/or lipids. Many chemicals, for example, mercury and chromium salts, are excellent fixatives; however, their low rate of penetration in a pure form makes them unsuitable. On the other hand, acetic acid is a rapid penetrant but a poor fixative. Commonly, acetic acid is used in conjunction with a heavy metal salt. The advantage is that the acetic acid can act as a vehicle for the transportation of the heavy metal compound so that excellent fixation can occur. There are a large number of fixatives available for general cytological work as well as for more specialized work in cytochemistry.

Formalin. Formaldehyde, alone or in mixtures, is probably the most widely used chemical for fixing tissue. It does not appreciably shrink or swell the tissues. Its reactions in the tissue are numerous and complex. It can combine with a large number of different kinds of functional groups and, in so doing, can form methylene bonds. For the most part the reaction results from its addition to a compound containing an active hydrogen atom to form hydroxymethyl compounds (French and Edsall, 1945) as follows:

$$RH + HCHO \rightleftharpoons R\text{—}CH_2OH$$

This can further react with another compound to produce a methylene bridging between the two:

$$R\text{—}CH_2OH + R'H \rightleftharpoons R\text{—}CH_2\text{—}R' + H_2O$$

The $-CH_2-$ represents the methylene bridge. According to French and Edsall a number of compounds are available for reaction with aldehyde; this is called *formation.* They include amino, imino, amido, peptide, guanidino, hydroxyl, carboxyl, and sulfhydryl groups, and a number of aromatic compounds. It can readily be seen that with such diversity of reactions numerous cross-linkages can occur between protein groups and readily bind them together to produce good fixation. In addition, it is important to remember that washing after fixation can disrupt many of these bonds and open up reactive groups for histochemical studies.

Usually a 10% solution is used for fixation. This would be roughly a 4% absolute formaldehyde solution, since commercial formaldehyde is only 38% to 40% concentrated. Wolman (1955) studied the reaction of formation and maintained that a neutral or slightly alkaline solution produces the best fixation. At that pH there is rapid depolymerization of formalin to produce the monomers, and the monomer exists in the more hydrated form known as methylene glycol, $CH_2(OH)_2$, which is much more efficient as a fixative.

Several other aldehydes have been utilized for fixation. Of particular importance is glutaraldehyde. Not only is the substance good for general fixation but it is also an excellent fixative for electron microscopy. It has an additional quality of not interfering with enzyme sites for subsequent study in enzyme histochemistry (Sabitini et al., 1963). Glutaraldehyde is a five-carbon compound containing two aldehyde groups. It is perhaps for this reason that there is increase in cross-linking between protein groups to produce excellent fixation.

Metal ions. Metal ions include those heavy metals that act as protein precipitants. In general, only three metal salts are widely used in cytology—mercury, chromium, and osmium ions.

Mercury. Mercury salts such as the bichloride are sometimes used for fixation. In this type of fixation the mercuric ion

(Hg^{++}) is important because this bivalent ion can combine with two different proteins and bridge them (Wolman, 1955). In this reaction they can combine with carboxyl and hydroxyl groups as well as with amines. One interesting aspect is the high affinity for the sulfhydryl group. If a small quantity of mercury salt is used, it will bind the sulfhydryls in preference to other groups (Pearse, 1960).

Chromium. Chromium salts combine with water to form Cr—O—Cr complexes, and these complexes can combine with the reactive groups in protein (Pearse, 1960). According to Wolman, chromium fixation involves two stages—the primary, which can be reversed by washing, and the secondary, in which the bound chromate group is reduced to a chromic group. In general, the initial reaction involves carboxyl groups and to a lesser extent the amino group. The primary reaction between the chromium complexes and carboxylic group is followed by coordination with amino and hydroxyl groups (Green, 1953).

Osmium. As a tissue fixative, osmium (O_8O_4) is not recommended because of its low rate of penetration. However, its importance lies in fixation for electron microscopy, and therefore its mechanism of action has been studied. It is known that osmium tetroxide is a strong oxidizing agent and is reduced by unsaturated fats to produce a black precipitate. In fact, osmium can be used to detect fat in histochemical studies because the reduced osmium will appear black. Its mechanism of action (Porter and Kallman, 1953) consists of oxidation of the fatty acid double bonds by osmium to produce a monoester. Furthermore, osmium will also react with aliphatic hydroxyl (1,2-glycols), sulfhydryl, and amino groups (Wolman, 1955).

In general, the nuclei are not well preserved after osmium fixation. According to Porter and Kallman, osmium is excellent for cytoplasmic fixation. The proteins are quickly gelated, and it may form polymers with protein, establishing a linkage at double bond positions.

Unfortunately, overfixation may produce soluble end products that can be washed from the cell.

Alcohols and acetone. Alcohols and acetone are valuable in enzyme histochemistry because in general they leave the enzyme group available for subsequent reactions. The great disadvantage of alcohol fixation is the morphological disturbance produced. Little is known of the mode of action of alcohols, except that they denature proteins and dissolve many organic molecules.

Acetic acid. Acetic acid precipitates nucleoprotein and dissolves most of the cytoplasmic proteins. In general, acetic acid fixes those proteins in which the isoelectric point is near the pH of the acid. The bound water about the protein disappears. There is loss of electric charge, the protein molecules can form new cross-linkages, and the reactive groups of the proteins move close together (Wolman, 1955).

In retrospect. Of the large number of fixatives available, only the most common have been mentioned. However, when special studies are initiated, other fixatives or combinations of fixatives are used. These will be mentioned later. From an examination of the theory behind the various fixatives mentioned, it is evident that chemical fixation involves linking by the fixative to other molecules in the cell so that with subsequent treatment the molecules are held in position. Furthermore, in the process of fixation the globular proteins may be involved. Generally this entails (1) the unfolding of the globular protein molecule, which results in (2) the increased availability of heretofore masked reactive groups that cannot react with the fixative or remain untouched and become available in subsequent histochemical methods.

It can also be noted that with certain fixatives the binding capacity of acid and basic dyes may be affected. In general, those fixatives (formalin, for example) that affect the basic groups shift the isoelectric point to the acid pH, which results in decrease of eosinophilia. The reverse also holds true with fixatives that bind the acid group (chromate fixatives); they render the tissue less basophilic.

Physical fixation

The physical methods of fixation include freeze-drying, frozen section, and freeze substitution. In all these methods the temperature of the tissues is lowered to a point where all or at least nearly all of the metabolic activity has ceased. Although these methods have been classed as fixing processes, it is doubtful whether they are such in the true sense. When the tissue is brought back to normal temperature, the metabolic activity commences again.

Freeze-drying. Freeze-drying is one of the best methods for the preservation of tissue. Not only is the morphological detail maintained but the enzyme systems are preserved. The freeze-dry procedure consists of several steps. The first step is quenching the tissue by very low temperature. This is brought about rapidly by immersing the tissue in a Dewar flask containing liquid nitrogen or in isopentane cooled in liquid nitrogen. The latter method has received wide acceptance because the isopentane acts as a good heat transfer, whereas the liquid nitrogen has an insulating effect and may delay the freezing of the tissue. (The insulating effect is due to the formation of nitrogen gas immediately around the warm tissue, and it is the gas that is supposed by many to have the insulating effect.) After the quench the tissue is placed in a tube or container to which a high-vacuum system has been applied. The temperature of the container is maintained at about −40° C during the drying period. The high degree of vacuum and the cold temperature allow the sublimation (evaporation from the solid state) of water molecules from the tissue. At the end of the process the tissue is preserved but is devoid of all water except that which is bound. After the drying period the tissues are generally embedded in paraffin or in Carbowax. The chief restriction of this technique is the length of time required to process the tissue (48 to 72 hours).

Frozen section. If tissues are frozen rapidly, the frozen water will serve as an embedding medium, and then sections can be cut if maintained at a suitable low temperature. This procedure is widely used for enzyme histochemistry and for routine studies in histology and cytology. Its advantage is the rapidity with which sections can be processed and the lack of chemical fixation which makes the method excellent for subsequent enzyme studies. Despite the advantages obtained, there are the following disadvantages to be coped with or at least to be aware of.

1. Freezing followed by thawing may possibly produce loss of architectural integrity. This is minimized by rapid cooling to prevent large ice crystals from forming and by placing sections into a fixative or incubation medium at the instant of thawing.
2. There can be loss of either the soluble enzyme or cofactors.
3. Diffusion of enzymes in unfixed tissues can lead to false positive results (Gomori, 1952). To prevent loss by diffusion the frozen sections can be placed in a fixative with a low freezing point such as acetone or ethanol to ensure some denaturation of the protein, which will, in many cases, fix the enzyme in postion and yet not inactivate them appreciably.

Generally the tissues are frozen with Dry Ice or cold carbon dioxide gas. The knife of the microtome used for cutting sections is likewise cooled to about the same temperature as the tissues. A refrigerated unit to cut frozen sections (cryostat) is now available. This unit has the advantage of maintaining the environment about the tissue and knife at the same low temperature, allowing more efficiency in cutting sections (Fig. 1-1).

Freeze substitution. Excellent morphological results are obtained with freeze substitution. In addition, many of the enzymes remain active for enzyme histochemical studies. Basically, freeze substitution consists of two steps: quenching of the tissue and extraction of the water at a low temperature. Isopentane cooled in liquid nitrogen, liquid nitrogen, ethanol at −65° C, an acetone-Dry Ice mixture at −60° C, or propylene glycol can be used as the quenching agent. Water can be extracted at low temperatures ranging from −20° to −75° C, depending on the technique or reagents used. There are also many substitute reagents. A few that we have used are ethanol, ethanol-methanol (usually in a 1:1 ratio), and osmium-acetone. Other investigators have used propylene glycol, Rossman's fluid, and ethanol with a metal salt (Pearse, 1960).

After dehydration the tissues are allowed to reach room temperature and are then embedded.

METHODS IN CYTOLOGY

Fluorescence microscopy

Fluorescence microscopy has become an important research tool in cytology and histology. A high degree of accuracy is obtained, the techniques are relatively simple, the cost is low, and the time necessary to complete the studies is relatively short when compared to autoradiography. In essence, the use of fluorescence microscopy involves the conjugation or labeling of a specific substance such as protein, serum antibodies, etc. with a suitable fluorochrome. At the present time a number of fluorochromes are available. The choice depends on the nature of the investigation. These include fluorescein isocyanate, fluorescein isothiocyanate, DANS (1-dimethylamino-naphthalene-5-sulfonic acid), lissamine, and rhodamine RB200. The tagged proteins or antibodies are examined under ultraviolet or ultraviolet-blue light. The sites of localization are indicated by visible fluorescent transmission, the color of which depends on the fluorochrome used.

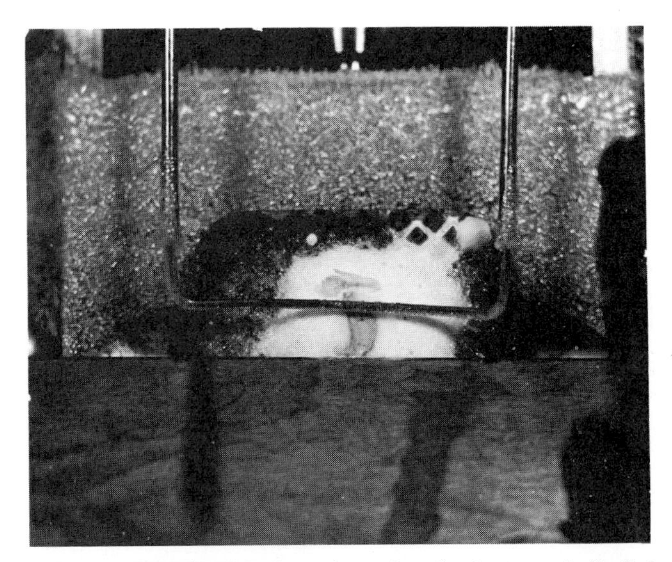

Fig. 1-1. Interior of a cryostat showing tissue (center) and microtome knife (below). The white material surrounding the tissue is the mounting medium. In the cryostat the environment is kept constant, thereby keeping both the tissue and the blade at the same low temperature.

Nature of fluorescence. To understand better the use of fluorochromes in cell research it is important to understand the theory by which fluorescence is accomplished. When a fluorochrome molecule absorbs a quantum of sufficient energy, it becomes excited, resulting in changes in its electron distribution. In many compounds this increased amount of energy is quickly dissipated to the surrounding molecules. However, in the case of fluorochrome the excited molecule is sufficiently stable so that it may return to ground state level and in so doing emit radiation. It is this usually visible emission that is called fluorescence, and its wavelength is always longer than the exciting radiation (Stokes's law).

This is visualized graphically in Fig. 1-2, in which *G* represents the ground state level and *E* represents the excited state level that results when the molecules absorb an exact amount of photon energy. The horizontal line at each level represents the vibrational state of the molecules. In general, when at equilibrium in their surroundings, these molecules are at the lowest of these levels *(E* and *G)*. The transition *(A)* represents the absorption of a specific quantum by the molecule that is transferred to one of the upper vibrational levels of the excited state. The excited molecule will then usually lose vibrational energy and reach the lowest vibrational energy of the excited state. If the state is stable for approximately 10^{-8} seconds, it is possible for the molecule to lose a quantum of radiation in the transition to one of the higher vibrational levels of the ground state. This results in fluorescence.

At the present time it is not possible to predict which compounds will fluoresce and which will not. However, Pringsheim (1949) suggested that the presence of fused aromatic rings may be at least one characteristic that is involved in producing fluorescence. For example, if one examines the structure of rosamine, which has a fluorescent characteristic, and compares it with malachite green, a nonfluorescent compound, a striking similarity is seen, the difference being, however, the presence of an oxygen bridge in rosamine and its absence in malachite green (Fig. 1-3). The oxygen bridging no doubt imparts rigidity to the molecule, which may be at least one requisite for fluorescence.

Autofluorescence. Many structures within the cell as well as some intercellular structures undergo fluorescence autonomously when merely examined under ultraviolet light. Most common is a blue to blue-green autofluorescence. Some cytoplasmic granules will at times produce a moderate to strong yellow fluorescence. Most of the cytoplasmic fluorescence is concentrated in the mitochondria. In addition to autofluorescence due to molecular structure, other inclusions also produce an autofluorescence; for example, ceroids produce a yellow to yellow-brown fluorescence, whereas calcium pro-

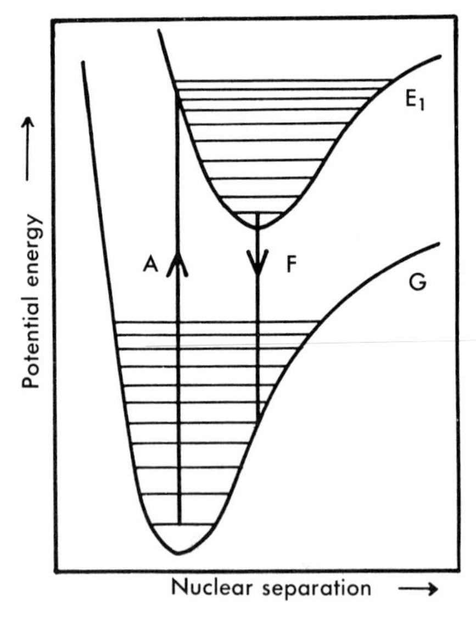

Fig. 1-2. Energy diagram of diatomic molecule showing absorption of radiation, **A,** and emission of fluorescence, **F. G** is the ground state level and **E** represents the excited state. (From Chadwick, C. S., and J. E. Fothergill. 1961. Fluorochromes and their conjugation with proteins. In R. C. Nairn [editor]. Fluorescent protein tracing. E. & S. Livingstone, Ltd., Edinburgh.)

duces a characteristic white fluorescence. Many of the vitamins as well as hormones produce a fluorescence ranging from yellow to green or even bluish. Venoms, particularly those from the family Crotalidae (rattlesnakes), produce a pale yellow fluorescence when exposed to an ultraviolet light source. Intercellular material, notably connective tissue, produces a blue-white fluorescence (Price and Schwartz, 1956).

Knowledge of autofluorescence is also important in conjunction with various tracing studies, particularly when the substance in question is labeled with a fluorochrome that fluoresces at the same or nearly the same color as some of the autofluorescent material within the cell.

Metachromasia

When a stain such as toluidine blue, thionine, or cresyl violet is applied to a tissue section, much of the cytoplasm will stain the color of the dye, yet certain other areas within this same cell or material found in the intercellular region will stain a purple to red color. This change from the blue toward the red produces the metachromatic color. Most of the dyes that are capable of producing metachromasia contain the thiazine groupings. From a histologist's view, metachromasia occurs in substances that are half esters of sulfuric acid with a polymeric carbohydrate. This is evident in such substances as mucoproteins, chondrin (chondroitin sulfuric acid, which is the matrix of cartilage), and many other carbohydrate macromolecules.

For a long time the mechanism producing metachromasia was poorly understood. However, in 1945 Michaelis and Granick suggested after a series of experiments that metachromasia may be the result of the conversion of the monomeric form of the dye (which is blue or blue purple, depending on the particular dye used) to the polymeric form, which has a changed color, red or a shade of green. Sylevén (1954) suggested that metachromasia depends on several factors, one of the most important being the reaction of the dye to the substrate. The point of reaction is between the anionic groupings of the compound with the cationic group of the dye and between adjacent dye molecules aggregated to the substrate. It is assumed that polymeric formation is due to hydrogen bonding, probably mediated by water molecules between adjacent dye molecules in the aggregation. Furthermore, meta-

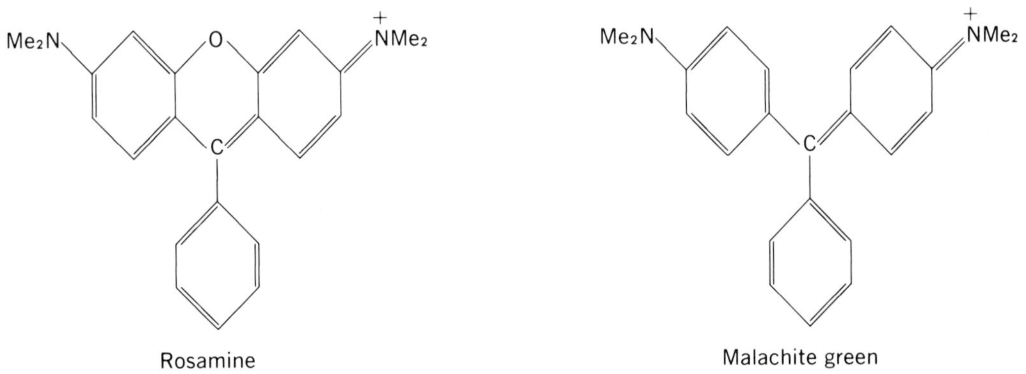

Rosamine

Malachite green

Fig. 1-3. Comparison of structure of rosamine (a fluorochrome) to that of malachite green, a nonfluorescing compound. Note absence of an oxygen bridge in malachite green. Probably the presence of the oxygen bridge is responsible for the fluorescing nature of rosamine. (From Chadwick, C. S., and J. E. Fothergill. 1961. Fluorochromes and their conjugation with proteins. In R. C. Nairn [editor]. Fluorescent protein tracing. E. & S. Livingstone, Ltd., Edinburgh.)

chromasia depends on a certain distance between available anionic surface charges. For example, in hyaluronic acid the anionic reaction groups are approximately 10 Å apart. This results in no metachromasia. On the other hand, when the densities are greater, that is, where a number of reactive groups are in the range of 4 Å, a stable metachromasia occurs.

Although it has been mentioned that metachromasia is specific for macromolecular carbohydrates, not all will give metachromasia. For example, polymers composed of hexosamine will not produce metachromasia. However, if the amino group is acetylated prior to treatment with a metachromatic dye, a positive reaction is produced.

Histochemistry

In a sense, histochemistry represents an extension of morphological staining techniques. Whereas the more routine techniques provide significant information regarding the morphology of the cell or tissue, little that is significant to the chemical implication involved can be noted. Histochemistry can be considered as the chemical identification and localization of various components in the cell, using techniques by which the end products are usually characterized by a colored precipitate or complex. In many reactions the final product can be quantitated spectrophotometrically.

The significance of histochemistry to cytological knowledge cannot be overemphasized. It is capable of changing a static field of morphology into a dynamic field closely related to biochemistry in which interpretation can be made on a structure-function basis.

Histochemistry, then, represents an interdisciplinary science that unites the various fields of chemistry, particularly organic chemistry and biochemistry, to the field of cellular or tissue morphology. Because of the dualistic nature of the field, the accuracy of localization is dependent on both the validity of the chemical reaction and on the ability of the reaction to maintain the architectural integrity of the tissue. Many basic reactions employed in biochemistry to identify specific compounds are useless in histochemistry because the reagents may be of such strength that they destroy the tissue. Often however, it is possible to so modify the reaction that the final result is not only valid for localization but does not unduly distort the tissue.

It is usually convenient to divide histochemistry into histochemistry per se and cytochemistry. Histochemistry consists of the chemistry of tissue. It is more general because it not only includes the identification of compounds within the cell and among various cells of the tissue but also the adjacent intercellular material and different adjacent tissues. On the other hand, cytochemistry is restricted to the chemistry of chemical changes observed within a particular cell or type of cell with little concern for the intercellular material.

As in the case of chemistry, the field of histochemistry can be subdivided into a number of specialized areas: (1) inorganic histochemistry, (2) protein histochemistry, (3) aldehyde histochemistry, (4) carbohydrate histochemistry, (5) lipid histochemistry, (6) nucleic acid histochemistry, and (7) the more functional field of enzyme histochemistry.

Inorganic histochemistry. Although numerous techniques for localization of metallic ions exist, only a few have been used with success. These include the localization of ion, calcium, and phosphate. Localization of other ions (for example, sodium and potassium), although techniques for identification and localization are available, involves a major problem produced by the interjection of the artifact of diffusion, which often can render the results useless. At best the results give merely regional distribution.

Several alternative methods are possible for distributional studies of inorganic material. Microincineration or autoradiography can be used. Microincineration involves the ashing of tissue sections at a temperature of about 600° C. This method can provide information regarding general distribution of certain minerals such as calcium, magnesium, iron, and silicon (Pearse, 1960). After radioactive isotopes of such minerals have been given, autoradiography can also provide much information on the distribution of the various inorganic components. This can be achieved using either the light microscope or electron microscope. (See discussion of autoradiography.)

Protein histochemistry. A large number of the classical tests used in biochemistry cannot be used in general histochemical studies because of the violent effects on the tissue or because the color intensity may not be sufficient for interpretation at the microscopic level. In effect, histochemistry of proteins consists of tests that are selective for a specific amino acid or specific groups. Therefore these tests only detect parts of the protein molecule. One can assume that if a positive reaction occurs, the amino acid indicated is included in the protein structure rather than being an isolated amino acid in the tissue. This is based on the premise that during the processing of tissues, the free amino acids which may have been present in the tissue are removed.

At the present time only a few specific amino acids can be identified histochemically. By their relative proportions they also indicate acid, basic, or neutral proteins. They include arginine, lysine, histidine, tyrosine, and tryptophan. Other tests can be used for the localization of sulfhydryl (–SH–) and disulfide groups (–S–S–), which in effect, can be used to identify cystine and cysteine. Other tests are based on reactions to detect the free amino acid (NH_2) or carboxyl (COOH) and histone groupings.

Aldehyde histochemistry. Many of the histochemical tests used depend on the production of and detection of the aldehyde group. Much of the histochemistry of carbohydrates as well as the plasmal reaction of lipids and the Feulgen reaction for identification of DNA depend on the detection of freed aldehyde groups. Although some aldehyde can be considered to occur naturally in tissues, aldehydes are produced experimentally by selective oxidation. Usually the naturally occurring aldehyde is associated with fatty acids. The detection of aldehyde groups, whether they are free in tissues or produced by a selective oxidation process, is accomplished by Schiff's reagent.

Schiff's reagent. Although there are a number of reagents that could be used, the most common is Schiff's reagent, which is prepared from a basic fuchsin solution. This dye is treated with a sulfurous acid solution that converts the dark blue purple into a colorless solution. In this form it is commonly called *leucofuchsin* or *fuchsin sulfurous acid* solution.

When leucofuchsin reacts with available aldehyde groups, a red to red-purple color is developed. It is believed that two aldehyde groups react with one leucofuchsin molecule. Although many users of the reagent refer to the development of the color as a "recoloration" of the dye, actually it is more than a recoloration due to the oxidation of the reagent by the aldehyde group. The final color developed is different from that of the original dye, and it may be reasonable to assume that the reaction of the aldehyde has a chromogenic effect which is reflected by the red to red-purple color.

Carbohydrate histochemistry. In the preceding section the nature of the Schiff reaction in the detection of aldehyde groups was discussed. Going one step further, it can be stated that the field of carbohydrate histochemistry, including the true sugar polysaccharides as well as those formed by uronic acids and glucosamines and the conjugated polysaccharides, is dependent on Schiff's reaction. The procedure for the detection of carbohydrate is known as the periodic acid–Schiff (PAS) reaction. In general, none of the carbohydrates will give a reaction by the direct use of Schiff's reagent. Instead, the aldehyde group must be produced by oxidation. In the PAS reaction periodic acid is used as the oxidant, which will break the C–C bonds where these are present as 1,2-glycol groups and convert them to dialdehyde (CHO–CHO). After oxidation the sections are treated with Schiff's reagent, which will develop a color where the aldehyde groups were formed (Fig. 1-4).

In addition to the PAS reaction a number of other carbohydrate tests are available. They include metachromasia as well as enzymatic action. The specific enzymes can be considered chemical reagents. The lack of staining characteristics after enzymatic action is indicative of the localization. Hyaluronidase, for example, is used for the detection of hyaluronic acid.

Lipid histochemistry. Because of the molecular structure of lipids, the histochemistry of this group is limited to the determination of classes of lipids rather than of the individual species. This is due to the similarity of both the chemical and the physical properties of the species within each class.

Probably the most interesting is known as the plasmal reaction. It was originally observed by Feulgen and Rossenbeck (Pearse, 1960). In this reaction a positive Schiff reaction was observed in the cytoplasm in sections that were not treated by acid hydrolysis. This indicates the presence of free aldehydes.

This reaction can be intensified by previous treatment with acid hydrolysis or by a short treatment with meruric chloride. This hydrolysis liberates the aldehyde group that can be detected by the Schiff reagent.

Nucleic acid histochemistry. Identification and localization are based on the following three components that compose nucleic acids: (1) the nitrogenous bases, (2) the deoxyribose sugar present in DNA, and

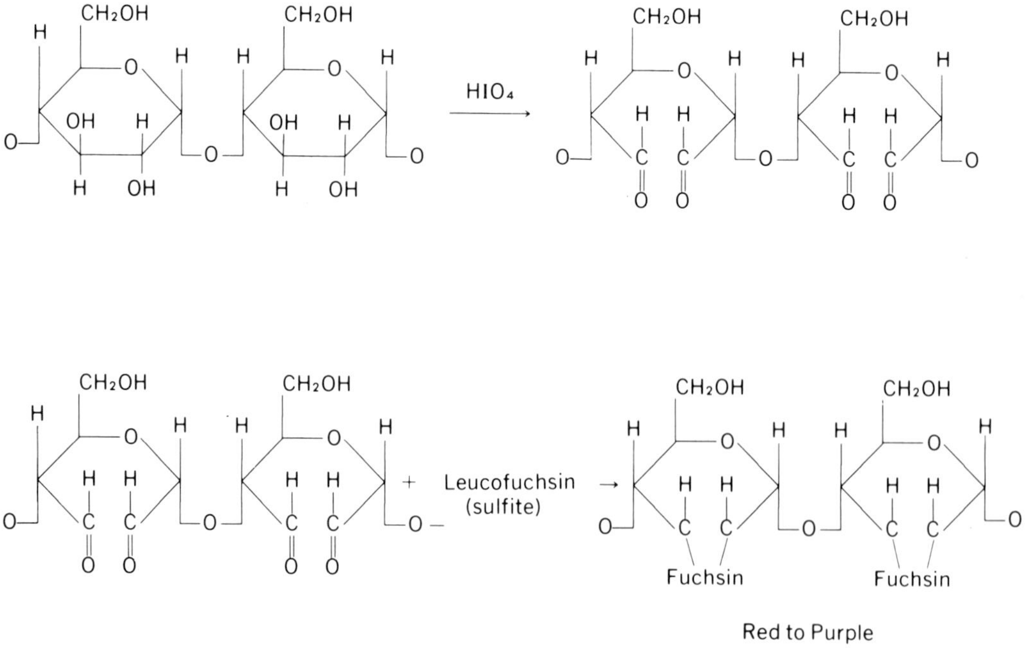

Fig. 1-4. Mechanism of periodic acid–Schiff reaction on carbohydrate.

(3) the phosphoric acid group associated with both DNA and RNA.

Nitrogenous bases. From the point of view of color identification, histochemical detection of purines and pyrimidines has been unsuccessful. However, the importance of the nitrogenous bases is that they will absorb ultraviolet light at 2,600 Å, and localization is made possible by microspectroscopy. However, the ultraviolet absorption technique will localize not only RNA but DNA as well.

Deoxyribose sugar. One of the basic differences between RNA and DNA is the sugar moiety present in the molecules. In DNA the sugar is deoxyribose, whereas in RNA the sugar is ribose. The presence of deoxyribose forms the basis of the Feulgen reaction, and so a positive reaction differentiates it from RNA, since the ribose sugar is not affected by the Feulgen reaction hydrolysis.

Feulgen reaction. As in the case of the PAS reaction, the basis of the Feulgen test is the detection of the presence of the aldehyde groups with Schiff's reagent. The Feulgen reaction can be divided into the following two stages:

1. The process of mild hydrolysis using a hydrochloric acid solution separates the purine bases from the deoxyribose sugar and exposes the aldehyde group of the latter. It is possible, however, by prolonged hydrolysis to separate the sugar group from the pyrimidine base as well.
2. The subsequent treatment of the aldehydes by Schiff's reagent produces a red-purple color.

This reaction can be studied photometrically to estimate the amount of DNA present. When used photometrically, the maximum absorption is at 550 nm.

Enzyme histochemistry. Enzyme histochemistry is not only the newest but the most expanding field of histochemistry. It represents a more functional approach to the study of cytology. Enzymatic studies at the cellular level can be of particular value in the field of pathology because they can explain the mechanism of action due to altered metabolism, but they can be equally important in helping to explain many of the reactions in cytological research.

The number of enzymes that can be visualized is large. To be sure, not all of those known can be detected and localized, but on the other hand, determining the distribution of those that are available can be used to obtain much of the information needed.

In general, the techniques used in enzyme studies are more exacting than those used in the other histochemical methods. In addition, the sources of error are more varied. Comparison of routine histochemical methods and enzyme studies reveals one striking difference. In the former the reagent will react with the constituent in the cell or intercellular material, and thus the final product is derived from the compound under study. In the latter the reagent is the substrate, which is acted on by the enzyme, and the product is the result of the enzymatic action. The resulting product must be highly insoluble when formed and should form a precipitate in situ so that the regions of the precipitate should be within the site of enzyme activity. In addition to its high insolubility in water, the precipitate should also have low solubility in lipids. Since many of the enzymes are situated on, in, or near membrane systems, solubility in the lipids would produce diffusion artifacts. The enzyme reaction must also obey the zero order of kinetics. That is to say, the rate of reaction must be independent of the substrate and related solely to the enzyme concentration.

Esterases. From the histochemical point of view esterases form a group of enzymes that catalyze or synthesize esters of carboxylic acids. The following diagram shows the reversible reaction:

RCOOR′	⇄	ROH	+ R′COOH
Carboxylic acid esters	Esterase	Alcohol	Carboxylic acid

A number of functions have been attributed to these enzymes. Meyers et al. (1957) suggest that esterase may play a role in protein metabolism because of its ability to hydrolyze amide and amino acid esters. It may also be related to the process of phagocytosis (Burstone, 1962). It is possible to divide the esterases into several groups: (1) aliesterases, which hydrolyze short-chain esters; (2) lipases, which hydrolyze fatty acids that have a long carbon chain; and (3) cholinesterases, which attack esters of choline.

Various histochemical methods are available for the demonstration of the different esterases. Among the most commonly used are indoxylacetate or the halogenated substituted form that reacts with an esterase to produce an indoxyl compound, which when followed by oxidation, produces an indigo dye. As in the case of phosphatases, a naphthol AS acetate can be used for a substrate, which when coupled with an azo dye, produces a colored precipitate. Gomori (1952) introduced the "Tween" method for detection of lipase. In this method a calcium salt soap of the fatty acid is produced, which on staining with, for example, Nile blue, produces a color indicating the localization of the enzyme.

Phosphatases. The phosphatases consist of a relatively large group of hydrolytic enzymes that catalyze the breakdown of phosphate esters to liberate phosphoric acid and an alcohol. Some of the phosphatases that can be demonstrated histochemically are listed in Table 1-1. Of particular importance are the phosphomonoesterases, which can be divided conveniently on the basis of their optimum pH. The phosphomonoesterases, broadly speaking, are nonspecific in that the enzyme will react with a number of different compounds or substrates. Within this nonspecific group of enzymes are the alkaline phosphatases (phosphomonoesterase I) and the acid phosphatases (phosphomonoesterase II). In addition to the nonspecific enzymes there are a number of enzymes that are substrate specific, including 5′-nucleotidase and glucose-6-phosphatase.

Visualization of phosphatase can be brought about by the metal salt method (Fig. 1-5) (Gomori, 1952) or by the use of one of the naphthol AS phosphates. In the former, either calcium or lead can be used, depending on the pH of the reaction. Calcium is used in an alkaline medium. The calcium combines with the phosphoric acid liberated to produce a calcium phosphate. The compound is converted successively to cobalt phosphate and finally to cobalt sulfide, which is a black precipitate. The lead method is similar. After the release of phosphates from the substrate a lead phosphate is formed, which is converted to lead sulfide

Table 1-1. Some common phosphatases that can be identified histochemically

Enzyme	Substrate
Phosphomonoesterase I (alkaline)	β-Glycerophosphate
Phosphomonoesterase II (acid)	β-Glycerophosphate
5′-Nucleotidase	Muscle adenylic acid
Adenosine triphosphatase	Adenosine triphosphate
Glucose-6-phosphatase	Glucose-6-phosphate
Glucose-1-phosphatase	Glucose-1-phosphate
Phosphoamidase	Phosphocreatine

for visualization. In the latter a number of naphthol AS phosphates are used. The phosphatases release the phosphate to produce highly insoluble naphthols, which are promptly coupled by an azo dye to produce a colored precipitate that can be visualized microscopically.

Dehydrogenases. Dehydrogenases consist of a group of enzymes that catalyze oxidation reactions by dehydrogenation. That is, these enzymes are capable of transferring the electrons from the substrate or proton donor to the oxidizing agent, which is the electron acceptor. Furthermore, these enzymes that catalyze dehydrogenation reactions are unable to utilize molecular oxygen directly as can the electron acceptor. Instead, there are a series of intermediate reactions in which the dehydrogenases transfer hydrogen to either NAD or NADP (di- or triphosphopyridine nucleotide) to produce the reduced state ($NAD \cdot H_2$ or $NADP \cdot H_2$). Furthermore, the reduced NAD and NADP are oxidized by a flavin nucleotide, FMN (flavin mononucleotide) or FAD (flavin adenine dinucleotide), which produce the oxidized NAD or NADP, but the flavoproteins are now reduced (Fig. 1-6). According to many investigators, the reduced flavoproteins under experimental conditions are capable of reducing dyes such as tetrazolium salts or methylene blue (Burstone, 1962). It is this point that forms the basis of the histochemical demonstration of a dehydrogenase enzyme. The reduced flavoprotein can be reoxidized by the dye, and the reduced dye formed will produce a colored insoluble formazan precipitate. However, there is some difference of opinion as to whether the reduced forms of FMN or FAD are capable of being oxidized directly by the dye.

A number of dehydrogenases can be localized histochemically. In Table 1-2 some of those that can be identified within cells are listed. By substituting the appropriate substrate and specific dehydrogenase in Table 1-2, the reaction as well as the mechanism of histochemical localization can be visualized.

Oxidases. Oxidases are enzymes that catalyze the transfer of electrons from a donor to oxygen. Many of the oxidases are metalloproteins and contain such metals as

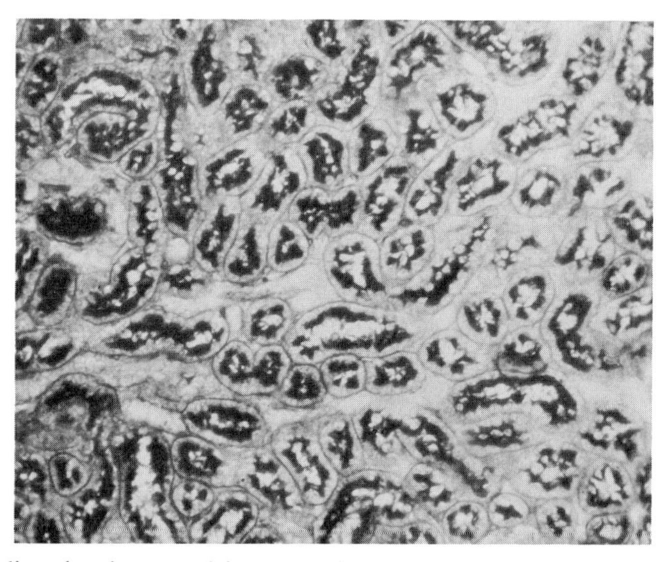

Fig. 1-5. Alkaline phosphatase activity in rat kidney. Note presence of enzyme activity along free surface of proximal convoluted tubules. Gomori's metal salt method.

iron or copper. Those that contain iron are the cytochrome oxidases, peroxidases, catalases, etc. An example of a copper-containing enzyme is tyrosinase.

Several methods are available for cytological demonstration of cytochrome oxidase, peroxidase, and monoamine oxidase.

Cytochrome oxidase is visualized by the Nadi reaction. In this reaction alpha naphthol and *N,N*-dimethyl-*p*-phenylenediamine

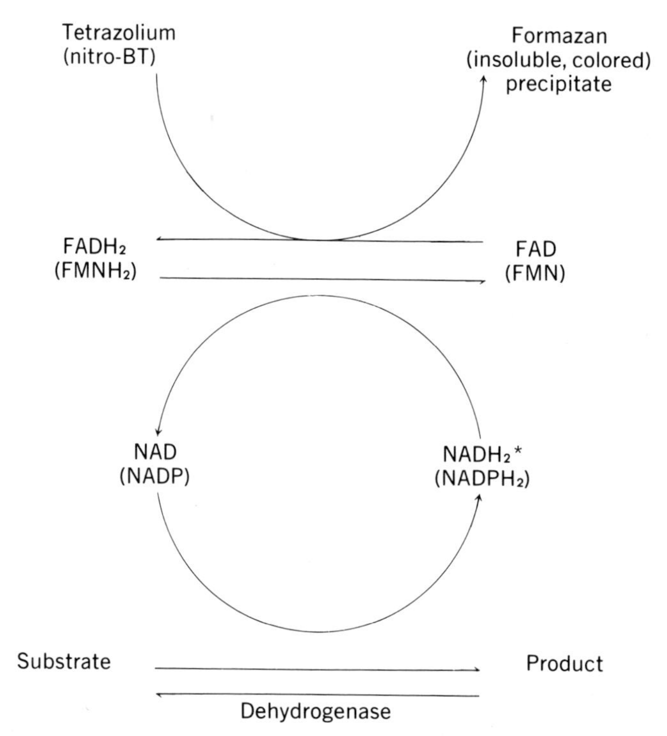

Fig. 1-6. Schematic drawing of dehydrogenase reaction as used in enzyme histochemistry. The final electron acceptor is nitro-BT, which is reduced to a highly insoluble chromogenic formazan. The asterisk marks the actual point where the transfer of electrons to nitro-BT may take place rather than where it is shown on the drawing. NAD, nicotinamide adenine dinucleotide; NADP, nicotinamide adenine dinucleotide phosphate; FAD, flavin adenine dinucleotide; and FMN, flavin mononucleotide.

Table 1-2. Some dehydrogenases that can be identified within the cell

Substrate	Enzyme	Product	Pyridine nucleotide
Sodium lactate	Lactic dehydrogenase	Pyruvate	NAD
Alcohol	Alcohol dehydrogenase	Acetaldehyde	NAD
Sodium malate	Malic dehydrogenase	Oxaloacetate	NAD
Sodium isocitrate	Isocitrate dehydrogenase	Oxalosuccinate	NADP
Sodium succinate	Succinic dehydrogenase	Fumarate	—

are used, and in the presence of cytochrome oxidase a blue indophenol is formed. The word "Nadi" is obtained from the first two letters in naphthol and diamine.

Peroxidases are enzymes that transfer two electrons from a substrate to hydrogen peroxide. In this reaction water and an oxidized dye are formed. The peroxidases are widely distributed in nature, in plants as well as in animals. Histochemically, peroxidases are identified by using benzene and hydrogen peroxide, which produce a brown precipitate as an end point.

Other enzymes. Sites of a number of other enzyme systems can be identified cytologically. Of some interest are the sulfatases, which hydrolyze the sulfate bonds. Of this group, perhaps the arylsulfatases deserve some special mention because of their presence in lysosomes (Chapter 12). Glycosidases, which attack the glycosidic linkage, are, like the arylsulfatases, of some importance (for example, β-glucuronidase in the lysosome fraction). Proteinases are poorly represented from a histochemical point of view in that only aminopeptidase can be localized within tissues.

Histoimmunology

The histoimmunology technique depends on the antigen-antibody reaction. The application of the method has proved useful in cytology for identification and localization of specific proteins, enzymes, and polysaccharides. In such studies those compounds within the cell are the antigens. If an antiserum is developed for such a specific compound, labeled with a suitable fluorochrome, and applied to the tissue, the position where the antigen-antibody reaction occurs will be the site or sites of a specific compound and can be visualized by fluorescence microscopy.

Generally the simplest method is to use fresh frozen sections and apply the fluorochrome-labeled antibody to the sections. At other times it is possible to inject into the animal the labeled compound and process the tissue by fixation, paraffin embedment, and sectioning. In this case knowledge of the stability of the labeled compound is necessary.

At times this simple method may not produce adequately intense fluorescence, and it may be necessary to use a layering technique (Coons, 1956) in which the unlabeled antigen is applied to the tissue, producing the antigen-antibody reaction; then a labeled anti-gamma globulin fraction is applied. The antibody can be considered to be the antigen for the anti-gamma globulin fraction. In this manner the labeled gamma globulin may have more bonding sites and produce a more intense fluorescence when it attaches to the antibody.

Ferritin, an iron-containing compound, has been conjugated to immune serum (Singer, 1959), the conjugate retaining its specificity; the antigen-antibody reaction can be visualized at the subcellular level with the electron microscope. The electron-dense points or patterns due to the electron scattering effect of the ferritin iron show the sites of the immune reaction.

Autoradiography

From the time of Becquerel (ca. 1895) it has been known that ionizing radiations act on photographic emulsions in much the same manner as does visible light. Thus one can think of the film as being a type of instrument for detecting nuclear radiation. Since the introduction of the method by Lacassogne and Cattes in 1924, it has become a valuable tool in cytology not only for the study of cell functions per se but also for correlations between morphology and cell physiology (biochemistry) as well as for localization of specific substances introduced into the cell.

Autoradiography is based on the fact that if a photographic film is placed over a tissue section which contains radioisotopic material, the radiation emitted by this substance will react locally with the photographic emulsion. A photographic image is produced that, on development, provides a means of visualizing the location of the radioactivity within the cell. This method as now developed provides a high degree of accuracy of localization. For highest resolution by this technique very thin tissue sections are necessary. On the other hand, when high resolution is not of great importance, thick sections may be used. Usually in this latter case a reversed radioautogram is produced in which the lighter areas represent areas of radioactivity.

In autoradiography two factors must be considered: (1) the properties of radiation and (2) the nature of the film used.

Properties of radiation. The following three types of radiation can be emitted by radioisotopes:

1. Alpha particles are helium nuclei consisting of two protons and two neutrons and are positively charged. Alpha particles produce good resolution primarily because of their short range within the emulsion. Their use in biological research is limited because they are produced essentially by heavy metals. They have been used on occasion to study the toxic effects caused by these metals on living systems.
2. Most of the autoradiograms are produced by beta particles, which are electrons of negative charge. Isotopes that emit beta particles of low energies give good resolution. These would include such elements as carbon-14 (^{14}C), tritium (^{3}H), calcium (^{45}Ca), etc. Of these, tritium is far more widely used because its beta particle has the lowest energy. Beta particles of high energies produce diffuse autoradiograms because the electrons form long tracks in the emulsion and the film is often useless.
3. Gamma particles have a low ionizing effect, and great range is not important in this technique.

Nature of the film. A number of different types of film are available and should be selected according to the particular study. In general, the film should be of the finest grain to increase the resolution. That is, the closer together the areas of darkening and yet still be distinguished from one another the higher the resolution. This, of course, follows the definition with regard to the resolving power of the microscope. In addition, the emulsion should be "fast" so that long exposure, particularly of high levels of radioactivity, can be avoided. Stripping film is useful for the study of cellular localization. In this procedure the emulsion is stripped from its base, inverted, and floated on water (Pelc, 1956). It is picked up directly on the mounted specimen. After exposure the emulsion-covered slide is developed. Quantitative results can be obtained by counting the grains. At times quantitation is possible by observing the density.

The time of exposure is difficult to predict, and there is no simple way of estimating it. A practical method for estimating time can be obtained by running preliminary tests using graded levels of radioactivity. This can give a fairly accurate estimate of exposure time.

Track autoradiography, which is the visualization of an ionizing particle in an emulsion, is also widely used. It can be used with both alpha and beta emitters. In this method both liquid emulsion as well as stripping film can be used. According to Comar (1955), stripping film is better for quantitative autoradiography because the emulsion thickness and the distance between specimen and emulsion are constant, which allow for reproducibility. Quantitative results can be obtained by grain counting, with the number being proportional to the amount of radioactivity.

Within the past few years a double-isotope autoradiographic technique has been developed (Baserga and Nemeroff, 1962; Trelstad, 1965). This technique permits two metabolic parameters to be studied simultaneously. In this type of study two different beta emitters of different energies of decay are used. They are carbon (^{14}C) and tritium (^{3}H). The principle behind this technique is based on the fact that the range of a beta particle is directly related to its energy of decay. Therefore ^{14}C can be distinguished autoradiographically from ^{3}H because the former has a greater distance of transmission. In addition, two emulsions are involved to distinguish the beta particles of ^{14}C and ^{3}H. Essentially, two layers of emulsion are separated by an inert layer of celloidin. The longer range of ^{14}C is recorded in the second emulsion, whereas the beta particles from ^{3}H are recorded in the first emulsion only. The autoradiograph is viewed on a single slide (Fig. 1-7).

Caro et al. (1962) described a method of autoradiography at the electron microscope level. This technique consists of applying a monolayer of silver halide crystals over the thin section. After exposure the film is developed, and the silver grains that were hit by beta particles stand out when examined with the electron microscope. A resolution of only 1,000 Å is possible with the presently available commercial emulsions (Caro, 1962).

Tissue culture

Tissue culture involves making small pieces of living tissue grow and multiply in vitro. Historically, tissue culture became a reality when small pieces of frog embryonic spinal cord were successfully cultured by Harrison in 1907. After Harrison's work significant studies were made by Alexis Carrel (1912, 1924), who worked out most of the procedures employed by tissue culturists today. He and his associates devised

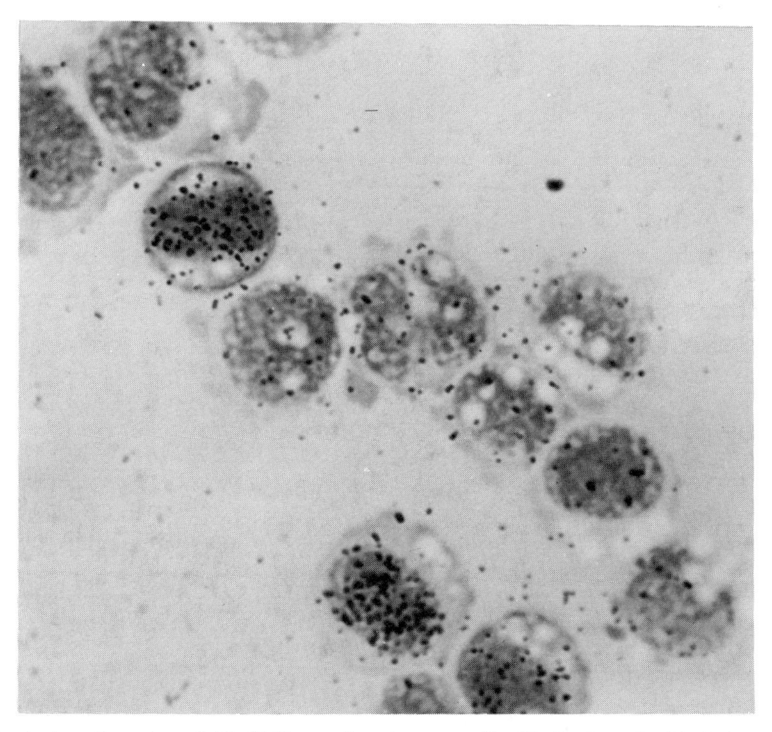

Fig. 1-7. Autoradiogram of Ehrlich's ascites tumor cells illustrating double-isotope tracing technique. In this study ^{3}H-thymidine and ^{14}C-leucine were used. Cells incorporating both tracers are more intensely labeled than cells labeled with only leucine. (From Baserga, R., and K. Nemeroff. 1962. J. Histochem. Cytochem. **10:**628-635.)

methods for serial propagation of a number of types of vertebrate cells. Plant tissue culture and isolated cell culture are also widely practiced. Another advance in tissue culture was the development of the technique for clonal isolation. This procedure involves isolating single cells derived from a single original cell; each single cell is isolated within a capillary tube (Sanford et al., 1948). The cell within the capillary tube proliferates prior to transfer to a suitable vessel for further cultivation. This technique is useful for various genetic studies because of the single cell origin and genetic equality of all cells of the clone.

The simplest method or technique for tissue culture consists of mincing tissue and placing some of the homogenate on a cover slip that contains several drops of sterile plasma and embryonic fluid. The cover slip containing the explant is inverted into a depression slide (usually a Maximow slide or similar type of chamber), and the edge of the cover slip is sealed to the slide with paraffin. The tissue is incubated at the temperature normal to the animal from which the explant was derived. Usually 24 hours later a zone of growth can be seen peripheral to the minced explant. This can be recultivated on several other slides. In this manner a population can be developed. The cover-slip method offers excellent preparations for studying cytologically the morphology or change in morphology as well as movements of cells and their inclusions.

With the increase in popularity of tissue culture for scientific investigation, synthetic media (rather than plasma or serum) have been developed. These media contain known amounts of amino acid, small peptides, vitamins, etc. They are used for large cultures, that is, flask culture when a large mass of cells is needed. In addition, such *defined media* have added value in that studies of a nutritional nature can be made.

A further advance in tissue culture is the technique of trypsinizing the tissue prior to culture. Larger tissues can be used and subjected to the enzyme trypsin. The enzyme separates the cells from the connective tissue, leaving a mass of individual cells available for culturing. This method is useful for establishing cultures on glass (Scherer et al., 1953). In addition to trypsin for dissociation of cells, collagenase and elastase have been used successfully.

In addition to the study of genetics, tissue culture is an important tool in the study of morphogenesis, for differentiation, in the study of nutritional requirements of specific cells, and in the study of virus propagation as well as the effects of virus on the host cells. Tissue culture is important in the field of pathology, where cytological changes due to the actions of various toxins, either of exogenous or endogenous origins, can be studied. In the assaying of drugs, for example, the action of carcinostatic agents on various carcinomas is evident.

Modifications of tissue culture techniques have been applied to organ culture. Small organs such as developing bone can be cultured and studied from a developmental point of view, or the effects of chemicals or biologicals such as hormones on the differentiation of this structure can be determined. Similarly, secreting organs can be studied experimentally.

Biological computing

The application of computer technology is becoming increasingly important in the field of biomedical sciences. Although used with any degree of seriousness for only the past few years, important strides have been made in solving some complex problems. Not only is the computer used for retrieval and analysis of data but it is equally important in the development of bioscientific theory, which opens the door to theoretical biology.

Although the scope of computer science is significant in biology, consideration will be restricted here to several examples of current use of computers in the field of cytology or in cell-related work. One of the

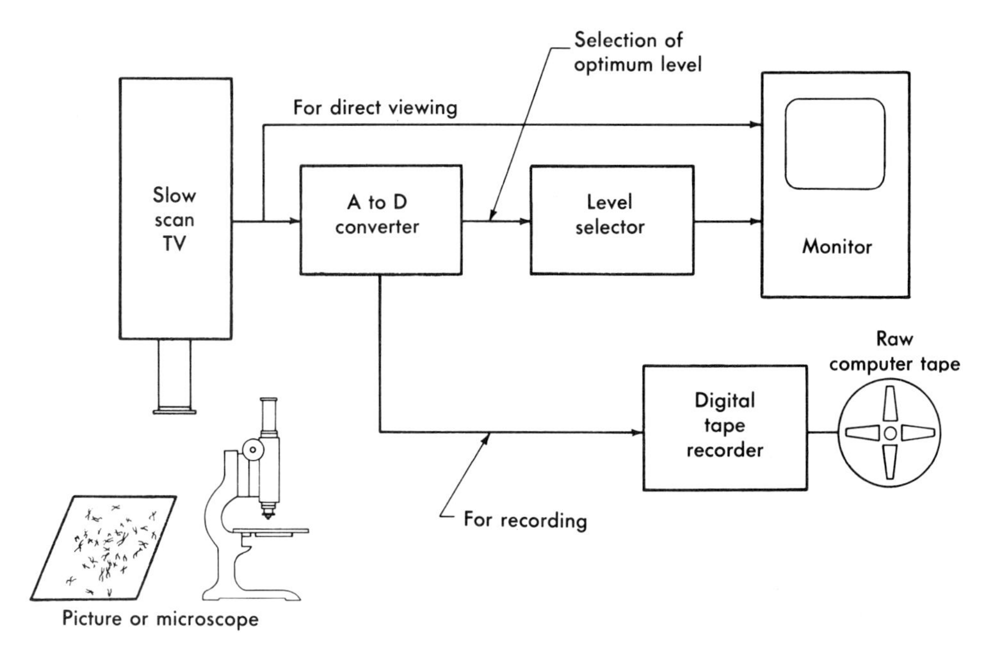

Fig. 1-8. Diagram of scanner and analog to a computer and tape recorder. (From Neurath, P. W., et al. 1966. Ann. N. Y. Acad Sci. **128:**1013-1034.)

Fig. 1-9. Computer print-out of a monocyte. (From Prewitt, J. M. S., and M. L. Mendelsohn. 1966. Ann. N. Y. Acad. Sci. **128:**1035-1053.)

important studies is the development of pattern-recognition techniques in conjunction with digitized cellular images (Waxman, 1966) (Fig. 1-8). The analysis of cellular image is brought about by using a scanning and recording cytophotometer, which is used as the sensor. The optical densities of the specimen are measured along lines spaced 0.25 μm apart, with intervals between successive samples on one line also fixed at 0.25 μm (Prewitt and Mendelsohn, 1966). The digital computer receives this information as a matrix of optical density. A set of symbols simulating a gray scale is used to reconstruct the image on a high-speed printer (Fig. 1-9). This technique has also been used by Neurath et al. (1966) in their study of the analysis of human chromosomes.

Another use of computers that touches the cellular level of organization is the construction of artificial "biochemical systems" (Garfinkel et al., 1966).

Cytophotometry

Cytophotometric techniques provide a method for quantitative study of cell components such as nucleic acids or proteins. This technique is based on the fact that the proportion of the light absorbed depends on the concentration of the absorbing substance. Therefore the concentration can be estimated by measuring the amount of absorption. Other factors that influence the amount of light absorbed include the wavelength of the light, the intensity of the light, and the thickness of the absorbing substance.

Basically, the cytophotometer consists of a sensor such as a photomultiplier, which is capable of scanning the sections and recording the different absorbencies on photographic plates or on rotating drums that have been calibrated previously. It is possible by a modification of this technique to feed this information into a computer and produce a biological image depicting the material quantitated, as discussed previously.

LITERATURE CITED

Baserga, R., and K. Nemeroff. 1962. Two-emulsion radioautography. J. Histochem. Cytochem. **10:**628-635.

Burstone, M. S. 1962. Enzyme histochemistry and its application in the study of neoplasms. Academic Press, Inc., New York.

Caro, L. G. 1962. High-resolution autoradiography. II. The problem of resolution. J. Cell Biol. **15:**189-199.

Caro, L. G., R. P. van Tubergen, and J. A. Kolb. 1962. High-resolution autoradiography. I. Methods. J. Cell Biol. **15:**173-188.

Comar, C. L. 1955. Radioisotopes in biology and agriculture. McGraw-Hill Book Co., New York.

Coons, A. H. 1956. Histochemistry with labeled antibodies. Int. Rev. Cytol. **5:**1-23.

French, D., and J. T. Edsall. 1945. The reaction of formaldehyde with amino acids and proteins. Advances Protein Chem. **2:**277-335.

Garfinkel, D., S. W. Ching, M. Adelman, and P. Clark. 1966. Techniques and problems in the construction of computer models of biochemical systems including real enzymes. Ann. N. Y. Acad. Sci. **128:**1054-1068.

Gomori, G. 1952. Microscopic histochemistry. University of Chicago Press, Chicago.

Green, R. W. 1953. The role of the amino and hydroxyl groups of collagen in chrome tanning. Biochem. J. **54:**187-191.

Meyers, D. K., J. W. Tol, and M. H. T. de Jonge. 1957. Studies on ali-esterases. V. Substrate specificity of the esterases of some saprophytic microbacteria. Biochem. J. **65:**223-232.

Michaelis, L., and S. Granick. 1945. Metachromasy of basic dyestuff. J. Amer. Chem. Soc. **67:**1212-1219.

Neurath, P. W., B. L. Bablouzian, T. H. Warms, R. C. Serbagi, and A. Falek. 1966. Human chromosomes analysis by computer, an optical pattern recognition problem. Ann. N. Y. Acad. Sci. **128:** 1013-1034.

Pearse, A. G. E. 1960. Histochemistry: theoretical and applied. 2nd ed. Little, Brown & Co., Boston.

Pelc, S. R. 1956. The stripping film technique of autoradiography. Int. J. Appl. Radiat. **1:**172-177.

Porter, K. R., and F. Kallman. 1953. The properties and effect of osmium tetraoxide as a tissue fixative with special reference to its use for electron microscopy. Exp. Cell Res. **4:**127-141.

Prewitt, J. M. S., and M. L. Mendelsohn. 1966. The analysis of cell images. Ann. N. Y. Acad. Sci. **128:**1035-1053.

Price, G. R., and S. Schwartz. 1956. Fluorescence microscopy. In G. Oster and A. W. Pollister (editors). Physical techniques in biological research. Vol. 3. Academic Press, Inc., New York.

Pringsheim, P. 1949. Fluorescence and phosphorescence. Interscience Publishers, Inc., New York.

Sabitini, D. D., K. G. Bensch, and R. J. Barrnett. 1963. Cytochemistry and electron microscopy. The preservation of cellular ultrastructure and enzymatic activity of aldehyde fixation. J. Cell Biol. **17:**19-58.

Sanford, K. K., W. R. Earle, and G. D. Likely. 1948. The growth in vitro of single isolated tissue cells. J. Nat. Cancer Inst. **9:**229-246.

Scherer, W. F., J. T. Syverton, and G. O. Gey. 1953. Studies on the propagation in vitro of poliomyelitis viruses. IV. Viral multiplication in a stable strain of human malignant epithelial cells (strain HeLa) derived from an epidermoid carcinoma of the cervix. J. Exp. Med. **97:**695-709.

Singer, S. J. 1959. The preparation of electron dense antibody conjugate. Nature (London) **183:**1523-1524.

Sylevén, B. 1954. Metachromatic dye-substrate interactions. Quart. J. Micr. Sci. **95:**327-358.

Trelstad, R. L. 1965. Double isotope autoradiography. Exp. Cell Res. **39:**318-328.

Waxman, B. D. 1966. Biomedical computing—1965. Ann. N. Y. Acad. Sci. **128:**723-730.

Wolman, M. 1955. Problems of fixation in cytology, histology, and histochemistry. Int. Rev. Cytol. **4:**79-102.

GENERAL REFERENCES

Bahr, G. F. 1955. Continued studies about the fixation with osmium tetra oxide. Exp. Cell Res. **9:**277-285.

Bell, L. G. E. 1952. The application of freezing and drying techniques in cytology. Int. Rev. Cytol. **1**:35-63.

Blumberg, J. M., J. F. Metzger, C. M. Smith, M. D. Hoggan, and S. I. Zacks. 1961. Demonstration of antigenic sites using ferritin conjugates. A.F.I.P. publication, Washington, D. C.

Coons, A. H., E. H. Leduc, and J. M. Connolly. 1953. Immunohistochemical studies of antibody response in the rabbit. Fed. Proc. **12**:439.

Eränkö, O. 1955. Quantitative methods in histology and micoscopic histochemistry. Little, Brown & Co., Boston.

Fitzgerald, P. J., E. Simmel, J. Weinstein, and C. Martin. 1953. Radioautography: theory, technique, and applications. Lab. Invest. **2**:181-222,

Glasstone, S. 1958. Source book on atomic energy. D. Van Nostrand Co., Inc., Princeton, N. J.

Gurr, E. 1965. Rational use of dyes in biology. The Williams & Wilkins Co., Baltimore.

Kamen, M. D. 1957. Isotopic tracers in biology. An introduction to tracer methodology. Academic Press, Inc., New York.

Marshall, J. M., Jr. 1954. Distribution of chymotrypsin, procarboxypeptidase, desoxyribonuclease, and ribonuclease in bovine pancrease. Exp. Cell Res. **6**:240-242.

Michaelis, L. 1947. The nature of the interaction of nucleic acids and nuclei with basic dyestuff. Cold Spring Harb. Symp. Quant. Biol. **12**:131-142.

Pollister, A. W., and H. Ris. 1947. Nucleoprotein determination in cytological preparation. Cold Spring Harb. Symp. Quant. Biol. **12**:147-154.

CHAPTER 2

Instrumentation

If one considers that the human eye is not capable of resolving objects smaller than 0.1 mm, it is no wonder that the science of cytology has not always existed. Few cells are large enough to be discerned without the aid of the microscope, let alone the organelles found within. What is known of the internal structures of cells is largely determined by the optical system used. With optical systems using visible radiation, details of about 0.1 μm in diameter can be observed, whereas using the electron microscope, biological structures in the range of 8 Å can sometimes be studied. This does not mean that electron microscopy makes the conventional light microscopy obsolete; on the contrary, each type of instrument has its advantages, depending on the nature of the study.

To understand better the relative sizes of cells, their organelles, and the approximate sizes of macromolecules, the student should familiarize himself with such measurements as the Ångstrom unit (Å), the nanometer (nm), and the micrometer (μm). Using the millimeter as a reference, Table 2-1 shows the conversion of the Ångstrom to nanometer to millimeter. Table 2-2 gives the approximate sizes of several cells as well as some macromolecules of biological importance.

The purpose of this chapter is to mention instruments used in cytology, to discuss briefly the theory of the various instruments used, and to cite several applications of these instruments to cell studies. For those who are interested in a more thorough discussion on the theory of the various instruments, a number of books and articles are available; several of these are included in the references at the end of this chapter.

The first successful compound microscope was developed in the last decade of the sixteenth century by Janssen. Its design remained static for almost 200 years. The greatest imperfection of the early microscopes as well as later models was the presence of chromatic aberration, that is, the color fringes about the images. In some microscopes the chromatic aberration was so bad they were practically useless. It was not until the middle period of the eighteenth century that achromatic lenses were designed and used in microscopes. This breakthrough in lens design and grinding paved the way for further changes, which ultimately led to the development of a microscope in which the practical limits of the power of resolution coincided with the theoretical resolving power obtained mathematically. This achievement was attributed to the work of the mathematician and physicist Ernst Abbe.

Further development of microscopy included the development of the phase contrast, interference, polarizing, dark-field,

Table 2-1. Conversion scale

Ångstroms	Nanometers	Micrometers	Millimeters
1	0.1	0.0001	0.0000001
10	1.0	0.001	0.000001
10,000	1,000.0	1.00	0.001
10,000,000	1,000,000	1,000.0	1.00

Table 2-2. Relative sizes of cells and macromolecules

	Average size	
Cell types	**Ångstroms**	**Micrometers**
Ovum (human, mature)	1,200,000	120
Liver (human)	200,000	20
Erythrocyte (human)	80,000	8
T phage (even)	650 × 950	0.065 × 0.095
Pf phage (DNA)	850 × 50	0.085 × 0.005
f2 phage (RNA)	250	0.025
Colloids (range)	10–1,000	0.001–0.1
Starch molecule	80	0.008

ultraviolet, x-ray, and electron microscopes.

As can be seen from the foregoing discussion, the most important component of the microscope is the lens system. In a compound microscope there are three such systems—the *condenser, objective,* and *ocular.* The condenser collects the light and concentrates or focuses the light onto the specimen. The objective produces the image and magnifies it. The ocular magnifies the image further.

The resolution of the microscope is the ability of the microscope's optical system to distinguish two points or lines that lie very close together. Mathematically, the resolution of the microscope is expressed by the formula

$$\Upsilon = \frac{\lambda\ 0.61}{NA}$$

where Υ = resolving power; λ = wavelength of light; and NA = numerical aperture or the light-gathering power.

The numerical aperture (NA) is determined by the sine of the half angle formed by the specimen and the maximum opening of the lens and also by the refractive index (n) of the medium through which the light passes, n being 1 for air and vacuum and about 1.5 for immersion oil such as cedarwood. At the present time the numerical apertures of oil-immersion objectives are between 1.3 and 1.5, although numerical apertures beyond 1.4 are rare.

It can readily be seen that with this formula the resolution of the microscope using blue light, which has a wavelength of 4,000 Å, is 0.17 μm (or 1,700 Å). That is, the lens system cannot discern two lines or points that are closer than 0.17 μm. Similarly, using white light, which has a wavelength of 5,000 Å, the resolution of the microscope is about 0.24 μm (or 2,400 Å). In general, the resolving power can be estimated by taking one half of the wavelength of radiation used.

By using a shorter wavelength of radiation, the resolution of the microscope can be increased. However, when the wavelength of light is much below 4,000 Å, glass lenses can no longer be used; instead, quartz lenses are needed (this will be discussed in the section on ultraviolet microscopy).

OPTICAL MICROSCOPY

Phase-contrast microscopy

When living cells are examined by conventional light microscopy, they appear transparent and largely homogeneous with visible radiation. The only structures that can be discerned are the chromogenic substances such as chloroplasts and plant and animal pigments. This transparency is due partly to the high water content of protoplasm and partly to the comparable refractive indices of the cell organelles. To see forms there must be contrast between them and the background. To study cells by conventional microscopic techniques it is necessary to use various stains, which produce differential absorption of visible light to provide the necessary contrast. At times it is possible to use various vital stains, but more often chemical killing and fixation followed by staining are necessary for adequate contrast.

Zernike, a Dutch physicist, developed the phase-contrast microscope. With this microscope it is possible to study structural details of living or dead cells. The function of the phase-contrast microscope is to convert, by optical means, the optical path differences into visible differences in intensity and therefore contrast, the optical path being the product of the refractive index of the medium through which the light passes and the thickness of the medium.

If two waves of light start out together in the same medium, that is, in air, their velocities will be the same at any point in time. If, however, a transparent nonabsorbing substance is placed some distance in front of one of these waves, the light will pass through this medium, but by doing so, the velocity will be altered. However, on emergence, its air velocity is again reestablished, but compared to the other light wave, which did not pass through this medium, it is retarded by some fraction of a wavelength and therefore has undergone a phase change. The amount of change depends on the index of refraction and the thickness of the medium through which the light wave passed. This phase change is measurable in degrees.

Similar changes occur when a transparent or nearly transparent cell is examined by conventional light microscopy. The difference in the refractive index between the cell and the surrounding medium and the differences in the refractive indices of the organelles produce small phase differences. The amplitude, that is, the distance from crest to crest of a sine wave, is not altered appreciably, and the intensity of the visible radiation remains constant. Thus the cell and its organelles remain essentially transparent to the eye. Phase contrast, however, converts the small phase differences into differences of contrast. To produce this contrast the phase microscope utilizes (1) an *annular diaphragm* located below the condenser (Fig. 2-1), which allows a hollow cone of light to impinge on the specimen, and (2) an objective, which contains a *diffraction* or *phase plate* located in the back focal plane. This plate separates the diffracted and direct light coming from the specimen and alters the intensity and phase relationship so that when combined at the eyepiece, a visible image is formed. Diffraction occurs when there is structural detail. This diffraction is 90 degrees out of phase with the direct light. The objective, containing the phase plate, receives both the

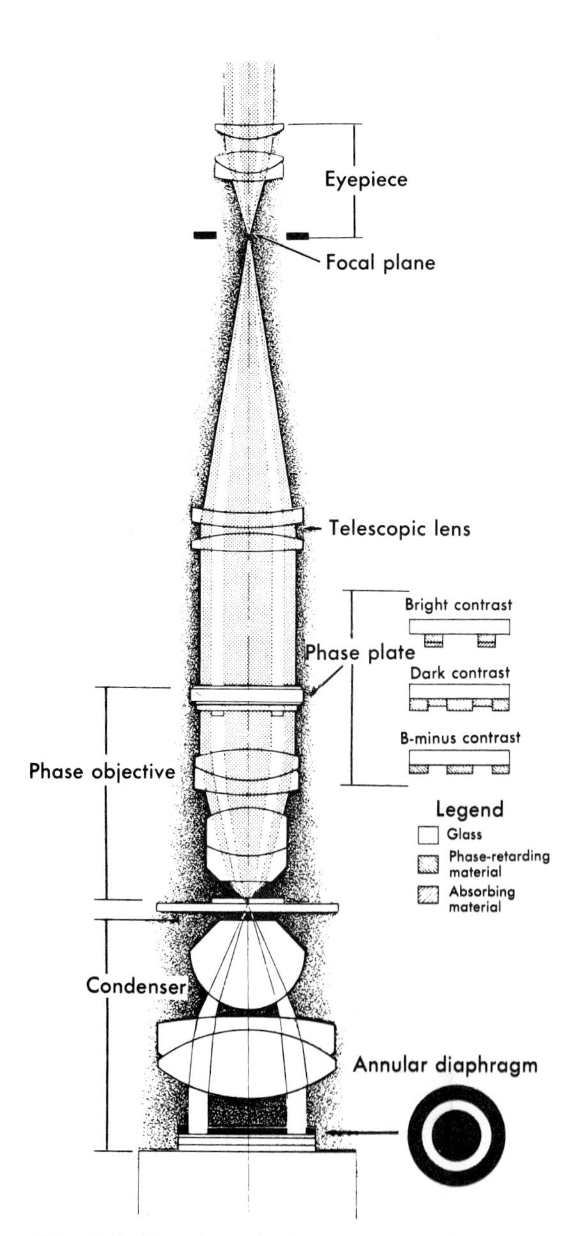

Fig. 2-1. Drawing of phase-contrast microscope showing the basis of this type of microscopy. The phase plates most commonly used are on the right. These phase plates are located in the objective. See text for theory. (Courtesy American Optical Co., Buffalo, N. Y.)

direct and diffracted rays. The direct light wave coincides with the phase ring, whereas the diffracted light is distributed over the whole aperture. To balance the direct and diffracted light waves absorbing material is coated on the phase ring. This material can alter by 90 degrees the wavelength of the direct light waves and bring it into phase with the diffracted light (Fig. 2-2). By this means the diffracted light is reinforced by the additive superposition of the direct light to produce a bright contrast (Fig. 2-3, *A*). On the other hand, it is also possible to add retarding material over the whole phase plate rather than just the phase ring. When this occurs, the diffracted light is retarded so that at the eyepiece the direct and diffracted waves are a half wavelength out of phase (Fig. 2-2). This results in subtractive superposition of the light wave to produce a dark contrast (Fig. 2-3, *B*). This microscope has contributed considerably to cytological knowledge, especially of living cells.

The disadvantage of phase contrast is that halos result from incomplete separation of the direct and diffracted light. The advantage, however, is its relatively low cost, which makes it almost a universal instrument for cytological studies.

Interference microscopy

The principle of the interference microscope is similar to that of the phase-contrast microscope. However, the interference microscope has the advantage of providing quantitative data as well as qualitative information. It is possible to obtain contrast of variable intensity, permitting the observer to select the best contrast for a specific detail. Similarly, with bright-light illumination, phase changes are enhanced by brilliant color contrasts. Thus one can select the best color contrast for specific features of the cell. Variable color contrast also permits semiquantitative results. Probably the most important function of the interference microscope is that of providing quantitative data such as dry weight determinations.

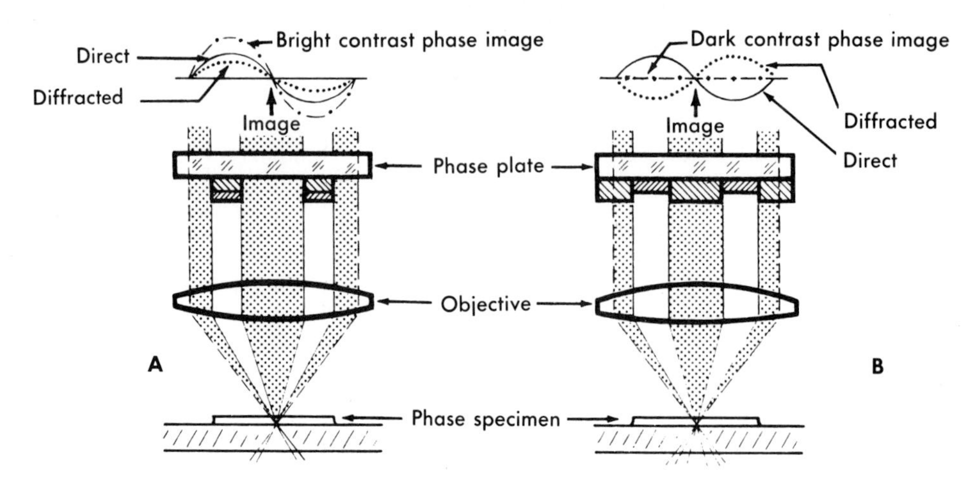

Fig. 2-2. Comparison of phase plates for bright contrast, **A,** and dark contrast, **B.** In bright contrast there is the additive superposition of light waves, and in dark phase there is a subtraction of light waves. Note the presence of phase-retarding material in the dark-contrast phase plate. (Courtesy American Optical Co., Buffalo, N. Y.)

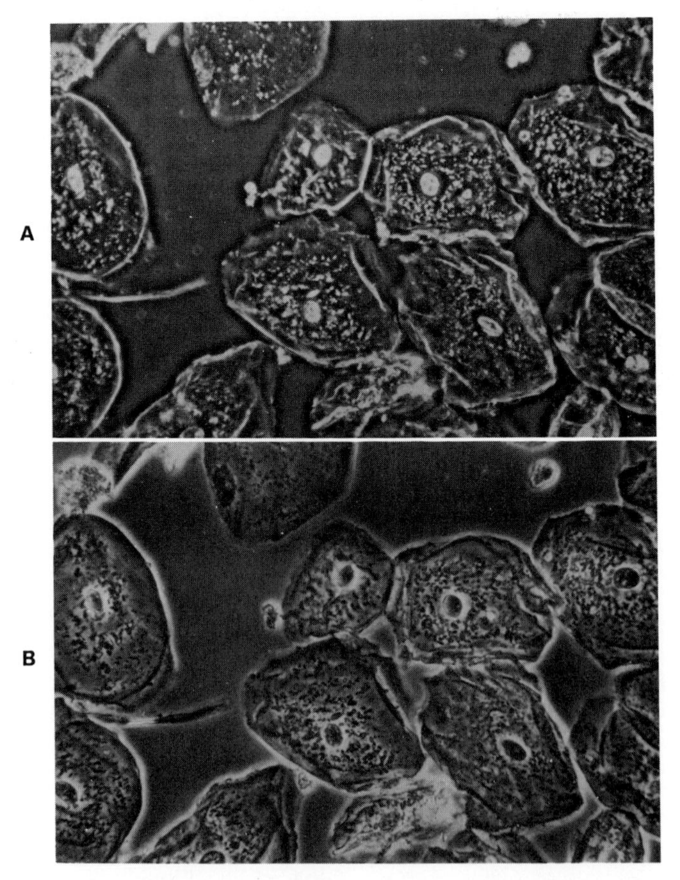

Fig. 2-3. A, Epithelial cells seen under bright contrast. Note bright nuclei and cellular inclusions. Compare with same cells viewed under dark contrast. **B,** Same epithelial cells as shown in **A** but viewed under dark contrast. Note that nuclei and cytoplasmic inclusions are dark. (Courtesy American Optical Co., Buffalo, N. Y.)

Interference can take place if two light waves originate from the same source. This is brought about in the interference microscope by a "beam splitter"; that is, the light from its source is split into two beams by semireflecting mirrors. One of the beams passes through the specimen, whereas the other bypasses it. These two beams are reunited and interfere with each other. The halos often seen in phase microscopy do not occur due to the complete separation of light.

One of the functions of the interference microscope is the ability to provide quantitative data. Since the refractive index of a cell is a measure of the solid concentration, and the phase change is dependent on the refractive indices of the cell and its thickness, one can assume that this phase change is a function of the dry mass of the cell, which can be expressed by the formula

$$\times = \frac{\Upsilon\ A}{100 - \alpha}$$

where Υ is the phase change $\Theta_0 - \Theta_1$, Θ_0 is the refractive index of the cell; Θ_1 is the refractive index of the intracellular fluid; A is the area that can be determined by planometric methods; and α is the specific refractivity increment, having a value of 0.0018 for proteins and 0.0016 for nucleic acids.

It can readily be seen that when the thickness is known, the refractive index can be determined, or conversely, when the refractive index is known, the thickness can be determined. At times, when tissues or other biological material are placed in media of known refractive indices, both the thickness and refractive index of the unknown can be determined.

With interference microscopy, changes in dry mass can be determined during growth and division of cell cultures (Mitchison, 1957). Changes in colloid deposition and other secretions can be studied, and an estimation of enzyme activity such as alkaline phosphatase activity in kidney tissue can be made (Barter et al., 1955).

Polarizing microscopy

Many compounds of biological importance such as fibers and crystals, which have a high degree of molecular orientation, exhibit *anisotropy* when examined under polarized light. These substances show differences in the velocity or light transmission in different directions. Such substances are also referred to as being *birefringent* because they show a double diffraction. *Isotropic* materials, on the other hand, have the same velocity of light transmission in all directions when polarized light passes through them.

The basis of the polarizing microscope is similar to that of a conventional microscope except that a *polarizer* is placed in front of the condenser and an *analyzer* is placed beyond the objective in the ocular. The polarizer and analyzer can be made either of Iceland spar or sheets of Polaroid film. The latter is preferred because correcting lenses are not needed. The ratio of light transmission when the polarizer and analyzer are in parallel and in crossed position is known as the *extinction factor.* Normally no light is transmitted beyond the analyzer when it is in a crossed position in relation to the polarizer.

When a beam of polarized light impinges on a substance showing high molecular orientation, it is split into two rays that are perpendicular to one another. One of these rays, the *ordinary* ray (Θ_0), obeys the law of refraction, whereas the other ray, known as the *extraordinary* (Θ_e) ray, passes through the material with a different velocity. On emerging, these rays recombine with a phase difference between the two. This phase difference or birefringence can be expressed by the formula

$$\Upsilon\ (\text{retardation}) = \Theta_e - \Theta_o\ t$$

where Θ_e is the extraordinary ray; Θ_o is the ordinary ray; and t is the thickness. Retardation or birefringence can be expressed in wavelengths either in Ångstroms or in millimicrons.

It can be seen from examination of the

formula that birefringence can be either positive or negative. Positive birefringence occurs when the refractive index parallel to a certain axis is greater than the refractive index of polarized light passing perpendicular to the axis. The converse is true for negative birefringence. That is, the refractive index of polarized light passing perpendicular to the axis is greater than that of the polarized light passing parallel to it. By and large, most biological fibers are uniaxial and show positive birefringence. For example, most proteins show a positive birefringence, whereas the birefringence of nucleic acids is negative. Some biological fibers may occasionally appear isotropic to polarized light. This is due at times to the presence of lipids, which are orientated in such a manner as to cancel out the positive birefringence of the protein. Extraction of the lipid moieties can usually reveal the positive value of the fiber.

Important distinction should be made between *intrinsic, form, strain,* and *streaming* birefringence as well as *dichroism.* Intrinsic birefringence, also known as *crystalline birefringence,* is due to the regularity of molecular arrangement of the compound. Consequently, it is independent of the refractive index of the medium in which the substance is placed. Form birefringence is due to submicroscopic asymmetrical particles or micelles, which may not necessarily be individually crystalline but are regularly orientated. Form birefringence disappears when the material is placed in a medium having a refractive index equal to that of the substance. By placing the substance in media of different refractive indices, one can distinguish between form and intrinsic birefringence as well as estimate the amount that each contributes to the total birefringence. Strain birefringence is the result of anisotropy, which occurs when an isotropic substance such as muscle is subjected to a strain such as stretching. Strain birefringence disappears when the strain is removed and the substance reverts back to its original shape or condition. Streaming birefringence occurs when asymmetrical particles in a solution tend to orient themselves in the direction of flow. However, when the streaming ceases, the solution becomes isotropic to polarized light.

Dichroism, or *anisotropic absorption,* occurs most commonly in structures containing chemical groupings that absorb light anisotropically. These changes are in the amplitude of the transmitted light. Dichroism can be induced in a number of biological materials with the use of certain stains. For example, dichroism can be produced in cellulose stained with Congo red. Similarly, with the use of a metallic salt such as silver nitrate, dichroism can be studied in some plant material. There is an apparent orientation of the stain molecules along the axis of the fibers to produce the dichroism observed.

Another example of material showing dichroic structure is chloroplast; when hemoglobin is observed by blue light, it also exhibits strong dichroism (Frey-Wyssling, 1957). It has also been shown that the eyes of bees probably contain three dichroic structures; this most likely explains the sensitivity of their eyes to polarized light.

Ultraviolet microscopy

The early development of the ultraviolet microscope was an attempt, in part, by microscopists to increase the power of resolution. From the formula used to determine the resolving power of the microscope it can readily be seen that the power of resolution will increase if a shorter wave-length is used. Unfortunately, however, when using radiations of wavelengths below 4,000 Å, glass lenses normally used for visible light are no longer transparent. Instead, lenses composed of fused quartz, calcium fluorite, or lithium carbonate must replace the glass lenses.

Although the power of resolution was increased by using radiation between 2,000 and 4,000 Å, the disadvantages outweigh the advantages gained in resolution. As it turned out, ultraviolet microscopy was damaging to the eyes, and therefore photographic techniques were necessary; when living cell cultures were used, the germicidal action of the ultraviolet radiation often destroyed the cells or the radiation caused genetic defects and other nuclear changes.

At one time ultraviolet microscopy was used in the study of colloid particles. The shorter wavelength allowed the observer to study particles in solution that were not observable with routine light microscopy. These colloid particles were visible but not resolvable. Hence the ultraviolet microscope was often referred to as the ultramicroscope.

The importance of the ultraviolet microscope since about 1940 has not been the increased power of resolution but its value in the fields of fluorescence microscopy and ultraviolet cytophotometry. In fluorescence microscopy the specimen, previously treated with a special stain, is illuminated by ultraviolet or ultraviolet blue light. These wavelengths excite the fluorochrome to produce visible fluorescence (see section on fluorescence microscopy in Chapter 1).

Dark-field microscopy

Dark-field microscopy is based on the fact that light is scattered at the boundaries between phases of different refractive indices. The dark-field microscope can be considered as a conventional microscope in which the usual condenser is replaced by one that causes the light to illuminate the object obliquely, with no direct light entering the objective. As a result, the specimen appears bright and the background dark. For example, in cells the organelles such as the nucleus, mitochondria, and granules appear bright against a dark background (Fig. 2-4). As in the case of the ultraviolet microscope, objects smaller than those observed by bright-field microscopy are visible as shining dots but cannot be resolved.

ELECTRON MICROSCOPY

Prior to the invention of the electron microscope, microscopists were hampered by the limitation placed on them by the wavelength of light. Attempts to increase the resolving power by the introduction of a shorter wavelength such as ultraviolet radiation proved futile. To be sure, the

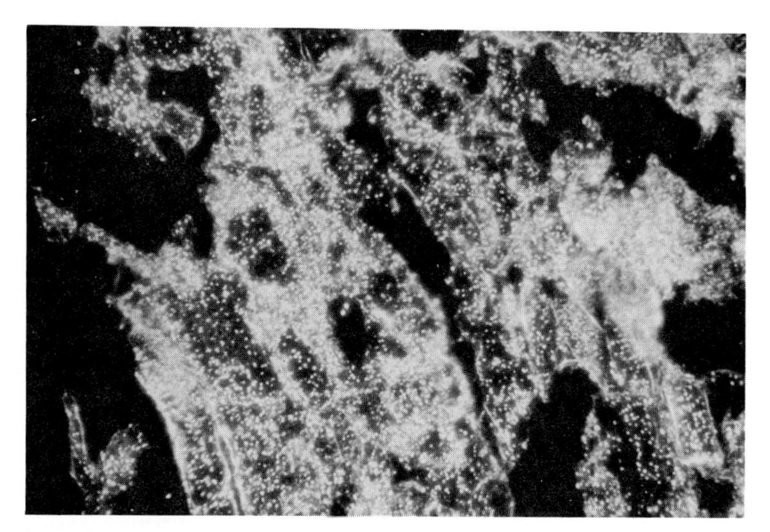

Fig. 2-4. Photomicrograph illustrating dark-field microscopy. The background is dark and the cellular inclusions are white.

resolving power was increased somewhat, but direct observations were not possible without the use of photographic plates. Physicists, particularly, were interested in trying to find a suitable type of radiation that would provide more extensive power of resolution. In 1924 de Broglie proposed an interesting hypothesis in which he stated that electrons under certain conditions may have characteristics of waves. In an instrument based on this phenomenon the optical system would be different from that of light microscopes in that glass optics would be useless. Instead, the optical system would be composed of electromagnetic lenses that would cause deflection of the charged particles, the electrons. In the 1930s the first electron microscope, based on the hypothesis of de Broglie, was constructed in Germany. Its subsequent success initiated the era of ultrastructural research in the physical and biological sciences. Image formation, however, was different from that obtained by the conventional light microscope. In light microscopy, image formation (contrast) depends on the various degrees of absorption of light. In the electron microscope, image formation and object details are represented by degrees of electron scattering, which can be considered equivalent to absorption.

As in the case of light microscopy, the power of resolution depends on the wavelength of the radiation. In the electron microscope the electrons have very short wavelengths.

According to the formula of de Broglie, the wavelength of the electrons is inversely proportional to the root of the voltage as follows:

$$\frac{12.3}{\sqrt{v}}$$

For example, if the voltage used is 100 kv (100,000 v), the wavelength is about 0.04 Å; that is:

$$\lambda = \frac{12.3}{\sqrt{100{,}000}} = \frac{12.3}{100\ \sqrt{10}}$$

Considering the wavelength of electrons at 100 kv to be about 0.04 Å, this should, by comparison with the wavelength of light (5,500 Å), improve the power of resolution approximately 140,000 times, that is, $\frac{5{,}500}{0.04}$. Unfortunately, this is not the case. Because imperfections of the magnetic lenses cause aberrations, it is impossible to attain the theoretical resolution of the ideal electron microscope. Instead, using the accelerating voltage of 100 kv, about the best one can hope to obtain at the present time is a resolution of about 8 Å, with an average routine resolution of about 10 to 15 Å or more.

The basis of the electron microscope is no different from that of the light microscope. The electrons are emitted at the cathode and are accelerated by the voltage at the anode. The latter contains a circular aperture through which the electrons pass at a constant velocity. There are magnetic lenses, the condenser, which concentrates the electrons on the specimen (much the same as in the light microscope) and then on a second magnetic coil that acts as the objective lens and magnifies the image. This is then received by the third lens, the ocular or projector lens, which projects the magnified image on a fluorescent screen for visual observation or on photographic film.

Scanning electron microscopy

Although the basic principle of the scanning electron microscope was suggested as far back as 1935, it was not until recently that it has been perfected and made available for physical and biological sciences. Scanning electron microscopy provides a methodology for studying solid specimens directly, particularly surfaces or surface characteristics that cannot be studied by conventional electron microscopy. The micrographs obtained by scanning electron microscopy provide the observer considerable depth of focus.

The principle involved in scanning electron microscopy is comparable to that in the conventional electron microscope. The electrons liberated from the specimen are detected by a scintillator-photomultiplier, which is synchronized with the electron probe scanner of the specimen. The resolution of the scanning electron microscope is 200 Å or less. The specimen is prepared by depositing vaporized metal at an angle on the surface, and the object is shadowed using the standard shadowing technique (Fig. 15-8).

Techniques used in preparing sections for electron microscopy

Two major obstacles present in electron microscopy require the use of specialized techniques that differ from the procedures used in light microscopy. One of the obstacles is the poor penetration of the electrons in tissues. If the sections are thick, the image seen is almost totally opaque, with little or no contrast. Therefore the thinner the section the better will be the resolution. However, too thin sections also lack contrast. At the present time it is possible to obtain sections as thin as 200 Å. The other major obstacle is that the tissues must be completely dry or dehydrated, since the specimen to be studied is placed in a high vacuum.

The tissue being prepared for study must be fixed with a minimal delay in order to prevent structural changes that would be readily observable under the electron microscope. Originally, the tissues were fixed in osmium tetroxide (O_sO_4). However, other fixatives such as glutaraldehyde followed by fixation in osmium have been used. In addition, formaldehyde and freeze-dry techniques have been used. The fixatives are most effective at a physiological pH, that is, 7.4. After fixation the tissues are dehydrated and embedded. At the present time a number of embedding compounds are available. They include epoxy resin (Epon 812), Maraglas, Durcupan, Ciba, Vestopal-W, Araldite, methacrylates (butyl and methyl methacrylates), and a water-soluble hydroxypropyl methacrylate. The latter may prove useful in the field of electron microscopic enzyme histochemistry. After embedding the tissues are cut using an ultramicrotome with a glass or diamond knife (Fig. 2-5). The ultramicrotome may have either a direct mechanical or a thermal advance, depending on the design. The sections are then placed on a grid coated with an extremely thin film of either Formvar, collodion, or carbon.

To improve the contrast the sections can be stained with "electron stains." These consist of heavy metal salts that are used for general contrast or to bring out specific structures. For example, osmium, which was used in the fixation, reacts with unsaturated fatty acids and is subsequently reduced; its deposition corresponds to the cell and organelle membranes. Some additional stains are potassium permanganate for both membrane and desmosomes, phosphotungstic acid for collagen, and lead salts (citrates, acetates, or hydroxides) for ribosomes and nucleic acids. These and other heavy metals, because of their high atomic number, increase the electron scattering and therefore improve the contrast.

Other techniques employed in electron microscopy include shadowing, spreading, negative staining, and freeze replication.

Shadowing. Shadowing consists of vaporizing dense metals in a vacuum. On striking the specimen at a low angle (like sunlight on the moon), the metal condenses on one side of an irregularity but not on the other (the shadow side). This method produces a three-dimensional image that not only improves contrast but also produces a depth that can add invaluable information. Specimens such as viruses, bacteria, and macromolecules can be studied by this shadow-casting method, as can large objects in scanning electron microscopy (Fig. 4-8).

Spreading. Filamentous molecules such as DNA, chromosomes, and viruses can be studied by spreading specimens on a water

Fig. 2-5. A, Ultramicrotome used for cutting thin sections for electron microscopy. This ultramicrotome is automatic and has a direct advance mechanism. Other ultramicrotomes may have a thermal advance mechanism rather than the direct drive. **B,** Close-up showing capsule containing the specimen. A glass knife is also visible immediately below the tissue. Diamond knives are also available for cutting tissue.

surface in a film of protein. This method takes advantage of cell lysis when the specimen is changed from a hypertonic to a hypotonic solution.

Negative staining. Negative staining is useful in the studying of tiny objects such as viruses, bacteria, and isolated cell organelles (mitochondrial membranes, ribosomes). This method consists of placing the specimen in a drop of "stain" such as phosphotungstic acid. The metal atoms penetrate between and around the smallest spaces and structures of the specimen and reveal images not seen by other methods. The spaces will appear well defined in negative contrast (Figs. 4-1 and 14-1).

Freeze replication. Freeze replication consists of a method whereby the tissue is frozen rapidly in liquid nitrogen or liquid helium. The tissue is then cleaved mechanically. In the cleavage the ice often cracks along the planes of membrane structure. This will give the topography of a pattern of membranes and organelles along the fractured surface. After cleavage the surface is shadow-cast in a vacuum. The tissue is dissolved away and the metal coating is then examined under the electron microscope.

The advantage of the freeze replication technique is that no chemical fixatives or stains are used. Thus membranes can be studied as they respond to a given physiological environment rather than to a fixative environment (Branton, 1966). Furthermore, all surfaces exposed are three dimensional, in which spatially extended areas of membranes can be studied.

X-RAY MICROSCOPY AND X-RAY DIFFRACTION

X rays, because of their short wavelengths, were first used to investigate crystalline structures. Their use in biological research has been fairly recent, being applied to obtain structural details and also the dry mass distribution of cells and tissues. In addition, x-ray diffraction studies have provided much information as to the structure of biologically important macromolecules such as fibrous and globular proteins, and DNA.

X-ray microscopy

Among the techniques employed are *microradiography* and *projection x-ray microscopy*. The simplest of the techniques consists of placing the tissue directly on a fine-grain photographic film and exposing it to x rays (preferably soft rays within the range of 1 to 10 Å). The tissue thickness should be less than 1 μm. This method is also referred to as the direct-contact method. A second method, called the projection method, consists of separation of the tissue from the photographic film. This allows for the enlargement of the image produced by the x ray.

As was mentioned, x-ray microscopy is invaluable for quantitative determination of cells. This method is based on the concept that monochromatic x rays are absorbed by biological tissue and that each of the elements has a specific limit of absorption of x rays. For example, carbon has a specific absorption edge at 43.5 Å, oxygen at 23.5 Å, nitrogen at 31.1 Å, and phosphorus at 5.77 Å. As a result, the presence of the elements within the cells is not only detected but can be quantitated by this means.

X-ray diffraction

When radiation impinges on matter, it becomes scattered. Thus if a monochromatic x ray having a wavelength of 1.54 Å is used, it will be diffracted by the specimen. The resulting pattern of this diffraction can be considered as a reflection of its structure. One can therefore see the detail of the structure on an atomic scale. If the material being studied has a periodic structure, the atoms are arranged in an orderly array. It is this regularity that impresses itself on the pattern of scattered radiation.

The technique of x-ray diffraction has a wide application in the study of crystal structures, both inorganic and organic. Thus one can determine not only the precise spatial relationships of atoms comprising the crystal but the orientation of the crystal pattern in the material being studied as well. The latter has important implications in the field of electronics in discerning the proper orientations of crystals within materials to be used. The use of x-ray diffraction studies has become an important phase in the newer field of molecular biology in determining the molecular patterns and structures of a number of macromolecules that are important in biology and cytology. These include collagen, hemoglobin, DNA, and a number of other substances of biological importance.

The basis of x-ray diffraction consists of passing a monochromatic beam through the object to be studied. The scattering or diffraction pattern observed is recorded on a photographic emulsion, which is placed beyond the specimen. The beam is made monochromatic by the use of a crystal monochromator, which is usually made of calcite. This crystal serves as a diffraction grating to obtain the monochromatic x ray. (In x-ray studies of this type the Kα line of copper, which has a wavelength of 1.54 Å, is most frequently used.)

The pattern observed on the photographic plate may consist of a series of concentrically arranged spots or bands that are caused by the interferences of the different diffracted rays. The distance between the dark bands or spots and the center is dependent on the space between the regularly repeating units of the specimen. In diffraction studies the smaller the angle of diffraction produced by the specimen, the greater the distance between the spots or repeating units and, in general, the greater the regularity of the spacings.

In diffraction studies of a crystal one can imagine that it is composed of a three-dimensional lattice structure in which the atoms are arranged in a regular fashion along their major axis. The interplanar distance is the distance of the superimposed lattice structure. This distance can be determined by the application of Bragg's law

$$N\lambda = 2d \text{ sine } \theta$$

where N is the order of reflection, which is an integral number; λ is the wavelength (usually 1.54 Å); d is the interplanar distance; and θ is the angle of incidence. Thus d can be expressed as follows:

$$d = \frac{N\lambda}{2 \text{ sine } \theta}$$

One of the biggest problems encountered in the study of biological macromolecules by x-ray diffraction techniques is the great number of atoms involved as well as the irregularities of the molecular architecture. Yet despite the difficulties, significant studies have been made in the elucidation of many macromolecules. The Watson-Crick double helix of DNA is an example known to most biologists.

LITERATURE CITED

Barter, R., J. F. Danielli, and H. G. Davies. 1955. A quantitative cytochemical method for estimating alkaline phosphatase activity. Proc. Roy. Soc. [Biol.] **44:**412-426.

Frey-Wyssling, A. 1957. Macromolecules in cell structure. Harvard University Press, Cambridge.

Mitchison, J. M. 1957. The growth of single cells. I. Schizosaccharomyces pombe. Exp. Cell Res. **13:**244-262.

GENERAL REFERENCES

Agar, A. W. 1961. The operation of the electron microscope. In D. Kay (editor). Techniques for electron microscopy. Blackwell Scientific Publications, Ltd., Oxford.

AO-Baker interference microscope. American Optical Co., Buffalo.

Barer, R. 1952. Interference microscopy and mass determination. Nature (London) **169:**366.

Bartels, P. The new Leitz interference microscope. Leitz, Inc., New York.

Branton, D. 1966. Fracture faces of frozen membranes. Proc. Nat. Acad. Sci. U.S.A. **55:**1048-1056.

Davies, H. G., and M. H. F. Wilkins. 1952. Interference microscopy and mass determination. Nature (London) **169:**541.

Guinier, A. 1963. X-ray diffraction. W. H. Freeman & Co., Publishers, San Francisco.
Kay, R. H. 1964. Experimental biology. Measurements and analysis. Reinhold Publishing Corp., New York.
Lipson, H., and C. A. Taylor. 1958. Fourier transforms and x-ray diffraction. G. Bell & Sons, Ltd., London.
Martin, L. C. 1966. The theory of the microscope. American Elsevier Publishing Co., Inc., New York.
Oster, G. 1955. Birefringence and dichroism. In G. Oster and A. W. Pollister (editors). Physical techniques in biological research. Vol. 1, pp. 439-460. Academic Press, Inc., New York.
Oster, G. 1956. X-ray diffraction and scattering. In G. Oster and A. W. Pollister (editors). Physical techniques in biological research. Vol. 2. pp. 441-466. Academic Press, Inc., New York.
Pease, D. C. 1964. Histological techniques for electron microscopy. 2nd ed. Academic Press, Inc., New York.
Reference manual AO series 10 phase microscope equipment. American Optical Co., Buffalo.

CHAPTER 3

Protoplasm

During the 1700s, it gradually became evident that the cell, the tiny compartment found by Hooke (1665), really contained some sort of material. Corti in 1774 reported movement within the cell walls of the huge plant cells of *Nitella* and *Chara*. Fontana in 1781 saw structures that were probably nuclei and perhaps also nucleoli within the epithelial cells of eels. Numerous observations during the first 30 years of the nineteenth century indicated the general presence of nearly structureless transparent material within the plant cell walls and animal cell membranes, and gradually it was realized that it was the contained substance which was actually the biologically important material, not the wall. In 1831 Robert Brown generalized that the nucleus is a characteristic structure of plant cells. Dujardin in 1835 called this thick, viscous, structureless, transparent material of the animal cell *sarcode*. A year later Valentin discussed the sarcode of a variety of animal cell types. Purkinje in 1839 used the term *"protoplasm"* for this material in plant cells. The same year von Mohl, and a few years later Nageli, related sarcode to protoplasm and concluded that the protoplasm of plant and animal cells was basically the same. Cohn (1850) and Virchow (1858) stressed the continuity of protoplasmic life, and the statement of Huxley in 1868 that protoplasm is "the physical basis of life" demonstrated that it had finally been established that the protoplasm is the really important biological material. Thus the concept of what a cell is developed simultaneously with the cell theory itself and is now a fundamental part of that theory. Still later the protoplasm was recognized as having two seemingly universal constituents, the *cytoplasma* (Kölliker, 1867) and the *kernplasm* or *nucleoplasm* (Strasburger, 1879).

The term "protoplasm" means "first formed" and had been applied earlier to Adam. The term reflects awareness of the fundamental nature of the material.

Simultaneously with that awareness the main chemical component of protoplasm was named *protein,* meaning "first," implying that the material is of first importance in life and closely related to protoplasm itself. In fact, one of the first cytochemical tests developed during the nineteenth century was the use of iodine solution to turn protein brown.

Since about 1850, the term "cell" has been applied to the living stuff, the protoplasm. The cell is the protoplasm and the protoplasm is the cell, although the walls in plants, fungi, and prokaryotes (bacteria, blue-green algae, etc.) are considered to be part of the cell.

Protoplasm has been described as the living stuff of organisms and cells. That is true. But on the other hand, are any of the particular subdivisions of protoplasm "living"? Is the plasma membrane, or a ribosome, or a Golgi apparatus, or a chromosome, or an enzyme, or pure hyaloplasm "living"? A good case can be made for the claim that a mitochondrion or plastid is "living," but are *their* contained ribosomes, or membranes, or genetic material "living"? The answer to these questions is probably not. No single visible structure or invisible molecule, such as a vesicle or ribosome or chromosome, no enzyme or messenger RNA polymer, no microtubule or membrane is, by itself, "living." What can be described as living is the organized system consisting of all such essential structures, polymers, and molecules functioning properly within adequate internal (substrate) and external environments. That is a properly functioning cell is living, but no individual unit of the system is "living." Protoplasm, then, can be "living" if it consists of an adequate mass that contains an adequate and proper number of each essential structure, polymer, molecule, and ion in the proper condition and the whole within an adequately proper environment.

Living also involves time, and for protoplasm to continue to live and function properly it must continue to maintain its adequacy. It must constantly produce the correct RNAs so that it can produce the proper proteins because RNAs and enzymes do not last long. That is, these and all cellular organic molecules and polymers except DNA must be constantly produced because they are constantly being destroyed. This is called *turnover,* a characteristic of living and of protoplasm. On the other hand, not just any proteins and molecules are produced. Each cell can produce only those for which it has the particular genes; it can produce no others. It is limited in its synthetic capacity by its inherited genetic content. But at any particular time a cell rarely has all genes functioning; many are inhibited temporarily or for long periods of time. Thus the same cell at different periods of its existence will differ in its structural and molecular content, and different cells vary widely, especially with respect to those structures and functions that are above and beyond those that are essential for the fundamental aspects of life.

The protoplasm of a cell, therefore, is a complex, specifically integrated and coordinated, rigorously balanced, dynamic, self-maintaining, and regulating system of organic molecules, polymers, structures, inorganic ions, and water that exists within an adequate external environment. The infinity of cell, tissue, organ, and organismal types present on earth indicate the plasticity of the basic "cell" that evolution has manipulated.

Biology and related subjects are studies of protoplasm, and cytology, the subject of this book, is the study of the protoplasm composing individual cells.

The protoplasm of a single cell is called a *protoplast,* consisting of the plasma membrane and all inside it except perhaps any nonliving material such as certain crystals, starch or glycogen grains, the contents of vacuoles, and stored fats. Protoplasm is the living stuff, now known to be complex in structure and possessing to some extent in every cell all of the unique structures and functions that characterize life, especially heritable coded information for self-sufficient metabolic activity and the functional structures required for that activity.

Differentiated cells are those that exploit or overemphasize a very limited number of those structural functions to the exclusion of many others. Evolution of multicellular organisms has consisted partly of the specialization of a number of highly differentiated cell types to form the various tissues and organs of the integrated whole individual. Often differentiation has produced cells of external forms that are far removed from the concept of a "typical" cell (for example, nerve cells, muscle cells, and retinal cells of animals and phloem, pollen grain, and root hair cells of plants).

Such cells often differentiate internally an overabundance of some speciality, for example, glandular secretion, cytoplasmic membranous or fibrous structures containing special molecules such as myosin or actin of muscle fibers, and chlorophyll of the photosynthetic membranous apparatus. Nevertheless, all such highly differentiated cells must retain the minimum of essential structures and functions to remain alive. Actually, some cells differentiate and die, for example, the outer skin cells, red blood corpuscles, and many plant cells.

Except for certain "lower" forms such as bacteria, blue-green algae, or actinomycetes, which may be called *procells,* all other kinds of organisms consist of one or an orderly aggregate of eucells (Fig. 3-1). The *eucell* contains within the plasma membrane a mass of *cytoplasm* and within the cytoplasm a more or less spherical membrane-enveloped structure called the *nucleus.* In turn, both cytoplasm and nucleus contain structures of various functions suspended in the nearly structureless ground substance called *hyaloplasm* and *nucleoplasm,* respectively. Eucells are almost always much larger than procells, the protoplasmic density is

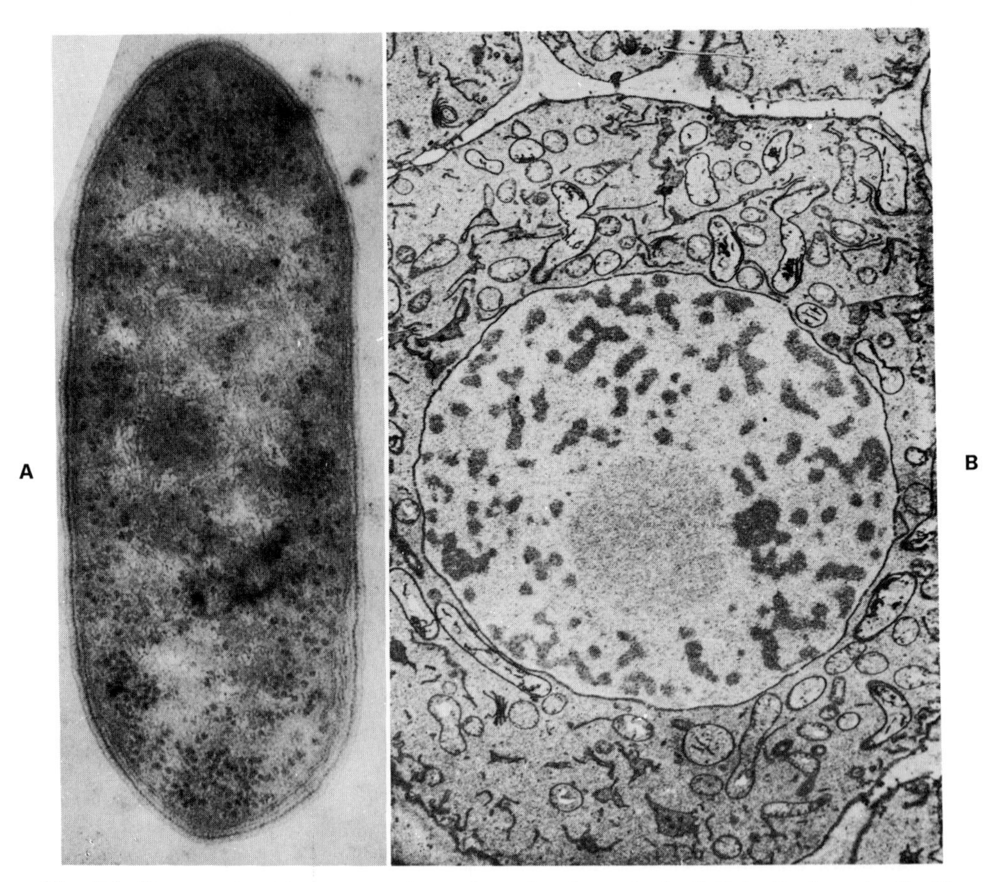

Fig. 3-1. Note contrast between prokaryotic and eukaryotic "cells." **A,** Prokaryote *Bacillus thiaminolyticus.* **B,** Eukaryotic cell from corn root tip. The differences are obvious. The magnification of the bacillus is much greater than the root tip cell. Actually, it is about the size of a mitochondrion or leukoplast in the root tip cell. (**A** courtesy Dr. J. L. Wittliff, Dr. J. F. Smith, and Dr. R. L. Airth; **B** courtesy University of Texas Cell Research Institute, Austin, Texas.)

much lower, and the fluidity is much greater. Nothing like protoplasmic streaming probably occurs in procells.

Procell protoplasm (Figs. 3-1, *A,* 13-12, and 15-1), on the other hand, is largely devoid of the familiar subcellular structures characteristic of eucells. Except for the few photosynthetic bacteria and blue-green algae, the protoplasm contains few if any membranous structures within the plasma membrane itself. The so-called nucleus, or *prokaryon,* is not limited by any membrane, and the details of "nuclear" division are poorly understood. In general, the protoplasm of procells is very dense and there is no endoplasmic reticulum (ER), vacuole, mitochondrion, etc., but the region outside the nucleus is packed with ribosomes. From time to time electron microscopy reveals some few structures of presently unknown functions. It is likely that the procell plasma membrane carries on all or most of the cellular functions that require membranes. Certainly the procell is remarkably different from the eucell, and so these terms are useful and meaningful.

Viruses and phages (to be discussed in Chapter 4) are even smaller and simpler than procells. Actually, the concept of protoplasm does not apply to them. They do contain RNA or DNA (but not both) and protein, but the structure is not a functioning, living, metabolic system. Without the protoplasm of a host cell to take control of, they achieve nothing that could be called "living."

Minimum mass

At this point the concept of minimum mass warrants inclusion (Morowitz and Tourtellotte, 1962). According to this concept there is a hypothetical and practical minimum protoplasmic mass below which active metabolic life cannot persist. Three points are made. First, a mass of protoplasm to be alive must have a plasma membrane. It has been well established that plasma membranes are approximately 75 Å thick, which means that an organism must have a diameter of at least 150 Å. Second, it has been estimated that to be described as living, a mass of protoplasm must contain enzymes for a minimum of about 100 reactions as well as molecules of substrate. These requirements would fill a volume of about 400 Å diameter. If, in addition, a long DNA double helix, various RNAs, and ribosomes sufficient to synthesize 100 different enzymes are required, a diameter of about 500 Å is needed. Thus a 500 Å mass surrounded by a 75 Å membrane would produce a minimum organism of about 650 Å diameter. Third, the famous physicist Schrödinger, in a discussion of life as an interested physicist sees it, points out that "living" is and must be an orderly process. However, all atoms and molecules at the temperature of life are in constant thermal motion (as demonstrated by brownian movement and diffusion), and so order is achieved statistically by large enough numbers of molecules, that is, by considerable redundancy, so that a uniform enough average is attained. The smaller the mass the more sensitive it is to thermal agitation or, as Schrödinger (1956) stated, an organism must have a comparatively gross structure to enjoy the benefit of fairly accurate laws, both for its internal life and for its interplay with the external environment. These things being physically true, even a 650 Å "organism" would be of very small mass.

Assuming, then, a 600 to 700 Å mass of "living" protoplasm, it would consist of about 3 to 4 million atoms, of about 75,000 to 100,000 molecules of the order of amino acids or nucleotides, and therefore of about 150 to 200 macromolecules such as protein or nucleic acid.

Actually, a 650 Å diameter is about the average size of viruses (they range from less than 300 to 5,000 Å) and about half the diameter of the smallest known "organisms," the rickettsias and the Mycoplasmatales. Perhaps organisms smaller than these exist; perhaps the figures given are incorrect and organisms smaller than about 1,000 Å diameter are impossible because far more redundancy than only two or three of each kind of ribosome or enzyme molecule is required. Therefore most viruses could not be alive; they are too small as well as lacking metabolism.

Plasmodia

It must not be assumed that all organisms consist of typical cells. The procells constitute one example. Some whole organisms that have the eucell type of protoplasm (numerous algae, protozoa, fungi, and especially Myxomycetes) consists of continuous cytoplasm undivided by plasma membranes or cell walls and have numerous scattered nuclei (Figs. 3-2 and 3-4). The myxomycete condition is called a *plasmodium* and technically is not cellular. The noncellular algae and fungi, which are filamentous and tubular, have a structure called a *coenocyte.* Among animals certain tissues may be noncellular, possibly striated muscle fibers or the epidermis of various Aschelminthes, for example. These are described by the word *"syncytium."* But in all of these, as in typical cellular structures, each nucleus "controls" its surrounding cytoplasm by the RNA (messenger and transfer) that it produces for the local protein synthesis. Some other examples of "free nuclear" protoplasm are the early embryos of insects, the early endosperm of many flowering plants, proembryos of gymnosperms and peony, the ameba-like *Pelomyxa* and other multinucleate Sarcodina, and the osteoclasts of vertebrates.

Although vigorous and heated attempts were made around 1900 either to fit these noncellular conditions (and also the cell wall) into the cell theory or exclude them, the present-day biologist considers them as natural conditions that do fit into an adequately broad concept of "the cell." Throughout biology such exceptions to man-made categories occur; in fact, they are to be expected.

Water

Protoplasm is generally described as a thick, elastic, contractile, viscous, transparent, proteinaceous colloid of about 80% water. It must be emphasized that the water is indeed part of the protoplasm and not just an inorganic solvent. No molecule known is living; life is the activity of a complex but orderly mass of matter. Water is as fundamental to life and as much a part of protoplasm as nucleic acids or proteins.

The water content of protoplasm usually remains constant. Further evidence that water is part of the protoplasm is illustrated by cellular death when heavy water (D_2O) replaces normal water in the protoplasm. Protoplasm is a dynamically stable, open

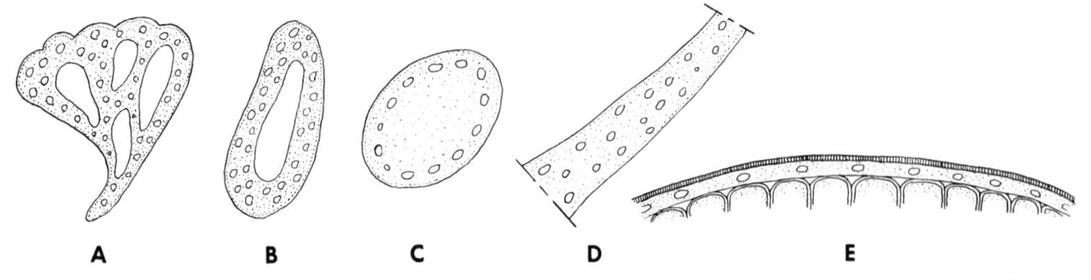

Fig. 3-2. Plasmodium, coenocyte, and syncytium showing nuclei in cytoplasm. **A,** Plasmodium, as in slime molds. **B,** Coenocyte of early embryo sac typical of many angiosperms with free early endosperm nuclei. **C,** Syncytial early embryo of an arthropod having superficial cleavage. **B** and **C** might also represent the gymnosperm female gametophyte or proembryo. **D,** Coenocytic filament of some algae and fungi in which there are no cross walls. **E,** Portion of syncytial epidermis of a rotifer covered externally with cuticle.

system of biochemical reactions. As such, water is constantly entering into molecules, for example, during hydrolysis, and leaving them during condensation and polymerization. Protein molecules and also ions such as K^+ and Na^+ are normally hydrated; that is, many water molecules are associated electrostatically or by hydrogen bonds with these other molecules and ions. This condition results from the dipole structure of the water molecule, positive at the hydrogen end and negative around the oxygen atom. It is the hydration of the proteins that produces the colloidal (gluey) consistency of protoplasm. Furthermore, all the water molecules in a cell could be bound to one another by hydrogen bonds between the protons of one water molecule and the oxygen of two others.

Even *pure* water, which is usually taken for granted as simple, is being found by the physicist to be a most unusual substance, with hitherto undreamed-of and still fantastic peculiarities; it is not even a typical liquid! If water were merely isolated molecules of H_2O, it would boil at $-168°$ C and would be lighter than ice; there would be no life on earth. Neither would it have the unique characteristics of viscosity, dielectric constant, surface tension, etc., that it has. There may be "kinks," or discontinuities, in certain physical properties at 30°, 45°, and 60° C. It is now considered to be a mixture of orderly crystalline arrays or clethrate-like "cages" and disordered (liquid) molecules. The structured arrays of 50 to 100 or more molecules last for about 10^{-11} seconds and "flicker" or "flip" on and off or collapse and re-form like waves. Water arrays may even determine to some extent macromolecular organic structure and, perhaps, protoplasmic function. These flickerings and orderly arrays of water molecules may be fundamental to life. The lethality of heavy water demonstrates the basic biochemical importance of water in protoplasm. Heavy water molecules (or O—D radicles) possess a different structure (bond length, for example) than H—O—H or O—H so that in enzymes the conformation of the globular protein is different, making it functionless, and thus the cell dies. Life has evolved in H_2O not D_2O, and the latter cannot replace the former in a living system. It must always be remembered that protoplasm is about 80% water and that fixed material for optical or electron microscopy is dehydrated and therefore abnormal and, to some extent, an artifact.

Of course, the water content may vary even in different parts of a protoplast. In some cells the outer region of the cytoplasm is often more viscous *(ectoplasm)* and has fewer ultrastructures than the inner cytoplasm *(endoplasm)*. Furthermore, a particular region may change from a more viscous *(gel)* to a less viscous *(sol)* condition and back again under some internal stimuli, as seems to occur in an ameboid cell when it moves by pseudopodial flowing.

Characteristics of life

Many biologists believe that a single protoplast possesses, perhaps only at a low level, all of the fundamental abilities possessed by any and all differentiated cells. It is *irritable;* that is, it is aware of conditions and changes in its environment such as temperature, acidity, light, pressure, chemicals, vibrations, and contact. Many unspecialized cells can respond by movement as do muscles, secrete as do gland cells, and transmit messages from one part of the cell to another as do nerve cells. Certainly the organs of a fish can be matched by the organelles of a complex ciliate.

It has often been stated that protoplasm does not act; rather it reacts to any change in order to reestablish, if possible, its optimum internal condition regardless of external changes. This characteristic of cells and organisms is called *homeostasis* and is often achieved by some sort of negative feedback system. Minor or major changes of homeostatic mechanisms may be described as *adaptations.* For example, marine protozoa do not need to pump out excess water from the protoplasm, but freshwater protozoa do. The latter have adapted to fresh water by evolving a water-eliminating pump called the *contractile vacuole,* which maintains the proper water content of the protoplasm.

The ultrastructures within the protoplasm produce heterogeneity and thereby provide definite places for particular chemical reactions without these reactions interfering with each other. That is, the membrane separates different phases of protoplasm from one another, but since a membrane is actually three dimensional, it constitutes a mediating third phase with which the other two phases are in contact.

Such organelle membranes also provide semirigid structures within which particular enzymes and other molecules may be embedded in an orderly fashion to produce a related sequence of chemical events. Their large surfaces also provide adequate areas of contact for such reactions. Furthermore, the membranes are locally modified into *macromolecular assemblies,* which are solid, three-dimensional, orderly aggregates of a group of specific enzymes and other molecules that are necessary for a closely related sequence of biochemical transformations. Examples are the pyruvate dehydrogenase particle, the hemocyanin particle, the fatty acid synthetase particle, the mitochondrial oxysome, and the photosynthetic quantasome.

One of the almost inconceivable aspects of the activity of a cell is how the subcellular membranous structures and macromolecular assemblies are formed and how they can rapidly increase or decrease in area and number. It can be assumed that there are no "little men" in the cell with hammers, nails, saws, rulers, and other equipment for "building" these structures. Therefore it must be concluded that whenever the proper kinds of molecules are synthesized, they spontaneously and automatically associate with one another in an exact relationship because of the particular forms of the particular molecules. This seems evident, since the molecular constituents can be separated, but when they are again mixed in vitro, the original macromolecular form is automatically reestablished.

The best model for this concept, and it is a simple one, is the duplication of a DNA polymer. After the double helix separates according to this scheme, each base becomes paired with its complementary base and no other (adenine with thymine and cytosine with guanine) because those pairs and only those pairs "fit" together. The "lock and key" model of enzyme action and protein synthesis on the ribosome are other models of particular molecules—only certain molecules that fit, coming together.

The building blocks of protoplasmic structures are, of course, molecules and macromolecules. These are arranged in orderly arrays and complexes because each constituent molecule or macromolecule has a unique structure that relates to and is bonded to other similar or different units; they fit together like parts of a jigsaw puzzle.

In membranes the polar lipid molecules seem to be the basic units that form the typical unit membrane of a layer of lipid sandwiched between two layers of protein. The addition of other specific molecules among these produces other unique types of membranes such as the plasma, Golgi, photosynthetic, endoplasmic reticular, nuclear, and mitochondrial membranes. These general types of membranes can also vary from place to place and from time to time, can increase in area or decrease, and can form membranes of a different type altogether.

Protein structure

Certain nonmembranous structures are formed of proteins more or less exclusively.

Examples are the microtubules, fibers of various sorts such as collagen and muscle fibers, certain crystals, hemoglobin, ribosomes, and the nucleolus. Protein is now considered to have at least four degrees of structure (Fig. 3-3). Its *primary structure* consists of its particular sequence of amino acids, each sequence (and there are thousands) producing a distinct protein. However, any amino acid sequence seems to produce a helix, called the *alpha helix,* because each amino acid is attached to the next at a definite angle. The alpha helix is the *secondary structure* of proteins. Lateral associations of many parallel alpha helices, or "flattened" alpha helices, can produce long and thick fibers such as silk, keratin, myosin, fibrinogen, and collagen. Many proteins, however, assume a more or less spherical configuration by the bending and folding of the alpha helix. This distortion is absolutely definite and depends on the primary structure. This globular form of the protein is its *tertiary structure,* which is made quite permanent by bonds between amino acids that are brought close to one another when the alpha helix is convoluted. For example, disulfide bonds form when two cysteine amino acids are close together, salt bonds can form when a basic amino acid is close to an acid amino acid, and hydrogen bonds and other vaguer forces exist between adjacent parts of the convoluted tertiary structure. *Quaternary structures* are produced when two or more globular proteins, alpha helices, or even primary structures become associated in a predetermined form. Thus the hemoglobin unit consists of four myoglobin (tertiary) units. Long, linear protein filaments of quaternary structure can form. It has been proposed that when a great many tertiary or quaternary protein structures are associated to form sheets, tubes, or filaments, the designation *quinary* structure is appropriate. The various sorts of microtubules that are so common in cells are quinary protein structures composed of thousands of regularly arranged globular proteins. Membranes are in part sheets of quinary protein structure. The protein coat of a virus is another example of quinary protein structure.

One of the best known protein structures is the *collagen fiber* of vertebrate connective tissue. The primary structure is an amino acid sequence. In this case the primary structures do not form alpha helices; they unite in three's parallel to one another but

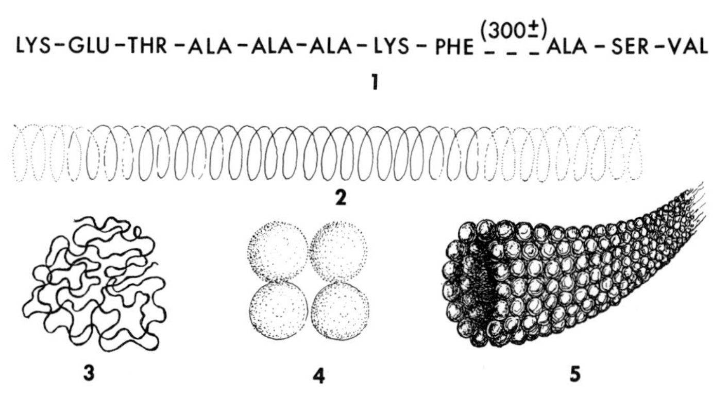

Fig. 3-3. Hierarchy of protein structure. **1,** Primary structure: amino acid sequence, about 1,000 Å long. **2,** Secondary structure: alpha helix of the primary structure, about 250 Å long. **3,** Tertiary structure: convoluted globular form of the alpha helix, 40 to 100 Å in diameter. **4,** Quaternary structure: association of two or a few globular proteins. **5,** Quinary structure: a large structure composed of hundreds or thousands of globular proteins or quaternary structures, as in microtubules and spindle fibers, up to 500,000 Å long or more.

forming a loose helix about 14 Å in diameter, 2,800 Å in length, and polar (the two ends are different). This unit is called *tropocollagen,* and many such units can unite end to end and associate laterally to form fibrils. The lateral union is very exact, the longitudinal head-to-tail unions between tropocollagen units being staggered by one quarter of their lengths laterally so that the unions correspond only in every fifth longitudinal strand. This staggering of unions produces longitudinal strength of the fibril. Fibrils are associated laterally to form the collagen fibers of vertebrate connective tissues seen under the light microscope.

Thus from small molecules of a few Ångstrom dimensions such as amino acids, structures of various subcellular sizes up to micron dimensions can be constructed. Chromosomes, among the largest of cellular organelles, have a definite structure of macromolecules of nucleic acids and various proteins, which must also be bonded to one another because of the structural organization of both the monomers and polymers.

Membrane structure

In some or all membranous structures, however, a preexisting structure seems to be required to start with. When a membranous structure grows, there may have to be some of that particular membrane already there. Thus the membrane increases in extent—it grows. It probably does not grow at an exposed edge because exposed edges of subcellular membranes do not occur; they are closed, as spherical or double membranes. It is likely, therefore, that the proper molecules are inserted into the preexisting membranes at many points. The membrane may grow thusly—by *intussusception.* Fibers such as cellulose microfibrils or microtubules, however, may actually grow at one or both ends.

It is evident, nevertheless, that the final structure does have its proper assortment of molecules exactly positioned with respect to one another in the arrangement necessary for its function. This arrangement is achieved automatically, even though, as in the membranes of mitochondria or chloroplasts, the number of the constituent kinds of molecules is large, consisting as it does of numerous kinds of proteins, lipids, cofactors, and others. It is probably the characteristic structure of each of the molecules that positions it exactly within the macromolecular structures. Since it is the particular set of molecules in exact spatial relationships to each other that permits the function of the molecules and membrane, the structure of the molecule is its function.

The plasma membrane itself is a protoplasmic organelle of unbelievable functional complexity in its multiplicity of activities and controls. It is the contact between the uniformity of internal complex conditions and the variability of the simpler outside environmental conditions. It is also the gateway controlling and even producing inward and outward movement of innumerable molecules and ions between the environment and the open system that is a cell. The open system maintains a constant inflow of matter, of high and low energy, using it to maintain and increase its complexity, its structure, and its low entropy, and simultaneously getting rid of the high entropy waste products. With the exception of DNA all molecules and atoms of the protoplasm are constantly being replaced by new ones, although the cell itself may continue as such for a long time.

Nucleus

Modern cytology still recognizes the two cellular constituents cytoplasm and nucleus. They are different in many ways other than the structures they contain. This difference is best revealed by what happens to each when separated from the other. It is possible to remove an intact nucleus from a cell, leaving an *enucleate cell,* the cytoplasm, and a nucleus nearly free of cytoplasm. When this is done, the nucleus can no longer function when put back into cytoplasm unless the transfer is extremely rapid. An isolated nucleus has a short life, measured in seconds or at most a few minutes.

Enucleate cytoplasm, on the other hand, can live and function to some extent for hours, weeks, or even months. It does lose some abilities of the intact cell and eventually dies, but very slowly. The marine alga *Acetabularia* can live for months after being enucleated, can regenerate lost parts, and can differentiate its cap to some extent. An enucleate ameba ceases to move and feed but lives for a number of days. Ciliary action continues for a long time in enucleate ciliates such as *Stentor*. The persistence of most cytoplasmic activity results from the presence of protein-forming RNA's and enzymes, most of which are exhausted only slowly.

Nevertheless, there are some cellular activities that require the continued presence of the nucleus, such as movement and feeding of amebas and the growth and regeneration of *Stentor*. Danielli et al. (1955) and Lorch and Danielli (1950) concluded that something in the cytoplasm is used up *at once* and is not stored. The nucleus determines the specific character of the macromolecules, but the cytoplasm is more important in the organization of the molecules into functional units. Furthermore, the plastids and mitochondria are almost as self-sufficient as symbiotic organisms living in the cytoplasm.

Movement of organelles

One of the fundamental characteristics of the nucleus is its ability to locate itself in a particular part of the cytoplasm and also to move from place to place within a cell by some sort of movement that is not random but definite, controlled, and predictable. Some examples are the movement of the nucleus in an animal egg cell as it moves to the plasma membrane to eliminate polar bodies, its subsequent movements back to the center of the cell, and the movement of the male nucleus to it to effect fertilization. When paramecia conjugate, a nucleus of each passes into the other. Nuclei move about in the angiosperm embryo sac to produce the triple fusion of the endosperm nucleus and fertilization of the egg. In Basidiomycetes, nuclei have exact pathways during clamp connection cell division. In *Acetabularia* after nuclear divisions the nuclei move from the base into various parts of the cap. Stebbins and Shah have presented evidence that the nucleus of a lateral cell, which is adjacent to two guard mother cells, moves adjacent to one guard mother cell to divide and then moves to and repeats the process opposite the other. As long ago as 1877 Haberlandt reported that the nucleus of a root epidermal cell moves to a certain part of the cell, somehow is responsible for the production of a root hair at that spot, and the nucleus then moves out into the root hair. In certain apomictic plants such as *Rudbeckia* (Battaglia, 1946) and *Cooperia* (Coe, 1953) the male gamete, instead of uniting with the egg nucleus, regularly moves to the base of the egg cell and divides there when the remote egg nucleus divides; this is called *semigamy*. The exact position of each nucleus in each cell of intestinal epithelium is striking.

Of course, cytoplasmic structures other than the nucleus are able to move, apparently autonomously. The nonrandom and predictable movements of chloroplasts in certain leaf cells in response to light intensity, and the movement back to the plasma membrane of chloroplasts that have been separated from it in *Chara* and *Nitella* are examples. There is little doubt that mitochondria aggregate in certain parts of the cell cytoplasm, predictable under certain normal conditions, such as around the nucleus, or into two groups in certain algal mitoses. The regular movement cycle of food vacuoles in ciliates such as *Paramecium* is a determined and predictable movement. Even the nucleolus seems to be able to move (or be moved) within the nucleus or, if persistent, during mitosis. It seems to be well established now that nuclei, nucleoli, mitochondria, vesicles, and plastids can move autonomously through protoplasm. Perhaps chromosomes can also move autonomously.

Protoplasm can also assume wide varieties of shapes. Variously shaped nuclei are known to be typical of certain cells or within particular cells at certain stages. The polymorphic nuclei of certain white blood cells, the gland cells of some insects, and the tube nucleus of pollen grains are examples. And, of course, all the various shapes of differentiated cells are determined by the cells themselves, although often influenced by outside factors around them.

Cytoplasmic movement such as streaming and cyclosis will be discussed later in the chapter. This includes movements of whole cells such as ameboid movement of certain protozoa and the ameboid cells characteristic of nearly all multicellular animals and the movements of cells during embryogenesis and later in animal ontogeny. Movement seems to be a fundamental characteristic of protoplasm; yet the mechanism or mechanisms are presently unknown.

Irritability

Protoplasm is also irritable (in the biological sense), which means that it responds to external and internal stimuli. Protozoa "know" when they are hungry or full of food. Even cell division may often be a response to internal conditions.

Many experiments have been made concerning responses to external stimuli, and all sense organs are examples of protoplasmic irritability to chemicals, contact, pressure, light or lack of light, gravity, temperature, etc. Even the response of a cat to the sight of a mouse, or a dog to the sight of a cat, or a boy to the sight of a girl are examples of protoplasmic irritability. Plants also respond in their simpler ways to light (phototropism) and gravity (geotropism), producing galls in response to insects and even catching insects (Venus's-flytrap) or roundworms (certain fungi) by movements.

Protoplasm is a wonderful and poorly understood material, rather uniform in composition, but through evolutionary processes able to produce the hundreds of millions of species that have existed or are extant on earth, the various kinds of tissues, and the wide assortment of cells and cellular processes known to cytology.

Unusual forms of protoplasm

"Plasmodium," "syncytium," and "coenocyte" are terms applicable to somewhat unusual forms of protoplasm.

Plasmodium. It is typical in eukaryotic organisms for each nucleus and its associated cytoplasm to be surrounded by a plasma membrane that separates it more or less from the cytoplasm associated with an adjacent nucleus. This cellular condition is not always complete, as in Ascomycetes (fungi) (Fig. 3-4), which have a large pore in the wall between adjacent "cells" big enough for nuclei and other structures to pass through easily. Many other organisms have binucleate cells, such as the ciliate protozoa and Basidiomycetes (fungi), or tapetal cells as in grass anthers. There are also whole organisms or particular tissues of otherwise cellular organisms in which numerous nuclei are contained within one continuous and common mass of cytoplasm. Such a multinucleate acellular mass of protoplasm may be called a plasmodium.

Among the protozoa the opalinids (ciliate flagellates), numerous ameboid forms such as *Pelomyxa,* most Heliozoa, and many Radiolaria are multinucleate and plasmodial. There are plasmodial stages in the life cycles or plasmodial reproductive cells in the small groups of animals called the Mesozoa. Probably the most famous plasmodial form of organism is the group of Myxomycetes. The plasmodia of some of the largest of these provide material for the study of protoplasm as pure as is available in large, living, and normal masses. The myxomycete plasmodium grows from a zygote by repeated nuclear divisions unaccompanied by cytoplasmic cleavage. The protoplasm flows along on a solid substrate in a reticulate system of channels, eating bacteria and sometimes other organic food along the way. Some of these forms have the fastest protoplasmic flowing rate known, as high as 8 cm per minute in *Physarum polycephalum* (Kamiya, 1959). In all cases the direction of flow reverses periodically in the veins behind the front, and yet the total plasmodium moves in one direction more or less continuously.

Pseudoplasmodia, that is, naked masses of protoplasm of cellular construction, are known that superficially look like the plasmodia of Myxomycetes, for example, the fungal Acrasiales and Labyrinthulales.

Plasmodial tissues of otherwise cellular organisms are also known. The early endosperm of many flowering plants such as grasses and lilies is plasmodial, as are the early embryo stages of gymnospermous plants and arthropodan animals. Often the development of such a plasmodium is described as *free nuclear,* that is, nuclear divisions unaccompanied by cytoplasmic separation into cells.

Syncytium. The term "syncytium" is sometimes applied to a multinuclear acellular tissue or organism. It is more often used by zoologists than botanists. For example, the multinuclear acellular epidermis of rotifers, gastrotrichs, and some roundworms, mammalian osteoclasts, and the trophoblast of many mammalian embryos are described as syncytia. The vertebrate polykaryocyte (osteoclast) of bone marrow may have as many as 100 nuclei. The term is also applied to the hypothetical multinuclear ciliate (protozoon), which, so goes the *syncytial theory* of the origin of metazoa from protozoa (Hanson, 1958), underwent division into cells later in phylogeny to form the first acoel worm. The multinucleate striated muscle fiber has been described as

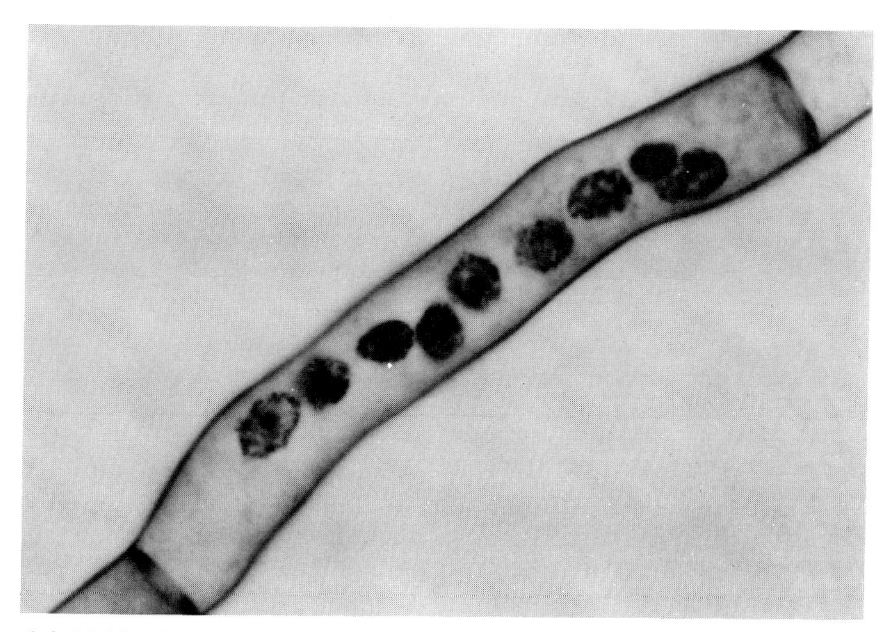

Fig. 3-4. Multinucleate "cell" of the ascomycete *Helminthosporium turcicum.* Chromonemata, nucleoli, and pores in transverse walls are visible. (Courtesy Dr. C. F. Robinow.)

a syncytium, although faint cytoplasmic separations have been observed under the electron microscope in some organisms. The syncytium may form either by nuclear divisions not followed by cytoplasmic divisions or by the breakdown of cell membranes in a cellular tissue. The terms "plasmodium" and "syncytium" are almost synonymous.

Coenocyte. The term "coenocyte" is used to describe the multinucleate, nonseptate, usually filamentous fungi and algae. Some coenocytic algae are *Hydrodictyon, Cladophora, Protosiphon,* such siphonaceous marine forms as *Bryopsis* and *Codium* of the green algae, and the chrysophytes *Botrydium* and *Vaucheria.* The so-called Phycomycetes, which includes chytrids, Oomycetes, and Zygomycetes, consist of multinucleate hyphae without cross walls. Except for lack of chloroplasts, some of these fungi are like coenocytic algae such as *Vaucheria.*

Summary

Protoplasm can be described as an intricately organized system of molecules, macromolecules, and structures in dynamic equilibrium. It is the material substrate for the particular orderly activities characterizing life—metabolism, irritability, growth, reproduction, adaptive response, self-maintenance, and repair.

Thus protoplasm adjusts to the environment, maintains itself, grows in amount, and reproduces. Although DNA is the hereditary information for carrying out, through RNA, the particular enzymatic syntheses of the particular species or cell, nevertheless, there must always be a preexisting mass of protoplasm as the proper and necessary complex milieu for the nucleoprotein activities.

Virchow's original aphorism, *"ommis cellula e cellula,"* can now be amended to "all protoplasm from preexisting protoplasm, all chromosomes from chromosomes, all mitochondria from mitochondria, all plastids from plastids, all DNA from DNA, and therefore, all life from preexisting life." All of these express growth and reproduction—basic attributes of life itself.

The subject matter of cytology is the study of the typical and also of the variations from the typical of these structural functions of protoplasm among a multitude of different types of cells and from time to time within a single cell. Cytology is the detailed study of the heterogeneous living stuff, protoplasm, within a single plasma membrane—what it is and what it does.

PROTOPLASMIC MOTION

Everyone is familiar with motion of protoplasm—the crawling of an earthworm, the walking of a dog, the flying of a bird, or the swimming of a fish. It is the ultimate cause of such gross motion, however, motion of a cell or of protoplasm within a cell, that is of concern here. Actually, there are a variety of easily observable intracellular motions of protoplasm, especially in plant cells. Probably the first observed cases were in *Amoeba* by von Rosenhof in 1755 and in the large cells of the water plants *Chara* and *Nitella* by Corti in 1772. These are still favorite materials for study. Ameboid movement is perhaps somewhat different from, and is often excluded from discussions of, protoplasmic streaming, as it occurs, for example, in *Chara.* Subsequently, during the nineteenth century, obvious protoplasmic streaming was reported in a variety of plant cells, stamen hairs, hair cells, and later the flowing of protoplasm of Myxomycetes by de Bary in 1859. Subsequently, other forms of local intracellular motion were noted—motion of plastids, nuclei, chromosomes, mitochondria, etc.

Before 1950 a large number of hypotheses were proposed to explain the cause or causes of the obvious mass motion called protoplasmic streaming, but none was better than a mere guess. However, a classification of the various types of streaming was achieved. At the present time there is no really satisfactory hypothesis that approaches completeness; the basic mechanism of any form of protoplasmic motion is still unknown. It is as difficult to understand this phenomenon as to try to explain a river flowing uphill without any pumping system of any sort. Of course, there must be an energy-using "pumping system" within a cell, or is there?

At the lowest level of protoplasmic motion is thermal agitation, molecular motion that occurs at all temperatures above absolute zero, and which is evident as brownian movement (Robert Brown, 1831). But such random molecular movement and its effects on somewhat larger particles, although chemically and therefore biologically important, are not included in this topic of protoplasmic movement, nor are the gross movements of whole organisms.

Following are some high and low rates of protoplasmic streaming given in millimeters per minute:

Physarum	18-80 mm	*Cucurbita*	0.48 mm
Rhizopus	3.3 mm	*Potomogeton*	0.006 mm
Chara	2-3 mm	*Avena*	0.30 mm
Nitella	2-3 mm	*Sagittaria*	0.24 mm
Vallisneria	1.5 mm	*Tradescantia zebrina*	0.36 mm
Elodea	1.5 mm	*Urtica*	0.30 mm

Seifriz (1943), who also listed rates in additional organisms, determined 0.6 mm per minute as the average rate.

Protoplasmic streaming

Seifriz (1943) defined true protoplasmic streaming as ". . . that activity within cells which is a general flow of the entire protoplasmic contents in a definite current." He excluded the movement of individual cell parts such as plastids, nuclei, granules, vacuoles, chromosomes, cilia, muscle fibrils, centrosomes, mitochondria, and even protozoan, euglenoid, ameboid, diatom, desmid, and blue-green algal movements, all of which are, of course, movements of protoplasm. He and Kamiya (1959, 1962) essentially agreed on the following classifications of types of protoplasmic streaming.

Agitation. Movement of this sort is a feeble activity in the protoplasm that is sometimes described as a "churning motion." Kamiya (1959) believed this pattern to be the most primitive of all and the type from which more complex movement developed. The movement resembles brownian movement, but the distances the particles move are greater, and agitation expends metabolic energy. Cells of *Closterium, Spirogyra,* and *Achlya* show this type of movement well.

Circulation. This movement is characteristic of cells having a centralized nucleus embedded in cytoplasm that is connected by many transvacuolar cytoplasmic strands to a peripheral layer of cytoplasm. The speed of flow varies in the strands. In individual strands movement is under little directional control. In fact, two particles in the same strand have been seen to approach each other from opposite directions, each traveling with a different speed, or coming from the same direction one overtakes the other, one particle moving faster than the other at all times.

The protoplasmic strands change continually in thickness, form, and location. They branch, unite, retract, or arise anew from the protoplasm lining the wall.

Circulation is a type of streaming characteristic, for example, of cells of *Spirogyra,* stinging cells of *Urtica,* hair cells of *Gloxinia,* and the cells of berries. This form of protoplasmic streaming may be included within the concept of cyclosis.

Rotation (also called cyclosis). Protoplasmic movement of the rotation flow type is limited to the periphery of the cell, just inside the cell wall. Kamiya (1959) describes it as resembling a "rotating belt." It is commonly seen in the leaf cells of many aquatic plants such as *Elodea, Vallisneria, Sagittaria,* and especially in *Nitella* and *Chara* as well as the root hairs of many other plants.

Shuttle. This type of streaming is best known in the myxomycete plasmodium. It is characterized chiefly by its periodic reversal of flow but also by the great volume of protoplasm transported and the great speed of the flow. The maximum speed recorded for streaming in any cell or plasmodium is 1.35 mm *per second* for *Physarum polycephalum.* This type of protoplasmic streaming is the basis for the "crawling" of a plasmodium across a substratum.

Seifriz also considered the protoplasmic streaming observed in the hyphae of some Phycomycetes as shuttle streaming. However, Kamiya separated this type of streaming, labeling it "tidal streaming." Protoplasm and cell sap are driven alternately in acropetal and basipetal directions. Variations on this plan include streaming in hyphae of certain coenocytic fungi that occurs spasmodically toward the hyphal tip and then basipetally after a period of rest.

Sleeve. This type of streaming is also characteristic of some Phycomycetes. The streaming occurs as an acropetal flow of most of the cytoplasm, including vacuoles, accompanied by a simultaneous, adjacent, peripheral, but basipetal flow. The peripheral layer carries few if any vacuoles. The contents of the vacuoles are supposed to be utilized in growth of the hyphal tip.

Kamiya considers this type of flow as a variation of "tidal streaming" when found in the fungi and as "fountain streaming" when observed in higher plant cells such as root hairs and pollen tubes.

• • •

Seifriz pointed out that very few cells show observable protoplasmic streaming, but he proposed that it is actually very common. Too little is known about slow movement in cells in general, animal and plant, to generalize safely. Time-lapse moving pictures often make evident movements otherwise too slow to be observed.

Hypotheses. There is no need here to enter into a discussion of the various hypotheses that have been published in the past to more-or-less explain protoplasmic streaming. Seifriz discussed (1) surface tension, (2) hydration, (3) osmosis, (4) sol-gel reversibility, (5) myelin processes, (6) coacervation, (7) autonomous propulsion of particles, (8) kinetic energy, (9) magnetism, (10) electrical forces, and (11) contractility. Not one of these attempts at explanation is at all convincing or probably correct, except that subsequent work tends to relate streaming to contraction, to microfibrils, or to both if one of these is an aspect of the other. For example, the flow of cytoplasm outward and back along the axopodia of Heliozoa has now been characterized as the cytoplasm flowing along the outer surfaces of an orderly system of microtubules (Fig. 14-4).

Actually, the relation of protoplasmic streaming to contraction is one of the oldest hypotheses, and Seifriz cited Corti (1774), Reichert (1866), Kuhne (1864), Verworn (1892), Pfeffer (1960), Vouk (1910), Scarth (1927), and Rashewsky (1939) as supporting this hypothesis, but until recently it was little more than an unsupported guess, based on the fact that the only other common protoplasmic movements are muscle contraction and possible contraction of spindle fibers during the anaphase stage of nuclear division.

During the 1950s, however, a number of workers have extracted from myxomycete, and also from the plant *Nitella,* contractile protein that hydrolyzes ATP and has the properties of myosin B. It has the form of long rigid rods 40,000 to 50,000 Å long and approximately 70 Å wide and has a molecular weight of about 6,000,000. Furthermore, sulfhydryl (free —SH groups) has been found, supporting the possibility that a cyclic conversion of —SH HS— to —S—S— (disulfide bonds) may be involved. Such observations and data seem to relate protoplasmic streaming to muscle contraction. Still more recently it has been found that muscle contraction, protoplasmic streaming, and the action of spindle fibers seem to have microtubules in common. Perhaps microtubules somehow underlie these (as well as other), phenomena; yet there is no evidence that microtubules ever contract, and if one watches protoplasmic streaming, the steady, continuous, unidirectional flowing like water in a river, it is difficult to imagine how contraction can be involved. Rapid streaming must be seen to be appreciated.

These newer concepts, however, justify Seifriz's conclusion in 1943 that "There is good reason to lump all forms of protoplasmic motion into one great class, for the basic mechanism may be the same in all; that is to say, protoplasmic streaming, amoeboid movement, ciliary motion, muscular activity, etc., may all involve one fundamental type of mechanism." And he favored the concept of rhythmic contraction and relaxation. These findings, although as yet only obscurely related to the phenomenon, do seem to be more reliable than the earlier more simple models.

The picture is certainly still unclear, except that the utilization of ATP (either glycolytic or mitochondrial) is well established. It is frustrating that the phenomenon is so obvious and yet not to be able to achieve an acceptable model of the driving mechanism or mechanisms. Ascribing protoplasmic movement to some vital or supernatural force does not explain anything. Perhaps movement is related to contractility. Perhaps contractility is not at all involved in protoplasmic streaming any more than it is in striated muscle. Perhaps there is some as yet uncharacterized basic attribute of protoplasm.

The "best" present hypothesis to account for protoplasmic streaming is naturally a synthesis of various proposals. It is generally agreed that there is usually a thin to thick layer of nonmoving protoplasm just inside the plasma membrane, often called ectoplasm or cortical protoplasm. Internal to the ectoplasm is the much more fluid, moving endoplasm. A number of workers in this field seem agreed that the movement is "produced" at the interface between the flowing endoplasm and the stationary ectoplasm. Jarosch (1964) has actually proposed a hypothetical pumping mechanism situated at this interface. It goes something like this. Because fibrils have been seen in cytoplasm, because these fibrils are possibly contractile, because the secondary structure of proteins is an alpha helix, and because a number of alpha helices would twist around one another to form a compound helix, changes in the gyres of such a helix would produce twisting and therefore contractions and extensions. These longitudinal movements of the gyres would produce movement of the surrounding protoplasm, provided one end of the fibril was somehow anchored, and mass movement of protoplasm would be produced if there were a great many such fibrils all somehow oriented properly with respect to the observed flow of the endoplasm.

It is obvious that there are a number of "if's" in all of these hypotheses. Data that negate these hypotheses are that presently revealed fibrils in the cytoplasms of Myxomycetes, *Chara,* and nearly all other cells do not seem to be properly placed or oriented; they usually lie either within the ectoplasm or the endoplasm, not extending from one into the other, and they always seem to lie parallel to the plasma membrane, not at a considerable angle to it. Furthermore, microtubules are always smooth; projections do not occur. But to repeat, there has to be an energy-using structural mechanism of some sort, and there is probably one basic (but somewhat modifiable) mechanism for all protoplasmic movement; it just is still unknown.

In addition to protoplasmic streaming there are numerous reports of movements of nuclei, plastids, mitochondria, vacuoles, muscle fibrils, chromosomes, centrosomes, nucleoli, and cytoplasmic granules. All of these are also examples of protoplasmic movement and may be very significant in cell function. Whether the displacements, rotations, or wiggling of such structures relates to protoplasmic streaming and cyclosis is, of course, not known. These latter movements are properly described in the discussions of the structures themselves.

Saltatory particle movement

Rebhun (1963) described a different sort of protoplasmic motion and presented a hypothesis to explain it. He studied and discussed the "saltatory" movements of a wide variety of particles from many different organisms, especially during mitosis. He noted that such particles as pigment granules, yolk granules, heme granules, and lipid droplets, which are often described as "inert" particles of the protoplasm, suddenly start to move rapidly in a linear and oriented manner and often for long distances (5 to 30 μm) at a constant velocity and then stop. Of two adjacent particles of the same sort, one may undergo saltatory movement and the other may not, and a moving particle may move among other sorts of stationary particles. Often such particles become nonrandomly distributed within a cell by such movement, for example, on one side of a nucleus, or at the poles of a spindle during mitosis, or at the periphery of a cell. Because these particles are described as "inert" (in contrast to "protoplasmic" particles such as mitochondria), it is assumed that their movement is not autonomous but that they are "moved."

Rebhun has proposed that the ER is involved in the movement. The ER may be considered the force-transmitting structure, although some rather hypothetical "moving fibrils" that are built into or otherwise associated with the ER are invoked as directed producing the movement of the particles. Although unproved, the suggestion that the ER is the causal agent of at least this sort of movement is interesting.

Cytology is to a large extent the study of protoplasm. Most cytologists, including biochemists, study particular structures or molecules of the protoplasm such as ribosomes, mitochondria, chromosomes, RNAs, enzymes, and ATP by any and all appropriate techniques and instruments. Since protoplasm is by far the most complex matter known in the universe, it is not surprising that many methods of study have been devised. Some of these are in vivo studies, that is, investigations of intact living cells or specific components in as nearly a normal condition and environment as the investigation permits. Other studies are in vitro investigations of cells or cellular components, that is, isolation of a mass of cells or cellular components (fractions). Components such as mitochondria, ribosomes, nuclei, ER, and satellite DNA are separated from destroyed cell debris and the specific component purified in bulk by appropriate methods in some sort of container. The pure (nonliving) fraction can then be subjected to various and specific environments (substrates) and their reactions in such a nonliving environment examined.

One of the important questions in biology is how accurately do conclusions from in vitro (dead) experiments reflect the actual structures and functions of living cells or components within normal living cells. The answer is clear; cellular structures and molecules are nonliving even within living cells, and conclusions from a large majority of in vitro studies accurately indicate in vivo functions, activities, and structures. Some of the cytological techniques and instruments used are discussed in the next two chapters.

LITERATURE CITED

Allen, R. D., and N. Kamiya (editors). 1964. Primitive motile systems in cell biology. Academic Press, Inc., New York.

Battaglia, E. 1946. Richerche cariologiche e embriologiche sul genere Rudbeckia (Asteraceae). VIII. Semigamia in R. laciniata L. Nuovo Gior. Bot. Ital. **53:**483-511.

Coe, G. E. 1953. Cytology of reproduction in Cooperia pedunculata. Amer. J. Bot. **40:**335-343.

Danielli, J. F., I. J. Lorch, M. J. Ord, and E. C. Wilson. 1955. Nucleus and cytoplasm in cellular inheritance. Nature (London) **176:**1114-1115.

Hanson, E. D. 1958. On the origin of the Eumetazoa. Syst. Zool. **7:**16-47.

Jarosch, R. 1964. Screw-mechanical basis of protoplasmic movement. In R. Allen and N. Kamiya (editors). Primitive motile systems in cell biology. Academic Press, Inc., New York.

Kamiya, N. 1959. Protoplasmic streaming. Protoplasmatologia **8**(3a):1-199.

Kamiya, N. 1962. Protoplasmic streaming. In W. Ruhland (editor). Encyclopedia of plant physiology. Vol. 17. Springer-Verlag, Berlin.

Lorch, I. J., and J. F. Danielli 1950. Transplantation of nuclei from cell to cell. Nature (London) **166:**329-333.

Morowitz, H. J., and M. E. Tourtellotte. 1962. The smallest living cells. Sci. Amer. **206:**117. Also in D. Kennedy (editor). 1965. The living cell: Readings from the Scientific American. W. H. Freeman & Co., Publishers, San Francisco.

Rebhun, L. I. 1963. Saltatory particle movements and their relation to the mitotic apparatus. In L. Levine (editor). The cell in mitosis. Academic Press, Inc., New York.

Schrödinger, E. 1956. What is life and other scientific essays. Doubleday & Co., Inc., Garden City, N. Y.

Seifriz, W. 1943. Protoplasmic streaming. Bot. Rev. **9:**49-123.

CHAPTER 4

Viruses and Prokaryota

Most present knowledge of the quasiorganisms, viruses, and the Prokaryota has derived from the utilization of new techniques in molecular biology, microbial genetics, and electron microscopy within the last 30 years. The electron microscope made it possible to even see viruses and finally to see the details of internal structure of the Prokaryota. Genetic study of certain viruses and bacteria, especially the colon bacillus *Escherichia coli* and its coliphages, has quite revolutionized knowledge of gene structure, gene action, and genetic control (Studier, 1972). Much knowledge of cell physiology has derived from biochemical study of bacteria. This chapter will stress structural knowledge, although functions, as of ribosomes, will be discussed in a subsequent chapter.

VIRUSES

At present the evolutionary origin (or origins) of viruses is unknown: whether they represent a very old and primitive form of prelife; whether some, at least, may be of very recent origin, as "wild" or "escaped" segments of chromosomes of prokaryotic and/or eukaryotic cells; whether they really have evolved; and, indeed, whether they are really "living" or "organisms." Whether they are organisms and living depends on arbitrary definitions.

Certainly viruses *could* have evolved, along with the evolution of their hosts. They mutate; they show relationships within groups of morphology (for example the structural uniformity of adenoviruses), of proteins (by serological studies), and of nucleic acids (from hybridization experiments); and they usually enter into and replicate within highly specific environments for which they are critically adapted. It is likely that viruses go all the way back to the first organisms and possibly appeared on earth before even very simple cells had evolved. Viruses and organisms may well have evolved together from the beginning of life on earth.

Certainly they are tiny particles, called in the infective stage *virions* or *nucleocapsids,* which range in size from about 0.015 to 0.35 μm (150 to 3,500 Å). The virion of a particular form of virus has a definite and characteristic shape and molecular composition. Every virion contains nucleic acid, either RNA or DNA but seldom both, and nearly all contain protein also. The tobacco mosaic virus (TMV), for example, is 94.4% protein and 5.6% nucleic acid. Some also contain lipid as membrane, derived in part from the host cell, nuclear envelope, cytoplasmic membrane, or plasma membrane. They consist of a protein sheath, the capsid, around the nucleic acid, the latter being single or double stranded. The nucleic acid is usually a single linear or circular strand of a number of units of heredity, although influenza and reoviruses have "segmented ribonucleic acid genomes" of up to ten more or less separate segments (Shatkin, 1971). The smallest viruses have rather short genophores, which are long enough for only about six "genes." More complex viruses have longer genophores, and the "tailed" phage particles have even longer strands. Virions contain few metabolic enzymes (the T-even phases and other large virions do have enzymes for penetration of the host cell wall and effects within the host cell). They have no ribosomes or any other typical cellular structures. They do not reproduce by division of the virion and are all "nonliving" and completely inactive, except when entering into, functioning, and replicating within a proper host cell. The protein and included nucleic acid of the inactive viral particle do have a characteristic particulate form that is rather com-

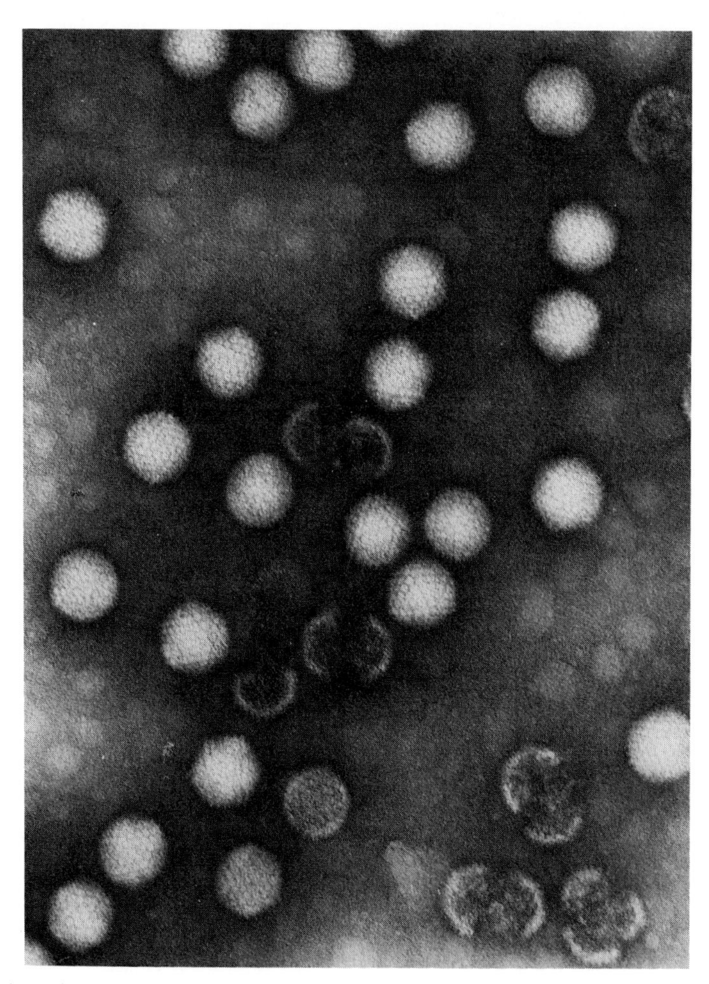

Fig. 4-1. Adenovirus type 12, revealed by negative staining. These virions are in the common form of the icosahedron; in this form there are 252 capsomeres composing the capsid, the number typical of adenoviruses. This is a DNA virus that commonly causes respiratory ailments in humans, but it can cause tumors in hamsters. Some virions have broken open. (Courtesy Dr. D. B. Stoltz, University of Texas, Austin, Texas.)

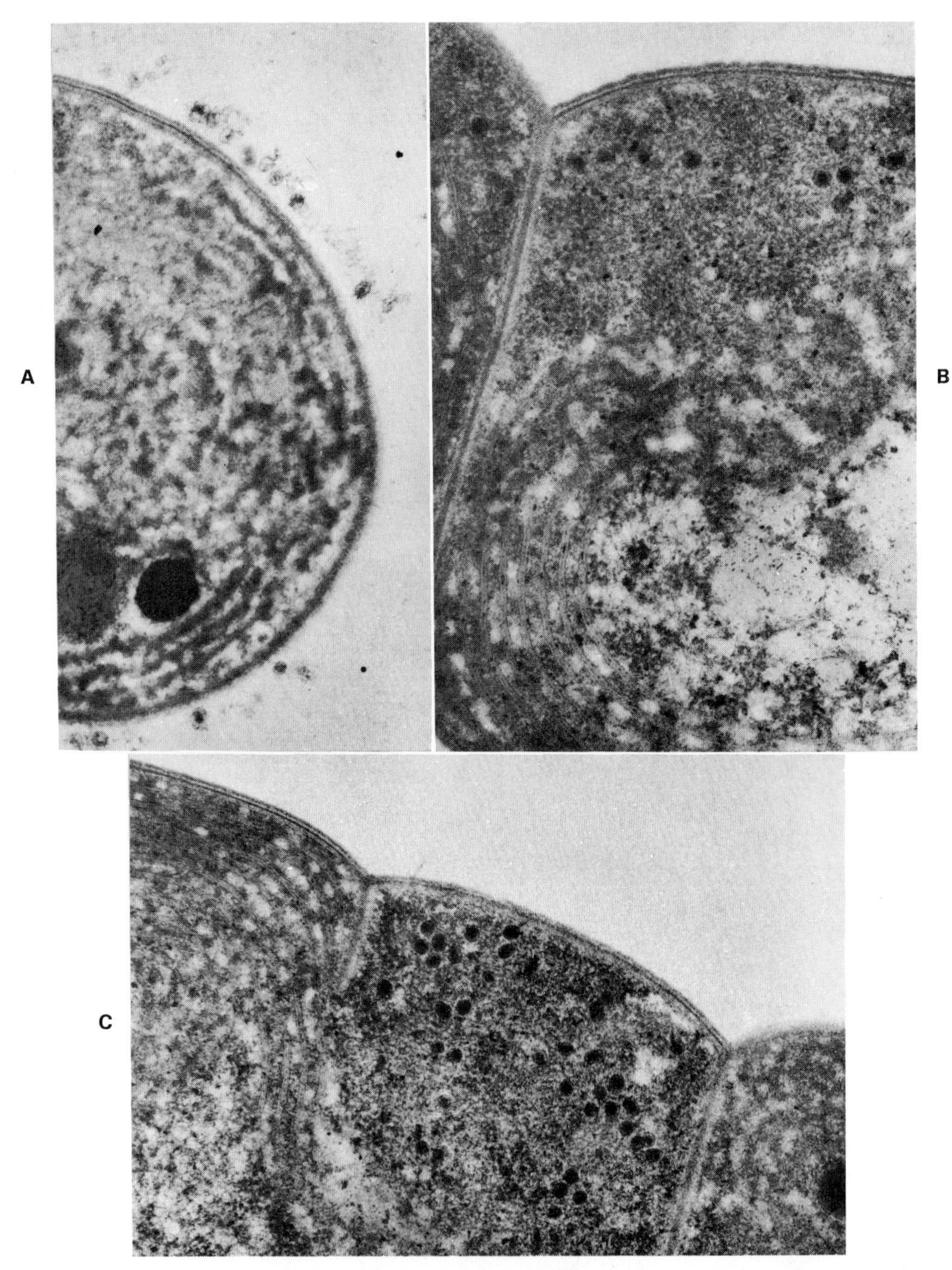

Fig. 4-2. Cyanophage (virus) and host; the species of blue-green alga is the cyanophyte *Plectonema baryanum*. **A,** T-even phagelike particles are absorbed on the outer surface of the host. In some the nucleic acid (darkly stained material) has already been "injected" into the host, leaving the lightly stained capsid ghosts attached by their tails. **B,** Virus particles being assembled in the procytoplasm. Some already have the dark nucleic acid core and less darkly stained protein capsid. Cores are probably forming in the region of the prokaryon. **C,** Later stage than that shown in **B,** but abundant particles still have no tails. (Courtesy Dr. R. M. Brown, University of Texas Cell Research Institute, Austin, Texas.)

plex in certain bacteriophage particles. They range in shape from polyhedrons, called *icosahedrons* (Fig. 4-1), to long thin rods (the famous tobacco mosaic virus particle is 150 × 3,500 Å), to the tadpole-shaped T_2 and other T-even phages of the *E. coli* bacterium.

A virus particle usually has the nucleic acid in the center (the *core*), which is surrounded by a protein sheath (the coat, or *capsid*) constructed of more or less identical spherical protein molecular called *capsomeres,* that is, the protein illustrates the quaternary protein structure. Reoviruses contain three types of proteins, one of which is the polymerase for replication. The reovirus cores can be isolated as spheres by removal of the capsid (Shatkin, 1971), and such condensed cores can transcribe mRNA (Gillies et al., 1971). Within the host cell the viral nucleic acid is sometimes replicated separately from the protein. For example, the nucleic acid may be replicated in the nucleus but the protein in the cytoplasm, or vice versa. Then the parts come together at some place within the cell and assemble into the complete virion.

Assembly of the virion is difficult to explain or even comprehend (Fig. 4-2). For example, in the infected *E. coli* procell, which is about 1.5 μm long, about twenty 65 μm long DNA viral genophores are pro-

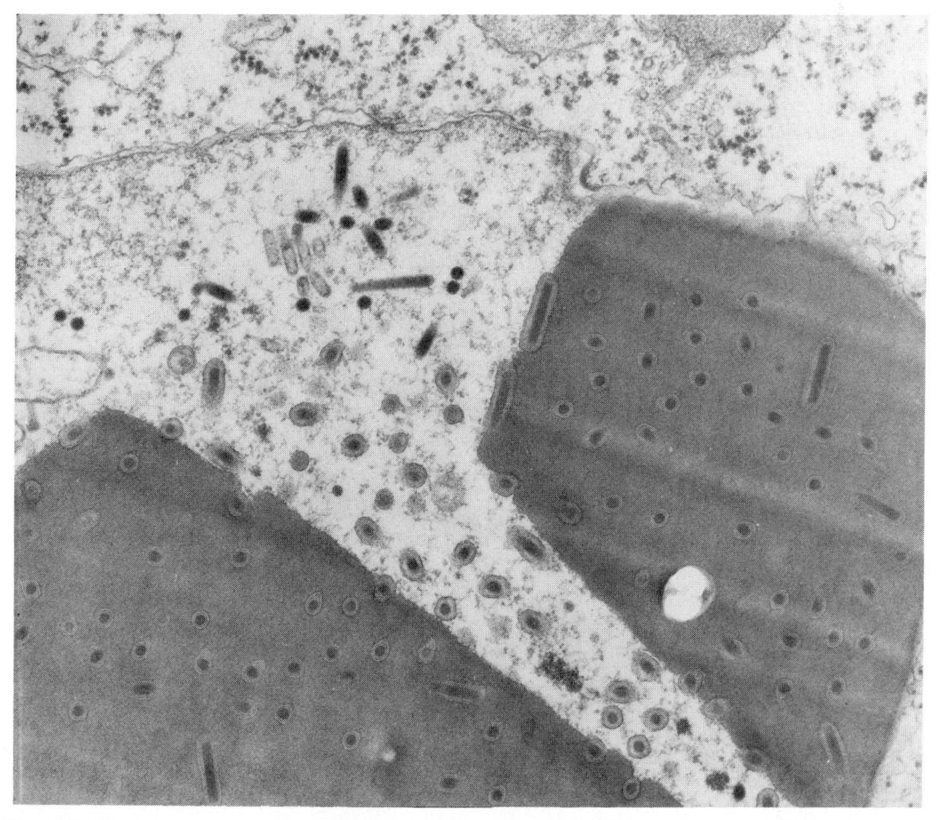

Fig. 4-3. Nuclear polyhedrosis (DNA) virus of an insect (fly) in the nucleus of a cecal cell of the larva. There are many rod-shaped virus particles, each consisting of the nucleocapsid (dark) surrounded by a unit membrane some distance from the capsid. Many particles are embedded (normally) in crystalloid protein polyhedrons, which start growth from the inner nuclear membrane. (Courtesy Dr. D. B. Stoltz, University of Texas, Austin, Texas.)

duced. Somehow these separate from one another, each "folds" up into an approximate sphere of 0.1 μm diameter, and then, or earlier, the capsomeres arrange themselves as an icosahedron with a tail and thin filaments. In viruses the assembly of the nucleic acid core with the protein coat is usually accomplished, although empty protein coats are often found. Virus particles themselves may associate in large amorphous (Fig. 4-3) or crystalloid masses (Fig. 4-4), often within membranes within the host cell nucleus or cytoplasm, and may even be liberated as such a crystalloid mass. Some viruses, as in fowl plague and the vaccinia viruses, also contain about 5% carbohydrate and 25% and 33% lipids, respectively, on the outer surface of the particle. It is likely, however, that the carbohydrate and lipid are often residues from the host cell protoplasm, especially membranes. Rod-shaped plant viruses often appear hollow, the longitudinal "hole" being about 30 to 40 Å in diameter.

The capsid

The globular protein of the virion covers the nucleic acid polymer as a single-layered envelope called the *capsid*. Each globular protein molecule of the capsid, whether a monomer or dimer, is called a *capsomer* (Fig. 4-1). Each capsomer, being about 60 Å in diameter, constitutes a significant portion of the capsid of small virions, about one twelfth of the tiny ØX-174 bacteriophage, but large virions have up to 3,000 capsomeres, the long tobacco mosaic virus having about 2,180.

The arrangement of the protein subunits determines the form of the virion, whether helix, rod, polygon, or more complex structure. The polygon is the commonest morphological form and is a twenty-sided figure called an *icosahedron*. Such a form permits

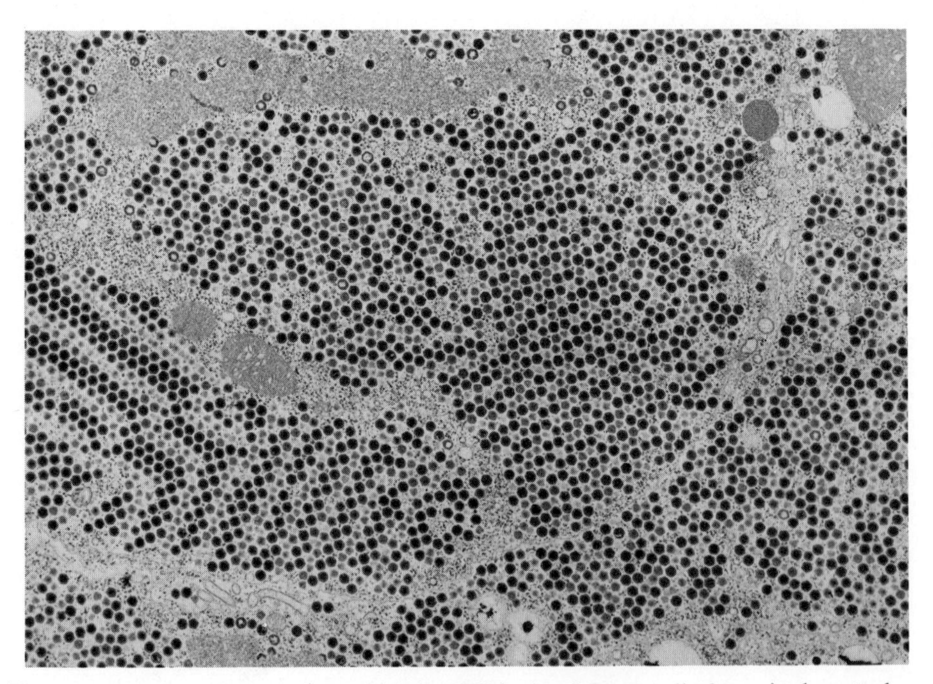

Fig. 4-4. Mosquito iridescent virus, which is a DNA virus but generally forms in the cytoplasm. Each virion (dark polygons) is 1,950 Å in diameter. Because the virions aggregate in large regular (crystalloid) masses, they refract the light (are iridescent), and the masses appear pinkish. (Courtesy Dr. D. B. Stoltz, University of Texas, Austin, Texas.)

only definite numbers of capsomeres, the smallest being 12. Other permitted numbers are 32, 42, 92, 122, 162, 252, 272, etc. For example, the *Tipula iridescent* virus has 812. A few virus particles are more complex, such as the T-even bacteriophages, which consist of an icosahedral head, a helical "tail," and some tail fibers (Fig. 4-2). All the capsomeres may be of one type of protein, or they may consist of a number of different proteins, some of which may be enzymes. Other functions of capsid proteins are as "recognizers" of the proper host cell, host specificity, and in phages to aid in attachment or adsorption to the host cell; also in phages the hollow, springlike "tail" is mechanically inserted through the bacterial wall as a tube for the injection of the nucleic acid from the head. Animal viruses seem to attach, often irreversibly and specifically, to the plasma membrane by electrostatic charges or chemical bonds (such as disulfide bonds) between capsomeres and membrane proteins. The virion is then taken into the cell either by fusion of plasma membranes of the cell and capsid of the virus so that the nucleic acid alone enters the cytoplasm or by the host cell membrane, in response to the virion, forming an invagination and eventually an internal vesicle. The viral nucleic acid is eventually liberated by dissolution of the membrane of the vesicle and the capsid.

The genophore

The nucleic acid of the virion is one (rarely two) continuous polymer of RNA or DNA. The DNA commonly exists as a double strand (a double helix) or uncommonly as a single strand, and it can be linear, circular, or circular that is supercoiled. The RNA is generally single stranded and linear, although double-stranded RNA viruses are known. Each consists of a few to many genes, from about 1 μm (2×10^6 daltons of molecular weight) to about 200 μm (400×10^6 daltons) (Table 15-1). Because the nucleic acid is a naked nucleic acid polymer without histones or other proteins, it is very different from a chromosome of a eukaryotic cell. Therefore it is better called a *genophore* than a chromosome, although virologists often refer to it as a "chromosome" or "genome."

Replication

After penetration into the protoplasm of a host cell the genophore, with or without some enzyme molecules from the virion and often using host cell enzymes, transcribes or replicates, or both, or the genophore becomes a prophage (see later).

An RNA genophore probably replicates viral RNA and transcribes mRNA. Some RNA viruses, however, transcribe a DNA copy by *reverse transcription* (Temin and Mazutani, 1970; Baltimore, 1970), using the recently detected RNA-dependent DNA polymerase enzyme. Such DNA may remain in the living host cell and modify (transform) it genetically, often into a tumor cell.

The original DNA or RNA genophore derived from the virion but within the host cell is able to transcribe mRNAs, which with the translational mechanism of the host cell produce proteins, some of which are enzymes and some usually structural (capsomeres). Some of the earliest formed proteins are replicases such as DNA-dependent DNA, or RNA-dependent RNA, or RNA-dependent DNA polymerases. Other early formed enzymes derived from the viral nucleic acids affect the host cell, such as causing destruction of its DNA. Late-formed enzymes include those that achieve assembly and lysis of the cell. Therefore there appear to be regulatory genes in the viral genome although in the T_7 coliphage the linear sequence of genes along the genophore corresponds to the temporal appearance of early, middle, and late enzymes (Studier, 1972, for an interesting account of the bacteriophage). Some viruses may bring in necessary enzymes from the virion. In general, most DNA viruses replicate within the eukaryotic host cell nucleus, whereas RNA viruses usually replicate in the cytoplasm. Eventually a number of viral genophores and capsid protein molecules are present within the host cell, often in rather specific regions of the cell such as nucleus of cytoplasm or associated with membranes.

Assembly

During the last phase of infection, these nucleic acid and protein molecules are assembled somehow into new infective virus particles or virions. In some viruses the empty capsids are formed, and the nucleic acid polymer is inserted into them (empty capsids are often revealed by electron microscopy [Fig. 4-4]). In other viruses the genophore and capsomers assemble together as a single process, as in the long rod-like tobacco mosaic virus. In the former type there is no molecular union within the virion between capsomeres and nucleic acid; in the latter the capsomeres are bonded to the genophore during and after assembly.

The effect of such activities of the viral nucleic acid on the host cell is usually death. The death of the cell may be violent and sudden destruction, called *lysis,* which is often produced by an enzyme, which liberates the virions formed. Other viruses escape continuously from the still living host cell over an extended period of time by causing a budding of the plasma membrane outward or penetration through a bacterial wall (Hofschneider and Preuss, 1963). Each bud contains a virion, and the bud separates from the host cell. The free virion, therefore, has a membrane derived from the plasma membrane external to its capsid. Other virions may pick up such an external membrane by causing budding of internal cellular membranes. Some viruses and host cells continue to live and divide but continually extrude virions during an indefinitely long period. Some insect virions, as part of their self assembly, form a massive proteinic crystal around themselves in which they remain until liberated by digestion in the digestive tract of a new host.

Satellitism

The simplest viruses, as "virions," seem to be composed of free nucleic acid without any capsid, such as the *potato spindle tuber* virus (Diener and Raymer, 1967). Other viruses may carry too little information to replicate themselves in a host cell. One such is the smallest plant virus known, the *tobacco necrosis satellite* virus, which is about the size of a ribosome, 50s.* It can increase itself only in the presence of the *tobacco necrosis* virus (Kassanis, 1962). The *tobacco rattle* virus consists of a mixture of short and long rods. The long rods, 1,900 Å long, carry the RNA information for, among others, more virion RNA; the short rods, 500 to 1,150 Å, carry the RNA information for, among others, the capsid protein. Thus infection by both forms is necessary for formation of complete virions (Semancik and Reynolds, 1969). Satellite viruses, which require the presence in the host cell of another virus, are known among both animal and plant viruses and, now that such a condition is known to exist (Kassanis, 1968), many such are being reported, and the condition is called "satellitism."

Prophage

Sometimes after penetration of the viral nucleic acid into a host cell, that viral genophore, if it contains a gene that represses the lytic cycle, associates with the genetic material of the host cell or remains separate, but in either case subsequently divides with it. The viral genophore is a symbiont that may not adversely affect the host cell. Such a viral genophore is called a *prophage,* especially if the virus is a phage of a bacterial cell. The viral strain that contains the repression gene is called *temperate;* strains that always produce lysis are called *virulent.* Prophages of temperate viral strains can become virulent, perhaps by mutation.

Whether "prophages" exist in eukaryotic cells is not clearly established. The *herpes*

*s = Svedberg unit.

simplex (cold sore) virus has been reported either to remain "dormant," as in neurons (Stevens and Cook, 1971), or it may not become "dormant" but be active always at a low level in gland cells (Kaufman et al., 1967) if there is much difference between the two proposals. Aaronson et al. (1971) and Lowy et al. (1971) have simultaneously reported the experimental proof that probably *all* cells of certain mouse strains contain some undetectable condition of *murine leukemia* (C-type) virus infection that is always passed on to daughter cells at division indefinitely. Occasionally spontaneously, and commonly by various methods of induction, these cells can be forced to produce detectable virus. This condition is certainly similar to the prophage condition of certain viruses in bacteria and may be rather common in eukaryotic cells. It seems evident that human viral cancers may be caused by latent viruses acquired years earlier by a "susceptible" individual. Viruses in viral cancer cells of animals do not destroy the host cells but stimulate their growth. Prophage in the bacterium *Corynebacterium diphtheriae* changes the bacterium from a harmless to a toxin- and disease-producing (diphtheria) organism (Freeman, 1951), and a prophage converts a harmless bacterium *Clostridium botulinum* into a producer of the deadly toxin that produces botulism (Eklund et al., 1971). Such alteration of host cell phenotype by prophage may be common.

Transduction

It is now well known that a viral genophore produced in a bacterial host cell can pick up a piece of host genophore and introduce the piece into a new host at infection. Thus the infected bacterial cell becomes diploid for a small segment of its genophore, recombination can occur, and genetic segregation for some bacterial genes is observed. This is called *transduction* and is a mechanism that permits genetic study of bacteria. It is possible that transduction may occur in eukaryotic organisms, perhaps producing some forms of cancer. It has been employed to introduce an effective bacterial gene into the defective genotype of a human tissue culture.

Hosts

Hundreds of different viruses are now known; for example, there are more than 300 known plant viruses. Viruses occur commonly in mammals, birds, insects, higher plants, and bacteria. They seem to be rare in other animal groups, although one is known in mites (red spiders), in earthworms, and in a nematode worm. Two also have been found in the protozoa and in blue-green algae (Fig. 4-2) and one in true algae; a few fungal viruses are known. One or more is known in fish and frogs, and some are specific in mitochondria or chloroplasts. It is highly likely, on the other hand, that all plant and animal groups have numerous viruses, but they have just not yet been detected.

The groups of tiny (0.2 to 1 μm) organisms known as the *Rickettsia, Mycoplasma,* and *Bedsonia,* which were formerly thought to be viruslike, are now known to be thin-walled Prokaryota, since each particle contains both DNA and RNA, ribosomes, some metabolic enzymes, and a bacterial type of cell wall, and divides by division. They are, however, obligate intracellular parasites of living cells.

PROKARYOTA

Electron microscopy has now demonstrated that the procell of the Prokaryota is quite distinct from the eucell (Fig. 3-1) and that the viruses are different from either of these. Since viruses possess few or no metabolic enzymes and only one type of nucleic acid (either RNA or DNA), it is unlikely that they should be described as organisms. *Rickettsia* and *Bedsonia,* although obligate parasites like viruses, do have some metabolism of their own and have procell structure. The procell, then, is the protoplasmic unit of the rickettsias, true bacteria, actinomycetes, myxobacteria, spirochetes, mycoplasmatales, and blue-green algae (Fig. 4-5). Some of the last group, such as *Beggiatoa,* are colorless. Protoplasmic streaming is unknown in procells (Stanier et al. [1970] give general coverage).

Following is a list of prokaryotic characters that contrast to those of eukaryotic cells:

Tiny size
70s rather than 80s ribosomes
Teichoic acid often
Muramic acid
Diaminopimelic acid
d-alanine and *d*-glutamic acid in walls
No Golgi membranes
No ER
No nuclear envelope
No nucleolus
No mitochondria or plastids
No spindle or aster
No centrioles or basal bodies
No mitosis
No meiosis
No sexuality
No known "chromosomal" contraction
Probably circular genophore
Probably only one genophore
No chromosomal histone
Constant DNA replication
Replication and transcription at same time
Flagella of a single microtubule-like filament

In all procells the protoplasm consists of two distinct regions. The more or less central region of indeterminate shape and no bounding membrane is sometimes called the nucleus but more properly the *prokaryon* (Fig. 3-1, *A*). The outer region, the *procytoplasm,* is more electron dense than the prokaryon and is, in fact, physically dense, since it contains many 70s ribosomes, in contrast to the 80s ribosomes of eukaryotes, and lacks vacuoles, ER, and various kinds of low-density vesicles (Fig. 4-6). The prokaryon consists of some sort of low-density ground material (Fig. 15-1) and the DNA in probably one double helix strand—the *"chromosome,"* or *genophore,* which is the term to be used here. These strands are very different from chromosomes of eucells; at least they do not go through a typical mitosis by coiling and are not segregated by a spindle; nor is there any detectable histone, although histone (or protamine) is present within the prokaryon

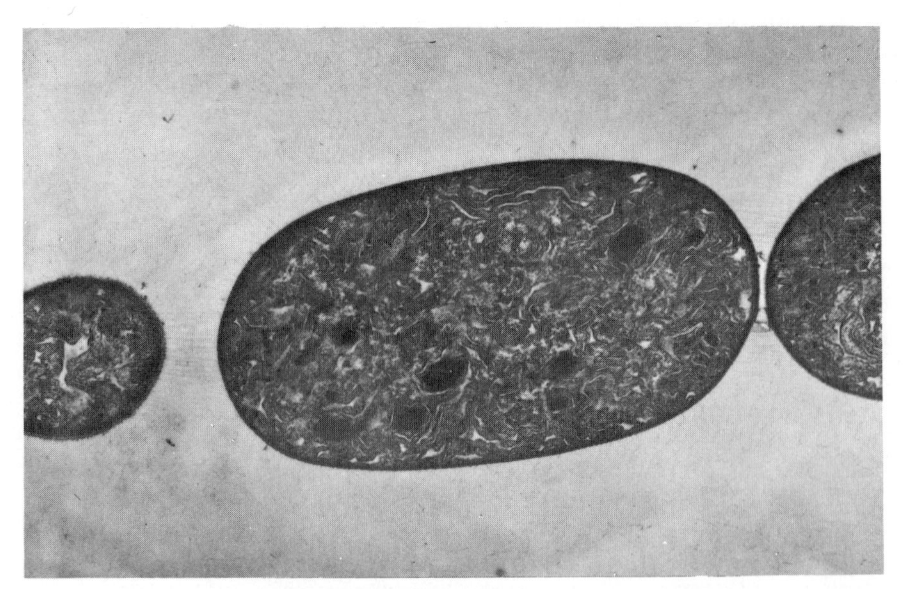

Fig. 4-5. Electron micrograph sections of the blue-green alga *Anabaena azollae* as an example of a photosynthetic prokaryote species.

but not in the procytoplasm. Rather than mitosis, in preparation for "nuclear" division the prokaryon seems to separate into non-fibrous material and DNA fibers, the latter dividing into two aggregates (Fig. 4-7). Later the fibers disperse within the two new prokaryons.

Furthermore, the outer region of the

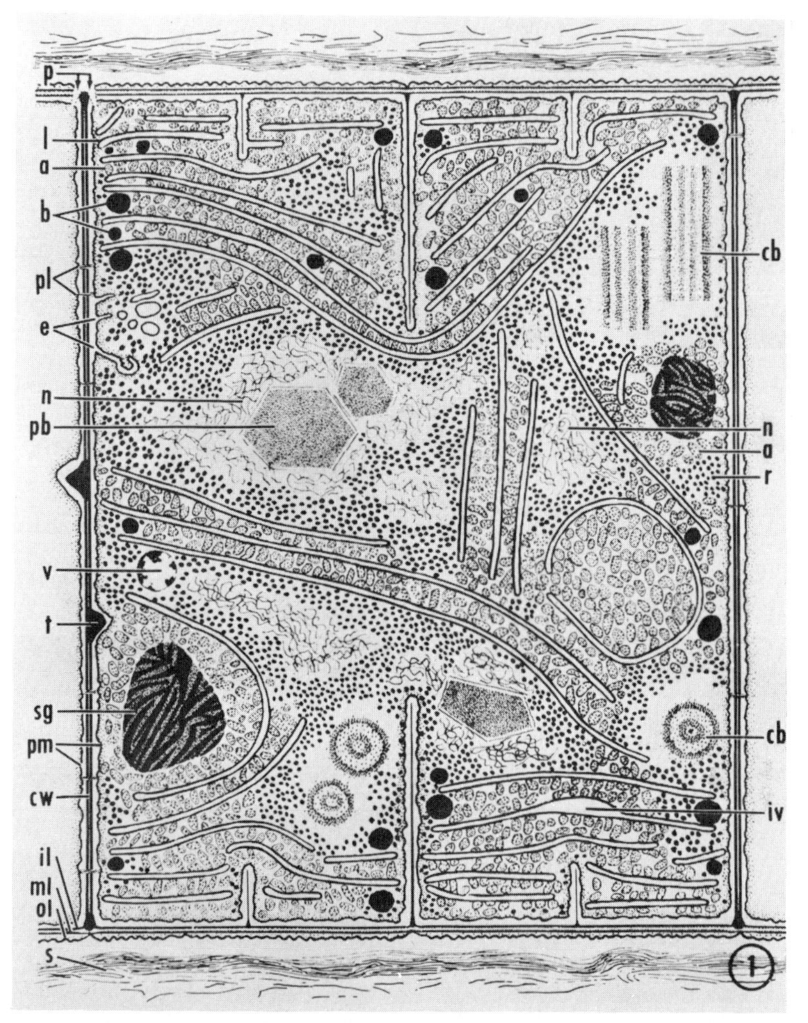

Fig. 4-6. Diagram of a composite median electron micrograph section of the procell of a blue-green alga showing that even the procell protoplasm is a heterogeneous system and the constant division by furrowing. **A,** Alpha granules among the photosynthetic lamellae; **b,** beta granules, which are also located randomly in the photosynthetic region; **cb,** cylindrical bodies; **cw,** cross wall (note that a half-completed wall will eventually bisect this procell and cross walls just started will later bisect those daughter procells); **e,** invaginations of plasma membrane; **il, ml,** and **ol,** inner, middle, and outer layers, respectively, of the surface wall; **iv,** intralamellar vesicle; **l,** lamellae (the sites of photosynthesis); **n,** nucleoplasm, which seems scattered and irregular in this single section but is located in central region of the procell; **p,** pores; **pb,** polyhedral bodies; **pl,** plasmodesmata in transverse wall; **pm,** plasma membrane; **r,** ribosomes; **s,** sheath; **t,** local thickening of transverse wall; **v,** vacuole-like inclusions. (From Pankratz, H. S., and C. C. Bowen. 1963. Amer. J. Bot. **50:**387-399.)

procell that is packed with ribosomes is essentially barren of membranous structures, except in the few photosynthetic bacteria and all of the photosynthetic blue-green algae. In the bacterial autotrophic forms the photosynthetic membranes form spherical vesicles, which are numerous in the outer protoplasm. In these photosynthetic bacteria (which have an incomplete photosynthetic process) the membranes are single.

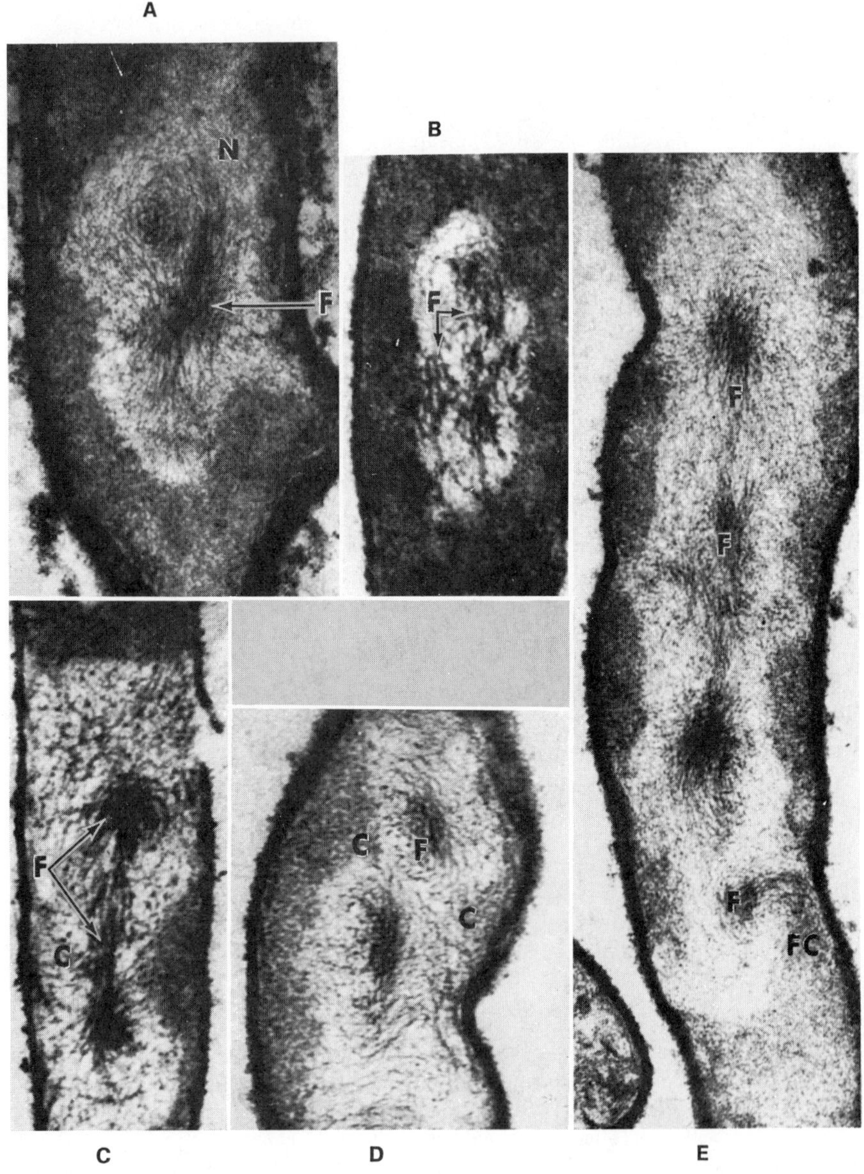

Fig. 4-7. Electron micrograph sections of *Streptomyces cinnamonensis,* a prokaryote, showing changes of prokaryon. **A** to **E** can be interpreted as divisions of the DNA fibrils into two **(C)** and then into four **(E)** masses within an enlarged prokaryon. Later these dense masses become more diffuse. **N,** Prokaryon; **F,** fibrils; **C,** cytoplasm; **FC,** fibrils in cytoplasm and associated prokaryon. (From Chen, P. L. 1966. Amer. J. Bot. **53**:291-295.)

The blue-green algae, on the other hand, have double membranes that are arranged, as in chloroplasts of eucells, concentrically in the procytoplasm. They have a complete photosynthetic mechanism that derives its electrons from water and produces free oxygen.

Occasionally there have been reports in the electron microscopic literature of small membranous structures in procytoplasm that are connected to the plasma membrane, such as the *chondroids* in *Bacillus subtilis* (Fig. 10-19) or the similar or identical *mesosome,* but most of the outer protoplasm is very homogeneous. Glycogen granules, volutin granules, and sulfur droplets are often present in certain forms.

It is likely that the plasma membrane of the procell is the site of most membrane-requiring cellular processes, except for photosynthesis, which requires its own unique membranous structure. Certainly the enzymes, and cytochromes for oxidative phosphorylation are restricted to the membranous cell debris when aerobic bacteria are ground up and centrifuged. Therefore it is not surprising that involuted membrane, the mesosome, also demonstrates oxidative phosphorylation when isolated. Some cell biologists believe that bacterial mesosomes (they are found also in some fungi), which are convoluted invaginations of the plasma membrane, represent specializations for respiration, since when isolated, they function thusly, but so does the whole plasma membrane. The proposal was inevitable that perhaps the mesosome itself represents a first step in the evolution of the mitochondrion. As in eucells, however, the plasma membrane is concerned also with transport of molecules, both inward and outward.

Bacterial flagella

Some procells of the bacterial and spirochete types have protoplasmic extensions called *bacterial flagella,* which confer motility to the procells possessing them (Fig. 4-8). They usually arise at one or both ends (called *polar insertion*) or at many points along the sides of the organism

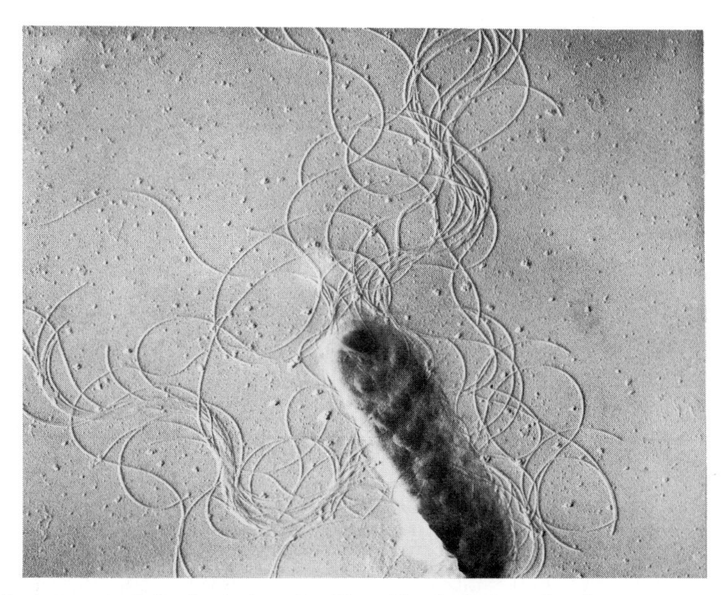

Fig. 4-8. Shadow-cast of the bacterium *Bacillus thiaminolyticus* showing numerous, long, thin, bacterial flagella. The bacterium itself is about 1.2 μm long and 0.5 μm wide. (Courtesy Dr. J. L. Wittliff, Dr. J. F. Smith, and Dr. R. L. Airth, University of Texas Cell Research Institute, Austin, Texas.)

(called *peritrichous insertion*). Some other eubacteria such as the famous *E. coli* have shorter and thicker (although still long and narrow) projections called *fimbriae* or *pili,* the function of which is unknown, but such organisms are not motile.

Procell flagella are very distinct from flagella of eucells. Bacterial flagella are much thinner, have a single fibril of truly molecular dimensions, and are often described as "macromolecular hairs." They are possibly contractile and may somehow produce movement of the procell through liquid. Each is now described as a single microtubule-like filament, since they are proteinaceous, "hollow," and have a diameter of about 250 Å. However, they are structurally different and are formed of different protein subunits, flagellin, from true microtubules. True microtubules have been reported within some Prokaryota. The axial filament of spirochetes is attached at both ends of the procell and consists of a bundle of parallel bacterial flagella. Certain bacteria (the myxobacteria) and blue-green algae have been thought to move without flagella or any known locomotor organelles. It is a gliding movement that is possible only when the organism is in contact with a solid or semisolid surface. In blue-green algae the direction is periodically reversed, but a net movement in some nearly random direction is achieved. When such filamentous blue-green algae are floating freely or one end only is firmly attached, the resulting movement achieved is a bending back and forth.

Division

Procell division, like eucell division, can be divided into prokaryon division and protoplast division. The prokaryon is irregular in shape and eventually seems to appear as two new prokaryons. It must be somewhat more organized than that statement implies, however, since there must be some mechanism for equal distribution of the double genome. Chen has recently illustrated by electron microscopy an aggregation of fibers (probably the genophore) at the center of the prokaryon in *Streptomyces* (Fig. 4-9). This is presumably followed by a "pulling apart" of the fibrous aggregate into two dense groups of fibers. There is indication that the procytoplasm then increases inward between the two new prokaryons. The pulling-apart phase can be compared to anaphase of mitosis but without any centrioles or spindles and is similar to some photomicrographs of Feulgen-stained bacteria.

There are, of course, schemes that present hypothetical models of genophore separation in bacteria. They all have some part of the circular genophore attached to the plasma membrane of the cell (Jacob et al., 1963) or to mesosomes (Ryter, 1968). The two daughter genophores somehow become attached to two separate but adjacent points of the membrane. These points of attachment then move apart a couple of microns, perhaps partly by the linear growth of the cell. Sueoka (1968) further proposed that there is then some sort of condensation of the daughter genophores to further separate them. Such a model is hardly adequate, however, to separate completely two 1,500 μm daughter genophores within a bacterium that is at most 2 or 3 μm long.

Furthermore, the work of Miller et al. (1970) indicates that a considerable amount of the genophore may be actually external to the prokaryon. The ribosomes outside the prokaryon are translating protein while attached to the numerous mRNA molecules that are being transcribed and are still attached to the DNA genophore. Either that or the genophore is confined to the prokaryon, and the ribosome-covered mRNA molecules extend outward into the riboplasm from the periphery of the prokaryon. Because transcription (DNA to RNA) and translation (mRNA sequences to amino acid sequences) apparently continue during genophore separation, the whole cell may be occupied by the geno-

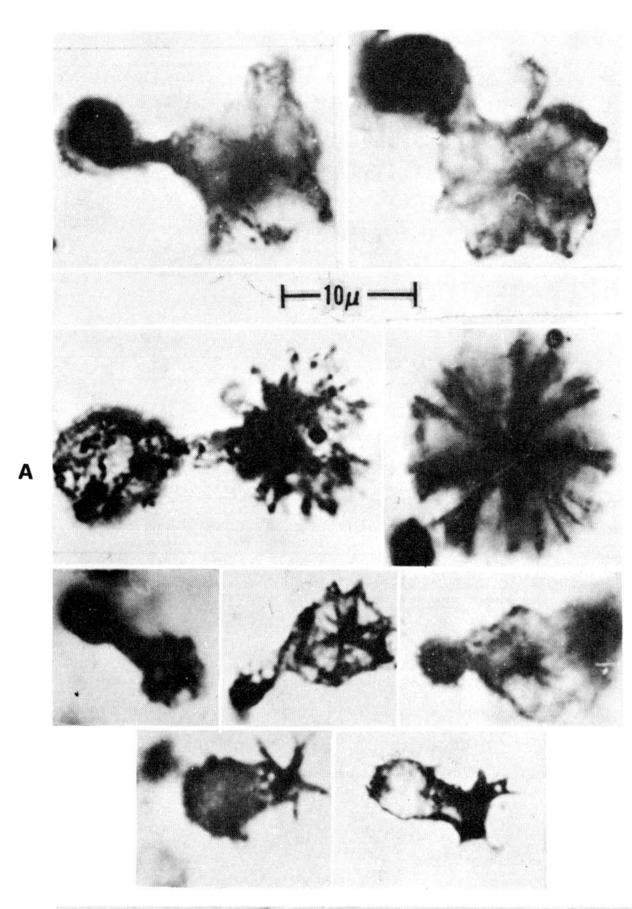

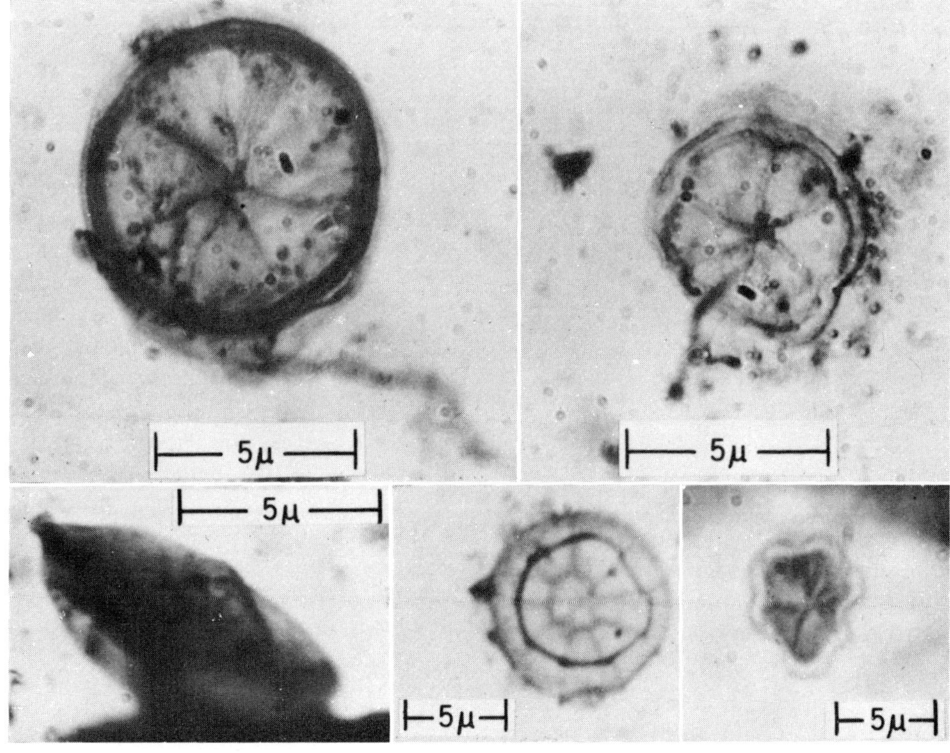

Fig. 4-9. A, Photomicrographs of the 2-billion-year-old fossil *Kakabekia umbellata.* Most examples consist of a bulb at one end connected by a stripe to an umbrella at the other end. Sizes of bulb and umbrella are inversely related. **B,** Photomicrographs of *Kakabekia*-like organism *(K. barghoorniana)* derived from soil at Harlech Castle, Wales, and grown in the presence of ammonia. The two are certainly similar. (**A** from Barghoorn, E. S., and S. A. Tyler. 1965. Science **147:**563-577; **B** from Siegel, S. M., K. Roberts, H. Nathan, and O. Daly. 1967. Science **156:**1231-1234.)

phore or strands attached to the genophore. Therefore the process of genophore separation must involve much more than is specified in the simple model just outlined.

Protoplast division seems to be the function of the plasma membrane. The first evidence is a circular ingrowth of the membrane and wall. That inward-directed ridge continues to grow toward the center until there is a complete separation into two protoplasts. In a long cell a number of such ingrowing ridges in various stages can often be seen under the electron microscope, giving the appearance of continuous protoplast division (Fig. 4-6).

No sexuality or meiosis is known in any prokaryote. It is possible, however, to get genetic recombination within such organisms, for exemple, in *E. coli.* That is, isolated DNA (transformation), bacterial DNA carried by phage (transduction), or DNA of another procell by rare conjugation can actually enter and combine with the DNA strand of the bacterial organism and become part of its hereditary genome. Such union and exchange of DNA between two strains of *E. coli* "cells" is a rare event but occurs often enough to permit genetic study of high resolution. The process involves segregation within genes and possibly even between two consecutive nucleotides of the DNA polymer.

The genophore of prokaryotes is probably a loop and a single linkage group of genes. This gene string is remarkably long relative to the size of the procell or prokaryon in which it is confined. A procell of *E. coli* that is 2 or 3 μm in length contains a genophore about 1,500 μm long.

Among eukaryotes, at least the higher multicellular forms, the chromosome seems to be nonfunctional in RNA synthesis when it is replicating and dividing. The prokaryotic genophore seems to be able to replicate and produce RNA at the same time; that is, it does both all of the time. This is achieved by replicating at only one point at any time, a point that moves around the loop. Thus genes in front of and behind the point are functional at any time.

Somewhat similar circular genophores have been extracted from mitochondria of animals, fungi, and chloroplasts. It does indicate a similarity between mitochondria and prokaryotes and can be used to support the theory of the symbiotic origin of mitochondria. Some mitochondria even seem to have a prokaryon (Fig. 10-10).

MESOKARYOTA

Mesokaryota is a designation that has been given to some flagellated algae, especially the dinoflagellates, because of their peculiar chromosomes and division (Zingmark, 1970). Such a group is hardly justified on that basis because among the less complex plants, animals, and fungi there are *many* variations of chromosomes and mechanisms of division. All of these have the general eukaryotic organelles and so are best considered as anomalous Eukaryota.

KAKABEKIA

Kakabekia is an organism of unknown affinity. In 1965 Barghoorn and Tyler published descriptions and illustrations of a number of fossil microorganisms from the Gunflint Chert of Western Ontario, Canada, dated by Hurley as having been deposited about 2 billion years ago. Among these mostly filamentous organisms, which appear similar to extant blue-green algae, there was one unique "organism" that consisted of a short stalk connecting a bulbous end with an umbrella-like end. The bulb varies inversely in size with the size of the umbrella-like crown; the latter has six to eight veinlike radial thickenings and varies in diameter from 12 to 30 μm. This organism was named *Kakabekia umbellata,* and the authors concluded that "It is difficult to assign an affinity of this organism to a living counterpart, providing any exists" (Fig. 4-9, *A*).

At the same time that the paleontologists were finding 2-billion-year-old fossils of

Kakabekia, microbiologists Siegel and Giummaro were trying to raise microorganisms from soil samples in exotic atmospheres such as air with various percentages of ammonia. In soil samples from Harlech Castle in Wales they "grew" some "microorganisms" in a partially ammonia atmosphere so unlike any known organisms that they hesitated to publish their work (Fig. 4-9, *B*).

However, when they saw the illustrations of the 2-billion-year-old *Kakabekia,* they recognized their living organism!

Both groups of authors indicated that the necessary condition of growth probably was and is an atmosphere that is at least partially chemically reduced and contains ammonia. Such an atmosphere is considered to have existed during the early epochs of terrestrial history. Thus fossil *Kakabekia* may provide a likely date when such a chemically reduced atmosphere still existed.

The affinities of fossil *Kakabekia* and the *Kakabekia*-like extant organism are unknown, whether they are eukaryotic, prokaryotic, or neither. It is likely, however, that the two samples, separated by 2 billion years, do represent the same type of organism and should be classified together. The extant form has now been named *Kakabekia barghoorniana.*

LITERATURE CITED

Aaronson, S. A., G. J. Todaro, and E. M. Scolnik. 1971. Induction of murine C-type virus from clonal lines of virus-free BALB/3T3 cells. Science **174:**157-159.

Baltimore, D. 1970. Viral RNA-dependent DNA polymerase. Nature (London) **226:**1209-1211.

Barghoorn, E. S., and S. A. Tyler. 1965. Microorganisms from the Gunflint Chert. Science **147:**563-577.

Diener, T. O., and W. B. Raymer. 1967. Potato spindle tuber virus: A plant virus with properities of a free nucleic acid. Science **158:** 378-381.

Eklund, M. W., F. T. Poysky, S. M. Reed, and C. A. Smith. 1971. Bacteriophage and the toxigenicity of Clostridium botulinum Type C. Science **172:**480-482.

Fraser, D. 1967. Viruses and molecular biology. A paper-back of the current concepts in biology series. The Macmillan Co., New York.

Freeman, V. J. 1951. Studies on the virulence of bacteriophage-infected strains of Corynebacterium diphtheriae. J. Bacteriol. **61:**675-688.

Gillies, S., S. Bullivant, and A. R. Bellamy. 1971. Viral RNA polymerases: electron microscopy of reovirus reaction cores. Science **174:**694-696.

Hanson, E. D. 1958. On the origin of the Eumetazoa. Syst. Zool. **7:**16-47.

Hofschneider, P. H., and A. Preuss. 1963. M13 bacteriophage liberation from intact bacteria as revealed by electron microscopy. J. Molec. Biol. **7:**450-462.

Jacob, F., S. Brenner, and F. Cuzin. 1963. On the regulation of DNA replication in bacteria. Cold Spring Harbor Symp. Quant. Biol. **28:** 329-348.

Kassanis, B. 1962. Properties and behaviour of a virus depending for its multiplication on another. J. Gen. Microbiol. **27:**477-488.

Kassanis, B. 1968. Satellitism and related phenomena in plant and animal viruses. Advances Virus Res. **13:**147-180

Kaufman, H. E., D. Brown, and E. M. Ellison. 1967. Recurrent herpes in rabbit and man. Science **156:**1628-1629.

Lowy, D. R., W. P. Rowe, N. Teich, and J. W. Hartley. 1971. Murine leukemia virus: high-frequency activation in vitro by 5-iododeoxyuridine and 5-bromodeoxyuridine. Science **174:** 155-156.

Miller, O. L., B. A. Hamkalo, and C. A. Thomas. 1970. Visualization of bacterial genes in action. Science **169:**392-395.

Morowitz, H. J., and M. E. Tourtellotte. 1962. The smallest living cells. Sci. Amer. **206:**117. Also in D. Kennedy (editor). 1965. The living cell: readings from the Scientific American. W. H. Freeman & Co., Publishers, San Francisco.

Semancik, J. S., and D. A. Reynolds. 1969. Assembly of protein and nucleoprotein particles from extracted tobacco rattle virus protein and RNA. Science **164:**559-560.

Shatkin, A. J. 1971. Viruses with segmented ribonucleic acid genomes: multiplication of influenza virus reovirus. Bact. Rev. **35:**250-266.

Siegel, S. M., and C. Giummaro. 1966. On the culture of a microorganism similar to the Precambrian microfossil Kakabekia umbellata Barghoorn in NH_3-rich atmospheres. Proc. Nat. Acad. Sci. U.S.A. **55:**349-353.

Siegel, S. M., K Roberts, H. Nathan, and O. Daly. 1967. Living relative of the microfossil Kakabekia. Science **156:**1231-1234.

Smith, K. M. 1965. The biology of viruses. Oxford University Press, Inc., New York.

Smith, K. M. 1967. Insect virology. Academic Press, Inc., New York.

Stanier, R. Y., M. Doudoroff, and E. A. Adelberg. 1970. The microbial world. 3rd ed. Prentice-Hall, Inc., Englewood Cliffs, N.J.

Stevens, J. G., and M. L. Cook. 1971. Latent herpes simplex virus in spinal ganglia of mice. Science **173:**843-845.

Studier, F. W. 1972. Bacteriophage T7. Science **176:**367-376.

Sueoka, N. 1968. A model of separation of daughter chromosomes by periodic condensation in bacteria. In W. J. Peacock and R. D. Brock (editors). Replication and recombination of genetic material. Australian Academy of Science, Canberra.

Temin, H., and S. Mazutani. 1970. RNA-dependent DNA polymerase in virions of Rous sarcoma virus. Nature (London) **226:**1211-1213.

Zingmark, R. G. 1970. Ultrastructural studies on two kinds of mesocaryotic dinoflagellate nuclei. Amer. J. Bot. **57:**586-592.

CHAPTER 5

Extraprotoplast material

CELL WALLS

The detailed study of cell walls certainly lies within the field of cytology. In fact, the term "cell" in biology was first used by Robert Hook in 1665 to describe the walls of cork. It was not until about 1825 that the concept of the protoplast as "the cell" became established. At the present time the cell wall is considered to be part of the cell. Detailed study of walls, however, is usually found in other disciplines: the bacterial wall in bacteriology, the walls of higher plants in plant anatomy, pollen grain and spore walls in palynology, walls of algae in phycology, and walls of fungi in mycology. An attempt will be made here to compare and relate these chemically and structurally different types of walls as an important area of cytology.

Walls, as distinct from intercellular material, are intimately associated with individual protoplasts. They can often increase in area and amount as the contained protoplast grows, and new walls can form during cytokinesis. Only occasionally do complete walls form at one time all around a mass of protoplasm, as they do around ascospores, when the egg of the Peronosporales (fungi) is formed, at a certain stage of the life cycle of diatoms, in the formation of the proembryo of *Ephedra,* and partly in spore formation in slime molds, some fungi and algae, pollen grains, and endosperm. Some cell walls cannot expand in area, for example, secondary walls of vascular plants, the quickly formed (20 minutes) silica walls of diatoms, and probably some others. Even some primary walls, which can expand when young, cannot do so after considerable thickening.

Cell walls are certainly necessary to the normal functioning of the plants having them, especially as protection and support of the cell or the whole multicellular organism. Epidermal and bark cell walls are specialized to protect the underlying tissues from drying out and from being invaded by bacteria and fungi; many xylem and other cells have thick walls for support of the plant as well as other functions.

Biochemically, cell walls are as complex as the extracellular material and, in general, are composed of the same types of monomers and polymers (Fig. 5-7 and Table 5-1). Most animals do not have enzymes such as cellulase for the digestion of plant cell wall polymers, but certain bacteria, fungi, protozoa, and snails do have one or more such enzymes and can therefore use this material as food.

Cell wall of prokaryotes

The procell is the structural and functional living unit of the bacteria, blue-green algae, and others. These groups are set apart from all other organisms by many characters of protoplast and extracellular material. Here, however, we are concerned with the wall and other organic material external to the plasma membrane.

Cell wall of bacteria. Bacterial cell walls (Salton, 1964; Stanier, Doudoroff, and Adelberg, 1970) differ chemically and structurally from walls of all other cells, even somewhat from walls of the otherwise quite similar blue-green algae. They do not consist predominantly of long linear polymers and microfibrils, and they have unique polymers and monomers. Some bacterial walls, as recently revealed by electron microscopy, consist of more or less spherical units, each from 80 to 800 Å in diameter, and these spheres (or hexagons) are packed tightly together in regular arrays (Fig. 5-1).

Fig. 5-1. Subunit structure of the inner wall of the bacterium *Bacillus thiaminolyticus* after lysis and shadow-casting for electron microscopy. This inner wall has a "screenlike" structure of nonlinear subunits unlike the walls of higher plants. (Courtesy Dr. J. L. Wittliff, Dr. J. F. Smith, and Dr. R. L. Airth, University of Texas Cell Research Institute, Austin, Texas.)

These structural units apparently consist of small polymers of perhaps up to 12 monomers of teichoic acid (ribitol phosphate or glycerol phosphate plus sugars and *d*-alanine) and also of glucosaminopeptides (a mucocomplex substance) and sometimes also of sugars, uronic acids, and hexosamines, or else the wall is continuous but with a "honeycomb network" produced by regularly arranged holes of about 80 Å diameter. This bacterial wall confers some rigidity, but the thickness of the wall and its substructure varies among bacterial species from almost none to quite thick and complex. The antigenic specificity of a bacterial cell is located in its wall, capsule, and flagella.

The walls of gram-positive bacteria are relatively simple. They are not layered and range in thickness from 150 to 800 Å. They contain large amounts of glucosaminopeptide material, some having only this type of macromolecular complex. Others contain teichoic acid and various sugars.

The walls of gram-negative bacteria are composed of at least two layers (the outer is the more rigid), consisting of a complex of protein, lipid, and polysaccharide and, as far as is known, no teichoic acid. The inner wall layer contains the mucocomplex substance. Retention of gram stain (crystal violet–iodine) in the protoplasm of the gram-positive bacteria has not been related to any particular chemical reaction; rather, the strong ethanol that is used is thought to affect the high muramic acid polymer content of wall material mechanically so that dye molecules are trapped within the protoplasm.

Bacteria and blue-green algae have from little to a great deal of secreted material external to the wall, called the *capsule* in bacteria and the *sheath* in blue-green algae. In both cases it is gellike, has a high water content (when in the presence of water), and varies greatly in amount. The bacterial capsule consists of polysaccharides with or without uronic acids. Occasionally, only teichoic acids or glucosaminopeptides are present. The capsule is not "necessary" to the normal life of the cell, at least experimentally. Enzymatic removal of bacterial walls demonstrates that the wall functions mechanically to prevent the protoplast from absorbing too much water by creating back pressure, and only rarely can bacteria survive without a wall.

Cell wall of blue-green algae. Blue-green algal cell walls are much less well known chemically and structurally than bacterial walls. They are intermediate between walls of bacteria and those of all other plants, since they contain, in common with bacteria, at least small amounts of muramic acids, the unusual amino acid diaminopimelic acid, glycosaminopeptides, no sterols, and no sulfuric acid. Their sheaths (not walls) differ from sheaths of bacteria in that they contain some cellulose, and the walls have some micellar structures like the walls of eucells.

Cytokinesis is essentially the same in bacteria, blue-green algae, fungi, and true algae. In these groups the plasma membrane invaginates to form a furrow, much as in animal cytokinesis, and cell wall material is formed in the furrow as it grows inward. Thus it looks as though centripetal growth of the cell wall in a ring, as an inwardly growing partition, accomplishes cytokinesis, but it is likely that the plasma membrane furrow is primary and transverse wall growth secondary. Adherence of the two daughter cells is simpler than separation of them; separation probably requires specific enzymes to hydrolyze the intercellular cement. In all cases except diatoms, growth of the longitudinal walls by intussusception, the insertion of new polymers and matrix almost anywhere within the old, is typical, at least of young cells.

Cell wall of true algae. The chemical composition and submicroscopic structure of the walls of true algae such as the reds, browns, and greens are not, in general, like those of primary walls of vascular plants (Fig. 5-2). The fundamental structural elements are seldom abundant micelles of cellulose. Rather, the algal wall is more like a matrix of polymers of uronic acids, hexosamines, various sugars, etc., often including some unique monomers and usually only a tiny percentage of microfibrils of cellulose or other polymer. However, as in all primary walls, from bacterial to those of flowering plants, wall growth occurs by the synthesis of polymers within the wall itself: the wall grows by intussusception. Cytokinesis in most algae is by furrowing of the plasma membrane and wall rather than by cell plate formation as in land plants.

Cellulose, that is, cellulose I, the natural micellar form of long glucose ploymers, does occur in many species of algae of most groups, but in many or most other species of these same groups it is completely lacking. Furthermore, in no algal walls is it much more abundant than about 15% and is usually 2% to 5%, in contrast to a much higher percentage of dry weight in seed plants. Thus algal walls consist mostly of matrix-type material of shorter polymers of pecticlike (uronic acid) or hemicellulose-like (pentose) polymers, although various hexose sugar polymers are usually present. Chitin has been reported in the walls of a few green algae, and in certain groups unique sugars and/or sugar derivatives such as alginic acid of the red and brown algae or fucinic acid of the brown algae are present. The diatoms and related algae have from a great deal to little "silica" in their walls; their walls are composed of no cellulose but of polymers of silicic acid and so-called pectin.

Algal walls, especially of many unicellular types, are often of complex form and

Fig. 5-2. Section of cell wall of the marine alga *Cladophora* showing the many layers of fibers of a complex wall. (Courtesy Dr. F. R. Turner, University of Texas Cell Research Institute, Austin, Texas.)

structure. Often the shapes of these cell walls are of taxonomic significance, as in diatoms, desmids, and dinoflagellates. The orderly arrangements of holes, called *puncta,* in the walls of diatoms are spectacular, and the ability of a compound microscope to resolve adjacent holes was long used as a test of the microscope's resolving power. Each punctum evidently contains a porous membrane across the opening. The complete cellular diatom wall (Fig. 11-2) is actually of two separate parts—the valves—the rim of one, the *hypothecium,* fitting inside the other, the *epithecium,* like a box and cover. Since the silica valves of the diatom cannot expand when formed, the protoplast cannot grow. When the cell divides, each daughter cell receives one of the valves and then secretes a new hypothecium. Thus in a reproducing population some of the protoplasts and valves become progressively smaller. Full size is restored by a protoplast discarding both valves, acting as a gamete, growing as a zygote (called an *auxospore*), and then secreting two new valves.

The unicellular green algae, called desmids, consist of two nearly separate *semicells,* each the mirror image of the other half. The shapes of these are frequently complex. The wall consists of a number of layers, the outermost sometimes of pectin. The wall of the desmid *Scenedesmus,* for example, consists of three layers. The innermost layer is of cellulose, there is a thin middle layer, and the outer pectic layer is a hexagonal meshwork supported by props from the middle layer and having structural openings. Furthermore, secretion of pectin through specific pores is thought to produce the movement of these cells. Movement of diatoms, on the other hand, is thought perhaps to be accomplished by protoplasm flowing in a grooved channel on the outside of the valves, somewhat like the track of a Caterpillar tractor.

The walls of the red, brown, and green algae are usually double layered, the inner one of parallel (in brown algae) or felted (in red algae) microfibrils. These microfibrils may be polyglucose (cellulose), polymannose (as in *Porphyra*), or polyglucose-xylose. The existence of cellulose in the walls of red and brown algae is still unresolved. The outer layer is matrix or "pectin" without microfibrils. Between adjacent cells there are either scattered tiny holes or holes grouped in large numbers to form pits. In many red algae there is a special "pit" in the transverse wall between adjacent sister cells.

The cell "walls" of *Volvox* and its relatives consist of a thick gelatinous matrix of scattered microfibrils and much nonfibrillar material, bounded on the exterior of the colony by a continuous double membrane but extending unbounded to near the center of the colony. Protoplasmic connections between all adjacent protoplasts penetrate these thick "walls."

Cell wall of fungi

The fungi, since they have no photosynthesis, are not typical plants; but since they do have walls, they can be and often are grouped with the true plants in classifications. Mycologists, the students of fungi, however, tend to think of them as constituting a separate kingdom. Certainly the cell wall polymer, chitin, which is fairly typical of the fungi, is rare to nonexistent in walls of algae and land plants. Much less is known about composition and ultrastructure of fungal walls than walls of bacteria or seed plants. Chitin occurs in the walls of many fungi in all groups but apparently not in all species or genera. Cellulose occurs widely also, sometimes in place of chitin, sometimes with it. Cellulose seems to be absent from walls of Ascomycetes and Basidiomycetes, although glucose polymers of some sort seem to be present in yeast (ascomycete) walls but not as microfibrils. Protein also seems to be characteristic of fungal cell walls, perhaps as a distinct middle layer between an outer layer of chitin and an inner layer of polysaccharides.

The difficulty of identifying polymers is that attempts to do so usually rely on identifying the monomer residues; but the presence of the residue, glucose, for example, does not necessarily specify cellulose in the wall. The iodine stain for the polymer is a good one, provided the cellulose is abundant enough to produce a visible reaction or is not covered by other material so that it cannot react. X-ray diffraction is difficult in mixtures. Electron microscopic evidence of long microfibrils is probably the best evidence for cellulose; such are not revealed in the walls of yeast, although glucose monomers are detected as residues.

Most fungi are filamentous, and the filaments grow at the tips. It is only at the tips, as the protoplasm elongates, that new cell wall material is formed. Nevertheless, the cell wall does seem in part to determine the form of the cell, since when the wall is prevented from forming by the action of wall-digesting enzymes, the form of the cell or filament is completely altered. Typically, wall material can form only where some wall already exists. The slime molds, however, are without walls during their growth and metabolic phase, but walls are formed as part of the development of the spore-forming phase. The walls of the spores of Ascomycetes also form entirely within the cytoplasm of the ascus, without contact with the ascus wall.

Electron microscopy of ascospore formation indicates that at numerous places the nuclear envelopes form thickenings when a piece of ER lies close to it and then bulge out as blebs and vesicles. These vesicles move outward almost to the plasma membrane of the ascus. There they "unite" to form an open-ended membranous tube around the protoplasm of the ascus, within which are the nuclei of the spores to be. This membrane then gradually envelopes the nuclei and extends inward between them eventually, thereby cutting out the spores. Walls are then formed between these double spore membranes. This is a case of membranes arising only from preexisting membranes, ER and nuclear. That is, although membranes may increase in extent by growth, some preexisting membrane must be present to begin the growth. That membranes do not rise de novo seems generally true, although there *may* be exceptions such as the apparent or possible formation of the nuclear envelope "on" the surfaces of telophase chromosomes.

The wall of the mycelium of the Phycomycetes is a long continuous tube with no cross walls. In the Ascomycetes occasional cross walls are formed, but they are incomplete and the protoplasm is continuous through a large hole in each cross wall (Fig. 3-4). During most of their life cycle, the Basidiomycetes form cells, each of which contains two nuclei. When such a *dikaryotic* cell divides, there are two separate nuclear divisions (Fig. 17-13). Then, as the cross wall is forming, one nucleus of one division passes through an external bypass tube around the cross wall (the so-called *clamp connection*) into the other end of the divided cell. Thus each daughter cell finally contains one of each of the two kinds of nuclei. Even Basidiomycetes have structurally complex pores in the transverse walls between adjacent cells.

When the fungal mycelium forms a compact tissue, the fruiting body, the packed mycelia are cemented together by some extracellular material. Such fructifications, some of which are very large, expand rapidly by uptake of water; many even secrete a varnishlike material onto the surface of the fruiting body.

Cell wall of land plants

Multicellular land plant protoplasts, except for some gametes and a few other special cases such as the generative cell in the pollen grain which has only intercellular material around it, have a *primary wall* (Esau, 1965). This wall is usually considered to be "hard." However, in the living tissue it is about 85% water and can most accurately be thought of as a firm jelly of pectic compounds (like the *middle lamella*), hemicellulose (pentoses and uronic acids), and a variable percentage of cellulose. There is also a small amount of protein in both the middle lamella and the primary wall. The protein of the middle lamella is evidently bound to the oriented gel structure of the pectic polymers by metallic ion cross-linkages. The protein of the primary wall consists at least of enzymes that perform the polymerization of the monomers within the wall itself. The monomers of the wall polymers may pass through the underlying plasma membrane as such or are actually formed in part within the wall.

The polymers of the wall material are formed outside the plasma membrane, within or on the inner surface of the wall. Addition of new polymers among the old produces growth of the wall in thickness and area and is described as growth by *intussusception*. In addition to wall growth by intussusception most walls also grow in thickness by addition of material to the internal surface, just outside the plasma membrane. This form of wall thickening by *apposition* frequently produces visible layers (Fig. 5-3), as though the wall thickening was periodic, which it often is. Such centripetal growth by apposition may produce thick primary and/or secondary walls. Centrifugal wall growth, the addition of material on the outside, occurs, if at all, only in isolated cells such as pollen grains and spores where external protoplasmic material is available for use. Secretions from the protoplast through the wall to the exterior produce extracellular material rather than a wall (e.g., the slime of root tips and the cuticle and wax of the epidermis).

The silica wall of diatomaceous algae (Fig. 11-2) is formed in a flat vesicle just inside the plasma membrane. Subsequently, the inner membrane of the vesicle becomes the new plasma membrane.

Wall growth in plants, that is, growth in

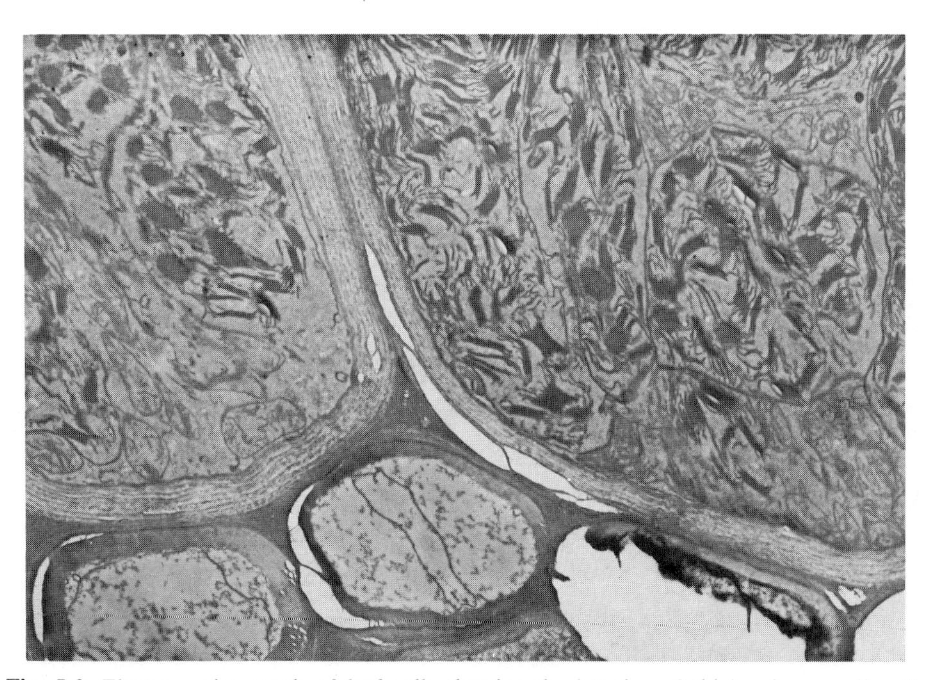

Fig. 5-3. Electron micrograph of leaf cells showing the layering of thick primary cell walls.

area of primary walls, must accompany protoplast growth. The increase in protoplast volume may include increase in amount of protoplasm and increase in volume of vacuoles, or either. Wall growth is accomplished by increase in area without decrease in thickness; wall material is formed as the wall enlarges. Whether a cell enlarges or not may be controlled by whether the wall itself can increase in area. Certainly the wall may have tensile strength (resistance to growth), which permits the cell to have high internal hydrostatic (turgor) pressure.

It has been established that cell growth rate is dependent on (1) the permeability of the cell to water, (2) the osmotic potential of the protoplast, and (3) the extensibility of the primary cell wall. Apparently, cell growth is permitted in part by the wall remaining or becoming extensible, that is, of lower tensile strength. Present evidence indicates that the plant hormone indoleacetic acid (IAA), at proper concentration (about 10^{-5}M), plays a major role in making the wall extensible, although it may also affect osmotic pressure and/or other cellular characteristics such as resumption of mitotic division. Other wall or protoplast factors must also exist to determine the final forms of cells—isodiametric, long and narrow, irregular, etc.

Some particular cells of vascular plants form *secondary walls* internal to the primary wall. Secondary walls are lower in water content, are higher in cellulose, often contain lignin, and are harder (woody) than primary walls. Primary walls differ from secondary walls in that the former often grow in extent, as the contained protoplast grows, by the addition of material throughout the volume of the wall. This process of wall growth can best be conceived if one keeps in mind that the primary wall is a highly hydrophilic amorphous colloid and not a hard structure. In fact, the primary wall has been defined as that wall which, at least in its young stage, is able to increase in area and amount by synthesis of its own material.

Older primary and secondary walls may add throughout their substance additional polymers and/or additional types of polymers such as more cellulose, and/or lignin, or "fatty" material (suberin or cutin, for example). The addition of lignin, cutin, or suberin usually takes place as the protoplast of the cell dies and disappears.

Perhaps the most unusual secondary walls are those of the tracheary elements of vascular plants. The secondary wall is deposited discontinuously in certain patterns on the inner surface of the more or less continuous primary wall. The pattern may consist of rings (annular) or a spiral; it may have the appearance of regular or irregular rungs of a ladder; or it may be continuous except for irregular or symmetrical pits. Walls with annular or spiral secondary walls are able to grow; the cells can elongate after such discontinuous secondary walls have formed. Cells having essentially continuous secondary walls cannot grow. Recently it has been noticed that there is a relationship between localized secondary wall deposition and the presence of adjacent microtubules just inside the plasma membrane. The meaning of this is unknown, especially since microtubules have also been related to protoplasmic streaming. Secondary walls are frequently layered, usually three layers, of which the last formed, the innermost, may be different in composition and submicroscopic structure from the two outer layers.

A *pit* in a secondary wall is a local region where the secondary wall does not form. Usually a pit in one cell is matched by another similar pit in the adjacent cell to produce a *pit pair.* Similar areas of primary walls are called *pit fields* (Fig. 11-8) to distinguish them from the true pits of secondary walls. Pits in secondary walls often form on top of the pit field of the primary wall, as though both are effects of one cause. Generally pits and pit fields have protoplasmic connections between the adjacent protoplasts called plasmodesmata.

Plasmodesmata (to be discussed later), in contrast to pits, which are large, are thin protoplasmic strands running through walls between protoplasts. Similar strands running outward through the exterior wall of an epidermal cell are called *ectodesmata.*

The *shapes* of plant cells are determined by genes and the immediate external environment, not the cell wall. The forms, functions, and fates of plant cells are aspects of growth and development just as in animals. There is a wide variety of cells and therefore cell wall shapes (Esau, 1965). The simplest are small and nearly cuboidal, such as meristematic cells, or nearly spherical, as in pith. Some may increase greatly in volume and become irregular in shape (long and narrow or short and wide). Wall thickness also varies from very thin (the walls of meristematic cells) to very thick (fibers or persimmon endosperm cell walls, Fig. 5-4). In certain cells such as the *vessel elements* of xylem and *sieve cells* of phloem, there must be enzymes for the breakdown of the end walls of the former or parts of the end walls in the latter. Thus at maturity the vessel elements, which are xylem cells arranged end to end, form a continuous, hollow, segmented tube, the *vessel,* which may be a number of inches in total length. The end walls between adjacent sieve cells are only partially destroyed. The result is the *sieve plate,* consisting of many circular holes. Sieve cells, in contrast to vessel elements, have protoplasmic contents, although each lacks a nucleus.

Most published discussions of plant cell wall ultrastructure are studies of bacteria or seed plants. Similar knowledge of walls of plants of other groups is limited. Seed plant cell walls all have some cellulose as well as hemicellulose and often pectic compounds. In some specialized walls, lignin, suberin, silica, or cutin is present and always considerable water. The main structural elements are cellulose microfibrils, which constitute from 3% to perhaps 50% of wall material. It has been estimated that each year about 10^{11} tons of polysaccharide is synthesized by the world's plants.

The cellulose polymers are unique among extracellular polymers because they are so long (10,000 to 50,000 Å in length) and have 1,000 or more glucose residues. Each such polymer is approximately 8 Å in diameter. Furthermore, glucose polymers associate in parallel arrays of about 100 to form a *micelle,* with a diameter of about 100 Å. Approximately twenty such micelles are associated in parallel to form the basic structural cellulose aggregate, the *microfibril,* of about 250 Å diameter. Among and between the microfibrils are water, other (shorter) polymers of glucose, uronic acids, some protein, and other organic and inorganic molecules. This composition of long cellulose microfibrils and short polymers has been compared to reinforced concrete.

The cellulose microfibrils grow at one or both ends as their constituent polymers grow, and new polymers and microfibrils can start among the old or be added by apposition just outside the plasma membrane. Subsequently, other kinds of polymers can be added among the microfibrils. For example, when lignification occurs, lignin polymers form in the secondary wall, the primary wall, and even in the middle lamella.

The number of glucose polymers in a wall of a cell is great. It has been estimated that in a cross section of one thick-walled cell (a fiber) there are about 2 billion cellulose polymers.

The amount and arrangement of the cellulose microfibrils within the walls (primary and secondary) of land plants vary with the stage of development. The first-formed primary wall is low in cellulose, and the microfibrils run in a more or less circular pattern (rather than longitudinally), with some interweaving by microfibrils, which run in various other directions. As additional layers are added centripetally by apposition, the microfibrils tend to run more and more longitudinally, either because they have been pulled into that orientation by the elongation of the cell and wall or because they are laid down more and more longitudinally. Late primary and secondary walls generally have fibrils running still more longitudinally. These are generalizations, of course, with many exceptions among cells or in different parts of one cell wall as, for example, near pits where microfibrils may even have a circular orientation. There are no known exceptions, however, to the generalization that the microfibrils run parallel to the plasma membrane; their variation is always with respect to the longitudinal axis of the cell.

The character of the plant cell wall often determines the type of tissue and the name of the tissue (Esau, 1965). Thus *parenchyma* is tissue consisting of cells with thin primary walls and little or no secondary wall (pith, cortex, root and stem apices). Parenchyma cells are usually nearly isodiametric, unspecialized enlarged cells with large vacuoles; in general, they can undergo further mitotic division when properly stimulated and are often endopolyploid. *Collenchyma* consists of cells having walls unevenly thickened, as in the corners only. The walls are unlignified, and the protoplast is alive. *Sclerenchyma* is supporting tissue with thick, hard, lignified walls, often of long, narrow cells. Walls are often pitted, and there are no protoplasts at maturity, except that there may be some parenchyma cells among the hard, thick-walled cells. Most sclerenchyma is wood, consisting of multicellular, long aggregates of tracheid and/or fiber cells; but sclerenchyma may also consist of more or less isolated groups of variously shaped cells and even of thick-walled seed coats. *Cork* is a tissue of thin-walled dead cells, the walls of which are infiltrated with suberin. It constitutes part of the bark of woody plants. *Xylem* and *phloem* are complex tissues composed of a variety of cell types. Wood of woody plants is xylem and derives its character from the prevalent thick-walled fibers and tracheids and usually vessels in angiosperms. Other tissues of land plants are not characterized as obviously by the contained cell walls.

Summary

Cell walls are characteristic of prokaryotes, fungi, and plants and are part of the cell, although not considered living in the usual sense. The wall is distinct from the extracellular material, which is called the middle lamella in multicellular land plants. Walls, from those of bacteria to flowering plants, consist of various polymers; bacteria have no cellulose; most algae have some cellulose, although it is lacking in many, and others have as much as land plants; all land plants have abundant cellulose, although the amount varies from 3% to 50%. All walls, except secondary walls, are more like a tough gel than wood and can grow by intussusception and/or by apposition. The many shapes of walls are genetically determined by the protoplast, and in multicellular plants there are thin strands of protoplasm called plasmodesmata running through the walls and connecting adjacent protoplasts. Cell walls give some rigidity to the protoplast and to the multicellular organism, permit turgor pressure, and probably are somewhat effective in the transport of water and dissolved molecules to the plasma membrane.

Zoologists often refer to the plasma membrane of animal cells as "walls." This is especially true of German cytologists, but the differences are obvious.

PLASMODESMATA

The protoplast of a plant cell is surrounded by a thick cell wall that tends to isolate adjacent protoplasts of multicellular plants from one another biologically, except for the movements of molecules through the walls. However, there seem to be actual protoplasmic connections between adjacent protoplasts that extend through the walls. These intercellular connections are called plasmodesmata and have been known at least since 1880 when Tangl saw them as long, very thin "lines" extending through the thick walls of the endosperm of *Strychnos,* similar to those in Fig. 5-4. During the subsequent years, plasmodesmata have been found in most tissues of all multicellular green land plants (mosses, liverworts, ferns, and other cryptogamic vascular plants and seed plants) as well as in some algae (Livingston, 1964).

Plasmodesmata are thin, always much less than 1 μm in diameter, and often at or below the limit of optical microscopic resolution. They are generally straight from the protoplast to the middle lamella and again to the adjacent protoplast. Frequently a swelling or granule has been described where a plasmodesma crosses the middle lamella, and there are numerous reports of granules in the protoplasts at the ends of a plasmodesma. These granules may or may not be artifacts. Plasmodesmata are usually simple, but reports of branching and anastomosing exist. Some of them seem to extend only to the middle lamella. Their distribution and number vary considerably. If there are pit fields in the cell walls, the plasmodesmata are restricted to the thin wall of the pit field. If no pit fields occur, the plasmodesmata are rather uniformly distributed. Some counts have indicated from 5 to $50/\mu m^2$, but those few figures mean little, since they vary so much.

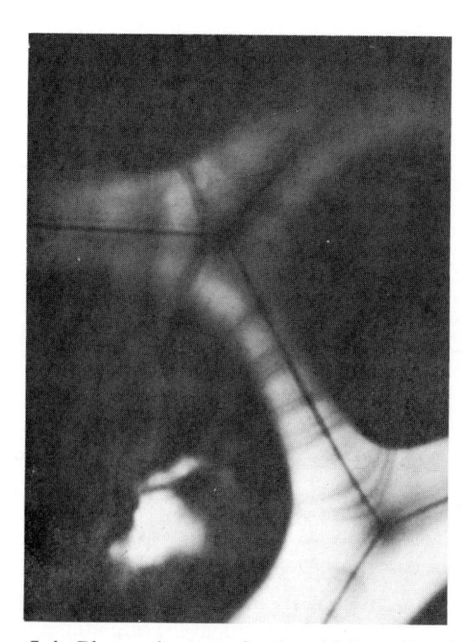

Fig. 5-4. Plasmodesmata in the thick walls of the endosperm of a mature seed of persimmon. Each plasmodesma is a fine protoplasmic connection between adjacent protoplasts.

Robards (1968) has reported desmotubules as substructures within certain types of plasmodesmata. Russow in 1883 and Krull in 1960 reported that plasmodesmata can split ("reproduce") longitudinally into two. As the wall containing it grows in surface area, a plasmodesma may widen and flatten laterally. If new wall material is deposited longitudinally as ingrowths along the midlines of the flattened surfaces, eventually two plasmodesmata would result, which could then move apart as the wall area continues to increase between them.

There are two probable origins of plasmodesmata. At cytokinesis, as the new transverse wall forms, strands of protoplasm (seemingly ER) extend across it and prevent wall formation at such points. These strands become plasmodesmata. Apparently, plasmodesmata can also form in existing walls, since they appear between stock and scion cells after a graft, in the thick walls of endosperm, and between cells that have slid into new contact with one another after the walls have elongated. There is still some question whether the plasmodesma is a section of unmodified ER or not, but certainly profiles of ER are frequently present in the the cytoplasm at the ends of plasmodesmata, and it is possible to trace ER right up to the opening of the plasmodesma and perhaps even through it. Because of these protoplasmic intercellular connections, it has been proposed that all cells of a plant are connected into one vast syncytium. Such a concept, however, may imply a biologically false model of a plant.

Plasmodesmata in the outer walls of epidermal cells are called *ectodesmata*. These extend outward to the base of the cuticle but not through it. It has been proposed that ectodesmata function in secretion of cuticle and/or wax onto the exposed surface of the cell.

Since the plasmodesma is probably an

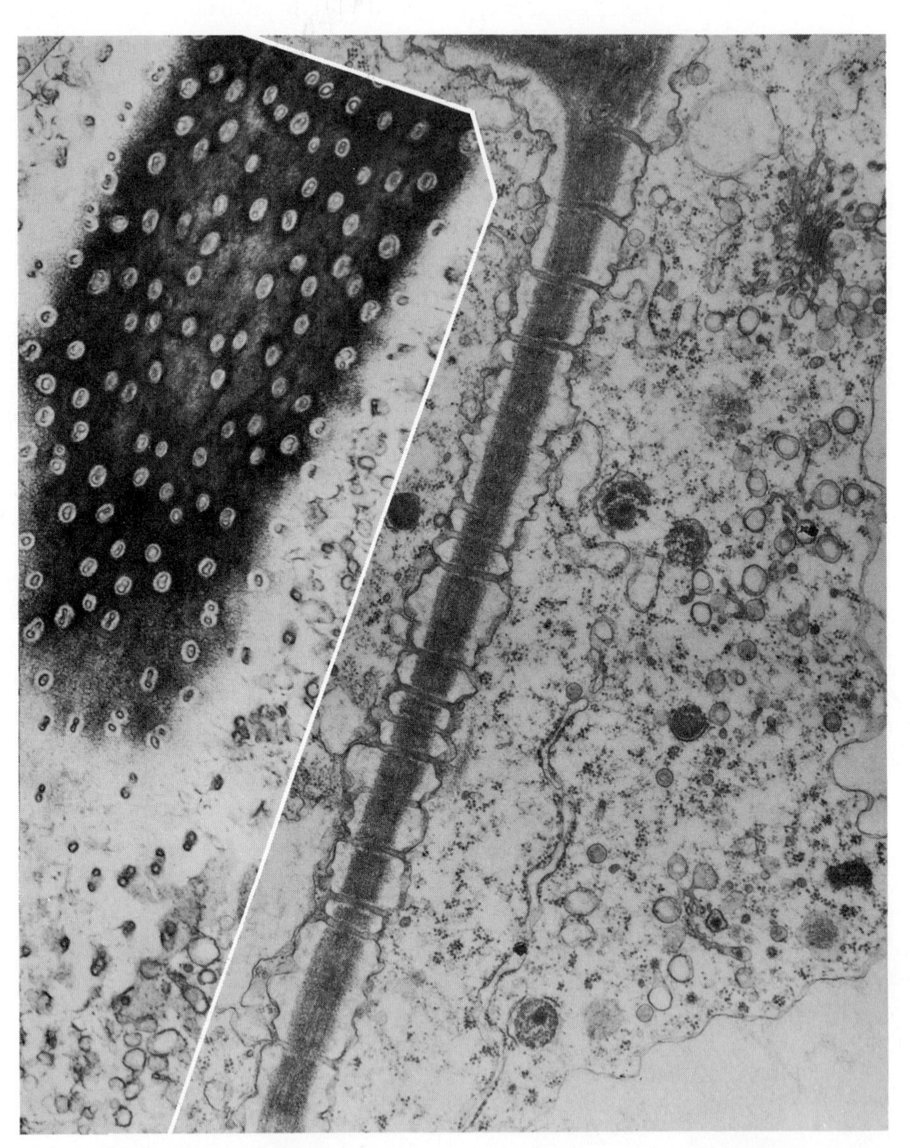

Fig. 5-5. Plasmodesmata in the cell wall of the aquatic charophyte *Nitella*. Right, transverse section of wall but longitudinal section of plasmodesmata. It seems evident that the plasma membranes of the two protoplasts are continuous through the plasmodesmata. Left, section parallel to the wall but perpendicular to plasmodesmata. A dictyosome with tubular extensions is evident, and polyribosomes are scattered through the cytoplasm in the transverse section. Also notice polyribosomes in the cytoplasm. (Courtesy Dr. F. R. Turner, University of Texas Cell Research Institute, Austin, Texas.)

intercellular protoplasmic connection (Fig. 5-5), it has been proposed that materials and stimuli are thereby transported between cells. It has been established that when thick endosperm cell walls, which represent stored food (Fig. 5-4), begin to be enzymatically attacked during seed germination, the first erosion of the wall appears at and along the plasmodesmata. It is reasonable, although it may not be necessary, to assign to plasmodesmata transport of enzymes and monomers into and out of the wall from and to the protoplast. Such a function would not require that a plasmodesma extend completely through both walls, from protoplast to protoplast, as they usually do. However, the ubiquity of plasmodesmata in plants certainly indicates considerable importance.

Electron microscopy has demonstrated plasmodesmata between cells in numerous tissues of many plants and is credited with revealing the origin and relationship to the ER. Treatment of living leaf tissue with silver nitrate (Fig. 5-6) has revealed reduction within the plasmodesmata as well as in "granules" in the cytoplasm at the openings of the plasmodesmata (Brown et al., 1962). This observation that conditions within plasmodesmata are probably different from those in the general cytoplasm supports similar conclusions by optical microscopists. The conclusion of Jungers (1930) that plasmodesmata are not protoplasmic connections but are elements of the wall may be at least as correct as the alternative.

Plant virologists have long suspected that virus particles may pass from cell to cell through plasmodesmata. Esau et al. (1967) presented electron microscopic evidence of such passage of beet yellows virus. The cytoplasm of an infected cell is full of the virus rods; they filled at least one plasmodesma between a sieve cell and a parenchyma cell. Thus it seems proved that viruses may pass through at least some plasmodesmata.

EXTRACELLULAR MATERIALS

It is a safe generalization that most protoplasts have some intimately associated, essentially nonliving material external to the plasma membrane that is derived directly from the protoplast itself, the composition and structure of which is genetically determined by the protoplast. Procells and all plant cells have cell walls, and the cells of multicellular animals have intercellular cement, which holds them together, or more

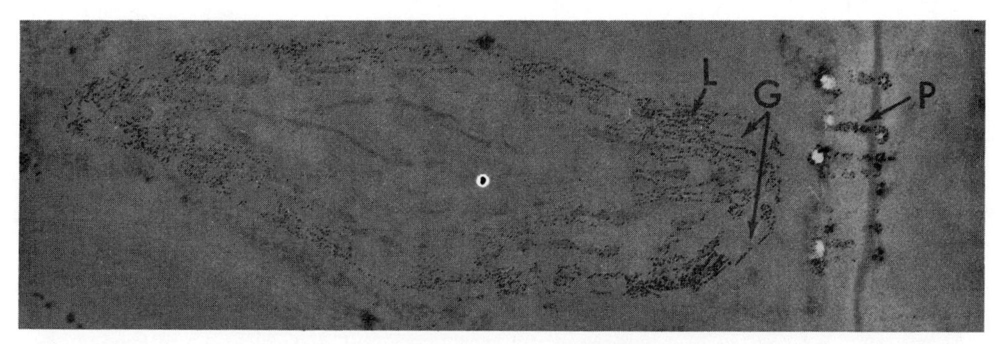

Fig. 5-6. Plasmodesmata and chloroplast reduction of $AgNO_3$ to tiny metallic silver particles at reductant sites. Silver particles occupy plasmodesmata, **P,** and also indicate cytoplasmic "granules" in the cytoplasm at each end of each plasmodesma. In the chloroplast, grana, **G,** are indicated by rectangular spaces devoid of silver, and the particles are arranged in evident intergranal lines, **L,** indicating that reduction is accompanied at, on, or in the stromal lamellae. (From Brown, W. V., H. Mollenhauer, and C. Johnson. 1962. Amer. J. Bot. **49:**57-63.)

voluminous material such as is present in the mesoglea of Coelenterata, bone, and cartilage. Most such organic material is in the form of polymers, usually sugars or derivatives of sugars. Additionally, there may be minerals, as in bone and the exoskeletons of some arthropods; in walls of certain plant cells there is also lignin, which is a polymer of phenolic (aromatic) compounds; in walls of bacteria there are teichoic acid and muramic acid polymers; and cell walls of certain algae and land plants have polymers of silicic acid. There is usually a small amount of protein also. This extracellular material should not necessarily be thought of as basically hard or rigid, like wood or bone, but as a firm gel consisting mostly of water, like firm agar. With respect to plants, however, extracellular material is external to the cell wall—the middle lamella.

AMINO ACID MONOMERS

It is possible that all extracellular material contains some protein or at least amino acids. The amount varies greatly, however, from more than 50%, as in animal connective tissue, to less than 1%, as in plant cell walls and middle lamella. The protein of the latter may consist mostly of enzymes that are functional in polymerizing the wall material itself, in dynamic aspects of wall growth, or in local lysis to produce in part the sculpturing of many plant

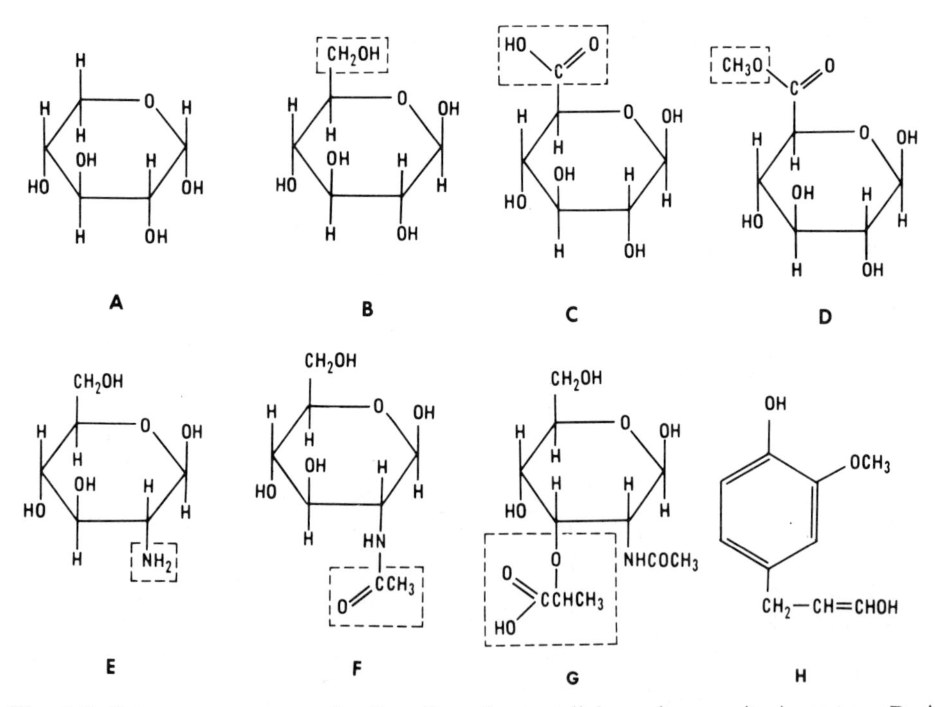

Fig. 5-7. Common monomers of cell walls and extracellular polymers. **A,** A pentose. **B,** A hexose (the six-carbon is boxed). **C,** A hexose is converted to a uronic acid by changes on the six-carbon. **D,** Occasionally, a methyl group is bonded through an oxygen to the six-carbon. **E,** A hexose is converted to a hexosamine by an amino group attached to the two-carbon. **F,** Hexosamine can be further modified by attachment of an acetyl group to the amino group to form *N*-acetylhexosamine. **G,** Another modification of hexosamine is muramic acid of prokaryotic walls. **H,** An entirely different monomer is coniferyl alcohol, an example of the type of monomer of lignin that is so common in cell walls of wood. From one or more than one of these kinds of monomers a wide variety of polymers can be formed, often with other constituents such as sulfuric acid or amino acids.

cell walls. Additionally, in multicellular plants there are plasmodesmata extending "through" the walls and thereby connecting adjacent protoplasts. Structural protein has been detected in the middle lamella of multicellular plants as perhaps one of the cementing materials.

The most abundant protein in mammalian connective tissue is collagen, a highly ordered fibrous material, each fiber of which is composed of parallel protein polymers. A nonprotein matrix called chondroitin sulfuric acid is also present, the monomers of which will be discussed later, and often there are minerals in that particular connective tissue called bone. One layer of the arthropod exoskeleton is of protein and is functionally important in the shedding process and in the resynthesis of the new chitinous exoskeleton.

Sugar and modified sugar monomers

Among prokaryotes, fungi, plants, and animals, most extracellular material consists of polymers of some form of sugar or sugar derivative (Fig. 5-7). Although there is a limited variety of such monomers, these may be polymerized in many different ways, and mixed polymers may also be present, making the chemistry often extremely complex. However, when reduced to a few of the most common monomers, the subject is comprehensible even to a nonchemist (Table 5-1).

The basic molecules are sugars, especially the six-carbon hexoses, but also the five-carbon pentoses. The hexoses occur as various steric arrangements of $C_6H_{12}O_6$ (glucose, galactose, mannose) in the six-membered cyclical pyranose ring form. These sugar monomers polymerize, often condensing at the one- and four-carbon positions, to form polysaccharides such as cellulose, which is the common polymer of plant cell walls and the tunic of tunicates. The pentoses, five-carbon sugars such as xylose and arabinose, also polymerize to form other polysaccharides, as in plant pectic materials, along with uronic acids.

Uronic acids such as glucuronic and

Table 5-1. Cell wall constituents

Polymers	Monomers
Cellulose	Glucose
Noncellulose polysaccharides	Mannose, galactose, glucose, xylose, or arabinose
Pentosans	Pentoses
Xylan	Xylose
Araban	Arabinose
Pectic acid	Galacturonic acid (often combined with calcium as calcium pectate)
Pectin and protopectin	Methylated galacturonic acid
Hemicelluloses	Pentoses and uronic acids
Chondroitin sulfuric acid	Galactosamine and glucuronic acid
Chitin	*N*-Acetylglucosamine
Glucosaminopeptides	Muramic acid and other monomers, including amino acids
Intercellular cement	Glucuronic acid and acetylglucosamine
Lignin	Phenylpropane (coniferyl alcohol)
Proteins	Amino acids (amino acids or small polypeptides may be united with sugarlike polymers, especially in bacteria)
"Silica"	Silicic acid, $Si(OH)_4$

galacturonic acids are derived from the respective hexose sugars glucose and galactose by conversion of the carbon-6 group (CH_2OH) to a carboxylic acid group (COOH). Some uronic acids may be methylated at C_6 or more rarely at C_3 or C_4; that is, the OH of the carboxylic acid group is replaced by —O—CH_3. When polymerized, these uronic acids constitute the chief components of plant wall pectic compounds as well as being constituents of many other kinds of extracellular material of plants, animals, and procells. Uronic acids are probably the most widespread monomers of extracellular material among terrestrial organisms.

Another common and widespread modification of hexose sugars is the replacement of the —OH on carbon-2 by an amino group to form a compound such as *glucosamine* or *galactosamine*. The latter is one constituent of chondroitin, a polymer of the connective tissue matrix. A further modification of the amine by the addition of acetic acid produces the monomer *N*-acetylglucosamine, which is present in the polymer of the intercellular cement of most animal tissues. It is also the monomer of chitin, a substance characteristic of arthropods, but also of molluscs, annelids, and the walls of most fungi. An additional modification of either type of hexosamine found in walls of procells is muramic acid. This acid has a three-carbon group attached through oxygen to carbon-3 of the hexosamine. Muramic acid is designated as 3-O-D-carboxyethyl hexosamine. It polymerizes in many combinations and is the characteristic monomer of bacterial walls. It is also present in walls of blue-green algae but not of eukaryotic cells.

Such monomers, when polymerized in a wide variety of combinations, produce much of the extracellular material of living organisms. Cellulose, the most abundant material of most land plant cell walls, is a polymer of glucose. In plant cell walls, cellulose is mixed with polymers of other sugars as well as with pectic compounds (polymers of uronic acids) and hemicelluloses (polymers of pentose sugars and uronic acids). Chondroitin sulfuric acid, the matrix of connective tissue, is a polymer of galactosamine, glucuronic acid, and sulfate. Chitin is a polymer of *N*-acetylglucosamine. The intercellular cement of animal tissues consists of hyaluronic acid, which is a polymer of glucuronic acid and acetylglucosamine.

Lignin

In most vascular plants the walls of a few particular kinds of cells eventually become impregnated with, among other polymers, lignin. The lignin monomers, however, are of a class of molecular type entirely different from any others discussed here. They have a six-carbon ring and a three-carbon side chain, essentially like coniferyl alcohol (Fig. 5-7, *H*). Lignin monomers differ especially in the composition of the side chain but also to a limited extent with respect to certain other groups on the ring. Condensation to form the polymers apparently occurs between the side chain of one monomer and the ring of the next, although various arrangements have been proposed. Lignin-impregnated walls are firm and rigid, as in wood, which, in fact, consists mostly of lignified cell walls. Eugenol, the chief aromatic constituent of clove oil, is very similar to coniferyl alcohol, and, in fact, a synthetic lignin called polyeugenol has been made in vitro from it.

Waxes

The cuticle that covers and permeates the outer wall of plant epidermal cells is complex and poorly known chemically. Some of the constituent compounds are true waxes, but paraffins, aliphatic acids, and aliphatic alcohols are also included as waxes. Many of these are not polymers, but the "estolides" are small polymers. These waxes are closely related to fatty acids.

Cutin, suberin, and sporopollenin. Cutin is the ground substance of plant cuticle. Cutin, suberin, and sporopollenin are complex polymers of aliphatic acids. Cutin is more highly polymerized than suberin and less so than the sporopollenin of pollen grain and spore walls, which is highly resistant to degradation and consequently forms fossils.

These superficial "waxes" and cuticular substances prevent the movement of water into or out of the protoplast or plant tissue and may act to screen out ultraviolet rays from the sun. Suberin is present in cell walls of cork, a cell type of tissue that composes part of the bark of trees and shrubs. Cells with suberized walls, like those having lignified walls, die and the protoplast disappears. Multicellular plants, unlike animals, thus have large amounts of tissue composed of dead although functional "cells," especially the tracheids, fibers, and vessels of xylem and also bark.

Minerals

The extracellular material of various plant and animal cells and tissues may be infiltrated with inorganic minerals. The extracellular material of bones of vertebrates is loaded with the salt hydroxyapatite, $3Ca_3(PO_4)_2$, in the form of tiny crystals (100 to 500 Å). These crystals are present in the ground substance of the connective tissue, forming a pattern related to the pattern of collagen fiber.

The chitinous exoskeletons of some arthropods, especially some Crustacea such as lobsters and crabs, contain and are hardened by the deposition of calcium carbonate. Extracellular secretions of corals, gastropods, brachiopods, and Bryozoa are also more or less pure secreted mineral.

Cell walls of certain plants such as grasses, diatoms, horsetails, sunflower, and *Lantana* contain considerable amounts of SiO_2, up to 10% or more of the cell wall material. This silica, at least in the diatoms, is amorphous, in the form of polymers of silicic acid, $Si(OH)_4$. In fact, silicified cells may have all the organic matter removed experimentally by incineration or all of the silica removed by hydrofluoric acid, and yet the cell walls and all their sculpturing are still evident. Certain peculiar cells of the grass leaf epidermis are called "silica cells" and have very thick walls of silica. Certain algae also produce limy material within or external to the walls.

Of course, small amounts of calcium, magnesium, and phosphorus are present in most plant cell walls, as in protoplasm itself.

Mucopolysaccharides, mucoproteins, and mucoids

Mucopolysaccharides, mucoproteins, and mucoids constitute a miscellaneous group of polymers universally present among organisms. They are of great significance and have numerous functions. Essentially all of them contain glucosamine and/or *N*-acetylglucosamine. Chemical analysis of these polymers is generally difficult because treatment so changes them that it is difficult to conclude the molecular association which probably existed in vivo. For example, is the protein actually part of a complex or merely loosely associated with the polysaccharide in mucoproteins and even mucoids? Furthermore, the terminology is confused. One classification is as follows:

A. *Mucopolysaccharides*—polymers containing glucosamine but no protein
   1. Neutral—*N*-acetylglucosamine (chitin), often with galactose or glucosamine and sugar
   2. Acid—glucosamine and uronic acids, often with sulfate (animal intercellular material, etc.)

B. *Mucoproteins*—acid mucopolysaccharides and protein as a complex, associated by polar or easily disassociated bonds (uncommon)

C. *Mucoids*—mucopolysaccharide and protein as a complex, associated firmly by covalent bonds and difficult to disassociate, neutral or acid, the latter often with sialic acid (common as blood group antigens, saliva, gastric mucosa, on membranes of animal cells, etc.)

Mucopolysaccharides have already been discussed as being important as extracellular materials in most organisms.

Mucoproteins and mucoids are both complexes of mucopolysaccharides and protein, are obviously quite similar, and in this discussion will be grouped together. They occur within the protoplasm and outside the plasma membranes and also as secretions of glands, in saliva, for example. They are most common outside cells, and it is there that they probably have their greatest significance. Ova of many animals, excluding arthropods, have a thick jelly layer of mucoid in which the sugar residues are esterified with $—SO_4$. It has been found that the polymers of the jelly coat of *Arbacia* eggs have a molecular weight of about 300,000 and contain about 20% dry weight of amino acids. Since the proteolytic enzymes trypsin and chymotrypsin, which break peptide bonds only, can hydrolyze these polymers, it seems that the polymers of jelly coats must contain regions of peptides, each containing a number of amino acids, probably of specific composition, and somehow "scattered" among the sugar residues.

It is certain that the mucoid of the jelly coats of ova are species specific, by which sperm recognize ova of the same species but are able to ignore ova of other species. It is likely that mucoids may also confer species, individual, and tissue specificity to cells of animal organisms generally, by which various sorts of cells can "recognize" one another. It is generally accepted that all animal cells have mucoid within or on the outer surface of the plasma membrane. Most cell antigens such as those of red blood cells as well as soluble blood-group substances are mucoids. The ability of unicellular forms to "recognize" individuals of their own species or opposite mating type probably depends on particular surface mucoids.

Mucoids are found within cells in vesicles of the gland cells that produce them, such as salivary glands, gastric mucosa, and lubrication glands elsewhere.

Summary

Extracellular material, then, is typical of cells of all groups of living organisms except probably many protozoans. The material is usually a water gel of polymers of sugars and/or derivatives of sugars, usually with some conjugated protein, and in some tissues with additions of lignin, minerals, and waxes. This material is not living, although some enzymatic activity may occur within it. It is, however, part of the cell in the modern concept, and some plant "cells" are functional units as cell walls only.

There is little doubt that extracellular material is essential to the life of the organism possessing it, but the functions are quite distinct from those of the protoplast. Extracellular material and cell walls are at most only slightly active metabolically; they have little control of molecular movement into and out of the protoplast except by creation of osmotic back pressure (turgor pressure) by cell wall rigidity. They do not determine shapes of cell; rather, it is the protoplast and adjacent cells that do so. Cell walls of multicellular plants provide rigidity, as do bones of vertebrates and exoskeletons of arthropods. The intercellular cement of multicellular animals and the middle lamella of multicellular plants have the same function—sticking adjacent cells together. In animals the intercellular material may function as nerve impulse insulation so that an impulse does not jump from cell to cell out of control. The cell wall of the procell or plant cell, being a secretion of a particular protoplast, is distinct from anything found in animals.

LITERATURE CITED

Brown, W. V., H. Mollenhauer, and C. Johnson. 1962. An electron microscope study of silver nitrate reduction in leaf cells. Amer. J. Bot. **49:**57-63.

Esau, K. 1965. Plant anatomy. 2nd ed. John Wiley & Sons, Inc., New York.

Esau, K., J. Cranshaw, and L. L. Hoefert. 1967. Relation of beet yellows virus to the phloem and to movement in sieve tubes. J. Cell Biol. **32:**71-87.

Jungers, V. 1930. Recherches sur les plasmodesmes chez les vegetaux. Cellule **40:**7-81.

Livingston, L. G. 1964. The nature of plasmodesmata in normal (living) plant tissue. Amer. J. Bot. **51:**950-957.

Robards, A. W. 1968. Desmotubule—a plasmodesmatal substructure. Nature (London) **218:** 784.

Salton, M. R. J. 1964. The bacterial cell wall. American Elsevier Publishing Co., Inc., New York.

Stanier, R. Y., M. Doudoroff, and E. A. Adelberg. 1970. The microbial world. 3rd ed. Prentice-Hall, Inc., Englewood Cliffs, N. J.

CHAPTER 6

Plasma membrane, phagocytosis, and pinocytosis

PLASMA MEMBRANE

Although early morphologists described the cell membrane as an interface separating the internal environment from the external medium, they were hampered by lack of instrumentation to further study the organization of this boundary. To many of them the plasma membrane was represented at most as a dark or refringment line at the cell surface. The physiologist, on the other hand, although accepting the term "cell membrane" from the morphologists, developed a different meaning that was based on numerous physiological studies to explain the phenomena of permeability and active transport as well as bioelectrical potentials. Later, other disciplines such as physics and chemistry and particularly physical chemistry and biochemistry were applied and eventually it was possible to propose a molecular model that would "explain" various functions attributed to the membrane. Interestingly enough, the pauci-molecular model of the plasma membrane as proposed by Davson and Danielli (1952) was based on indirect evidence from numerous and diverse kinds of studies, and when compared to the unit membrane proposed much later by Robertson (1959), which was the result of more direct examination by means of the electron microscope, one is impressed by the similarities of these two molecular models.

Historically, Overton (1895) was among the first to study the structure or composition of the plasma membrane. He was primarily interested in the rates of entry of a number of substances into the cell and showed that ions had a low permeability rate and nonelectrolytes entered the cell at rates that dependend on their *partition coefficient.* Those substances that had a higher coefficient entered faster than those that had lower partition coefficients. Partition coefficient can be stated as the ratio of solubility of a substance in oil to its solubility in water. Therefore it can readily be seen that those substances having a higher solubility in oil than in water will have a higher partition coefficient number. These studies led Overton to postulate that the cell membrane is composed of a continuous layer of lipid material.

Later, Collander and Bärlund (1933) modified the lipoidal theory of Overton, proposing that the membrane, although lipid in nature, also contains pores that extend through this layer to permit entrance of hydrophilic molecules and ions.

Gortner and Grendell (1925), using

erythrocyte ghosts, extracted the lipid content from these cell remnants and noted that the total lipids extracted occupied twice the original area of the membrane when spread on a water surface. This led to the assumption that the plasma membrane is composed of bimolecular leaflets (two molecular layers) of lipid material. These lipids are orientated in such a manner that the polar grouping (or hydrophilic ends) are at the surface, whereas the hydrocarbon groups of the fatty acids form the interior (Fig. 6-1). The basis of this concept was derived from the original work on surface tension by Langmuir (1917), who found that the hydrophilic portion of the lipid, being the most active, is drawn inward at the water-lipid interface, and the less active, or the hydrocarbon portion, forms the free surface.

Studies by Fricke and Curtis (1934, 1935) supported the concept of a plasma membrane being composed of lipid. They showed that membranes exhibit low electrical conductivity, which agrees with characteristics of lipids in general.

Indirect studies by Cole (1932) and Harvey and Shapiro (1934) on plasma membrane showed that the surface tension of cells is much lower than those obtained using pure lipid material. The results indicated the surface tension of lipids to be about 5 dynes/cm^2, but only 0.2 dyne for the cell membrane. This means that the plasma membrane is not composed entirely of lipid as was previously thought, but some other substance or substances must be present to produce the low surface tension. Danielli and Harvey (1935) suggested that in addition to the lipids already proved to be present, proteins may be responsible for the low values obtained. This concept led to the formulation of the pauci-molecular model of the plasma membrane by Davson and Danielli (1952). According to this concept, the membrane

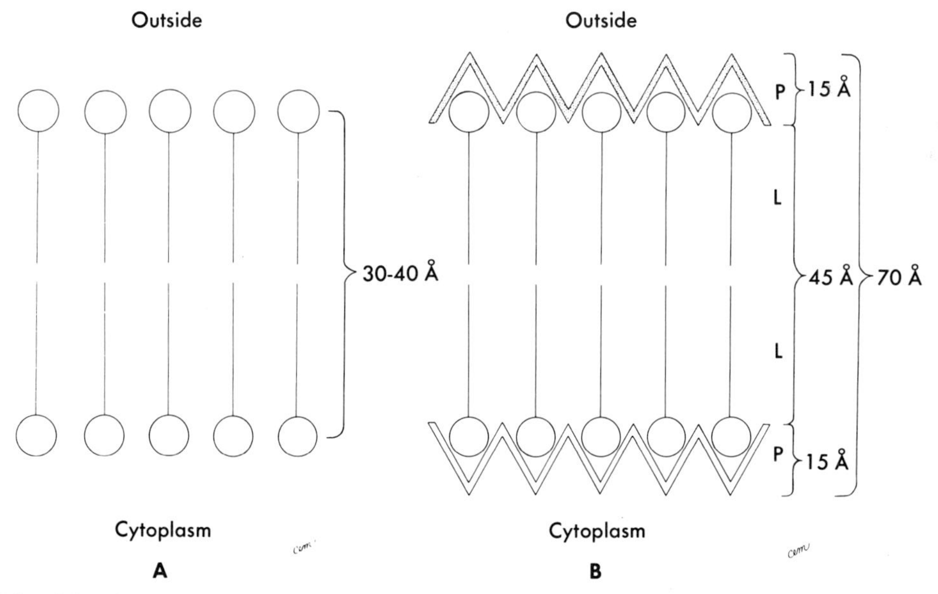

Fig. 6-1. Diagrammatic representation of the plasma membrane based on the concept of Gortner and Grendell, **A,** and the unit membrane as conceived by Robertson, **B.** Stippled region indicates the outer layer is probably composed of polysaccharides in addition to proteins. (Courtesy Dr. C. E. Mays, De Pauw University, Greencastle, Ind.)

consists of one or more bimolecular leaflets orientated in the manner described by Gortner and Grendell. That is, the polar groups of the lipids are at the two surfaces, whereas the two layers of interdigitating hydrocarbon moieties form the interior. Overlying the polar group surfaces are the proteins, which are orientated tangentially. One can visualize the model as lipid layers sandwiched between the proteins, the proteins forming both the outer and inner surfaces.

Thickness of the plasma membrane

Many of the early studies of membrane thickness and composition were done with erythrocyte ghosts. These ghosts are erythrocytes of mammals, which have no nucleus and from which all the contents (mostly hemoglobin) have been removed by suspension in hypotonic solution, leaving only the membrane. Another advantage of using mammalian red blood cell ghosts is the ease of obtaining large numbers for study as well as the fact that their homogeneity provides consistent results. Since the membrane thickness is well below the resolution of the light microscope, Waugh and Schmitt (1940) studied these membranes with the analytical leptoscope. Although this method is probably little used today, it did provide much needed information. The thickness of a film deposited on a surface can be determined from the intensity of reflected light, provided that the indices of glass, film, and external medium are known. For this study they used a barium stearate–calibrated step film. Comparison of the intensities of reflected light of the step film of barium stearate and of the membrane when adjusted to equal intensity permitted the thickness of the membrane to be determined. The thickness of rabbit erythrocyte membranes was found to range between 215 and 230 Å. Other measurements varied between 50 and 300 Å. Wolpers (1941), using membranes from erythrocytes and electron microscopy, determined the thickness of the plasma membrane to range between 150 and 300 Å. Hillier and Hoffman (1953), also using erythrocyte ghosts and electron microscopy, obtained the value of 50 Å ± 10 Å for the thickness of the membrane. Of this figure, they estimated that 30 Å was composed of lipids; the remaining 20 Å they considered to be protein. The figure cited by Hillier and Hoffman, as will be shown later, is low but within the range generally accepted for membrane thickness at the present time. During this same period, numerous other figures were recorded for membrane thickness. In some instances a thickness of as much as 600 Å has been reported (Ponder, 1961). The variances obtained were in all cases due to the method of preparing the ghost cells by hemolysis. It was assumed that after a number of washings the thickness remains constant. The possibility always exists, however, of some hemoglobin remaining even after several washings.

Unit membrane

It must be remembered that the model of Davson and Danielli provided a molecular concept of the plasma membrane, but it was, nevertheless, constructed from indirect evidence. It was not until the 1950s when the unit membrane concept was developed that measurements were based upon electron microscopic studies of myelin sheaths as well as the embryogenesis of myelinated nerves and numerous other cellular membranes.

It has been shown from electron microscope studies that myelin is composed of multiple repeating layers of an average thickness of about 120 Å. Each of these layers contains a dense osmiophilic line 25 Å thick, followed by a light layer 80 to 110 Å across (Fig. 6-2). The light zones are bisected by another less dense line, known as the intraperiod line. At times these intraperiod lines are almost nonexistent or may appear as dotted lines. During the period of early studies, it was not known specifically whether the myelin was produced by the Schwann cell or by the nerve axon itself, and further study was initiated to determine its origin. Studies of the ontogeny of myelinated nerve sheaths as well as studies of mature myelin that included low-angle x-ray diffraction techniques and polarizing microscopy of myelin led to the concept of the unit membrane as proposed by Robertson.

For more detailed discussion of membrane structure see Branton and Park (1968).

Embryology of myelin sheath. Early studies by Gasser (1952) showed that the Schwann cell does not completely enclose

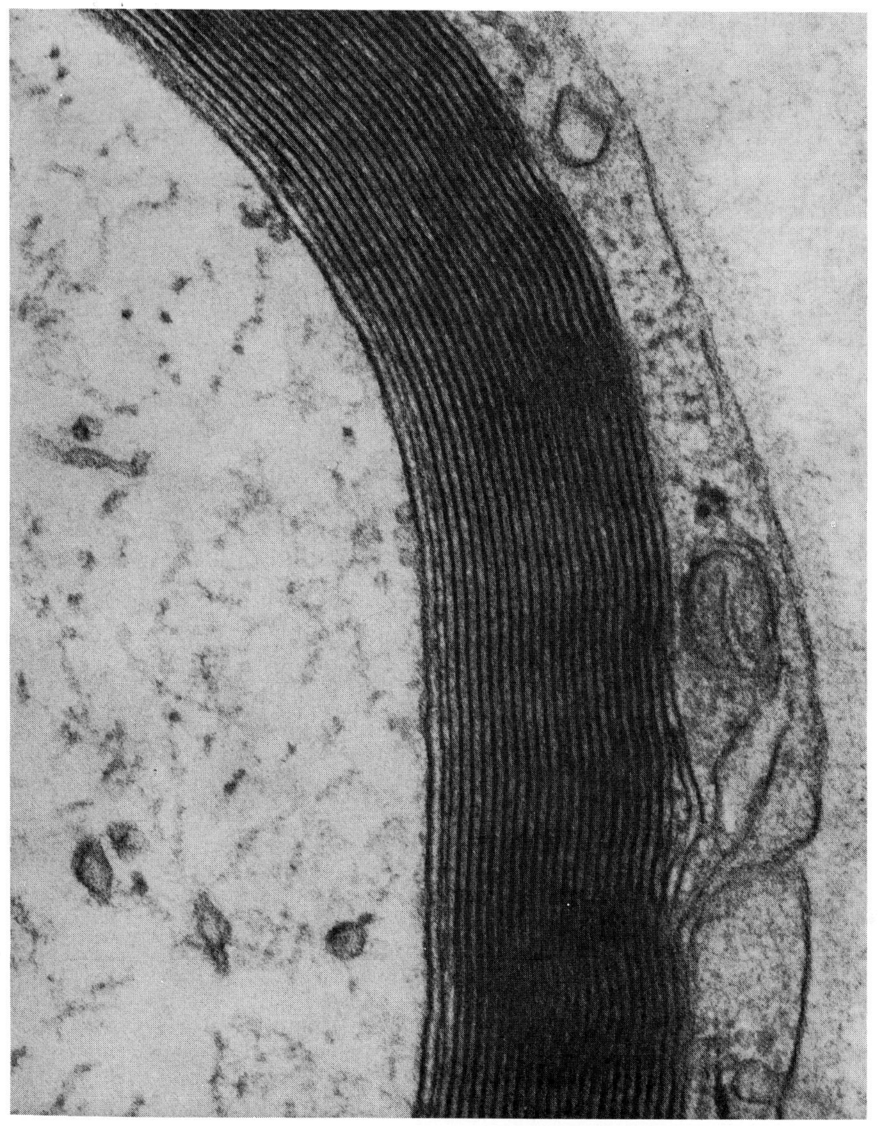

Fig. 6-2. Electron micrograph of myelin. The dark osmiophilic lines are period lines. Intraperiod lines, which bisect the light areas, are not evident. (Courtesy J. Beggs, Laboratory of Neuropathology, Barrow's Neurological Institute, Phoenix, Ariz.)

the nerve fiber of unmyelinated nerves. The lips or edges of the Schwann cells do not touch. These lips, which do not fuse, form the *mesaxon*. Geren (1954), while studying the ontogeny of myelin formation in chick embryos, observed that some of the nerve fibers had long mesaxons which could be described as spiraling rather loosely about the axon fibers (Fig. 6-3). At that point it was highly suggestive that the characteristic lamellated pattern of myelin may be nothing more than greatly extended plasma membranes of the Schwann cells. The difficulty was that the membrane itself was not clearly discernible. However, with the introduction of the new fixative potassium permanganate, rather than osmium which had been used previously, the relatively indiscrete lines became prominent (Fig. 6-4). As a consequence, three distinct layers were visible. Next to the cytoplasm was a dense line that measured approximately 20 Å, followed by a light central zone of 35 Å thickness, and an outer dense line of 20 Å, making the membrane approximately 75 Å thick. Therefore, when applied to the Schwann cells in developing myelin, this fixative shows that myelin is a double layer of Schwann cell unit membranes wound together, in which the intraperiod line is represented by the cytoplasmic surface of the membrane alone, and the major line is formed by the two outside layers coming together.

• • •

It has been shown that the staining characteristics of the inner and outer layers of the unit membranes show differences in chemical composition. The outer membrane may be mainly carbohydrate, whereas the inner (cytoplasmic) membrane is primarily lipid and protein. From the study of myelin membranes and many others, Robertson (1959) proposed that all cellular membranes are fundamentally of the same dimensions that is, 20, 35, and 20 Å. Such a theoretical membrane he called the *unit membrane*.

If one were to compare the unit membrane with the one proposed earlier by Davson and Danielli, no significant difference between the two appears at first glance.

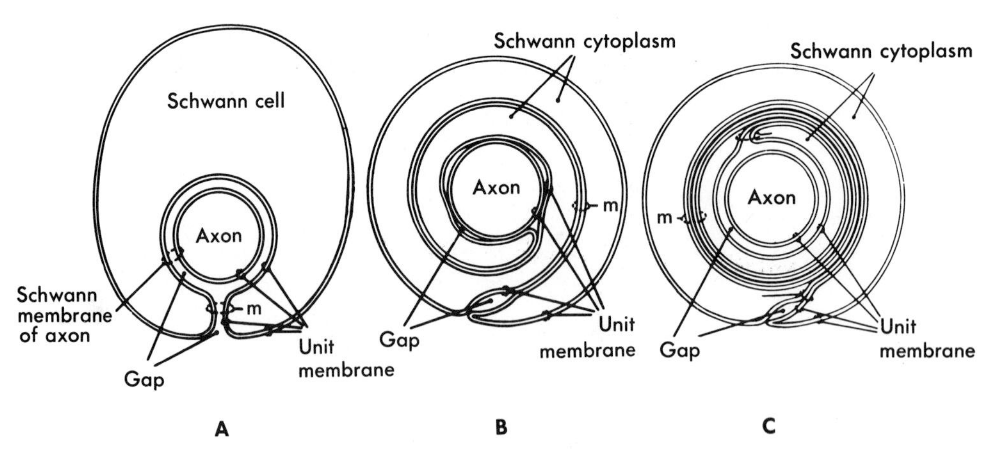

Fig. 6-3. Diagram showing formation of myelin. **A,** In early stage of myelin formation the mesaxon, **m,** surrounds the axon. **B,** Elongated mesaxon is spiraling about the axon. **C,** A later stage in the formation of myelin. Note compact myelin. (From Robertson, J. D. 1964. Unit membranes. A review with recent new studies of experimental alterations and a new subunit structure in synaptic membranes. In M. Locke [editor]. Cellular membranes in development. Academic Press, Inc., New York.)

Yet despite the similarity in structure, the following basic differences do exist:

1. Because of lack of available information, the older concept did not specify the number of lipid monolayers, whereas the unit membrane model includes a bimolecular structure.
2. The older model suggested that the nonlipid layer is composed essentially or entirely of a globular protein, whereas the unit membrane model suggests a fully spread fibrous protein layer.
3. The pauci-molecular model of Davson and Danielli suggested a symmetrical membrane in which the proteins in the inner and outer layer were essentially similar. On the other hand, differences in staining characteristics obtained by Robertson (1962) suggest the membrane is asymmetrical in this respect. That is, a difference in chemical composition exists between the inner and outer layers, and the latter could conceivably contain polysaccharide (Fig. 6-1).

The unit membrane, as proposed by Robertson, provides invaluable information concerning the molecular structure of the plasma membrane as well as other cellular membranes such as the membranes of the ER, Golgi complex, and mitochondria. Yet the present model does not provide for selective channels or pores. In addition, it is also known that the membrane can show changes in state, as is evident in nerve depolarization or changes in membrane transport followed by hormones in certain cells (Hechter, 1965a).

Lamellar and globular models. One can consider the membrane as being a dynamic and highly labile structure shifting between various substructural states with different phases of function. As a result, Kavanau (1963, 1965) developed a molecular theory based on membrane in function. In essence the membrane shifts between different sub-

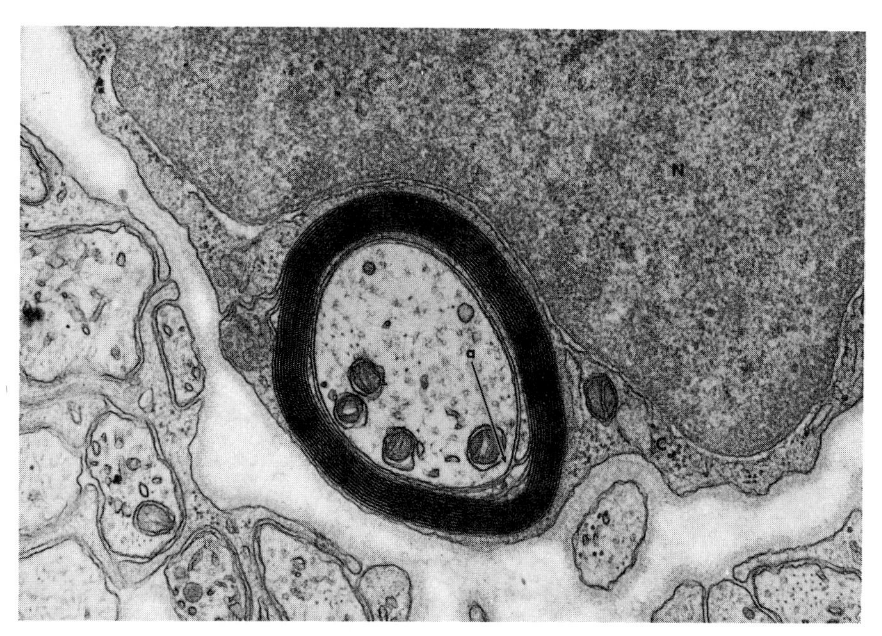

Fig. 6-4. Electron micrograph of human myelinated nerve fiber. Note relationship of mesaxon (arrow) to axon fiber, **a,** and nucleus, **N; C,** cytoplasm of the Schwann cell. (Courtesy J. Beggs, Laboratory of Neuropathology, Barrow's Neurological Institute, Phoenix, Ariz.)

structural states with different phases of function. The differences are in the arrangement of the lipid moieties within the membrane. The two extremes are the open and closed configurations.

The open configuration consists of regularly arranged hexagonal (cylindrical) micelles or pillars 80 Å wide and between 180 and 200 Å high, the center-to-center spacing between pillars being about 150 Å (Fig. 6-5). The ends of the pillar bases are bound to the envelopes by relatively stable bonds.

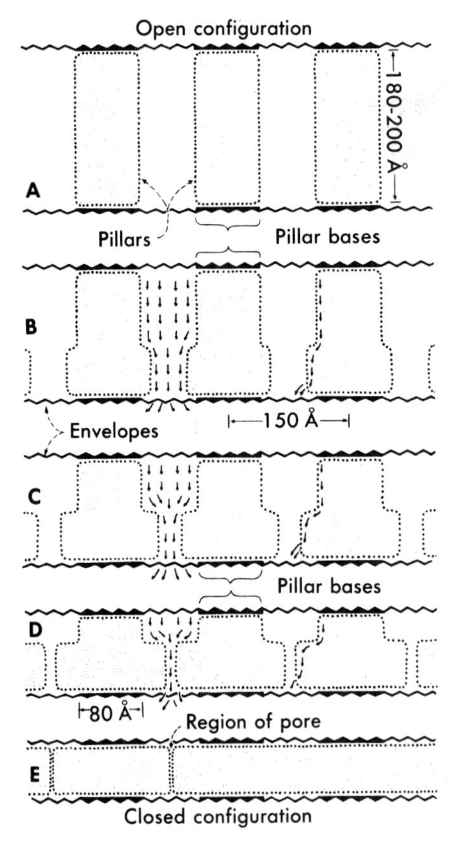

Fig. 6-5. Diagrammatic cross section showing changes in micellar form in transformation from open to closed configuration of a membrane. Heavy dots show the region of lipid polar groups. Zigzag lines indicate protein layers. Arrows between the pillars show direction of flow of collapsing cylindrical micelles. See text for further explanation. (From Kavanau, J. L. 1963. Nature [London] **198:**525-530.)

The envelopes are protein monolayers 10 to 15 Å thick. The closed formation, on the other hand, results when the pillars collapse and the lipid micelles coalesce or closely abut (Fig. 6-6). If the collapse goes to completion, it results in the formation of the bimolecular leaflets of the unit membrane. In the partially opened state, pores exist among the closely abutted lipid units. When the closed configuration occurs, the bimolecular leaflets, which average 50 to 60 Å, are sandwiched between the protein monolayers (Fig. 6-5). The relation between the pillar bases and overlying and underlying protein layers are unchanged because of the stable lipid-to-protein bonding of the open configuration.

Kavanau proposed that the transformations between these membrane configurations provide a basis for protoplasmic streaming and movements of cell organelles, for ameboid locomotion, for active transport and impulse conduction, and for the coalescence, fragmentation, growth, degrowth, contraction, and expansion of components of the ER and of the membranes enclosing other cell organelles. He postulated that mem-

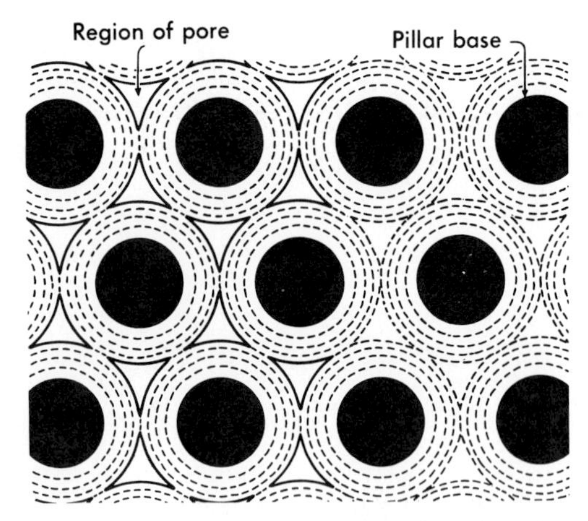

Fig. 6-6. Top view of Fig. 6-5. Dashed lines show the same position of the bimolecular disks. Pore regions are formed on the assumption that bimolecular disks abut but do not obliterate these regions. The area to the right shows obliteration of pore region. (From Kavanau, J. L. 1963. Nature [London] **198:**525-530.)

branes transform chemical energy to kinetic energy by mechanisms involving reversible transformations between assemblies of micellar units of complementary asymmetry.

Structure of protein envelopes

The protein envelopes, of about 15 Å thickness, are postulated to play at least five basic roles. They function (1) in the catalysis of metabolic reactions; (2) as molecular sieves, probably at the same time having catalytic roles in active transport; (3) as structural stabilizers of the lipid micelles of different membrane configuration; (4) in intramembranous transformations, and (5) as "triggers" for certain intermembranous (topological) transformations that occur during the fusion and fragmentation of membrane-bounded bodies (Kavanau, 1965).

Several theories exist as to the molecular configuration of these protein envelopes. One incorporates the beta helix configuration and one, suggested by Hechter (1965a,b), incorporates the hexagonal protein configuration.

Beta configuration. The envelope can be conceived as being composed of proteins in an extended but not completely unfolded or uncurled beta configuration. This will allow for greater interaction between the peptide bonds of the proteins and the polar group of the lipids. In addition, there would be possible in this configuration greater penetration of these groups into the hydrocarbon moieties of the lipid layers. Since these proteins are not completely unfolded, they possess potentially extensible segments that may be coiled to various degrees into compact knots and globules. This becomes important because the knots permit the membrane to extend rapidly over a large area of cytoplasm but yet have the capacity to recover to the original size without the intervention of growth or degrowth. Catalysis is carried out by the proteins in the fibrous state as well as in the partially globulated state (Kavanau, 1965).

Hexagonal configuration. Hechter (1965a), on the other hand, conceived the cell membrane as possibly being composed of hexagonal protein disks. This type of configuration is based on the work of Warner (1961a,b), who studied the possible molecular configurations of several antibodies as well as other polypeptides to determine the possible unifying structural arrangement of active biological compounds. Although biopolymers are customarily considered as being of the alpha helical configuration, many proteins do not exist in that form, and in an aqueous biological solution the protein may consist of a hexagonal arrangement (Fig. 6-7).

To fully understand the concept of Hechter it is well to consider the genesis of the hexagonal disk before its application to the structure of the membrane. All the peptides could be arranged in a regular strainless hexagonal pattern (Fig. 6-7). In this form the hexagons could be envisioned as consisting of two planar surfaces, one surface being hydrophilic and the other surface hydrophobic. This configuration can be brought about if the carbonyl oxygens formed the outer corners of the hexagon and the peptide bonds occupied the positions on one planar surface, which would be the hydrophilic surface. The amino acid side chains would project downward to form the second surface (called hydrophobic). The distance between the carbonyl oxygens on the hydrophilic surface measures 4.8 Å, that is from oxygen center to oxygen center (Fig. 6-8).

The carbonyl oxygen of these hexagonal peptides would coincide with the "second neighbor's" oxygen pattern of water and could possibly provide additional stabilizing forces. Furthermore, the polar amino acid chains located on the hydrophobic surface are at times placed to provide stabilized hydrogen bonds between neighboring polar groups. Hydrophobic forces from nonpolar interactions may also contribute to the conformational stability.

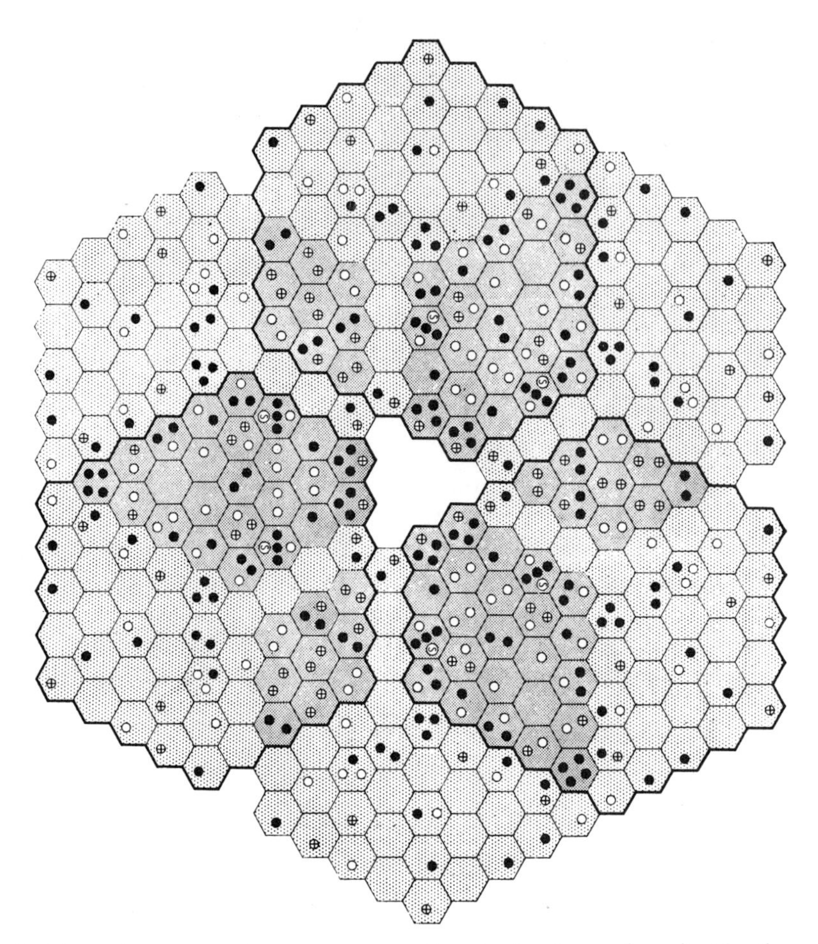

Fig. 6-7. Schematic representation of overlap pattern in the A protein unit. The three upper units are outlined in black. ⊕, Carboxyl chain; Ⓢ, sulfhydryl groups; ○, amide groups; ●, aliphatic hydroxyl side chains. (From Warner, D. T. 1964. J. Theor. Biol. **6:**118-136.)

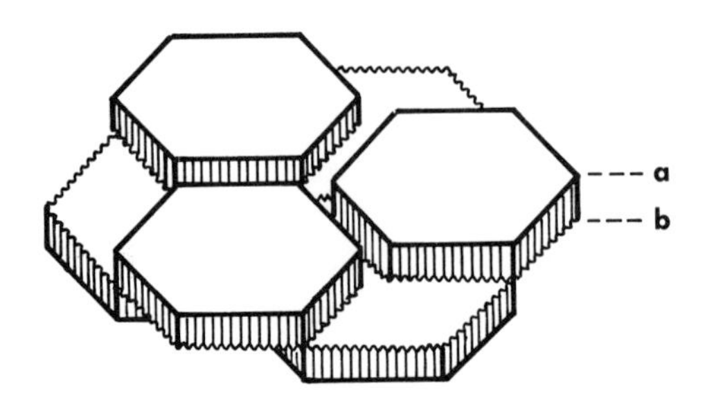

Fig. 6-8. Concept employed to show packing of hexagonal protein units of tobacco mosaic virus (TMV). This is the A protein, which is composed of six subunits. Top view of this arrangement is shown in Fig. 6-7. (From Warner, D. T. 1964. J. Theor. Biol. **6:**118-136.)

Warner (1964) utilized this information to study the protein configuration of tobacco mosaic virus (TMV). This was possible because the protein subunit is known; that is, the amino acid sequences are known. In his work the peptide subunits were considered to be locked together by means of the hydrophobic surface forces to form what is known as the hexameric A protein (Fig. 6-8). Furthermore, these A units are cemented together at their hydrophilic surfaces. In this manner the protein coat is visualized. Examination of the overlay of these six units shows a resulting central opening where the hexagonal disks do not overlap. This gives rise to channels lined with carbonyl and hydroxyl groups. It can be seen, then, that the hydroxyl group can represent hydrogen bonding sites available to water. These channels form an aqueous passage containing bound water and COO^- sites for cationic bonding.

Hechter (1965a) applied this type of configuration to the protein layers of membranes. These protein layers can be envisioned as being built of two layers of peptide-antipeptide units. Each such interlock system is 6.9 Å thick and separated, by two water layers in a hexagonal icelike arrangement (Fig. 6-9), hydrogen bonded via "second neighbor" relations to the carbonyl oxygens of the peptide hydrophilic surface. The outer layer is calculated to be about 19 Å thick. This protein layer is associated with the mixed lipid layer via two water layers in an ordered icelike arrangement. In Robertson's unit membrane concept the innermost protein layer of the membrane is different from the outer surface, perhaps because of the presence of polysaccharides in the outer layer. Despite the asymmetry, one can consider the inner protein layer to consist of locked hexagonal units also.

As noted in the design for the TMV model (Figs. 6-8 and 6-9), channels are edged with hydroxyl groups and either a positively or negatively charged side group. These channels are filled with ordered water, some water layers being highly hydrogen bonded to the edges and other water molecules being more mobile. In such channels, selection between cations would depend on the size as well as the shape of the hydrated ion. For example, taking potassium and sodium ions as examples, the former has one to two water layers in its

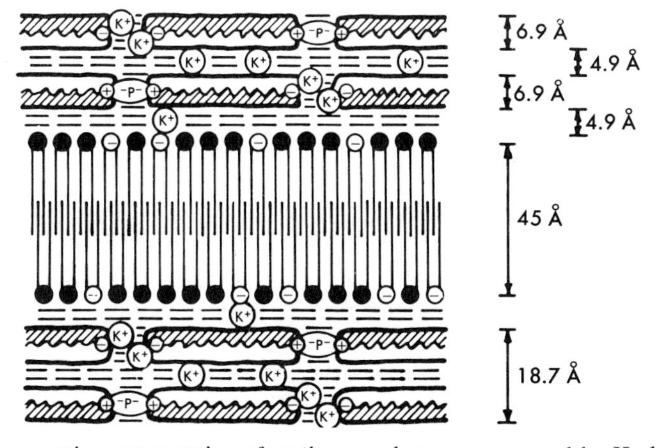

Fig. 6-9. Diagrammatic representation of resting membrane as proposed by Hechter. Basically, the unit membrane is preserved. Protein layers consist of interlocked hexagonal disks cemented together by water molecules (refer to Figs. 6-7 and 6-8). Aqueous channels in the protein layers possess fixed charge sites. (From Hechter, O. 1965. Fed. Proc. **24:**91-102.)

immediate hydration shell, whereas sodium has at least six layers. Such a sodium ion is considerably larger than the hydrated potassium ion, and one can see how a cation channel can be selectively available for potassium but not for sodium.

At some points the interlocked hexagonal units may be cross-linked by disulfide bonds (—S—S—).

If the membrane is disturbed, the hexagonal pattern of the subunits can change in molecular configuration toward a more globular form, possibly tending toward the development of a partial helix, accompanied by the lipid layers assuming a more random micellar arrangement (Fig. 6-10). In general, the fixed electronegative sites in the depolarized region of the membrane no longer exhibit high selectivity for potassium and sodium. In addition, the mobile water becomes available to provide relatively free diffusion of cations along the electrochemical gradients.

High electron microscopy of membranes has indicated that many, in addition to those of mitochondria and chloroplasts, may be composed of a layer of not too tightly packed spherical globules of lipoprotein.

Lipid-globular protein mosaic model. The lipid-globular protein mosaic (LGPM) model was proposed as an alternative to the Davson-Danielli-Robertson model for the organization of lipids and protein in biological membranes (Lenard and Singer, 1966). In essence this model consists of globular proteins embedded within a lipid matrix (Figs. 6-11 and 6-12).

The LGPM model is thermodynamically more stable than the unit membrane and encompasses in its structure recent knowledge of the action of macromolecules in aqueous solutions. Notably important are the hydrophobic and hydrophilic interactions. Thus in hydrophobic reactions the nonpolar hydrocarbons of lipids as well as nonpolar residues of proteins are aggregated away from contact with the aqueous medium and are therefore found in the interior. On the other hand, the polar or ionic groups of proteins and lipids are in contact with the aqueous phase. In this manner hydrophilic interactions are maximized (Singer, 1972). This arrangement tends to be extremely stable and is the predominant state of lipids in membranes (Vanderkooi, 1972). These lipid layers can form perme-

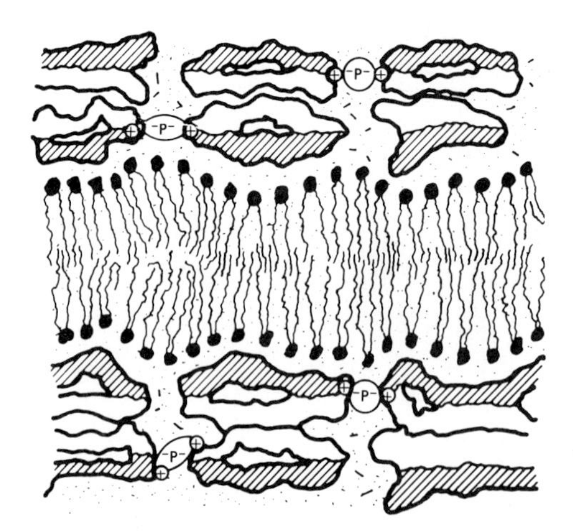

Fig. 6-10. Diagram of depolarized membrane. Protein subunits have lost their hexagonal arrangement and have assumed a more random micellar arrangement. (From Hechter, O. 1965. Fed. Proc. **24:**91-102.)

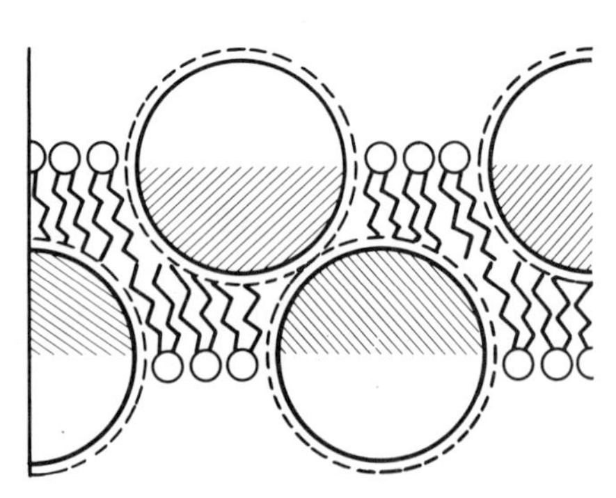

Fig. 6-11. Model of retinal disk membrane. The large circles represent protein; the small circles represent the polar lipid heads; the wavy lines represent the nonpolar phospholipid tails. The cross-hatching in the proteins denotes the nonpolar surface. (From Vanderkooi, G., and M. Sundaralingam 1970. Proc. Nat. Acad. Sci. U. S. A. **67:**233-238.)

able barriers around the cell or organelles. These barriers can be considered to be modified over part of the area, depending on the functional requirement (Stoeckenius, 1972). Thus the membrane proteins can supply the specialized sites on these membranes.

Concerning the protein moieties of membranes, two atypical membrane proteins have been isolated, and from these proteins it is possible to begin to obtain significant data on the shape and properties of the protein as well as the possible role played in the molecular structure of membranes. These two proteins are rhodopsin and cytochrome oxidase. The former is a retinal rod protein whose function is that of a photondetector. It is a globular protein of approximately 40 Å in diameter and has a molecular weight of about 28,000. The latter, cytochrome oxidase, is a multimeric globular protein, the molecular weight being about 200,000 to 250,000. It is located on the mitochondrial membrane and is one of the proteins involved in the electron transfer system. Both of these proteins appear to require lipids for full activity.

Based on the arrangement of rhodopsin and cytochrome oxidase, two similar yet different models can be obtained.

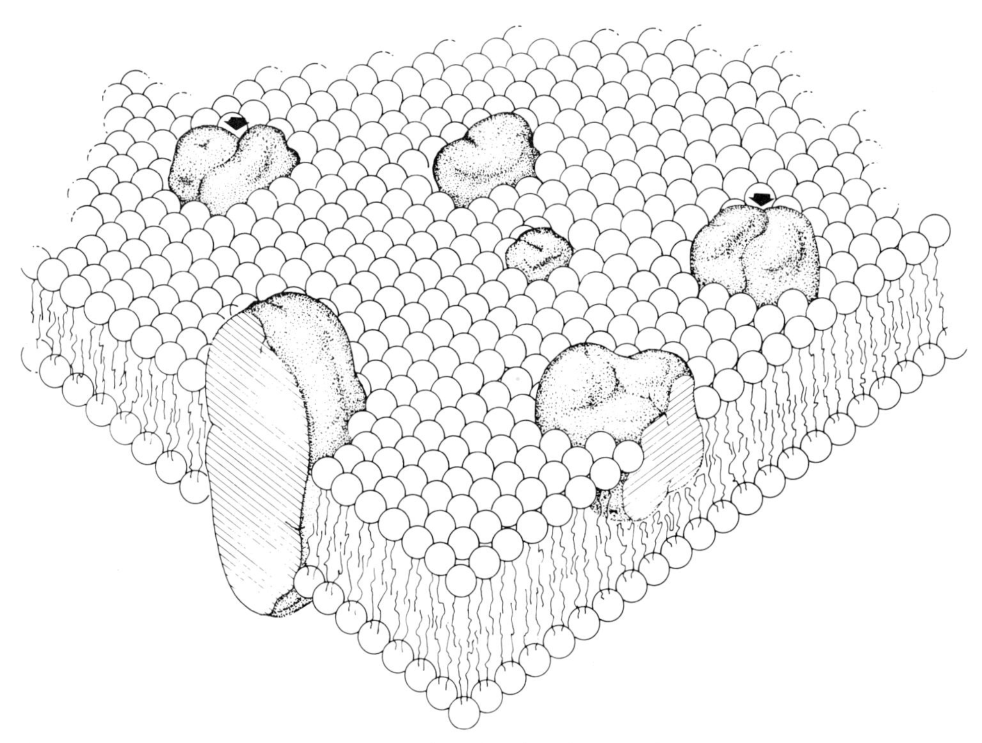

Fig. 6-12. Three-dimensional representation showing the mosaic structure of the membrane. The smaller proteins are embedded in the matrix and partially protruding from it (as in Fig. 6-11). A large protein molecule is seen penetrating the lipid matrix. In this schematic representation the distribution of the membrane proteins is depicted as being random; however, some protein or lipoprotein aggregates may exist (at arrows), probably due to short-range protein-to-protein interactions. The small spheres between the proteins are depicted as phospholipids and form the matrix of the membrane. (From Singer, S. J. 1972. A fluid lipid-globular protein mosaic model of membrane structure. In D. E. Green [editor]. Membrane structure and its biological applications. Ann. N. Y. Acad. Sci. **195:**16-23.)

Various data obtained from chemical analysis, x-ray diffraction studies, and data revealed by electron microscopy indicate that in membranes from retinal rods the rhodopsin molecules are embedded deeply within the lipid matrix. If one assumes that rhodopsin is about 40 Å in diameter, to maintain the thickness of the membrane as revealed by electron microscopy the rhodopsin molecule must penetrate approximately halfway into the lipid moiety (Fig. 6-11). The rhodopsin molecule is presumed to be amphipathic or bipolar. The hydrophobic part of the molecule interacts with the hydrophobic regions of the lipid, which not only maintains the stability of the protein in the lipid matrix but also has the advantage of keeping the protein orientated in the same direction, that is, in relation to the incident of the beam of light on the retina (Vanderkooi, 1972).

X-ray diffraction analysis of the membrane surface reveals that rhodopsin is distributed randomly throughout the membrane (Blasie and Worthington, 1969a,b).

On the other hand, the arrangement of cytochrome oxidase protein is more ordered. The arrangement and the position of these molecules is revealed by glutaraldehyde-fixed, phosphotungstic acid–stained sections. A regularly arranged pattern is indicated in which the arrangement is herringbone in style. Calculation of the thickness of the cytochrome oxidase complex is about 80 to 85 Å. These large complexes, unlike those of rhodopsin, are not inserted in the lipid complex but, instead, extend through the lipid in such a manner that the lipids appear to fill in the spaces between them. Presumably a protein-to-protein contact is present. It is assumed that the hydrophobic or nonpolar regions are in contact with the nonpolar areas of the lipid, and the hydrophilic areas of cytochrome oxidase would then be in contact with the aqueous regions as well as with the hydrophilic areas of the lipids (Vanderkooi, 1972).

In this model the protein and lipid alternate to form a mosaic in the plane of the membrane.

The advantage of this type of model is that it is dynamically stable, and furthermore, many diverse kinds of proteins and enzymes can be integral membrane protein if they can exhibit appropriate amphipathic qualities. On the other hand, those proteins that do not have these qualities may be excluded. As a result this model can provide a basis of determining the proteins that are membrane bound and those that are soluble (Singer, 1972).

Using the two models, several possibilities can exist as to the role these membranes play. The model depicting cytochrome oxidase, assuming its periodicity and protein-to-protein interaction, produces a membrane that is rigid or crystalline. On the other hand, the model of the membrane containing rhodopsin, in which the lipids form the continuous phase, can be assumed to be fluid. It is possible to explain both morphological and physiological phenomenon on this basis.

Chemical composition

Most of the information obtained on the composition of cell membranes resulted from chemical studies of erythrocyte ghosts. Parpart and Ballentine (1952) showed that the lipid-to-protein ratio of these cells, although somewhat variable, was in the range of 1:1.60 to 1.82. Various types of lipids have been identified as being present in membranes. Moskowitz and Calvin (1952) found that lipids in membranes consist of cholesterol, 30%; cephalin, 46%; lecithin, 11%; sphingomyelin, 8%; and 5% unaccountable.

Membrane proteins. Historically, red blood cell membranes were the primary source for the study of membrane proteins. Jorpes (1932) described a fibrous protein derived from erythrocyte ghosts as being *stromatin.* Its elastic and shrinkage characteristics are similar to those of fibrin. Possibly because of the acid nature of the protein, it contributes to the negative change observed in membranes. Later, Moskowitz and Calvin (1952) obtained a creamy white substance from ghosts (stromin or reticulin), which when further separated, yielded *elenin* and *s* protein. The *s* protein, according to Moskowitz et al. (1950) is similar to stromatin. Elenin is a long rod-shaped polymer, which when linked with the extracted lipid, comprises the main framework of the cell. Furthermore, the Rh and AB factors of erythrocytes lie in this fraction. Elenin was the substance used by Hillier and Hoffman (1953) in the plaque theory of the protein structures of membranes.

Later studies, using other than erythrocyte ghosts, revealed that membranes are not only grossly heterogeneous but it is unlikely that there is a single unique protein which is responsible for maintaining the structure of membranes. These proteins can be classified as being either intrinsic or extrinsic (Vanderkooi, 1972) or integral or peripheral according to Singer (1952). The intrinsic or integral proteins probably constitute the largest fraction and are characterized by being insoluble in neutral aqueous solutions. The second group, the extrinsic proteins, are associated with membranes. The following criteria distinguish these proteins: (1) their release by high ionic strength and also by metal chelation, (2) when released, their freedom from any lipids, and (3) in general, their water solubility (Singer, 1972).

Cytochrome oxidase and rhodopsin, as seen in the LGPM and possibly the Rh and AB factors found previously in red blood cell membranes, can be considered as being intrinsic proteins. Cytochrome *c* (Singer, 1952) and magnesium-dependent ATPase (Lenaz, 1972) of mitochondrial membranes are considered to be extrinsic or peripheral proteins.

Polysaccharides. Robertson suggested the possibility of carbohydrates being present as constituents of the plasma membrane when he observed the different staining characteristics between the outer and inner layers. The polysaccharides in the outer layer could be attached to the protein by a reaction of some of their active groups with the active end groups of the protein. Histidine may be considered significant in the protein-carbohydrate bond found in the outer surface (Bell, 1962). A possible function of the carbohydrates may be the stabilization of the cell surface protein against possible denaturation. In addition, the mucopolysaccharides may be involved in cell mobility (Bell, 1961), and the carbohydrates may be the basis for the range of membrane properties (Bell, 1962).

Laico and Eylar (1966) showed that almost all the erythrocyte glycoprotein (containing sialic acid and galactose) is found in the membrane. Furthermore, sialic acid makes a major contribution to the negative charge of the surface (Wallach and Eylar, 1961).

Water. Water constitutes 30% to 50% of the bulk component of a membrane system. In this amount it is apparent that water must play an important role in the molecular organization. It may be reasonable to assume that it is present in an ordered arrangement in relation to the polar groups of not only the protein layers but of the lipids as well.

Cations. Recent information indicates that inorganic cations may play an important role in maintaining the structural integrity of biological membranes. Based on the role of cations in red blood cell membranes, it was shown that, as far as these membranes were concerned, cations played a significant role in maintaining their stability. Although the actual mechanism involved is unknown, several models have been proposed as to how these cations probably interact with the lipids and proteins of these membranes. They are as follows: (1) a ternary complex may be formed between the protein cation and the hydrophilic moieties of lipids; (2)

a lipid protein complex may be bound to the lipid leaflets through a ternary cationic bridge; and (3) a binding site for protein may be stabilized by a ternary cation bridge between several hydrophilic ends of lipids (Reynolds, 1972).

These various models can provide important information on membrane stability, even though it has been shown that the lipid and protein composition vary considerably from membrane to membrane. There now appears to be no common structural protein as was previously thought (Dreyer et al., 1972). Thus cations may be necessary for maintaining structural stability for some membranes but not necessarily for all (Reynolds, 1972).

Enzymes. Studies have shown that enzymes are also associated with cell membrane metabolic pathways that are mediated by macromolecular proteins. Many may be integrated into the molecular structure itself, whereas others may be attached to the membrane and can be considered as detachable structures. A number of enzymes have been identified as part of the plasma membrane. It is possible that a number of these same catalysts will be present in other membrane systems as well, notably the membranes that comprise the ER (Chapter 7). Some of these enzymes associated with the cell membranes include glyceraldehyde-3-phosphate hydrogenase and 3-phosphoglyceric acid kinase (Dixon et al., 1966). Eicholz and Crane (1966) fractionated the membranes present in the brush borders of hamster epithelia and found alkaline phosphatase, maltase, isomaltase, invertase, and lactase activity. In addition, galactosyl transferase and acid sodium-potassium–activated ATPase (adenosine triphosphatase) have been found in or associated with the membrane. The latter can be considered part of the active transport system of these cations.

Junctional complexes

Histologically, epithelial tissue consists of cells that are closely held together by a scant amount of intercellular material. Functionally, epithelial tissue forms membranes and coverings such as are observed in the linings of the digestive tract and gallbladder, and also forms all of the glands of the body. In most cases the tissue is subjected to wear and tear in performing its activities, and yet the cementing material does not pull apart and cause separation of the cells from one another in the tissue. Electron microscopy of these tissues shows a characteristic junctional complex (Fig. 6-13) composed of three parts that can be identified as (1) the tight junction *(zona occludens),* (2) the intermediate junction *(zona adhaerens),* and (3) desmosomes *(macula adhaerens)* (Farquhar and Palade, 1963).

Tight junction (zona occludens). The tight junction is located at the distal region between adjacent cells nearest to the free surface of the epithelial layer and extends completely around each cell. This zone is brought about by the actual fusion of the outer membrane leaflets of the adjoining cells to form a single intermediate layer and produce an apparent five-layered unit at that region. Among animals and plants this is a unique case where membranes of adjacent cells are in actual contact. It acts as a seal.

Nexus. The nexus (gap junction or fascia occludens) represents a speciliazed region of contact between opposed plasma membranes of adjacent cells. It was described by McNutt and Weinstein (1970) in cardiac muscles of several mammals, including adult and fetal humans, as well as in uterine cells. Functionally the nexus appears to mediate a type of cell-to-cell communication for the direct passage of small molecules between the interiors of the cells. Thus in cardiac muscle it apparently functions physiologically because it represents a probable site for rapid spread of membrane depolarization and thereby provides for coordinate heart contraction. In electron micrograph sections it appears as a honey-

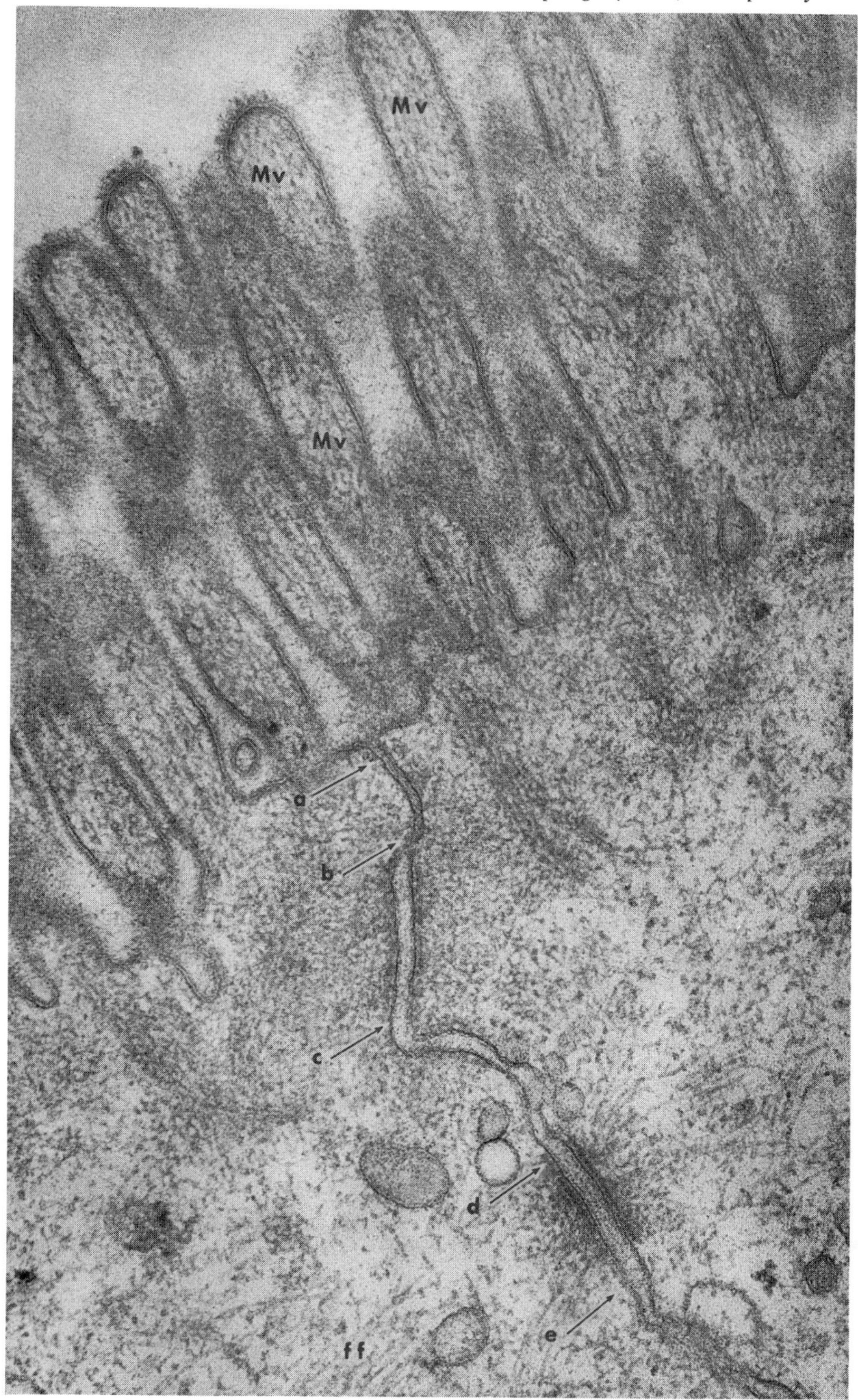

Fig. 6-13. Electron micrograph showing junctional complex between two adjacent epithelial cells from intestinal mucosa. **a** to **b,** Tight junction (zona occludens); **b** to **c,** intermediate junction (zona adhaerens); **d** to **e,** region of desmosome. **Mv,** Microvillus; **ff,** fine filaments. (From Farquhar, M., and G. E. Palade. 1963. J. Cell Biol. **17:**375-412.)

comb structure with a central lucent area separating the nexus membranes.

Intermediate junction (zona adhaerens). The length of this zone is variable and can be identified by the presence of an intercellular space that measures approximately 200 Å. The intercellular space is composed of homogeneous amorphous material. Bands of somewhat dense cytoplasm are generally located just beneath the membrane.

Desmosomes (macula adhaerens). In this region of the junctional complex the intercellular space measures approximately 250 Å and contains a central disk of dense material. In addition, there are dense cytoplasmic plaques arranged parallel to the inner membranes of each cell and microfibrils that radiate from this region a short distance into the cytoplasm (Fig. 6-14).

The desmosomes appear to be scattered along the adjacent membranes. With special staining, light microscopy reveals dark dotlike structures.

Oosaki and Ishii (1964) demonstrated that not only do epithelial tissues show junctional complexes as just described but a similar condition exists in smooth muscles. They observed the obliteration or fusion of adjacent membranes that seals

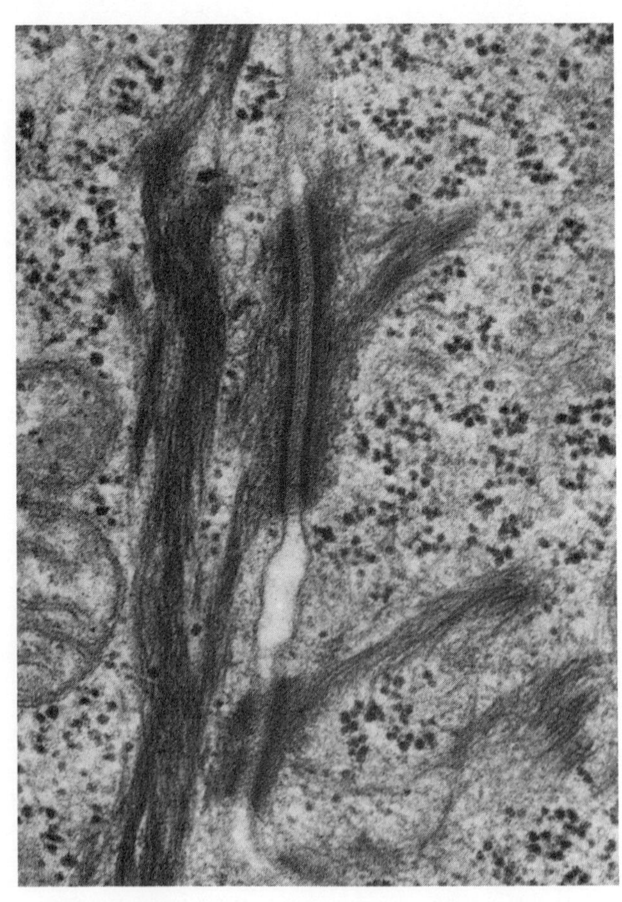

Fig. 6-14. Electron micrograph of a desmosome from the choroid plexus of a cat. See text for description. (Courtesy J. Beggs, Laboratory of Neuropathology, Barrow's Neurological Institute, Phoenix, Ariz.)

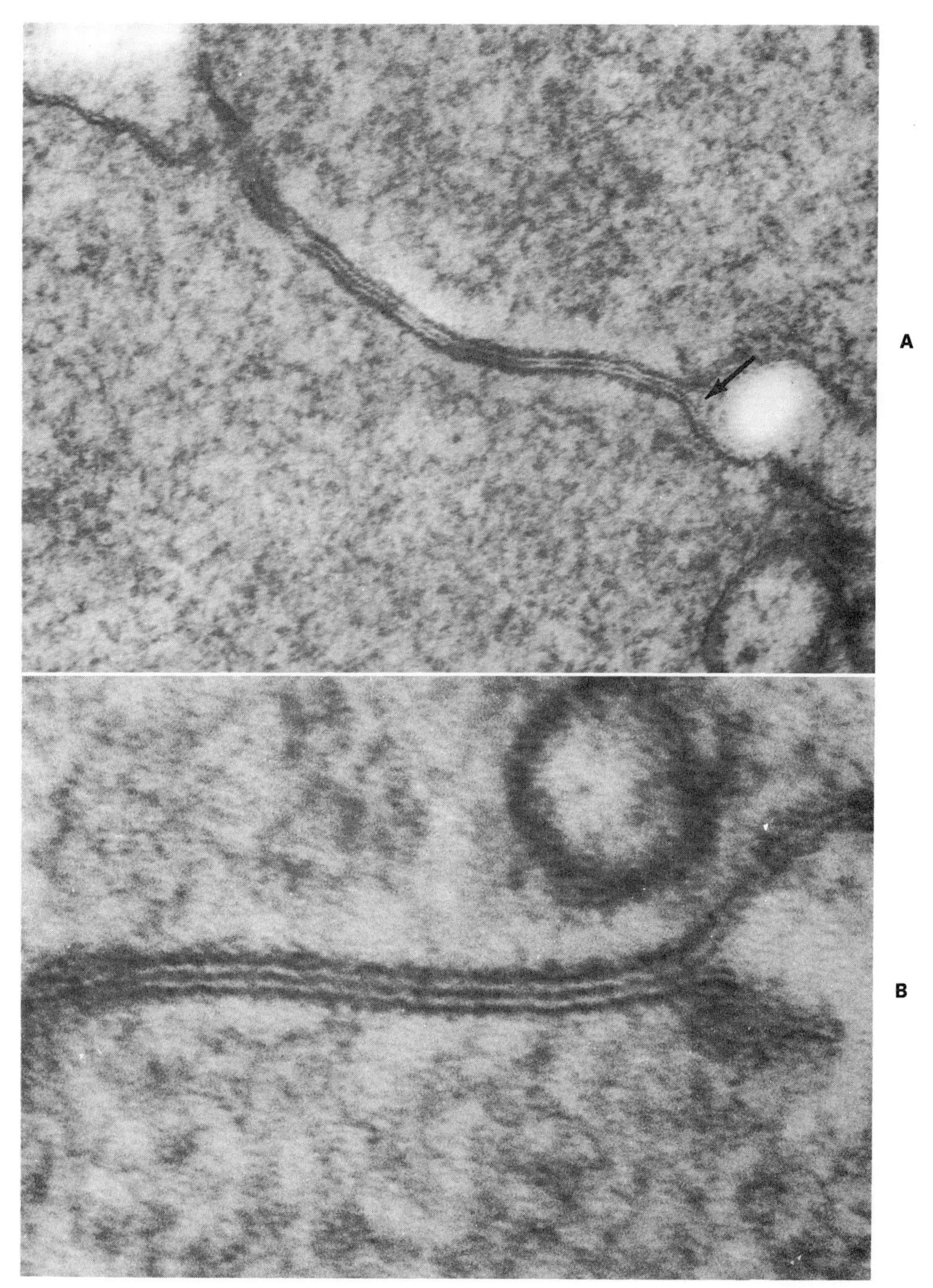

Fig. 6-15. A, Electron micrograph showing fusion junction of plasma membranes of two smooth muscle cells. Arrow shows converging of opposing membranes to form intermediate line of the junction. **B,** Higher magnification of **A** showing fusion junction that results in a pentalaminar arrangement. (From Oosaki, T., and S. Ishii. 1964. J. Ultrastruct. Res. **10:**567-571.)

the intercellular space. Apparent fusion of the outer layers of the adjoining membranes results in the formation of a single intermediate layer that is visible when examined by electron microscopy (Fig. 6-15). Elsewhere the fusion is not seen, and the intercellular space is characterized by a width of about 30 to 100 Å and comprises amorphous material of moderate density.

In descriptive histology of epithelia another term is commonly used—"terminal bars." With special staining such as iron hematoxylin, fine black lines extend parallel with the cell surface and between the edges of the more distal part of the cell. The terminal bar is associated with condensed intercellular cement, which tenaciously holds the cells together at that region and at the same time prevents material from reaching or leaving the space by lumens bounded by these epithelial cells. It is possible that the occluding zone is that part of the complex best suited to seal up the intercellular space. The staining reaction may be due to the dense cytoplasm associated with this region.

Functionally, the complex may play the role of a diffusion barrier by sealing the intercellular spaces of epithelia. Evidence has shown that intercellular material cannot pass this complex (Farquhar and Palade, 1963).

Septate desmosomes. Invertebrate animals have a common type of adherent region between two plasma membranes that is known as the septate desmosome (Fig. 6-16). The plasma membranes are joined together by parallel arrays of lamellae arranged at right angles to the surface. In the caterpillar *(Calpodes ethlius)* the membranes are separated by a distance of about 140 Å and are joined by a septum that is about 85 Å thick, spaced at intervals of 190 Å. The septa form a hexagonal network arranged as the walls of a symmetrical intracellular compartment (Fig. 6-17). Each space in the network is about 105 Å in diameter. The walls of the spaces are formed from the three arrays of septa, which are orientated 120 degrees to one another. Apparently, the arrays are not all alike; those in one direction are more dense than the other two (Locke, 1965).

Cell surfaces

In the study of histology or cytology modifications of the cell surfaces are often encountered. Some of the modifications consist of specialization of the plasma membrane and underlying cytoplasm, whereas others represent the products of cellular secretion that can form various kinds of crusts. Only the actual cellular modification will be discussed here.

Probably the most important structures associated with the free surfaces of certain animal cells are *microvilli.* They are found in cells that comprise the mucosal linings of the small intestines and produce what is known as the *striated border.* The *brush borders* of the proximal convoluted tubules of the kidney and the free surface of cells that make up the lining of the gallbladder are quite similar. In all these surfaces the prime function is apparently that of absorption. The microvilli of some glandular tissue probably have some function, but it is poorly understood because absorption is not seemingly involved.

Prior to the era of electron microscopy the striate border was considered to be a cellular secretion covering the free surface. The surface appeared as a homogeneous strip of secretion. With the use of better techniques striations became visible. Electron microscopy shows this layer to be composed of closely packed projections of the cytoplasm, uniform in height, that are called *microvilli.* The average height ranges from 80 to 100 nm. The plasma membrane of the microvilli is composed of a unit membrane that is continuous with the plasma membrane of the rest of the cell. The core of the villi consists of the extension of the cell cytoplasm into this area. It is apparent from the large num-

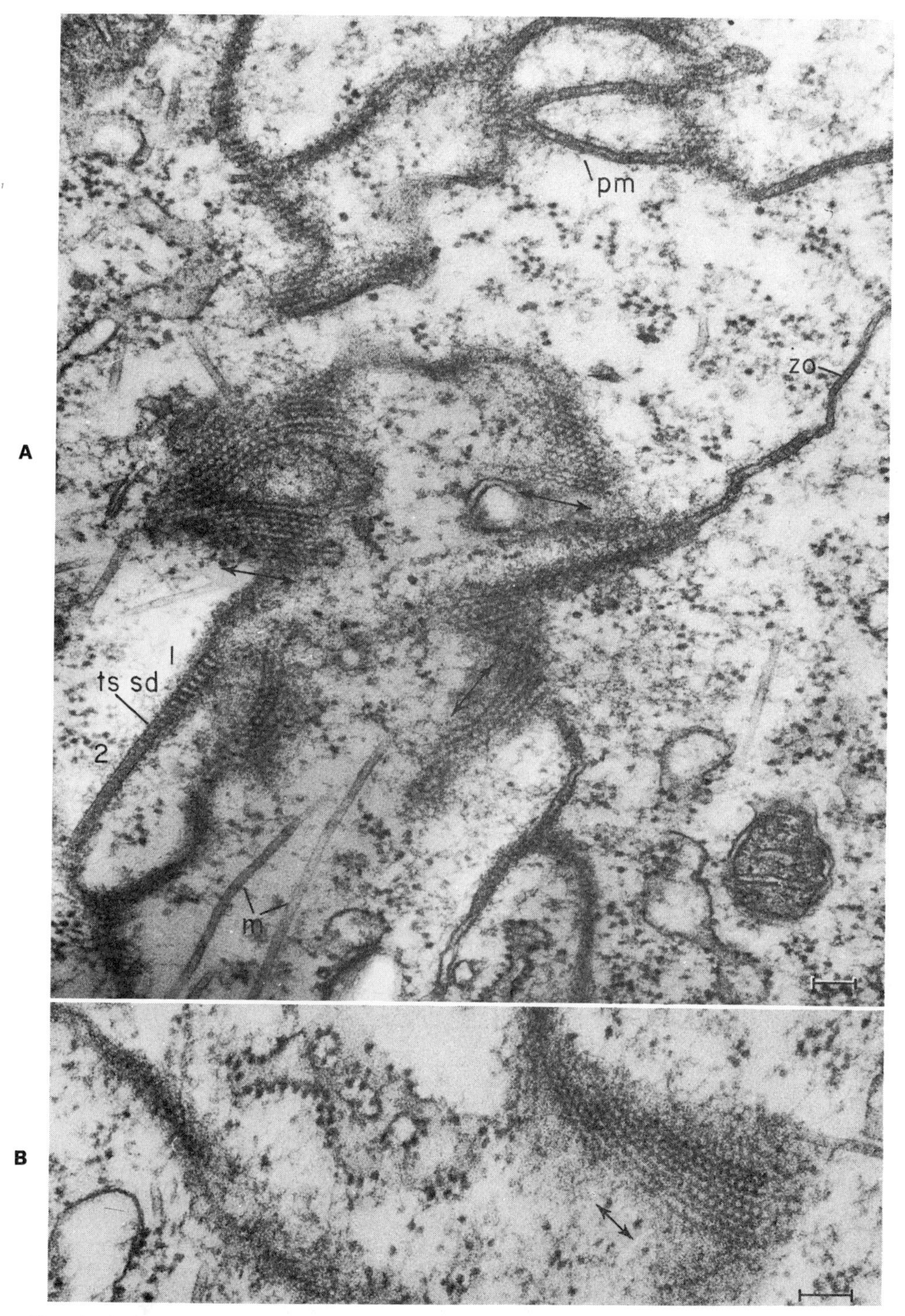

Fig. 6-16. A, Tangential and transverse sections through septate desmosomes in epidermis of *Calpodes ethlius* (order Lepidoptera, family Hesperiidae). Most of the septate desmosomes are sectioned tangentially. Arrows indicate the axis of the main septa. **m,** Microtubules; **ts sd,** desmosome cut transversely; **pm,** plasma membrane; **zo,** zona occludens. Note also rough ER and polyribosomes. **B,** Electron micrograph of a section transverse to the membrane but no longer in a normal relation to the main septum. Intercellular spaces appear uniformly dense. (From Locke, M. 1965. J. Cell Biol. **25:**166-169.)

ber of microvilli present per cell that the total surface area available for absorption is extremely great.

The aggregate of microvilli in the kidney tubule is referred to as the brush border. The microvilli are much larger in size and appear irregular when observed by light microscopy. In a sense the cell surface appears ragged. These cytoplasmic structures also exhibit a plasma membrane that is continuous and part of the plasma membrane of the cell. The brush border, as is true of the microvilli of the intestinal epithelium, is primarily involved in absorption.

A modification of microvilli was observed in the venom gland of the scorpion *Centruroides sculpturatus* (Fig. 6-18). The microvilli arise in the usual manner, but a short distance from their origins they immediately branch into a large number of long secondary branches. These *dendritic* microvilli project into the luminal spaces of the gland. Their function is unknown, but presumably they play a role in reabsorption of water and thereby concentration of the venom.

Hanssen and Herman (1962) observed the presence of an axial filament in the microvilli of the proximal convoluted tubule of the kidney (Fig. 6-19). They reported the presence of similar filaments in microvilli of the oviduct and microvilli of jejunal epithelium of rats. They proposed that the axial filament may play a role functionally in the reconstruction of the brush border, may be related to the production of enzymes, and finally, may be involved in the mechanism of reabsorption by selectively picking up and transporting water and *solute from the lumen of the cytoplasm.* They may, however, be microtubules that function to give some rigidity to the microvilli.

Modification of the plasma membrane can be seen in cells involved in rapid transport of water. An excellent example is the basal layer in the cells from the proximal and distal convoluted tubules of the kidney (Fig. 6-20). In cells such as these there are deep interdigitations of the plasma membrane into each of the contiguous cells. The cytoplasm between folds contains large mi-

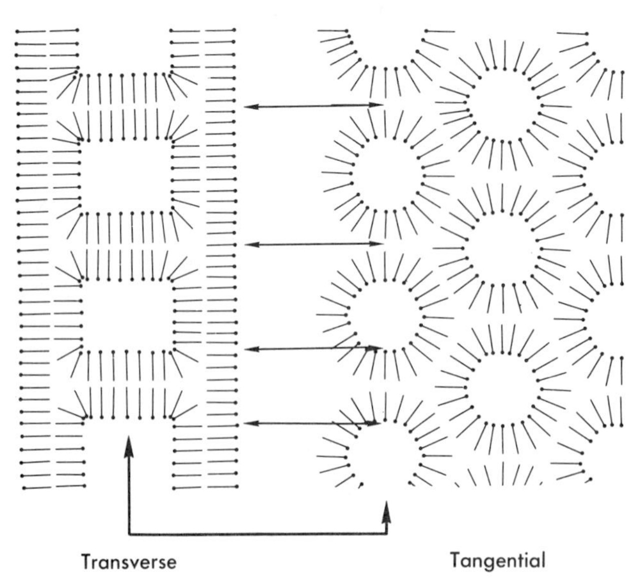

Fig. 6-17. Possible arrangement of lipid components in the septate desmosome. Note similarities to lipids in the hexagonal phase. (From Locke, M. 1965. J. Cell Biol. **25**:166-169.)

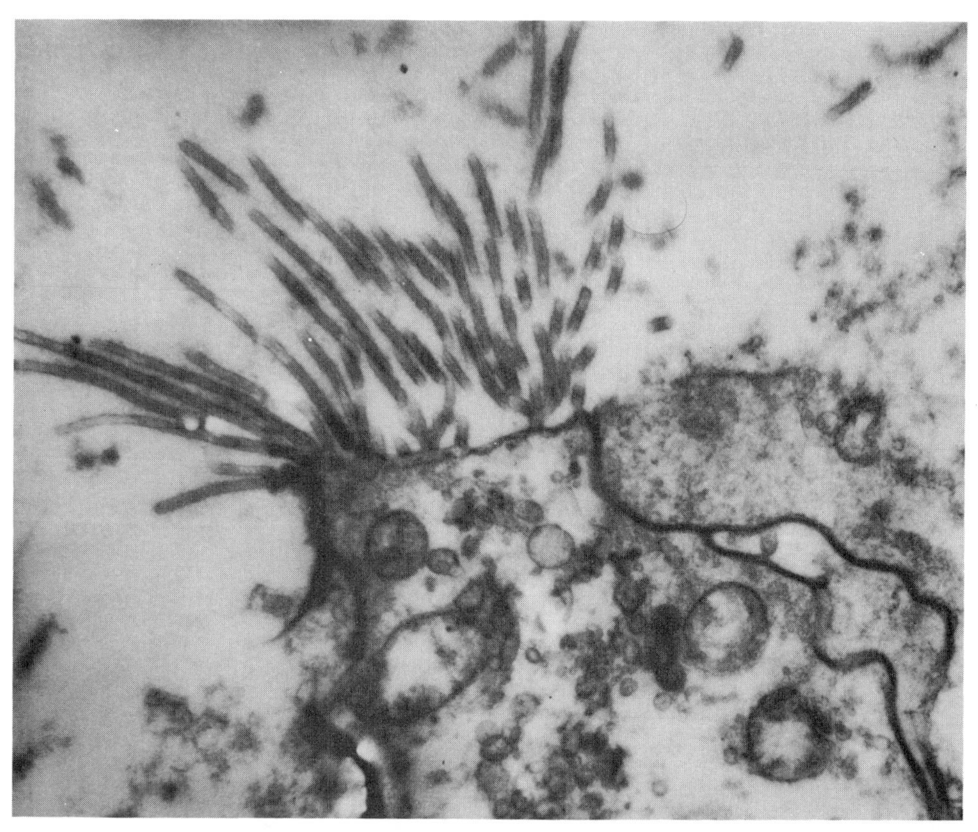

Fig. 6-18. Electron micrograph of part of cellular complex of venom gland from the scorpion *Centruroides sculpturatus* showing dendritic type of microvilli.

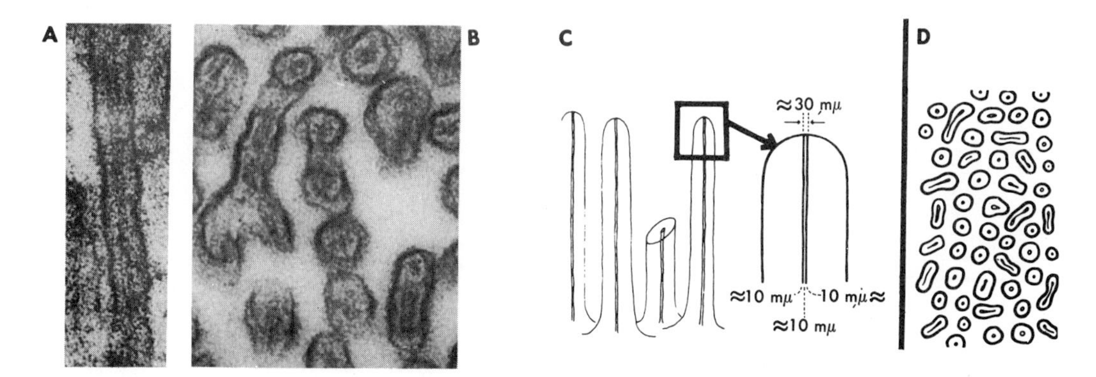

Fig. 6-19. A, Electron micrograph of longitudinal section through microvilli. Note presence of double parallel lines suggestive of an axial filament. **B,** Oblique section through a number of microvilli showing double parallel lines as well as circles. **C,** Diagrammatic drawing of **A. D,** Schematic representation of oblique section shown in **B.** (From Hanssen, O. E., and L. Herman. 1962. Lab. Invest. **11:**610-616.)

tochondria (Pease, 1955a,b; Ruska et al., 1957). An intercompartmental space exists between the folds. These spaces or labyrinths are homologous to those in the glomerular epithelial cells of the kidney. The compartments and the mitochondria and the intercompartmental spaces comprise the functional unit. According to Ruska et al., these intercompartmental spaces may widen considerably and may represent pathways of fluid for excretion. The pressure in the intercompartmental

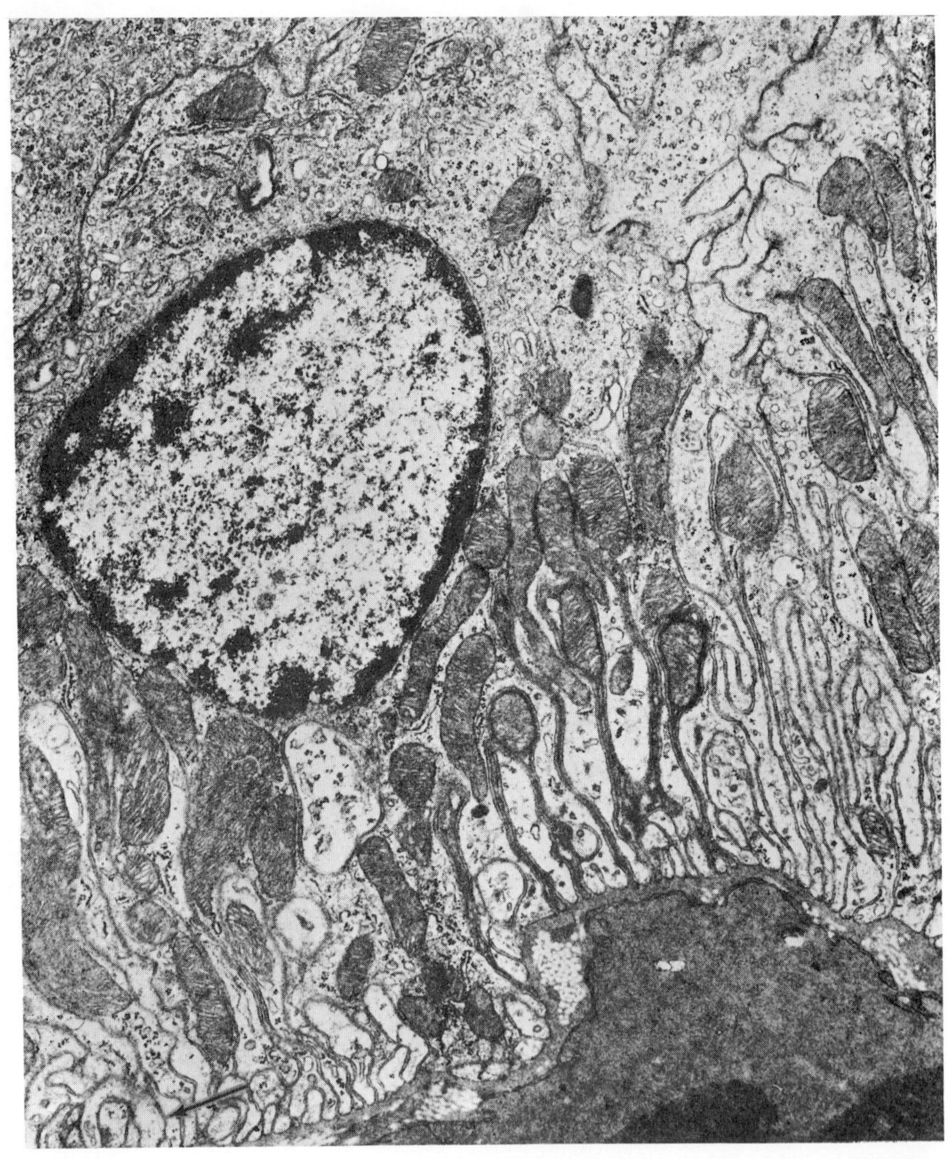

Fig. 6-20. Electron micrograph of basal region of cells from distal convoluted tubules of kidney showing basal infoldings of the basal membranes containing mitochondria. Note polarization of mitochondria between membrane infoldings. Arrow indicates intermembranal space. (Courtesy J. Mazurkiewicz, Arizona State University, Tempe, Ariz.)

space overcomes the capillary pressure to cause reabsorption. The mitochondria as well as the enzyme system present on the membranes are directly involved in the process of water transport.

PHAGOCYTOSIS AND PINOCYTOSIS

Changes in plasma membrane configuration can give rise to two basic phenomena known as phagocytosis and pinocytosis. These processes result in the ingestion of bulk solid and fluid materials, respectively. Although these two cellular activities were known for a number of years from light microscopic observations, it was not until electron microscopic studies that the mechanisms involved were fully understood and their physiological importance fully appreciated.

Phagocytosis

Phagocytosis (Gr. *phagein,* meaning "to eat"; *kytos,* meaning "cell") is a process whereby certain cells and unicellular organisms are capable of ingesting and digesting solid material. As observed under the light microscope, phagocytosis is accomplished by the cell (or organism) extend-

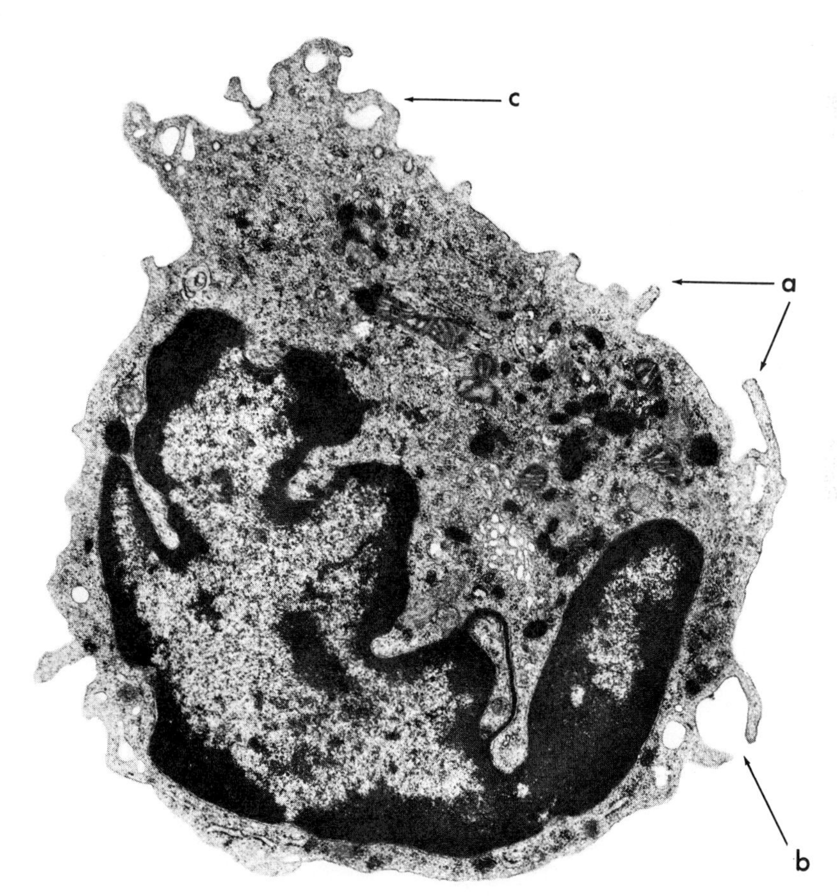

Fig. 6-21. Electron micrograph section of a whole neutrophil obtained from arachnoid space of guinea pig. Phagocytic response was initiated by injecting bacteria into arachnoid space. **a,** Early stage of phagocytosis in which pseudopodia are extending outwardly; **b,** pseudopodia are forming a cuplike vesicle; **c,** pseudopodia have fused to form a phagocytotic vesicle. (Courtesy J. Beggs, Laboratory of Neuropathology, Barrow's Neurological Institute, Phoenix, Ariz.)

ing pseudopodia, which encircle and enclose the particle completely, engulfing it. (Fig. 6-21). Part of the plasma membrane becomes the food vacuole membrane.

In the lower invertebrate animals phagocytosis is an important or the only means for obtaining nutrition, sometimes called protozoal nutrition. In the Protozoa, phagocytosis is the means whereby rhizopods (amebas, etc.) obtain their food. Some of the flagellates and some of the Sporozoa also obtain nutrition by this means in certain developmental stages. Phagocytosis as a means of acquiring food for digestion is characteristic of a number of lower Metazoa; in the Mesozoa and porifera (sponges) it is the only means. In the Coelenterata (hydrozoan animals), free-living flatworms of phylum Platyhelminthes, and some Mollusca it is part of the digestive process. In these animals, cells that are capable of phagocytosis are scattered throughout the lining of the gastrovascular cavity among the enzyme-secreting cells. Although the major part of digestion is extracellular, phagocytic activity as a means of obtaining nutrition is still evident (Barnes, 1963). In addition to nutrition, phagocytosis is important in the physiological involution of organs, as can be observed in the echinoderms, tunicates, and tadpoles as well as in the metamorphosis of some insects.

In higher forms of animals, especially the mammals, phagocytic activity is limited to the general defense against infection and cellular scavenging within the body (Fig. 6-21).

The role of leukocytes as a part of the scavenging mechanism in mammals was described as early as 1870 by Langhans, who observed the phagocytosis of old erythrocytes by white blood cells. Later, Rosser (1881) suggested that leukocytes may also be involved in the destruction of microbes (Wright and Dodd, 1955). It was during the early 1890s that Metchnikoff developed the concept of phagocytosis in immunity from observations made after inserting rose thorns under the skins of starfish larvae. He observed that the thorns

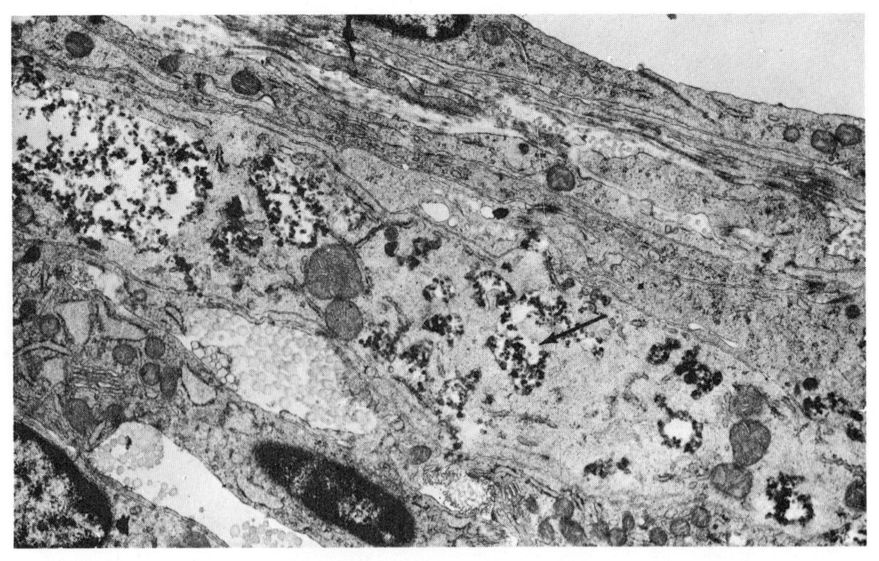

Fig. 6-22. Electron micrograph of arachnoid tissue from guinea pig. This section shows a number of phagocytic vesicles containing carbon particles in the cytoplasm. (Courtesy J. Beggs, Laboratory of Neuropathology, Barrow's Neurological Institute, Phoenix, Ariz.)

were then surrounded by motile cells that were capable of phagocytosis, and he suggested that cellular phagocytosis is actually the primary means of body defense.

Among the phagocytic cells found in the mammalian system the neutrophil is the most active. It is the first white blood cell to be found in the area of inflammation. The young mature neutrophils, those containing two nuclear lobes, are the most effective (Wright and Dodd, 1955). On the other hand, phagocytosis may be decreased by vitamin and/or protein deficiencies. This may be a reason why malnutrition may lower resistance to bacterial infection (Mills, 1949).

Also important in phagocytic activities are the cells that comprise the macrophage system—the reticuloendotheliel system of Aschoff. Included in this system are the macrophages (histiocytes) found in the connective tissue and the phagocytic reticular cells of the lymphoid tissue, myeloid tissue, and spleen; the von Kupffer cells that line the sinusoids of the liver; the lining cells of the sinusoid of the adrenal gland, the hypophysis, and some of the perivascular cells; and the "dust cells" of the lung. These cells not only are capable of phagocytizing bacteria but can ingest worn-out blood cells and cellular debris as well as colloidal particles (Fig. 6-22).

After phagocytosis in lower animals the digestive or food vacuole is formed as a result of the lysosome uniting with the phagocytized particle (see Chapter 12 for a discussion of the sequence of events following the formation of the digestive vacuole). The resulting products of enzymatic action can be utilized by these organisms for growth and other synthetic activities of the cell, for reproduction, and for locomotion. On the other hand, a similar sequence occurs in the case of white blood cells, but it is doubtful whether the breakdown of the ingested bacteria, protozoa, or other extraneous material is used for any synthetic activity because of the short lifespan of these white blood cells. Probably the prime purpose of lysosomal activity is to destroy the bacteria or to contain the extraneous material.

Theory of phagocytosis. The formation of the superficial food cup is a response to the external environment. This formation and the closure can take place within 2 seconds or may take as long as 12 seconds. It begins as a doughnut-shaped outsurging of cytoplasm that lifts the plasma membrane outward and around a central fixed region that has received the contact of the material to be phagocytized. The cytoplasm beneath the fixed region shows no cytoplasmic motion or movement. The lips of the pseudopodia converge and overlap. The lips then fuse, beginning from the inward side and progressing to the outward side. The time required for fusion to occur may range from 1 to 10 minutes (Christiansen and Marshall, 1965).

One of the interesting problems in phagocytosis has been the physical or chemical stimulus that triggers the sequence of events culminating in the formation of the food vacuole. It has been shown that contact by itself does not necessarily produce phagocytic activity. According to numerous studies on phagocytosis and pinocytosis, the surface charge of the particle to be engulfed is of utmost importance. In all cases organisms or substance that can be engulfed are cationic in nature. Those substances exhibiting an anionic or neutral charge will not stimulate a phagocytic response.

Phagocytosis by mammalian white blood cells has the same requirement—response only to cationic particles. There are times when the bacteria will be phagocytized very slowly or not at all, but later, when a phagocytosis-promoting substance is present, the process is greatly accelerated (Menkin, 1956). This substance, known as *opsonin,* is specific and forms a coating about the bacterium which alters the surface so that neutrophils and monocytes can act. This substance is cationic in charge.

Similarly, the ability of the macrophage to engulf dilute colloidal material such as nontoxic dyes depends on the cationic (acid) charge of these particles. Being cationic, substances such as trypan blue, carbon particles, and metals like colloidal silver and iron are readily taken up by the macrophage (Ham, 1957). Dyes that are neutral will not be engulfed unless they are complexed with a cationically charged particle. It is sometimes convenient to refer to the uptake of these colloidal and larger particles as *microphagocytosis* because of their submicroscopic size. In fact, the use of these dyes in a colloidal state offers an excellent means of studying phagocytosis of the reticuloendothelial system. If intravenous injections of dilute solution of the dyes are given for several days, the cytoplasm will become gorged with the dye or other marker, which indicates the function of the reticuloendothelial system in the removal of extraneous material from the general circulation.

Pinocytosis

Pinocytosis (Gr. *pinein,* meaning "to drink"), like phagocytosis, represents changes in the free surface whereby the pinocytotic process transports solutes in mass inward across the surface membrane. It offers a means whereby materials, including relatively large macromolecules, can enter the cell. Changes in surface configuration that can lead to pinocytosis are (1) the elevation of an undulating membrane to entrap a relatively large droplet of fluid; (2) the inpocketing of the free plasma membrane surface to form vesicles of submicroscopic size; and (3) semipermanent tubular invaginations of the cell membrane to form long channels (Fawcett, 1961, 1965).

Historically, the concept was first described by Lewis (1931) from study of living cells in culture. He described the uptake of fluids by an active movement of undulating membrane that appeared to arise at the periphery of the cell. This membrane extended upward from the free surface and entrapped the fluid into a vesicle. After the entrapment of the fluid the vesicle moved into the exterior of the cell, and in so doing became progressively smaller. The entrapment of fluid could be easily studied because the vesicles formed were more than 1 μm in diameter, which is well within the resolving power of the light microscope. Later, studies by Mast and Doyle using fluorescence microscopy indicated that pinocytosis may be important for the cellular uptake of proteins. Time-lapse cinematography has demonstrated this process dynamically. It was not, however, until electron microscopic studies, coupled with the use of markers, that the full significance of pinocytosis became evident.

Electron microscopic studies of capillary endothelial cells have shown that at the free margins of these cells are projections or flaps that project into the lumen (Fig. 6-25). These flaps usually are located adjacent to the terminal bars (Fawcett and Wittenberg, 1962; Donahue, 1964). Such marginal folds are about 80 nm thick and are devoid of organelles. The folds appear to impound material by curving over and coalescing with the plasma membrane. In this manner large vesicles are formed that are visible by light microscopy, and a continuous series of events can be traced by phase cinematography.

Early electron microscope studies of endothelial cells showed a large number of vesicles of approximately 650 Å diameter immediately under the cell membrane. They were found facing the capillary lumen and the pericapillary spaces. Many of these minute vesicles, which can be described as flask shaped, appear to open onto the free surfaces (Fig. 6-23) (Palade, 1953). Since these vesicles appeared on both sides of the cell, they may represent the transport of fluid across the cell and may well account for the high permeability of capillaries (Fig. 6-24). It was not until electron-opaque markers were employed that such a concept could be established. Most of the markers used for tracing pinocytotic vesicles were and are ferritin, gold, thorium dioxide, and saccharated iron. In all instances the uptake begins when the particles of the substance first become attached to the cell surface (Fig. 6-25) and later appear in open pits on the luminal surface. They are later observed within vesicles that are still attached to the membrane. These vesicles become detached (Fig. 6-26), and the markers are carried across to the pericapillary membranes, where fusion of the vesicles is observed.

The markers are set free by a "reverse pinocytosis" in the pericapillary spaces, where they later accumulate in the adventitial histiocytes and fibroblasts (Wissig, 1958; Palade, 1960; Kaye et al., 1961; Florey, 1961; Choi, 1962). Because the tracer material was transported and set free at the opposite side, pinocytosis may well be involved in the "active transport" of not only fluids but macromolecules as well.

A number of cell types such as those of the proximal convoluted tubules of the kidney, the *efferent ductule* of the testes, and

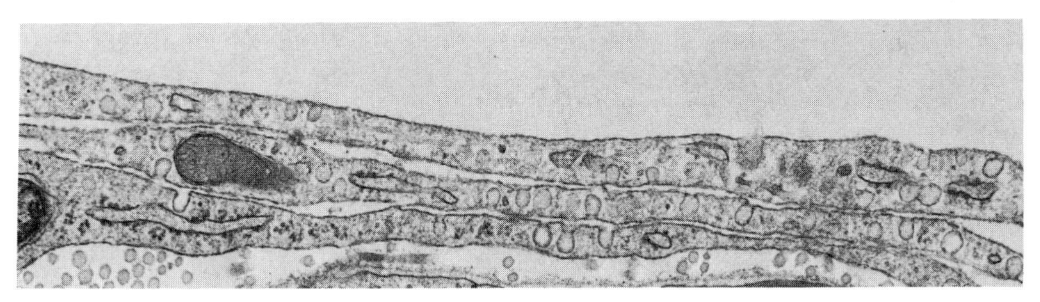

Fig. 6-23. Electron micrograph of arachnoid tissue of guinea pig showing a number of pinocytotic vesicles. A number of vesicles are still attached to the cell membrane, whereas others have become detached and are visible within the cytoplasm. (Courtesy J. Beggs, Laboratory of Neuropathology, Barrow's Neurological Institute, Phoenix, Ariz.)

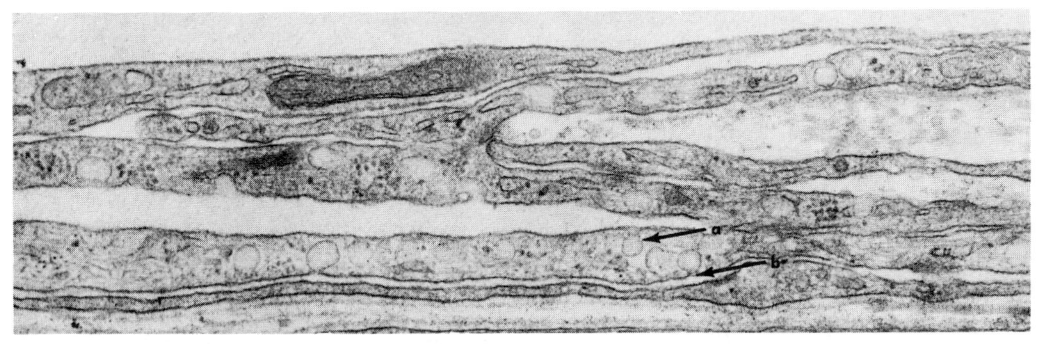

Fig. 6-24. Electron micrograph of arachnoid tissue showing a number of pinocytotic vesicles. **a,** Vesicle that is still open to the free surface; **b,** a similar vesicle that is probably opening into a space on the opposite side of the cell by a "reverse pinocytotic" process. This may represent a means whereby fluids are carried across the cell. A vesicle within the cytoplasm is also evident. (Courtesy J. Beggs, Laboratory of Neuropathology, Barrow's Neurological Institute, Phoenix, Ariz.)

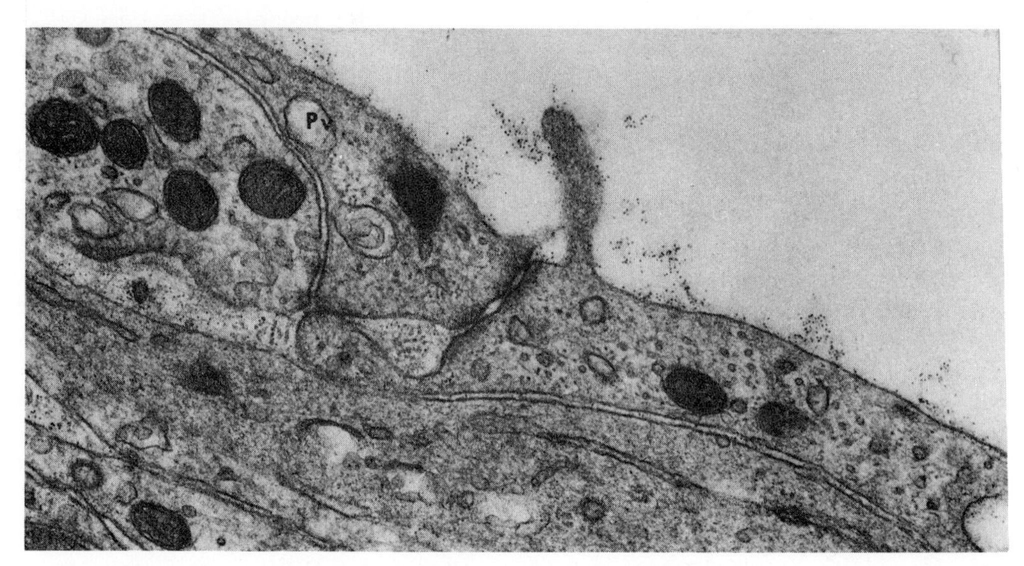

Fig. 6-25. Ferritin accumulating on the free surface of arachnoid tissue. Note projection or flap, **Pv**, which projects into arachnoid space. Folds such as these appear to impound fluid by curving over and coalescing with the plasma membrane. (Courtesy J. Beggs, Laboratory of Neuropathology, Barrow's Neurological Institute, Phoenix, Ariz.)

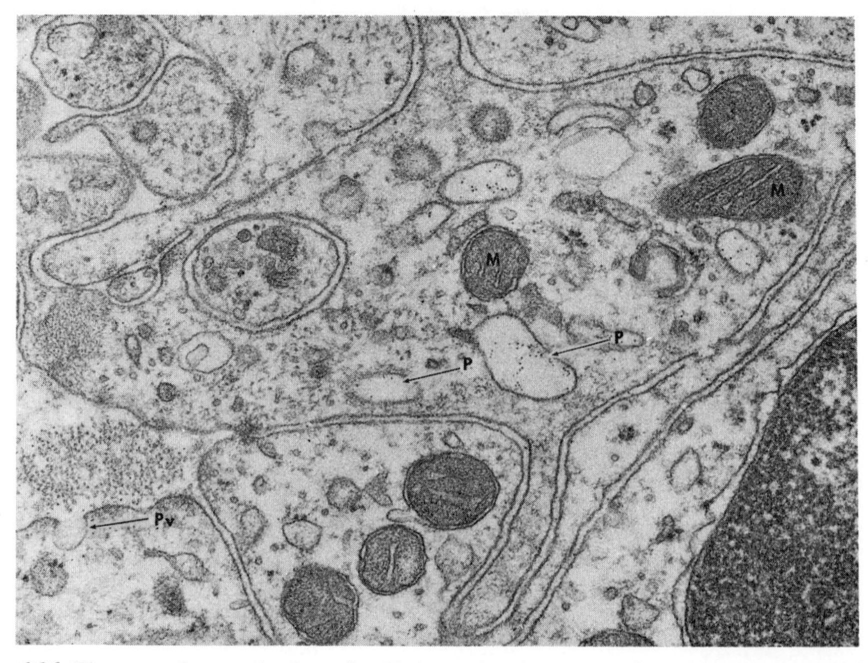

Fig. 6-26. Electron micrograph of arachnoid tissue showing penetration of ferritin, **P**, by micropinocytosis. Pinocytotic vesicle, **Pv**, is forming at a free surface. **M,** Mitochondria. (Courtesy J. Beggs, Laboratory of Neuropathology, Barrow's Neurological Institute, Phoenix, Ariz.)

the visceral layers of the yolk sac (known to be capable of rapid absorption of material of relatively large molecular weight) contain a number of permanent or semipermanent channels through which material can gain entrance into the cytoplasm. They are somewhat like the gullet of *Paramecium,* at the bottom of which food vacuoles form. These *apical canaliculi* run a tortuous course but do not anastomose. They can be differentiated from the membranes of the ER by the fact that they appear to be thicker and darker than the ER membranes. Large vacuoles are usually associated with the ends of these canaliculi. When marked colloidal hemoglobin was injected into mice, the hemoglobin could be traced through these canaliculi and into the vacuoles, which seems to prove the concept that such structures are utilized for absorption by certain cells (Fawcett, 1961).

Extraneous coats. Studies of phagocytosis and pinocytosis using amebas have shown that an extraneous coat is present which covers the cell membrane. This fuzzy coat consists of filaments about 1,000 Å long and about 100 Å thick that give a positive periodic acid–Schiff reaction (PAS), indicating that the material is composed of polysaccharides (Wolpert and O'Neill, 1962). When markers such as thorium dioxide or ferritin were used to study pinocytosis, they were first absorbed onto these filaments. Such observations indicate that this layer may function in selectivity.

Later, similar layers were found in many mammalian cells involved in the pinocytic process (Fig. 6-27). In the toad urinary bladder this layer is found in three types of cells, but most frequently in the mitochondria-rich fraction. When saccharated iron oxide was used, this material was first absorbed to this coating. Later the marker material was found in vacuoles that also contained this coat material (Choi, 1965). The coated layers are also found in gallbladder cells, where they are called *antennules microvillares* (Yamada, 1955). They are present as filiform processes on the cell surfaces of hepatic cells that face the sinusoids (Fawcett, 1953). The uptake of ferritin by erythroblasts has also been shown to take place by micropinocytosis (Bessis and Breton-Gorius, 1959; Fawcett, 1964). Electron microscopy of the erythroblasts shows the surface to have small local coated

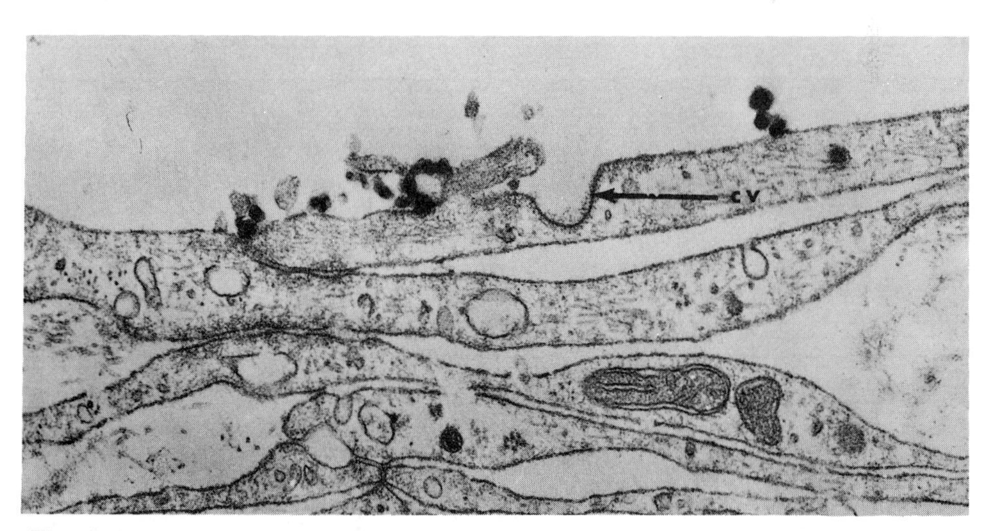

Fig. 6-27. Electron micrograph of a coated micropinocytotic vesicle, **cv.** Other vesicles are evident within the cytoplasm as well as one that is forming at a free surface. (Courtesy J. Beggs, Laboratory of Neuropathology, Barrow's Neurological Institute, Phoenix, Ariz.)

areas, whereas the remaining membranous regions are smooth. The extraneous coat is characterized by striations that indicate similarity to the filamentous material found in other cells. It is this localized area with the extraneous coating that will form the micropinocytotic vesicles (Fig. 6-27). Ferritin, when present, will adhere to this coated layer but not to the smooth regions of the membrane. After adherence there is an invagination of the coated area to form vesicles that carry the ferritin into the cells. The smooth and fuzzy regions may differ somewhat in function; the coated areas may be selective for a specific type or class of compounds, whereas the smooth region may be involved in more general pinocytotic processes (Fawcett, 1964).

These varied activities are apparent by the different types of micropinocytotic vesicles formed from the free surfaces and from the coated or fuzzy surface. Fawcett (1965) compared these differences. At the smooth surface there is a paucity of images of intermediate stages, which may mean that this step takes place fairly rapidly. Accumulations of vesicles also remain attached to the surface, whereas few are found free in the cytoplasm below. This may mean that there is considerable delay in the separation of these vesicles from the surface. On the other hand, pinocytosis of the coated surface shows a number of intermediate stages of invaginations, with no large accumulation of fully formed vesicles at the surface, indicating a constant sequence with no appreciable rate variations.

Theory of pinocytosis. As in the case of phagocytosis, pinocytosis is a response to an external stimulus. It is appropriate, then, to show what external stimuli are necessary for pinocytosis to proceed. When *Amoeba* is given ^{14}C glucose alone, pinocytosis will not occur; yet if an inducing protein is present, the radioactive glucose is taken in by the organism (Chapman-Andresen and Holter, 1955). Substances that induce pinocytosis consist of simple salts, amino acids, proteins (Marshall and Nachmias, 1965), RNAase, and cytochrome *c* (Schumaker, 1958). In all cases the effective agents are cationic, positively charged particles. Anions, anionic dyes, or negatively charged proteins do not induce pinocytotic processes. Similarly, uncharged solutes like simple sugars do not induce pinocytosis. Yet if complexed with a positively charged particle or even in a medium containing positively charged substances, both anionic and neutral compounds can be pinocytized by the cell.

In the uptake of substances such as proteins three stages are recognized (Marshall et al., 1959). The first stage consists of the initial binding of the protein to the plasma membrane. This is a reversible binding that is a function of concentration and independent of pH. Brandt (1958) showed that pinocytosis appears to be independent of the hydrogen ion concentration within the pH range of 6.5 to 8.0. The initial binding also appears to be independent of temperature and is not greatly affected by metabolic inhibitors. In the second stage when the binding of proteins exceeds a certain level, there is a sudden increase in binding, as though new binding sites on the cell had become available. The third and final stage is characterized by insensitivity to inhibitors and cooling. The bound protein is no longer in equilibrium with the protein in the medium. It is during this stage that ingestion by the membrane containing the bound proteins takes place. At certain low external concentrations *Amoeba* can bind fifty times as much protein as is present in the solution within 5 minutes after immersion (Schumaker, 1958).

Pinocytosis is suppressed both by respiratory inhibitors and high pressure (Zimmerman and Rustad, 1965). If pressure of 2,000 lb./in.^{2} is applied to an organism, most of the pinocytotic channels disappear, whereas at 3,000 lb./in.^{2} all channels disappear within a relatively short period of time. With release of pressure the channels appear once again. The inhibition of pinocytosis by this means may involve changes in the sol-gel equilibrium, whereby the cortical plasma gel is changed to the sol state under pressure; or as an alternative, since channel formation involves or requires energy such as ATP, thermodynamic disturbances may result from such pressure, which could produce the same result.

It was pointed out that pinocytosis may be a form of active transport. Like active transport in the conventional sense it is energy dependent. The importance of this process in transporting macromolecules across the membrane barriers into the underlying cytoplasm is uncertain. For one thing it is not known how many cell types are or can engage in this mechanism of transport. This uncertainty is especially true of cells having walls, although there are reports that some pinocytosis, probably only micropinocytosis, may occur in some plant cells. Under certain conditions all cell types may be capable of pinocytosis. If this were true, pinocytosis as a means of active transport would take on added importance. Since our knowledge is limited as to the cell types involved, it can be stated that pinocytosis may be a collateral method of active transport through membranes, working in conjunction with the active transport used in the normal physiological sense and perhaps negating some conclusions drawn from such experiments.

PLASMA MEMBRANE

Literature cited

Bell, L. G. E. 1961. Surface extensions as a mechanism at cellular movement and cell division. J. Theor. Biol. **1:**104-106.

Bell, L. G. E. 1962. Polysaccharides and cell membrane. J. Theor. Biol. **3:**132-133.

Blasie, J. K., and C. R. Worthington. 1969a. Molecular localization of frog retinal receptor photopigment by E. M. and low angle x-ray diffraction. J. Molec. Biol. **39:**407-416.

Blasie, J. K. and C. R. Worthington. 1969b. Plainer liquid-like arrangement of photopigment molecules in frog retinal receptor disk membrane. J. Molec. Biol. **39:**417-439.

Collander, R., and H. Bärlund. 1933. Permeabilitäts-studien an Chara ceratophylla. Acta Bot. Fenn. **11:**1-14.

Davson, H., and J. F. Danielli. 1952. The permeability of natural membranes. Cambridge University Press, London.

Dixon, E., T. J. McManus, and D. C. Tosteson. 1966. Glycolytic enzymes in pig and sheep red cells. Fed. Proc. **25**(1)**:**641.

Dreyer, W. J., D. S. Paperman, and H. Kuhn. 1972. On the absence of ubiquitous structural protein subunits in biological membranes. In D. E. Green (editor). Membrane structure and its biological applications. Ann. N. Y. Acad. Sci. **195:**61-74.

Eicholz, A., and R. K. Crane. 1966. Fractionation of membrane enzymes present in brush borders of hamster epithelial cells. Fed. Proc. **25**(1)**:** 656.

Farquhar, M. F., and G. E. Palade. 1963. Junctional complexes in various epithelia. J. Cell Biol. **17:**375-412.

Fawcett, D. W. 1961. The membranes of the cytoplasm. Lab. Invest. **10:**1162-1188.

Fricke, H., and H. J. Curtis. 1934. Electric impedence of suspensions of yeast cells. Nature (London) **134:**102-103.

Fricke, H., and H. J. Curtis. 1935. Electric impedance of suspensions of leucocytes. Nature (London) **135:**436.

Gasser, H. 1952. Saltatory conduction hypothesis (discussion). Cold Spring Harb. Symp. Quant. Biol. **17:**32-36.

Geren, B. B. 1954. Formation from Schwann cell surface of myelin in the peripheral nerves of chick embryos. Exp. Cell Res. **7:**558-562.

Geren, B. B., and F. E. Schmitt. 1954. The structure of the Schwan cell and its relation to the axon in certain invertebrate nerve fibers. Proc. Nat. Acad. Sci. U.S.A. **40:**865-870.

Ham, A. W. 1961. Histology. J. B. Lippincott Co., Philadelphia.

Hanssen, O. E., and L. Herman. 1962. The presence of an axial structure in the microvillus of the mouse convoluted proximal tubular cell. Lab. Invest. **11:**610-616.

Hechter, O. 1965a. Role of water in the molecular organization of cell membranes. Fed. Proc. **24:** 91-102.

Hechter, O. 1965b. Intracellular water structure and mechanisms of cellular transport. Ann. N. Y. Acad. Sci. **125:**625-646.

Hillier, J., and J. H. Hoffman. 1953. On the ultrastructure of the plasma membrane as determined by the electron microscope. J. Cell. Comp. Physiol. **42:**205-247.

Jorpes, E. 1932. The protein component of the

erythrocyte membrane and stroma. Biochem. J. **26:**1488-1503.

Kavanau, J. L. 1963. Structure and functions of biological membranes. Nature (London) **198:** 525-530.

Kavanau, J. L. 1965. Structure and functions in biological membranes. Vol. 1. Holden-Day, Inc., San Francisco.

Laico, M. T., and E. H. Eylar. 1966. Cell free biosynthesis of glycoproteins. Fed. Proc. **25**(1): 587.

Lemanski, L. F. 1971. Histological, histochemical, and ultrastructural study of myocardiogenesis in Mexican axolotls, Ambystoma mexicanum. Ph.D. Thesis, Hayden Library, Arizona State University, Tempe, Ariz.

Lenard, J., and S. J. Singer. 1966. Protein conformation in cell membrane preparation as studied by optical rotatory dispersion and circular dichroism. Proc. Nat. Acad. Sci. U.S.A. **56:**1828-1835.

Lenaz, G. 1972. Studies on the organization of proteins and lipids in the inner mitochondrial membrane. In D. E. Green (editor). Membrane structure and its biological applications. Ann. N. Y. Acad. Sci. **195:**39-49.

Locke, M. 1965. The structure of septate desmosomes. J. Cell Biol. **25:**166-169.

McNutt, N. S., and R. S. Weinstein. 1970. The ultrastructure of the nexus: a correlated thin-section and freeze-cleave study. J. Cell Biol. **47:**666-688.

Mills, C. A. 1949. Bone marrow nutrition in relation to the phagocytic activity of blood granulocytes. Blood **4:**150-159.

Moskowitz, M., and M. Calvin. 1952. On the components and structures of the human red cell membrane. Exp. Cell Res. **3:**33-46.

Moskowitz, M., W. B. Dandliker, M. Calvin, and R. S. Evans. 1950. Studies on the antigens of human red cells. J. Immun. **65:**383-392.

Oosaki, T., and S. Ishii. 1964. The ultrastructure of the regions of junction between smooth muscle cells in the rat intestine. J. Ultrastruct. Res. **10:**567-571.

Parpart, A. K., and R. Ballentine. 1952. Molecular anatomy of the red blood cell membrane. In R. Barron (editor). Modern trends in physiology and biochemistry. Academic Press, Inc., New York.

Pease, D. C. 1955a. Fine structure of the kidney seen by electron microscopy. J. Histochem. Cytochem. **3:**295-301.

Pease, D. C. 1955b. Electron microscopy of tubular cells of the kidney cortex. Anat. Rec. **121:** 723-736.

Ponder, E. 1961. The cell membrane and its properties. In J. Brachet and A. F. Mirsky (editors). The cell. Vol. 2. Academic Press, Inc., New York.

Reynolds, J. A. 1972. Are inorganic cations essential for stability of biological membranes. In D. E. Green (editor). Membrane structure and its biological applications. Ann. N. Y. Acad. Sci. **195:**75-85.

Robertson, J. D. 1959. Ultrastructure of cell membranes and their derivatives. In E. M. Crook (editor). Structure and function of subcellular components. Biochemical Society Symposium No. 16. Cambridge University Press, London.

Robertson, J. D. 1962. The membrane of the living cell. W. H. Freeman & Co., Publishers, San Francisco.

Ruska, H., Moore, D. H., and J. Weinstock. 1957. The base of the proximal convoluted tubule cells of the rat kidney. J. Biophys. Biochem. Cytol. **3:**249-253.

Singer, S. J. 1972. A fluid lipid-globular protein mosaic model of membrane structure. In D. E. Green (editor). Membrane structure and its biological application. Ann. N. Y. Acad. Sci. **195:**16-23.

Stoeckenius, W. 1972. Membrane models. In D. E. Green (editor). Membrane structure and its biological application. Ann. N. Y. Acad. Sci. **195:**35-36.

Vanderkooi, G. 1972. Molecular architecture of biological membranes. In D. E. Green (editor). Membrane structure and its biological application. Ann. N. Y. Acad. Sci. **195:**6-15.

Vanderkooi, G., and D. E. Green. 1970. Biological membranes. I. The protein crystal model for membranes. Proc. Nat. Acad. Sci. U.S.A. **66:**615-621.

Vanderkooi, G., and M. Sundaralingam. 1970. Biological structure. II. A detailed model for the retinal rod segment membrane. Proc. Nat. Acad. Sci. U.S.A. **67:**233-238.

Warner, D. T. 1961a. Proposed molecular models of gramicidin s and other polypeptides. Nature (London) **190:**120-128.

Warner, D. T. 1961b. Proposed molecular models. II. Conformation of Staphylomycin and other polypeptides and possible relation to the structure of water. J. Theor. Biol. **1:**514-528.

Warner, D. T. 1964. IV. A suggested conformation for the protein sub-unit of tobacco mosaic virus. J. Theor. Biol. **6:**118-136.

General references

Ballentine, R. 1944. Stromatin. J. Cell. Comp. Physiol. **23:**21-26.

Barnard, E. A., and J. F. Danielli. 1962. A cytochemical reaction for nucleoproteins. Nature (London) **178:**1450-1453.

Branton, D., and R. C. Park (editors). 1968. Papers on biological membrane structure. Little, Brown & Co., Boston.

Fawcett, D. W. 1964. Cell movement and cell contact. Exp. Cell Res. supp. **8:**174-187.

Fernández-Móran, H. 1959. Fine structures of biological lamellar system. In J. L. Oncley (editor). Biophysical science. John Wiley & Sons, Inc., New York.

Frankenhaeuser, B., and P. L. Hodgkins. 1956. The after effects of impulses in giant nerve fibers of Loligo. J. Physiol. (London) **131:** 341-376.

Geren, B. B., and J. Raskins, 1953. Development of the fine structure of the myelin sheath in sciatic nerve of chick embryos. Proc. Nat. Acad. Sci. **39:**880-884.

Griddle, R. S., R. M. Bock, D. E. Green, and H. Tisdale. 1962. Physical characteristics of protein of the electron transport system and interpretation of the structure of the mitochondrion. Biochemistry (Wash.) **1**(5)**:**827-842.

Harris, E. J. 1956. Transport and accumulation in biological systems. Butterworth & Co., Ltd., London.

Osterhout, W., Jr. 1940. Some models of protoplasmic surfaces. Cold Spring Harb. Symp. Quant. Biol. **8:**51-60.

Parpart, A. K. 1942. The preparation of red blood cell membranes. J. Cell. Comp. Physiol. **19:** 248-249.

Schmitt, F. O. 1936. Nerve ultrastructure by x-ray diffraction and polarized light studies. Cold Spring Harb. Symp. Quant. Biol. **4:**7-11.

Sjöstrand, F. S. 1956. Ultrastructure of cells as revealed by electron microscope. Int. Rev. Cytol. **5:**456-552.

Soloman, A. K. 1960. Pores in the cell membrane. W. H. Freeman & Co., Publishers, San Francisco.

Soloman, A. K. 1960. Red cell membrane and ion transport. J. Gen. Physiol. **43:**1-15.

Vandenheuvel, F. A. 1965. Structural studies of biological membranes in demyelinating diseases. Ann. N. Y. Acad. Sci. **122:**57-76.

Warner, D. T. 1965. A proposed water protein interaction and its application to the structure of tobacco mosaic virus particles. Ann. N. Y. Acad. Sci. **125:**605-624.

PHAGOCYTOSIS AND PINOCYTOSIS

Literature cited

Barnes, R. D. 1963. Invertebrate zoology. W. B. Saunders Co., Philadelphia.

Bessis, M. C., and J. Breton-Gorius. 1959. Ferritin and ferruginous micelles in normal erythroblast and hypochromic hypersideremic anemias. Blood **14:**423-432.

Brandt, P. W. 1958. A study of the mechanism of pinocytosis. Exp. Cell Res. **15:**300-313.

Chapman-Andresen, C., and N. Holter. 1955. Studies on the ingestion of C^{14}-glucose by pinocytosis in the amoeba Chaos chaos. Exp. Cell Res. supp. **3:**52-63.

Christiansen, R. G., and J. M. Marshall. 1965. A study of phagocytosis in the amoeba Chaos chaos. J. Cell Biol. **25:**443-457.

Choi, J. K. 1962. Electron microscopy of absorption of tracer material by the toad (Bufo marinus) epithelium. Anat. Rec. **142:**222.

Choi, J. K. 1965. Electron microscopy of absorption of tracer material by toad urinary bladder. J. Cell Biol. **25:**175-192.

Donahue, S. 1964. A relationship between fine structure and function of blood vessels in the central nervous system of rabbit fetuses. Amer. J. Anat. **115:**17-26.

Fawcett, D. W. 1953. Observation on the fine structure of hepatic cells. J. Appl. Physiol. **24:**1424-1425.

Fawcett, D. W. 1964. Local specialization of the plasmalemma in micropinocytosis of erythroblasts. Anat. Rec. **148:**370.

Fawcett, D. W. 1965. Surface specializations of absorbing cells. J. Histochem. Cytochem. **13:** 75-91.

Fawcett, D. W., and J. Wittenberg. 1962. Structural specialization of endothelial cell junctions. Anat. Rec. **142:**231.

Florey, H. 1961. Exchange of substance between the blood and tissue. Nature (London) **192:** 908-912.

Ham, A. W. 1957. Histology, 5th ed. J. B. Lippincott Co., Philadelphia.

Kaye, G. I., G. D. Pappas, and A. Donn. 1961. An electron microscope study of the rabbit corneal epithelium in relation to uptake and transport of colloidal particles. Anat. Rec. **139:** 244-245.

Lewis, W. H. 1931. Pinocytosis. Bull. Hopkins Hosp. **49:**17-37.

Marshall, J. M., and V. T. Nachmias. 1965. Cell surface and pinocytosis. J. Histochem. Cytochem. **13:**92-104.

Marshall, J. M., V. N. Schumaker, and P. W. Brandt. 1959. Pinocytosis in Amoeba. Ann. N. Y. Acad. Sci. **78:**515-523.

Menkin, V. 1956. Biochemical mechanisms in inflammation. Charles C Thomas, Publisher, Springfield, Ill.

Palade, G. E. 1953. Fine structure of blood capillaries. J. Appl. Physiol. **24:**1424.

Palade, G. E. 1960. Transport in quanta across the endothelium of blood vessels. Anat. Rec. **136:**254.

Schumaker, V. M. 1958. Uptake of protein from solution of Amoeba proteus. Exp. Cell Res. **15:**314-331.

Wallach, D. F. H., and E. H. Eylar: 1961. Sialic acid in cellular membranes of Ehrlich's ascites carcinoma cells. Biochim. Biophys. Acta **52:** 594-596.

Wissig, S. L. 1958. An electron microscope study of the permeability of capillaries in muscles. Anat. Rec. **130:**467-468.

Wolpert, L., and C. H. O'Neill. 1962. Dynamics of the membrane of Amoeba proteus studied with labelled specific antibody. Nature (London) **196:**1261-1266.

Wright, C. S., and M. C. Dodd. 1955. Phagocytosis. Ann. N. Y. Acad. Sci. **59:**945-950.

Yamada, E. 1955. The fine structures of the gall bladder epithelium of the mouse. J. Biophys. Biochem. Cytol. **1:**445-457.

Zimmerman, A. M., and R. C. Rustad. 1965. Effects of high pressure on pinocytosis. J. Cell Biol. **25:**397-400.

General references

Bennett, H. S. 1963. Morphological aspects of extracellular polysaccharides. J. Histochem. Cytochem. **11:**14-23.

Ito, S. 1964. The surface coating of enteric microvilli. Anat. Rec. **148:**294.

Mitchisen, J. M. 1950. Birefringence in Amoeba. Nature (London) **166:**313-314.

Ray, D. L. 1951. Agglutination of bacteria: A feeding method in the soil Amoeba, Hartmanella sp. J. Exp. Zool. **118:**443-465.

Rustad, R. C. 1959. Molecular orientation at the surface of Amoeba during pinocytosis. Nature (London) **183:**1058.

Saslaw, S., and C. A. Doan. 1947. The role of phagocytosis as related to age of granulocytes following primary and reinfection studies with hemolytic streptococci in Macacus rhesus. J. Lab. Clin. Med. **32:**878-885.

CHAPTER 7

Endoplasmic reticulum

Prior to electron microscopy the cell cytoplasm was considered as being a homogeneous colloidal mixture, the hyaloplasm, composed almost entirely of water and protein material. Depending on the type of fixation used, the cytoplasmic ground substance was variously described as granular, reticular, or vacuolar. Within the ground substance the Golgi material (as a filamentous apparatus), mitochondria, and at times vacuoles, plastids, and spherosomes could be identified. One could conceive of these as free-floating bodies within the homogeneous hyaloplasm.

It was not until the development of the electron microscope that a system of cytoplasmic membranes was conclusively "discovered." These membranes were first described by Porter et al. (1945) using tissue-cultured animal cell preparations. The membranes were described as forming lace-like reticulations, like strings of beads, in the ground substance of the cell. These reticulations showed a center of less density and ranged in size from 100 to 150 nm. Early studies had indicated that this reticulation was confined entirely within the endoplasmic portion of the cell, and from its position it was originally referred to by Porter as the endoplasmic reticulum (ER).

In a sense this system of membranes was known for a number of years. It was described by optical microscopy as a filamentous structure within the cell. Partly because the membrane thickness is less than 100 Å, which is below the resolution of the light microscope, and partly because investigators did not know what to look for, it eluded definite identification. In a historical review, Haguenau (1958) attributed the early descriptive morphology of this system to Garnier. It was described as a specialized region in the cytoplasm that was basophilic to stains. Its first evidence in cells was in the highly secreting pancreas and salivary glands. Garnier noted that portions of these basophilic regions contain rods or filamentous structures, which varied and appeared not to be permanent entities. Their development seemed to vary in direct relation to the activity of the cell. The filaments were more numerous in cells that were in an active state, and conversely, the filaments progressively disappeared when zymogenic granules were present within the cell. This basophilic material found at the base of the pancreatic cell was named the *ergastoplasm* (Gr. *erazamai,* meaning "to elaborate and transform") by Garnier because of its close association to the synthetic activity of the cell. The "structure" was assumed to be present in other cells. Interestingly, the ergastoplasm had been noted previously by Pflüger in 1869 and Heidenhain around 1875.

After the turn of the century little significant work was done with regard to the ergastoplasm. There were those who thought the ergastoplasm was the result of pleomorphic mitochondria, whereas others believed that although there was a structure comparable to that described by Garnier, the fibrillar configuration was probably more dependent on the type of fixation used.

After the first descriptions by Porter, other studies (Porter, 1953; Weiss, 1953; Porter and Palade, 1957) using thin sections obtained from the newly developed ultramicrotome allowed more detailed characterization of the ER. These and other studies have shown that the ER is a constant entity of all cells found in animals and plants. The only exceptions are mature erythrocytes and prokaryotes. For a time a number of individuals believed the ER to be an artifact that resulted from the fixation process; yet the same system of cytoplasmic membranes was described in pancreatic cells that were prepared by the freeze-dry technique (Grunbaum and Wellings, 1960). Further studies indicated that these membrane-bounded units could be separated and identified by physical methods such as ultracentrifugation (see discussion of microsomes).

Although it has been stated that the ER is well below the resolution of the light microscope, it is nevertheless identifiable by phase-contrast microscopy if one knows what to look for. It appears as linear contours in the basal cells of the pancreas as well as in the testicular tissue (Fig. 7-1). In testicular tissue it first appears as a mottling within the cytoplasm. However, with the passage of time the ER undergoes further changes, perhaps as a result of injury, in which the contours become more extensive and show a concentric arrangement. The underlying causes that produce these changes are poorly understood. One explanation is that there is a colloidal transformation taking place that shifts the cytoplasm from a gel to a sol state, presumably due to changes in hydration or alteration in the physicochemical changes taking place within the cell (Ito, 1962).

Because of electron microscopy the ER is now well recognized as a fundamental organization of the eukaryotic cell. It is basically an interconnecting system of tubules that extends throughout the cell, being continuous with the nuclear membranes, and rarely, shows communication with the plasma membrane. It is not restricted to the endoplasm. In the region of the Golgi complex, connections are occasionally observed. These tubules can be considered as constituting a network of cavities, with the

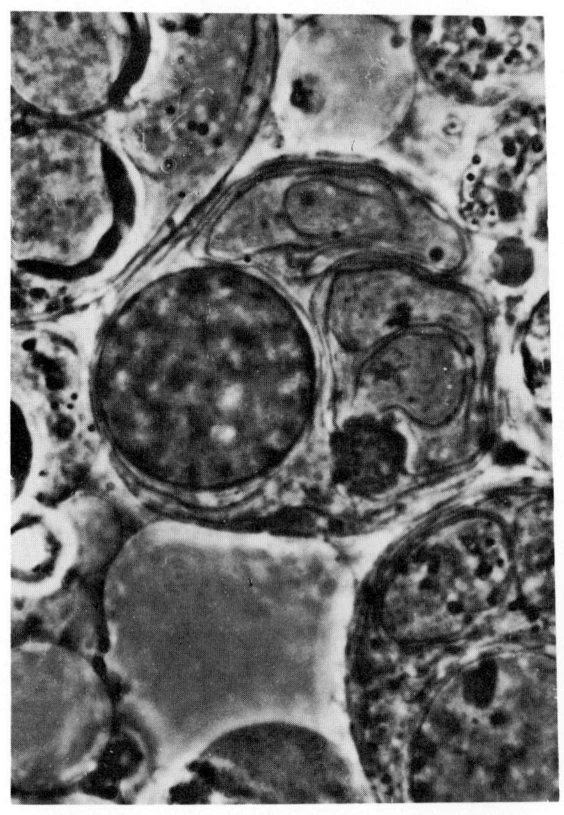

Fig. 7-1. Phase-contrast micrograph of guinea pig spermatocytes that were allowed to stand in a slide preparation for some time. Note concentric arrangement of ER. (From Ito, S. 1962. Light and electron microscopic study of membranous cytoplasmic organelles. In R. J. C. Harris [editor]. Interpretation of ultrastructure. Academic Press, Inc., New York.)

boundaries limited by a membrane. Generally the cavities appear empty. At times, however, they may appear to be filled with material of varying electron densities. These cytoplasmic membranes can assume various forms such as cisternal, vesicular, and tubular. At times it is possible to see all three forms within a single cell. In vivo the ER is a labile system.

Configurations of cytoplasmic membrane

Cisternal arrangement. The cisternal arrangement is characteristic of cells that are actively engaged in protein synthesis, particularly if the material synthesized is for secretory purposes. This form is characterized by ER tubules in broad flat sinuses in which the profiles appear long and flat (Fig. 7-2). Generally the cisternae maintain a depth of about 50 nm. When seen, the cisternae are usually loosely stacked in a parallel manner to produce lamellae. Anastomoses of the profiles can be seen within a single section, suggesting that continuity may exist throughout the cytoplasm. The term "cisternae" was chosen to designate large reservoir-like formations in a system of cavities (Porter and Palade, 1957).

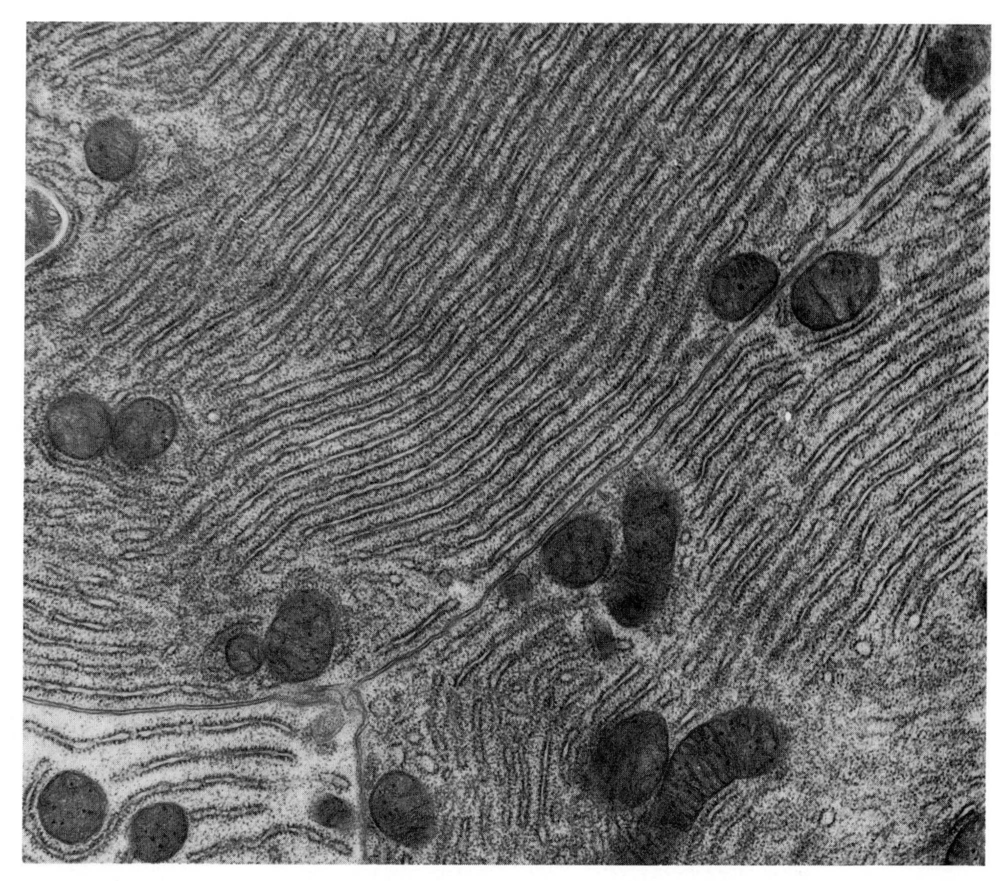

Fig. 7-2. Electron micrograph of pancreatic acinar cells from starved bat showing closely packed cisternal arrangement of granular ER. This is a good example of "rough," or "granular" ER. (From Ito, S. 1962. Light and electron microscopic study of membranous cytoplasmic organelles. In R. J. C. Harris [editor]. Interpretation of ultrastructure. Academic Press, Inc., New York.)

Weiss (1953), on the other hand, referred to the cisternal elements as *ergastoplasmic sacs*.

Vesicular arrangement. Vesicles or sacs may occur as membrane-lined cavities that range from a rounded shape to a more globose configuration. Vesicles do not always appear to show communication with other vesicles or cisternae. The sizes of these vesicles are variable, but on the average they range from 40 to 500 nm (Fig. 7-3).

In addition to such large ER vesicles, cells often contain other sorts of vesicles. In fact, the term is applied to most small, spherical, membrane-bounded structures regardless of origin, size, or content. The term "microbody" is sometimes applied.

Tubular arrangement. In an electron micrograph section the tubules may appear as circles. However, tubular configurations show much branching and anastomoses, and these profiles more often show pleomorphic figures. The sizes of these tubules are variable also, but on the average they range from 50 to 100 nm in diameter (Fig. 7-4).

Distribution of membrane within cytoplasm

The cytoplasmic membranes not only vary in form but also in amount and in cellular disposition. In fact, change in quantity and distribution can be regarded as one of the most evident responses to cellular conditions and differentiation. The ER can shift from a continuous phase to one in which the vesicles show discontinuities, depending on the physiological and biochemical state of the cell. This phase change represents a reversible process.

From an embryonic point of view the ER appears early in the developmental stage of the embryo and can be recognized

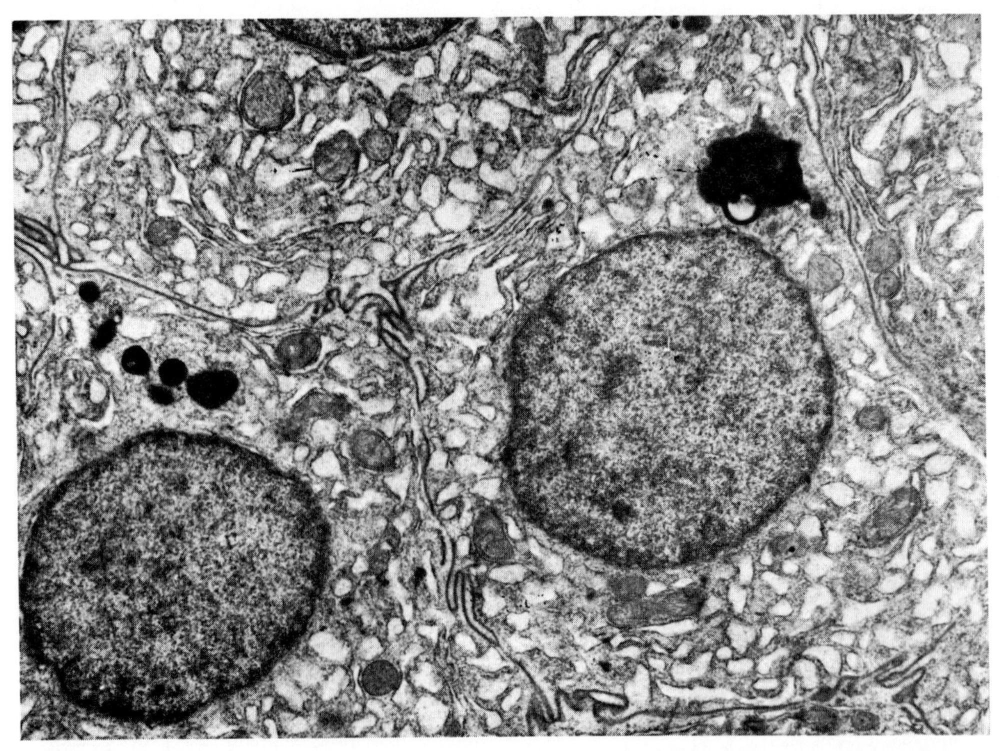

Fig. 7-3. Electron micrograph of venom gland cells from rattlesnake *(Crotalus atrox)* illustrating vesicular arrangement of ER.

as early as the two-cell stage and increases during the process of cellular differentiation (Slautterback and Fawcett, 1959). In the early stages of cnidoblast development the basophilic cytoplasm contains numerous small vesicles. As differentiation progresses, there is an increase in the number of vesicles with a subsequent elongation and coalescence to form a continuous system. In a more advanced state of development these tubular profiles develop cisternae that tend to be arranged in a parallel manner. After the formation of the cnidocil the ER undergoes a regression, with only a few membrane-lined vacuoles persisting in the cytoplasm.

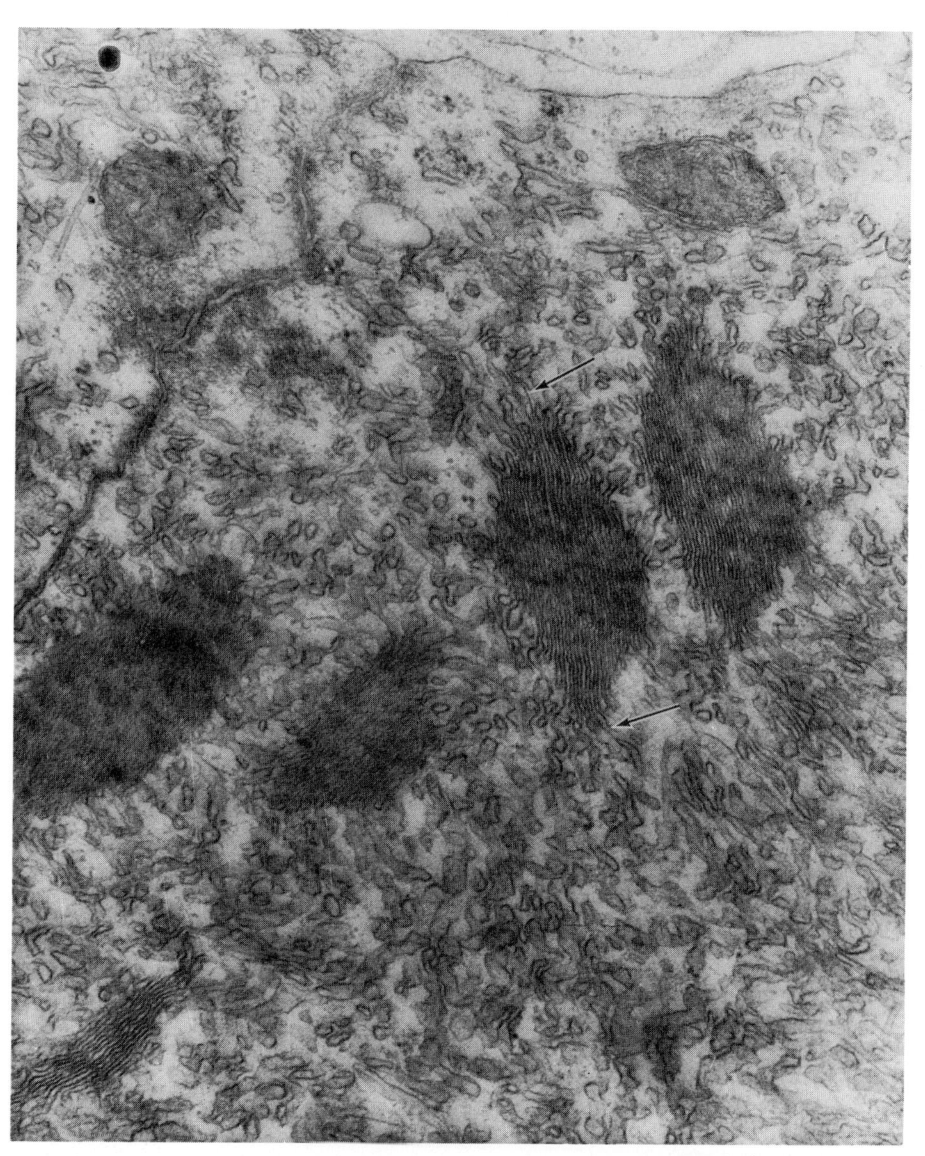

Fig. 7-4. Electron micrograph of pigmented epithelial cell of frog retina showing myeloid bodies. Arrows show continuity between membranes of myeloid body and agranular ER. (From Porter, K. R., and E. Yamada. 1960. J. Biophys. Biochem. Cytol. **8:**181-205.)

Types of endoplasmic reticulum

Two basic morphological types of ER are visible and identifiable. They are (1) the granular ER, sometimes called the *rough ER* or the *ergastoplasm,* and (2) the agranular or the smooth ER.

The *granular* ER (Fig. 7-2) is identified by the presence of small electron-dense particles attached to the *outer surfaces* of the membranes. These electron-dense granules are composed of ribonucleoproteins and are referred to as ribosomes (Chapter 9). On the average they are about 150 Å in diameter. The basophilic characteristics of cells seen by light microscopy are associated with this type of membrane system. However, the ribosomes and not the membrane system per se are responsible for the basophilic staining characteristics.

The *smooth* ER, on the other hand, does not have ribosomes attached to its membranes; hence it appears smooth. Generally the staining characteristics are different in that cells viewed by light microscopy which contain a large amount of smooth membranes take acidophilic stains. This is due to the lack of ribosomes. On a purely morphological basis the difference between the two types of membranes is the presence or absence of ribosomes. However, the differences between the two types involve function as well as stability. Functionally, the granular ER is involved in protein synthesis, whereas the smooth ER is involved in a multiplicity of functions other than protein synthesis (see following discussion of agranular ER). Another major difference between the smooth and rought ER is their stability. It has been shown (Ito, 1962) that the smooth ER is less stable than the granular form. The agranular ER may vesiculate a short time after the death of or even slight damage to the cell, whereas the granular ER may persist as such for several days after death. The stability of the rough ER is apparently due to the presence of attached ribosomes. It has been shown that chemically and enzymatically the membranes of the total rough and smooth microsomes are similar and that the membrane properties are modified by the attached ribosomes (Eriksson and Dallner, 1972).

Both the rough and smooth types of ER can be present within the same cell. There is no sharp division where one begins and the other ends. Generally one will predominate over the other when both types are present. It was originally postulated from studies of regeneration of liver tissue that the smooth ER gave rise to the rough form.

Granular ER. As stated previously, the granular ER is involved in protein synthesis. Much of this evidence is derived from biochemical studies of the microsome fraction, from autoradiographic studies using labeled amino acids, and from electron micrographs.

The amount and distribution of the granular ER are correlated with the biosynthetic activity of the cell. Thus in cells that synthesize small to moderate amounts of protein the ER may consist of few tubules with an occasional cisternal expansion. On the other hand, in actively synthesizing gland cells such as the pancreas the ER consists of extensive arrays of parallel cisternae.

The role of the granular ER in protein synthesis is well demonstrated in a number of electron microscopic studies (Weiss, 1953; Fawcett, 1961). In a starved animal or an animal in hibernation the granular ER is characterized by narrow and uniformly spaced cisternae that are parallel to the lateral and basal surfaces. After feeding there is a change in the ER characterized by extensive cisternae that execute sweeping curves or multilayers of concentric whirls (Weiss, 1953; Fawcett, 1961), and the cisternal spaces increase in volume (Helender, 1964). Frequently the cisternal spaces may contain granules of homogeneous material presumed to be the products of secretion that were synthesized on the ribosomes attached to these membranes.

Similar cisternal arrangements of the ER

have been described in the basophilic area of liver cells (Porter and Bruni, 1959; Moulé, 1963), in the parotid gland cells of mammals, and in the cells from the venom glands of rattlesnakes *(Crotalus atrox).* The latter gland is homologous to the parotid gland of mammals.

The presence of a basophilic cytoplasm does not necessarily mean that the ER is extensive or necessarily indicate the presence of a rough ER. In embryonic cells, for example, the granular ER is not extensive, and at times the membranes of the ER may be of the smooth variety. The ribosomes, which are responsible for the basophilic staining observed by light microscopy, are scattered throughout the cytoplasm either singly or, as is more often observed, in clusters (polysomes) (Chapter 9). It has been established that the ribosomes function in protein synthesis, but the products of synthesis in this condition are used by the embryonic cells immediately for growth and development. Another example is the reticulocyte, in which the ribosomes synthesize hemoglobin. More will be said of this in Chapter 9.

Agranular ER. The term "agranular reticulum" was applied to a system of cisternae and vesicles that were originally observed in neurons (Palay, 1953; Palay and Palade, 1955). The system observed, however, was later reassigned as a Golgi complex. Morphologically, the agranular reticulum is identified by the *lack* of ribosomes attached to the membrane; hence they are also referred to as the smooth ER. In addition, other differences that delineate it from the granular ER are present, including the type of configuration within the cell. The smooth ER tends to be tubular rather than cisternal. An additional difference is the stabilities of these two forms. As mentioned previously, the smooth ER is less stable and undergoes postmortem autolysis readily, whereas the granular ER may persist for some time after the death of the cell.

As in the rough form, the smooth ER can vary in amount and in position within the cytoplasm. In general, the smooth ER in such cells as liver (Fawcett, 1955; Porter and Bruni, 1959) and testicular interstitial cells (Christensen and Fawcett, 1960, 1961) consists of networks of anastomosing tubules. The tubules by and large show a uniform diameter throughout (Fig. 7-7). The diameters of these tubules range from about 100 nm in liver to about 300 to 450 Å in interstitial cells. At times some cisternae can be observed as well as intermediate forms between the two (Christensen and Fawcett, 1961). Communication or association is often observed between the smooth ER and the Golgi complex (Fig. 8-8) as well as continuity with the nuclear envelope (Fig. 8-8) and with the granular ER.

The functions of the smooth ER are more varied than those of the granular liver. In the liver, for example, the smooth ER was first noted to be associated with regions of glycogen storage (Fawcett, 1955; Porter and Bruni, 1959). In fasted animals it was observed that residual glycogen was associated with the smooth ER. When these animals were fed, the ER greatly increased but still remained in close association with the glycogen area. This suggested that in liver the smooth reticulum was related to glyconeogenesis and glycogenolysis (Fawcett, 1961). The presence of the enzyme glucose-6-phosphatase in or on the smooth reticulum strongly suggests glycogenolysis activity (Peters et al., 1962). Electron micrographs in later studies on the relationship of the smooth ER to glycogen-rich areas indicated that the granular ER may be involved in glycogen formation; the activity may be intimately related to the disappearance of the ribosomes rather than to the membrane system per se. Thus glycogen formation in the liver may be related to degenerative changes in the granular ER that result in the disappearance of the ribosomal particles and appearance of smooth ER.

Because of the multiplicity of functions performed by the hepatic cell, glycogenolysis may be only one of a number of functions carried out by this membrane system.

The interstitial cells of the testes (Christensen and Fawcett, 1960, 1961), in which the only known function is androgen synthesis, contain agranular ER exclusively. The reticulum is abundant throughout the cell. Furthermore, biochemical studies lend support to this contention as well as similar development of the agranular form at other steriod-synthesizing sites such as the ovarian interstitial cells and corpus luteum (Fawcett, 1961). Similarly, agranular ER is present in the meibomian gland (Parakkal and Matoltsy, 1964), which is considered to be a sebaceous gland that is also involved in lipid synthesis.

The smooth ER is also present in the chloride glands of fish (Threadgold and Houston, 1964; Datta Munshi, 1964). These glands apparently serve in extrarenal excretion in the saltwater teleosts, and are also present in a number of freshwater forms. The nature of its function in the latter is unknown, but Copeland (cited by Datta Munshi, 1964) suggests a reverse polarity may exist in which absorption of the chloride ion may take place by these cells.

Modifications of agranular reticulum

Sarcoplasmic reticulum. The sarcoplasmic reticulum found in skeletal and cardiac muscles is also considered to be a highly modified form of smooth reticulum.

The *skeletal* or *striated muscle* is formed of long cylindrical cells of uniform diameter. Each cell is multinucleated, the nuclei occupying a peripheral position within the large cell or fiber. The cell is bounded by the plasma membrane, called the *sarcolemma.* The plasma membrane, of course, contains all of the protoplasmic mass, which can be subdivided into *sarcoplasm* and *myofibrils.* The myofibrils, which occupy most of the volume of the fiber, may be distributed more or less evenly within the sarcoplasm or in compact bundles with the spaces between occupied by the sarcoplasm. The myofibril seems to be composed of two main types of materials alternating in a regular fashion along its length. With light microscopy one of the transverse markings appears as a dark band, which is referred to as the *A band* (anisotropic band). Alternating with the A band is a light band, the *I band* (isotropic band) (Fig. 7-5). Bisecting the I bands is the *Z line (Zwischenscheibe).* In the midregion of the A band is the *H band* and bisecting the H band is the M line *(Mittlescheibe).* The structural and functional unit is called the *sarcomere.* It includes the A band and one half of each I band adjacent to it, that is, from one Z line to the next Z line. Cardiac muscle is similar

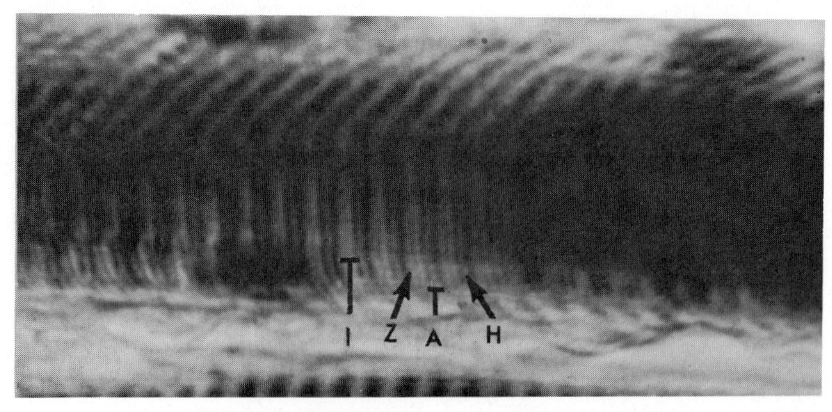

Fig. 7-5. Photomicrograph of rat skeletal muscle showing characteristic cross striations. **A,** Anisotropic band; **I,** isotropic band; **Z,** Z band bisecting I band; **H,** H band, or Hensen's band, which is the pale central region of A band.

to the skeletal muscle except that the fibers are shorter and branched and the nuclei are found in the central region of each fiber rather than lying at the periphery.

The myofibril consists mostly of thick and thin filaments. The M line is a membrane of sorts that binds a bundle of thick filaments together at their midregion. The Z line is a membrane of sorts that binds a bundle of thin filaments together at their midregion. These bundles overlap and regularly interdigitate in the dark regions of the A bands shown in Fig. 7-6. The thin filaments are composed of the protein *actin;* the thick filaments consist of molecules of the protein *myosin* that have projections (bridges) that extend to the adjacent thin filaments. The Sliding Filament Model of striated muscle contraction of Hanson and Huxley assumes that somehow the thick and thin filaments "walk" past each other: They slide relatively in among each other. The bridges are somehow involved in producing a ratchetlike motion, the shortening of sarcomere lengths, and muscle contraction.

The first microscopic report of sarcoplasmic reticulum was by Veratti (ca. 1902), who observed delicate plexuses in skeletal muscles that surrounded the myofibrils. These plexuses showed a periodicity in which the more transverse elements were located in a constant relationship to the banding. Many cytologists of that period gave little importance to this structure (Porter, 1961a; Fawcett and Revel, 1961). Porter, in the same review, noted that a few cytologists interpreted this reticulum as an image of slender extensions of extracellular trophocytes that apparently served a nutritional function. In the same manner it was also interpreted as a homologue of the Golgi complex. However, with the advent of electron microscopy the reticulum of Veratti was shown to be composed of a network of membranelike tubules.

In the muscles studied (Porter and Palade, 1957; Porter, 1961a; Fawcett and Revel, 1961; Peachey, 1965) the sarcoplasmic reticulum was observed to consist of a network of membrane-bounded tubules, which are found in striated (skeletal) muscles as well as cardiac muscles. Despite the differences and complexities encountered with the sarcoplasmic reticulum, including differences between muscles within a species or in various species, a certain pattern appears to be common to all. The tubules that make up the sarcoplasmic reticulum run longitudinally in the interfibrillar sarcoplasmic space for the length of each sarcomere. These tubules, at the levels of the H and I bands, run into or merge with large cisternal structures. At the H band level this cisterna, called the *central cisterna,* girdles or forms a sleevelike structure around the myofibrils (Figs. 7-6 and 7-7). The central cisterna is apparently the result of the fusion of the longitudinally oriented tubules. Furthermore, part of this irregular sleeve may be shared with the surrounding myofibrils and thereby produce a transverse channel across the fiber at the H band level (Porter and Palade, 1957).

The membranes of the central cisternae appear to be penetrated by numerous circular to elongate fenestrations. These circular openings average 300 to 400 Å in diameter. They appear to be arranged in a regular hexagonal pattern in which the center-to-center spacing is about 700 Å (Peachey, 1965) (Figs. 7-6 and 7-7). Similar disklike regions were observed previously (Porter and Palade, 1957) but were believed to be a thinner area rather than actual openings.

At the levels of the I band these longitudinally arranged tubules merge with the large *terminal cisternae.* These large vesicles are, like the central cisternae, transversely disposed and also form a sleeve around each myofibril. Where one such terminal cisterna is present, another of approximately the same size is found on the opposite side of the Z line. The surfaccs of the opposing vesicles are somewhat flattened and separated by a dense zone measuring about 500

Fig. 7-6. Longitudinal electron micrograph section through sartorius muscle of frog. Myofibrils are labeled **mf.** Z lines, **Z,** are located in center of each I band. A band, **A,** shows a light H zone, **H,** and denser outer regions where the primary and secondary filaments overlap. At the center of the A bands are the light L zones, **L,** containing a dark M line, **M,** down the middle. In this section the triads are the two terminal cisternae, **tc,** and the transverse tubule, **tt.** Intermediate cisternae are designated by **Is.** Adjacent to A bands are elongated profiles of longitudinal tubules, **It,** as well as oval profiles of fenestrated collars, **fc.** Glycogen granules, **gly,** are large, densely stained granules; smaller granules, **gr,** are found within the I bands. (From Peachey, L. D. 1965. J. Cell Biol. **25:**209-233.)

Å. This dense region coincides with the Z line. Sections showing profiles of the terminal cisterns indicate that the sacs are filled with diffuse granular material containing very dense granules 50 to 100 Å in diameter (Fig. 7-6).

The dense material between the paired terminal cisternae consists of a number of small circular profiles ranging between 200 and 250 Å in diameter (Porter and Palade, 1957; Peachey, 1965; Walker and Schrodt, 1965). Peachey (1965) has also shown that this intermediate or transverse tubule (part of the *T system*) is sometimes continuous across the width of the whole muscle fiber (Fig. 7-7). From the terminal cisternae the transverse (T) tubules extend peripherally to the sarcolemma and are continuous with and are deep invaginations of it. The T system is somewhat convoluted and expanded at the subsarcolemmal level (Walker and Schrodt, 1965).

The *triad,* which is important in the coupling of surface excitation to contraction in skeletal muscle, consists of the *tripartite complexes* of two terminal sarcoplasmic cisternae and the smaller tubule of the T system that is interspaced be-

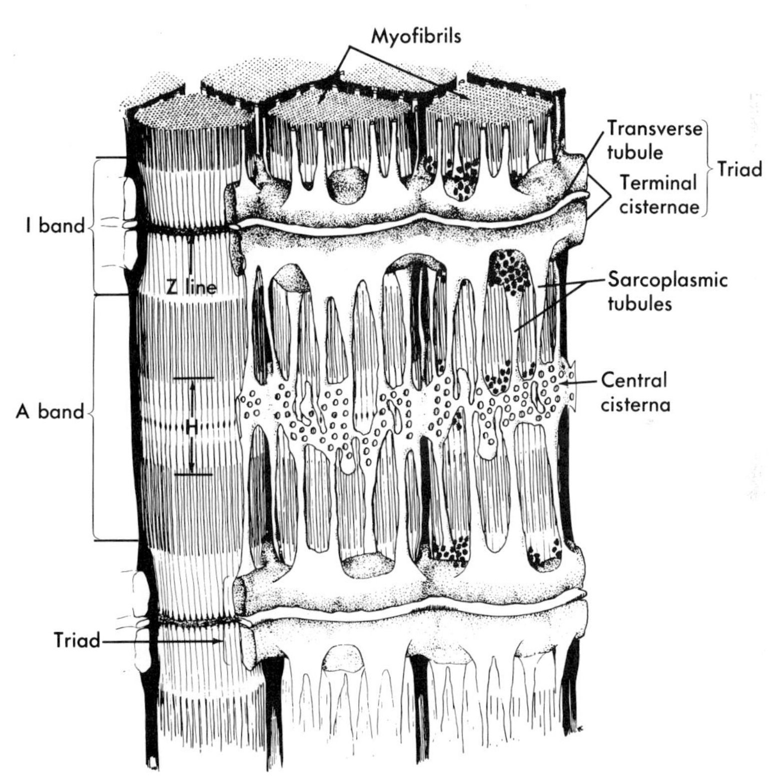

Fig. 7-7. Three-dimensional drawing of the sarcoplasmic reticulum associated with several myofibrils. The longitudinal sarcoplasmic tubules merge into or form a larger transverse sleeve-like element, the terminal cisterna. Another terminal cisterna from the adjacent sarcomere lies in close proximity. Between these two cisternae is a slender tubule (T tubule), which originates in the plasma membrane. The two terminal cisternae and the smaller transverse tubule constitute the triad. The confluency of the longitudinal sarcoplasmic tubules in the A band at the H band level produces the central cisterna. Note fenestrations in the central cisterna. In some muscles the triad is located at the A-I junction; thus there are two triads per sarcomere. (From Peachey, L. D. 1965. J. Cell Biol. **25:**209-233.)

tween the two, that is, the transverse tubule.

A modification of this pattern was described by Fawcett and Revel (1961) in the striate muscle bands from the swim bladder of the Atlantic toadfish *(Opsanus tau).* In this case the sarcomere contains a long A band and shorter I band. The two diads are found at the opposite ends of the A-I junction. Slender longitudinal branches arise laterally and extend toward the H band and Z line, respectively. These tubules anastomose and form a complex network between successive diads. The branches emanating from these two diads become confluent at the level of the H band and form the central cisterna. Also, lateral branches extend into the I band. At the Z line the fingerlike projections from one terminal cisterna interdigitate with the fingerlike projections from the diad of the opposing sarcomere.

The transverse tubules originate from the terminal cisternae and extend peripherally, becoming continuous with the sarcolemma at the level of the A-I junction.

With the discovery of the network of tubules that comprise the sarcoplasmic reticulum, several functional possibilities were advanced. This system might play an important role not only in distributing energy-rich material needed for muscular contraction but also in providing the necessary channels for transmitting impulses along the surface and conveying the action potential from the surface to the myofibrils within.

In a series of experiments it was shown that when microelectrodes were applied to the surfaces of skeletal muscle fibers, they were able to depolarize only an area of sarcolemma a few micrometers in diameter and produce a very localized contraction in the muscle fiber (Huxley and Taylor, 1955, 1958; Huxley, 1957; Peachey, 1965). These sensitive areas were localized in precise register to the striation patterns of the skeletal muscle fibers. Interestingly enough, these sensitive areas are at times different in muscles of various species or may vary from one set of muscles to another within the same species or individual. In the tendinous muscle of the frog the sensitive areas are found only at the I band. Prior to electron microscope studies, evidence suggested that the internal spread of the impulse might be mediated by a thin band, the Z line, which bisects the I band, because it was at these precise locations where the microelectrodes produced localized contractions. On the other hand, in muscles from the crab, an arthropod, and in muscles from the swim bladder of the toadfish (Fawcett and Revel, 1961) the regions about the Z line are insensitive to stimulations. Instead, there are now two sensitive spots per sarcomere that are located at the A band near the A-I junctions. When these fibers are stimulated, half of the I band can be made to contract when microelectrodes are applied at one A-I junction.

Clarification was made when these sensitive areas, which were demonstrated by microelectrode studies, were compared with electron micrographs of similar muscles. In the amphibian muscle the area most sensitive to microelectrode stimulation contains the triad, that is, the terminal cisternae of the sarcoplasmic reticulum and the T system, or transverse tubule system. The transverse tubule coincided with the Z line, which was the area sensitive to depolarization. As was mentioned previously, it was thought that the Z line itself was somehow involved, but it was admirably demonstrated that the Z line was not a continuous membrane across the whole fiber but was limited to each myofibril.

Likewise in muscles of the crab, which are sensitive to microelectrode stimulation near the A-I junction, electron micrographs show a picture similar to that observed in amphibian muscles. At each A-I junction a triad was located, the location of the transverse tubule corresponding to the area sensitive to depolarization. Furthermore, as evidenced by ultrastructural studies of the sarcoplasmic reticulum, the transverse tubule is continuous with the sarcolemma at the surface. It was therefore concluded that the T system was responsible for the inward spread of activation from the depolarized muscle surface. The T system can in a sense represent the inward extension of the impulse-transmitting sarcolemma.

Since the surface area of the T system is at least several times greater than the area of the membrane, it is reasonable to assume that ionic currents might flow between the sarcoplasm and extracellular space by means of the transverse tubules. As a result of depolarization of the sarcolemma, there is a flow of positive current from the sarcolemma through the lateral tubules and along the transverse tublules to the outside of the sarcomere (Freygang, 1965).

A hypothesis of the possible mechanism of excitation-contraction coupling may involve the release of calcium ions stored in the lateral tubules or cisternae of the sarcoplasmic reticulum by electrical impulse. The calcium ion will diffuse across the membrane to the contractable filament to cause muscle contraction by activating the actomyosin ATPase. Relaxation occurs as calcium ions reaccumulate back into the sarcoplasmic reticulum (Winegrad, 1965).

Myeloid body. Another possible modification of the agranular reticulum was observed in the pigment cell of the frog retina (Porter and Yamada, 1960), which appears as stacked membrane structures where function may be involved in controlling pigment migration.

These structures, called myeloid bodies, are about the size of mitochondria and have an angular outline. They have a basophilic staining characteristic and give a positive periodic acid–Schiff (PAS) reaction.

Electron micrographs show that the myeloid body consists of tubules approximately 75 nm in diameter (Figs. 7-4 and 7-8). They appear as stacks of membranes, being somewhat more dense and thicker than the tubules of the ER. The spacings between membrane pairs are rather constant, and the spaces limited by the membranes of the myeloid body are continuous with the cavities or spaces of the ER.

The lamellar units that comprise the myeloid body are flat disks that differ from one

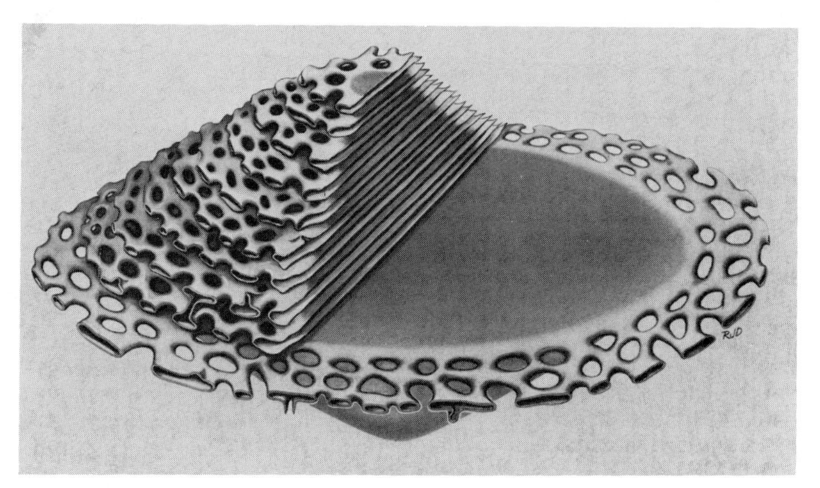

Fig. 7-8. Three-dimensional drawing of myeloid body based on a number of electron micrograph sections comparable to Fig. 7-4. The paired membranes of the lamellar units are thicker than the membranes of the ER. (From Porter, K. R., and E. Yamada. 1960. J. Biophys. Biochem. Cytol. **8:**181-205.)

another by a constant amount. The central disk is the largest, and each successive disk becomes smaller by a uniform amount that ultimately produces a double conical form (Figs. 7-4 and 7-8).

It is not uncommon to find myeloid bodies connected by their convex surfaces to form groups of five or even six. They can also be seen attached to the surface of the nucleus and have been seen associated with lipid bodies.

Nuclear membrane

By tradition the nuclear membrane is considered in the discussion of the nucleus (Chapter 15), where it forms an interface between the nucleoplasm on the inside and the cytoplasm on the outside. Yet ultrastructural studies demonstrate that the nuclear membrane is intimately related to and forms a contiguous part of the ER. Its behavior after cell division also indicates that it is possibly a specialized part of the ER. For this reason the nuclear membrane will be considered along with the cytoplasmic membranes.

Until electron microscopy was used for cytological studies, the concept of the nuclear membrane was that of a single membrane structure, presumably exhibiting selective permeability like its counterpart the cell membrane. Some indications of the possible complexity of the nuclear membrane were made in 1883 by Flemming, who described a clearly visible double-layered membrane. This was later confirmed by Scott (cited by Wischnitzer, 1958) by means of micromanipulation. One of the first electron microscope studies on the observation and description of the double membrane was made by Callan and Tomlin in 1950. Using amphibian oocyte nuclear envelopes that were shadow-cast, they observed and described the double membrane encircling these nuclei. They noticed also discontinuities in the outer membrane. Later, Watson (1955) showed that these discontinuities were really pores in these double membranes (Fig. 7-9).

Ultrastructure. The nuclear membrane, or *nuclear envelope,* appears as a unit of modified ER encircling the nuclear region (Chapter 15). The inner membrane is locally in contact with the chromatin material and as a result, the perinuclear chromatin often condenses along this inner membrane. Although these membranes may be about 75 Å or slightly more in thickness, the membrane bounding the nuclear side appears thicker because of this chromatin condensation. The outer membrane is constantly parallel to the inner membrane and continuous with the membranes of the ER. At times ribosomes can be found attached to the outer membrane of some nuclei and can be considered as part of the granular ER. The *perinuclear space* between the two membranes is somewhat variable but generally averages about 200 to 400 Å wide. In plant cells the perinuclear space ranges from 100 to 250 Å, with an average width of about 140 Å (De, 1957).

In sections through the nuclear envelope discontinuities can be seen in which the inner and outer membranous components unite a U form at their margins to produce pores (Figs. 7-9, 15-3, and 15-5). If there is a condensation of chromatin associated with the inner membrane unit, there is usually a less dense area at the position of the pores. These pores show that a continuity exists between the nucleoplasm and the cytoplasm. Another continuity exists but is not associated with the pore; it is the continuity resulting from direct communication between the cisternae of the ER and the perinuclear space.

In animals the pores consist of circular to oval areas about 500 to 1,000 Å in diameter (Fig. 7-10). In the salivary glands from the larvae of *Chironomus* these pores show a center-to-center spacing that ranges between 800 and 900 Å. Often the pore spaces appear to be plugged with dense granular material that is electron dense and is found in both the inner and outer regions. The granules are approximately 90 Å in diameter (De, 1957). In the sea urchin

(Afzelius, 1955), in addition to a granule or central globule, the space inside the pore also contains what can be described as loose gellike material, which presumably holds the globule or granule in place.

Further observations in the regions of the pores show that they appear to be encircled by rings of rather electron-dense material. These rings, or *annuli,* were observed in a number of animals such as the

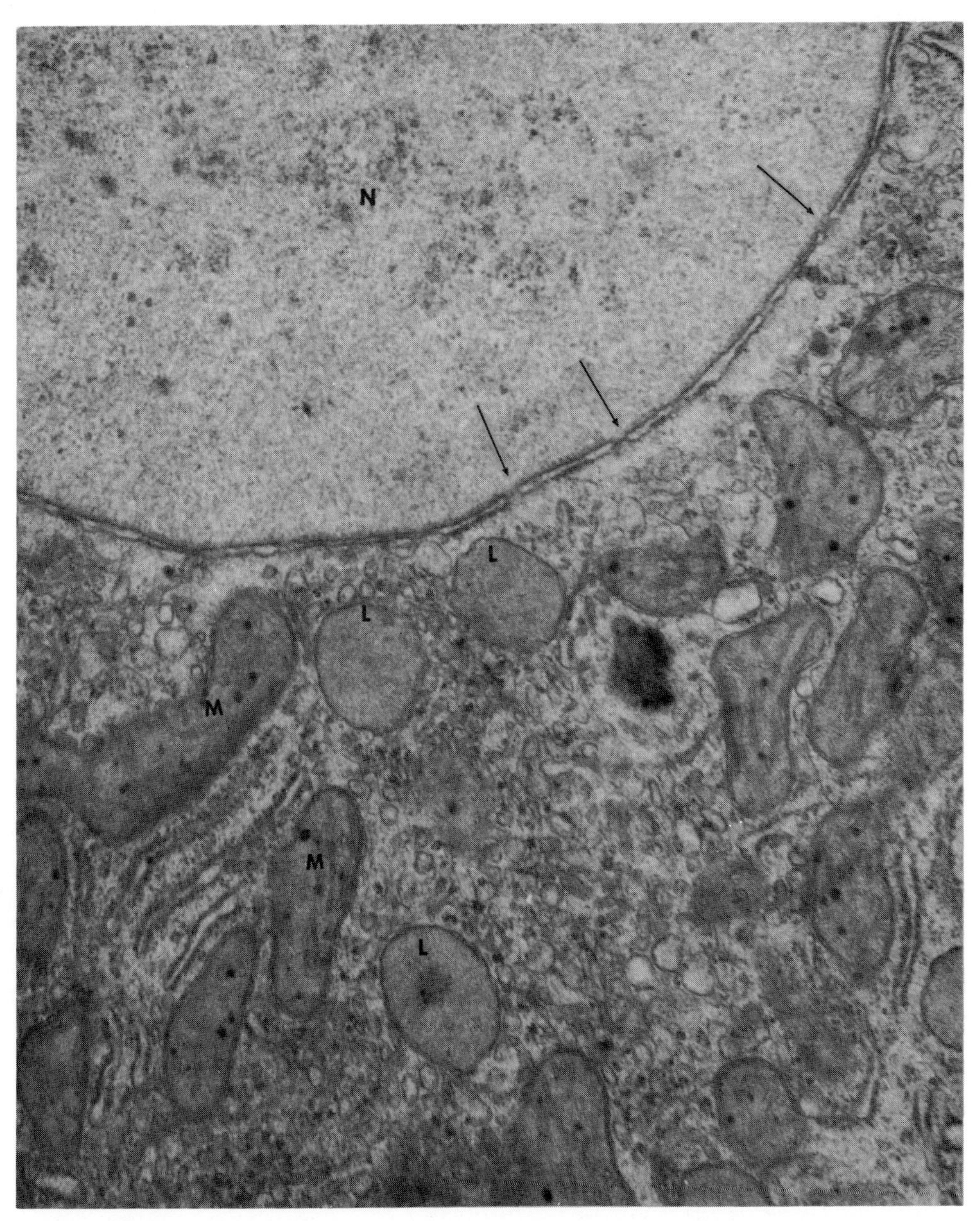

Fig. 7-9. Electron micrograph of rat liver showing presence of nuclear pores (arrows). **M,** Mitochondria; **L,** lysosome; **N,** nucleus. (Courtesy J. Swafford, Arizona State University, Tempe, Ariz.)

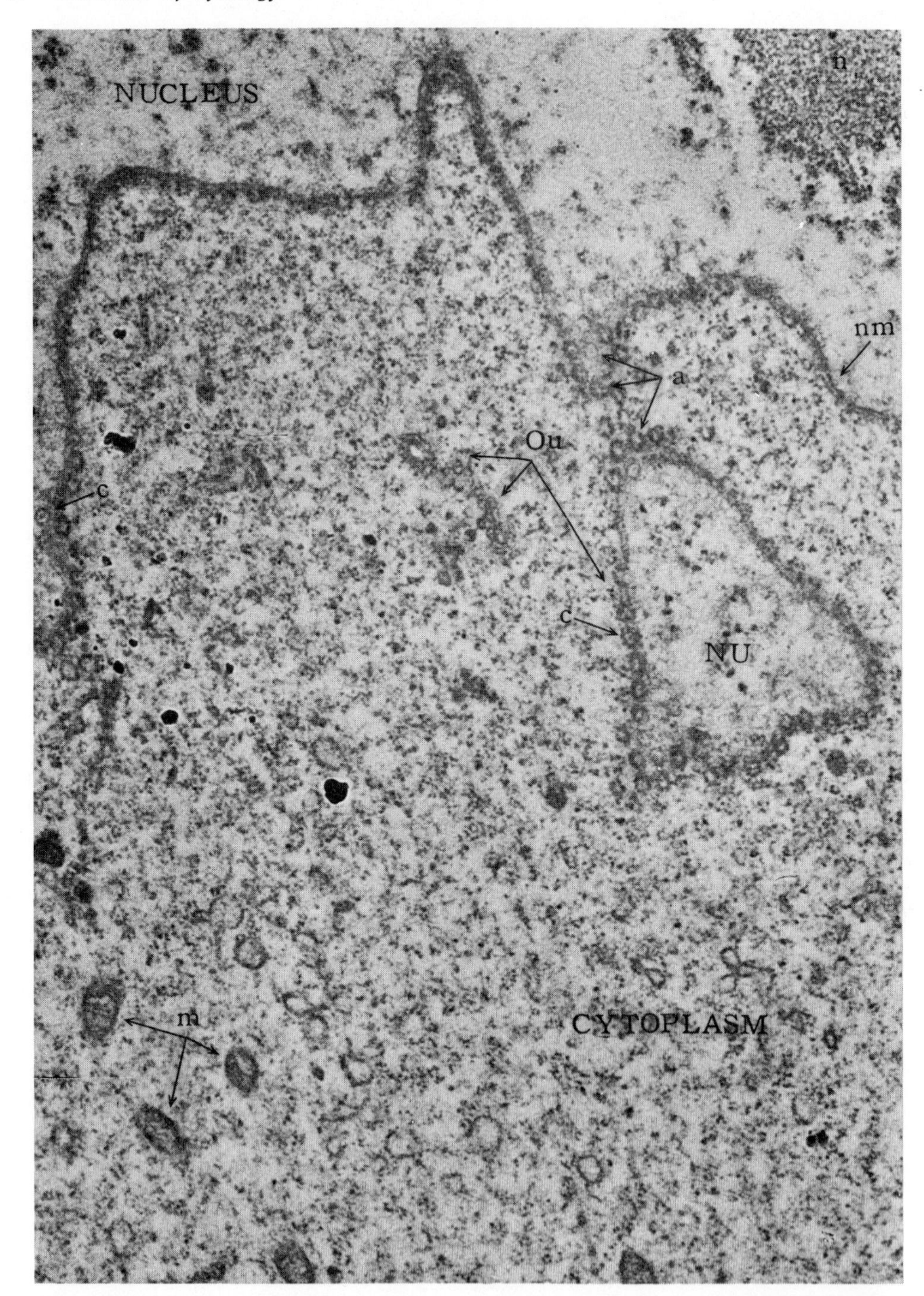

Fig. 7-10. Electron micrograph of nuclear envelope from oocytes of the amphibian *Triturus viridescens* showing a number of annuli, **a,** which can be seen on the nuclear side (upper arrow), at the level of the nuclear envelope (middle arrow), and on the cytoplasmic side (lower arrow). The annulus at **c** appears to contain a central granule. **Ou,** Outpocketing of nuclear envelope due to shrinkage irregularities. **m,** Mitochondria; **n,** nucleolus; **nm,** nuclear membrane; **NU,** nucleus. (From Wischnitzer, S. 1958. J. Ultrastruct. Res. **4:**201-222.)

midgut of *Chironomus* (Bahr and Beerman, 1954) and in oocytes of sea urchins (Afzelius, 1955) and amphibians (Fig. 7-10) (Wischnitzer, 1958).

Within the discontinuities the annuli extend about 600 Å inward on the nuclear side and about 200 Å outward on the cytoplasmic side of the membranes (Afzelius, 1955). In sections from the nuclei of amphibians Wischnitzer observed about the same distance of 600 Å on the nuclear side and on the cytoplasmic side, with some tendencies for deeper projections of the annuli into the nuclear region. The total length of annuli is about 1,500 Å. Afzelius often observed that the pores are covered by a single membrane that is thinner than the other two membranes comprising the nuclear envelope.

In cross section the annuli appear as rings that have diameters corresponding to the diameters of the pores. Within the annuli there are six to eight vague subunits that have an average size of 175 to 225 Å and that consist of a dark rim of 50 Å and a center of 100 Å (Fig. 7-11). These subannuli are visible from micrographs taken at the nuclear and the cytoplasmic surface (Fig. 7-10). In cross section they are termed *microcylinders* and are continuous throughout the length of these annuli (Wischnitzer, 1958).

Afzelius had calculated from his studies that there are about forty to eighty holes or pores per square micrometer. In *Drosophila* the pores appear to be arranged in a roughly hexagonal pattern.

Function. It has been suggested that there are two pathways available for nuclear-cytoplasmic exchange: one would be via the perinuclear space and the second through the pores or at least through the center of the microcylinders. The sizes of the pores, which average 300 to 400 Å, ap-

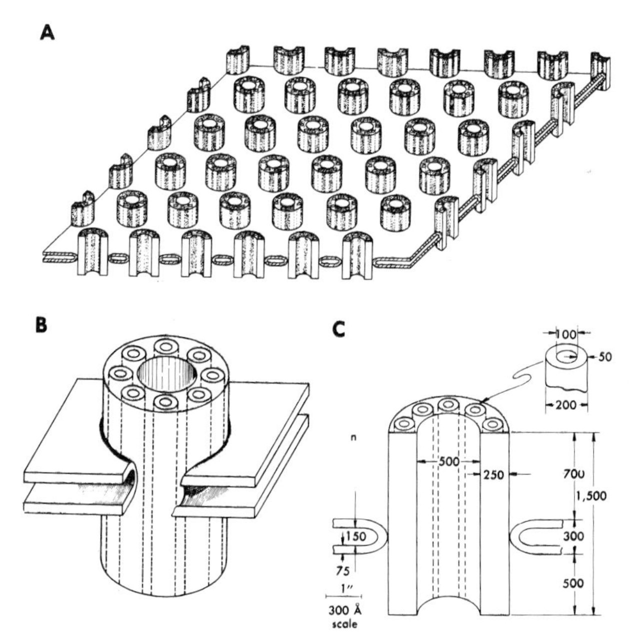

Fig. 7-11. A, Diagrammatic representation of nuclear envelope and pores from oocyte of the amphibian *Triturus viridescens.* The outer nuclear surface is upward. **B,** Detailed diagram of a pore tube or annulus and portion of nuclear envelope. **C,** Dimensions of various components of the tube. See text for description. (From Wischnitzer, S. 1958. J. Ultrastruct. Res. **1**:201-222.)

parently exceed the size of any macromolecule that may assume to pass through by at least 100 Å.

At the present time there is little information as to the role played by the nuclear envelope in selective permeability. It has been shown that the nuclear envelopes of oocytes from *Xenopus* and *Triturus* are highly permeable to ionic flow. On the other hand, the nuclear membranes from *Drosophila* and *Chironomus* larvae offer strong barriers to ion flow (Wiener et al., 1965). It was also shown that the nuclear membranes of cultured renal cells as well as nuclear membranes of hepatic cells obtained by partial hepatectomy show a rise in electrophoretic mobility that occurs early in the DNA presynthetic period (Kishimoto and Lieberman, 1965).

Some insight on the selective permeability and biochemical characteristics of the nuclear envelope may be inferred by utilizing information gleaned from the ER or from the microsomal fraction because, as was stated previously, the nuclear membrane can be considered part of the ER system.

The localization of the enzyme glucose-6-phosphatase in or on the nuclear membrane may indicate both a morphological as well as a functional relationship with the ER (Tice and Barrnett, 1962).

• • •

With the discovery of a system of membranes permeating the cytoplasm, the cytoplasm could no longer be considered a single-phase system. Instead, these membrane-bound tubules convert the cytoplasm into a multiphasic system (Porter, 1961b; Moulé, 1963). Porter considered that the ER produces a three-phase system, whereas Moulé believed it to consist of two phases. According to Porter, the three phases include (1) the spaces within the limiting membranes of the ER, (2) the limiting membrane per se, and (3) the external cytoplasm. It is possible to add a fourth phase or at least a partial phase system, the aqueous phase, particularly on the cytoplasmic side of the membrane, which is produced by orientation and binding of water molecules by the hydrophilic moieties of the membrane. From a physicochemical point of view phase boundaries represent active surfaces.

According to biochemical studies, the membranes probably represent one of the most important entities of the cell. They are important (1) for active transport, (2) as a diffusion barrier, (3) as an ionic gradient, and (4) for bioelectric potential. Furthermore, these membranes contain enzyme systems that are either structured into the molecular configuration of the membranes or bound tightly to them.

The membrane of the ER is about the same thickness and composition as the plasma membrane. It is composed of lipoproteins in which the lipid moieties are sandwiched between the two protein layers. This, of course, follows the basic molecular configuration of the unit membrane concept as proposed by Robertson. To this configuration one can superimpose the pillar concept of Kavanau and the hexagonal protein configuration proposed by Warner to help explain the dynamic nature of this membrane system (Chapter 6).

Noticeably lacking is specific information on or evidence of pores. However, since these membranes act as diffusion barriers coupled with ion transport, it is possible that extremely minute molecular pores do exist which are comparable to those proposed for the plasma membrane.

Most if not all of the biochemical studies of the ER are based on information derived from the microsomal fraction obtained by ultracentrifugation of the cytoplasmic fraction.

Microsomes

Microsomes can be described as components of the high-speed pellet that is spun down after the mitochondrial fraction has been separated. They were in the supernatant fluid after mitochondrial sedimentation. Generally in this preparation the force used is 25,000 to 100,000 *g* for 60 to 120 minutes (Siekevitz, 1965). The morphological nature of this fraction is not constant but depends on the nature of the cells from which it was derived. From liver one can expect to obtain membranes that contain attached ribosomes as well as remnants of membrane without ribosomes. These latter membranes enclose a vesicular space. On the other hand, the microsomal fraction obtained from pancreatic cells shows oval to circular profiles of about 80 to 300 nm diameter (Palade and Siekevitz, 1956). In general, there is more flattened appearance, which is probably due to the more parallel arrangement of the cisternae. Microsomes obtained from the pancreas are more homogeneous than those of the liver, and there is probably more fragmentation in the pancreas than in the liver. Most of the membrane fragments contain ribosomes attached to their surfaces. These membrane-bounded vesicles may contain material of appreciable density within. At times these vesicles may appear from partly full to empty. Smooth membrane-bounded vesicles are rare. It has been postulated that as far as the pancreas is concerned, and presumably this may occur in other cells, the vesicles obtained are probably due less to fragmentation as to pinching off of the vacuolar system (Palade and Siekevitz, 1956). The microsome fraction from muscle contains smooth membranes as well as free ribosomes. From the reticulocytes the microsome fraction may contain only ribosomes (Sievkevitz, 1965).

Since the microsomal fraction contains membranes as well as ribosomes attached to them, a detergent such as sodium deoxycholate generally acts on the membrane system by solubilizing them to thus release the ribosomes. Both can be used for further biochemical studies. The morphology and functions of the ribosome will be discussed in Chapter 9. In addition to the lipids and proteins comprising the molecular structure of the ER membranes, further chemical studies of the microsomal fraction show that RNA is also present in a significant amount (Chaveau et al., 1958). It was first believed that the RNA present in the analysis of the microsomal membranes may have been due to ribosomal contamination. However, comparison of the chemical analysis of the RNA found in the membrane with the RNA in the ribosome showed that membrane RNA has a significantly higher amount of guanylic acid than does either ribosomal or soluble RNA (tRNA). Its role in the structure of the ER is somewhat obscure, but Moulé (1963) suggested that the membrane RNA may serve as a device to anchor or attach the ribosomes to the membrane. It is also tempting to speculate that it may also play a role in membrane replication.

Microsomal studies have shown that numerous enzyme systems are present within the structure of the membranes. One group of enzyme systems found is that involved in the electron transport system (such a system is also present in the mitochondria —see Chapter 10 for comparison). These include the NAD and NADP-linked systems, which have been found in all microsomal fractions thus far tested in animal and plant tissues. It appears that this electron transport system is distinct from that found in mitochondria, since it contains a cytochrome b_5 not found in mitochondria as well as another heme protein, the CO-binding pigment, also not found in mitochondria (Siekevitz, 1965). Kinetic studies have shown that the flow of electrons is about the same as in mitochondria. Also present and associated with the ER are the mixed-function oxidases (Mason et al., 1965), which represent a large class of enzymes. They are found throughout the animal kingdom and can be divided into two groups: the internal mixed-function oxidases and the external mixed-function oxidases. Functionally, these mixed-function oxidases are active in the metabolism of lipids and steroids as well as compounds foreign to the metabolic network (Mason et al., 1965). Within the group are enzymes functional in the metabolism of carcinogenic agents and drugs.

In addition to those enzymes, esterase and sulfatases have been identified as being part of the enzyme system associated with the microsomal fraction. Likewise, cholinesterase has been found in the microsomal fraction from brain cells, which shows enzymatic properties that differ slightly from cholinesterase obtained from whole brain tissue (Toschi, 1959; Hanzon and Toschi, 1959).

Although the ribosomes are the sites for protein synthesis, the membranes associated with the ribosomes may also play an important role in the overall synthesis of some proteins. It has been shown that carbohydrate-containing proteins such as prothrombin are found in the microsomal fraction of the liver. It is suggested that protein synthesis takes place on the ribosome but that the ER may function in conjugating the protein moiety to the carbohydrates (Helgeland, 1965).

Origin of endoplasmic reticulum

Various studies have indicated that the cytoplasmic ER may be derived from the nuclear envelope. Gay (1956), in a series of studies, had described bleb formations arising from the nuclear envelope and extending into the cytoplasm. These outgrowths could become detached from the nuclear envelope and change into flattened saclike membranes. The cytoplasmic ER is derived from replication, as in the formation of annulate lamellae. Interestingly enough, the contact relationship existing between the inner membrane of the nuclear envelope and the chromosome of the nucleus suggested that these outgrowths from the outer nuclear membrane are replications of the nuclear envelope, thereby providing a means of transferring genetic material into the cytoplasm. Since ER is always present in cells, perhaps ER comes from ER.

Valuable as this hypothesis may be in describing the possible origin of the ER from the nuclear envelope, particularly in undifferentiated cells, it does not give an insight as to its behavior during cell division. Present knowledge of the behavior of the nuclear envelope was obtained mostly from studying mitosis in cells of onion root tips (Porter and Machado, 1960). Although this study was done with plant tissue, presumably the same events occur in animal tissues as well (Chapter 17).

During the later stage of prophase, the nuclear membrane breaks down into fragments. These remnants and the cytoplasmic ER, which is morphologically very similar, surround the spindle in a region from which the mitochondria and proplastids are excluded. During the metaphase stage of mitosis these elements possibly persist, migrate, and become concentrated near the poles of the spindles. The ER belonging to the cytoplasm remains outside the spindle. From the two polar regions of the cell, elements of the ER begin proliferation in which extensions grow into the spindle area and into the regions between the chromosomes, which at this time are grouped at the poles. By the end of anaphase and during telophase, some cytologists believe that some of the units of the ER fuse to the chromosomes to form the nuclear envelope so that by the end of telophase the nuclear membrane is complete (Fig. 17-17). Occasionally, pieces of ER appear to be trapped within the developing daughter nuclei.

The ER that lies outside the spindle and that did not appear to participate in the mitotic process ultimately becomes distributed fairly equally between the daughter cells.

A more detailed account of the events leading to the reconstruction of the nuclear membrane is by Barer et al. (1959). They observed vesicles comparable to the ER appearing around and between the mitochondria. These vesicular elements nearest to the chromosomes are randomly arranged at first, but later they become lined up along the chromosomal surfaces as though they are pressed onto them. Each of the chromosomes is partially surrounded by the vesicular elements at first. These elements that lie on or are pressed onto the chromosomes increase in length, presumably by fusion, until the nuclear membrane is completed. Finally the nuclear membrane is partially separated from the chromosomes. This process of separation may be due to the accumulation of the nucleoplasm. Although the nuclear envelope may form from ER, in all probability the ER, which is always present in a cell, can increase itself.

Endoplasmic reticulum and its relation to cell differentiation

An interesting relationship exists between the development of the ER and cell differentiation. For example, in a fully differentiated cell such as occurs in the pancreas and parotid gland the ER is well developed. On the other hand, animal cells that are not significantly specialized either morphologically or physiologically do not have a well-developed ER system. This can be seen in cells obtained from the crypts of the intestinal tract, sebaceous glands (Palade, 1955a), and spermatocytes. Furthermore, examination of embryonic tissue shows the ER to consist of a few scattered vesicles in the cytoplasm. Porter (1961b) suggested that the cell as it forms its own surface configuration and distribution of organelles is greatly influenced by the patterns of the ER.

There have been a number of electron microscope studies of the behavior of cells during the process of differentiation. Slautterback and Fawcett (1959) studied the development of the cnidoblast of *Hydra,* which is a primitive form of animal in the phylum Cnidaria. These cnidoblasts are important in the production of nematocysts, which are the stinging devices used by the coelenterate animal to paralyze and kill its prey. In the early stage of differentiation of the cnidoblast there are numerous isolated vesicles in the cytoplasm. Later the vesicles increase in number, elongate, and coalesce to form a more or less continuous system. At this time the beginning of the attachment of ribosomes to this membrane system can be seen. In the more advanced state the profiles are much enlarged, with subsequent development in broad, flat cisternae. The ER becomes arranged into parallel arrays. Electron-lucent material is often observed in the lumen of this ER system. At that time also the Golgi complex enlarges, and there appears to be a continuity between the membranes of the ER and the Golgi complex. Continuity probably allows for coordination of function of these two organelles as well as the transfer of synthesized material from the ER to the Golgi complex. As the nematocyst matures, there is a regression of the Golgi complex and the ER becomes broken up into isolated vesicles with ribosomes adhering to them.

Waddington and Perry (1962) studied the development of the notochord of the urodele. In the very early stage of development the notochordal cells are almost devoid of formed cytoplasmic structures. Occasionally, some Golgi elements and a few double membranes of the ER are visible as well as the nuclear envelope. One of the first changes observed is the formation of fluid-filled vacuoles formed by cavities resulting from the lifting away of the outer nuclear membrane from the inner membrane. Concomitantly, near the nucleus a series of flattened cisternae appear that seem to be derived by a peeling-off process from the nucleus. With continued development of the membrane system of the ER the cells comprising the notochordal tissue become filled by these membranes, with ribosomes becoming attached to them. The cisternae appear to be continuous with the fluid-filled vacuoles. The cells comprising the outer surface, which forms the sheath, develop a second ER system. This ER is abundant and contains ribosomes. The cisternae contain electron-dense material. At this time also the Golgi complex consists of numerous elements.

In the study of the ultrastructure of the

developing eye of *Drosophila* (Waddington, 1960) similar changes were noted. The undifferentiated cells showed little in the way of formed elements within the cytoplasm. Later, as differentiation occurred, the ER began to appear as undulating double profiles with ribosomes attached to their outer surface. These membranes showed continuity with the nuclear envelope.

In retrospect, embryonic cells are characterized by a paucity of ER within the cytoplasm. The ribosomes, scattered about the cyptoplasm, presumably function in protein synthesis. As differentiation ensues, cytoplasmic membranes increase in number and complexity. The ribosomes that were free in the cytoplasm become attached to these membranes. It is difficult at this time to determine whether these developing cytoplasmic membranes persist in the next generation of the cell. Evidence does suggest the possibility, however, that with each cell division some or a completely new ER is formed which persists and functions during that interphase only to be replaced wholly or in part by a slightly different ER in the successive generation. These changes continue until the form characteristic of the postmitotic differentiated cell is achieved (Porter, 1961b).

Knowledge of the role played by the ER in cellular differentiation is by no means clear. To be sure, fundamental differentiation is brought about by the interaction between the gene and the cytoplasm. Yet a significant intermediary role in the overall process of differentiation may be played by the ER. In the early embryonic stage the nuclear membrane can be considered to act as a barrier, but as the ER develops, possibly from the nuclear envelope, this structure may act as a pathway between the nucleus and the cytoplasm for passage of products of gene action. This information passed from gene to ribosomes may not be exclusively by means of the soluble polynucleotide, but perhaps it is in some way facilitated by the structure of the ER (Waddington, 1962). Furthermore, the ER may be concerned not with single genes and the ribosomes but may somehow be involved with the coordination of numerous gene activities that may be progressing in an organized fashion for greater efficiency of the biosynthetic mechanism.

Evolution of cell membranes

It is tempting to speculate on the evolution of the cell membranes such as the plasma membranes and the membranes of the ER as well as the nuclear envelope. All these membranes are essentially similar in molecular configuration. The nuclear envelope is continuous with the ER and at times connected through the ER with the plasma membrane. In a sense all three can be considered to be continuous. Robertson (1962) conceived the evolution of membranes as though at one time a simple primordial organism existed in which a unit membrane bounded protoplasmic material. This protoplasmic material pushed outward to form pseudopodia. Later these evaginated membranes began to fold back on themselves so as to produce the nuclear membrane as well as a simple and primitive ER. Further development of the ER resulted in increased configuration to produce the ER system as seen in a fully differentiated cell.

LITERATURE CITED

Afzelius, B. A. 1955. The ultrastructure of the nuclear membrane of the sea urchin oocyte as studied with the electron microscope. Exp. Cell Res. **8:**147-158.

Bahr, G. F., and W. Beerman. 1954. The fine structure of the nuclear membrane in the larval salivary gland and midgut of Chironomus. Exp. Cell Res. **6:**519-522.

Barer, R., S. Joseph, and G. A. Meek. 1959. The origin of the nuclear membrane. Exp. Cell Res. **18:**179-182.

Chaveau, J., Y. Moulé, and C. Rouillier. 1958. Localisation de l'acide ribonucléique dans les diverse structures morphologiques des microsomes de foie de rat. Exp. Cell Res. **13:**398-400.

Christensen, A. K., and D. W. Fawcett. 1960. Fine structure of testicular interstitial cells in the oppossum. Anat. Rec. **136:**333.

Christensen, A. K., and D. W. Fawcett. 1961. The

normal fine structure of opossum testicular interstitial cell. J. Biophys. Biochem. Cytol. **9:** 653-670.

Datta Munshi, J. S. 1964. Chloride cells in the gills of fresh-water teleosts. Quart. J. Micr. Sci. **105:**79-87.

De, D. N. 1957. Ultrastructure of nuclear membranes of plant cells. Exp. Cell Res. **12:**181-184.

Eriksson, L. C., and G. Dallner. 1972. Membrane biogenesis and rough microsomal subfractions. J. Cell Biol. **55:**70A.

Fawcett, D. W. 1955. Observations on the cytology and electron microscopy of hepatic cells. J. Nat. Cancer Inst. **15**(supp.)**:** 1475-1502.

Fawcett, D. W. 1961. The membranes of the cytoplasm. Lab. Invest. **10:**1162-1188.

Fawcett, D. W., and J. P. Revel. 1961. The sarcoplasmic reticulum of a fast acting fish muscle. J. Biophys. Biochem. Cytol. **10:**89-94.

Freygang, W. H. 1965. Tubular ionic movement. Fed. Proc. **24:**1135-1140.

Gay, H. 1956. Nucleocytoplasmic relation in Drosophila. Cold Spring Harb. Symp. Quant. Biol. **21:**256-269.

Grunbaum, B. W., and S. R. Wellings. 1960. Electron microscopy of cytoplasmic structures in frozen-dried mouse pancreas. J. Ultrastruct. Res. **4:**73-80.

Haguenau, F. 1958. The ergastroplasm: its history, ultrastructure, and biochemistry. Int. Rev. Cytol. **7:**425-482.

Hanzon, V., and G. Toschi. 1959. Electron microscopy of microsomal fractions from the rat brain. Exp. Cell Res. **16:**256-271.

Helender, H. F. 1964. Ultrastructure of secreting cells in the pyloric gland area of the mouse gastric mucosa. J. Ultrastruct. Res. **10:**145-159.

Helgeland, L. 1965. Incorporation of radioactive glucosamine into submicrosomal fraction isolated from rat liver. Biochim. Biophys. Acta **101:**106-112.

Huxley, A. F. 1957. Local activation of striate muscle from the frog and the crab. J. Physiol. (London) **135:**17P-18P.

Huxley, A. F., and R. E. Taylor. 1955. The function of Krause's membrane. Nature (London) **176:**1068.

Huxley, A. F., and R. E. Taylor. 1958. Local activation of striate muscle fibers. J. Physiol. (London) **144:**426-441.

Ito, S. 1962. Light and electron microscopic study of membraneous cytoplasmic organelles. In R. J. C. Harris (editor). Interpretation of ultrastructure. Vol. 1. Academic Press, Inc., New York.

Kishimoto, S., and I. Lieberman. 1965. Nuclear membranes of cultured mammalian cells in the period preceding DNA synthesis. J. Cell Biol. **25:**103-107.

Mason, H. S., J. C. North, and M. Vanneste. 1965. Microsomal mixed function oxidations: The metabolism of xenobiotics. Fed. Proc. **24:** 1172-1180.

Moulé, Y. 1963. Endoplasmic reticulum and microsomes of rat liver. In M. Locke (editor). Cellular membranes in development. Academic Press, Inc., New York.

Palade, G. E. 1955a. Studies on the endoplasmic reticulum. II. Simple disposition in cells in situ. J. Biophys. Biochem. Cytol. **1:**567-582.

Palade, G. E. 1955b. A small particulate component of the cytoplasm. J. Biophys. Biochem. Cytol. **1:**59-67.

Palade, G. E., and K. R. Porter. 1954. Studies on the endoplasmic reticulum. I. Its identification in situ. J. Exp. Med. **100:**641-656.

Palade, G. E., and P. Siekevitz. 1956. Pancreatic microsomes. An integrated morphological and biochemical study. J. Biophys. Biochem. Cytol. **2:**671-690.

Palay, S. L. 1953. Fine structures of neuronal cytoplasm. J. Appl. Physics **34:**1419.

Palay, S. L., and G. E. Palade. 1955. Fine structures of neurons. J. Biophys. Biochem. Cytol. **1:**68-88.

Parakkal, P. F., and A. F. Matoltsy. 1964. The fine structure of lipid droplets in the meibomian gland of the mouse. J. Ultrastruct. Res. **10:**417-421.

Peachey, L. D. 1965. The sarcoplasmic reticulum and transverse tubules of the frog's sartorius muscle. J. Cell Biol. **25:**209-233.

Peters, V. B., H. M. Dembitzer, G. W. Kelly, and E. Baruch. 1962. Endoplasmic changes associated with glycogenolysis. Proc. 5th Int. Congr. Electron Microscopy **2:**TT-7.

Porter, K. R., A. Claude, and E. F. Fullam. 1945. A study of tissue culture cells by electron microscopy. J. Exp. Med. **81:**233-245.

Porter, K. R. 1953. Observations on a submicroscopic basophilic component of cytoplasm. J. Exp. Med. **97:**727-751.

Porter, K. R. 1954. Electron microscopy of basophilic components of cytoplasm. J. Histochem. Cytochem. **2:**346-355.

Porter, K. R. 1961a. The sarcoplasmic reticulum: its recent history and present status. J. Biophys. Biochem. Cytol. **10:**219-225.

Porter, K. R. 1961b. The ground substance in the cell. In J. Bracket and B. Mirsky (editors). The cell. Vol. 2. Academic Press, Inc., New York.

Porter, K. R., and G. E. Palade. 1957. Studies of the endoplasmic reticulum. III. Its form and distribution in striate muscle. J. Biophys. Biochem. Cytol. **3:**269-300.

Porter, K. R. 1957. The submicroscopic morphology of protoplasm. Harvey Lect. **51:**175-225.

Porter, K. R., and C. Bruni. 1959. An electron microscope study of the early effects of 3′-Me-DAB on rat liver cells. Cancer Res. **19:**997-1009.

Porter, K. R., and E. Yamada. 1960. Studies on the endoplasmic reticulum. V. Its form and differentiation in pigment epithelial cells of the frog retina. J. Biophys. Biochem. Cytol. **8:** 181-205.

Porter, K. R., and R. D. Machado. 1960. Studies on the endoplasmic reticulum. IV. Its form and distribution during mitosis in cells of onion tip. J. Biophys. Biochem. Cytol. **7:**167-180.

Robertson, J. D. 1962. The membrane of the living cell. Sci. Amer. **206:**65-72.

Siekevitz, P. 1965. Origin and functional nature of microsomes. Fed. Proc. **24:**1153-1163.

Slautterback, D. B., and D. W. Fawcett. 1959. The development of the cnidoblast of *Hydra*. An electron microscopic study of cell differentiation. J. Biophys. Biochem. Cytol. **5:**414-452.

Threadgold, L. T., and A. H. Houston. 1964. An electron microscope study of the chloride cell of Salmo solar L. Exp. Cell Res. **34:**1-23.

Tice, L. W., and R. J. Barrnett. 1962. The fine structural localization of glucose-6-phosphate in rat liver. J. Histochem. Cytochem. **10:**754-762.

Toschi, G. 1959. A biochemical study of brain microsomes. Exp. Cell Res. **16:**232-255.

Waddington, C. H. 1960. The ultrastructure of the developing eye of Drosophila. Proc. Roy. Soc. [Biol.] **153:**155-178.

Waddington, C. H. 1962. Specificity of ultrastructure in developing cells and its genetic control. J. Cell. Comp. Physiol. **60**(supp.):93-105.

Waddington, C. H., and M. M. Perry. 1962. The ultrastructure of the developing urodele notochord. Proc. Roy. Soc. [Biol.] **156:**459-482.

Walker, S. M., and Schrodt, G. R. 1965. Continuity of the T system with the sarcolemma in rat skeletal muscle. J. Cell Biol. **27:**671-677.

Watson, M. L. 1955. The nuclear envelope. Its structure and relation to cytoplasmic membranes. J. Biophys. Biochem. Cytol. **1:**257-270.

Weiss, J. M. 1953. The ergastoplasm. Its structure and relation to protein synthesis as studied with the electron microscope in the pancreas of the Swiss albino mouse. J. Exp. Med. **98:**607-618.

Wiener, J., D. Spiro, and W. R. Loewenstein. 1965. Ultrastructure and permeability of nuclear membranes. J. Cell Biol. **27:**107-117.

Winegard, S. 1965. Role of intracellular movements in the excitation-contraction coupling in skeletal muscle. Fed. Proc. **24:**1146-1155.

Wischnitzer, S. 1958. An electron microscope study of the nuclear envelope of amphibian oocytes. J. Ultrastruct. Res. **1:**201-222.

GENERAL REFERENCES

Bessis, M., and J. Breton-Gorius. 1957. Accumulation de granules ferrugineux dan les mitochondries des erythroblastes. C. R. Acad. Sci. (Paris) **244:**2846-2847.

Boell, E. J., and R. Webber. 1955. Cytochrome oxidase activity in mitochondria during amphibian development. Exp. Cell Res. **9:**559-567.

Brodie, B. B., J. Axelrod, J. R. Cooper, L. Gaudette, B. N. La Du, Metoma, and S. Udenfriend. 1955. Detoxification of drugs and other foreign compounds in liver microsomes. Science **121:**603-604.

Carasso, N., and P. Favard. 1958. L'origine des plaquettes vitellines l'oeuf de planorbe. C. R. Acad. Sci. (Paris) **246:**1594-1597.

Claude, A. 1946. Fractionation of mammalian liver cells by differential centrifugation. I. Problems, methods and extract. J. Exp. Med. **84:** 51-59.

Coupland, R. E. 1965. Electron microscopy on the structure of the rat adrenal medulla. J. Anat. **99:**231-254.

Epstein, M. A. 1957. The fine structural organization of Rous tumour. J. Biophys. Biochem. Cytol. **3:**851-858.

Fitz-James, P. 1964. The fate of mesosomes of Bacillus megaterium during protoplasting. J. Bact. **87:**1483-1491.

Fletcher, M. J., and D. R. Sandi. 1961. Turnover of rat liver mitochondria. Biochim. Biophys. Acta **51:**356-360.

Parks, H. F. 1961. On the fine structure of the parotid gland of mouse and rat. Amer. J. Anat. **108:**303-329.

Peachey, L. D. 1962. Accumulation of divalent ions in mitochondrial granules of intact cells. Proc. 5th Int. Congr. Electron Microscopy **2:** 003-004.

Tedeschi, H., and D. L. Harris. 1958. Some observations on the photometric estimation of mitochondrial volume. Biochim. Biophys. Acta **28:**392-402.

Yamamoto, M. 1965. Intracisternal granules of the endoplasmic reticulum in the periblast of the fish egg. Exp. Cell Res. **40:**655-657.

Yoshida, Y. 1964. Glycogen formation in the cytotrophoblast of human placenta in early pregnancy as revealed by electron microscopy. Exp. Cell Res. **34:**293-304.

CHAPTER 8

Golgi apparatus

In 1898 Camillo Golgi revealed the presence of the *apparate recticulare interne* in the Purkinje cells from the cerebellar cortex of the barn owl. This "structure," which became known as the Golgi apparatus, consists of an argentophilic network that surrounds the nuclei of these cells. Despite the speculations that were raised as to the possible function of this newly described structure, most of the early work was primarily involved with descriptive morphology and attempts to demonstrate this new structure in other cells. As more and more information became available, doubts were expressed by many who maintained that the Golgi apparatus was an artifact rather than a true structure. Part of this doubt was derived from the fact, and with good reason in some instances, that almost anything that was capable of reducing silver salts was termed the Golgi apparatus. Also, it was found that the Golgi apparatus did not always surround the nucleus as Golgi had observed, but intead the silver-reducing region formed what could be described as a spheroidal mass, often located in the supranuclear position. Others contended it was an artifact, the result of fixatives used that were harsh in action and many of which contained solvents that produced a network of fibers or altered the "older" structures through dissolution or fragmentation. In fact, in the 1940s the structure that was referred to as the Golgi apparatus was considered very generally to be merely an artifact, the network probably representing a postmortem liberation of myelin. This, biologists contended, was due either to slow fixation or to unequal rates of penetration of the fixatives used, either of which would be capable of liberating myelin to form the figures that were described as the Golgi substance.

The pleomorphic configurations that were observed also contributed to the concept of the Golgi apparatus as an artifact. There seemed to be a wide range of sizes and shapes of the network, with no apparent morphological consistency.

By the 1920s, despite the arguments for or against the nature of the network, work was undertaken to establish a relationship between the structure and its function. In 1924 Parat and Painleve introduced the "vacuome theory" in a series of papers. This theory disagreed with the original concept of the Golgi apparatus that the network was a true structure. Instead, these investigators contended that the Golgi apparatus in the living system consisted of vacuoles or droplets that could be stained with neutral red or methylene blue. In fact, Haguenau and Bernhard (1955) contended that the Golgi net was the artifact that was created during the process of fixation and subsequent impregnation with metals such as silver or osmium.

It is interesting to note also at this time

that although the Golgi apparatus was thought to be an artifact, the dictyosome was considered a true structure. This was possibly because of the following reasons:

1. The dictyosome could be seen in living sections, whereas the Golgi apparatus as found in the vertebrates was not visible.
2. The dictyosome could be seen in stained sections with the use of the more conventional stains, whereas the Golgi apparatus could be seen only with the more special staining techniques using silver salts or osmium.

It was not until the late 1920s that Bowen was able to show a similarity between the dictyosome as typically seen in the invertebrates and the Golgi apparatus in vertebrates.

Whether plant cells ever have a Golgi apparatus was debated pro and con until electron microscopy settled the argument in favor of its ubiquitous presence.

Most of the subsequent interpretations of the Golgi complex followed the concept of the "vacuome theory" as proposed by Parat and Painleve. Baker (1950) showed that the spheres were composed of lipids and phospholipids and proposed the term "lipochondria" for these spheres. Montagna (1950) suggested that these sudanophilic spherules mark in some way the activity of the Golgi bodies. Worley (1951) was able to recover the Golgi apparatus from homogenates. However, he believed that the networks obtained were artificially produced by the stain that he used. He also concluded that the Golgi network was artificially produced, and therefore the Golgi network was not a natural feature within the living cell. Xeros (1951) showed a functional relationship between the lipochondrial vesicles and zymogen formation and concluded that these lipid globules (lipochondria) found within the Golgi zone are the Golgi bodies seen in living cells. Gatenby (1951) observed the Golgi network as a canalicular and subspheroidal system. He quoted Thomas as believing that the network appearance of the Golgi apparatus was due to an artificial entanglement of elongated mitochondria with "Baker's bodies" or vesicles.

It was not until the advent of phase and electron microscopy that the Golgi apparatus was established with certainty as a ubiquitous cytoplasmic entity. Also contributing to knowledge of the existence of the Golgi apparatus was the use of the freeze-dry technique.

In retrospect, Hibbard (1945) noted in a review article that between 1898 and 1945 there were several thousand articles written about the Golgi apparatus. In view of this, coupled with a myriad of names applied to what was seen, it is no wonder confusion existed. Hirsch (1939) listed approximately 150 names given to this "structure," some of which are *Golgi body dictyosomes, Golgi, Golgi dictyosomes, lipochondria,* and *Baker's bodies.* Dictyosome commonly refers to individual Golgi associations found in the invertebrate animals and plants and the Golgi apparatus to those found in vertebrates. Among botanists the term "dictyosome" refers to a single association of cisternae and the Golgi apparatus to the sum total of the dictyosomes of a single cell. The distribution can be considered to be universal throughout the eukaryotic animal and plant kingdoms.

Morphology

Light microscopy, using such techniques as De Fano's silver or Kopisch's osmium method for the demonstration of the Golgi apparatus in certain mammalian cells, showed that a reticulate structure is present in the supranuclear position somewhere between the nucleus and the distal surface (Figs. 8-1 and 8-2). In the past and to some extent at the present time many investigators have used the Golgi morphology and its pleomorphism as an index for cell activity. The Golgi configurations have been used as an indication of a phagocytic response as well as an estimation of the cellular function of some secretory glands (the thyroid, for example). More will be said later in the section on the function of the Golgi complex.

Electron microscopy

Electron microscopic studies have shown the Golgi complex to be composed of about three types of membrane-bounded units (Fig. 8-3). The most characteristic of these assemblages are the closely packed parallel cisternae. They consist of paired parallel membranes, each of which is about 60 Å in thickness. At the edges of these cisternae the two adjacent membranes fuse to enclose a cavity about 100 to 150 Å in width. Usually there are four to eight or more of these profiles spaced approximately 250 to 300 Å apart. These multilayered profiles have a somewhat curved appearance; at times they may appear oval, surrounding a central vacuolar region. According to the numerous descriptions made of this organelle, there appears to be no communication between adjacent cisternae. In comparing the cisternae of the Golgi complex to those of the ER, the cisternae of the Golgi network are narrower.

Associated with the multilayered arrays of cisternae are numerous small vesicles that range in size from approximately 400 to 800 Å. These small vesicles are clustered about the edges of the cisternae as well as along the outer surfaces. The inner cisternae and larger vacuoles close by may contain a homogeneous material of low to moderate density. This material is presumed to be a secretory product that is in the process of being concentrated or modified. All these membrane-bounded elements are embedded in a homogeneous ground substance that is called the *Golgi ground substance.* The parallel membranes are the sites of metal deposits and can be referred to as the *Golgi externum,* whereas the vacuolar region is called the *Golgi internum.* These terms were first used by Hirsch (1939) in referring to the Golgi apparatus as seen with the light microscope. The membrane-bounded units of the Golgi externum are of the smooth type; they do not contain ribosomal par-

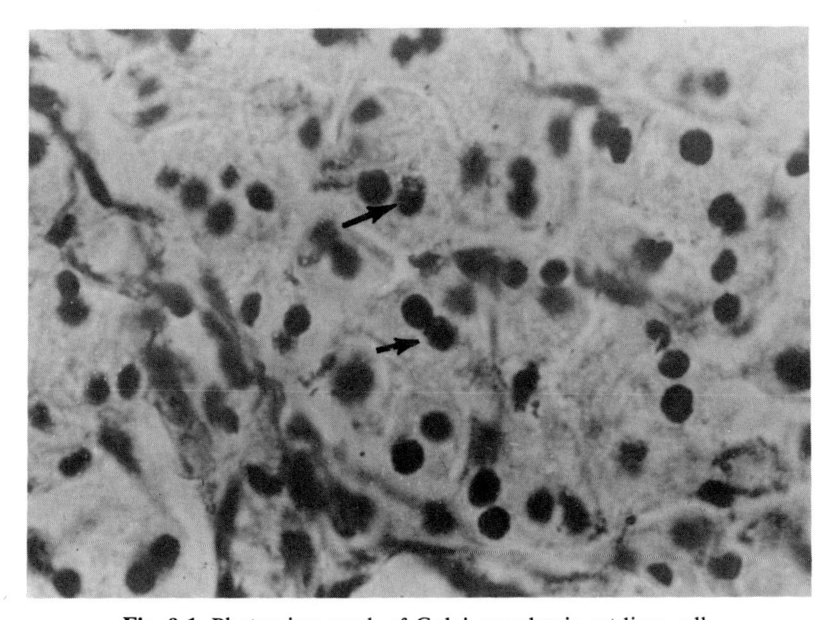

Fig. 8-1. Photomicrograph of Golgi complex in rat liver cell.

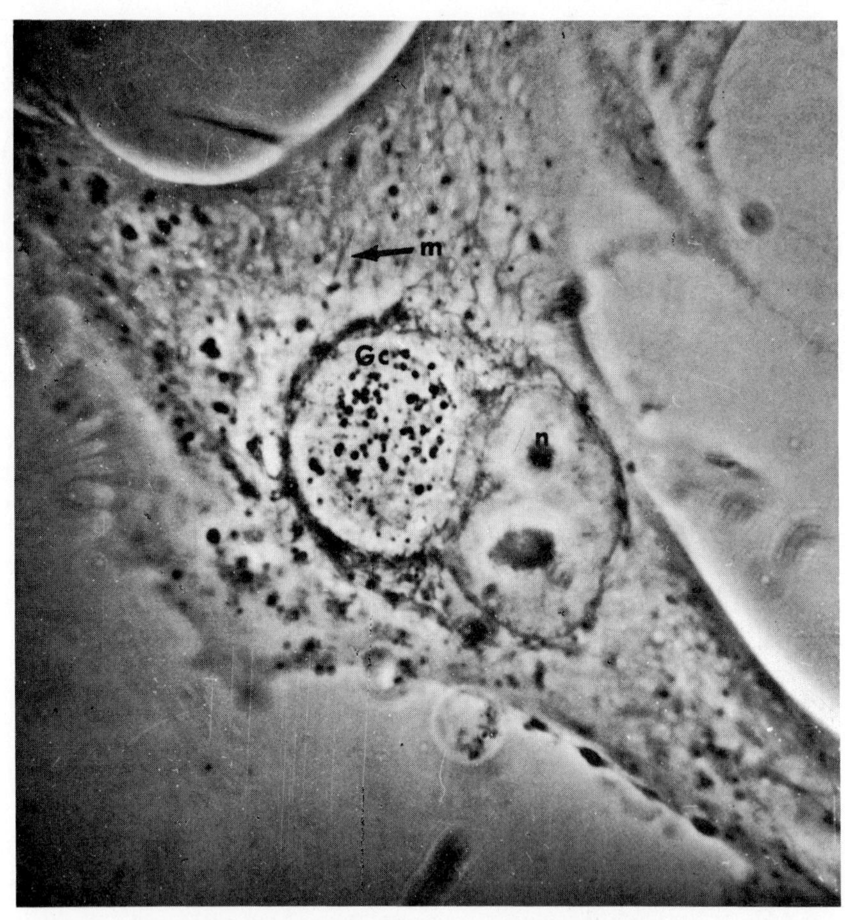

Fig. 8-2. Phase-contrast micrograph of melanoma cell showing large and prominent Golgi complex, **Gc,** adjacent to nucleus containing a number of Golgi granules. **m,** Mitochondria; **n,** nucleus. (From Rose, G. G., and J. S. Stehlin. 1961. Cancer Res. **10:**1456-1460.)

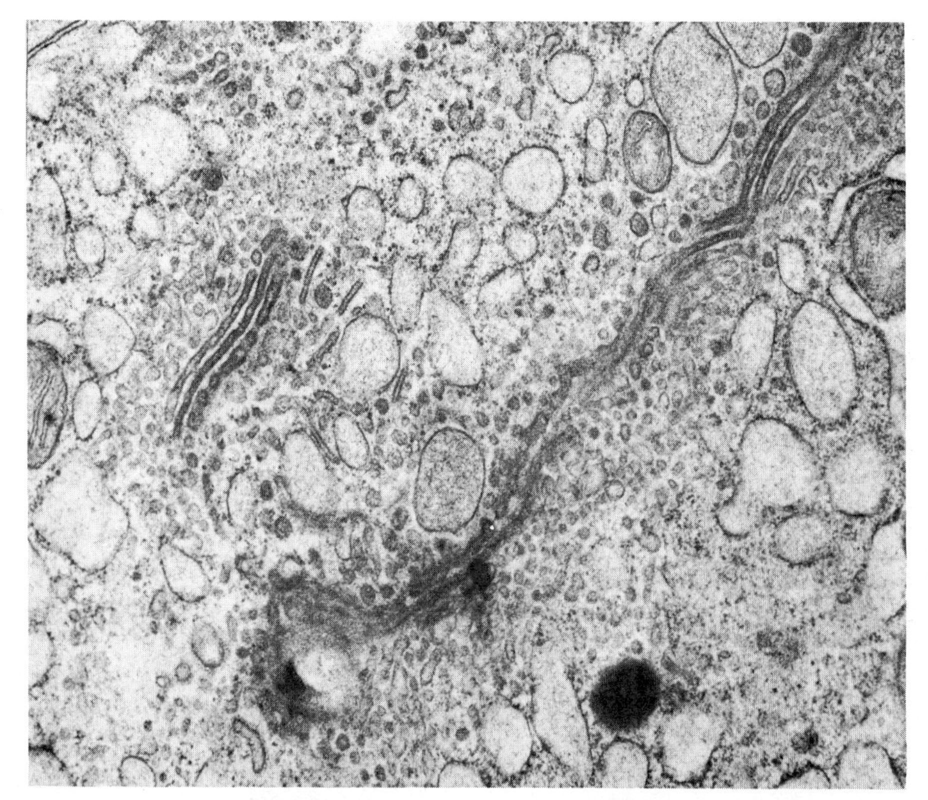

Fig. 8-3. Electron micrograph of venom gland epithelium of western diamondback rattlesnake *(Crotalus atrox)*. Inner cisternae have a beaded appearance suggesting the simultaneous pinching off of a number of vesicles. Note also the numerous vesicles associated with the Golgi complex.

ticles attached to their outer membranes (Lacy, 1957; Essner and Novikoff, 1962).

Thus on the basis of EM studies the Golgi apparatus can be considered morphologically as being a heterogeneous organelle. As a result, many cytologists have preferred to use the term "Golgi complex" rather than the older term "Golgi apparatus."

Mollenhauer and Morré (1966a) proposed a terminology that appears to offer flexibility of interpretation as to Golgi function and that stresses the homology of animal and plant Golgi apparatuses. The simplest unit is the *cisterna* (Fig. 8-4). It is within this membrane-bounded space that the products of secretion accumulate. It probably represents the smallest functional structure. The *dictyosome* consists of a number of associated cisternae, ranging from two to seven and upward to about twenty or more. The dictyosome represents a functional unit. The term "Golgi apparatus," either singular or plural, is reserved for a larger aggregate structure consisting of many dictyosomes participating in a common function or the sum total of dictyosomes within one cell. The manner in which the dictyosomes are associated may vary. They may be widely spaced in plant and invertebrate cells, that is, possibly randomly scattered throughout the cytoplasm, or they may form tight aggregates as in vertebrate animal cells. The extent of the Golgi apparatus, then, is determined by the extent to which the dictyosomes are interassociated.

With the use of glutaraldehyde as a fixative, coupled with low-shear homogenization and differential centrifugation, it is possible to obtain free concentrated Golgi apparatus material that comprises the intact membrane systems (Morré et al., 1965). These structures have the same appearance

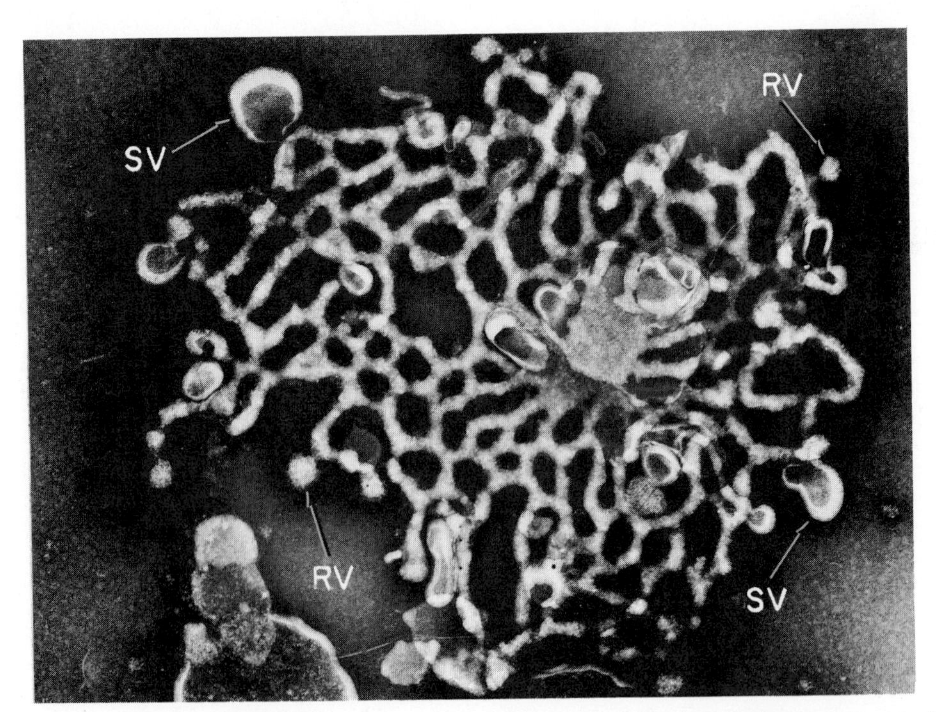

Fig. 8-4. Negatively stained section of a single plant cisterna showing nonfenestrated central region and two types of vesicles associated with it. **SV,** Smooth vesicle; **RV,** rough vesicle. Compare with Fig. 8-5. (From Cunningham, W. P., D. J. Morré, and H. H. Mollenhauer. 1966. J. Cell Biol. **28:**169-179.)

as when seen in electron micrographs of intact cells. Negative staining with phosphotungstic acid has extended detailed knowledge of the structure of the Golgi apparatus. The cisternae appear as fenestrated plates composed of tubules ranging from 300 to 500 Å in diameter (Figs. 8-4 and 19-19). These tubules branch and anastomose to produce the fenestrated systems. With separation of the dictyosome into individual cisternae a central disklike region has been made evident (Fig. 8-4) that measures approximately 1 μm in diameter. Several regions of morphological specialization can also be seen. One consists of protuberances and has a shaggy surface texture similar to that of the membranes of the rough ER. This form appears to be present in all cisternae and has been seen located at the ends of tubules. The smooth surface vesicles vary from 200 to 600 Å in diameter. They are attached to the sides of tubules or may be interposed between several segments.

The *dictyosome* (Figs. 8-7 and 8-8) itself (*dictyo,* meaning "net or network") consists of a small number of stacked cisternae joined together by some bonding material within the intercisternal matrix. The intercisternal region contains intercisternal elements 70 to 80 Å in diameter (Fig. 8-5). In cross sections these show a repeating substructure with the same orientation between all cisternae of a dictyosome. After negative staining this structure appears as a system of parallel fibers that extends over part of the cisternal face (Fig. 8-6). The center-to-center spacing of the intercisternal elements within the central part of the dictyosome is approximately 150 Å. The appearance of the intercisternal elements varies within the dictyosome; at times they may extend beyond the periphery of the dictyosome. These intercisternal elements are not in direct contact with the cisternal membrane. Furthermore, they are not the same as the bonding material. At the present time their function is unknown (Mollenhauer and Morré, 1966a).

The Golgi apparatus, then, represents an aggregate of dictyosomes. However, the extent to which the dictyosomes are interconnected within the cell, as the Golgi apparatus, is not known with certainty. However, tubular interconnections between adjacent dictyosomes have been observed (Mollenhauer and Morré, 1966a) and may

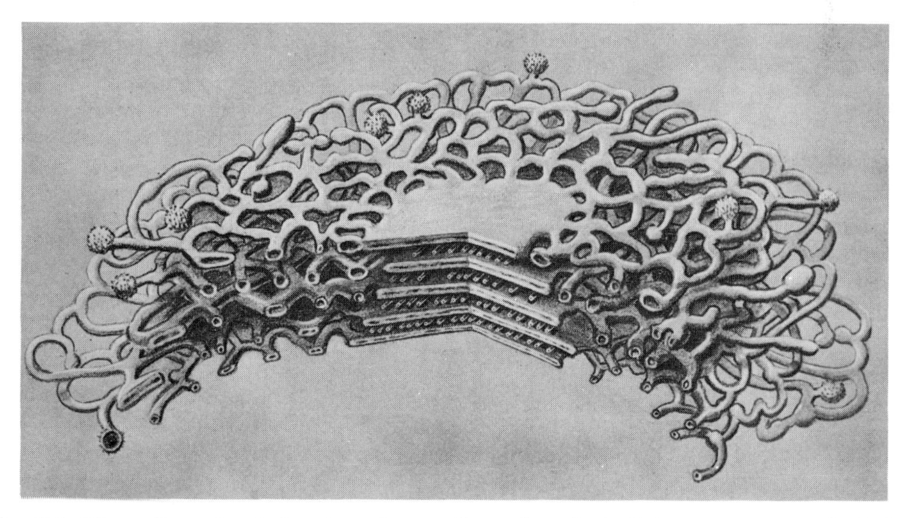

Fig. 8-5. Three-dimensional drawing of a portion of a plant dictyosome composed of five cisternae. See text for description. (From Mollenhauer, H. H., and D. J. Morré. 1966. Ann. Rev. Plant Physiol. **17**:27-46.)

be responsible for synchronous changes in secretory activity among all the dictyosomes within a cell, which suggests that they are informationally related. In cells that contain a single dictyosome the dictyosome is equivalent to a Golgi apparatus. Similarly, in the synergid cells of cotton the dictyosomes may number several thousand and can be interpreted as forming three functionally distinct Golgi apparatuses, one producing secretion, one for cell wall formation, and the third, consisting of a few vesicles of loosely arranged cisternae, located next to the filiform apparatus at the micropylar end of the cell (Mollenhauer and Morré, 1966a). Similarly, pairs of Golgi apparatuses have been observed in the diatom *Pinnularia nobilis* (Drum, 1966) (Fig. 8-7).

"Amplexus" is a term used to denote a specific structural arrangement of ER and Golgi apparatus (Fig. 8-8). It is characterized by a broad sheet of ER branching off from the outer nuclear envelope membrane and forming an extensive cisterna in the form of a hood. Within the hood or between it and the nuclear envelope are one or two large dictyosomes, each with the *forming face* (the presumed youngest cisterna) adjacent to the ER. There is accumulating evidence that the inner surface of the hood which lies close to the dictyosome is smooth, whereas all the other surfaces of the hood are rough (their surfaces possess ribosomes). Vesicles appear to bud off from this smooth surface of the ER hood and become new Golgi cisternae of the forming face of the dictyosome. If this scheme is true, it would provide a mechanism for direct transport and transformation of intercisternal ER material to intracisternal Golgi material. The cisternae of the

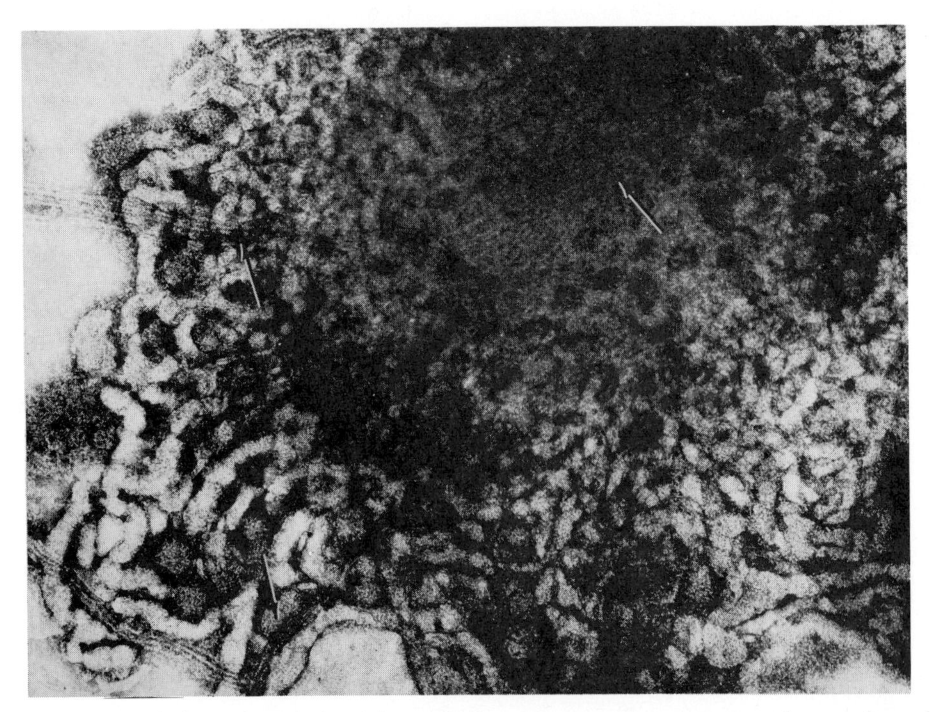

Fig. 8-6. Negatively stained isolated internal plant cisterna. Note presence of a number of parallel intercisternal fibers along the outer surface. These fibers extend beyond the dictyosome. (From Cunningham, W. P., D. J. Morré, and H. H. Mollenhauer. 1966. J. Cell Biol. **28:**169-179.)

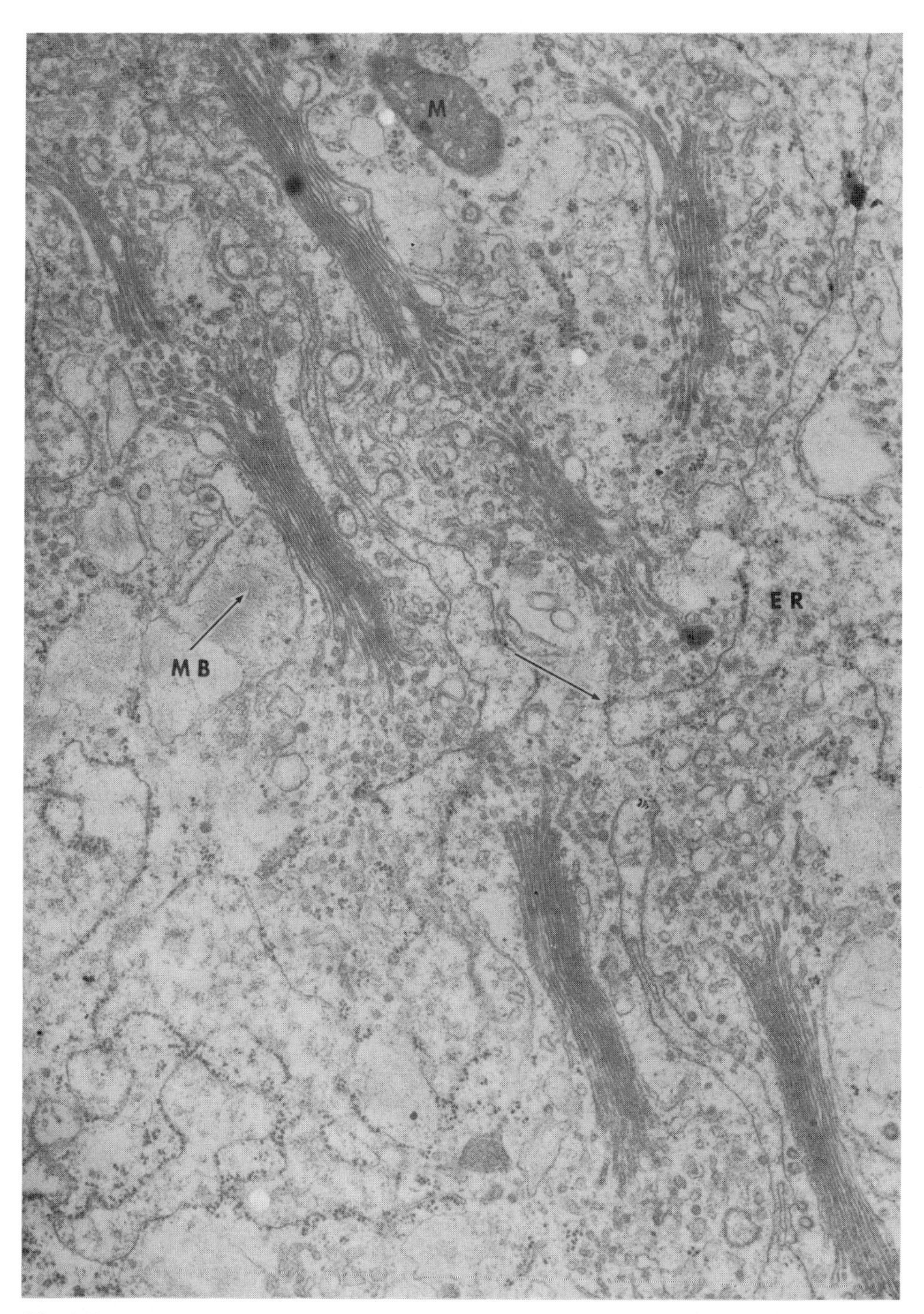

Fig. 8-7. Electron micrograph of paired Golgi apparatuses from the diatom *Pinnularia nobilis*. (From Drum, R. W. 1966. J. Ultrastruct. Res. **15:**100-107.)

dictyosome become increasingly swollen (hypertrophied) as they "move" toward the *maturing face* (if they actually are so displaced). At least the cisternae near the maturing face are more swollen than those nearer the forming face.

Amplexi have been seen by electron microscopy in a large number of algae (greens,

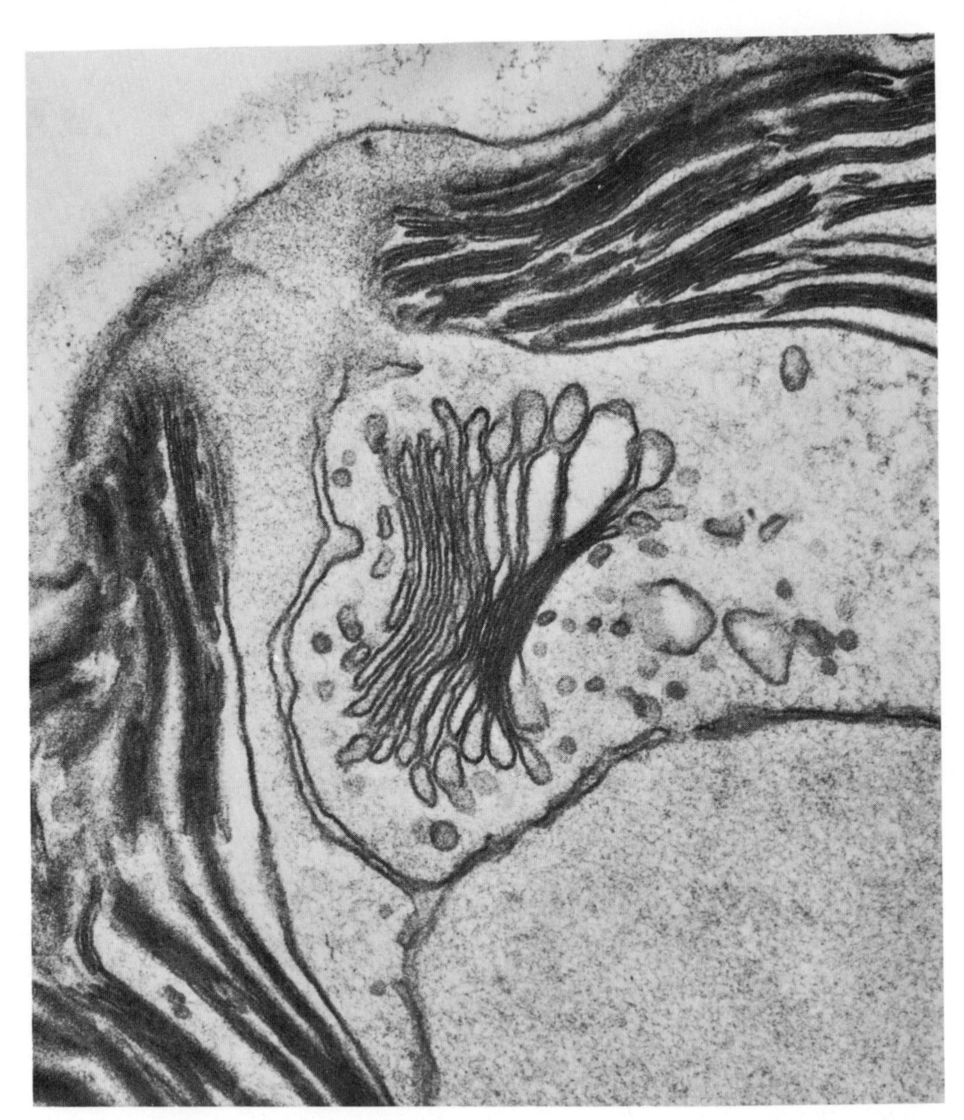

Fig. 8-8. Amplexus of the unicellular green alga *Tetracystis excentrica* showing also the nucleus and chloroplasts. The ER comes off from the nuclear envelope as a sheet that forms a hood within which is a large dictyosome; the forming face of the latter is close to the ER, and the maturing face is directed more toward the nucleus. The gradual increase in hypertrophy of cisternae from forming to maturing face is evident. It is possible, if not likely, that the vesicles lying between the ER and the forming face of the dictyosome are derived from the adjacent ER (note one protuberance of that part of the ER) and aggregate to form a new cisterna on the forming face of the dictyosome. (Courtesy Dr. R. M. Brown, University of Texas Cell Research Institute, Austin, Texas.)

browns, yellow-greens, and Cryptophyceae) and in one fungus but in no other sort of organism. Perhaps amplexi are restricted to organisms having nuclear envelopes that persist throughout cell division. In the mature, vegetative, unicellular green alga *Tetracystis* there are two to eight ER hoods and four to sixteen dictyosomes; generally, there are two dictyosomes per hood. The number of zoospores into which such a cell can divide is determined by the seeming requirement that two dictyosomes must be present in each zoospore.

The amplexus has also been reported to be a specialized and more elaborate example of a dictyosomal-nuclear envelope association, which reflects growing knowledge that dictyosomes are often or typically related to the ER structurally and functionally.

Functions

Historically, light microscopy indicated the Golgi apparatus to be the site of secretory granule formation. Some of the early evidence was based on the enlarged Golgi apparatus observed in cells that were known to be highly secretory in nature, as compared to the relatively small size of the Golgi apparatus in cells that have little or no secretory function. Other evidence of the secretory function was based in cyclical changes observed in the Golgi apparatus of living cells (Wallgren, 1951). Worley (1943) studied the structure and function of the Golgi complex in developing mollusc embryos and observed that after gastrulation the Golgi apparatus became exceedingly active. Yolk accumulated in the region and formed elaborate compound vesicular bodies. After this stage there was discharge of the protein spheres containing the yolk material. The Golgi apparatus then became reduced in size, followed by the development of a number of small spherical vesicles, and the cycle was repeated. Yet despite the accumulation of information suggesting the secretory function, its role was still controversial. Conclusive evidence was obtained finally from electron microscopy in conjunction with autoradiographic techniques. Electron microscopy had shown that the membranes bounding the secretory vesicles in the Golgi region are derived from the membranes of the Golgi complex rather than from the membranes of the ergastoplasm. Later studies using combined autoradiographic techniques and electron microscopy (Caro, 1961) have shown an earlier transfer of some synthesized material from the ER to the Golgi complex.

Another function of the Golgi apparatus is the formation of the acrosome in spermatids (Burgos and Fawcett, 1955) (Fig. 19-19). In the early stages of spermatid formation the Golgi apparatus is large and spherical and consists of numerous parallel membranes and a number of small vacuoles. As development continues, the Golgi apparatus becomes irregular because of vacuoles that develop between these membranes and alter the earlier architecture. Within one or more of these vacuoles a dense granule, the *proacrosome granule,* surrounded by a clear material, develops. This granule, which is derived from the Golgi apparatus, continues to grow within the vacuole by a process known as accretion. The vacuole (by this stage of development a vesicle) then moves to the nucleus, where it adheres to the nuclear membrane. The acrosomal granule becomes attached to the vesicle membrane at a point where the latter becomes attached to the nuclear membrane. During this time the acrosomal granule has continued to grow. During a late stage of spermateliosis (the conversion of the spermatid into a sperm), the Golgi apparatus leaves the region of the acrosomal granule and moves back along the sides of the nucleus. The vesicle finally collapses and forms the *head cap.* The acrosomal granule becomes the *acrosome* (Chapter 19).

The Golgi apparatus is also involved in the synthesis and concentration of products rich in carbohydrates. There is an indication that both glycoproteins and mucopolysaccharides are synthesized in the Golgi complex (Peterson and LeBlond, 1964; Neutra and LeBlond, 1965). Electron microscope studies have shown that the Golgi apparatus is the region where mucin is formed in the goblet cells of intestinal epithelia. It is also in the Golgi region that mucin droplets first appear and coalesce to form large vacuoles prior to release into the distal region of the cell (Freeman, 1966) (Figs. 8-9 and 8-10).

It has been shown from studies using ^{35}S-sulfate that carbohydrates are sulfated in the Golgi region (Ostero-Vilardebó et al., 1964); proteoglycans, a noncollagenous organic material found in odontoblasts is also sulfated in the Golgi region (Weinstock and Young, 1972).

In animals the Golgi complex has been shown to be involved in the segregation of the products of secretion of hormones (Rinehart and Farquhar, 1953) and pigments (Kessel and Beams, 1965). The Golgi apparatus has also been implicated in the formation of plasma membrane (Grove et al., 1968) and both the membranes of the ER and mitochondria (see discussion on origin of mitochondria for further details). The Golgi apparatus is involved also in the segregation of collagen (Porter, 1964). It has also been established that melanin is transferred from the ER to the Golgi apparatus (Sieji et al., 1963). The smallest melanin granules first appear in the Golgi region (Wellings and Siegel, 1959; Rose and Stehlin, 1961).

In plants the Golgi apparatus has been visualized as participating in the formation of the cell plate. It has been shown or estimated that the cell plate is formed by the union of droplets (Becker, 1938; Bajer, 1965; Cronshaw and Bouck, 1965) that arise from the Golgi apparatus. This apparatus, then, can be conceived as being capable of synthesizing substances that can serve as precursors for cell wall matrix

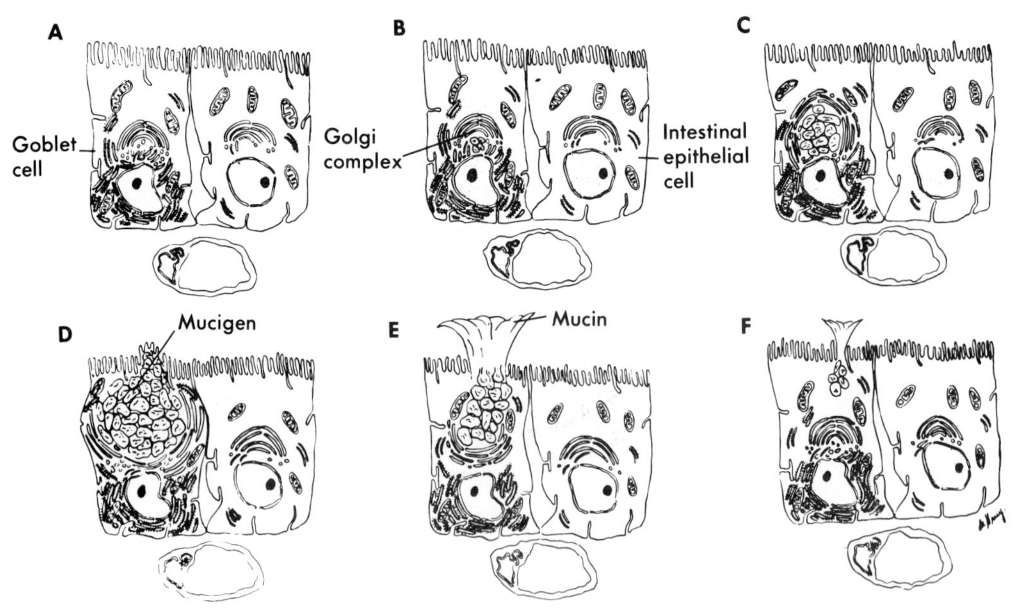

Fig. 8-9. Depiction of the sequence of changes in goblet cell during mucus formation. **A,** Golgi membranes and the membranes of the rough endoplasmic reticulum proliferate. **B,** Accumulation of mucinogen droplets in Golgi complex. **C** to **E,** As the mucus formation increases, there is proliferation of Golgi membranes. **F,** Presecretory stage after secretion of mucus. The process repeats itself. (From Freeman, J. A. 1966. Anat. Rec. **154:**121-148.)

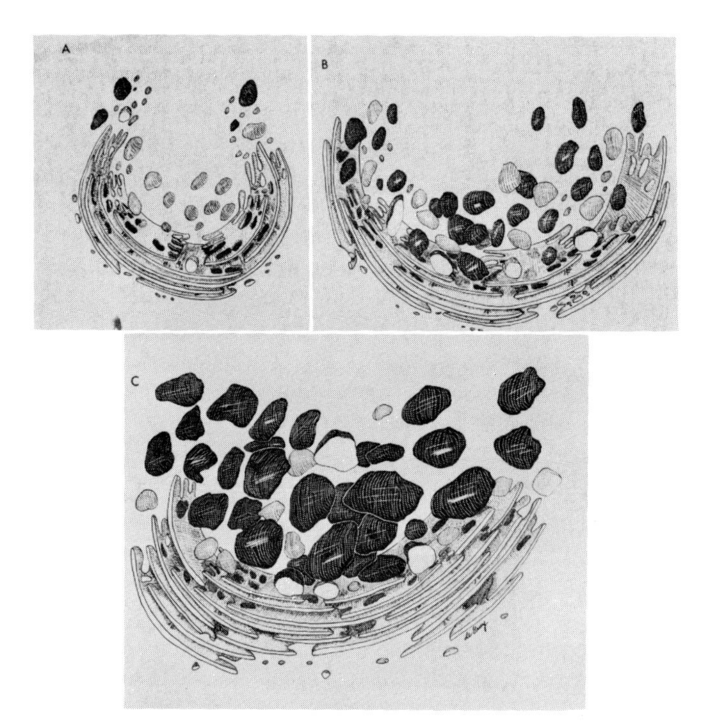

Fig. 8-10. Diagrammatic representation showing relationship of Golgi apparatus and accumulation of mucus. **A,** Mucus is in small vacuoles located at the periphery of the Golgi apparatus. **B,** Mucus droplets are increasing in number and begin to accumulate and fill the central region of the Golgi apparatus. **C,** Coalescence of many individual mucus droplets. Fig. 8-9 shows relation of mucus accumulation and secretion. (From Freeman, J. A. 1966. Anat. Rec. **154:** 121-148.)

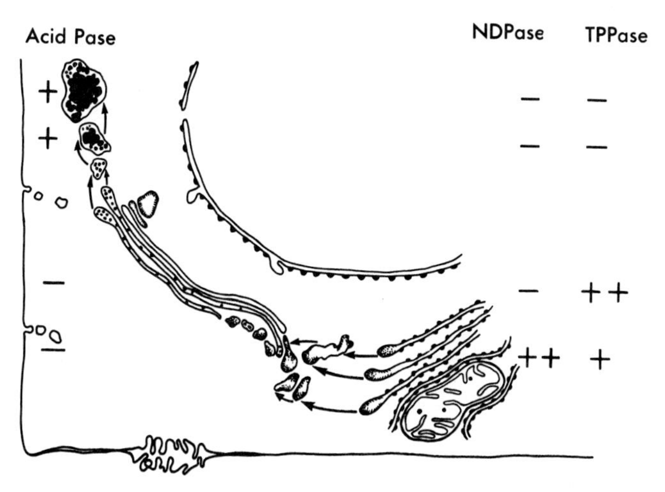

Fig. 8-11. Diagram showing possible relationship between smooth ER derived from the distal region of the granular ER and the Golgi complex, secretory vesicles, and lysosome. Relationships were based on a number of enzyme reactions and a number of electron micrographs. Acid Pase is acid phosphatase, NDPase is nucleoside diphosphatase, and TPPase is thiamine pyrophosphatase. (From Essner, E., and A. B. Novikoff. 1962. J. Cell Biol. **15:**289-312.)

and plant slime. The membranes of the vesicles on coalescence constitute the plasmalemma of the new cell surfaces. Since these vesicles were possibly derived from the Golgi apparatus, at least in part, there is indication that Golgi membranes and cell membranes can be ontogenetically related (Frey-Wyssling et al., 1964). Similarly, vesicles arising from the Golgi apparatus that migrate to the cell surface to contribute to the pollen tube walls and plasmalemma have been observed (Rosen et al., 1964; Larson, 1965), and in root cap cells the hypertrophy of cisternae is remarkable, since they provide material outside the plasma membrane. An interesting problem is the role of the Golgi apparatus in the diatoms, *Equisetum,* and grasses, which are known to have siliceous walls.

Transfer of synthesized protein from the ER to the Golgi complex has been shown by autoradiographic studies in conjunction with electron microscopy (Caro, 1961). How the transfer takes place is not known with certainty. Only at times do electron micrographs show the ER to be continuous with the cisternae of the dictyosome. This would allow direct transfer of the synthesized proteins from the ER to the Golgi apparatus. On the other hand, it has also been suggested that small vesicles, or transitional elements, bud off from the ER and carry the products to the Golgi apparatus. One can conceive that near the distal ends are special protuberances of the ergastoplasm, in close proximity to the Golgi apparatus. The membranes are agranular in nature (Essner and Novikoff, 1962), and it is this portion of the ER that gives rise to the small vesicles, or *quanta.* This would provide a bridge between the ER and the cisternae of the Golgi apparatus. In the region of the Golgi apparatus these vesicles will fuse with the membranes of the cisternae (Fig. 8-11). At the present time it is difficult to determine whether any other regions of the cytoplasm also contribute material to the Golgi apparatus.

Vesicles similar to those produced during phagocytosis and pinocytosis can at times be seen near the region of the Golgi apparatus. The production of the secretory vesicles appears to progress along the length of the cisternae, beginning at the point where the products of synthesis are accumulated. As maturation ensues, the distally attached vesicles increase in size and change in staining characteristics. The vesicles are released with the loss of the terminal cisternae (Fig. 8-11). At other times the secretory vesicles are arranged in rows adjacent to undilated Golgi apparatuses; the cisterna may pinch off a number of vacuoles simultaneously (Fig. 8-3). Each of these vesicles is bounded by a single membrane. The nature of the transformation is unknown. It has been assumed that the Golgi apparatus may be involved in the concentrating of the material; that is, one of the functions may involve resorption of water and thereby concentration of the secretion. Some other transforming function may also be involved. It is obvious, however, that dictyosomes, even within one cell, may be "processing" a variety of secretions. The "factories" are structurally the same, but the products are varied.

Grove et al. (1968) have argued from electron microscope studies, especially of dictyosomes in the mycelium of the fungus *Pythium,* that ER membrane and the membrane of the cisternae of the forming face (the proximal pole) of the dictyosome are identical (25 to 40 Å thick and not trilaminar). Membranes of cisternae at the maturing face (the distal pole) are identical not only to membranes of the secretory vesicles produced but also to the plasma membrane (up to 75 Å thick and trilaminate unit membranes). Internal cisternae show a progressive change from resembling ER to resembling plasma membrane. They propose that ER membrane structure is converted in the dictyosome into the structure comparable to that of the plasma membrane because the secretory vesicles produced *must* fuse with the plasma membrane to discharge their contents to the exterior. They consider certain parts of the ER, the Golgi dictyosome, and the secretory vesicles produced as constituting the *endoplasmic reticulum—Golgi apparatus–vesicle complex* (the EGV complex). Thus both the cisternal membranes and cisternal contents show a progressive change from the proximal to the distal pole, and the dictyosome is visualized as being in a dynamic steady state.

Histochemistry

The argentophilic and osmiophilic nature of the Golgi apparatus indicates the presence of lipids. Studies have shown that the Golgi membranes are composed essentially of equal parts of lipids and proteins. Of the lipids, both phospholipids and phosphatides have been identified (Schneider and Kuff, 1954). In addition, the Golgi complex shows a positive periodic acid–Schiff (PAS) reaction. This may have several implications, one being the presence of polysaccharides as a constituent, another that it may represent a lipid moiety (Dalton and Felix, 1954). RNA has also been identified, but only from density gradient separation. It is quite possible that ribosomes may have been present as a contaminant. However, the possibility of some RNA being present cannot be ruled out because it has also been identified as a chemical component in the membranes of the ER. The case of RNA in the Golgi membranes is speculative at this time.

Knowledge of the enzymes present in the Golgi complex is limited. There apparently is little in common between the enzyme system found in the Golgi apparatus and those present in the membranes of the ER. Schneider and Kuff (1954) demonstrated the presence of alkaline phosphatase. Later studies, however, have shown that alkaline phosphatase is not in the Golgi complex as such but, rather, in small granules located in the Golgi region (Novikoff and Goldfischer, 1961). Acid phosphatase has also been demonstrated in the Golgi complex (Shanthaveerappa and Bourne, 1965). A significant biochemical activity found in the Golgi membrane indicates the presence of enzymes that hydrolyze nucleoside diphosphates. Novikoff and Goldfischer showed that diphosphates of guanosine, inosine, and uridine are hydrolyzed rapidly, whereas cytidine and adenosine are split rather slowly. Unfortunately, the variability of these enzymes limits their use as markers and thereby materially hampers interpretation of their function. Thiamine pyrophosphate is also hydrolyzed rapidly in the Golgi region.

Origin of Golgi apparatus

At the present time knowledge of how the dictyosomes replicate themselves, if they do reproduce in that manner, is poorly understood. It has been shown that daughter cells in the division of the maize root meristem have as many or more Golgi structures as the original cell preceding division. It must be assumed that the structures must have formed either at the time of or after division (Whaley et al., 1960). A number of possibilities have been proposed to explain replication of the Golgi apparatus. Some include formation by fragmentation and resynthesis of cisternae (Mollenhauer and Morré, 1966a). Vesicles derived from the ER may become cisternae of dictyosomes.

Kessel (1971) demonstrated that in embryonic cells from grasshoppers the Golgi apparatus appears to be derived from blebbing from the nucleus, with subsequent fusion of these small vesicles to produce progressively longer saccules. Later, part of the ER becomes associated with the forming face of the dictyosome and then produces the vesicular component for the dictyosome by means of bleb formation.

Other means of replication have been suggested such as reorientation of smooth membranes, de novo synthesis from lipid spherulite, and division by means of constrictions (Buvat, 1963).

LITERATURE CITED

Bajer, A. 1965. Cell plate formation in endosperm. Exp. Cell. Res. **37:**376-398.

Baker, J. R. 1950. Morphology and fine structures of organisms. Nature (London) **165:**585-586.

Becker, W. A. 1938. Recent investigation in vivo of the division of plant cells. Bot. Rev. **4:**446-472.

Burgos, M. H., and D. W. Fawcett. 1955. Studies on the fine structure of the mammalian testis. I. Differentiation of the spermatids in the cat. J. Biophys. Biochem. Cytol. **1:**287-299.

Buvat, R. 1963. Electron microscopy of plant protoplasm. Int. Rev. Cytol. **14:**41-155.

Caro, L. G. 1961. Electron microscopic radioautography of thin sections, the Golgi zone as a site of protein concentration in pancreatic acinar cells. J. Cell Biol. **10:**37-44.

Cronshaw, J., and G. B. Bouck. 1965. The fine structure of differentiating xylem elements. J. Cell. Biol. **24:**415-431.

Cunningham, W. P., D. J. Morré, and H. H. Mollenhauer. 1966. Structure of isolated plant Golgi apparatus revealed by negative staining. J. Cell Biol. **28:**169-179.

Dalton, A. J., and M. D. Felix. 1954. Cytologic and cytochemical characteristics of the Golgi substance of epithelial cells of the epididymus—in situ, in homogenates, and after isolation. Amer. J. Anat. **94:**171-207.

Drum, R. W. 1966. Electron microscopy of paired Golgi structures in the diatom Pinnularia nobilis. J. Ultrastruct. Res. **15:**100-107.

Essner, E., and A. B. Novikoff. 1962. Cytological studies on two functional hepatomas. Interrelations of the endoplasmic reticulum, Golgi apparatus, and lysosomes. J. Cell Biol. **15:**289-312.

Freeman, J. A. 1966. Goblet cell fine structure. Anat. Rec. **154:**121-147.

Frey-Wyssling, A., J. F. Lopez-Saex, and K. Müllethaler. 1964. Formation of the cell plate. J. Ultrastruct. Res. **10:**422-432.

Gatenby, J. B. 1951. The Golgi apparatus of liver and nerve cells. Nature (London) **167:**185-186.

Grove, S. N., C. E. Bracker, and D. J. Morré. 1968. Cytomembrane differentiation in the endoplasmic reticulum-Golgi apparatus-vesicle complex. Science **161:**171-173.

Haguenau, F., and W. Bernhard. 1955. L'appareil de Golgi dans les cellules normales et cancéreuses de vertèbres. Arch. Anat. Micr. Morph. Exp. **44:**27-56.

Kessel, R. G. 1971. Origin of the Golgi apparatus in embryonic cells of grasshoppers. J. Ultrastruct. Res. **34:**260-275.

Kessel, R. G., and H. W. Beams. 1965. An unusual configuration of the Golgi complex in pigment-producing "test" cells of the ovary of the tunicate, Styela. J. Cell Biol. **25:**55-67.

Lacy, D. 1957. The Golgi apparatus in neurones and epithelial cells of the common limpet Petella vulgata. J. Biophys. Biochem. Cytol. **3:**779-796.

Larson, D. A. 1965. Fine structural changes in the cytoplasm of germinating pollen. Amer. J. Bot. **52:**139-154.

Mollenhauer, H. H., and D. J. Morré. 1966a. Golgi apparatus and plant secretion. Ann. Rev. Plant Physiol. **17:**27-46.

Mollenhauer, H. H., and D. J. Morré. 1966b. Tubular connections between dictyosomes and forming secretory vesicles in plant Golgi apparatus. J. Cell Biol. **29:**373-376.

Montagna, W. 1950. Perinuclear sudanophil bodies in mammalian epidermis. Quart. J. Micr. Sci. **91:**205-208.

Morré, D. J., H. H. Mollenhauer, and J. E. Chambers. 1965. Glutaraldehyde stabilization as an aid to Golgi apparatus isolation. Exp. Cell Res. **38:**672-675.

Neutra, M., and C. P. LeBlond. 1965. Synthesizing complex carbohydrates in the Golgi regions as shown by the uptake of tritiated galactose. J. Cell Biol. **27:**72A.

Novikoff, A. B., and S. Goldfischer. 1961. Nucleosidediphosphatase activity in the Golgi apparatus and its usefulness for cytological studies. Proc. Nat. Acad. Sci. U.S.A. **47:**802-810.

Ostero-Vilardebó, L. R., N. Lane, and G. C. Godman. 1964. Some characteristics of cells secreting sulfated mucopolysaccharides. J. Histochem. Cytochem. **12:**34.

Peterson, M. R., and C. P. LeBlond. 1964. Uptake by the Golgi region of glucose labelled with tritium in the 1 or 6 position as an indicator of synthesis of complex carbohydrate. Exp. Cell Res. **34:**420-423.

Porter, K. R. 1964. Cell fine structure and biosynthesis of intercellular macromolecules. J. Biophys. **4:**167-196.

Rinehart, J. F., and M. G. Farquhar. 1953. Electron microscopic studies of the anterior pituitary gland, J. Histochem. Cytochem. **1:**93-112.

Rose, G. G., and J. S. Stehlin. 1961. The Golgi complex and melanin elaboration of human melanomas in tissue culture. Cancer Res. **10:** 1456-1460.

Rosen, W. G., S. G. Gawlik, W. V. Dashek, and K. A. Siegesmund. 1964. Fine structures and cytochemistry of Lilium pollen tubes. Amer. J. Bot. **51:**61-71.

Schneider, W. C., and E. L. Kuff. 1954. On the isolation of some biochemical properties of the

Golgi substance. Amer. J. Anat. **94:**209-224.

Shanthaveerappa, T. R., and G. H. Bourne. 1965. Histochemical demonstration of thiamine pyrophosphatase and acid phosphatase in the Golgi region of the cells of the eye. J. Anat. **99:**103-118.

Sieji, M., K. Shimao, M. S. C. Birbeck, and T. B. Fitzpatrick. 1933. Subcellular localization of melanin biosynthesis. Ann. N. Y. Acad. Sci. **100:**497-533.

Wallgren, I. 1951. Observation of the Golgi apparatus in living plasma cells and in erythroblasts with dark ground illumination. Exp. Cell Res. **2:**10-19.

Weinstock, A., and R. W. Young. 1972. Sulfate-S uptake by the Golgi apparatus of odontoblasts and the migration of label to the mineralization front of dentin. J. Cell Biol. **55:**276A.

Wellings, S. R., and B. V. Siegel. 1959. Role of Golgi apparatus in the formation of melanin granules in human malignant tumor melanomas. J. Ultrastruct. Res. **3:**147-154.

Whaley, W. G., and H. H. Mollenhauer, and J. H. Leech. 1960. The ultrastructure of the meristematic cell. Amer. J. Bot. **47:**401-449.

Worley, L. G. 1943. The structure and function of the Golgi system in the living cells of developing molluscs. Proc. Nat. Acad. Sci. U.S.A. **29:**228-231.

Worley, L. G. 1951. Recovery of the Golgi apparatus from homogenates of normal mammalian liver. Exp. Cell. Res. **2:**684-687.

Xeros, N. 1951. Lipid bodies, Golgi apparatus and zymogen formations. Nature (London) **167:** 448-449.

GENERAL REFERENCES

Bensley, R. R. 1951. Facts versus artefacts in cytology. The Golgi apparatus. Exp. Cell Res. **2:**1-9.

Buvat, R. 1958. Nouvelles observations sur l'appareil de Golgi dans les cellules des vegetaux vasculaires. C. R. Acad. Sci. (Paris) **246:**2157-2160.

Buvat, R., and A. Puissant. 1958. Observations sur la cytodiérè et l'origine plasmodesmes. C. R. Acad. Sci. (Paris) **247:**233-236.

Clowes, F. A. L., and B. E. Juniper. 1964. The fine structure of the quiescent centre and neighboring tissues in root meristems. J. Exp. Bot. **15:**622-630.

Dalton, A. G., and M. D. Felix. 1956. A comparative study of the Golgi complex. J. Biophys. Biochem. Cytol. **2**(suppl.):79-83.

Farquhar, M. G., and S. R. Wellings. 1957. Electron microscopic evidence suggesting secretory granules formation within the Golgi apparatus. J. Biophys. Biochem. Cytol. **3:**319-322.

Grassé, P. P. 1957. Ultrastructure, polarité et reproduction de l'appareil de Golgi. C. R. Acad. Sci. (Paris) **245:**1278-1281.

Grassé, P. P., and N. Carasso. 1957. Ultrastructure of the Golgi apparatus in protozoa and metazoa (somatic and germinal cells). Nature (London) **179:**31-33.

Grenne, L. J., C. H. Hirs, and G. E. Palade. 1963. On the protein composition of bovine pancreatic zymogen granules. J. Biol. Chem. **238:**2054-2070.

Karrer, H. E. 1960. Electron microscopic observations on developing chick embryo liver and the possible role in the formation of glycogen. J. Ultrastruct. Res. **4:**149-165.

Lane, N. J. 1964. Elementary neurosecretory granules in the neurones of the snail Helix aspera. Quart. J. Micr. Sci. **105:**31-34.

Lazarus, S. S., and B. J. Wallace, 1964. Nucleoside and thiamine pyrophosphatase activity of rabbit Golgi apparatus. J. Histochem. Cytochem. **12:**729-736.

Morré, D. J., and H. H. Mollenhauer. 1964. Isolation of the Golgi apparatus from plant cells. J. Cell Biol. **23:**295-305.

Nath, V., and G. P. Dutta. 1962. Cytochemistry of protozoa with particular reference to the Golgi apparatus and the mitochondria. Int. Rev. Cytol. **13:**323-355.

Rose, G. G. 1961. The Golgi complex in living osteoblast. J. Biophys. Biochem. Cytol. **9:**463-478.

Zeigel, R. F., and A. J. Dalton. 1962. Speculations based on the morphology of the Golgi systems in several types of protein-secreting cells. J. Cell Biol. **15:**45-54.

CHAPTER 9

Ribosomes

Ribosomes are submicroscopic particles that are composed of RNA and protein and constitute approximately 85% of the cytoplasmic RNA (Figs. 9-6 to 9-8, 10-1 and 10-8). No true ribosomes are recovered from the nucleus. It is assumed that precursors of ribosomes occur in nucleoli and nucleoplasm. Functionally, they serve as the sites for protein synthesis of the cell. Because of their smallness, they remained unknown as structural entities until electron microscopic techniques were applied to biological material. They can be identified from electron micrographs as being small, round to spherical, electron-dense bodies. The average size ranges from 150 to 200 Å, although at times they may be as small as 80 Å or as large as 300 Å in diameter (Palade, 1955).

Ribosomes are universally distributed throughout the animal, fungal, and plant kingdoms and occur in prokaryotes. Possibly the only cell type devoid of ribosomes is the mature mammalian erythrocyte. The mammalian erythrocyte, however, cannot be considered a true cell because during its final maturation process the nucleus is extruded, which results in an anucleated "cell."

The density of ribosomes per unit area varies from one cell type to another, being rather constant for any given type. The density per area is high for cells active in protein synthesis and low for cells in which protein synthesis is low. Examination of tissues by light microscopy will show that in cells where protein synthesis and therefore ribosomal concentration is high, the cytoplasm stains basophilic, whereas in cells in which protein synthesis is low the cytoplasm stains acidophilic.

Electron micrographs of cells of the pancreas, liver, and parotid glands, which are known for their high protein synthesis as well as secretion of their products, show that the ribosomes have a great affinity for the membranes of the ER. In these cells some to most of the ribosomes are attached to the outer surfaces of the ER membranes. In general, the ribosomes appear to be attached in a random fashion. At times, however, a regular interval between granules appears to be evident (Palade, 1955) as well as clusters of ribosomes that form diverse patterns such as crescents, spirals, circles, and rosettes (Baglio and Farber, 1965). Such clusters of ribosomes are actually functional units called *polysomes* (see later discussion (Fig. 7-2).

The manner in which ribosomes are attached to the membranes is somewhat obscure. However, as noted in the section on microsomes, the RNA present within these membranes may serve as anchoring points for ribosomal attachments. Unattached ribosomes can often be seen within the cytoplasm. Some occur singly or in small clusters (polysomes). On the other hand, cells such as those comprising the basal cell layer of the epidermis (Palade, 1955) and embryonic cells contain large numbers of ribosomes. However, unlike the cells described, they do not generally have their ribosomes attached to the membranes. Instead, the ribosomes are all scattered individually or as clusters throughout the cytoplasmic ground substances.

The position of the ribosomes depends on the particular function of the cell. In those cells that have ribosomes attached to the membranes of the ER the protein synthesized is secreted. On the other hand, cells such as the basal cells of the epidermis and embryonic cells, although they have a high rate of protein synthesis, synthesize proteins for additional protoplasm for growth.

Physical characteristics

Two classes of ribosomes are evident: (1) the 70s ribosome found in prokaryotes and in cell organelles such as mitochondria and chloroplasts and (2) the 80s ribosome found in the cytoplasm of eukaryotic cells. The 80s ribosome has a molecular weight of 2.6×10^6 daltons (T'so et al., 1958; Tissières et al., 1959), and the 80s ribosome has a molecular weight of 4.1×10^6 daltons (T'so et al., 1958). Furthermore,

Table 9-1. Summary of some physical characteristics of ribosomes*

Source	Subunits		Ribosome	Molecular weight*
E. coli	30s	50s	70s	30s: 0.7×10^6 50s: 1.8×10^6 70s: 3.6×10^6
Liver (guinea pig)	40s	60s	77s (80s)†	77s: $5.0 \pm 0.2 \times 10^6$
Liver (rat)	(40s) 39s	58s (60s)	80s	
Liver (calf)	(40s) 47s	62s (60s)	80s	
Yeast (bakers')	40s	60s	80s	40s: $1.4 \pm 0.1 \times 10^6$ 60s: $2.8 \pm 0.2 \times 10^6$ 80s: 4.1×10^6
Pea	40s	60s	80s	40s: $1.4 \pm 0.1 \times 10^6$ 60s: $2.8 \pm 0.2 \times 10^6$ 80s: 4.2×10^6
S. pombe	(40s) 38s	60s	83s (80s)	
Reticulocytes (human)	40s	58s (60s)	78s (80s)	78s: 4.1×10^6
Reticulocytes (sheep)	40s	58s (60s)	78s (80s)	78s: 4.1×10^6
HeLa cells (human)	40s	60s	74s (80s)	40s: 1.4×10^6 60s: 2.7×10^6 74s: 4.1×10^6
B. subtilis	30s	50s	70s	70s: 3.6×10^6

*Data from various sources.
†Accepted general values.

each of these ribosomes is composed of two subunits of unequal size. The 70s ribosome is composed of a 30s subunit, which has a molecular weight of 800,000 daltons, and the 50s subunit, which is roughly twice the size of the smaller subunits. The average molecular weight is about 1.8×10^6 daltons (Kurland, 1960). The 80s ribosome is composed of a 40s and 60s subunit. The molecular weights of the two subunits are 1.4×10^6 daltons and 2.7×10^6 daltons, respectively (Table 9-1).

It has been shown that ribosomes require about 0.001M of magnesium for structural formation. When this concentration falls below 0.001M, the ribosomes dissociate reversibly into subunits. If, on the other hand, the magnesium concentration is increased ten times, ribosomes can form dimers or twin particles (Fig. 9-1). The 70s will form a 100s particle, and two 80s ribosomes will form a 120s particle. The function of magnesium may be in the formation of primary linkages with the phosphate groups of some of the RNA molecules in the ribosome, with subsequent interaction between the RNAs and the proteins (Lederberg and Lederberg, 1961). In addition to magnesium, calcium ions (Ca^{++}) can also be used (Chao, 1957).

Ribonucleic acids

In the 70s bacterial type of ribosome the larger subunit contains a 23s rRNA, whereas the smaller 30s subunit contains a 16s rRNA. The molecular weights of these two RNAs are 1.1×10^6 daltons and 5.5×10^5 daltons, respectively (Kurland, 1960, 1970). On the other hand, in eukaryotic ribosomes the larger 60s subunit contains a

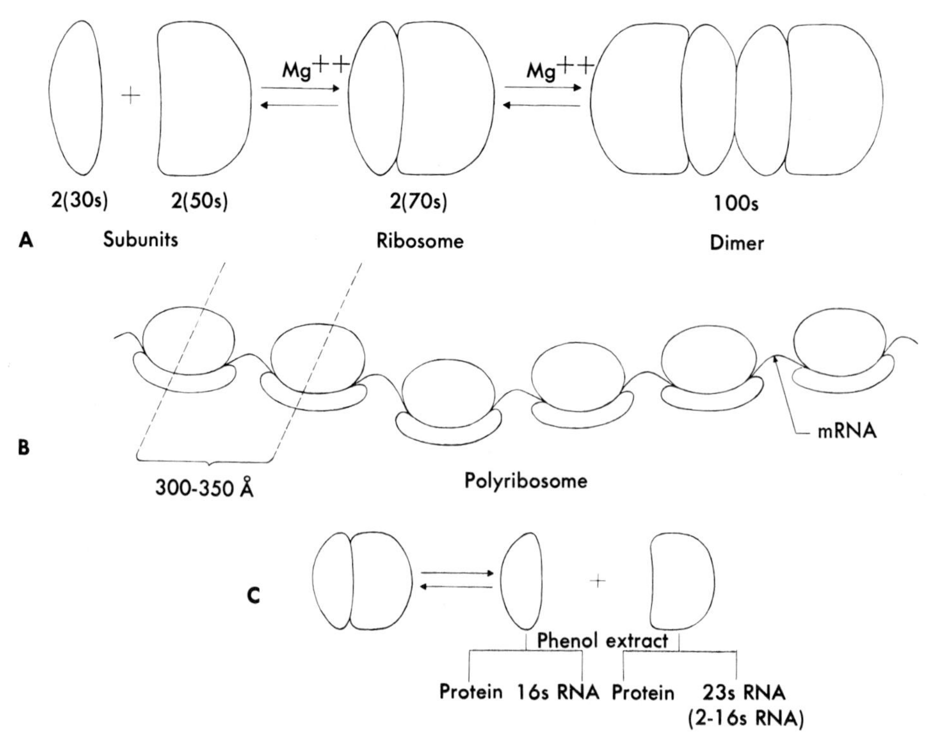

Fig. 9-1. A, Illustrating role played by magnesium ions in maintaining the structure of ribosomes. **B,** Depicting mRNA uniting a number of ribosomes to produce a polysome. **C,** Showing the RNA content of the 30s and 50s subunits.

28s rRNA (molecular weight 1.3×10^6 daltons) and in the 40s particle, contains an 18s rRNA (molecular weight 6×10^5 daltons) (Hall and Doty, 1959). Recent studies have shown that eukaryotic ribosomes vary somewhat in the RNA content and are less constant than in prokaryotes. For example, a 25s rRNA and a 16s to 18s rRNA are more often found in lower eukaryotic cells and plants. Furthermore, in ribosomes that contain the smaller 17s to 18s rRNA, the larger RNA species increase in size when going up the evolutionary scale in the animal kingdom (Attardi and Amaldi, 1970).

Beside the major RNA in ribosomes several minor forms are present as well. A 5s rRNA is found in the large subunits of prokaryotic and eukaryotic ribosomes. Also present is a 7s rRNA. However, this rRNA species has been found only in the large subunits of eukaryotic ribosomes. It is assumed that this fraction arises from the splitting of larger 28s rRNA during the maturation of this large RNA. The 7s rRNA is obtained by a process that disrupts hydrogen bonds.

It is of interest to note that the large 23s rRNA found in prokaryotic cells is twice the size of 16s rRNA found in the smaller subunits. This originally led to the hypothesis that the 23s rRNA could be a dimer of the 16s rRNA. Furthermore, phenol extraction of the 50s particle revealed a heterogeneous fraction containing both 23s and some 16s rRNAs. In addition, the conversion of the 23s rRNA into two 16s rRNAs was observed under varying conditions (Midgley, 1965). It was suggested that these 16s rRNAs might be joined together not unlike those of the phosphodiester-type linkages found in polynucleotides (Midgley, 1965). Additionally, the effect of T_1 ribonuclease produces 2 moles of 16s per mole of 23s rRNA (Fellner and Sanger, 1968). These results also indicate that the 23s rRNA can consist of two similar or identical portions (Davis and Sells, 1969). However, differences in the base composition refute the concept that the 23s rRNA is a dimer of two identical 16s rRNAs (Aronson, 1962; Stanley and Bock, 1965). Thus it can be assumed that the 23s rRNA is composed of two similar but not necessarily identical halves (Fellner and Sanger, 1968). It has been suggested that the 23s rRNA cistron arose by gene duplication (Woese, 1968). Furthermore, RNA-DNA hybridization studies show that both the 16s and 23s rRNAs compete for the same site (Attardi et al., 1965; Nomura, 1970). This competition suggests that possibly the 16s and 23s rRNAs had evolved from gene duplication starting from a common gene. An alternative concept is that common sequence homologies suggest a common function (Nomura, 1970).

Structure of ribosomal RNA

The primary structure of rRNA can be conceived as being a long flexible molecule that seems to have an asymmetrical base composition that is relatively high in guanine and low in cytosine, at least as far as lower forms are concerned (Osawa, 1968). It has also been shown that the guanine-cytosine (G-C) percentage varies among different organisms, and in general the percentage is lower in the lower eukaryotes and in plant cells. Furthermore, there is an increase in the G-C percentage when going up the evolutionary scale in the animal kingdom (Attardi and Amaldi, 1970). In addition to the major nucleotides (adenine, uracil, guanine, and cytosine) a number of unusual nucleotides have been obtained as well. They are the methylated nucleotides, in which the methyl group can be either on the base or ribose (2′—OH) moieties, and pseudouridylic acid.

Secondary structure. Evidence of the existence of a secondary structure was obtained by various techniques such as infrared spectroscopy (Howard et al., 1964; Miles, 1958), x-ray diffraction and gel diffusion patterns (Klug et al., 1961; Lefkovits and Di Girolamo, 1969), viscosity studies (Gall, 1968), and ultraviolet absorption. As mentioned previously, the primary structure can be considered as a long flexible strand, which is capable of folding upon itself. Thus sections can run in an antiparallel direction. If the nucleotide sequences are complementary, a helical configuration can be obtained. Looping can occur in the secondary structure, where no pairing occurs. As a result, one can envision the secondary structure of rRNA as forming a cloverleaf arrangement similar to that of tRNA.

Tertiary structure. At the present time two models have been proposed for the possible tertiary structure of the rRNAs. One model describes the tertiary structure as consisting of the stacking of the RNAs to form a rod-shaped structure. The other model describes the tertiary structure as helices, which appear to radiate in all directions from their long axis. The primary forces involved are presumed to be electrostatic (Attardi and Amaldi, 1970).

5s rRNA. In 1963 a low molecular weight rRNA was obtained from the large subunit of *Escherichia coli* (Rosset and Monier, 1963). Since that time, this small rRNA has been found in all ribosomes from bacteria to animal and plant cells (Comb and Katz, 1964; Comb et al., 1965; Attardi and Amaldi, 1970). This rRNA has a sedimentary coefficient of 5s (molecular weight of about 40,000). Analysis of the base composition shows that it is similar to the base composition of tRNA, except that it does not contain methylated bases or pseudouridylic acid. Furthermore, this 5s rRNA has no amino acid–accepting ability and is not complementary to the tRNA of the

Table 9-2. Correlation of the nomenclature for ribosomal proteins of *E. coli**

30s proteins				50s proteins			
Berlin	**Uppsala**	**Madison**	**Geneva**	**Berlin**	**Uppsala**	**Berlin**	**Uppsala**
S1	1	P1	13	L1	7	L20	36
S2	4a	P2	11	L2	28	L21	—
S3	5 + 9	P3	10b	L3	11	L22	20
S4	10	P4a	9	L4	14	L23	—
S5	3	P4	8a	L5	6II	L24	21
S6	2	P3b + 3c	10a	L6	9	L25	12
S7	8	P5	7	L7	1	L26	—
S8	2a	P4b	8b	L8	3	L27	30
S9	12	P8	5	L9	3	L28	—
S10	4	P6	6	L10	4	L29	10
S11	11	P7	4c	L11	—	L30	19
S12	15	P10	—	L12	1	L31	—
S13	15b	P10a	—	L13	—	L32	—
S14	12b	P11	—	L14	16	L33	27
S15	14	P10b	4b	L15	25	—	A
S16	6	P9	4a	L16	26II	—	6I
S17	7	P9	3a	L17	26I	—	22
S18	12a	P12	2b	L18	24	—	34
S19	13	P13	2a	L19	23	—	—
S20	16	P14	1				
S21	15a	P15	0				

*From Kurland, C. G. 1972. Structure and function of the bacterial ribosome. Ann. Rev. Biochem. **41:**377-408.

bacterial chromosome. When first studied, it was thought to be a precursor of the tRNA.

The 5s rRNA consists of about 120 nucleotides and, in general, has a high guanine-cytosine content. Yeast is the only exception, where the four bases are in approximately equal amounts. Furthermore, the base sequence shows that the various sequences are repeated twice in the molecule. It is possible to postulate that the 5s molecule is the result of gene duplication, or the symmetry may be related to its function (Brownlee et al., 1967, 1968).

Although it is not known for certain whether the 5s rRNA participates directly in a specific function of the large subunits, it has been shown that it participates in the structural role in the assembly of the large subunit. Fractionation studies have shown that proteins L2, L6, L18 and L25 (Table 9-2) are necessary to bind the 5s rRNA to the 23s rRNA (Monier, 1972).

Ribosomal proteins

Waller and Harris (1961) and Waller (1964) have shown that ribosomes from *E. coli* contain at least twenty-four proteins. Previously it was thought that the ribosome was a relatively simple structure containing multiple copies of one or a few proteins. Since that time, a number of methods have been used to separate the proteins. Among the techniques employed are Lubrol-W (Setterfield et al., 1960), acetic acid (Waller and Harris, 1961, and Waller, 1964), 2-chloroethanol (Fogel and Sypherd, 1968), urea-lithium (Spitnik-Elson, 1965), and the enzyme ribonuclease. These methods yield a variable number of proteins that, by and large, are basic and comparable to histones found in the nucleus. At the present time twenty different proteins are found in the smaller 30s subunits of prokaryotes, and about thirty-four proteins are found in the 50s subunits. In eukaryotic ribosomes the number of proteins is about twenty-three in the smaller 40s subunits and from thirty to thirty-four in the larger 60s subunit (Bielka, et al., 1972). By vigorous purification and separation of proteins by polyacrylamide gels at different concentrations (Nomura, 1970) it is possible to obtain proteins with less than 1% contamination (Kurland, 1972).

Comparison of tryptic peptides (Craven et al., 1969; Stöffler and Wittman, 1971) between various ribosomal proteins show few similarities. Additionally, immunological studies have failed to show cross-reactions between any of the 30s proteins (Kurland, 1972; Nomura, 1970) or with the 50s protein, with the exception of L7 and L12 (Tables 9-2 and 9-3). These two proteins give a complete cross-reaction that demonstrates at least a high sequence homology (Wittman, 1972). Thus it can be assumed that each of the ribosomal proteins is unique.

Stoichiometry

There is strong evidence that ribosomes may be heterogeneous rather than homogeneous due to the number of proteins present. In *E. coli,* for example, the twenty proteins will not fit into the size of the 30s subunit at any one time. Furthermore, the molecular weights of these proteins average about 420,000 daltons compared to the weight of 250,000 daltons for the actual subunit. Thus one would suspect that a class of proteins exists that corresponds to one copy per ribosome (Kurland, 1970).

Analysis of these proteins shows that two classes of proteins do indeed exist: those proteins that range from 0.8 to 1.2 copies per ribosome and those that range from 0.65 to 0.8 copy. The proteins of the former group are classified as unit proteins and are present in all ribosomes. These proteins are necessary for physical assembly (Nomura, 1970). The latter proteins are classified as being fractional proteins and are functional in nature.

It can be assumed that heterogeneity of ribosomes may exist in vivo. If indeed this condition does exist, two interpretations can be formulated to explain this heterogeneity. One is the *static model,* which would mean a permanently differentiated class of ribosomes having different functions. These ribosomes are permanently fixed with the association of specific fractional proteins. The second model is the *steady state model,* in which the unit proteins form the permanent core and the fractional proteins exchange from one ribosome to another in an orderly manner. In protein synthesis each phase, such as initiation, elongation, and termination, is mediated by specific fractional proteins (Nomura, 1970; Kurland, 1972).

Reconstitution of ribosomes

The methodology for the reconstitution of ribosomes had its beginning with the experiment conducted by Brenner, Jacob, and Meselson (1961), when they observed anomalous ribonuclear particles from a bacterial extract in a CsCl density gradient. Later studies showed these anomalous particles to be degraded ribosomes (Meselson et al., 1964), which was the result of splitting between 30% and 40% of their proteins. The degraded ribosomes are called the core particles (CP); the proteins removed are called the split proteins (SP). When the core particles and split proteins are mixed together and incubated, complete ribosomal subunits are again obtained. Each component by itself is inactive, which indicates that each of the proteins contributes to the total overall function of the ribosome.

When the split proteins from the 30s and 50s particles were further separated, acidic (A) and basic (B) fractions were obtained from each subunit (Traub et al., 1967). When 50s core is mixed with sp 50A, a partial activity was obtained. When sp 50B was also added to the mixture, greater activity was observed. It was concluded that sp 50A is essential for function and sp 50B is stimulatory. It was true also with the use of core 30s and mixed with sp 30As and 30Bs. In this case sp 30B was essential for function and sp 30A was stimulatory.

Later, studies were performed on the complete reconstitution of ribosomes (Traub and Nomura, 1969). The 30s subunit and even the 23s core particle were treated with phenol to extract the RNA. The proteins were prepared using lithium chloride methods. One study involved the role of RNA in reconstitution. It was found that RNA must be present for assembly to take place. In addition, 16s RNA from a distant species can replace 16s RNA of *E. coli;* 17s or 18s rRNA would not facilitate ribosomal assembly. This may indicate that there is some similarity of base sequences and that only small segments of the rRNA are involved with the protein interaction (Nomura, 1970).

The second significant group of studies was undertaken to determine the function and assembly of ribosomal proteins in the ribosomal particle (Nomura, 1969, 1970). The method used in the reconstruction consisted of omitting one protein after another in the assembly process. In this manner a number of proteins were found that apparently were necessary for the physical assembly of ribosome or for function. If the reconstituted ribosome sedimented at 20s to 25s or disrupted during centrifugation, it was assumed that the omitted protein was necessary for physical assembly; or if altered function occurred, the protein was necessary for protein synthesis (Table 9-3). One criticism that has been made with this method is that it is assumed that each of the proteins are well defined and that the omission of a protein would lead to the loss of a single function; however, the possibility exists that a loss of any protein could lead to a coordinated loss of all functions (Kurland, 1972).

New techniques to study the structure and function of ribosomes consist of using whole ribosomes and attempting to induce a lesion that can affect a protein and then determining the function of the altered protein (Kurland, 1972). These newer techniques include (1) genetically altered components, (2) alteration of proteins by chemical means, and (3) immunological techniques.

The genetic method has been used with varying success primarily because of the difficulty of finding appropriate components (Nomura, 1970; Kurland, 1972). At the present time only a small number have been studied with sufficient detail (Table 9-3).

Inactivation of ribosomal proteins by the use of various chemicals has been used with varying success, such as chemicals that react with tyrosine, sulfhydryls, and those that show amino group specificity (Moore et al., 1968; Retsema and Conway, 1969). One difficulty with this technique is that it is possible to modify more than one component.

Immunological methods have the advantage of a high degree of specificity (Stöffler and Wittman, 1971a,b), and fortunately all of the 30s and 50s proteins appear to have antigenic characteristics. Furthermore, the antigenic sites of the ribosomal proteins are presumably assessable for interaction with the specific antibodies. This method has been used to identify a 50s fraction, which is required for GTPase activity (Kurland, 1972).

Table 9-3. Summary of data for 30s proteins of *E. coli**

Protein	Molecular weight		Required for assembly	Unit protein	Site-specific RNA complex	Function and mutant phenotype
	Equil.	SDS				
S1	65,000	65,000				mRNA binding
S2	30,000	28,300				A site
S3	31,000	28,200				A site
S4	26,700	26,700	+	+	+	*rpxD, ram* suppressors
S5	24,000	19,600				Spec R
S6	18,000	15,600				
S7	21,500	22,700	+	+	+	
S8	17,600	15,500	+	+	+	
S9	21,600	16,200	+	+		
S10	16,000	12,400				
S11	18,300					mRNA-tRNA interaction
S12	19,000	17,200				SmD, SmR
S13		14,900				
S14	15,600	14,000				A site
S15	13,200	12,500			+	
S16	13,500	11,700	+	+		
S17	10,700	10,900	+	+		
S18	14,600	12,200				
S19	15,000	13,100				
S20	14,000	12,000			+	
S21	13,000	12,200				mRNA-tRNA interaction

*From Kurland, C. G. 1972. Structure and function of the bacterial ribosome. Ann. Rev. Biochem. **41**:377-408.

Spec R (spectinomycin resistant); SmD (streptomycin dependence); SmR (streptomycin resistance).

Biosynthesis of ribosomal proteins

At the present time two theories have been proposed to account for the source of ribosomal proteins. One states that the nascent rRNA can function as its own mRNA for the synthesis of ribosomal proteins (Otaka et al., 1964). It was shown that nascent rRNA was able to stimulate amino acid incorporation. One disadvantage of this theory is that the size of the 16s or 23s rRNA, for example, is not large enough to specify all the proteins in either the 30s or 50s subunits. Probably at the most the 16s could synthesize three to five proteins, and the 23s could synthesize about six to ten. If indeed there is a messenger function in rRNA, proteins that directly interact with the RNA could be synthesized by the rRNA and properly aligned on the molecule (Nomura, 1970).

The other theory proposes that the synthesis occurs typically in the cytoplasm on ribosomes or polysomes by mRNA rather than by nascent rRNA.

Synthesis of ribosomes in prokaryotic cells

Early tracer studies using ^{14}C-uracil on *E. coli* cultures showed that material incorporated into the ribosomes passes through several precursor stages prior to becoming ribosomal (McCarthy and Aronson, 1961; McCarthy et al., 1962). These studies showed that radioactivity first appeared in a group of particles sedimenting between 8s and 20s, having a peak at 14s. Later, radioactivity was found in particles sedimenting at 30s and 43s and, still later, in the 30s and 50s ribosomal subunits. The 14s particle was called the *eosome* and was considered to be the precursor particles of the 16s and 23s rRNA. Eosomes could be considered unfinished chains of RNA and, with the addition of some protein, would become 30s and 40s *neosome* particles. Finally, with the addition of more ribosomal protein the definitive 30s and 50s subunits would be formed. Although these early studies indicated the stepwise assembly of ribosomes, they were complicated by the fact that mRNA contaminated their results.

Later, studies using pulse labeled ^{3}H-uridine from "shift-up" cultures of *E. coli* (Kono and Osawa, 1964) and from "fragile" *E. coli* cultures confirmed the stepwise assembly of ribosomes. In these studies the shift-up cultures yielded a number of ribosomal particles sedimenting at 26s, 30s, and 40s and, finally, the 30s and 50s particles. (The 30s pulse-labeled particle was differentiated from the 30s subunit by having a slightly lower density in CsCl.) The results from the fragile culture yielded 26s, 32s, and 40s ribonuclear protein particles. Comparison of these results show that 26s, 30s, and 32s particles contain 16s rRNA and can be considered precursors of the 30s subunit. Similarly, the 40s and 43s subparticles contain 23s mRNA and are the precursors of the 50s subunit.

Use of protein inhibitors such as chloramphenicol (Nomura and Watson, 1959), puromycin (Sells, 1964; Nakada, 1956b), and streptomycin also confirms the stepwise assembly of prokaryotic ribosomes.

The conversion of nascent rRNA to the mature form evidently involves the addition of methyl groups, the conversion of uridylic acid to pseudouridylic acid, and the cleavage of nonribosomal stretches (Nomura, 1970).

Synthesis in eukaryotes

Many studies have shown the nucleolus to be the exclusive region for ribosomal synthesis. Such function of the nucleolus was probably first demonstrated by histochemical techniques (Caspersson and Schultz, 1940) and later by autoradiographic techniques (Karasaki, 1965; Granboulan and Granboulan, 1965). When the nucleoli are irradiated and then treated with ^{3}H-cytidine, nucleolar activities are abolished (Perry, 1960). In this method irradiation destroys the nucleolar region so that ribosomal synthesis is abolished. Probably the most significant is the *Xenopus laevis* mutant in which no nucleoli are formed and, as a result, no ribosomes are produced (Brown and Gurdon, 1964).

Historically, T'so et al. (1958), using ribosomes from pea seedlings, demonstrated that the 80s particle first dissociates into the 60s and 40s component. When more magnesium (Mg^{++}) is removed from the system, the 60s is further degraded into 40s particles, each of which breaks down into two 26s units. This subunit preparation appears to be homogenous in composition, which suggests that the 80s, 60s, and 40s components represent hexamers, tetramers, and dimers of 26s particles. The molecular weight of the 26s subunit is approximately 700,000. Similar composition was obtained from hepatic ribosomes.

Recent studies using HeLa cells and L cells have shown the presence of a large 45s precursor molecule. When RNA preparations were labeled with ^{3}H or ^{14}C uridine, the 45s molecule appears within 5 minutes, and after 25 minutes the radioactivity appeared in the 32s and 18s rRNA and later in the 28s rRNA. When RNA synthesis was inhibited with the use of actinomycin, no new 45s rRNA was synthesized. The 45s rRNA that was originally present disappeared, and 32s and 18s rRNA was present. Still later, the rRNA contained 28s units. It was concluded that the 45s rRNA by cleavage will give rise to 28s and 18s rRNA (Scherrer et al., 1963).

Probably simultaneously or shortly after synthesis the 45s rRNA undergoes methylation. Evidence shows that most methylation occurs at this early stage (Greenberg and Penman, 1966). It has been shown (Aronson and Holowczyk, 1965) that the amount of methylation corresponds with an equimolar 28s and 18s rRNA. Furthermore, if one assumes that methylation occurs at the time of synthesis of 45s rRNA, the total time for synthesis is 2 to 3 minutes. Also, the conversion of uridylic to pseudouridylic acid presumably takes place either exclusively or at least primarily at the 45s stage and perhaps while the molecule is being synthesized (Greenberg and Penman, 1966).

The technique of cell fractionation whereby the nucleolus, nucleoplasm, and cytoplasm can be separated has made it possible to study not only the conversion of the 45s rRNA into the 18s and 28s rRNA but also to study the stepwise assembly of the ribonucleonic subunits.

Tracer studies have shown that the 18s rRNA, which arises from the cleavage of the 45s rRNA, is rapidly transferred to the cytoplasm. This occurs 20 to 25 minutes after the incorporation of the tracer precursors. The 32s rRNA, on the other hand, remains in the nucleolus for about 1 hour after the incorporation of the tracer material. It is transformed into the 28s rRNA and then transferred to the cytoplasm (Greenberg and Penman, 1966).

Furthermore, with the use of ultraviolet absorption sedimentation profile as well as polyacrylamide gel electrophoresis it is possible to trace the stepwise conversion of the 45s precursor molecule into the 28s and 18s rRNAs (Weinberg et al., 1967). Ultraviolet profile has shown a number of major and minor peaks, which indicate that the 45s rRNA is converted to a 41s, to a 36s, to a 32s, and finally, to the 28s rRNA. Similarly, peaks corresponding to 24s, 20s, and 18s rRNA were observed. Thus it can be assumed that the 41s, 36s, and 32s rRNAs are precursors of the 28s rRNA and that the 24s and 20s rRNAs are precursors to the 18s rRNA. (Fig. 9-2).

Sedimentation analysis has shown that the 45s molecule is much longer than the combined 18s and 28s molecules. Furthermore, in the conversion of the 45s precursor molecule to the 32s rRNA approximately 50% of the molecule was not conserved. About 20% of the 32s was not conserved when converted to the 28s rRNA (Attardi and Amaldi, 1970) (Fig. 9-2).

Analysis of the nonribosomal stretches

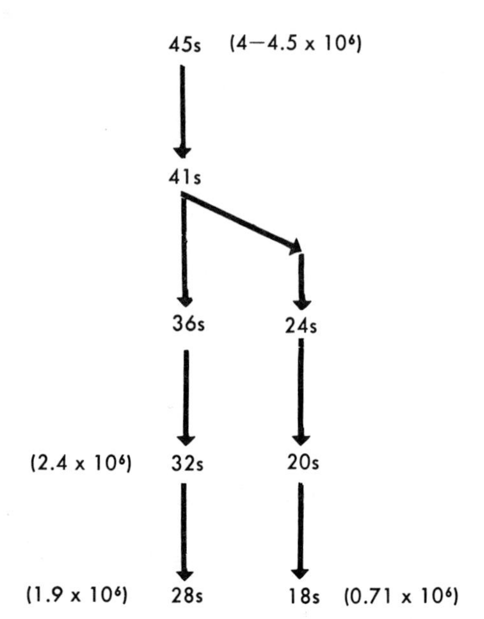

Fig. 9-2. Flow diagram showing the conversion of 45s rRNA into 18s and 28s rRNAs. Figures in parentheses are the molecular weights of the various precursor molecules. The maturation of the large molecules implies a nonconservative transition to the mature rRNAs. (Data from Weinberg et al., 1967; McConkey and Hopkins, 1969; Liau and Perry, 1969.)

that were discarded shows that they are high in guanine and cytosine and are nonmethylated (Willems et al., 1968).

At the present time it is difficult to postulate the functional role played by these nonribosomal stretches. In the section on the biosynthesis of ribosomal proteins it was mentioned that rRNA may have a messenger function, yet the analysis of the nonribosomal stretches would seem to rule out this function because of its repetitive sequences (Weinberg et al., 1967). An alternative may be that it is involved in the formation of the secondary structure.

Subunit formation

There is evidence that as the 45s rRNA molecule is being synthesized, it becomes associated with some proteins (Liau and Perry, 1969). Several nascent ribonuclear particles were isolated from nucleoli of L cells. In the presence of EDTA buffer these particles had the sedimentation coefficient of 80s, 65s, and 55s. Analysis of these ribonuclear protein particles has shown that the 80s particles can contain 45s, some 36s, and possibly 41s or 36s rRNAs. The 55s ribonuclear protein particles contain 32s and 28s rRNAs, as well as some 5s rRNA. In general, the 7s rRNA is absent from the

Table 9-4. Summary of the biogenesis of eukaryotic ribosomes from HeLa and L cells*

Particle size	Protein composition	rRNA present
Nucleolus		
80s	57%	45s, 41s, 32s
65s	53%	36s, 32s
55s	44%	32s, some 28s Some 5s
Cytoplasm		
50s (60s)†	43.4%	28s, 7s, 5s
30s-33s (40s)	58%	18s

*Data from Warner and Soeiro, 1967; Liau and Perry, 1969.
†60s and 40s sediment at a lower s value in EDTA buffer.

55s but becomes evident in the 50s cytoplasmic particle. The 30s, containing an 18s rRNA, arises early in the maturation of the ribosome (Table 9-4).

Similar results were obtained from HeLa cell nucleoli (Warner and Soeiro, 1967).

Regulation of rRNA synthesis

Regulation of rRNA synthesis is poorly understood at this time. In bacteria the rate of protein synthesis is apparently directly related to the number of ribosomes present (Kennel and Magasanik, 1962; Kjeldgaard, 1961). If, for example, bacteria are transferred from a minimal to a rich culture, there is an immediate acceleration of rRNA synthesis, whereas the overall synthesis of DNA and protein are delayed for a period of time (Schleif, 1967). The reverse is also obtained when bacterial cultures are shifted from a rich to a minimal culture. The rate of rRNA synthesis is inhibited temporarily and then resumes at a rate characteristic for the medium. Several hypotheses have been proposed, yet none seems to explain the regulation adequately. One hypothesis is that the presence of uncharged tRNA acts as a repressor of rRNA synthesis (Kurland and Maaloe, 1962). Another is that the presence of free ribosomes or subunits acts as a repressor of rRNA synthesis (Morris and DeMoss, 1966).

With the regulation there must be some coordination among all the rRNAs. In bacteria, as seen previously, all the rRNAs are synthesized independently, yet hybridization studies indicate that the genetic loci of the 16s, 23s, and 5s rRNAs are clustered together (Dubnau et al., 1965). It is possible that a promoter region that uses a α-like factor of RNA polymerase may be specific for these genes and therefore lead to coordination of synthesis (Nomura, 1970).

Eukaryotes, by having a single 45s rRNA, can ensure coordination with the 18s and 28s rRNAs. However, the coordination with the 5s rRNA is difficult to conceive because the cistrons for the 5s rRNA are not linked with the 45s molecule, yet coordination does occur. As mentioned previously with regard to the nucleolar location for the synthesis of rRNA, it was stated that the *Xenopus laevis* mutation fails to form the nucleoli and therefore lacks the cistrons for producing the 18s and 28s rRNAs. It does, however, have cistrons for the 5s rRNA, yet also fails to produce 5s rRNAs.

Electron microscopy

Detailed electron microscopic studies of purified ribosomes from *E. coli* show the 30s particle to be an asymmetrical prolate ellipsoid that has an average measurement of approximately 95 × 170 Å (Hall and Slayter, 1959) and is somewhat concave or indented at one end. On the other hand, the 50s subunit is more nearly spherical but is flattened on one side. Its measurements are approximately 170 × 140 Å (Hall and Slayter, 1959) or about 140 × 160 Å in diameter (Huxley and Zubay, 1960). When the 70s ribosome is seen, it is composed of two subunits of unequal size, that is, a 30s and a 50s particle. The larger (the 50s unit) has its more flattened side in contact with the smaller, or 30s, unit (Figs. 9-1 and 9-3). The overall dimension of the 70s ribosome is about 130 × 160 Å; the shorter dimension is in the direction of the axis, joining the large and small units together (Huxley and Zubay, 1960). When the 100s particle (a dimer of the 70s particle) is seen under the electron microscope, it consists of two 70s particles in which the two small 30s subunits are opposed to one another (Figs. 9-1 and 9-3).

After negative staining with phosphotungstic acid the ribosomes, that is, the 70s particles, appear to be irregular in outline and to have a distinct cleft present between the 30s and 50s subunits. In the 100s dimer the opposed subunits (the two 30s subunits) may have a crescentic or triangular shape. The area of contact is displaced to one side of the long axis so that a

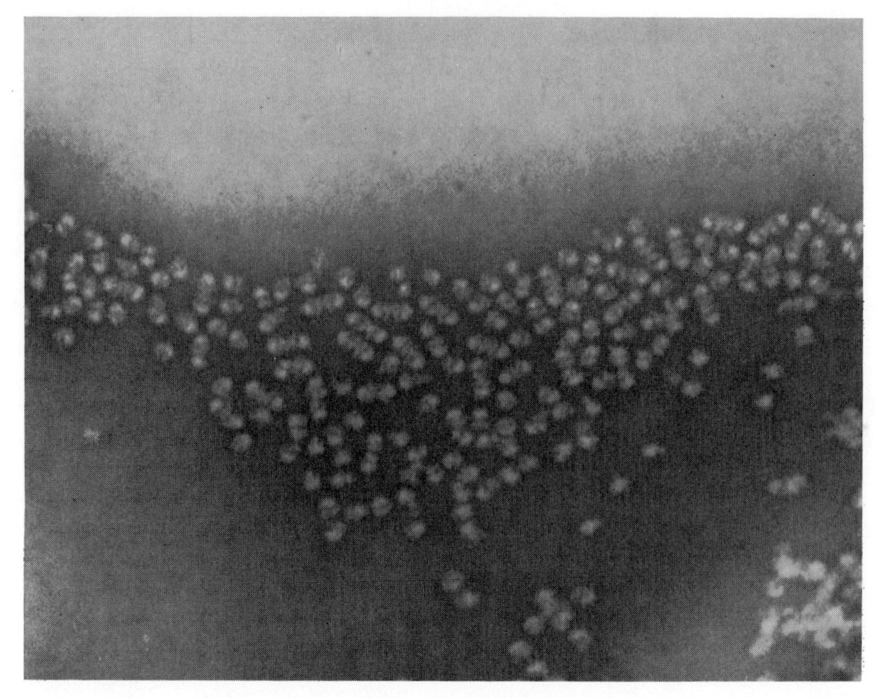

Fig. 9-3. Negatively stained mixture of 100s and 70s particles from *E. coli.* The 70s component can be identified as containing two unequal subunits, whereas the 100s particles contain two monomeric forms joined together at their smaller (30s) subunits. (From Huxley, H. E., and G. Zubay. 1960. J. Molec. Biol. **2:**10-18.)

wedged space can often be seen. In general, the shape of the 30s particle is less distinct with negative staining. When uncombined, they may appear as triangles and polygons. In addition, they show a lower contrast than do the 50s particles and are presumed to be much thinner (Huxley and Zubay, 1960) (Fig. 9-3).

When stained with uranyl acetate (a stain for the demonstration of nucleic acids and other substances), there is no visible cleft in the region of the junction between the subunits in the 70s ribosome (Fig. 9-4). This may indicate that these two units are in close contact, presumably in molecular contact, which obliterates the gap, whereas in negative staining, the lower protein concentration at the junction allows for penetration.

Further structure revealed by electron microscopy is that occasionally the 50s and 30s subunits appear to have a fibril attached to each, which suggests that the 30s unit is tightly bound to the fibrillar component of the 50s unit.

Electron microscopy of ribosomal subunits from eukaryotes reveals that they are essentially the same in size and shape. The 40s subunit, like the 30s prokaryotic unit, is a prolate, but it is divided into two regions of unequal size, the contact between appearing in electron micrographs as a dense line. The 60s subunit is isometric with a flattened face that binds to the smaller subunit (Sabatini et al., 1972).

Polysomes

Although ribosomes serve as sites for protein synthesis, numerous studies have shown that the functional units are clusters of ribosomes, collectively called *polysomes, polyribosomes,* or *ergosomes* rather than

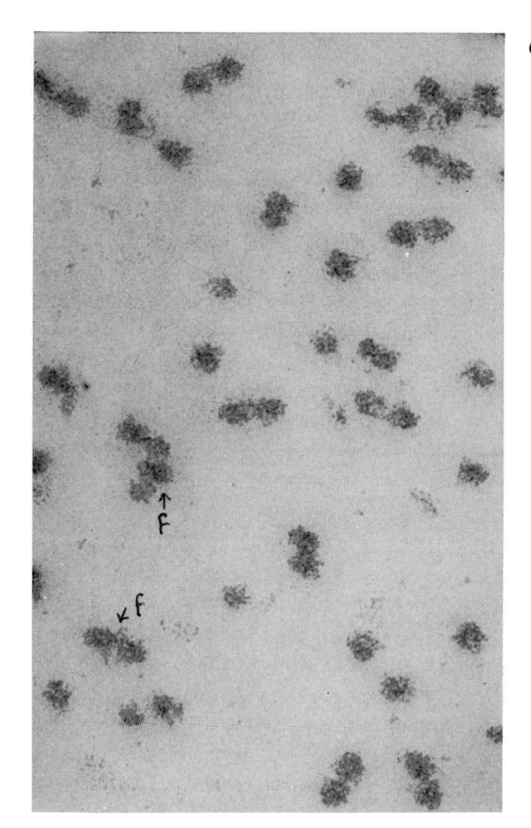

Fig. 9-4. Mixture of both 100s and 70s particles stained with uranyl acetate. The 70s particles show no divisions into subunits. Several particles show internal structures such as a fenestrated appearance as seen opposite the arrows. (From Huxley, H. E., and G. Zubay, 1960. J. Molec. Biol. **2:** 10-18.)

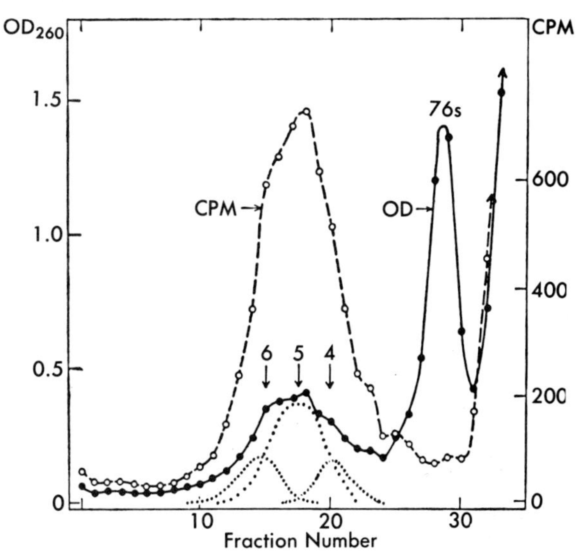

Fig. 9-5. Graphic representation of experiments demonstrating that protein synthesis (hemoglobin) takes place on polysomes. In this experiment, rabbit reticulocytes were incubated for 45 seconds in amino acids labeled with ^{14}C. Cells were osmotically lysed, and 1 mm of the lysate was layered on sucrose gradient and centrifuged at 25,000 rpm for 2 hours. Optical density at 260 nm for RNA showed two peaks, one sedimenting at 76s corresponding to single ribosomes and another sedimenting several times faster corresponding to tetramers, pentamers, and hexamers (arrows labeled 4, 5, and 6 represent the various polysomes). The high radioactivity, **CPM,** is associated with ribosomal tetramers, pentamers, and hexamers. Dotted curves represent distribution of the various polysomes. Electron micrographs of reticulocyte polysomes are shown in Figs. 9-6 to 9-8. (From Warner, J. R., A. Rich, and C. E. Hall. 1962. Science **138:**1399-1403.)

single ribosomes. Electron micrographs show that all the ribsomes of a polysome are attached to an mRNA (Figs. 9-1 and 9-5 to 9-7). Early evidence of the possible existence of polysomes was obtained from sedimentation constants obtained from bacteria, which indicated that, in addition to single ribosomes, some dimers and trimers were also present. Much of the difficulty of studying and establishing polysome formation centered about the means of preparation of tissues and organisms. The harshness to which the tissues are subjected to study ribosomes also destroys these functional clusters.

The establishment of the polysome as a functional entity was derived from rabbit reticulocytes (Warner et al., 1962, 1963; Rich et al., 1963). These cells represent a stage in the development of the mature erythrocyte and are characterized by a basophilic cytoplasm. This cell type synthesizes only hemoglobin molecules and has the added advantage that it can be broken up with minimal manipulation.

Collections of these cells were treated

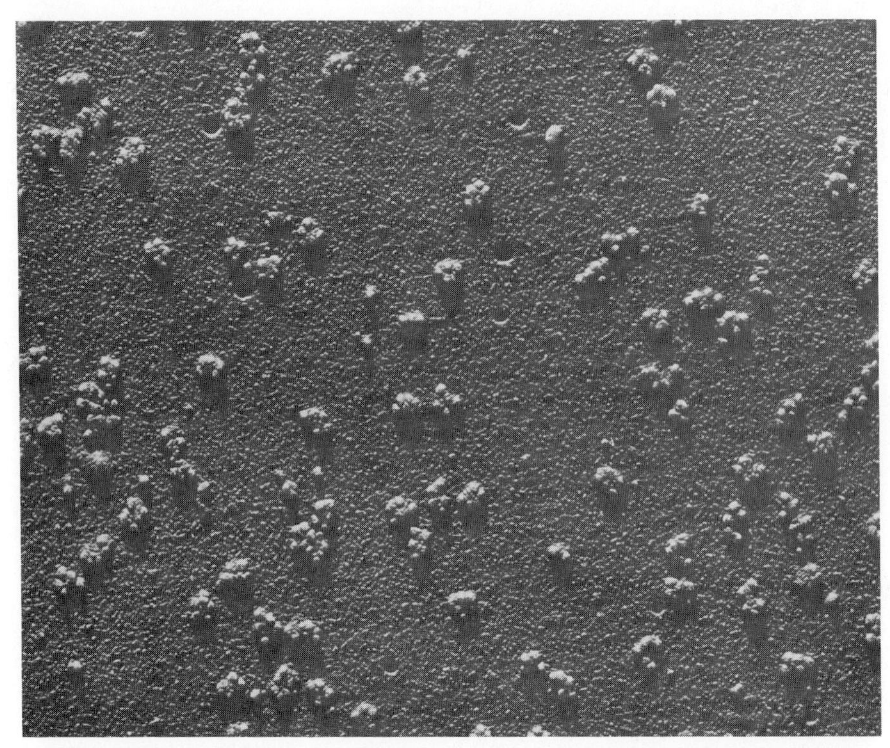

Fig. 9-6. Electron micrograph of reticulocyte polysomes. These polysomes represent the 170s fraction. (From Warner, J. R., A. Rich, and C. E. Hall. 1962. Sciences **138:**1399-1403.)

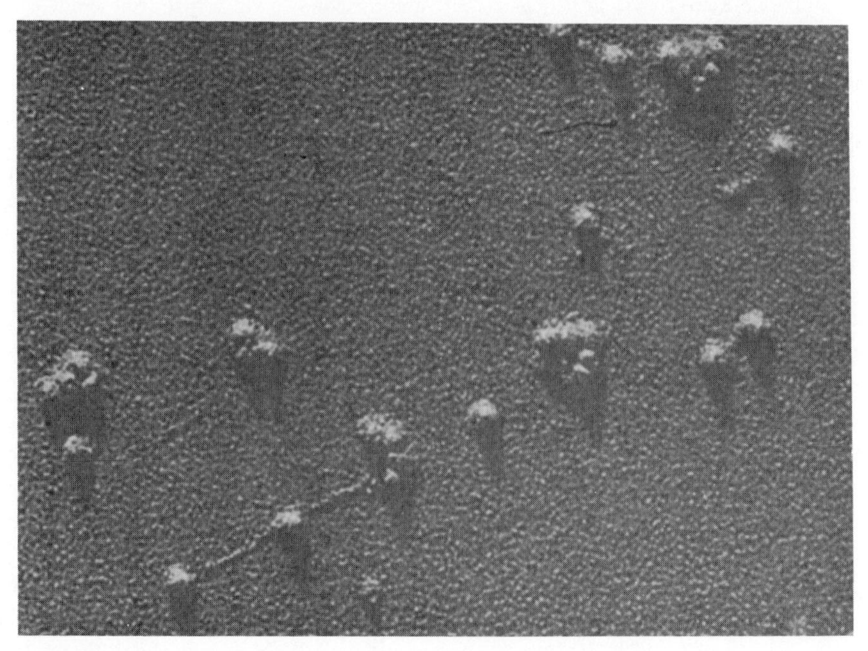

Fig. 9-7. The 170s fraction showing strands connecting the ribosomal units. These strands presumably represent mRNA. (From Warner, J. R., A. Rich, and C. E. Hall. 1962. Science **138:**1399-1403.)

with ^{14}C amino acids for 45 seconds, after which the reaction was stopped and the cells disrupted by osmotic lysis. Density gradient studies established the presence of a single sharp band and a broader and heavier band (Fig. 9-5). The latter contained the radioactive material. The sharp peak corresponded to single 78s particles, whereas the 170s band contained aggregates of ribosomes. From the sedimentation constant obtained the 170s band probably contained a cluster of five ribosomes. In addition, the broad band indicated this presence of tetramers as well as hexamers. The latter constituted 10% of the total, the 170s particles about 75% of the total.

It was assumed that the 170s band represented aggregates of ribosomes held together by mRNA. Furthermore, it was assumed that if this were the case, treatment with low-level amounts of ribonuclease should destroy the mRNA and produce individual 76s particles, each of which should contain nascent proteins attached to them. Such was the case, and 76s particles were formed from the 170s aggregate, and

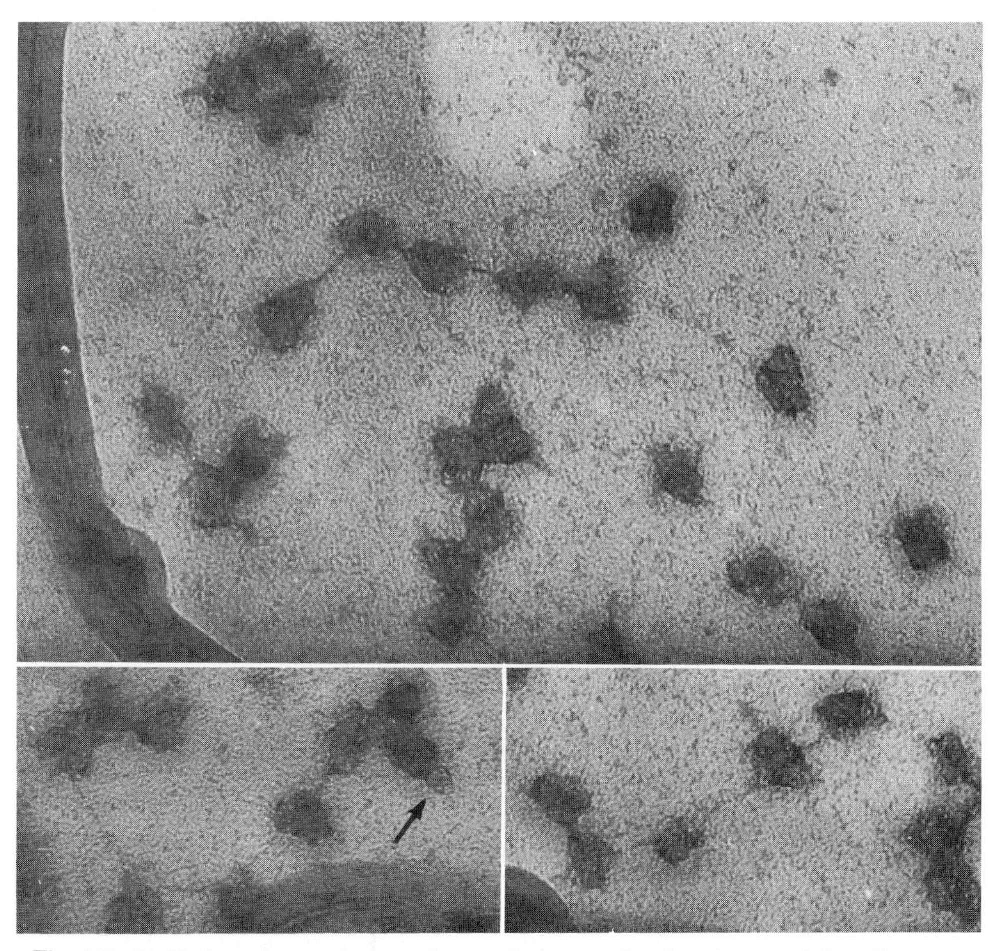

Fig. 9-8. Positively stained polysomes from reticulocytes showing clusters of five ribosomes connected by mRNA. The mRNA measures approximately 10 to 15 Å in diameter. A ribosomal subunit can be seen at the end of the arrow. (From Rich, A., J. R. Warner, and H. M. Goodman. 1963. Cold Spring Harbor Symp. Quant. Biol. **28**:269-285.)

each contained a polypeptide that could be identified by ^{14}C-tagged amino acids incorporated onto these ribosomes.

Some of the 170s polysomes were air dried, and electron micrographs showed clusters of polysomes, usually five in number (Fig. 9-6). The center-to-center spacing between the ribosomal units measured 300 to 350 Å. It was possible at times to see a fiber measuring 10 to 20 Å thick connecting the ribosomes together (Fig. 9-7). With uranyl acetate stain a definite fiber of similar thickness was observed (Fig. 9-8). Since uranyl acetate is somewhat specific for nucleic acid, this fiber connecting the ribosome is probably mRNA. The length of this mRNA was about 1,500 Å.

Hemoglobin consists of four polypeptide units, each with a molecular weight of 16,000. Each of these polypeptide subunits contains 150 amino acids. Assuming a triplet coding, that is, a code of three bases per amino acid, the mRNA would contain 450 bases. Furthermore, each base is approximately 3.4 Å thick, giving the mRNA a 1,500 Å length, which corresponds to the length of mRNA obtained by electron microscopy.

In general, the number of ribosomes per polysome depends on the length of the particular mRNA (Penman et al., 1963). It has been shown, for example, that the number of ribosomes per cluster may be as many as fifty or more in poliovirus polysomes (Rich et al., 1963).

The flexibility of the mRNA is partly responsible for the various shapes of polysomes observed. It has been shown (Wettstein et al., 1963) that in a curved polysome aggregate the 30s particles of the ribosomes are oriented toward the center.

Function

The precise role of ribosomes in the synthesis of proteins was not fully understood at first. It was thought that they performed the passive role of holding the mRNA; the surface acted as a condensing site for the growing polypeptide chain. With more information of the composition of the ribosome it became increasingly evident that the two subunits are structurally and functionally different and act in a coordinated manner to synthesize proteins. One can conceive the ribosome as forming a two-site structure, in which the smaller subunit acts as a binding site for the mRNA. The larger subunit has one site for the growing peptide, called the D, or *donor site* (peptidyl site) and a second site the A, or *acceptor site* (aminoacyl site). In addition to the ribosome, mRNA and tRNAs are also involved, as are the various fractions necessary for initiation, elongation, and termination.

Messenger RNA (mRNA)

The term "messenger RNA" was proposed by Jacob and Monod (1961) for a polynucleotide that contains the information for determining protein structure. Accordingly, mRNA is transcribed from the DNA template and embodies in it the necessary genetic information as to the sequence and number of amino acids necessary for a specific protein. Such mRNA contains sequences for a number of different proteins. One characteristic is that the length of the molecule should be variable, depending on the size of the protein it codes. Another characteristic is that it should be complementary to a portion of one strand of DNA and should have a base composition similar to DNA, with the exception that uracil replaces thymine. It should therefore hybridize with the DNA from which it was transcribed.

In eukaryotic cells each mRNA strand codes for one protein, whereas in some bacteria such as *E. coli* and *Salmonella typhimurium* and in some phages such as QβRNA and R17 phage, mRNA forms polycistronic strands that code for more than one protein. Some information is available as to the nature of the secondary structure of the various mRNAs. The mRNAs that code for a single protein have, presumably, a coiled structure, but whether this condition exists on the ribosome is poorly established at this time (Geiduschek and Haselkorn, 1969). On the other hand, in polycistronic mRNA there are intensive regions of looped structures (Steitz, 1969; Hindley and Staples, 1969). There is evidence also of extensive regions that form double helices, and this helical arrangement may play a role in the regulation of gene expression; that is, the only initiation site is exposed to start the synthesis of a protein, whereas the other initiation sites are concealed within the secondary structure. As protein synthesis progresses, the coiling loosens and exposes the initiation site to start the second protein while the first protein goes on to completion. Other initiation sites on a polycistronic strand can be exposed in this manner.

Transcription of mRNA involves RNA polymerase and ribonucleotide triphosphates. These enzymes catalyze the polymerization; they join together the various nucleotides and catalyze the chain in vitro and in vivo in a 5′ → 3′ polarity (Geiduschek and Haselkorn, 1969). In the process of polymerization the RNA polymerase attaches to the DNA strand at the initiator site and continues to catalyze the action until the terminator site is reached. The specificity of binding and initiation is determined by the DNA and RNA polymerase alone.

Generally, the life-span of mRNA is relatively short, although in some eukaryotic

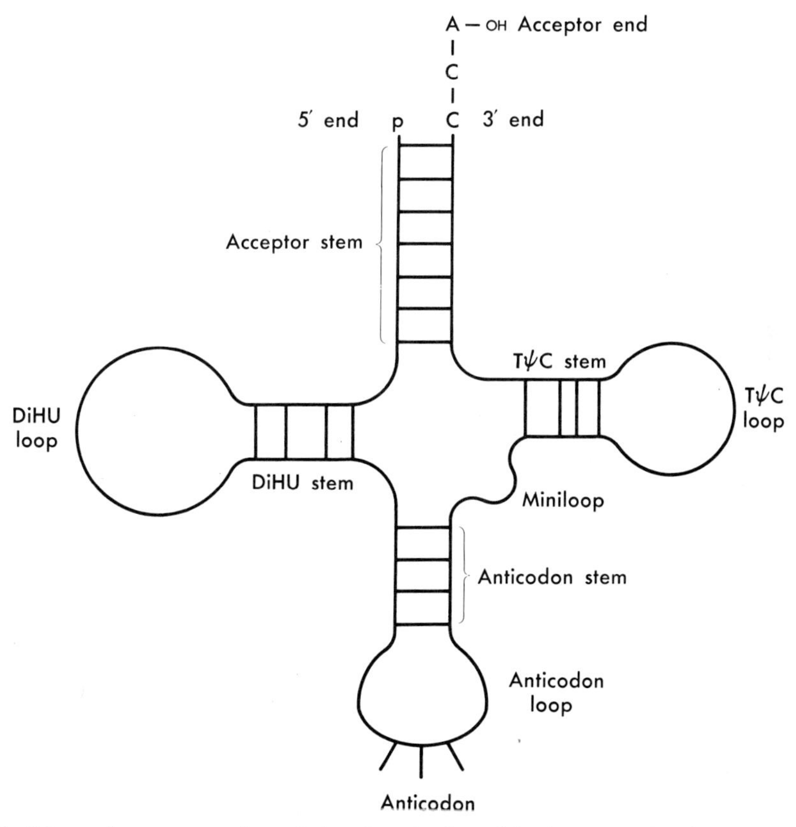

Fig. 9-9. Schematic representation of the cloverleaf model of transfer RNA. C-C-A located on the acceptor arm is common to all tRNAs as is T-ψ-C located at the bottom of the T-ψ-C loop. DiHU is dihydrouridine; T, ribothymidine; ψ, pseudouridylic acid.

cells there is evidence of some degree of stability. The degradation of mRNA is probably achieved by action of polynucleotide phosphorylase and potassium-activated RNAase II (Geiduschek and Haselkorn, 1969).

Transfer RNA (tRNA)

tRNA constitutes the third type of RNA. This class of small ribonucleic acids functions as amino acid adapter molecules, carrying specific amino acids into specific places on the protein synthesizing mechanism.

This class of small RNAs has a sedimentation value of about 4s and a molecular weight of approximately 25,000 daltons. Each tRNA is composed of about eighty nucleotides. In most prokaryotes they constitute 10% to 20% of the RNA.

From available evidence it is generally agreed that the cloverleaf model (Fig. 9-9) is probably the best two-dimensional representation. Little is known of the three-dimensional form itself (Zachau, 1972). Analysis of the cloverleaf shows that all tRNAs show the same composition of (CCA—OH) at the 3′ end. This constitutes the acceptor end for receiving the amino acids; the 5′ end of most tRNAs is guanine. At the opposite end of the acceptor site is the anticodon loop, which contains a specific triplet code for a specific amino acid. Thus there is one (or more) specific tRNA for each of the twenty naturally occurring amino acids. Involved in transferring the amino acid to the tRNA is a specific aminoacyl-activating enzyme (aminoacyl-RNA-synthetase). The specificity of the enzyme-tRNA-amino acid reaction appears to lie in a specific region of the tRNA configurative, the recognition site for the synthetase enzyme, which, for different tRNAs lies in different loci on the molecule. In general, the acceptor stem, the stem of dihydrouridine, and the miniloop region have been implicated as the recognition site for many tRNAs. The anticodon is, of course, essential in all tRNAs (Zachau, 1972).

As mentioned earlier, there is a specific aminoacyl synthetase enzyme for each of the twenty amino acids. The enzymatic reaction involving the loading of tRNAs with amino acid represents the following two-step sequence:

1. Aminoacyl synthetase + AA + ATP $\rightleftharpoons$ Aminoacyl synthetase · AA · AMP + P_i
2. Aminoacyl synthetase · AA · AMP + tRNA $\rightleftharpoons$ AA · tRNA + Aminoacyl synthetase + AMP AA = amino acid; ATP = adenosine triphosphate; AMP = adenosine monophosphate; P_i = inorganic phosphate

In this reaction the carboxyl group of the amino acid reacts with the 2′ or 3′ hydroxy group of the ribose moiety of the terminal adenosine (Novelli, 1967).

Initiation of protein synthesis

Initiation of protein synthesis in the ribosome is a complex step involving mRNA, formyl methionine-tRNA (′fmet-tRNA), the initiation factors F_1, F_2, and F_3, GTP, and the 30s subunit. In this process the smaller subunit recognizes the initiation codon AUG on the mRNA and binds to it. The ′fmet-tRNA attaches to the 30s mRNA complex. After the initiation of this complex the 50s subunit combines with the complex to form the complete prokaryotic 70s ribosome.

Prokaryotes have two species of methionine-tRNA, only one of which is formylated. ′fmet-tRNA is formylated by the enzyme met-tRNA transformylase (Marcker and Sanger, 1964; Marcker, 1965) after the attachment of methionine. The function of the formyl group may be to block the amino end of the amino acid to prevent any reaction with other amino acids. ′fmet-tRNA recognizes the codons AUG and GUG and will deliver methionine only to the terminal position. met-tRNA will deliver methionine only to an internal position. It, too, recognizes the codon AUG for methionine (Clark and Marcker, 1965). It is not known why met-tRNA will deliver methionine to internal positions only and not to the initiation site.

In polycistronic mRNA each of the proteins produced is initiated by 'fmet-tRNA.

In all protein synthesis in prokaryotes as well as in eukaryotic cells all initiation starts with the codon AUG located on the mRNA. Unfortunately the codon AUG does not always occupy the 5'-terminus position. Frequently it is preceded by a large number of bases (Billeter et al., 1969).

The role of initiation factors is unclear, yet they are required. Factor F_2 seems to stabilize the subunit mRNA complex (Kurland, 1972), and at the same time guides 'fmet-tRNA to the initiation complex. In this process the complex that binds to the ribosomal subunit is a ternary complex, consisting of F_2-GTP-fmet-tRNA. F_2 has a GTPase activity and catalyzes the hydrolysis of GTP to GDP after the 50s subunit has joined the 30s subunit (Kolakofsky et al., 1969).

F_3 appears to be necessary when natural mRNA is used, but apparently it is unnecessary when synthetic mRNAs are used. It may function in fixing the reading frame of the translation of mRNA. Involved would be 30s-mRNA-F_3 (Kurland, 1972).

The precise role of F_1 is not well known. In general, if the 50s subunit is absent from the initiation complex, F_1 is not needed, although some exception may occur. It appears to form a complex with the 30s subunit and is released when the 50s subunit is present to form the 70s monomer. There is some evidence that either F_1 or F_3 may function as a dissociation factor for the dissociation of the intact ribosome, and dissociation is necessary for initiation to take place (Lucas-Lenard and Lipman, 1971; Kurland, 1972).

Initiation of protein synthesis in the cell organelles, mitochondria, and chloroplasts is, in general, similar to that of prokaryotes. Two types of met-tRNA are present, one of which is formylated and will deliver methionine to the terminal position; the other, as in prokaryotes, will deliver methionine to the internal positions (Lucas-Lenard and Lipman, 1971).

Biosynthesis in eukaryotic cells is less well known than in prokaryotes. However, it was shown that eukaryotes contain two species of met-tRNA, one of which can be formylated by the enzyme transformylase (Caskey et al., 1967) obtained from *E. coli.* When formylated, the met-tRNA is capable of initiating protein synthesis in an *E. coli* cell-free system (RajBhandary and Ghosh, 1969). Further studies, however, have shown that this enzyme transformylase does not exist in eukaryotic cytoplasm. To differentiate these two met-tRNA, $tRNA^{Met}_{F*}$ and $tRNA^{Met}_{M*}$ are used (Smith and Marcker, 1970). Thus $tRNA^{Met}_{F*}$ is homologous with 'fmet-tRNA in prokaryotes and cell organelles and is the initiation of protein synthesis. Met-$tRNA_{M*}$ is homologous to met-tRNA and delivers methionine to internal positions. In addition, the initiation factors M_1, M_2, and M_3 are involved. They are no doubt homologous to factors F_1, F_2, and F_3 found in prokaryotes.

Fate of formyl and methionine

Not all proteins have methionine in the terminal position. Since all proteins when initiated begin with formyl methionine in prokaryotes and methionine in eukaryotes, some mechanism must be present to selectively cleave off the formyl from the polypeptide as well as methionine from a number of proteins. An enzyme deformylase has been found in a number of bacteria, *E. coli* for example (Takeda and Webster, 1968; and Adams, 1968), which is capable of cleaving the formyl group from methionine. In addition, an enzyme (amino peptidase) has been found in extracts of bacteria that is capable of removing methionine from the polypeptide. Presumably an enzyme similar or identical to amino peptidase is present in eukaryotes that is capable of removing methionine from some of the proteins. In a number of studies (for example, in the synthesis of hemoglobin) it has been shown that methionine is removed from the growing polypeptide chain early in the biosynthetic process (Jackson and Hunter, 1970). It has been estimated that this amino acid is removed by the time the first fifteen to twenty amino acids have been added.

It is of interest to note that if met-tRNA is formylated and used in the synthesis of hemoglobin, the formyl methionine remains attached. The cytoplasm of eukaryotes contain no deformylase enzyme to cleave the formyl group from the methionine, and amino peptidase action is blocked by the presence of formyl (Housman et al., 1970).

Elongation process

The process of elongation consists of adding amino acids to the growing polypeptide chain. The following three steps are involved:

1. The anticodon of the aminoacyl-tRNA (AA · tRNA) reacts with the codon on the mRNA. Hydrogen bonds are involved in this reaction. Bonding is also achieved with several proteins present in the 30s and 50s subunits. The aminoacyl-tRNA is attached to the A site of the ribosome (Gilbert, 1963).
2. This step results in the formation of a peptide bond between the amino acid and the growing polypeptide or 'fmet-tRNA if initiation has just been completed. The polypeptide chain (or fmet) is transferred from its position at the P site to the aminoacyl-tRNA located at the A site.
3. This step includes the discharge of the unloaded tRNA from the P site. The mRNA moves one codon in relation to the ribosome, and the polypeptide chain is also moved back again to the P site, leaving the A site open to receive another aminoacyl-tRNA. This step is repeated after the addition of each amino acid until the polypeptide is discharged.

In the mechanics of elongation the first step is insertion of the amino acid into the acceptor site. Involved in this process is tRNA and the T factor (transfer factor). Initially the adapter hypothesis was proposed in which the tRNA was necessary to carry a specific amino acid into its proper place on the mRNA. Later studies have shown a more complicated mechanism in which two proteins, found in the soluble fraction, are also involved. These two proteins are Ts and Tu. In the cytoplasm they are associated with each other and are designated the T factor; in addition, GTP is involved. The complex that is bound to the ribosomal A site is a ternary complex consisting of AA · tRNA · Tu · GTP. Ts seems to accelerate the rate at which this complex is formed (Ravel et al., 1969; Weissbach et al., 1969; and Lucas-Lenard et al., 1969). Tu appears to act as a carrier of AA · tRNA.

The formation of the ternary complex probably proceeds in the following manner:

1. (Tu – Ts) + GTP + AA – tRNA $\rightleftharpoons$ (Tu · GTP · AA – tRNA) + Ts
2. (Tu · GTP · AA – tRNA) + mRNA – Ribosome $\rightarrow$ (mRNA – Ribosome · AA tRNA) + Tu GDP + Pi
3. Tu · GDP + Ts $\rightleftharpoons$ (Tu – Ts) + GDP

After attachment to the ribosomal A site, peptide bond formation takes place, in which the polypeptide is cleaved from the tRNA at the P site and becomes attached to the aminoacyl-tRNA at the A site. In this process, bond formation is mediated by the enzyme peptidyl transferase. This enzyme is located on the 50s subunit, between the P and A sites. GTP is hydrolyzed to GDP plus inorganic phosphate.

There are several proposals for the role of GTP hydrolysis in this model. When GTP is replaced by an analogue GMPPCP (5′-guanyl-methylenediphosphate), the formation of the peptide bond is inhibited because of the failure of the analogue to be hydrolyzed. The binding of the ternary complex is unaffected, which indicates the binding to be spontaneous (Lipman, 1969). One proposal is that the energy needed for the formation of the peptide bond could be obtained from the ester bond, which links the polypeptide to tRNA at the P site. Other alternatives are that GTP hydrolysis may be needed to release the Tu factor. This will not occur if the analogue GMPPCP is used. Another possible role of GTP hydrolysis may be its effect on ribosome structure. The derived energy from the hydrolysis may have a warping effect on the ribosome so that peptidyl-tRNA can be aligned for bond formation between the polypeptide and the amino acid (Kurland, 1972).

The translocation of the polypeptide from the A site to the P site requires the supernatant G factor, which is a ribosome-dependent GTPase. GTP is required as well. As translocation occurs, the peptidyl-tRNA is moved from the A site to the P site, and the mRNA moves one codon. The uncharged tRNA from the P site is discharged. The role played by the G factor is that by reacting with GTP to produce energy, this energy might be converted to mechanical energy, resulting in translocation and movement of the mRNA (Kurland, 1972).

Elongation in eukaryotes. Mitochondria and chloroplasts presumably have the same factors as those seen in prokaryotes. Both the T factors (Tu and Ts) and G factors are involved. In the cytoplasm of eukaryotes are factors T_1 and T_2. T_1 apparently functions on the T factor but at present cannot be resolved into Tu and Ts. T_2 functions as the G factor (Lucas-Lenard and Lipman, 1971).

Termination of protein synthesis

A number of studies based on genetic mutations of prokaryotes (Brenner et al., 1965; Zipser, 1967), and supportive studies based on poly U–directed phenylalanine synthesis indicate that codons UAA, UAG, and UGA signal the termination of protein synthesis. In addition, three factors are also involved. Two factors are called *release factors* and are designated R_1 and R_2. R_1 is needed to translate codons UAA and UAG. R_2 translates UAA and UGA. The third factor is the s factor (Milman et al., 1969; Goldstein et al., 1970b), which does not have any release capacities but stimulates the rate of release. It may stimulate binding to the terminator codon rather than peptidyl-tRNA hydrolysis (Lucas-Lenard and Lipman, 1971). The s (Tu) factor does not affect the codon specificity of the R factors.

The mechanism of release of the protein seems to be the formation of a complex that involves the R factor-terminator codon and the ribosome. The terminator signals the attachment of either R_1 or R_2. The ester linkage between the tRNA and polypeptide is cleaved, and the polypeptide is released from the ribosome. There is evidence that the R factor converts peptidyl transferase into a hydrolase. This, in effect, transfers the polypeptide to water rather than to an aminoacyl-tRNA.

The tRNA that carried the polypeptide is still attached to the ribosome. Another factor, the TR factor, has been isolated, which releases the tRNA from the ribosome and appears to act only in termination (Kaji et al., 1969).

In a number of prokaryotes there are two terminator codons that lie next to each other (Ishitsuka and Kaji, 1970). It is believed that if one terminator fails, the other terminator ensures that termination will take place. Also, although two release factors are present, only one is needed to facilitate the release. If antibodies are produced against R_1 and R_2, it was shown that release would take place if either anti-R_1 or anti-R_2 was present. However, if both were present at the same time, no release was possible because both factors were inactivated (Lucas-Lenard and Lipman, 1971).

Although information on the mechanism of termination in eukaryotes is fragmentary, evidence so far indicates the presence of

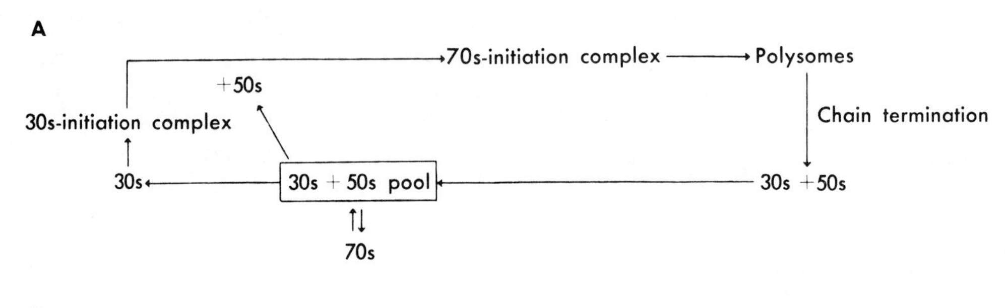

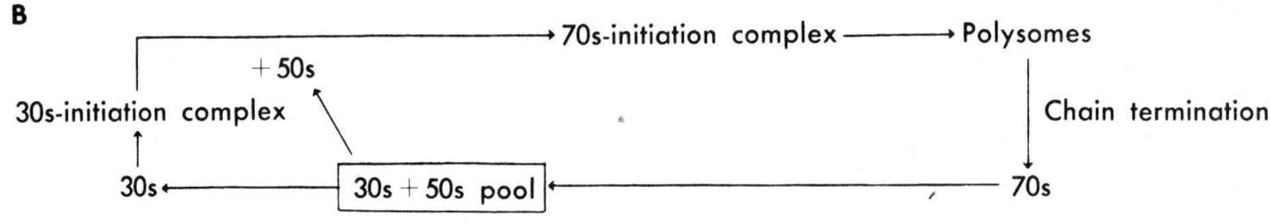

Fig. 9-10. Flow diagram showing two alternative models for the role of "free" 70s ribosomes in the ribosome cycle in vivo. (From Nomura, M. 1970. Bact. Rev. **34:**228-277.)

codons UAA and UAG (Hawthorne, 1969) as well as the R factor (Goldstein et al., 1970b).

Dissociation of ribosomes

After the termination of protein synthesis the monosomes are not conserved but dissociate into subunits. These subunits will again reform into 70s or 80s monosomes at the initiation of protein synthesis. Indirect evidence of ribosomal dissociation was observed when *E. coli* organisms were gently lyzed and the ribosomal profile studied. The results showed profiles of polysomes and subunits in equal proportion. No 70s monosomes were observed (Mangiarotti and Schlessinger, 1966). More direct evidence was later shown when *E. coli* cultures were shifted from a heavy culture medium that contained ^{13}C, ^{2}H, and ^{15}N to a light culture medium containing ^{12}C, H, and ^{14}N. Two kinds of 70s ribosomes were present. One contained heavy 30s and light 50s subunits, and one contained light 30s and heavy 50s subunits. These were stable and suggested subunit exchange (Kaempfer et al., 1968; Nomura, 1970). Similar results were obtained when heavy 70s ribosomes were mixed with an excess of 50s light subunits together with the necessary initiation factors, 'fmet-tRNA, valine-tRNA, and synthetic mRNA. Analysis showed that the 'fmet-tRNA became attached to hybrid 70s and val-tRNA to heavy 70s ribosomes. This means that noninitiation tRNA (for example, val-tRNA) can be bound directly to 70s subunits, whereas 'fmet-tRNA must be bound to the 30s, then the 50s combines with the smaller subunit (Guthrie and Nomura, 1968).

Although it is known that ribosomes dissociate, it is uncertain whether the "run-off" is in subunits or in monosomes, that is, 70s or 80s particles (Fig. 9-10). When protein synthesis is blocked by puromycin, free 70s ribosomes accumulate; this could mean that the run-off is in 70s monosomes. If so, dissociation must occur prior to initiation phase of protein synthesis. A factor found in the cytoplasm called the *dissociation factor* (DF) rapidly dissociates the monosomes into subunits. This factor is probably similar to or identical to the initiation factor F_1.

LITERATURE CITED

Adams, J. M. 1968. On the release of the formyl group from nascent protein. J. Molec. Biol. **33:**571-589.

Adams, J. M., and M. R. Capecchi. 1966. *N*-Formylmethionyl-sRNA as the initiator of protein synthesis. Proc. Nat. Acad. Sci. U.S.A. **55:**147-155.

Aronson, A. I. 1962. Sequence differences between ribonucleic acid isolated from 30s and 50s ribosomes. J. Molec. Biol. **5:**453-455.

Aronson, A. I., and M. A. Holowczyk. 1965. Composition of bacterial ribosomal RNA: heterogeneity within a given organism. Biochim. Biophys. Acta **95:**217-231.

Attardi, G., and F. Amaldi. 1970. Structure and synthesis of ribosomal RNA. Ann. Rev. Biochem. **39:**183-226.

Attardi, G., P. C. Huang, and S. Kabat. 1965. Recognition of ribosomal RNA sites in DNA. I. Analysis of *E. coli* systems. Proc. Nat. Acad. Sci. U.S.A. **53:**1490-1498.

Baglio, C. M., and E. Farber. 1965. Correspondence between ribosome aggregation pattern in rat liver homogenates and in electron micrographs. J. Molec. Biol. **12:**466-467.

Bielka, H., H. Welfe, P. Westermann, F. Noll, F. Grummt, and J. Stahl. 1972. Isolation and properties of protein from animal ribosomes. In R. A. Cox and A. A. Hadjiolov (editors). Functional units in protein synthesis. Vol. 23. Academic Press, Inc., London and New York.

Billeter, M. A., J. E. Dahlberg, H. M. Goodman, J. Hindley, and C. Weissman. 1969. Sequence of the first 175 nucleotides from the 5′-terminus position of QβRNA synthesized in vitro. Nature (London) **224:**1083-1086.

Brenner, S., and J. R. Beckwith. 1965. Ochre mutants, a new class of suppressible nonsense mutants. J. Molec. Biol. **13:**629-637.

Brenner, S., F. Jacob, and M. Meselson. 1961. An unstable intermediate carrying information from gene to ribosome for protein synthesis. Nature (London) **190:**576-581.

Brenner, S., A. O. W. Stretton, and S. Kaplan. 1965. Genetic code: the "nonsense" triplet for chain termination and their suppression. Nature (London) **206:**994-998.

Britten, R. J., B. J. McCarthy, and R. B. Roberts. 1962. IV. The synthesis of ribosomal proteins and assembly of ribosomes. Biophys. J. **2:** 83-93.

Brown, D. D., and J. B. Gurdon. 1964. Absence of ribosomal RNA synthesis in anucleolate mutant of Xenopus laevis. Proc. Nat. Acad. Sci. U.S.A. **51:**139-146.

Brown, J. C., and A. E. Smith. 1970. Initiator codon in eukaryotes. Nature (London) **226:** 610-612.

Brownlee, G. G., F. Sanger, and B. G. Barrell. 1967. Nucleotide sequence 5s ribosomal RNA from Escherichia coli. Nature (London) **215:** 735-736.

Brownlee, G. G., F. Sanger, and B. G. Barrell. 1968. The sequences of 5s-ribosomal ribonucleic acid. J. Molec. Biol. **34:**379-412.

Caskey, C. T., B. Redfield and H. Weissbach. 1967. Formylation of guinea pig liver methionyl-sRNA. Arch. Biochem. Biophys. **120:** 119-123.

Caspersson, T., and J. Schultz. 1940. Ribonucleic acid in both nucleus and cytoplasm and the function of the nucleolus. Proc. Nat. Acad. Sci. U.S.A. **26:**507-515.

Chao, F. 1957. Dissociation of macromolecular ribonucleoprotein of yeast. Arch. Biochem. Biophys. **70:**426-431.

Clark, B. F. C., and K. A. Marcker. 1965. Coding response of *N*-formyl-methionyl s-RNA to UUG. Nature (London) **207:**1038-1039.

Cohn, P. 1962. Studies of ribosomal proteins from reticulocytes. Biochem. J. **84:**16.

Comb, D. G., and S. Katz. 1964. Studies on the biosynthesis and methylation of tRNA. J. Molec. Biol. **8:**790-800.

Comb, D. G., N. Sarkar, J. DeVallet, and C. J. Pinzino. 1965. Properties of transfer-like RNA associated with ribosomes. J. Molec. Biol. **12:** 509-513.

Craven, G. R., P. Voynow, S. J. Hardy, and C. G. Kurland. 1969. The ribosomal proteins of Escherichia coli. II. Chemical and physical characterization of the 30s ribosomal proteins. Biochemistry (Wash.) **8:**2906-2915.

Davis, F. C., Jr., and B. H. Sells. 1969. Synthesis and assembly of ribosomal proteins in 50s subunit during recovery from chloramphenicol treatment. J. Molec. Biol. **39:**503-521.

Dubnau, D., I. Smith, and J. Marmur. 1965. Gene conservation in Bacillus species. II. The location of genes concerned with the synthesis of ribosomal components and soluble RNA. Proc. Nat. Acad. Sci. U.S.A. **54:**724-730.

Fellner, P., and F. Sanger. 1968. Sequence analysis of specific areas of 16s and 23s ribosomal RNAs. Nature (London) **219:**236-238.

Fogel, S., and P. S. Sypherd. 1968. Chemical basis for heterogeneity of ribosomal proteins. Proc. Nat. Acad. Sci. U.S.A. **59:**1329-1336.

Gall, J. G. 1968. Differential synthesis of the genes for ribosomal RNA during amphibian oogenesis. Proc. Nat. Acad. Sci. U.S.A. **60:**533-560.

Geiduschek, E. P., and R. Haselkorn. 1969. Messenger RNA. Ann. Rev. Biochem. **38:** 647-676.

Gilbert, W. 1963. Polypeptide synthesis in Escherichia coli. II. The polypeptide chain and s-RNA. J. Molec. Biol. **6:**389-403.

Goldstein, J., G. Milman, E. Scolnick, and C. T. Caskey. 1970b. Peptide chain termination. VI.

Purification and site of action of S. Proc. Nat. Acad. Sci. U.S.A. **65**:430-437.

Goldstein, J. L., A. L. Beaudet, and C. T. Caskey. 1970a. Peptide chain termination with mammalian release factor. Proc. Nat. Acad. Sci. U.S.A. **67**:99-106.

Granboulan, N., and P. Granboulan. 1965. Cytochemie ultrastructurale du nucleole. II. Etude des sites de synthese du RNA dans le nucleole et le noyau. Exp. Cell Res. **38**:604-619.

Greenberg, H., and S. Penman. 1966. Methylation and processing of ribosomal RNA in HeLa cells. J. Molec. Biol. **21**:527-535.

Guthrie, C., and M. Nomura. 1968. Initiation of protein synthesis: a critical test of the 30s subunit model. Nature (London) **219**:232-235.

Hall, B. D., and P. Doty. The preparation and physical chemical properties of ribonucleic acid from microsomal particles. J. Molec. Biol. **1**: 111-126.

Hall, C. E., and H. S. Slayter. 1959. Electron microscopy of ribonucleoprotein particles from E. coli. J. Molec. Biol. **1**:329-332.

Hawthorne, D. G. 1969. Identification of nonsense codons in yeast. J. Molec. Biol. **43**:71-75.

Hindley, J., and D. H. Staples. 1969. Sequence of a ribosome binding site in bacteriophage QβRNA. Nature (London) **224**:964-967.

Housman, D., M. Jacobs-Lorena, V. L. Rajbhandary, and H. F. Lodish. 1970. Initiation of haemoglobin synthesis by methionyl t-RNA. Nature (London) **227**:913-918.

Howard, F. B., J. Frazier, M. N. Lipsett, and H. T. Miles. 1964. Infrared demonstration of two and three strand helix formation between poly c and guanosine mononucleotide and oligonucleotide. Biochem. Biophys. Res. Commun. **17**:93-102.

Huxley, H. E., and G. Zubay. 1960. Electron microscope observations of microsomal particles from Escherichia coli. J. Molec. Biol. **2**: 10-18.

Ishitsuka, H., and A. Kaji. 1970. Release of tRNA from ribosomes by a factor other than G-factor. Proc. Nat. Acad. Sci. U.S.A. **66**:168-173.

Jackson, R., and T. Hunter. 1970. Role of methionine in the initiation of haemoglobin synthesis. Nature (London) **227**:672-676.

Jacob, F., and J. Monod. 1961. Genetic regulatory mechanisms in protein synthesis. J. Molec. Biol. **3**:318-356.

Kaempfer, R. O. R., M. Meselson, and H. J. Raskas. 1968. Cyclic dissociation into stable subunits and reformation of ribosomes during bacteriological growth. J. Molec. Biol. **31**:277-289.

Kaii, A., K. Igarashi, and H. Ishitsuka. 1969. Interaction of tRNA and release of tRNA. Cold Spring Harbor Symp. Quant. Biol. **34**: 167-177.

Karasaki, S. 1965. Electron microscopic examination of the sites of nuclear RNA synthesis during amphibian embryogenesis. J. Cell Biol. **26**:937-958.

Kennel, D. E., and B. Magasanik. 1962. The relation of ribosome content to the rate of enzyme synthesis in Aerobacter aerogenes. Biochim. Biophys. Acta **55**:139-151.

Kjeldgaard, N. O. 1961. The kinetics of ribonucleic acid and protein formation in Salmonella typhimurium during transition between different states of balanced growth. Biochim. Biophys. Acta **49**:64-76.

Klug, A., K. C. Holmes, and J. T. Finch. 1961. X-ray diffraction studies on ribosomes from various sources. J. Molec. Biol. **3**:87-100.

Kolakofsky, D., K. Dewey, and R. E. Thach. 1969. Purification and properties of factor F_2. Nature (London) **223**:694-697.

Kono, M., and S. Osawa. 1964. Intermediary steps of ribosome formation in Escherichia coli. Biochim. Biophys. Acta **87**:326-334.

Kurland, C. G. 1960. Molecular characterization of ribonucleic acid from Escherichia coli. J. Molec. Biol. **2**:83-91.

Kurland, C. G. 1970. Ribosome structure and function. Science **169**:1171-1177.

Kurland, C. G. 1972. Structure and function of the bacterial ribosome. Ann. Rev. Biochem. **41**:377-408.

Kurland, C. G., and O. Maaloe. 1962. Regulation of ribosomal and transfer RNA synthesis. J. Molec. Biol. **4**:193-210.

Lefkovits, I., and M. Di Girolamo. 1969. Reutilization of ribosomal proteins in vivo for the formation of new ribosomal particles in Escherichia coli B. Biochim. Biophys. Acta **174**:566-573.

Liau, M. C., and R. P. Perry. 1969. Ribosomal precursor particles in nucleoli. J. Cell Biol. **42**:272-283.

Lederberg, S., and V. Lederberg. 1961. Hybridization between bacteria ribosomes. Exp. Cell Res. **25**:198-200.

Lipman, F. 1969. Polypeptide chain elongation in protein synthesis. Science **164**:1024-1031.

Lucas-Lenard, J., and F. Lipman. 1971. Protein biosynthesis. Ann. Rev. Biochem. **40**:409-448.

Lucas-Lenard, J., P. Tao, and A-L. Haenni. 1969. Further studies on bacterial polypeptide elongation. Cold Spring Harbor Symp. Quant. Biol. **34**:455-462.

Madison, J. T. 1968. Primary structure of RNA. Ann. Rev. Biochem. **37**:131-148.

Mangiarotti, G., and D. Schlessinger. 1966. Polysome metabolism in E. coli. J. Molec. Biol. **20:**123-143.

Marcker, K. 1965. The formation of *N*-formylmethionyl-sRNA. J. Molec. Biol. **14:**63-70.

Marcker, K., and F. Sanger. 1964. *N*-Formylmethionyl-s-RNA. J. Molec. Biol. **8:**835-840.

McCarthy, B. J., and A. I. Aronson. 1961. The kinetics of the synthesis of ribosomal RNA in E. coli. Biophys. J. **1:**227-245.

McCarthy, B. J., and R. J. Britten. 1962. The synthesis of ribosomes in E. coli. I. The incorporation of C^{14}-uracil into the metabolic pool and RNA. Biophys. J. **2:**35-47.

McCarthy, B. J., R. J. Britten, and R. B. Roberts. 1962. The synthesis of ribosomes in E. coli. III. Synthesis of ribosomal RNA. Biophys. J. **2:**57-83.

McConkey, E. H., and J. W. Hopkins. 1969. Molecular weights of some HeLa ribosomal RNAs. J. Molec. Biol. **39:**545-550.

Meselson, M., M. Nomura, S. Brenner, C. Davern, and D. Schlessinger. 1964. Conservation of ribosomes during bacterial growth. J. Molec. Biol. **9:**696-711.

Midgley, J. E. W. 1965. Studies on the structures of a 23s ribosomal nucleic acid from Escherichia coli. Biochim. Biophys. Acta **108:**348-354.

Miles, H. T. 1958. Quantitative infrared spectra in D_2O of some nucleosides, nucleotides and polynucleotide: a new measure of polynucleotide interaction. Biochim. Biophys. Acta **30:** 324-328.

Milman, G., J. Goldstein, E. Scolnick, and T. Caskey. 1969. Peptide chain termination. III. Stimulation of in vitro termination. Proc. Nat. Acad. Sci. U.S.A. **63:**183-190.

Monier, R. 1972. Recent studies on the structure and function of 5s RNA. In R. A. Cox and A. A. Hadjiolov (editors). Functional units in protein biosynthesis. F. E. B. S. Proc. Varna (Bulgaria). Vol. 23. Academic Press, Inc., London and New York.

Moore, P. B., R. R. Traut, H. Noller, P. Pearson, and H. Delius. 1968. Ribosomal proteins of Escherichia coli. II. Proteins from the 30s subunit. J. Molec. Biol. **31:**441-461.

Morris, D. W., and J. A. DeMoss. 1966. Polysome transitions and the regulation of ribonucleic acid synthesis in Escherichia coli. Proc. Nat. Acad. Sci. U.S.A. **56:**262-268.

Nakada, D. 1965a. Formation of ribosomes by a "relaxed" mutant of Escherichia coli. J. Molec. Biol. **12:**695-725.

Nakada, D. 1965b. Ribosomes formation by puromycin-treated Bacillus subtilis. Biochim. Biophys. Acta **103:**455-465.

Nomura, M. 1969. Ribosomes. Sci. Amer. **221:** 28-35.

Nomura, M. 1970. Bacterial ribosomes. Bact. Rev. **34:**228-277.

Nomura, M., and J. D. Watson. 1959. Ribonucleoprotein particles within Chloromycetin-inhibited Escherichia coli. J. Molec. Biol. **1:** 204-217.

Novelli, G. D. 1967. Amino acid activation for protein synthesis. Ann. Rev. Biochem. **36:**449-484.

Osawa, S. 1968. Ribosome formation and structure. Ann. Rev. Biochem. **37:**109-133.

Osawa, S., E. Otaka, T. Itoh, and T. Kukui. 1969. Biosynthesis of 50s ribosomal subunit in Escherichia coli. J. Molec. Biol. **40:**321-351.

Otaka, E., S. Osawa, and A. Sibatani. 1964. Stimulation of ^{14}C-leucine incorporation into proteins in vitro by ribosomal RNA of Escherichia coli. Biochem. Biophys. Res. Commun. **15:**568-574.

Palade, G. E. 1955. A small particulate component of the cytoplasm. J. Biophys. Biochem. Cytol. **1:**59-79.

Penman, S., K. Scherrer, Y. Becker, and J. E. Darnell. 1963. Polyribosomes in normal and poliovirus infected HeLa cells and their relationship to messenger-RNA. Proc. Nat. Acad. Sci. U.S.A. **49:**654-662.

Perry, R. P. 1960. On the nucleolar and nuclear dependence of cytoplasmic RNA synthesis in HeLa cells. Exp. Cell Res. **20:**216-220.

Retsema, J. A., and T. W. Conway. 1969. Reversible dissociation of E. coli by *N*-ethylmaleimide. Biochim. Biophys. Acta **179:**369-380.

RajBhandary, H., and P. Ghosh. 1969. Studies on polynucleotides. XCI. Yeast methionine transfer ribonucleic acid: purification, properties and terminal nucleotide sequences. J. Biol. Chem. **244:**1104-1113.

Ravel, J. M., R. L. Shorey, C. W. Garver, R. C. Dawkins, and W. Shive. 1969. The role of aminoacyl-tRNA-CTP-protein complex in polynucleotide synthesis. Cold Spring Harbor Symp. Quant. Biol. **34:**321-330.

Rich, A., J. R. Warner, and H. M. Goodman. 1963. The structure and function of polysomes. Cold Spring Harbor Symp. Quant. Biol. **28:**269-285.

Rosset, R., and R. Monier. 1963. A propos de la d'acide ribonucleique de faible poids moleculaire dans les ribosomes d'Escherichia coli. Biochim. Biophys. Acta **68:**653-656.

Sabatini, D., Y. Nonomura, T. Moromoto, and

G. Blobel. 1972. Structural studies on rat liver and chicken embryo ribosomes. In R. A. Cox and A. A. Hadjiolov (editors). Functional units in protein biosynthesis. F. E. B. S. Proc. Varna (Bulgaria). Vol. 23. Academic Press, Inc., London and New York.

Schaechter, M., D. Maaloe, and N. O. Kjeldgaard. 1958. Dependency on medium and temperature of cell size and chemical composition during balances growth of Salmonella typhimurium. J. Gen. Microbiol. **19:**592-606.

Scherrer, K., H. Latham, and J. E. Darnell. 1963. Demonstration of an unstable RNA and of a precursor to ribosomal RNA in HeLa cells. Proc. Nat. Acad. Sci. U.S.A. **49:**240-248.

Schleif, R. 1967. Control of production of ribosomal protein. J. Molec. Biol. **27:**41-55.

Schultz, J., T. Caspersson, and L. Aquilonius. 1940. The genetic control of nucleolar composition. Proc. Nat. Acad. Sci. U.S.A. **26:**515-523.

Sells, B. H. 1964. RNA synthesis and ribosome production in puromycin-treated cells. Biochim. Biophys. Acta **80:**230-241.

Sells, B. H., and F. C. Davis, Jr. 1968. Ribosome biogenesis: non random addition of structural proteins to 50s subunits. Science **159:**1240-1242.

Setterfield, G., J. M. Neelin, and S. T. Bagley. 1960. Studies on basic proteins from ribosomes of buds of pea seedlings, J. Molec. Biol. **2:** 416-424.

Smith, A. E., and K. A. Marcker. 1970. Cytoplasmic methionine transfer RNAs from eukaryotes. Nature (London) **226:**607-610.

Spitnik-Elson, P. 1965. The preparation of ribosomal proteins from Escherichia coli with lithium chloride and urea. Biochem. Biophys. Res. Commun. **18:**557-562.

Stanley, W. M., Jr., and R. M. Bock. 1965. Isolation and physical properties of the ribosome ribonucleic acid of Eschericha coli. Biochemistry (Wash.) **4:**1302-1311.

Steitz, J. A. 1969. Polypeptide chain initiation: nucleotide sequences of three ribosomal binding sites in bacteriophage R17 RNA. Nature (London) **224:**957-964.

Stöffler, G., and H. G. Wittman. 1971a. Ribosomal proteins. XXV. Immunological studies on Escherichia coli ribosomal proteins. J. Molec. Biol. **62:**407-409.

Stöffler, G., and H. G. Wittman. 1971b. Sequence differences of Escherichia coli 30s ribosomal proteins as determined by immunological methods. Proc. Nat. Acad. Sci. U.S.A. **68:**2283-2287.

Takeda, M., and R. E. Webster, 1968. Protein chain initiation and deformylation in B. subtilis homogenates. Proc. Nat. Acad. Sci. U.S.A. **60:**1487-1494.

Tamaoki, T. 1966. The particulate fraction containing 45s RNA in L cell nuclei. J. Molec. Biol. **15:**624-639.

Tissières, A., J. D. Watson, D. Schlessinger, and B. R. Hollingworth. 1959. Ribonucleoprotein particles from Escherichia coli. J. Molec. Biol. **1:**221-233.

Traub, P., K. Hosokawa, G. R. Craven, and M. Nomura. 1967. Structure and function of E. coli ribosomes. IV. Isolation and characterization of functionally active ribosomal proteins. Proc. Nat. Acad. Sci. U.S.A. **58:**2430-2436.

Traub, P., and M. Nomura. 1969. Structure and function of *Escherichia coli* ribosomes. VI. Mechanism of assembly of 30s ribosomes studied in vitro. J. Molec. Biol. **40:**391-413.

Ts'o, P. O. P., J. Bonner, and J. Vinograd. 1958. Structure and properties of microsomal nucleoprotein particles from pea seedlings. Biochim. Biophys. Acta **30:**570-582.

Wagner, E. K., S. Penman, and V. M. Ingram. 1967. Methylation patterns of HeLa cell ribosomal RNA and nuclear precursor. J. Molec. Biol. **29:**371-387.

Waller, J. P. 1964. Fractionation of the ribosomal protein from *Escherichia coli*. J. Molec. Biol. **10:**319-336.

Waller, J. P., and J. I. Harris. 1961. Studies on the composition of the protein from Escherichia coli ribosome. Proc. Nat. Acad. Sci. U.S.A. **47:** 18-23.

Warner, J. R., P. M. Knopf, and A. Rich. 1963. A multiple ribosomal structure in protein synthesis. Proc. Nat. Acad. Sci. U.S.A. **49:**122-129.

Warner, J. R., A. Rich, and C. Hall. 1962. Electron microscope studies of ribosomal clusters synthesizing hemoglobin. Science **138:**1399-1403.

Warner, J. R., and E. Soeiro. 1967. Nascent ribosomes from HeLa cells. Proc. Nat. Acad. Sci. U.S.A. **58:**1984-1990.

Weinberg, R. A., U. Loening, M. Willems, and S. Penman. 1967. Acrylamide gel electrophoresis of HeLa cell nucleolar rRNA. Proc. Nat. Acad. Sci. U.S.A. **58:**1088-1995.

Weissbach, H., N. Brot, D. Miller, M. Rossman, and R. Ertel. 1969. Interaction of guanosine triphosphate with E. coli soluble transfer factors. Cold Spring Harbor Symp. Quant. Biol. **34:**419-431.

Wettstein, F. O., T. Staehlin, and H. Noll. 1963. Ribosomal aggregates engaged in protein synthesis: characterization of the ergosome. Nature (London) **197:**430-435.

Willems, M., E. Wagner, R. Laing, and S. Penman. 1968. Base composition of ribosomal RNA precursors in HeLa cell nucleolus: further evidence of nonconservative processing. J. Molec. Biol. **32:**211-220.

Wittman, H. G. 1972. Ribosomal proteins from prokaryotes. In R. A. Cox and A. A. Hadjiolov (editors). Functional units in protein biosynthesis. F. E. B. S. Proc. Varna (Bulgaria). Vol. 23. Academic Press, Inc., London and New York.

Woese, C. R. 1968. Primary structure homology within 23s ribosomal RNA. Nature (London) **220:**923.

Zachau, H. G. 1972. Recognition of transfer ribonucleic acids by aminoacyl tRNA synthetase. In R. A. Cox and A. A. Hadjiolov (editors). Functional units in protein bioysnthesis. F. E. B. S. Proc. Varna (Bulgaria). Vol. 23. Academic Press, Inc., London and New York.

Zimmerman, E. E. 1968. Secondary methylation of ribosomal ribonucleic acid in HeLa cells. Biochemistry **7:**3156-3164.

Zipser, D. 1967. UGA: a third class of suppressible polar mutants. J. Molec. Biol. **29:**441-445.

CHAPTER 10

Mitochondria

Mitochondria (Gr. *mitos,* "thread"; *chondron,* "grain") are organelles found in the cytoplasm of plants and animals. In bacteria the counterpart is suspected to be the *mesosome* (Fig. 10-19). Mitochondria have been referred to in most biology and biochemical courses as the "powerhouse" of the cell because of the enzyme systems found within that produce much of the energy necessary for the cells to carry out their processes of secretion, movement, locomotion, reproduction, etc.

The mitochondrion has been known for many years. Historical reviews (Novikoff, 1961; Lehninger, 1964) cite that the first mention or description of a likely granular cytoplasmic structure was made by Kollicker (ca. 1850) while examining muscle tissue. These granules were later named *sarcosomes* by Petzius in 1890. Flemming (ca. 1882) described these structures as *filia.* In 1890 an interesting postulation was made by Altmann, who referred to these granules, sarcosomes, or filia as *bioblasts* (living germs). From this he introduced the bioblast theory, in which these organelles were elementary particles somewhat comparable to bacteria, which presumably were symbionts within the cell. Fortunately, or unfortunately, this concept was received with much criticism and eventually forgotten. It is of interest to note, however, that with the chemical identification of DNA and the observation that ribosome-like particles are present as an integral part of mitochondria there has been within the past few years a revival of the bioblast concept of Altmann (see following discussion of evolution and Chapter 11). Benda (ca. 1898) devised a staining technique using crystal violet that revealed these structures brilliantly, and he was able to describe their morphology accurately. He renamed them mitochondria. In 1900 Michaelis used Janus green B as a vital stain to observe mitochondria in living cells. In effect, the use of a vital stain substantiated the existence of mitochondria because they were made visible as such in living cells. Prior to that time most of the descriptions were made from fixed tissue, which was responsible for the argument that mitochondria were possibly artifacts. Regaud (ca. 1908) observed by means of new staining techniques that the composition of mitochondria is a mixture of phospholipids and proteins. Meves (1918) described mitochondrial transformation, that is, long threads converted into many tiny spheres. With the introduction of electron microscopy in the late 1940s and early 1950s and with the perfection of microtomes for cutting thin sections, Palade and Sjöstrand were able to study the fine structural arrangements of mitochondria. Since that time, a voluminous accumulation of information from electron microscopy has been recorded (Lehninger, 1964).

Isolation of mitochondria for biochemical studies was credited to Bensley and Hoerr in 1934 when they separated mitochondria by differential centrifugation. By the 1950s, with improved methods of mitochondrial isolation by Claude, Hogeboom, and others, coupled with knowledge gained from electron microscopy, confluence between biochemistry and morphological cytology became a reality in explaining the physiology of mitochondria on a structure-function basis.

Staining techniques

The particular visualization of mitochondria at the light microscope level, either in living or fixed tissue, is dependent on the techniques used and the material studied.

In working with fixed tissue it is customary to use fixatives very low in lipid solvents and containing osmium or chromium. Staining of fixed sections can be accomplished by a number of techniques such as the Altmann, iron hematoxylin, or Regaud fast green methods.

Vital staining can be accomplished by several methods. In all cases, however, it is necessary to adjust the osmotic concentration of the staining fluid to that of the mitochondria. The mitochondrion can behave like an osmometer, swelling in a solution hypotonic to the organelle or contracting in a hypertonic solution.

One of the earliest and most successfully used vital stains is Janus green B (JG-B). Although it can be used for both animal and plant tissue, it is more successful with animal cells. This reaction depends on cells that are capable of reducing JG-B. In this type of reaction JG-B is reduced by the enzyme system of the cytoplasm to the leukoderivative. There is also an enzyme system within the mitochondria that prevents this reduction and is both oxygen dependent and cyanide sensitive. The only system having these characteristics is the cytochrome oxidase system. Therefore when a section is treated with a dilute solution of JG-B, a blue-green coloration appears within the cytoplasm that is restricted to the mitochondria. When cyanide is added, the color disappears due to the accumulation of the reduced form of the dye (Lazarow and Cooperstein, 1953; Cooperstein et al., 1953).

One can also employ enzyme histochemistry to detect mitochondria. The use of a tetrazolium compound such as nitro-BT as a staining method has proved successful (Chapter 1). The reduced flavoprotein is oxidized by the nitro-BT, and the tetrazolium salt is thus converted into a highly insoluble, colored formazan precipitate. The structures containing the formazans are mitochondria. Similarly, one can also use the Nadi reaction (Chapter 1) to detect mitochondria. This is normally used to detect cytochrome oxidase, but since the cytochrome system is located in mitochondria, the localization of the cytochrome is tantamount to localization of mitochondria. A vital stain known as the LBC reaction (leuco brilliant cresyl blue reaction) has also been employed to demonstrate mitochondria (Tarao, 1964).

Shapes

The shapes of mitochondria are highly variable, but it can be stated generally that they range from a short rod shape to an elongate filamentous form. Within each group there may be many gradations; for example, the rod shape form may range from oval (in which the length and width are almost the same) to long. Similarly, various gradations can also be seen in the filamentous forms. Pleomorphic forms are often seen in which the mitochondria may contain swellings at their ends or have a vesiculated matrix (Fig. 10-1). Much of this pleomorphism, however, may be partly due to the methods used in fixation, that is, improper pH of the fixing solution or improper osmotic concentration of the staining solution if living cells are used for study.

Sizes

Although the size of mitochondria is variable, they generally measure about 0.5 to 1 μm in diameter and have an average length of 3 to 4 μm, with lengths up to 7.5 μm in yeast cells (Kawakami, 1961) and 8 μm in the comb plates of Ctenophora (Horridge, 1964). For any particular tissue, however, the lengths and widths are about the same.

In addition, mitochondrial size can also be affected by the physiological and pathological state of the tissue (Fig. 10-2). Since mitochondria can act as osmometers, the increase or decrease in size can be mediated by altering the pH appreciably from that of the cell and by using unbuffered fixing and/or staining solutions. Imbibition of water into mitochondria can be brought about by toxins that alter the osmotic gradient and that change the homeostatic condition within the cell, resulting in swelling.

Number

The number of mitochondria varies from one cell type to another but is rather constant for any one type of cell. The number correlates with the metabolic activity of the cell. Thus if the metabolic activity is high, the number of mitochondria is likewise high. Conversely, a small number of mitochondria generally indicates cells of low

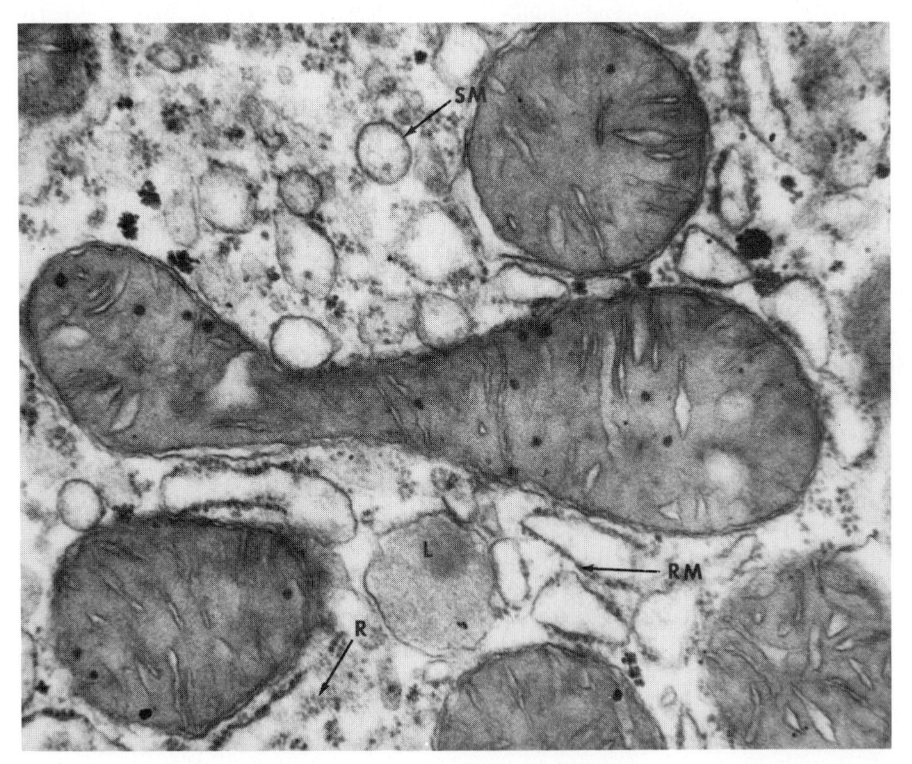

Fig. 10-1. Electron micrograph of liver mitochondria of an animal treated with an experimental antibiotic. Note the dumbbell-shaped mitochondrion and presence of vacuoles in the mitochondrial matrix. Numerous microsomes are evident, some with smooth membranes, **SM,** and some with ribosomes attached, **RM.** A microbody (peroxisome), **L** is also present, as are free ribosomes, **R.** (Courtesy Dr. R. Guillory, Department of Chemistry, Cornell University, Ithaca, N. Y.)

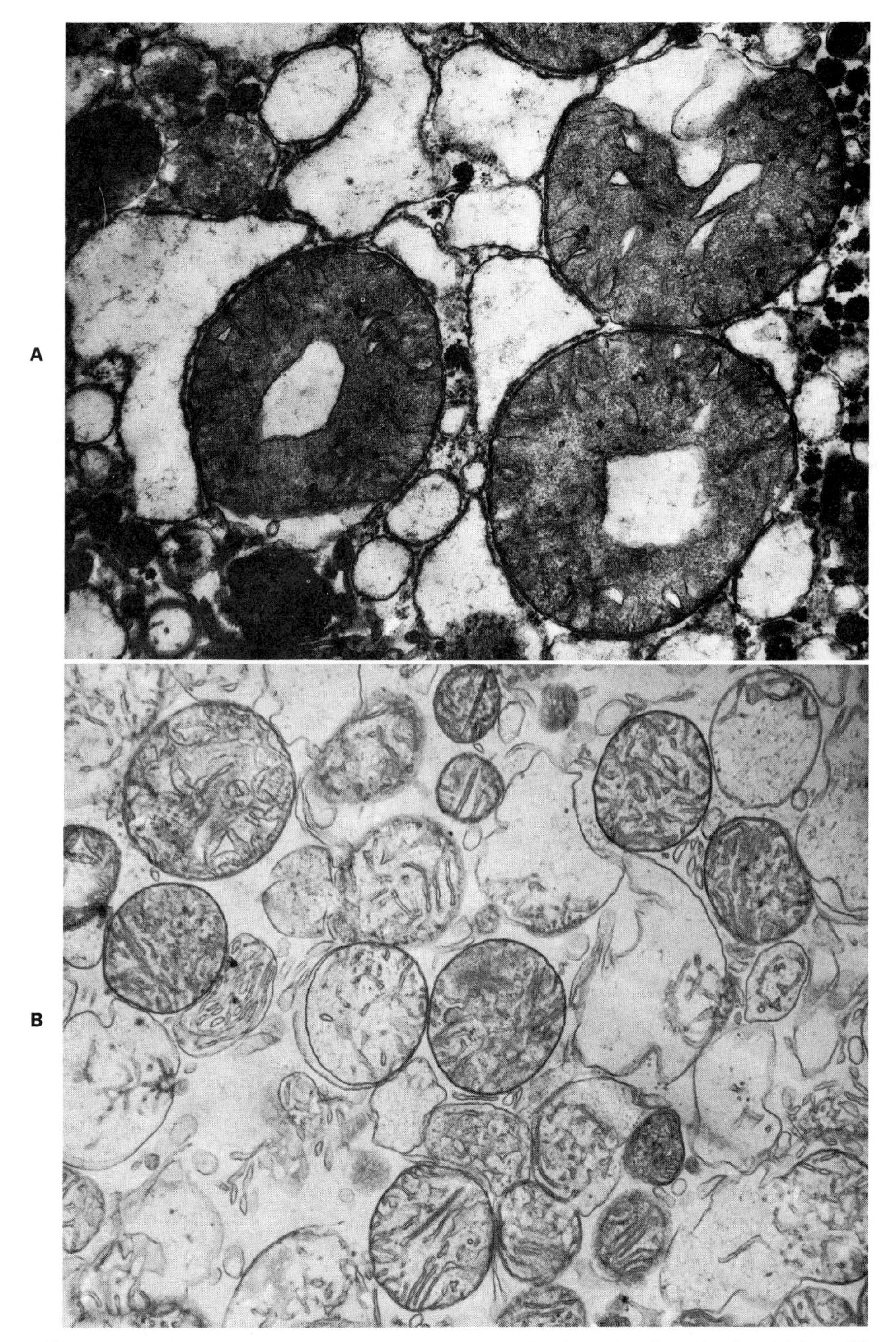

Fig. 10-2. Electron micrograph of isolated liver mitochondria. **A,** Mitochondrial swelling caused by an experimental antibiotic. Note presence of large vacuoles in the matrix. **B,** Normal untreated mitochondria. There is little evidence of swelling. (Courtesy Dr. R. Guillory, Department of Chemistry, Cornell University, Ithaca, N. Y.)

metabolic activity. Attempts have been made to estimate the number of mitochondria per cell by statistical analysis. The numbers may range from 500,000 in the large multinucleate ameba *Chaos chaos* to 20 to 24 per cell in sperm (Lehninger, 1964). Liver contains approximately 800 per cell; large sea urchin eggs, 13,000 to 14,000 per cell; and renal tubules, 300 to 400 per cell.

Studies have indicated that mitochondria may comprise a significant fraction of the mass and volume of the cytoplasm. In rat liver cells, for example, the mitochondria may account for 15% to 22% of the total nitrogen content and about 20% of the cytoplasmic volume.

Distribution within cell

Ordinarily, mitochondria are distributed evenly throughout the cell cytoplasm. Yet at times variability is encountered in which the mitochondria are polarized or show a definite alignment within the cell. This is particularly true of cells such as those comprising the proximal convoluted tubule of the kidney. In these cells the mitochondria are concentrated at the basal region, opposite the renal capillaries. They are intimately related to the infoldings of the plasma membrane (Fig. 6-20). A similar arrangement is also evident in the cells of the salt gland of the fairy shrimp *Artemia.* In both examples the energy derived from the oriented mitochondria is used or involved in active transport in the polarized direction. Orientation is also evident in skeletal muscles, where the mitochondria become aligned between the myofibrils. At times mitochondria may be in intimate contact with the nucleus, chloroplasts, basal body of cilia, and other structures.

In glands such as the prostrate or venom glands of a number of poisonous snakes the mitochondria may be more or less concentrated in the basal region.

In the development of sperm in the grasshopper or many other insects there is fusion of mitochondria into one or two long configurations, the *mitochondrial derivative,* located in the midpiece of the sperm tail. In the unfertilized sea urchin egg the mitochondria may aggregate into bundles containing as many as sixty individual mitochondria. Interestingly enough, after fertilization, with the formation of the zygote, there is disaggregation of the aggregates into single forms. Concomitant with this transformation is a large increase in the respiration rate (Lehninger, 1964).

In general, mitochondria have a tendency to assume some orientation within the cell. In cells that are columnar or prismatic in shape they tend to be orientated within the cell parallel to the major axis, that is, in a lengthwise direction. On the other hand, in such cells as leukocytes the mitochondria are somewhat more radially arranged and in the direction of diffusion (Novikoff, 1961).

Mitochondria within the cell may also show a certain degree of freedom. They are able to move from one position to another within the cytoplasm. In general, however, the degree of freedom existing in an animal cell is much less than that observed in plants, where movement within the cytoplasm is dramatic and the mitochondria move either autonomously or as though they were being swept along by protoplasmic streaming.

In other cells (for example, in some reptilian venom glands) the mitochondria occupy a fixed position within the cell, there being almost no degree of freedom. Positioned mitochondria presumably function in regional control over biosynthetic activity and perhaps also in secretion when they are located near the free surface.

Another type of movement has also been described as inherent to mitochondria. From phase-contrast studies using fibroblasts and Ehrlich's ascites tumor cells (Packer and Golder, 1960) it was shown that mitochondria continually change shape and volume. Often these movements can be described as being rhythmical. More will be said about the mitochondrial swelling-contraction phase later in this chapter.

Structure

Prior to electron microscopy the mitochondria appeared to be solid structures floating within the cytoplasm. Little thought was given to the probability of more detailed and internal structure. With the development of a suitable microtome and embedding matrix for cutting ultra-thin sections it became apparent that mitochondria consist primarily of membrane systems.

Morphological studies obtained from electron microscopy show the mitochondria to be enclosed by an outer trilaminar membrane 60 to 70 Å thick. It consists of two protein layers with a lipid layer sandwiched between. The protein layers average 15 to 20 Å in thickness, whereas the central lipid layer is approximately 30 Å in thickness (Fig. 10-3). Between the outer membrane and the inner membrane is a space of 40 to 70 Å. The inner membrane, which is also trilaminar, is continuous and encloses a central space. However, the inner membrane sends folds into this central space to provide shelf like structures, which are referred to as *cristae* or the *cristae mitochondrialis.* The

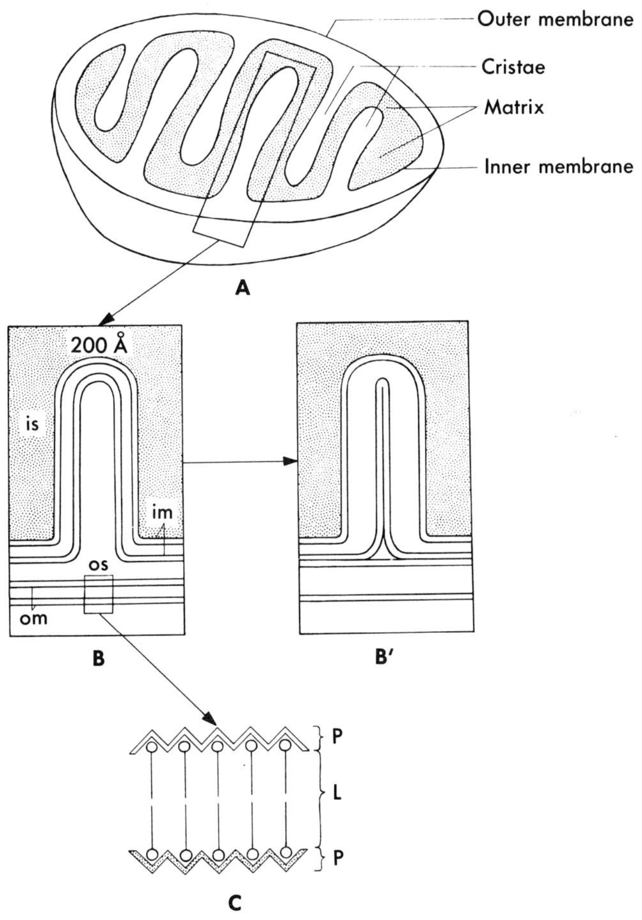

Fig. 10-3. Drawing of a generalized mitochondrion. **A,** Three-dimensional drawing of membrane system and cristae resulting from infolding of the inner membrane system. **B,** Enlarged view of crista and outer membrane. **C,** Molecular organization of the membrane system. **B′** shows the obliteration of the outer space and intercristal space, which may represent the position of membranes in a living cell. (See text for explanation.)

narrow space between the outer and inner membrane also extends between the leaves of the cristae to produce the *intracristal spaces*. They usually appear optically empty. The inner chamber, which is bounded by the inner membrane and cristae, is filled with a homogeneous or a finely granular *matrix*. The density of this matrix can vary from one cell type to another as well as with different fixatives used. At times small electron-dense granules scattered in the matrix can be observed. The sizes of these mitochondrial granules range from 250 to 600 Å (Fig. 10-4).

Thus the mitochondrial membranes bound two chambers—the *outer chamber,* which is between the outer and inner membranes and within the cristae, and the larger *inner chamber,* which is bounded by the inner membrane and the usually transversely directed cristae.

Despite this description, which is the accepted model obtained from electron microscopy, some conceptual changes may be required as more information becomes available. It has been shown that mitochondrial membranes, including membranes that comprise the cristae, may have a pentalaminar pattern (Malhotra, 1966); that is, there is fusion of these membrane systems similar to the *zona occludens* seen in junctional complexes of epithelial tissue (Chapter 6). The membranes along the fusion line appear darker and heavier and have dimensions similar to the two protein layers of the respective membranes (Fig. 10-5). It can be likened to the fusion of myelin, where the opposing membrane surfaces meet and fuse. This, then, under living conditions of the cell would eliminate the outer chamber and the central core in the cristae. Most of these new results were obtained from the freeze-

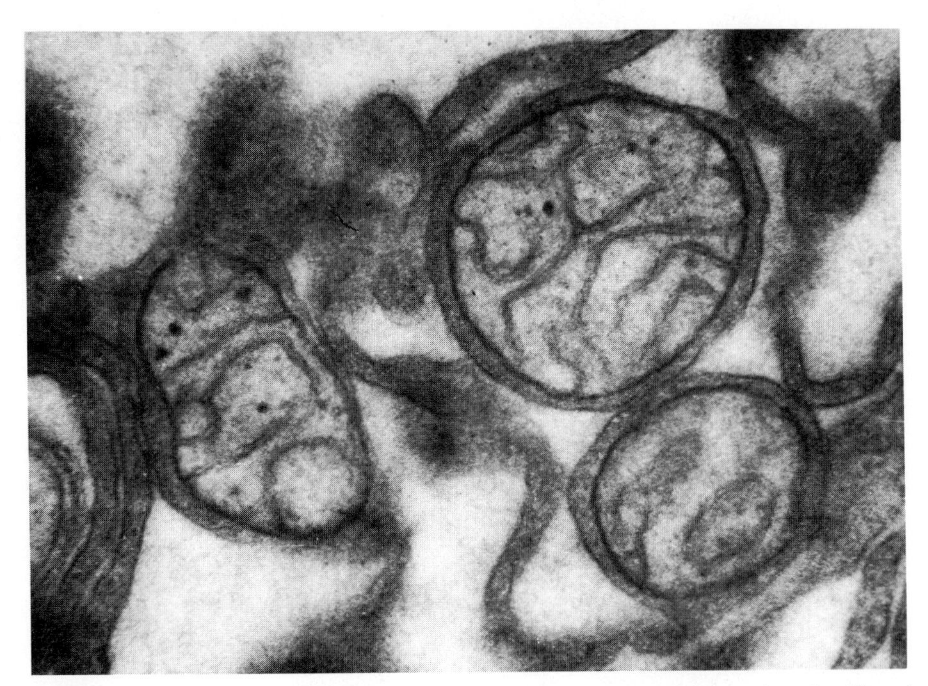

Fig. 10-4. Mitochondria from venom gland cell of western diamondback rattlesnake *(Crotalus atrox)*. Cristae are few in number, and some are fused with one another. Mitochondrion on the left is a longitudinal section, whereas mitochondria on the right are cross-sectional views. Several electron-dense mitochondrial granules are seen in the matrix. Each mitochondrion is surrounded by a layer of electron-dense cytoplasm.

substitution method. The outer chamber generally does appear if there has been a delay in fixation after the extirpation of the organ. It is considered to be something of an artifact.

With negative staining using phosphotungstate on lysed mitochondria the cristae reveal subunits resembling "lollypops" (Fig. 10-6). They consist of a stem approximately 30 to 35 Å wide and 45 to 50 Å long and a round head that measures 75 to 80 Å in diameter. The center-to-center spacing between subunits is 100 Å (Parsons, 1963). The subunits, called *elementary particles* and *oxysomes,* presumably contain all molecules of phosphorylation but not the electron transport system. It has been calculated that the number of subunits or elementary particles may be approximately 10^4 to 50^5 per mitochondrion.

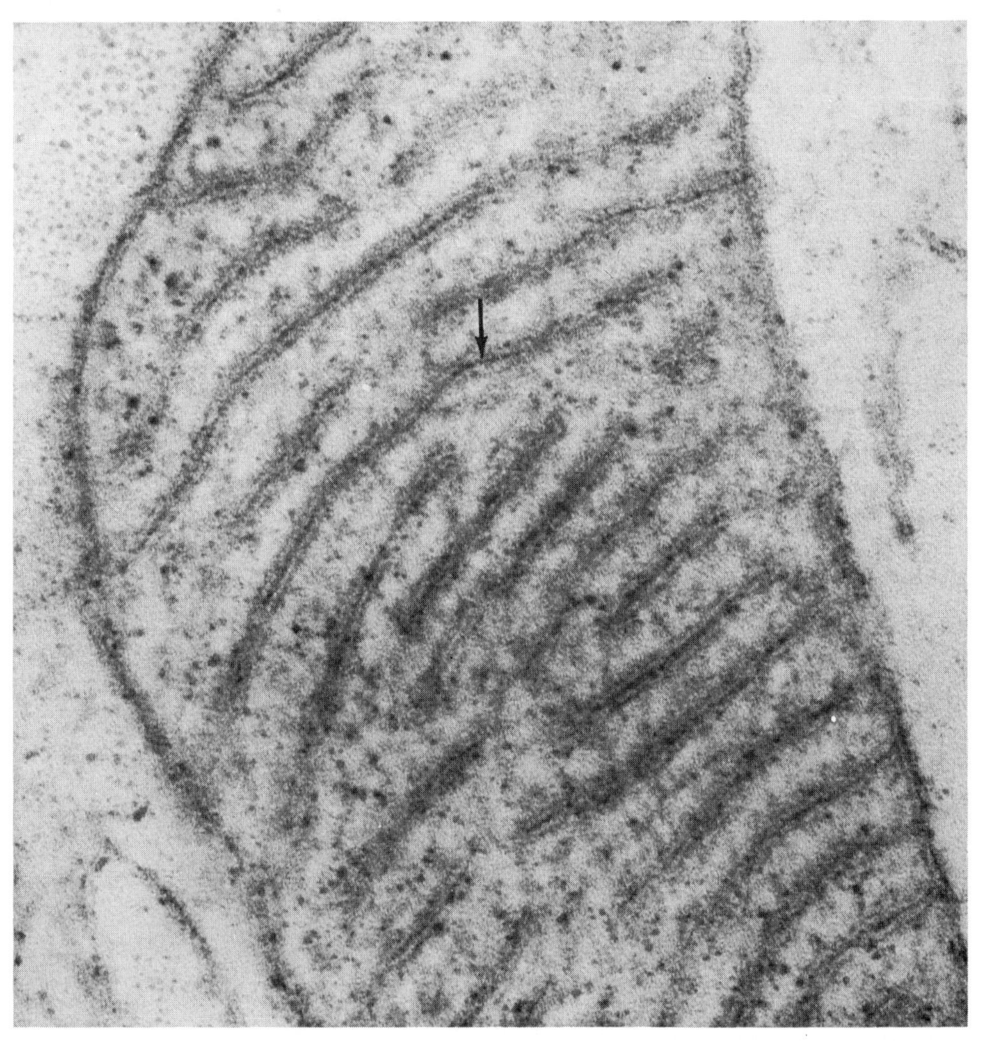

Fig. 10-5. Section of mitochondrion of cerebellar tissue that was frozen 30 seconds after decapitation. Note obliteration of intercristal spaces. Arrow shows fusion of outer lamellae of adjacent cristae to produce a pentalaminar layer. (From Malhotra, S. K. 1966. J. Ultrastruct. Res. **15:**14-37.)

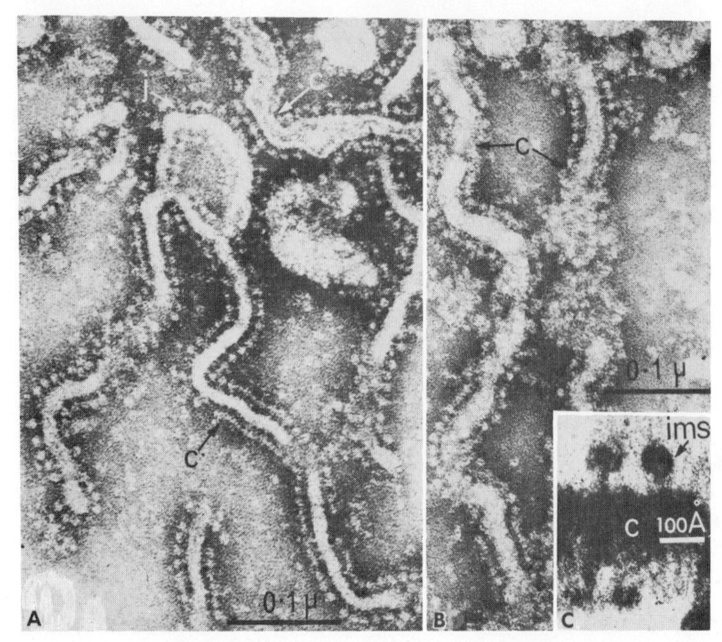

Fig. 10-6. Negatively stained section of mitochondrial cristae showing associated subunits. **A** shows several cristae, **C,** and points of branching, **j.** Note "lollypop" units along the surfaces. **B,** Negatively stained lysed rat liver mitochondria. Subunits are comparable to those seen in **A. C,** Two subunits from **B** at higher magnification. (From Parsons, D. F. 1963. Science **140:** 985-987.)

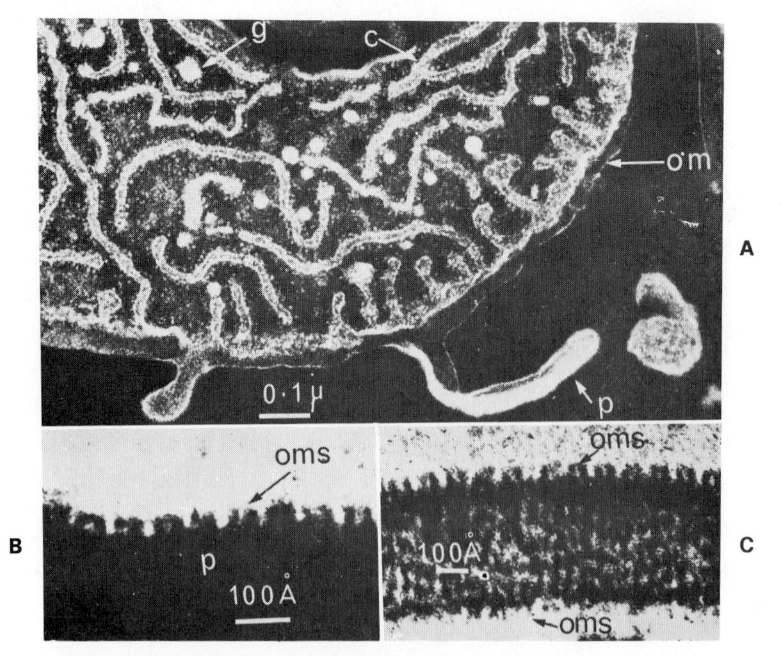

Fig. 10-7. A, Negatively stained mitochondrion showing projection, **p,** on the outer membrane, **om. B,** Higher magnification of outer membrane subunits, **oms,** shown at **p.** These subunits consist of numerous hollow cylinders approximately 60 Å wide and 60 Å high. The center-to-center spacings are approximately 80 Å. **C,** Negatively stained spread preparation of lysed mitochondria. (From Parsons, D. F. 1963. Science **140:**985-987.)

Another type of subunit has been observed in the outer membrane of rat liver mitochondria (Parsons, 1963; Guillory, personal communication). These structures consist of hollow cylinders 60 Å wide and 60 Å long, with a central hole 20 Å in diameter. The center-to-center spacing is approximately 80 Å. The major axis of these cylindrical units is perpendicular to the membrane surface (Fig. 10-7).

Mitochondrial inclusions. In addition to the electron-dense bodies often seen in the mitochondrial matrix, other types of inclusions have been described. Many of them are no doubt limited to mitochondria from special cell types; others are the result of some pathological condition; still others may have been present in all mitochondria but have eluded early observation.

Helical filaments have been observed in mitochondria from the *corpus striatum* of rats (Behnke, 1965; Mugnaini, 1963). They consist of separate parallel filaments within the dilated intracristal spaces. They appear at times to be separated from the mitochondrial matrix by a membrane (Behnke, 1965). In general, these filaments consist of helices that are about 30 Å thick and a pitch of 120 Å. At times as many as fifteen helices can be seen in some of the intra-

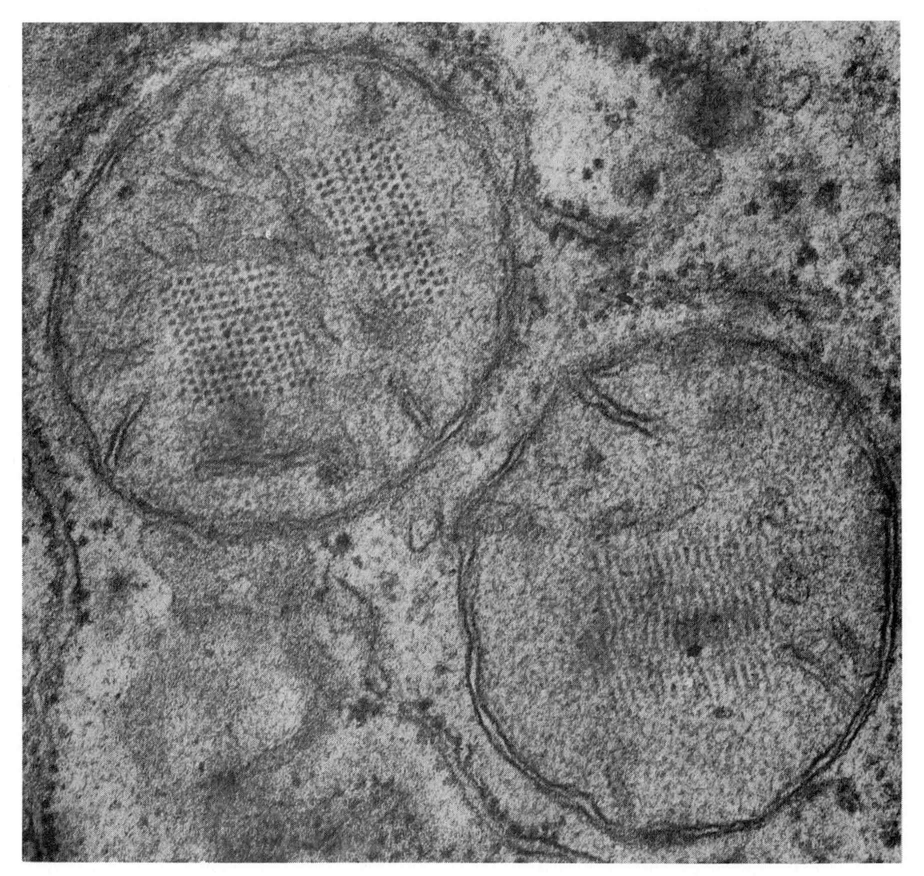

Fig. 10-8. Mitochondria showing crystalline inclusions. These crystalline inclusions are rectangular and are composed of parallel repeating strands that lie about 20 nm apart (right). In the mitochondrion on the left they appear as dots because these strands were cut transversely. (From Wills, E. J. 1965. J. Cell Biol. **24:**511-514.)

cristal spaces. These structures were found in mitochondria that were in intimate association with the cisternae of the rough ER, particularly at the periphery of the glycogen area at the point of transition from the granular to the agranular ER. This structure was thought to be a phospholipid synthesized in the mitochondria (Behnke, 1965) because of a similarity of pattern to mixtures of lipids in an aqueous dispersion that assume a comparable helical structure by spontaneous aggregation of the lipid micelles (Lucy and Glauert, 1964). On the other hand, Mugnaini (1963) believes that they may represent fibrous proteins synthesized within the cell. Non-DNA helices, but of larger size, have been reported in nuclei and cytoplasm of certain eukaryotic cells, of ameba, and of the developing spermatozoid of *Zamia*.

Crystalline structures previously described in pathological tissue have also been observed in normal human liver cells (Wills, 1965). These intramitochondrial inclusions are nearly cuboidal. In profile they are approximately 200 to 350 nm across. In longitudinal section these bodies show a crystalline structure of parallel, repeating, opaque strands 8 to 10 nm in diameter that are separated by gaps of approximately 20 nm (Fig. 10-8). Protein crystals within mitochondria have been reported in oocytes of animals, as one source of yolk platelets, and in some plant cells (Fig. 14-8). Small membrane-bounded granules that range in size from 0.1 to 0.2 μm have been described in mitochondria from mucoid cells of the mouse gastric mucosa, the uterine epithelium of the mouse (only in the estrous phase), and in the inflammatory and hyperplastic condition of the ear epidermis (Deschner, 1963; Nilssen, 1958). At one time these granules were believed to be related to the secretory process because they were first observed in the mucoid cell and later in the uterine epithelium. However, they have also been described in the epithelial cell, which has no known secretory function; thus the function of these granules remains unresolved.

Ishikawa and Pei (1965) described glycogen particles in mitochondria from rat retinal receptors. They appear as dense elliptical masses enclosed by a membrane. Their sizes may vary greatly, ranging up to 3 nm, which is well above the resolution of the light microscope. The distribution of the intramitochondrial glycogen is variable, with no apparent specific region of localization. Small membrane-bounded clusters of glycogen granules can be found within the cristae, within the space between the inner and outer membrane, and inside the mitochondrial matrix. In some mitochondria, however, glycogen bodies have no apparent membrane and they are assumed to be membraneless. The distribution of these granules is apparently limited to the mitochondria of the visual receptor cell and may have some relationship to age. These glycogen particles are not seen in the newborn but first became observable in the mitochondria of rats as early as 3 months of age.

Other accumulations such as ferritin or ferritin-like bodies have been observed in mitochondria of individuals suffering from thalassemia major, or Cooley's anemia (Bessis and Breton-Gorius, 1957). The cause of this type of anemia is poorly understood but is presumed to be hereditary in nature. Yolk granules have also been observed in the mitochondria from the eggs of *Planorbis* (Carasso and Favard, 1958).

Variations in mitochondrial patterns. Examination of mitochondria from a large number of cells of numerous animal and plant tissues, whether lower or higher plants, invertebrate or vertebrate animals, shows the basic mitochondrial pattern is the same for all. They all contain paired membranes separated (or presumably separated) by a narrow space, the inner membrane enclosing a matrix of variable density. The inner membrane penetrates this matrix to form invaginations. Despite these basic similarities in structure, one is impressed by variations in their pattern, especially of the invaginations, not only between groups of animals and plants but also between different tissues from the same organism.

Structural variations can include size and shape, matrix densities, the kinds of inclusions present, and the number and shape of the invaginations. Additional variations are observed in the length of the cristae, ranging from rather short and blunt structures to long cristae extending the width or even the length of the matrix. In some mitochondria there are relatively few cristae, and in other mitochondria the cristae are numerous and closely packed together. Biochemical studies indicate that mitochondria with few cristae have a lower metabolic activity than mitochondria in which the cristae are numerous and closely packed together.

In liver and most plant mitochondria the cristae are irregular in occurrence and sparsely distributed. The cristae extend a short distance into the matrix. They are transversely arranged and may form an extended arc around the inside of the mitochondrion. On the other hand, mitochondria from kidney tubules have many cristae that are transversely arranged and extend across the entire width of the mitochondrial matrix. Often the actual continuity between the cristae and inner membrane is not visible. It is probable that the connection may be mediated by a narrow neck (Sjöstrand, 1953).

In Protozoa and the slime molds, for example, the cristae are in the form of tubules, which may be closely packed and may not show a regular organization (Figs. 10-9 and 17-4).

Several different types of arrangement may occur within the same mitochondrion.

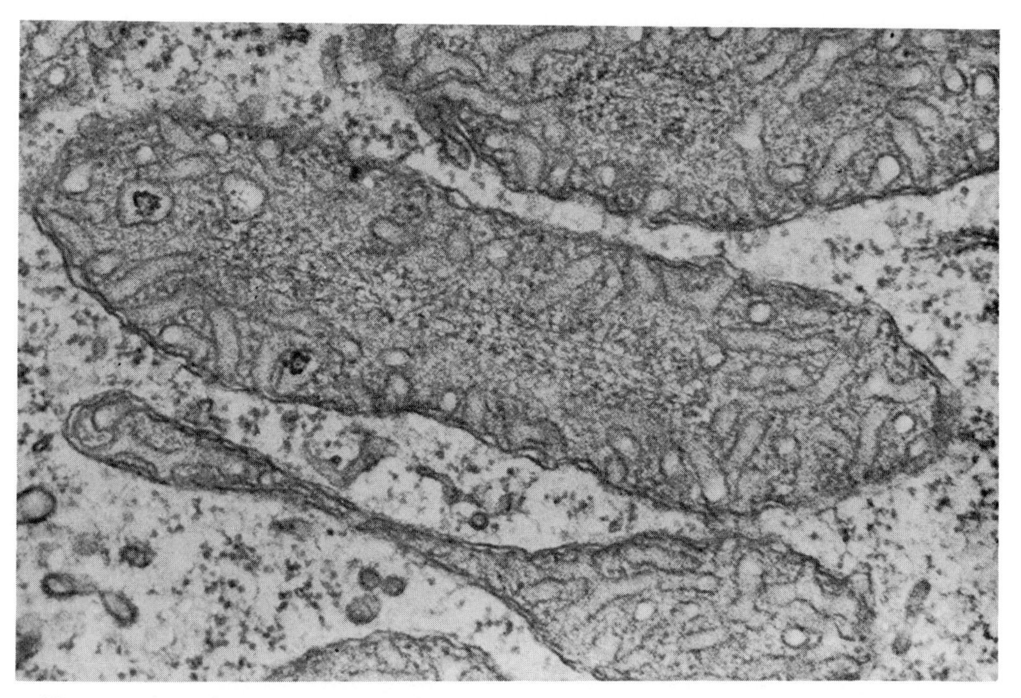

Fig. 10-9. Mitochondria from the flagellate stage of the protozoan *Didymium* showing the presence of centrally located DNA. It appears as electron-dense threads. Each of the paired units consists of tightly coiled helices. Note also the tubular "cristae" typical of many lower organisms. (From Schuster, F. L. 1965. Exp. Cell Res. **39**:329-345.)

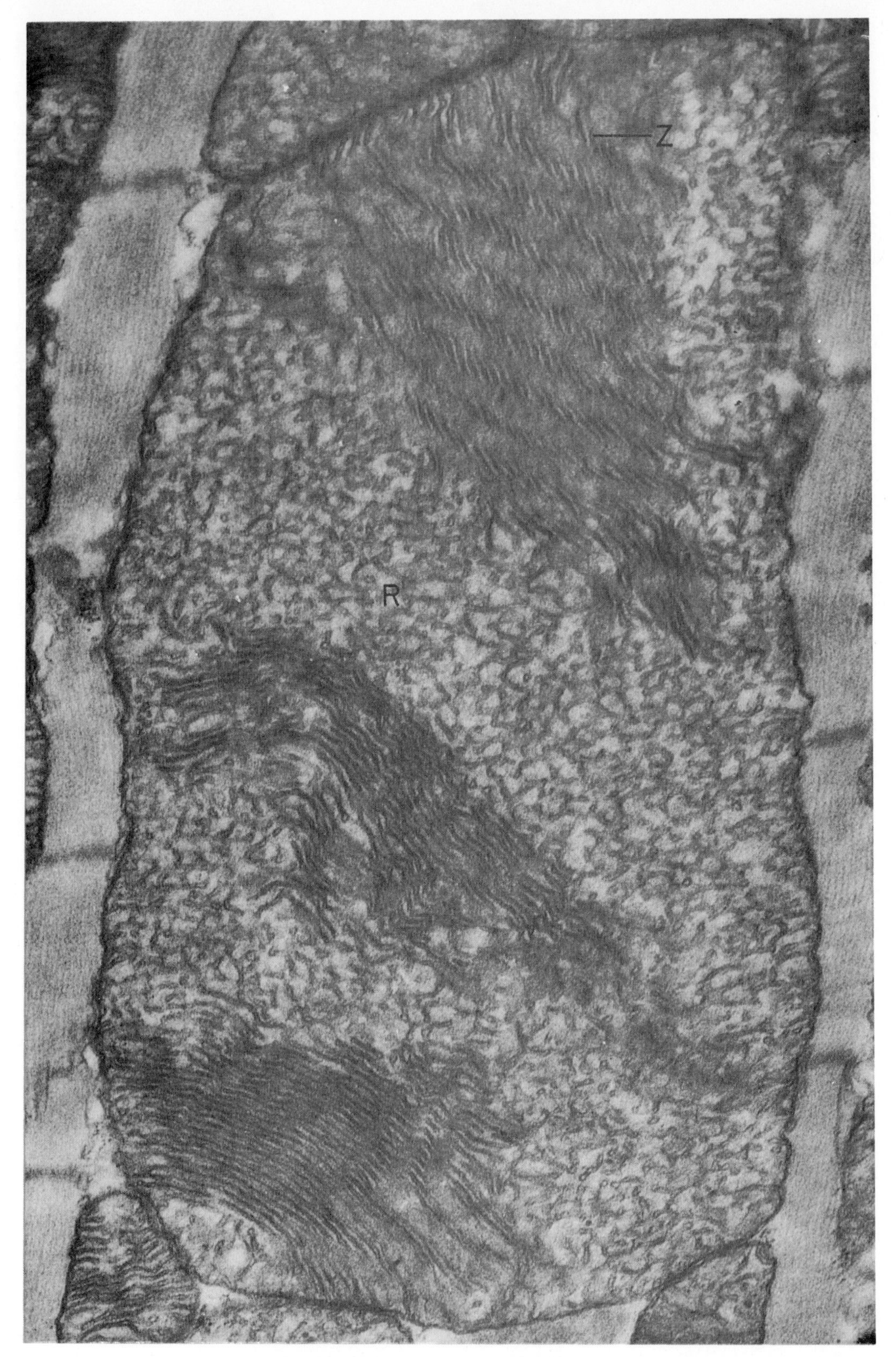

Fig. 10-10. For legend see opposite page.

An interesting arrangement involving several patterns was observed in mitochondria of cardiac muscle cells of the canary (Slautterback, 1965). They appear separate within the mitochondrion but merge at the boundary. These two forms were designated zigzag and retiform. The former consists of "cristae" that are tubular and measure 150 to 175 Å in diameter. These tubules are packed in a hexagonal or staggered array (Fig. 10-10) and pursue a straight course in a zigzag manner. The retiform cristae consist of tubules that also measure 150 to 175 Å in diameter. They are, however,

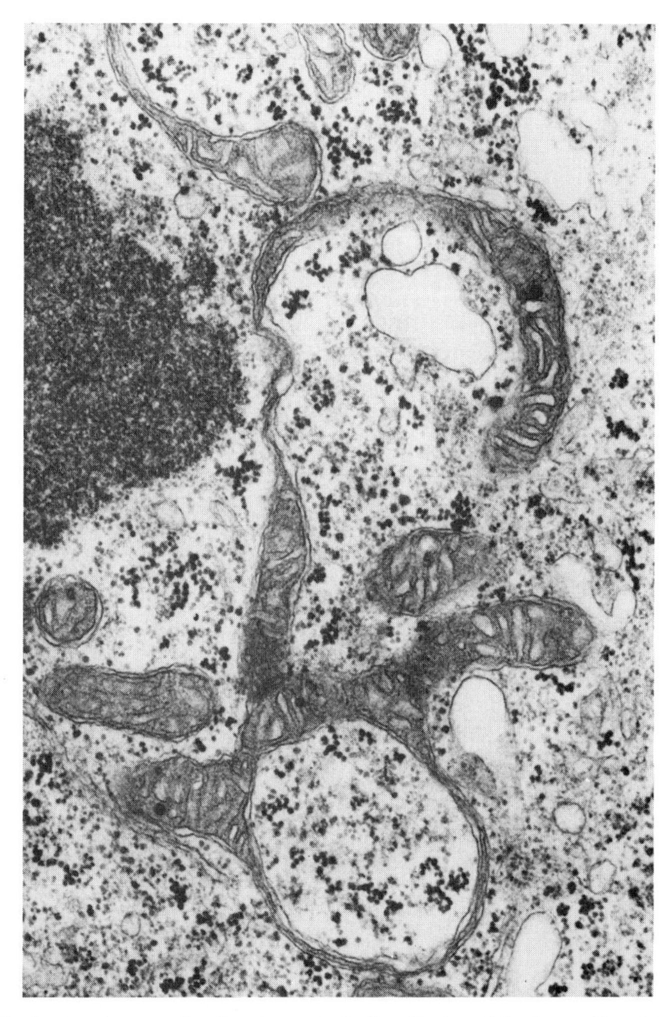

Fig. 10-11. Electron micrograph showing atypical mitochondria from the developing heart of a cardiac lethal mutant *Ambystoma mexicanum* (Mexican axolotl). The mitochondrion at the bottom appears to have engulfed cytoplasm. (Courtesy Dr. L. F. Lemanski, Department of Biology, University of Pennsylvania, Philadelphia, Pa.)

Fig. 10-10. Electron micrograph of mitochondrion from cardiac muscle of canary. This section shows numerous Y-shaped retiform arrays, **R,** which suggest a possible hexagonal pattern alternating with a zigzag array of cristae, **Z.** (From Slautterback, D. B. 1965. J. Cell Biol. **24:**1-22.)

highly anastomosed and less regularly arranged. Continuity exists between these two systems. It is common for cristae from mitochondria from slower hearts to be disposed in whorls (Slautterback, 1965).

Occasionally, atypical mitochondria can be seen in presumably normal tissue. Stephens and Bils (1965) observed mitochondria from normal rat liver that appear to have engulfed a small portion of cytoplasm. Similar results were observed from developing myocardial cells of the cardiac lethal mutant of *Ambystoma mexicanum* (Mexican axolotl) (Lemanski, 1971) (Fig. 10-11). Another explanation of this apparent engulfment may be the highly pleomorphic configuration assumed by the mitochondria and that a cross section or tangential section through the pleomorphic regions can produce the same apparent effect.

In some organisms the mitochondria may be long and branching, such as those in yeast cells (Kawakami, 1961). In these cells the mitochondria appear to be connected to the internal membrane system as well as to the nuclear and cytoplasmic membranes (Thygarajan et al., 1961).

The cristae represent a mechanism for increasing the surface area of the mitochondrion. It is in these cristae that the enzymes involved in oxidative phosphorylation and the electron transport system are found. It is conceivable, then, that when more cristae are present, more assemblies of these enzymes are also found.

Suppose for illustrative purpose that the liver cell is a sphere of a diameter of 30 μm. Its surface area ($4\pi r^2$) would be about 3,000 μm^2. Furthermore, if one assumes that a single liver cell may contain 1,000 mitochondria whose average dimensions are 1.3 $\times$ 10 μm, the surface area of a single mitochondrion would be about 13 μm^2. One thousand mitochondria would make a total surface area of 13,000 μm^2. Compared to the surface area of the liver cell the mitochondria have a surface area about 4.3 times greater than the surface area of the cell. In addition, if one assumes that there are about ten cristae per mitochondrion, each having an area equal to the base of the mitochondria, a single mitochondrion will have an additional surface area of 16 μm^2. Multiplying this figure by 1,000 (the number of mitochondria), the surface area due to cristae will be 16,000 μm^2. The total mitochondrial surface area is the simple addition of the area of the mitochondria and the total surface area of the cristae, giving a total area of 29,000 μm^2, which when compared to the area of a single hepatic cell, is about ten times greater (Lehninger, 1964).

Pathological changes

Although all pathological changes are not included in the scope of this book, certain general mitochondrial alterations will be mentioned to illustrate changes that may be encountered. One of the most common changes is mitochondrial swelling. The cause may be due to a toxin that acts presumably by alterating the osmotic pressure within the cells, thereby causing imbibition of water. The cells and the inclusions, including mitochondria, appear swollen. Generally this process is reversible when the toxic substance is removed. The imbibition of water causes the tissue to swell and appear cloudy under the microscope, hence the term "cloudy swelling." This condition may also result from a delay in fixation after extirpation of tissue from the animal.

Another change affecting the mitochondria may be lysis of the organelle; at times the mitochondria may appear to show hyalinization, which results in complete or almost complete cessation of function. When fluoracetate is administered to chick embryos, for example, mitochondrial alterations include irregularity in shape. Structural damage involves both matrix and cristae: The density of the matrix decreases, and the inner membrane becomes displaced and collapsed onto a limited area of the external membrane (Pucci, 1964). In lead poisoning (Watrach, 1964) there is a formation of closely packed arrays of lamellae, some of which may measure only 55 to 65 Å in thickness and 0.1 to 0.5 μm in length. Such few, small, and short cristae are a sign of mitochondrial malfunction and degeneration. The origin of this condition is unknown, but the filaments represent multiple membranes packed together in a highly regular fashion. The alterating mechanism may be triggered by modifications in lipid-

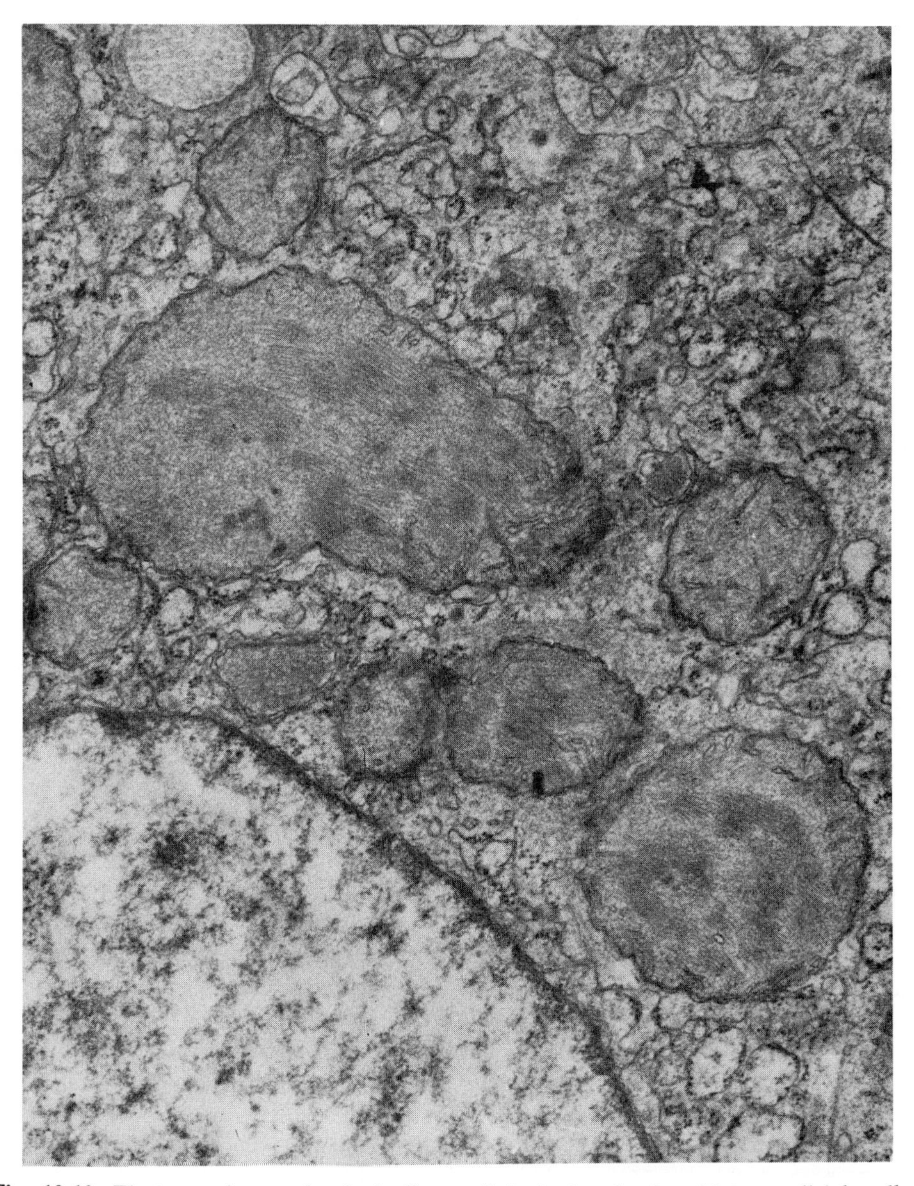

Fig. 10-12. Electron micrograph of pig liver cell in lead poisoning. Note parallel lamellar formation in mitochondria. Some of the lamellae appear to be continuous with the cristae. (From Watrach, A. M. 1964. J. Ultrastruct. Res. **10:**177-181.)

protein complexes. This change may cause impaired function by affecting the elementary particles (Fig. 10-12).

Other changes affecting mitochondria involve vacuolation and increased deposition of electron-dense material within the matrix.

Chemical composition

It is customary to consider the chemical composition of the mitochondrion on the basis of the membrane system and the various assemblies of enzyme systems associated with it.

The composition of the membrane systems is similar to that of the plasma and endoplasmic membranes; that is, the membranes are composed of lipids and proteins, the lipids being sandwiched between two protein layers. In the composition of lipids from mitochondrial membranes, phospholipids comprise 26% of the mitochondrial dry weight; cholesterol, 6%; and neutral fat, 4%. Of the phospholipid moiety, 50% is present as phosphatidyl serine and phosphatidyl ethanolamine, 30% as lecithin, 13% as phosphoinositides, 2% as polyglycerophosphatides, and 17% as plasmalogens (Ball and Joel, 1962).

The protein composition of mitochondrial membranes is not well known. However, an actinlike and myosin-like protein has been extracted from liver mitochondria (Onishi and Onishi, 1962a,b). These substances showed cross-reactions with actin and myosin prepared from skeletal muscles. It was suggested that contraction of mitochondria by ATP is partly due to these proteins. However, the concept and presence of such contractile proteins has been discredited, and they no longer appear in models of mitochondrial structure and function.

Immunological and electrophoretic studies on rat mitochondria treated with deoxycholate have shown that mitochondria contain at least three groups of antigens: (1) one specific for membranes, (2) one soluble in deoxycholate, and (3) one shared by both (D'Amelio et al., 1963).

The structure and function of mitochondria are intimately related to the biochemical actions. Because of this relationship, it is impossible to discuss the one without the other. If mitochondria are sonicated, which disrupts them, the soluble proteins are released in solution and the membranes are present in the sediment fraction. Analysis of the membranes shows that the electron-transferring enzymes, the flavoproteins, and cytochomes b_1, c , c, a, and a_3 oxidase as well as the energy-coupling enzymes of oxidative phosphorylation are located on them. The soluble fraction contains most of the enzymes of the fatty acid oxidase system as well as sites for oxidation of some of the amino acids.

It has been suggested that the oxidation-reduction components in the electron transfer system are connected to each other through lipoproteins. They can be conceived as structural devices that not only hold the parts together but also as functional devices that serve as shuttles; that is, they shuttle electrons from one to another of a pair of oxidation-reduction components to which each lipoprotein is attached. It is of interest to note that some of the subparticles resulting from sonification still contain oxidative phosphorylating properties (Ziegler et al., 1958). Two subparticles obtained were designated the *electron transport particle* (ETP) and the *phosphorylating electron transport particle* (PETP). The ETP catalyzes the rapid oxidation of $NADH_2$ and succinate by molecular oxygen. The PETP contains the properties (or at least many of the properties) of the ETP but is capable of carrying on oxidative phosphorylation and yet still contains the citric acid cycle dehydrogenases.

In addition to the soluble enzymes present in the matrix the matrix includes adenosine triphosphate (ATP), adenosine diphosphate (ADP), coenzyme A (CoA), diphosphopyridine nucleotide (NAD), triphosphopyridine nucleotide (NADP), coenzymes, and inorganic electrolytes such as K^+, HPO^-,

Mg^{++}, Cl^{-}, and $SO_4^{=}$ (Lehninger, 1964).

In considering the function of mitochondria we are discussing primarily the enzymatic mechanism involved in cellular respiration as well as mitochondrial swelling and contraction cycles. An additional function identified in mitochondria is protein synthesis, which on the part of the mitochondria is independent of cytoplasmic ribosomes.

Nucleic acid

After the detection of DNA in mitochondria (mtDNA) of both plants and animals (Bell and Mühlethaler, 1964; Luck and Reich, 1964; Nass et al., 1965; Schuster, 1965), it was suggested that mitochondria are capable of self-duplication as well as protein synthesis, and they possibly may play an important role in cytoplasmic inheritance. As knowledge of the biosynthetic activity increased during the past 10 years, these early postulations proved correct. However, it was somewhat disappointing to learn that the biosynthetic activity was limited. The biosynthetic activity seems to be the result of an interplay between two genetic systems consisting of the nucleocytoplasmic system on the one hand and the mitochondrial matrix on the other (Borst, 1972).

After the identification of mtDNA the various mtRNAs were soon found.

Mitochondrial DNA

mtDNA is, by and large, located in the central region of the mitochondrion (Fig. 10-9 and 17-4) (Schuster, 1965). It may appear as 20 to 50 Å fibers or as rodlike structures with a thickness of up to 250 Å. It was observed that mtDNA from cells in a rapid proliferative state contains thicker fiber than from cells with a lower metabolic rate (Schuster, 1965).

DNA genophores can be isolated from mitochondria. As far as is known they are all circular, double-stranded structures (Fig. 10-13). At the present time no single-stranded DNAs have been found (Helinski and Clewell, 1971). At times an open ring structure may be observed, but this may be due to extraction procedure rather than being the true configuration. In addition to the small circular form some animal mtDNA may exist as a circular dimer, which can be considered a double length circular model or a catenate form in which the single length submolecules can be connected to each other as in links of a chain (Hudson and Vinograd, 1967; Clayton and Vinograd, 1967, 1969).

One significant feature about mtDNA is the uniformity in size of the circles, as seen in various animals. They all have a contour size of about 5 μm, the range being 4.45 μm in sea urchins to 5.15 μm in the echuriod worms. The molecular weight average is about 1×10^7 daltons (Ashwell and Work, 1970; Helinski and Clewell, 1971; Borst, 1972).

The buoyant density in CsCl is generally somewhat lower than the nuclear DNA, being about 1.701 in mtDNA, whereas the density for nuclear DNA is about 1.712. In addition, the cytosine-guanine ratio in mtDNA is 41% to 53% for the nuclear DNA (Luck, 1965a,b). (The difference in buoyant density implies a difference in base composition.)

DNA replication

The presence of DNA polymerase in the mitochondria suggests that mitochondria might be able to replicate themselves.

Two opposing views were proposed, one being that mtDNA is synthesized by a master gene in the nucleus and the resulting DNA is transferred to the mitochondria. The function of DNA polymerase is solely for repairing the damaged mtDNA. Hybridization studies between mtDNA and nuclear DNA were mostly unsuccessful, indicating that nuclear DNA probably does not synthesize mtDNA. The second view, which is readily testable, is the study of mtDNA replication in vitro. When isolated mitochon-

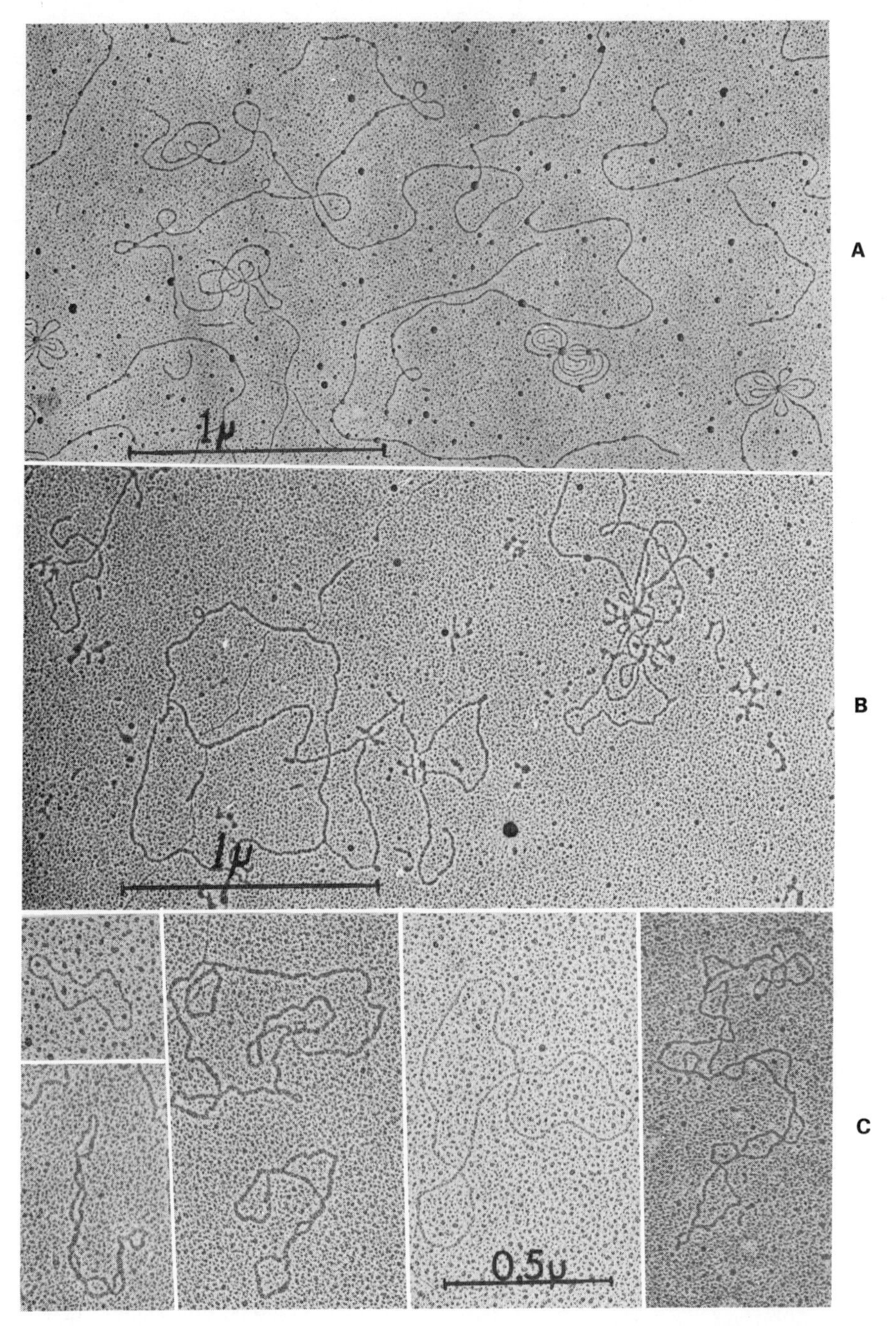

Fig. 10-13. A and **B,** Noncircular mitochondrial DNA from yeast mitochondria. **C,** Circular DNA from whole yeast cell DNA. Although most mitochondrial DNA is circular, the noncircular DNA *may* truly represent the condition in yeast. (From Sinclair, J. H., et al. 1967. Science **156:**1234-1237.)

dria are incubated with the essential triphosphates (ATP, CTP, GTP, and UTP), replication of mtDNA is achieved (Brewer et al., 1967). In addition, experiments using ^{3}H-bromodeoxyuridine show that mtDNA replicates in a semiconservative manner (Gross and Rabinowitz, 1969). Evidence indicates that the rate of synthesis is under the influence of the nucleus, and the rate can be altered by a number of environmental conditions (Ashwell and Work, 1970).

Mitochondrial RNA

Studies have shown that the amount of mtRNA is about ten to twenty times that of the mtDNA (South and Mehler, 1968). At the present time ribosomal RNA, the various tRNAs, and possibly mRNA have been identified. The latter consists of a rather heterogeneous group of RNAs.

Mitochondrial ribosomes. After the identification of ribosomes in *Neurospora* (Küntzel, 1969 a,b) ribosome-like particles were later found in mitochondria from several animals and plants. Although the size of the mt ribosome is generally given as a 70s particle, comparable to prokaryotes, a fairly wide range in sizes has been obtained. For example, fungal ribosomes sediment at about 73s, whereas ribosomes from several animals sediment at about 55s (Ashwell and Work, 1970; Borst, 1972).

The 73s particle dissociates into a large 50s subunit and a 30s to 33s subunit. The larger subunit contains a 23s to 27s RNA, and the smaller subunit contains a 16s to 18s RNA (Ashwell and Work, 1970). The 55s ribosome dissociates into a 40s and 30s subunit. The RNAs are 16s for the larger subunits and 12s for the smaller 30s subunits. The molecular weights of the two RNAs from *Xenopus* and HeLa cells are 0.53 to 0.56×10^{6} for the large molecule and 0.3 to 0.36×10^{6} for the smaller RNA (Ashwell and Work, 1970; Borst, 1972).

Protein analyses show that there is little in common with the proteins obtained from cytoplasmic ribosomes. No 5s RNAs have so far been identified from the large subunits.

Mitochondrial tRNA. At the present time all 20 tRNAs have been found in mitochondria from *Neurospora.* In other cells the number of tRNAs are variable, which may mean that because of technical difficulties not all were isolated. All tRNAs obtained hybridize with mtDNA, thereby indicating that they were synthesized within the mitochondria and not derived from the outside. One unique species of tRNA found is ′fmet-RNA, which is not present in the cytoplasm of eukaryotic cells (see discussion on protein synthesis, Chapter 9). The tRNAs sediment at 4s like their counterparts in the cytoplasm.

Mitochondrial messenger RNA. There is little available information regarding the presence of mRNA of mitochondrial origin. However, studies have shown the presence of 11s, 12s, and 21s RNAs, which are believed to have a messenger function (Vesco and Penman, 1961).

Protein synthesis

In the section on the function of ribosomes it was noted that mitochondria synthesize proteins in much the same manner as do prokaryotes. However, the amount of mtDNA per mitochondrion indicates that the total genetic information probably does not exceed 15,000 base pairs. This means that mtDNA requires the proper number of enzymes to translate and transcribe these base pairs. The implication at this time indicates that many more genes are needed for expression of mtDNA than are contained on these molecules. Thus it is estimated that only about 5% of the mitochondrial proteins can be coded for by the DNA (Borst, 1972).

In general, mitochondria can code and synthesize proteins of a structural nature such as cytochrome oxidase. On the other hand, it is believed that the nuclear genes code for much, if not all, of the soluble proteins of the matrix as well as the proteins of the outer membrane and a number of proteins located on the cristae (Ashwell and Work, 1970; Borst, 1972).

Of the proteins coded for by nuclear genes, it has been proposed that the mitochondria translate these mRNAs (Dawid, 1972). The major difficulty is in the manner by which these mRNAs enter the mitochondria. A second hypothesis that seems to have more evidence is that the mRNAs derived from the nucleus are translated in the cytoplasm, and the resulting proteins are then transported into the mitochondria. The following two methods of entrance of these proteins have been proposed:

1. The precursors enter the mitochondria and inside are converted into the end product, thereby affecting a unidirectional flow of material into the organelle.
2. There is the synthesis of lipoprotein vesicles, and these vesicles can merge and combine with the growing mitochondria.

Cellular respiration

Cellular respiration involves the enzymatic breakdown of carbohydrates, fats, and amino acids, with the carbohydrate being the predominant form of substrate. The end product of this oxidative process is the liberation of energy along with water and carbon dioxide. The liberated energy can be stored as ATP or can be utilized directly for a number of cellular functions, including heat.

In the enzymatic breakdown of foods, that is, carbohydrates, fats, and protein, the initial degradation is extramitochondrial. The final products of these substances are ultimately degraded in the cytoplasm to a two-carbon compound, acetate, which is then bound to coenzyme A (CoA) to form acetyl-CoA. The acetyl-CoA enters the mitochondria, and the acetate group couples with oxaloacetic acid of the Krebs tricarboxylic acid cycle (TCA) to form a six-carbon compound, citric acid. After a series of steps involving enzymatic action it is decarboxylated; that is, it loses carbon dioxide. Also in this cycle five pairs of hydrogens are removed by dehydrogenase and ultimately enter into the electron transport system, in which the hydrogen protons and "de-energized" electrons finally combine with molecular oxygen to form water (Fig. 10-14).

Electron transport system

The electron transport system (or the cytochrome system) is coupled with the TCA system. The hydrogens that were released from the substrate to NAD or NADP are passed to the oxidized form of the flavoprotein to reduce it. The hydrogens are released from the electrons by the flavoprotein and enter into the mitochondrial matrix, the electrons being transferred to the cytochrome system. The cytochromes are iron-containing compounds (see discussion of histochemistry in Chapter 1) that are capable of receiving the electrons from the flavoproteins and transferring them successively from cytochromes b to c, to a, to a_3 and from cytochrome a_3, along with the protons, to molecular oxygen. The acceptance of the electron by molecular oxygen activates the oxygen and causes it to combine with the protons in the matrix to form water (Fig. 10-15). Coenzyme Q (ubiquinone) is found at some position in the electron transport system. Its function is not known for certain, and its role in the electron transport system is somewhat elusive. It is not only found in the mitochondria but also in the cell nuclei and microsomes. It is possible that it participates in oxidative phosphorylation, if not in the electron transport system per se (Lehninger, 1964).

Transforming mechanisms are involved at three points along the electron transport system in the release of energy by pairs of electrons to produce ATP from ADP and phosphate (Fig. 10-15). Oxidative phosphorylation is probably the most important function of mitochondria. In fact, the coupling of the TCA cycle with the

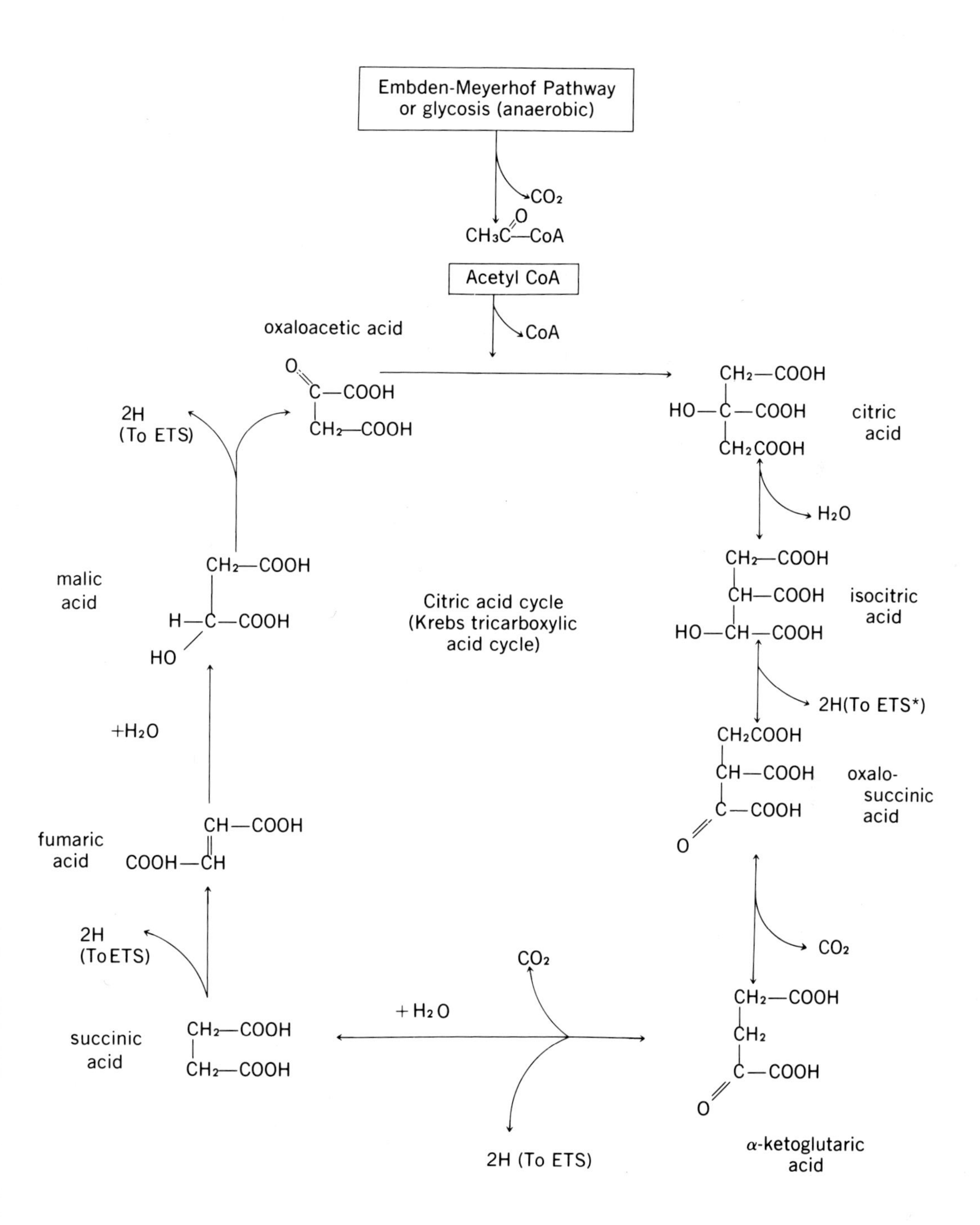

*ETS = electron transport system

Fig. 10-14. Diagrammatic representation of Krebs citric acid cycle.

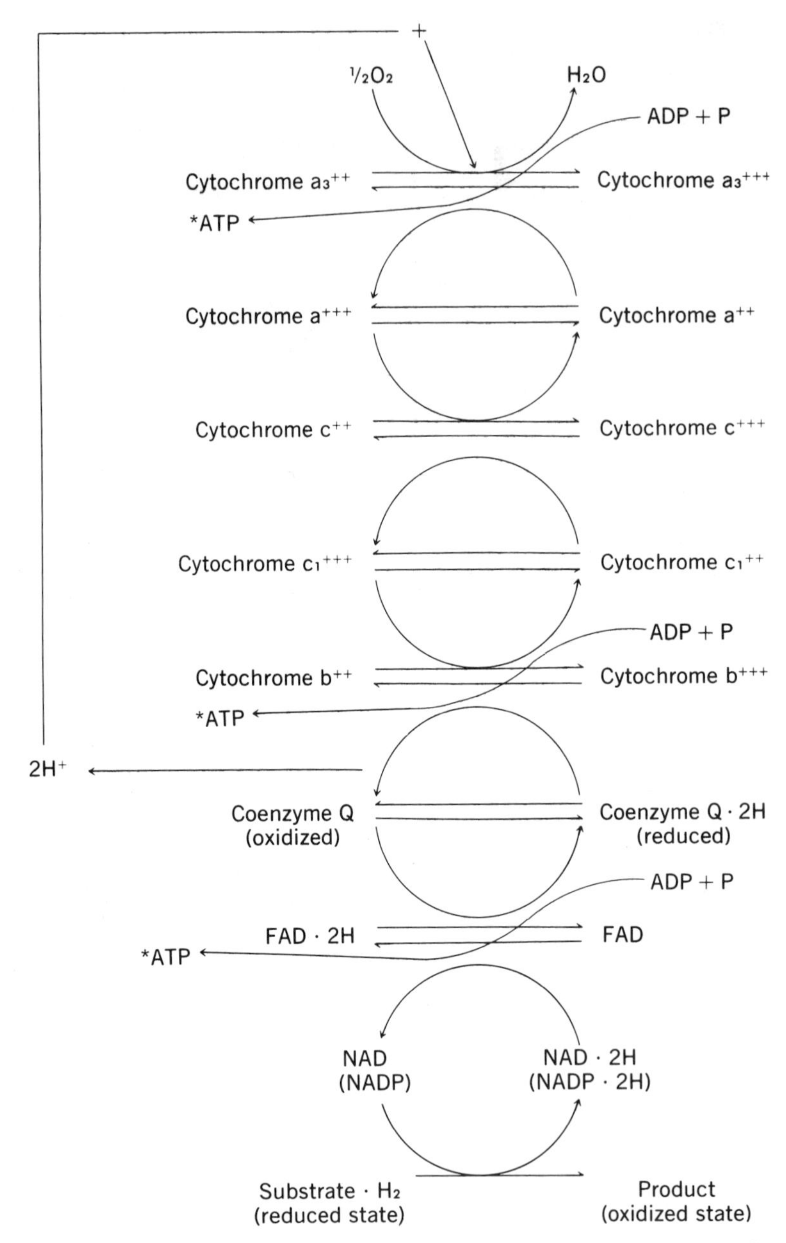

Fig. 10-15. Scheme of electron transport system. Asterisks indicate points of oxidative phosphorylation.

electron transport system produces thirty-eight molecules of ATP from one glucose molecule, as compared to the production of only two ATP molecules by the anaerobic glycolytic pathway.

Mitochondrial changes in volume

Earlier it was stated that phase-contrast studies of living cells demonstrated that mitochondria have a characteristic swelling and contraction cycle that appeared to be respiration dependent (Packer and Golder, 1960). At times the cycle appears to be rhythmical in nature. Other studies using isolated liver mitochondria also showed that mitochondria are capable of undergoing swelling, which can be classified as either passive or active in nature.

Passive swelling is of little significance and results when mitochondria are placed in hypotonic solutions. In fact, they behave much like an osmometer when suspended in mannitol solution (Lehninger, 1962, 1964), the degree of swelling depending on concentration. Ledeschi (1958) had shown that isolated mitochondria obey rather exactly the osmotic laws when placed in solutions of sucrose. It is of interest in this respect that sucrose penetrates the outer membrane rather quickly but the inner membrane more slowly. This produces a ballooning effect in the outer chamber of the mitochondria. On the other hand, certain substances such as phosphates, calcium (Ca^{++}), thyroxine, glutathione (Lehninger, 1962, 1964), ferrous iron (Hunter et al., 1963), and ascorbic acid (Utsumi et al., 1965) produce swelling when added to isolated mitochondria that is out of proportion to the concentrations used. Furthermore, when ATP is added, the mitochondria undergo contraction, which results in the extrusion of water. In fact, it has been shown that approximately 400 moles of water are extruded per mole of ATP added (Lehninger, 1962). This indicates that substances which uncouple phosphorylation are associated with mitochondrial swelling and the intake of water. The oxidation-phosphorylation function occurs after the mitochondria undergo contraction.

The swelling of mitochondria by phosphate is due to the enzymatic uptake of this substance during the mechanism of oxidative phosphorylation. Calcium causes swelling because it acts as an uncoupling agent. In addition, calcium, ascorbic acid, thyroxine (Lehninger, 1964), and ferrous iron (Hunter et al., 1963) cause swelling because free fatty acids are formed by enzyme action within the mitochondria and accumulate there. At times extensive accumulations can occur and lead to lysis and disintegration of the mitochondria. These accumulated fatty acids that uncouple phosphorylation have been called the *U factor,* or *uncoupling factor* (Wojtczak and Wojtczak, 1960). Utsumi et al. (1965) have shown that when exposed to such substances as ferrous iron and ascorbic acid, mitochondria of hepatomas did not show this mitochondrial swelling. This lack of mitochondrial change appeared to be due to the low content of polyenoic acids found in hepatoma cells.

The structural basis of mitochondrial contraction was mentioned in the section on the chemical composition of mitochondria. There is apparently an actinlike and myosin-like substance present in mitochondria (Ohnishi and Ohnishi, 1962a,b). This has been confirmed with some reservation by others (Vignais et al., 1963). This actinlike and myosin-like substance shows contractibility when ATP is added. Another contraction factor known as the *C factor* was also observed (Neubert et al., 1962). These C factors are heat-labile mitochondrial materials that are required in contraction of reduced glutathione swelling. The C factor restores the ATP-linked contraction. The amount of water extruded is proportional to the concentration of the C factor. These factors are found in mitochondria of all tissues of higher animals. The contraction factors can be divided into C factor I, which is an enzyme called *glutathione peroxidase;* C factor II, an enzyme called *catalase;* and C factor III, an unidentified heat-labile substance of small molecular weight.

The amount of mitochondrial swelling in cells is small and is referred to as "low-amplitude swelling," in contrast to the large amount of swelling in isolated mitochondria, which is called "high-amplitude swelling."

Origin of mitochondria

Available evidence concerning the lifespan of mitochondria, at least their molecular material, indicates ranges somewhere between 5 and 10 days. This would mean that several new mitochondria must be produced within this period of time. Several different possible mechanisms of mitochondrial genesis have been suggested, including (1) division of preexisting mitochondria, (2) infolding of the plasma membranes and/or membranes of the ER, (3) changes in nuclear membranes, and (4) de novo formation in which the proteins and lipids are produced and spontaneously assembled into mitochondria.

One of the views of the earlier cytologists was that mitochondria underwent a division during mitosis and that each half went into the daughter cells (Novikoff, 1961). In effect, this view held that mitochondria, like the chromosomes, play a part in inheritance; that is, at fertilization the sperm as well as the egg contributes a complement of mitochondria to the zygote. In each successive mitotic division these mitochondria would divide and approximately one half would go to each daughter cell.

Robertson (1964) conceived of mitochondria as originating from the plasma membrane and membranes of the ER as well as from the nuclear envelope (Fig. 10-16). Electron microscopy shows that the mitochondria are continuous with the cytoplasmic and nuclear membranes; the mitochondria may be formed when the cytoplasm fills the cavity of the membrane and becomes detached or pinched off to produce the individual mitochondria. Somehow it must acquire a peculiar sort of circular DNA strand. It might do so if derived from the nuclear envelope, but it is not clear how it could acquire DNA if derived from ER or plasma membrane.

Hoffman and Gregg (1958) postulated that mitochondria are formed within the nucleus from the nuclear membrane. The mitochondria would later be extruded from within the nucleus to the cytoplasm. In an actively dividing cell this method would be the principal means of replication. This concept was based on nuclei demarcated by invaginations of the nuclear membrane, which was suggestive of developing mitochondria. This hypothesis is not supported by observation.

Luck (1965a,b), using radioactive choline, studied mitochondrial genesis from a mutant strain of *Neurospora crassa.* He showed that mitochondria increase in number and that during the exponential growth phase the mitochondrial mass doubles. It is his contention that mitochondria increase by accretion and growth and division of existing individuals (Luck and Reich, 1964).

An interesting study of mitochondrial genesis was based on the electron microscopic studies of the retinal photoreceptor inner segment (Berger, 1964). Electron mi-

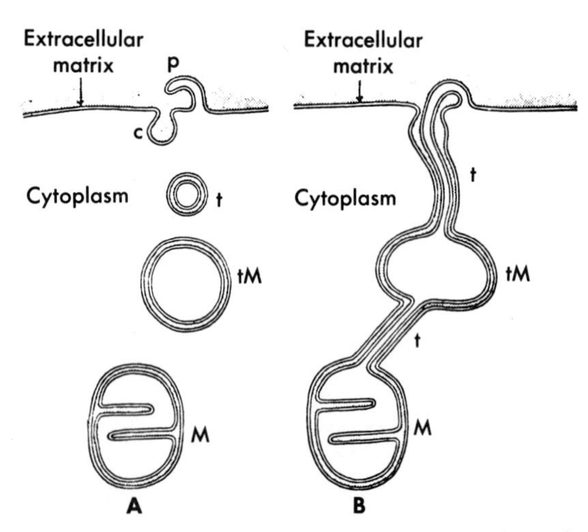

Fig. 10-16. Possible mechanism of formation of mitochondria from the cell membrane. **t,** Tubule; **tM,** tubular mitochondrial form; **M,** mitochondrion; **p,** process; **c,** caveola intracellularis. (From Robertson, J. D. 1964. Unit membranes: a review with recent new studies of experimental alterations and a new subunit structure in synaptic membranes. In M. Locke (editor). Cellular membranes in development. Academic Press, Inc., New York.)

croscopy revealed the mitochondria as being larger in size toward the scleral end and smaller toward the ventral end. In addition, differences in organization were observed such as the inner membranes toward the vitreal end are vesicular and distributed at random. There is also irregularity of the dimensions of the inner space in the smaller mitochondria. Small opaque bodies that average 120 Å in diameter were observed within the smaller mitochondria, but never in the larger ones. The structure is a spherical invaginated membranous sac 340 nm in diameter (Fig. 10-17). A pore that is continuous with the cytoplasm is present. The interspace between the membranes is irregular. The matrix contains vesicles and occasional opaque bodies of 150 Å.

The cytoplasmic continuity with the mitochondria matrix suggests the origin of mitochondria as being cytoplasmic. At first the pore is large, but it becomes progressively smaller until no pore is present. The engulfed cytoplasm becomes the matrix.

The limiting membranes appear to be derived from the Golgi complex; thus one of the importances of this structure would be the synthesis of membrane material. This method of mitochondrial genesis represents a de novo origin of mitochondria in at

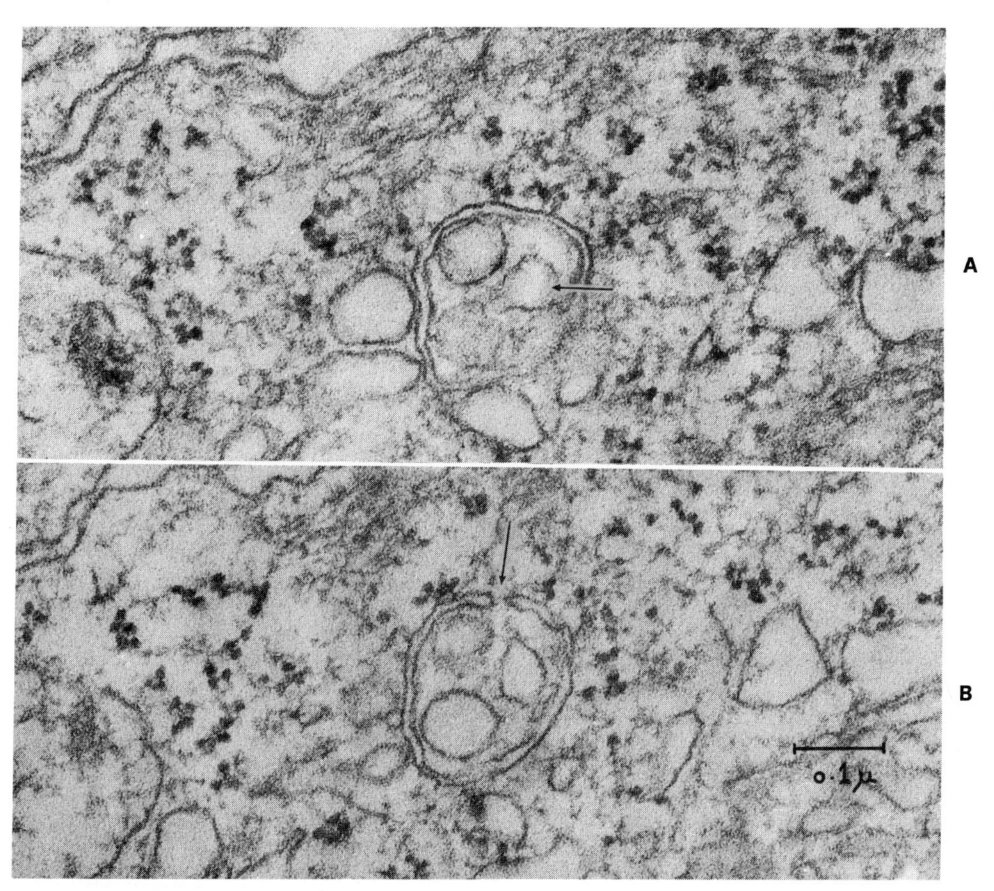

Fig. 10-17. Electron micrographs showing events in the possible formation of mitochondria as observed in the photoreceptor inner segment. **A,** Electron micrographic section showing vesicular inner section. **B,** Limiting membranes have almost fused. A small pore is still evident. Note also the polyribosomes. (From Berger, E. R. 1964. J. Ultrastruct. Res. **11**:90-111.)

least one type of cell, if not a common origin.

Evolution of mitochondria

Recent accumulated information, particularly that of nucleic acids in mitochondria, has led to the revival of the bioblast theory, or at least a concept that closely parallels it. Comparison of the nucleic acids between mitochondria and prokaryotes shows a high degree of similarities. Both contain circular DNA, and nuclear envelopes are lacking. Probably the strongest evidence derives from the mechanism of protein synthesis. In both prokaryotes and mitochondria the initiation of protein synthesis uses formylmethionyl-tRNA, whereas eukaryotes use unformylated tRNA (see section or ribosomal function). Furthermore, chloramphenicol inhibits protein synthesis in mitochondria and prokaryotes but has no effect on protein synthesis in eukaryotes. Conversely, cycloheximide inhibits protein synthesis in eukaryotes but has no effect on protein synthesis in mitochondria or prokaryotes. The s value of ribosomes in eukaryotes is 80s, whereas in mitochondria and prokaryotes it is about 70s (some animal cell mitochondria contain 55s mini-ribosomes). Analysis of plasma membrane shows cholesterol to be present as a constituent in eukaryotes but absent from prokaryotes and the mitochondrial inner membrane (Rothfield and Finkelstein, 1968).

Thus one can conceive of mitochondria as being evolved from an ancient prokaryote (Swift, 1965) possessing all the attributes of an independent, probably aerobic organism. However, with adaptation over a long period of time it became an essential and dependent symbiont, lost some of its identity to the cell, and conversely, the ancient cell lost some of its function, deriving it now from the endosymbiont or mitochondrion. As a result, both became obligatory symbionts to each other. Similar relationships exist today, as for example, the kappa granules found in some paramecia. In this case one can conceive of these granules and cells as having a symbiotic relationship to each other, as can be shown with the cell and mitochondria.

Although the theory of the symbiotic origin of mitochondria and plastids has achieved wide popularity and is supported by numerous characters shared by prokaryotes and the quasiorganisms mitochondria and plastids, all biologists do not necessarily accept it. Raff and Mahler (1972) have recently reexamined the question and have concluded "that while the symbiotic theory may be esthetically pleasing, it is not compelling." They presented extensive evidence and proposed that mitochondria arose by inward blebbing from the plasma membrane, by the acquisition somehow of an outer membrane, and by the additional acquisition of a DNA genophore from the DNA of the protoeukaryote in which the evolution of mitochondrion occurred. This hypothesis is largely a repeat of the older proposal that mitochondria might have evolved from some prokaryotic structure like mesosomes (Fig. 10-19). The DNA of the mitochondrion was supposed to have left the "nuclear" DNA by a sort of amplification to become a cytoplasmic plasmid or episome, which might then have become wrapped within a membrane containing the respiratory chain (Borst, 1972). This model has been called the *episome theory*.

Promitochondria

When yeast cells such as *Saccharomyces cerevesiae* are grown under anaerobic conditions, no recognizable structures are seen in their mitochondria with routine electron microscopy. However, when these cells are shifted to an aerobic environment, these promitochondria will acquire all the morphological characteristics of typical mitochondria and biochemically will contain cytochrome oxidase activity (Morpurgo et al., 1964; Wallace and Linnane, 1964; Wallace et al., 1968). Isolation of these promitochondrial structures revealed the presence of DNA, cytochrome, succinic dehydrogenase, and ATPase.

During the anaerobic phase, the enzymes cytochrome a and a_3 are lacking (Ashwell and Work, 1970).

Petite mutant

When yeast cells, which are susceptible to the action of certain dyes such as acridines and ethidium bromide, are exposed to these dyes, mtDNA synthesis ceases and degradation of mtDNA begins. This degradation process will continue until the dye is removed. When the mtDNA is degraded completely, neutral petites are formed that contain no mtDNA, although the nuclear DNA of the yeast cell is intact and functional. In other forms, where complete degradation does not occur, the mtDNA that remains can undergo replication. However, the resulting mtDNA will show changes in its base composition, which results in low-density petites (Nagley and Linnane, 1970; Goldring et al., 1970; Borst, 1972). There is a change in the guanine-cytosine ratio and a loss of mitochondrial genes that can be recognized by hybridization studies. Often there are changes in the physical morphology of the mtDNA, in which the normal circular form is converted into several heterogeneous circles (Hollenberg et al., 1969).

Lomasomes and mesosomes

Lomasomes, as they appear in some fungi (Fig. 10-18), are inward elaborations of the plasma membrane in the form of tubules or vesicles. Their function has not been determined. Structurally, they are somewhat like the mesosomes of some bacteria and may have a similar function.

Mesosomes are complex membranous invaginations of the plasma membranes of some bacteria (Fig. 10-19). The invaginations, about 2,500 Å in diameter, are in the form of interdigitating tubules or vesicles or have four concentric shells of 75 Å thick membranes. Biochemical study of isolated and concentrated mesosomes has indicated that their membranes are active in oxidative phosphorylation. Thus they are functionally comparable to mitochondria of eucells, and it has been proposed that they may be the prokaryotic evolutionary predecessors of mitochondria. Supporters of that concept must "explain" the acquisition of the surrounding double membranes, which are different from each other; the genophore, which is typical of mitochondria but not of mesosomes; and the ability to divide by furrowing. These problems do not exist for the supporters of the symbiotic hypothesis of the origin of mitochondria.

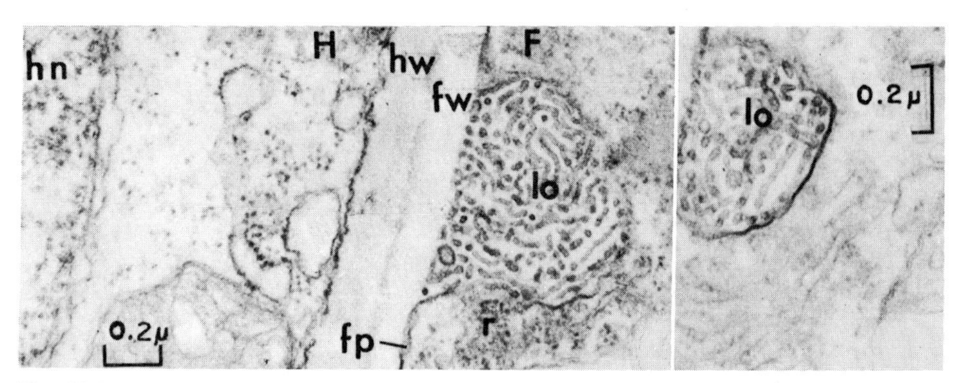

Fig. 10-18. Lomasomes, **lo,** in cells of the fungus *Peronospora manshurica.* The tubules that compose the lomasome in this species and the tubules or vesicles of other species of fungi are internal elaborations of the plasma membranes. (From Peyton, G. A. 1963. Amer. J. Bot. **50:** 787-797.)

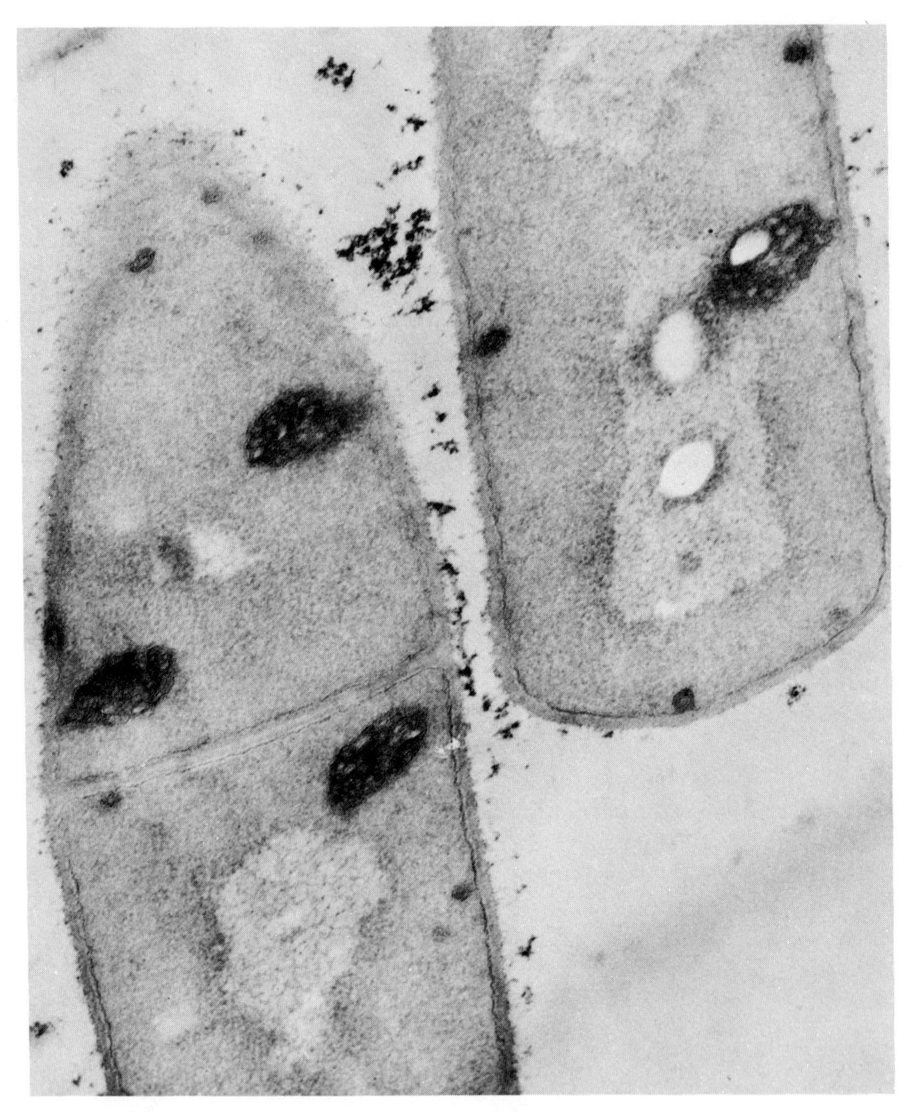

Fig. 10-19. Mesosomes (dark bodies) in bacilli at the end of log phase growth. These mesosomes are attached to or are modified invaginations of the plasma membrane. Note also DNA-containing prokaryons. (Courtesy Dr. P. C. Fitz-James, University of Western Ontario, London, Ont.)

LITERATURE CITED

Ashwell, M., and T. S. Work. 1970. The biogenesis of mitochondria. Ann. Rev. Biochem. **39:**251-290.

Ball, E. G., and C. D. Joel. 1962. The composition of mitochondrial membranes in relation to its structure and function. Int. Rev. Cytol. **13:**99-133.

Behnke, O. 1965. Helical filaments in rat liver mitochondria. Exp. Cell Res. **37:**687-689.

Bell, P. R., and K. Mühlethaler. 1964. Evidence for the presence of deoxyribonucleic acid in the organelles of the egg cells of Pteridium aquilinum. J. Molec. Biol. **8:**853-862.

Berger, E. R. 1964. Mitochondrial genesis in the retinal receptor inner segment. J. Ultrastruct. Res. **11:**90-111.

Bessis, M., and J. Breton-Gorius. 1957. Accumulation de granules ferrugineux dans les mitochondries des érythroblasts. C. R. Acad. Sci. (Paris) **244:**2846-2847.

Borst, P. 1972. Mitochondrial nucleic acid. Ann. Rev. Biochem. **41:**333-376.

Brewer, E. N., A. De Vries, and H. P. Rusch. 1967. DNA synthesis by isolated mitochondria of Physarum polycephalum. Biochim. Biophys. Acta **145:**686-692.

Carasso, N., and P. Favard. 1958. L'origine des plaquettes vitellines de l'oeuf de Planorbe. C. R. Acad. Sci. (Paris) **246:**1594-1597.

Clayton, D. A., and J. Vinograd. 1967. Circular dimer and catenate forms of mitochondrial DNA in human leukaemic leucocytes. Nature (London) **216:**652-657.

Clayton, D. A., and J. Vinograd. 1969. Complex mitochondrial DNA in leukemic and normal human myeloid cells. Proc. Nat. Acad. Sci. U.S.A. **62:**1077-1084.

Cooperstein, S. J., A. Lazarow, and J. W. Patterson. 1953. II. Reaction and properties of Janus Green B and its derivative. Exp. Cell Res. **5:** 69-82.

D'Amelio, V., V. Mutolo, and A. Barbarino. 1963. Immunological and electrophoretic analysis of rat liver mitochondria and other cellular fractions. Exp. Cell Res. **29:**1-16.

Dawid, I. B. 1972. Mitochondrial RNA in Xenopus laevis. I. Expression of the mitochondrial genome. J. Molec. Biol. **63:**201-216.

Deschner, E. E. 1963. A membrane bounded intramitochondrial granule in untreated mouse sigmoid-rectal epithelial cells. Exp. Cell Res. **31:**428-431.

Ephrussi, B. 1958. Cytoplasm and somatic variations. J. Cell Comp. Physiol. **52**(supp. 1):350.

Goldring, E. S., L. I. Grossman, D. Krupneck, D. R. Cryer, and J. Marmur. 1970. The petite mutant of yeast: loss of mitochondrial deoxyribonucleic acid during induction of petites with ethidium bromide. J. Molec. Biol. **52:** 323-335.

Green, D. E., P. V. Blair, and T. Oda. 1963. Isolation and characterization of unit electron transport in heart mitochondria. Science **140:** 382.

Gross, N. J., and M. Rabinowitz. 1969. Synthesis of new strands of mitochondrial and nuclear deoxyribonucleic acid by semiconservative replication. J. Biol. Chem. **244:**1563-1566.

Helinski, D. R., and D. B. Clewell. 1971. Circular DNA. Ann. Rev. Biochem. **40:**899-942.

Hoffman, H., and G. W. Gregg. 1958. An electron microscopic study of mitochondrial formation. Exp. Cell Res. **15:**118-131.

Hollenberg, C. P., P. Borst, R. W. J. Thuring, and E. F. G. van Bruggen. 1969. Size, structure and genetic complexity of mitochondrial DNA. Biochim. Biophys. Acta **186:**417-419.

Horridge, G. A. 1964. The giant mitochondria of Ctenophora complates. Quart. J. Micr. Sci. **105:**301-310.

Hudson, B., and J. Vinograd. 1967. Catenated circular DNA molecules in HeLa cell mitochondria. Nature (London) **216:**647-652.

Hunter, F. E., J. M. Gebicki, P. E. Hoffstang, J. Weinstein, and A. Scott. 1963. Swelling and lysis of rat liver mitochondria, induced by ferrous ions. J. Biochem. **238:**825-835.

Ishikawa, T., and Y. F. Pei. 1965. Intra-mitochondrial glycogen particles in rat retinal receptor cell. J. Cell Biol. **25:**402-407.

Kalf, G. E. 1963. The incorporation of leucine-1-C-14 into protein of rat heart sarcosomes: an investigation of the optimal conditions. Arch. Biochem. **101:**350-359.

Kawakami, N. 1961. Thread-like mitochondria in yeast cell. Exp. Cell. Res. **25:**402-407.

Küntzel, H. 1969a. Proteins of mitochondrial and cytoplasmic ribosomes from Neurospora crassa. Nature (London) **222:**142-146.

Küntzel, H. 1969b. Mitochondrial and cytoplasmic ribosomes from Neurospora crassa: characterization of their sub-unit. J. Molec. Biol. **40:** 315-320.

Lazarow, A., and S. J. Cooperstein. 1953. Studies on the mechanism of Janus Green B staining on mitochondria. Exp. Cell Res. **5:**56-69.

Lehninger, A. L. 1962. Water uptake and extrusion by mitochondria in relation to oxidative phosphorylation. Physiol. Rev. **42:**467-517.

Lehninger, A. L. 1964. The mitochondrion. W. A. Benjamin, Inc., New York.

Lemanski, L. F. 1971. Histological, histochemical, and ultrastructural study of myocadriogenesis in Mexican axolotls *Ambystoma mexicanum.* Ph.D. thesis, Hayden Memorial Library, Arizona State University.

Luck, D. J. L. 1965a. Formation of mitochondria in Neurospora crassa. Proc. Nat. Acad. Sci. U.S.A. **52:**931-938.

Luck, D. J. L. 1965b. Formation of mitochondria in Neurospora crassa: a study based on mitochondrial density changes. J. Cell Biol. **24:** 461-470.

Luck, D. J. L., and E. Reich. 1964. DNA in mitochondria of Neurospora crassa. Proc. Nat. Acad. Sci. U.S.A. **52:**931-938.

Lucy, J. A., and A. M. Glauert. 1964. Structure and assembly of macromolecular lipid complexes composed of globular micelles. J. Molec. Biol. **8:**727-748.

Malhotra, S. K. 1966. A study of structure of the

mitochondrial membrane system. J. Ultrastruct. Res. **15:**14-37.

Montague, M. D., and R. K. Morton. 1960. Chemical and physical properties of small deoxyribonucleic acid component of crystalline cytochrome b_2. Nature (London) **187:**916-917.

Morpurgo, G., G. Serlupi-Crescenzi, G. Teece, F. Valente, and D. Venettacci. 1964. The influence of ergosterol on the physiology and ultrastructure of Saccharomyces cerevisiae. Nature (London) **201:**897-899.

Mugnaini, E. 1963. Helical filaments in mitochondria of neuroglial cells in the rat corpus striatum. J. Ultrastruct. Res. **9:**398-399.

Nagley, P., and A. W. Linnane. 1970. Mitochondrial DNA deficient petite mutants in yeast. Biochem. Biophys. Res. Commun. **39:** 989-995.

Nass, M. M., S. Nass, and B. A. Afzelius. 1965. The general occurrence of mitochondrial DNA. Exp. Cell Res. **37:**516-539.

Nass, S. 1969. The significance of the structural and functional similarities of bacteria and mitochondria. Int. Rev. Cytol. **25:**55-129.

Neubert, D. A. B., A. B. Wojtczak, and A. L. Lehninger. 1962. Purification and enzymatic identity of mitochondrial contraction factors I and II. Proc. Nat. Acad. Sci. U.S.A. **48:** 1651-1658.

Nilssen, O. 1958. Ultrastructure of mouse uterine surface epithelium under different estrogenic influences. I. Spayed animals and oestrous animals. J. Ultrastruct. Res. **1:**375-396.

Novikoff, A. B. 1961. Mitochondria (chondriosomes). In J. Brachet and A. E. Mirsky (editors). The cell. Vol. 2. Academic Press, Inc., New York.

Ohnishi, T., and T. Ohnishi. 1962a. Extraction of actin- and myosin-like proteins from liver mitochondria. J. Biochem. (Tokyo) **52:**230-231.

GENERAL REFERENCES

Ashhurst, D. E. 1965. Mitochondrial particles seen in section. J. Cell Biol. **24:**497-499.

Beams, H. W., and T. N. Tahmisian. 1964. Study of mitochondria in the male germ cells of Helix as revealed by electron microscopy. Exp. Cell Res. **6:**87-93.

Deutsch, K., and W. Krause. 1964. An electron microscopical study of isolated mitochondrial membranes treated with osmium tetraoxide, potassium permanganate, and formaldehyde. Quart. J. Micr. Sci. **105:**319-323.

Enders, A. C. 1961. Cytological studies on the corpora lutea of delayed implantation. Anat. Rec. **139:**225.

Fitz-James, P. 1964. Fate of the mesosomes of Bacillus megaterium during protoplasting. J. Bact. **87:**1483-1491.

Hedman, R. 1965. Properties of isolated skeletal muscle mitochondria from rat. Exp. Cell Res. **38:**1-12.

Ohnishi, T., and T. Ohnishi. 1962b. Extraction of contractile protein from liver mitochondria. J. Biochem. (Tokyo) **21:**380-381.

Packer, L., and R. H. Golder. 1960. Correlation of structure and metabolic changes accompanying the addition of carbohydrates to Ehrlich ascites tumor cell. J. Biochem. **235:**1234-1240.

Parsons, D. F. 1963. Mitochondrial structure: two types of subunits on negatively stained mitochondrial membranes. Science **140:**985-987.

Pucci, I. 1964. Mitochondrial changes induced by fluoroacetate in chick embryo myocardium in vivo. Exp. Cell Res. **35:**412-414.

Raff, R. A., and H. R. Mahler. 1972. The nonsymbiotic origin of mitochondria. Science **177:** 575-582.

Rendi, R. 1959. On the occurrence of intramitochondrial ribonucleoprotein particles. Exp. Cell Res. **17:**585-587.

Robertson, J. D. 1964. Unit membranes: a review with recent new studies of experimental alterations and a new subunit structure. In M. Locke (editor). Cellular membranes in development. Academic Press, Inc., New York.

Roodyn, D. B., P. J. Reis, and T. S. Work. 1961. Protein synthesis in mitochondria. Biochem. J. **80:**9-21.

Rothfield, L., and A. Finkelstein. 1968. Membrane biochemistry. Ann. Rev. Biochem. **37:**463-496.

Rouiller, C. 1960. Physiological and pathological changes in mitochondrial morphology. Int. Rev. Cytol. **9:**227-292.

Salton, M. R. J., and J. A. Chapman. 1962. Isolation of the membrane-mesosome structures from Micrococcus lysodeikticus. J. Ultrastruct. Res. **6:**489-498.

Schuster, F. L. 1965. A deoxyribose nucleic acid component in mitochondria of Didymium nigripes, a slime mold. Exp. Cell Res. **39:**329-345.

Sjöstrand, F. S. 1953. Electron microscopy of mitochondria and cytoplasmic double membranes. Nature (London) **171:**30-32.

Sjöstrand, F. S. 1963. A new ultrastructural element of the membrane in mitochondria and some cytoplasmic membranes. J. Ultrastruct. Res. **9:**340-361.

Slautterback, D. B. 1965. Mitochondria in cardiac muscle cells of the canary and some other birds. J. Cell Biol. **24:**1-22.

Smith, D., P. Tauro, E. Schweizer, and H. O. Halborson. 1969. The replication of mitochondrial DNA during cell cycle in Saccharomyces lactis. Proc. Nat. Acad. Sci. U.S.A. **60:** 936-942.

South, D. J., and H. R. Mahler. 1968. RNA synthesis in yeast mitochondria. Nature (London) **218:**1226-1232.

Stasny, J. T., and F. L. Crane. 1964. Separation of elementary particles from mitochondrial cristae. Exp. Cell Res. **34:**423-426.

Stephens, R. J., and R. F. Bils. 1965. An atypical mitochondrial form in normal rat liver. J. Cell Biol. **24:**500-504.

Swift, H. 1965. Nucleic acids of mitochondria and chloroplasts. Amer. Nat. **99:**201-227.

Tarao, S. 1964. The LBC reaction (leuco brilliant cresyl blue reaction), a new method for demonstrating mitochondria in living cells. Cytologica **29:**424-434.

Tatum, E. L. 1964. Genetic determinants. Proc. Nat. Acad. Sci. U.S.A. **51:**908-915.

Thygarajan, T. R., S. F. Conti, and H. B. Naylor. 1961. Electron microscopy of yeast mitochondria. Exp. Cell Res. **25:**216-218.

Truman, D. E. S., and A. Korner. 1962. Incorporation of amino acids into proteins of isolated mitochondria. Biochem. J. **83:**588-596.

Utsumi, K., K. Nishikaze, and S. Seno. 1965. Failure of lipid peroxidation and swelling of mitochondria isolated from ascites hepatoma cell. J. Cell Biol. **27:**108A-109A.

Vasconcelos, A. C. L., and L. Bogorad. 1971. Proteins of cytoplasmic, chloroplasts and mitochondrial ribosomes of some plants. Biochim. Biophys. Acta **228:**492-502.

Vesco, C., and S. Penman. 1961. The cytoplasmic RNA of HeLa cells: new discrete species associated with mitochondria. Proc. Nat. Acad. Sci. U.S.A. **62:**218-225.

Vignais, P. V., P. M. Vignais, C. Rossi, and A. L. Lehninger. 1963. Restoration of ATP-induced contraction of pre-heated mitochondria by "contractile protein." Biochem. Biophys. Res. Commun. **11:**307-312.

Wallace, P. G., and A. W. Linnane. 1964. Oxygen induced synthesis of yeast mitochondria. Nature (London) **201:**1191-1194.

Wallace, P. G., M. Huang, and A. W. Linnane. 1968. The biogenesis of mitochondria. II. The influence of medium composition and the cytology of anaerobically grown Saccharomyces cerevisiae. J. Cell Biol. **37:**207-220.

Watrach, A. M. 1964. Degeneration of mitochondria in lead poisoning. J. Ultrastruct. Res. **10:**177-181.

Wills, E. J. 1965. Crystalline structures in the mitochondria of normal human liver cells. J. Cell Biol. **24:**511-514.

Wojtczak, L., and A. B. Wojczak. 1960. Uncoupling of oxidative phosphorylation and inhibition of ATP-Pi exchange by a substance from insect mitochondria. Biochim. Biophys. Acta **39:**277-286.

Ziegler, D. M., A. W. Linnane, D. E. Green, C. M. S. Dass, and H. Ris. 1958. Studies on the electron transport system. XI. Correlation of the morphology and enzymatic properties on mitochondrial and sub-mitochondrial particles. Biochim. Biophys. Acta **28:**497-499.

CHAPTER 11

Plastids

All life on the earth now and for the past hundreds of millions of years, all the organic molecules in and out of organisms, and all the oxygen that makes the activity and efficiency of most of that life possible is the direct or indirect result of one specific biological process—photosynthesis. That process had probably been completed in its evolution 2 billion years ago, that is, the evolution of the minimum of essential enzymes, cofactors, cytochromes, chlorophylls, carotenoids, lipids, xanthophylls, etc., and these molecules had been placed into rigidly exact spatial relationships to one another as the double cytoplasmic photosynthetic membrane (Fig. 11-9).

The first organisms to possess the complete photosynthetic process and membranes were probably like the present-day simple, tiny, bacteria-like, ubiquitous blue-green algae, of which 2-billion-year-old fossils have been found. The photosynthetic membranes in blue-green algae are unconfined, being distributed more or less throughout the procytoplasm of the procell (Figs. 4-2, 4-5, and 4-6). However, in all other photosynthetic plants (except the few photosynthetic bacteria) these membranes are confined within fairly large cytoplasmic structures called *plastids* (Fig. 11-1).

Origin of plastids

The evolutionary origin of plastids is unknown, but two possibilities have been suggested. One proposal is that they "just evolved" from a previously unconfined condition, the double plastid membrane having been derived somehow from the plasma or nuclear membrane. The bacterial mesosome (Fig. 10-19), which is active in oxidative phosphorylation like a mitochondrion, has been proposed as an example of how the mitochondrion might have just evolved. The plastid might have done the same. The alternative, which is not as farfetched as it at first seems and is becoming widely accepted as a likely possibility, is that plastids and also mitochondria may have originated as symbiotic blue-green algae living within the cytoplasm of another organism, as proposed long ago by Mereschkowsky (1905) and Famintzin (1907) and later by Ris and Plaut (1962), Margulis (1967), Whitfield and Spencer (1968), and others. It has been argued that the blue-green algal procell, the mitochondrion, and the chloroplast have similar lamellar structure; contain DNA in a loop form similar to the loop genophore of bacteria; possess RNA, 70s ribosomes, enzymes, carotenoids, and cytochromes for their activities; can divide; cannot arise de novo; and can mutate and evolve. A secondary function both blue-green algae and plastids possess is the elaboration of soluble or insoluble food reserve. Even functional hybrid 70s ribosomes have been produced in vitro between 30s chloroplast and 50s bacterial subunits (Lee and

Evans, 1971). In addition, both chloroplast and bacterial ribosomes are inhibited by chloramphenicol, whereas eukaryotic ribosomes are less inhibited (Ellis, 1969). Thus plastids fit the definition of prokaryota.

The argument that mature plastids develop in vascular plants from proplastids and proplastids from tiny primordia lacking internal membranes and that these may form de novo from existing membranes

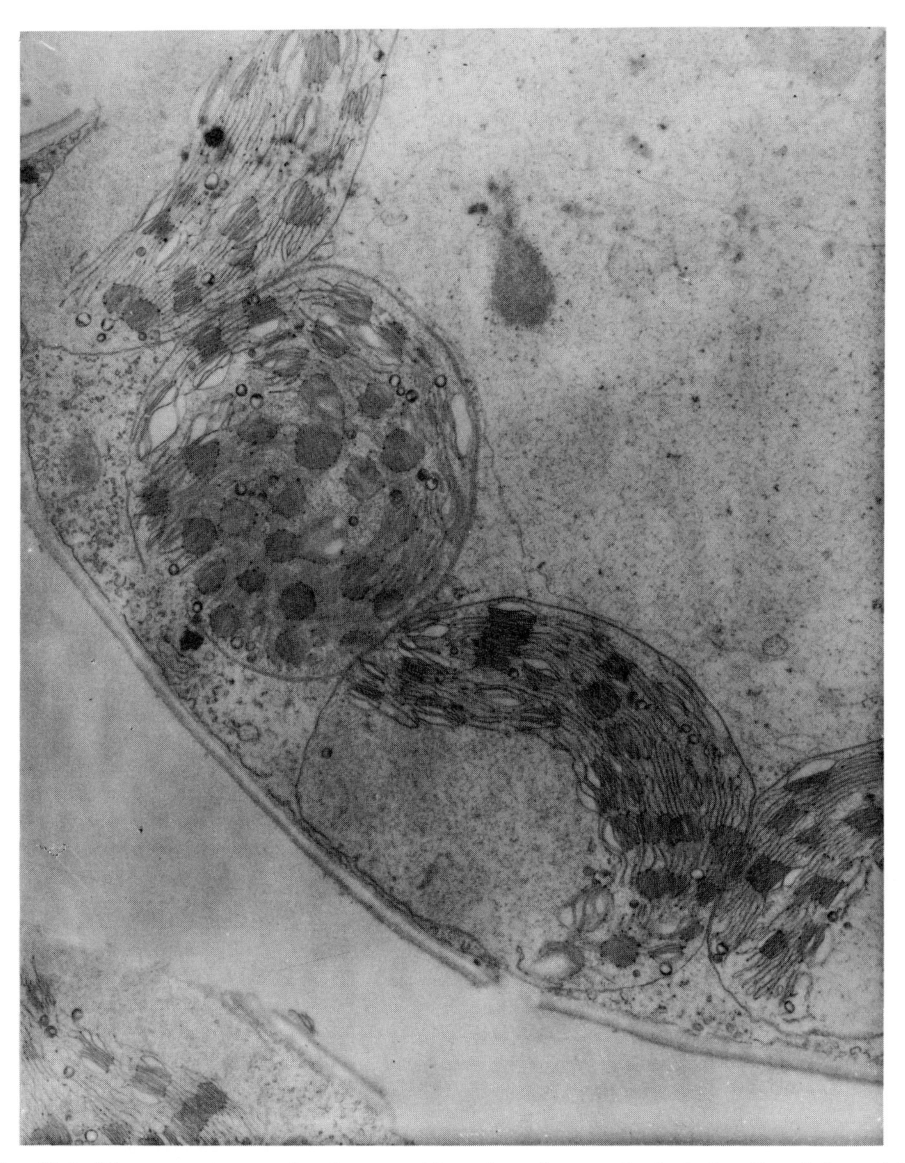

Fig. 11-1. Electron micrograph of some chloroplasts from a leaf of the dicotyledon white clover. This shows longitudinal, diagonal, and almost cross-sectional views of grana with puncta (black dots) on their circular surfaces. These chloroplasts have no starch, and a considerable volume is stroma without lamellae, always toward the cell wall. Lipid granules are scattered among stromal lamellae (or frets). The center of the cell is occupied by a large vacuole, the membrane (tonoplast) of which is evident.

such as the nuclear membrane (the last point, however, has not been established) is negated by the evolutionary fact that this developmental sequence occurs rarely in the green or other algae (but see Brown and Weier, 1968), which are the probable ancestors of the vascular plants. If the de novo origin does prove to be correct for vascular plants (a remote possibility), it would indicate a truly major biological change from the algae to the vascular plants. Even electron microscopy has not as yet resolved the hundred-year-old question of whether plastids arise de novo in vascular plants; they evidently do not in nonvascular plants.

Symbiosis. Furthermore, in support of the symbiotic origin of plastids, symbiotic unicellular algae, mostly green algae, living within the protoplasm of animal cells are far more common than generally realized. There are many green Protozoa such as *Paramecium, Stentor,* and numerous Foraminifera, Radiolaria, and other Sarcodina; green freshwater sponges; many green Cnidaria, including a green hydra; several green flatworms and green ctenophores; a few green rotifers; and some annelid worms and molluscs that have cells of some tissues containing symbiotic algae. Symbiotic (not parasitic) intracellular spirochetes, yeasts, rickettsiae, and bacteria are also known in a variety of animals and plants. Thus intracellular symbiosis is certainly not rare among present-day organisms, and in many cases divisions, loss of the cell wall, and physiological characteristics of the symbiont have become correlated with activities of the host cell for persistence and mutual advantage. The symbiotic origin of plastids (and also mitochondria) would relate the outer of the two membranes with an original "food vacuolar membrane" of the host cell, the inner being the plasma membrane of the symbiont. Both might have evolved subsequently, and they are certainly different now. The symbiotic origin of plastids is at least a logical and sound hypothesis but probably an unprovable one.

Furthermore, it is now generally conceded that it is often difficult or impossible to clearly distinguish between normal cell constituents and internal foreign "organisms" if an infectious "organism" is conceived as hereditary material that can enter a "host" cell and replicate within it. Thus defined the DNA introduced in transformation experiments, the sperm nucleus in the egg, all intracellular symbiotes, the lambda particle of *Paramecium aurelia,* and lysogenic viruses, all of which modify the traits of the host, are "infectious" only in a sense. There is an excellent example of the difficulty of distinguishing between a symbiont and a "normal" cell constituent. For many years a freshwater organism called *Glaucocystis nostochinearum* has been known as a colorless algal cell (it has a wall) within which is a symbiotic blue-green alga. An electron microscope study by Hall and Claus (1967) indicated that this symbiotic relationship can be interpreted equally well as a normal unicellular red alga with chloroplasts having a blue-green color. Certainly the "plastids" have a pyrenoid much like pyrenoids of some red algae and, like red algae in general, the "starch" grains form outside the plastids in the cytoplasm. Schnepf et al. (1966), however, concluded that *Glaucocystis* cannot be a red alga because it has rudimentary flagella and basal bodies—structures lacking in red algae. Which is *Glaucocystis,* a red alga or a symbiotic relationship? Certainly the plastids of red algae are similar to blue-green algae in certain pigments, and the presence of these common pigments as grains on the photosynthetic membranes is common to both. Perhaps all plastids are the descendants of "infective" organisms of hundreds of millions of years ago.

Evolutionary development

Regardless of how they originated, plastids at first were probably rather simple, chlorophyll-containing, membranous, double-membrane–bounded cytoplasmic bodies

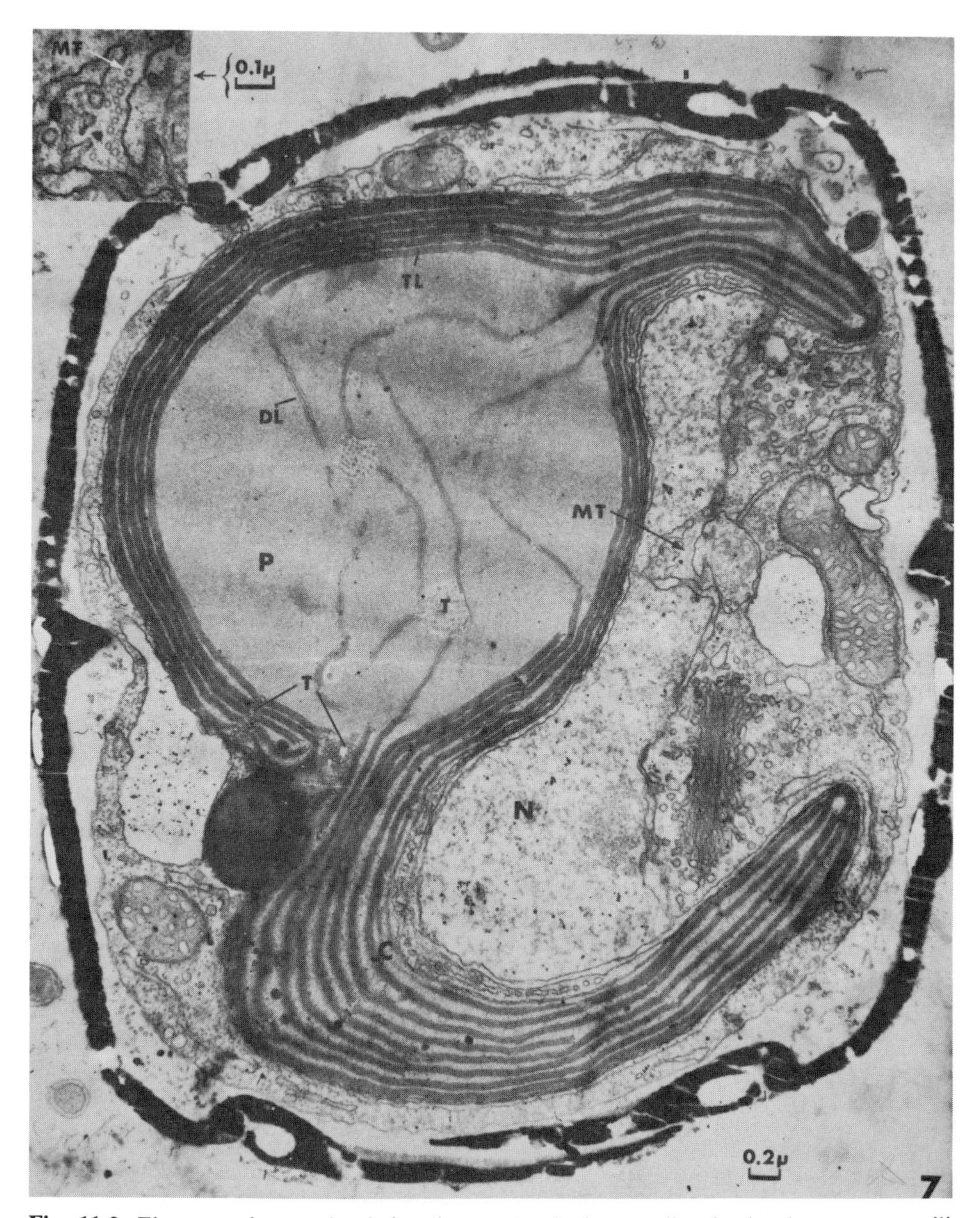

Fig. 11-2. Electron micrograph of the diatom *Amphipleura pellucida* showing two-part, siliceous, cover-and-box wall; mitochondria with tubular cristae; large Golgi apparatus; nucleus, **N;** row of microtubules, **MT** (enlarged in the inset); and large chloroplast. Within the chloroplast are a large, rather blank, amorphous pyrenoid, **P,** with a few membranes, **DL,** running across; a few organized systems of tubules, **T;** and outside the pyrenoid, eight or nine long groups of photosynthetic membranes, **TL,** each of which consists of about six membranes. The new silica wall is deposited in a thin flat vesicle just under the plasma membrane so that later the inner vesicle membrane becomes the functional plasma membrane. The outer nuclear envelope encloses the chloroplast, an unusual condition. (From Stoermer, E. F., H. S. Pankratz, and C. C. Bowen. 1965. Amer. J. Bot. **52:**1067-1078.)

that produced more organic molecules such as sugars and amino acids than they "themselves" could use, and so contributed to the welfare of the rest of the cell (or host). Furthermore, for them to persist they must have divided more or less synchronously with the growth and division of the cells containing them. During early evolution when all organisms were unicellular, several types of pigment molecules must have evolved. Except for the few photosynthetic bacteria, all photosynthetic structures contain chlorophyll a. However, in addition, there are at least ten different chlorophylls and about thirty different carotenoids, including six to eight carotenes and twenty or more xanthophylls, variously present in different plant groups. Beside chlorophyll a, which is common to all, the green algae and land plants contain chlorophyll b; the brown algae, diatoms, and dinoflagellates contain chlorophyll c; the red algae contain chlorophyll d; and the yellow-green algae contain chlorophyll e. There is even more diversity among the carotenoids. The blue-green algae, flagellated cryptomonads, and red algae uniquely contain two types of accessory pigment-protein molecules called the phycobilins (phycocyanin and phycoerythrin), which may set off these groups of organisms from other plant groups.

Additional plastid evolution involved the elaboration of more photosynthetic membranes and the organization of them into functional groups of parallel arrays comprising from two to five in various algal classes (Fig. 11-2). Other parts of chloroplasts differentiated into the pyrenoid, and in some organisms such as *Chlamydomonas* and *Volvox* an eyespot evolved. There was also evolution of chloroplast form, and eventually, in some algae and especially in the vascular plants, specialization by loss of chlorophyll into colorless leukoplasts and colored (but not green) chromoplasts. It also appears that male gametes (except in a few algae) of plants do not carry plastids, whereas female gametes always do.

Cytological history

Because of their large size and inherent color, plastids, especially the green chloroplasts and orange, carotenoid-containing chromoplasts, were among the first subcellular structures seen by the early microscopists. Starch grains, because of their large size and light diffraction, were also seen early. As early as 1676 and 1678, Leeuwenhoek described the large chloroplasts of the filamentous alga *Spirogyra* and others. Comparetti (1791), Mirbel (1799), and Sprengel (1802) described chloroplasts in various plant cells.

By 1881 Schimper concluded that chloroplasts arise de novo and that the chloroplasts of flowering plants arise from colorless plastids, which he called leukoplasts. In 1882 Strasburger actually followed under the microscope the division of the single plastid of *Spirogyra* during cell division, and Schmitz also reported that in algae the chloroplasts pass by division into the two daughter cells. He also named the pyrenoid of algal chloroplasts. In 1883 Schimper claimed that plastids always arise from preexisting plastids, and Meyer supported that claim. Meyer saw green grains within the chloroplasts of some flowering plants (for example, orchids), which he called *grana.*

With respect to grana, after about 1890 chloroplasts were generally considered to be homogeneous (grana did not exist). In 1932, however, Heitz "rediscovered" grana in flowering plant chloroplasts, and Doutreligne corroborated this claim in 1935. In 1947 Granick and Porter observed spinach leaf grana under the electron microscope and reported about fifty per chloroplast; they noted that the protein content was very low. Since then, grana have been established as real and ubiquitous structures within the chloroplasts of land plants and green algae (but of no other algae).

From about 1910 to 1955 there were two schools of thought concerning the origin of plastids. One claimed that plastids arise either from mitochondria or that both of these cellular components arise from a common precursor. The other group, equally numerous, believed that plastids and mitochondria are inherently different. At present nearly all plant cytologists agree with Mottier's conclusion in 1918 that mitochondria and plastids are distinct and permanent components of plant cells, that neither arises de novo, and that both increase only by division. It is also known now that both are surrounded by a double membrane; both have internal functional membranes; both have DNA, RNA, ribosomes, and many enzymes and metabolic pathways; both react internally to changes in their environments; and both have some of their own genes. Is not this a rather complete description of a living organism? Except for the lack of cell walls, this would describe symbiotic procells. It has often been reported that when unicellular algae become intracellular symbionts, they do lose their walls.

Algal chloroplasts

The plastids of algae, as well as mosses, contain chlorophyll and are therefore called chloroplasts or sometimes chromatophores (Fig. 11-1). Leukoplasts or chlorophyll-lacking plastids are uncommon in the algae or mosses; they seem to have evolved mostly among the vascular plants (Fig. 3-1, *B*). Within the algae there is a remarkable diversity of numbers and shapes of chloroplasts per cell; consequently, they provide a useful taxonomic character for classification. The number of chloroplasts may range from a single large one, as in *Spirogyra,* to many small ones, as in *Vaucheria.*

The most common chloroplast shape in algae and land plants is a somewhat flattened circular or elliptical disk, especially when there are many per cell. But in algae having one or a few chloroplasts per cell the shapes are diverse and often complex. One of the best known is the spiral chloroplast of *Spirogyra.* It is obvious that if a cell contains only one chloroplast, the chloroplast must divide into two at cell division and the two "new" plastids must be equally distributed to the two daughter cells. Mere random distribution, which may be adequate for cells having numerous small chloroplasts, does not occur because the large chloroplast is cut in half as the cytoplasm is cleaved by cytokinesis.

The chloroplasts of many algae contain one or more rather large proteinaceous structures called *pyrenoids* (Fig. 11-2). Although a pyrenoid occurs in some species of nearly all algal groups, it is largely absent in the red algae, the brown algae, and the Pyrrophyta. It is much more common in the green algae, Euglenophyta, and Chrysophyta. It lies within the chloroplast and among the photosynthetic membranes. In fact, there are usually one or more membranes extending through it. Pyrenoids can apparently arise de novo or divide. In many green algae (for example, *Chlamydomonas*) the pyrenoid is closely surrounded by a layer of thick *starch plates.*

Two proposals have been made with regard to the nature of the pyrenoid. One is that it is simply a mass of reserve protein. The other, which is held by most phycologists, is that it is somehow involved in solid carbohydrate (starch, paramylum, leukosin, etc.) formation. At least in the green algae the first starch grains to appear in a chloroplast do seem to lie very close to the pyrenoid. In red algae and *Euglena,* however, starch grains form uniquely outside the chloroplast itself.

The organization of the unit of chloroplast membrane structure is that of a greatly flattened sac called a *thylakoid;* it is continuous all around and so produces a pair of membranes. Each membrane is about 85 Å thick but is separated from the other membrane of the same sac by 100 to 200 Å. It is often a much greater distance from adjacent sacs except in grana or equivalents where adjacent sacs are separated by only about 50 Å. Each membrane apparently consists of organized, unit, spherical structures of 75 to 85 Å diameter. Furthermore, the membranes of adjacent sacs may lie close together. The distance between the membranes of one sac is uniform; distances between pairs or groups of pairs may vary, especially when starch grains form between pairs.

In all algae except the green algae the chloroplast membranes, although grouped in parallel arrays of pairs, seem to be homogeneous or uniform throughout, with little or no internal differentiation (Fig. 11-2). Therefore such chloroplasts are described as *agranal*. Apparently all green algae, on the other hand, have membranes, various areas of which are different from one another, or else there are two sorts of membranes. Mostly the pairs are independent of one another and rather widely separated. In places, however, from two to a few such pairs come close together, lie in close parallel to one another, and seem to consist of specialized regions of the membranes. Such local aggregates in chloroplasts of green algae appear in the electron microscope like a sloppily piled stack of hollow pancakes. Somewhat similar aggregates in chloroplasts of flowering plants were given the name

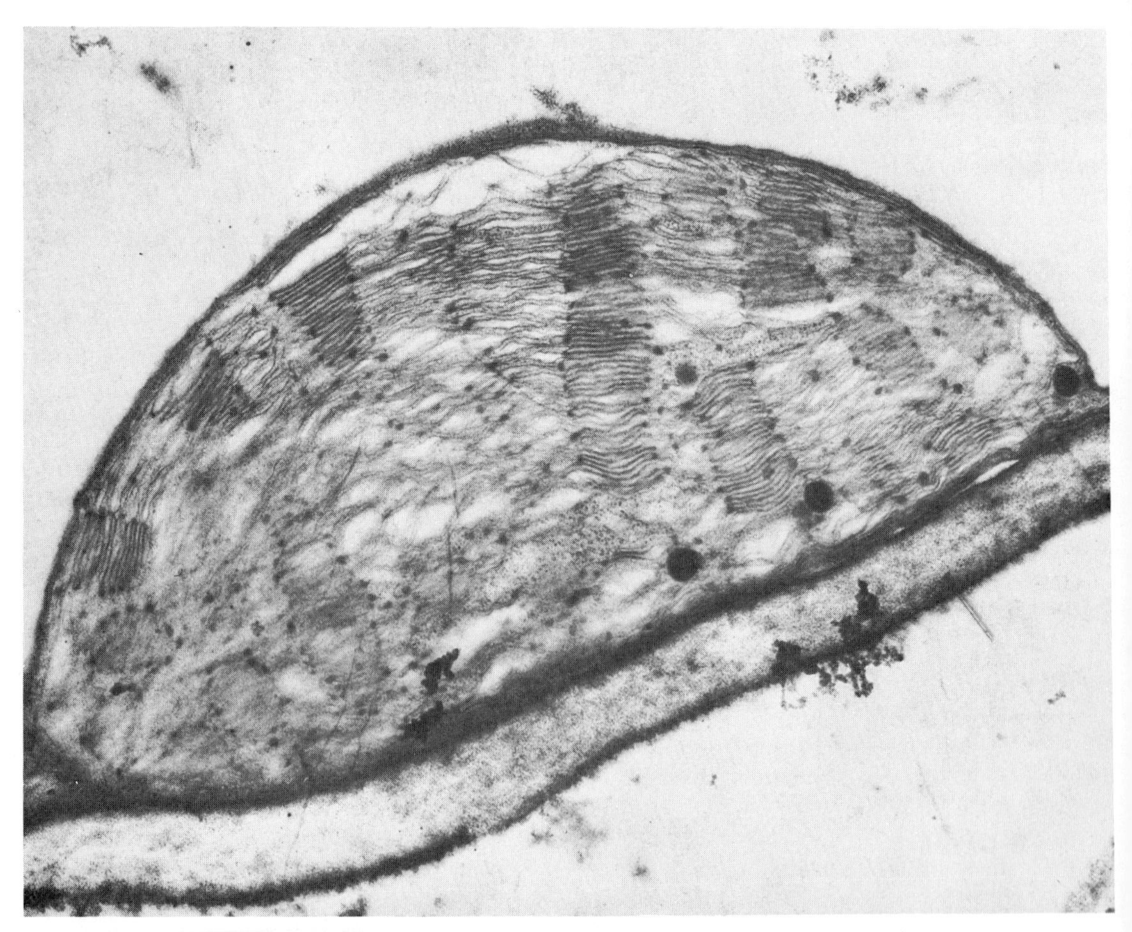

Fig. 11-3. Chloroplast of the grass *Eragrostis* showing stromal lamellae, grana with puncta on their margins, granal lamellae, and osmophilic granules.

grana by Schimper in 1883, but the lamellar aggregates of green algal chloroplasts are different enough to be designated *granoids.* Granoids are generally lower in height (fewer lamellar pairs) and more irregular in form; the lateral contact between the granoidal and stromal lamellae is simpler; and *puncta,* which are dotlike, nonmembrane-bounded structures always revealed by osmic acid fixation on the curved surfaces of seed plant grana (Figs. 11-1 and 11-3), have not been revealed on algal granoids (Johnson and Brown, 1964). Lamellae between adjacent grana, which traverse the amorphous material of the chloroplast called the *stroma,* are called *stromal lamellae* if very wide or *frets* (Fig. 11-6) if narrower anastomosing tubes. There is evidence that some plastid lamellae originate from inblebbing of the inner plastid lamella. However, most increase in extent and number of lamellae arises from growth and branching of preexisting lamellae. Grana form by local transformation of stromal lamella.

Some flagellated algae, gametes, and zoospores of algae have a red or orange modified region of the chloroplast that is called an *eyespot.* The electron micrograph reveals that the eyespot consists of one or more rows of spheres containing carotenoids regularly arranged between the lamellae. These eyespots are known to be photosensitive and usually lie close to the bases of the flagella. The eyespot of *Euglena* and its relatives, however, is separate from the chloroplast, which sets this group of algae off from the others.

Land plant chloroplasts

The chloroplasts of land plants present what might be considered an evolutionary sequence from chloroplasts of green algae to those of the most highly specialized flowering plants, to those of certain Kranz plants. Among the bryophytes and the cryptogamic vascular plants (lycopods, psilotums, horsetails, etc.) the internal structure of the chloroplast is granoidal, much as in the green algae. However, in one of these, *Selaginella,* special treatment has revealed small puncta, and in the horsetails the overall structure is more granal than granoidal. In the ferns almost true grana are found, similar to those in the seed plants.

It was among the ancient vascular plants with thick woody stems and underground roots that specialization occurred to produce *leukoplasts.* These colorless plastids may produce chlorophyll and become chloroplasts, but in certain cells and tissues such as roots they generally seem unable to do so. A leukoplast that can become a chloroplast is often called a *proplastid.* Leukoplasts do possess many of the enzyme systems characteristic of chloroplasts, however, and certainly can synthesize and hydrolyze starch or other carbohydrate polymers. Leukoplasts containing one or more large starch grains are often called *amyloplasts;*

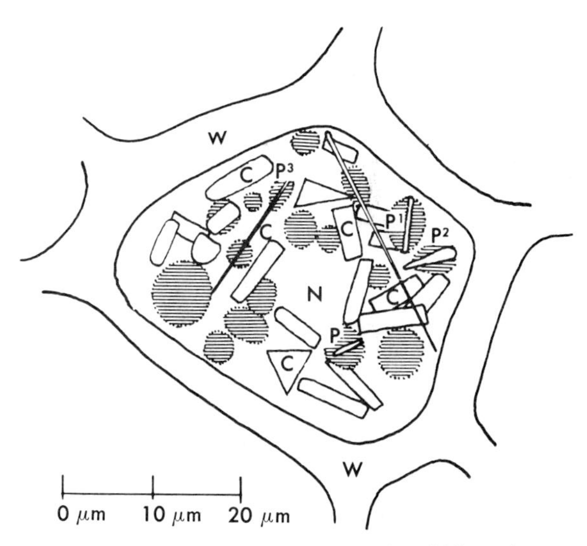

Fig. 11-4. Chromoplasts and crystals within red epidermal cell of the fruit of *Ibervillea.* Chromoplasts are crosshatched. **C,** Crystals of various shapes; **P,** small crystal within a chromoplast; **P¹,** small needle-shaped crystal; **P²,** small triangular crystal; **P³,** chromoplast at one end of a long needle-shaped crystal illustrating that the crystal grows at one end; **N,** nucleus; **W,** wall.

if grains of protein, they are called *proteinoplasts;* or if droplets of oil, they are called *elaioplasts.*

Starch grains are characteristic of both chloroplasts and most leukoplasts and are formed among the lamellae; in chloroplasts they are found among the stromal lamellae, never within grana or granoids. Chloroplasts or leukoplasts may produce large amounts of solid-colored structures of carotenoids such as crystals or sheets and are then called *chromoplasts* (Fig. 11-4). Examples occur in carrots, tomatoes (Fig. 14-13), and petals of *Nasturtium.* Electron microscopy has revealed numerous sorts of chromoplasts. One kind, described as *fibrillar,* has small granules of carotene integrated among fibrils of some sort. Another kind is called *globular* and possesses numerous larger lipid globules in which carotenoids are dissolved. It seems that there are numerous methods of chromoplast formation and organization, each perhaps having evolved separately from others. The development of the fruit chromoplasts of the cucurbit *Ibervillea* out of many small units is one of the most complex known (Fig. 11-5). Chromoplasts probably cannot (or at least do not in nature) change back into leukoplasts or chloroplasts, although experimentally they may do so.

Chloroplast evolution within the flowering plants seems to have produced rather broad *stromal lamellae* in the monocotyledons but narrow lamellae called *frets* (Fig. 11-6) in the dicotyledons. Unique chloroplast evolution has occurred in the grass family, especially the most specialized tribes but also in other families both monocotyledons and dicotyledons. In these Kranz plants (Fig. 11-8), the chloroplasts of the mesophyll tissue do not form starch grains, as is typical of chloroplasts, and in the most modern tribes, including the Andropogoneae (such as corn and sorghum), the chloroplasts of the cells of a sheath around the vascular bundles no longer form grana; they have again become *agranal* (Figs. 11-7 and 11-8). It is only in the agranal plastids of these sheath cells that starch is formed in Kranz plants. Whether the agranal chloroplasts of the parenchyma sheath of Kranz plants can photosynthesize or not is unknown. If they can, and they are pale green in color, it is also likely that the stromal lamellae of all land plants can do so, although it is generally assumed that all or most photosynthesis occurs within grana.

Although chloroplasts in most cells may move about autonomously or by protoplasmic streaming, the chloroplasts of the sheath cells of many grasses permanently occupy certain regions of the cells. In Andropogoneae and Panicoideae, for example, they occur in the centrifugal region (Fig. 11-8), whereas in the Eragrostoideae (for example, Bermuda grass) they seem to be "attached" permanently to the centripetal wall. The chloroplasts of *Chara* and *Nitella* are permanently attached to the wall.

Electron miscroscopy has revealed in surface view and cross section tiny structural units called *quantasomes* that make up the granal lamellae (Fig. 11-9). These are arranged in regular ranks and files probably throughout the whole granal lamella. The fact that two lamellae are intimately associated in the granum is probably functionally very significant (Weier et al., 1965; Weier and Benson, 1967). In contrast, the stromal or fret lamellae are composed of a single array of such 70 to 80 Å subunits.

The lamellar system of a granum can be visualized (Fig. 11-6) as consisting of a stack of flattened sacs that are closed all around the nearly circular circumferences. Apparently the two surfaces of adjacent sacs lie close together and may have a functional relationship with each other. When a granum is isolated by maceration and centrifugation, the sacs may separate from each other and appear like a stack of coins that has tipped over. It is the flat surfaces of these sacs that consist largely of quantasomes.

The details of the curved surfaces of

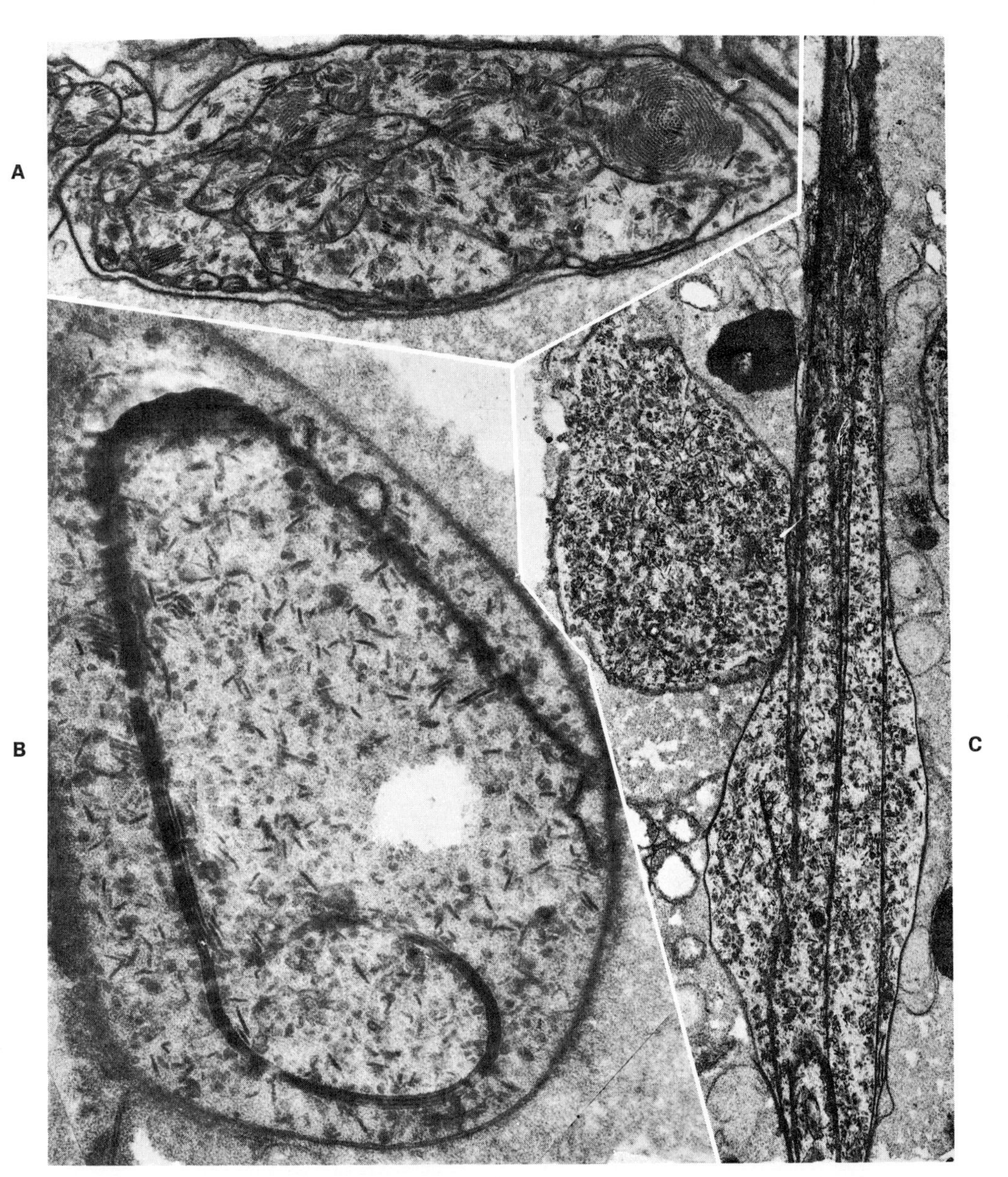

Fig. 11-5. Chromatophore crystal development and structure in the fruit of the cucurbit *Ibervillea.* **A,** Electron micrograph of a plastid in transition from chloroplast to chromoplast. Typical internal chloroplast membrane system, including grana, has broken down. New membranes have formed, and many groups of short "rods" have appeared, often aggregated into or being formed in a paracrystalline array. **B,** Cross section of mature "crystal." It consists of numerous parallel membranes bent into a U shape that are probably built up from the short rods that can be seen. **C,** Longitudinal section of a needle-shaped "crystal." Membranes and short rods, usually in parallel groups, are evident. The plastid seems to be extended by growth of the red, carotenoid "crystal," and much of its bulk is concentrated around the crystal at the lower end. Actually, plastid membranes surround the whole "crystal." (Courtesy Dr. H. Arnott and L. V. Ansell, University of Texas Cell Research Institute, Austin, Texas.)

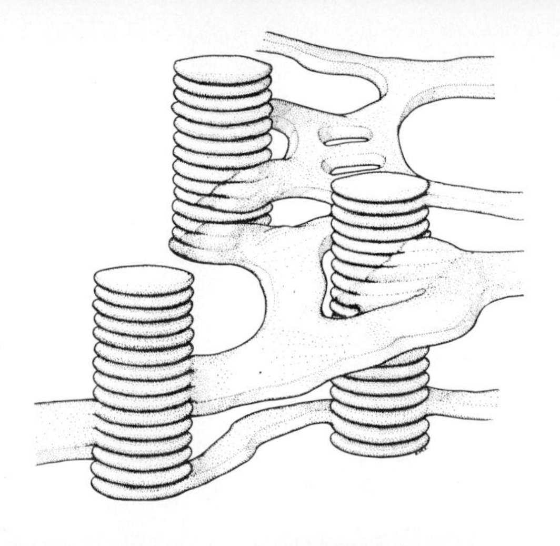

Fig. 11-6. Three-dimensional scheme of chloroplast membranes of flowering plant. Three grana are represented as stacks of thylakoids. Frets or stromal lamellae interconnect the grana and they, too, are closed sacs. When a stromal lamella intersects or connects with a granum, it forms at an angle to the axis of the granum, making contact progressively with a sequence of adjacent thylakoids. (From Weier, T. E., C. R. Stocking, and L. K. Shumway. 1966. Brookhaven Symp. Biol. **19:** 353-374.)

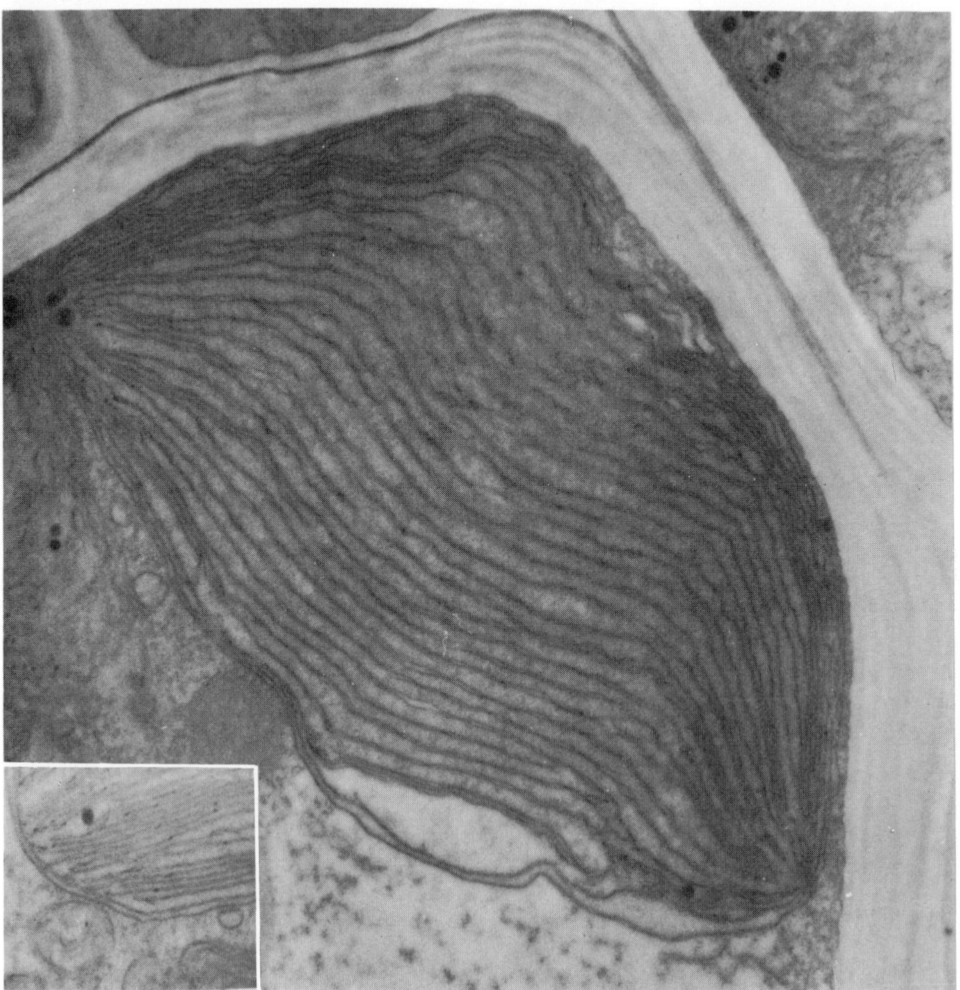

Fig. 11-7. Agranal chloroplast as found in parenchyma sheath cells from leaves of grasses of the tribe Andropogoneae (including *Zea mays*) and some Panicoideae. Inset shows membrane organization at the "end" of another such agranal chloroplast from the same cell. Notice double plastid membrane, seeming lack of contact between it and stromal lamellae, and closed ends or edges of paired stromal lamellae (thylakoids). Layering in thick primary wall can also be seen.

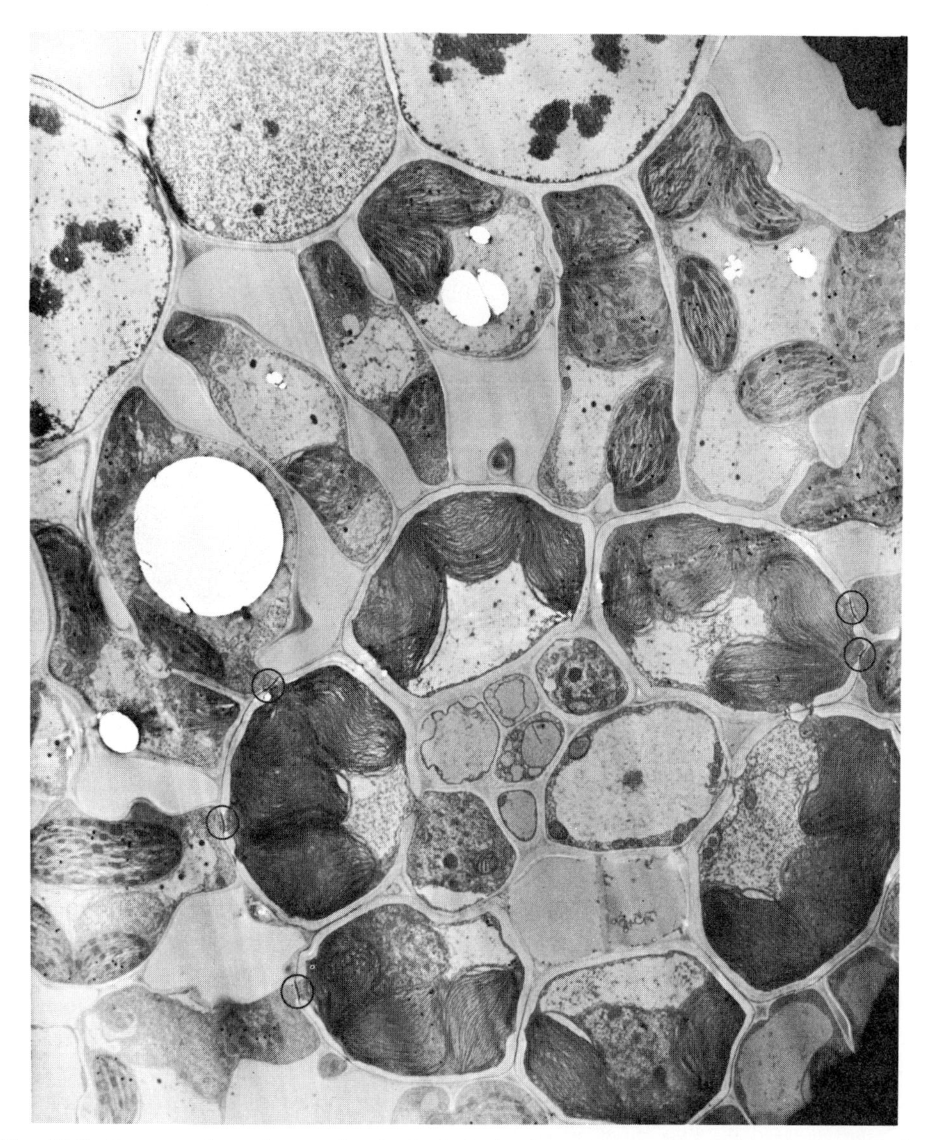

Fig. 11-8. Cross section of part of a leaf of *Anthephora cristata* (Panicoideae) showing the typical circular parenchyma sheath surrounded by radiating chlorenchyma cells of Kranz plants. The latter have granal chloroplasts, the former agranal chloroplasts that always occupy the outer, centrifugal regions of parenchyma sheath cells. Within the circles note intercellular connections (plasmodesmata) between cells. Often these form a group where there is a thin region of the thick primary wall called a pit field. These chloroplast conditions are characters useful in classification.

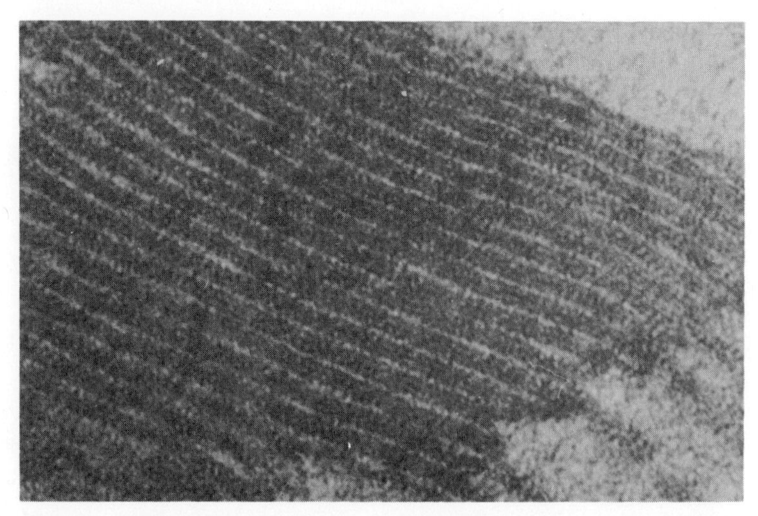

Fig. 11-9. Highly magnified electron micrograph of granal membranes (partitions) of chloroplast in cross section showing what are assumed to be quantasomes. Each dark band is really two juxtaposed membranes of two adjacent thylakoids of a granum. Each light band is the central space loculus of a thylakoid. (From Weier, T. E., C. R. Stocking, and L. K. Shumway. 1966. Brookhaven Symp. Biol. **19**:353-374.)

grana where they "attach" to stromal lamellae are uncertain. Apparently there are various configurations rather than just one, but it seems likely that the margins of adjacent granal sacs are structurally attached, since whole grana may survive vigorous maceration or natural dissociation of chloroplasts. Furthermore, scattered rather regularly on the curved surface of a granum are so-called *puncta,* the function of which is unknown (Figs. 11-1 and 11-3). It is possible, but unlikely, that they are partially artifacts. They have so far been revealed only by osmium fixation for electron microscopy. There seems to be some sort of attachment of stromal lamellae (or frets) to the granal sacs also, as though the two types of membranes are continuous, although the space between a pair of stromal lamellae and the space within a granal sac are not confluent (Fig. 11-10). It also seems that the membranes of grana are much firmer than the stromal lamellae, since granal sacs hold together during maceration, but stromal lamellae are not recovered as such. The relationship of stromal lamellae to grana has been interpreted as the parallel stromal lamellae arranged or tilted at an angle to the parallel planes of the granal lamellae (Fig. 11-6) (Heslop-Harrison, 1963; Weier et al., 1966). Thus a stromal lamella makes contact with a number of granal lamellae in sequence and may function to hold the granum together and/or as a tubular intercommunication between and among granal spaces. Visualization of this scheme is difficult from an electron micrograph but is likely. The relationship of puncta to this granal surface arrangement is presently unknown.

Paolillo and Falk (1966) and Paolillo and Reighard (1967) have proposed that there is a pattern of *helical* interconnections among granal compartments and the tilted stromal lamellae or frets. Wehrmeyer and Röbbelen (1965) have related this helical arrangement of interconnections to a concept of spiral-cyclical growth of granal stacks. These interpretations are still tentative.

In numerous chloroplasts, especially when they do not contain starch grains, the lamellae do not completely fill the plastid;

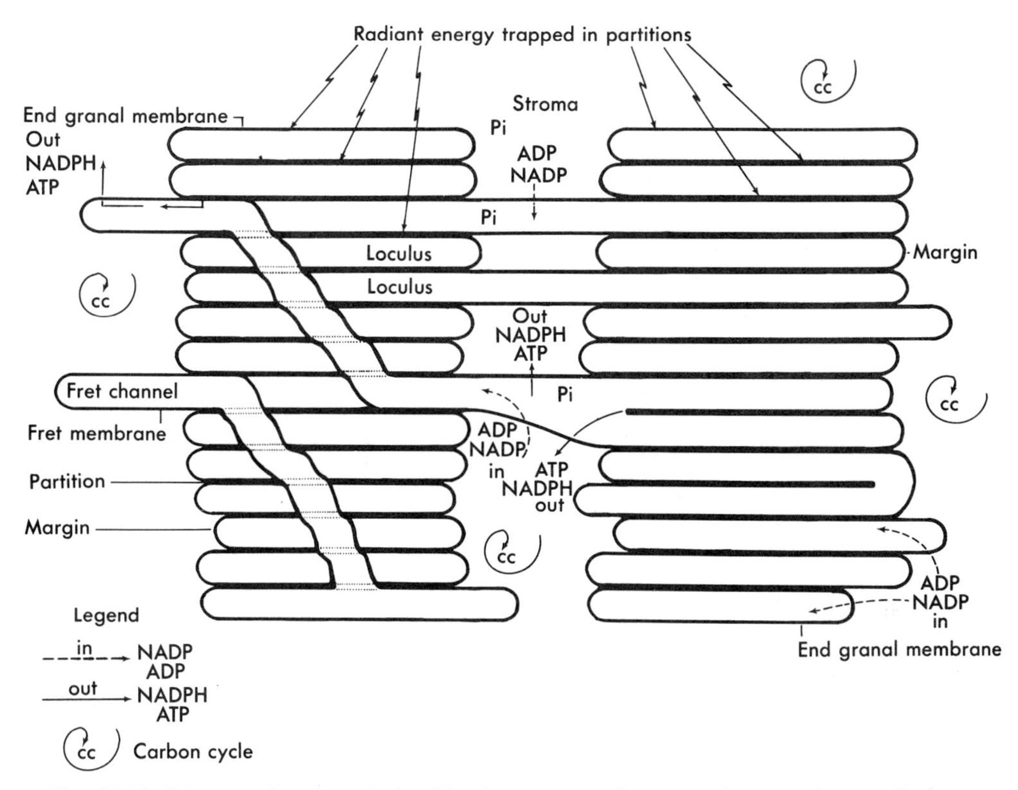

Fig. 11-10. Diagram showing relationships between membranes and stroma in overall photosynthetic reactions. The interior of each thylakoid is called a loculus, and the double membrane formed where two thylakoid membranes abut is called a partition. The end granal membrane is single, only half of a partition. The closed circumference of a thylakoid is called the margin. Diagonal fret channel–thylakoid contact is indicated. (From Weier, T. E., C. R. Stocking, and L. K. Shumway. 1966. Brookhaven Symp. Biol. **19**:353-374.

often a large region of pure stroma exists (Fig. 11-1), but as a chloroplast becomes loaded with starch after exposure to light, the lamellae are distorted and separated and may eventually occupy most of the plastid. As just stated, starch grains never form within grana but only between the stromal lamellar pairs. There seem to be no particular structures or modified lamellae where starch grains form, and, unlike many algae, pyrenoids do not seem to be associated with starch grain formation in the algae possessing them.

Chloroplasts of flowering plants when fully formed are of various shapes, often disk shaped or ovoid. Their axes are generally only a few micrometers long, usually about 5 μm, but they vary somewhat among species and tissues. They occur in most living cells of leaves, superficial or deeper cells of stems that are exposed to light, some structures of flowers, bracts of various sorts, most young unripe fruits, some embryos, and roots of some aerial plants. Most epidermal cells of leaves and leaf hairs do not seem to have chloroplasts, although they are more common in such cells than is generally known. However, when present in typical epidermal cells, they are generally few, small, and functionally distinctive. The epidermal cells, which almost always contain large, green, functional chloroplasts, are the guard cells of stomata, where their photosynthetic activity may be important in stomatal movement. Guard cells of grasses, however, have plastids that are more like leukoplasts but do contain a small amount of chlorophyll. Furthermore, the plastids of grass guard cells are restricted to the bulbous ends of the "cells" which, derived by cytokinesis from one mother cell, are not completely separated by a plasma membrane or wall; the protoplasms of the two cells are confluent at both ends, or they may be considered to constitute one binucleate cell.

Chloroplasts of flowering plants are rather numerous in the specialized cells of leaves and add up to large numbers per unit area of a leaf. It has been estimated that there are about 250 million within a square inch of leaf of one type of plant. Of course, numbers vary considerably among species. In some species or tissues the chloroplasts may be permanently fixed in position within a cell, as in the parenchyma sheath cells of some grasses. In many other leaf cells, however, chloroplasts may move around carried by cyclosis. There are reports also of autonomous chloroplast movements, even ameboid movements, by which they assume certain positions within the cell in dim light but different positions in bright light. Most spectacular movements have been reported in the very large cells of *Chara*. In this aquatic plant all chloroplasts are normally fixed against the cell wall, but if some become detached, they rotate rapidly and move back to a normal position against the wall. Also in *Chara* as well as flowering plants, division of chloroplasts by constriction has been observed by time-lapse photography under the microscope.

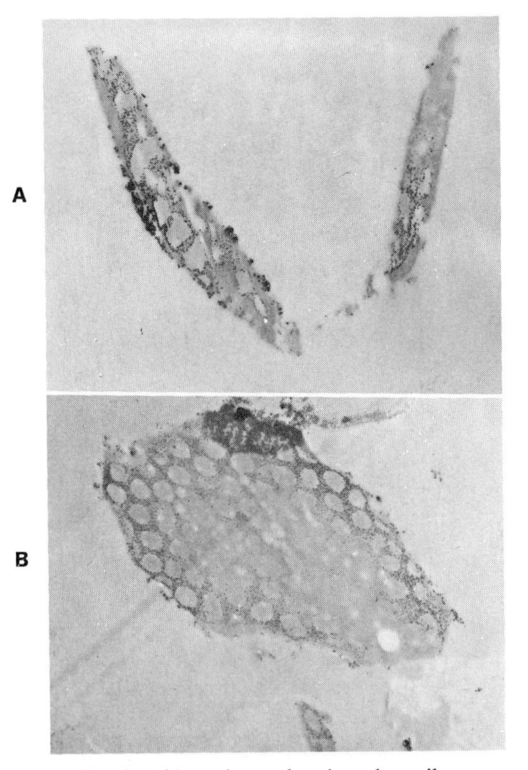

Fig. 11-11. Chloroplasts showing that silver particles produced by $AgNO_3$ reduction are distributed in stroma (really on stromal lamellae) but not in grana. **A,** Section cut perpendicular to **B** and showing rectangular aspect of grana. **B,** Electron micrograph of section cut to show the round aspect of grana (clear circular areas). In **A** an indication of silver grains lined up on the profiles of stromal lamellae is slightly evident. (See also Fig. 5-6.) (From Brown, W. V., H. Mollenhauer, and C. Johnson. 1962. Amer. J. Bot. **49:** 57-63.)

The chemical composition of plastids is essentially the same as that of general protoplasm, except for special chlorophylls, carotenoids, enzymes, cytochromes, quinones, and nucleotides, which are necessary as functional-structural molecules in the photosynthetic and related processes. Statements concerning the total protein, carbohydrate, lipid, or ash of chloroplasts contribute little to cytological knowledge.

A chemical reaction, known at least since 1918 as the *Molisch reaction,* seems limited to chloroplasts. That is, if living leaf tissue is immersed in silver nitrate solution in the dark or light so that the solution gets to the cells quickly, as at a cut surface, the chloroplasts turn black or brown. This color results from metallic silver, which has been reduced by the chloroplast from the silver ions. In the 1930s many observations of the Molisch reaction were made in various plants and tissues and with various conditions of acidity and strength of solution, light or darkness, living or dead tissue, but no positive knowledge was achieved as to where the reduced silver was located or what the reducing agent or process was. Electron microscopy has now demonstrated that in the light the silver is formed on the stromal lamellae of flowering plant chloroplasts (Fig. 11-11) and on the lamellae of algae (Brown et al., 1962; Giraud, 1963). Silver nitrate is not reduced within grana. Reduction is probably achieved by some molecule (ascorbic acid is the most likely) and some process, since in the light much more silver nitrate is reduced more quickly and the patterns of reduction sites are different than in darkness (McHale, 1965).

Leukoplasts that are destined to become chloroplasts eventually form colorless protochlorophyll. Some algae and the female gametophytes of *Ginkgo* and conifers contain the enzyme(s) necessary for the conversion of protochlorophyll to the green functional chlorophyll. In angiosperms, other algae (including *Euglena*), and some other land plants, light is necessary for conversion of protochlorophyll to chlorophyll and for maintenance of chlorophyll. In flowering plants a light reaction of some sort is required; therefore tissues or whole plants grown from seed in the dark are not green but yellowish (because of the carotenoids) and are described as *chlorotic*. Green plants put into the dark lose their green color rapidly (grasses) or very slowly (many dicotyledons). The change from green to not green is associated with the decline and disappearance of grana and most stromal lamellae. Whether the chloro-

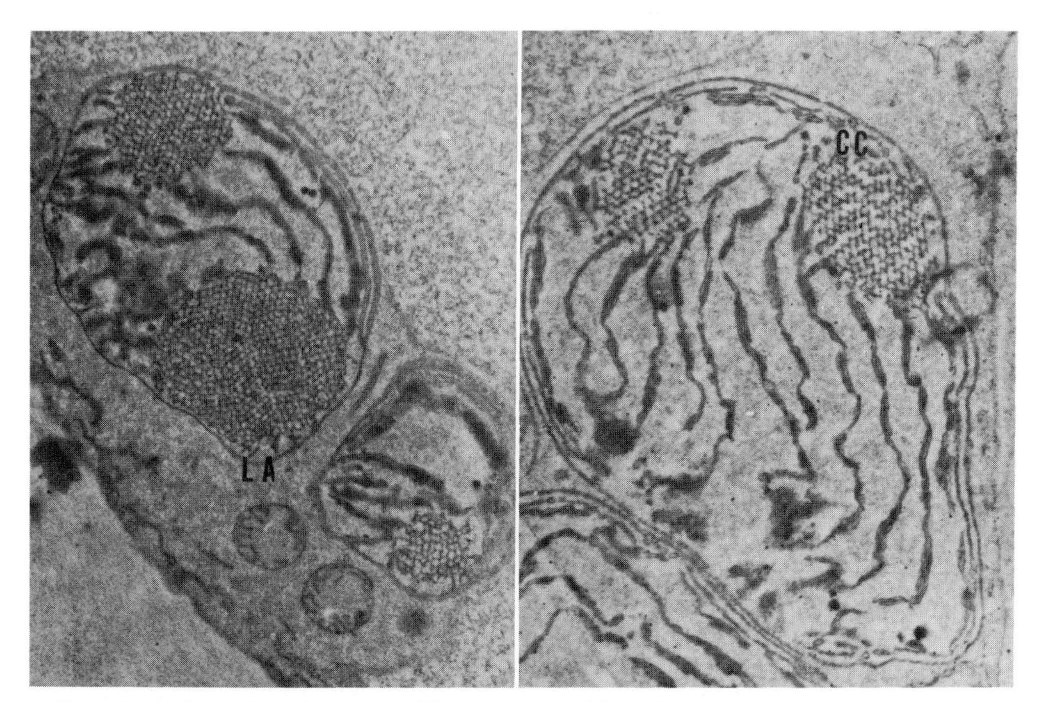

Fig. 11-12. Examples of paracrystalline arrays in chloroplasts of dark-treated corn plants. When green grass plants are put into total darkness for 3 days, the normal lamellar system, including grana, breaks down into a few lamellae, and paracrystalline arrays appear, **LA** and **CC**. When placed in light again, paracrystalline arrays quickly break up, and by 12 hours the normal membrane system, including grana, has re-formed.

plasts revert all the way back to leukoplasts is unknown. In the dark and for a short time when such plastids are again exposed to light, an odd but orderly arrangement of regularly interconnected tubes called the *prolamellar body* is evident (Fig. 11-12); this body is also called the dense core, primary granum, plastid center, vesicular center, vesicular body, crystalline center, and the Heitz-Leyon crystal. There may be one to three in each plastid, and later, still in light, the prolamellar body is converted back into the usual stromal and granal lamellae. During normal conversion of a leukoplast to a chloroplast no prolamellar body forms; it is an abnormal structure.

The normal development of the lamellar system is partly under the control of nuclear genes, and known nuclear mutations stop development at different stages. Plastid gene "mutations," as in leaves of various plants that are partially green and partially white, are also known to occur; these are transmitted from generation to generation only through the egg.

It seems evident that as a leukoplast transforms into a chloroplast, some membranous vesicles destined to become lamellae originate by inward budding from the inner plastid membranes. It is also likely that all chloroplast membranes extend and increase in area by intussusception. They can also decrease by loss of molecules, as in the dark. All these membranes occur in pairs as more or less flattened vesicles or sacs. The ends or edges are never open, whether

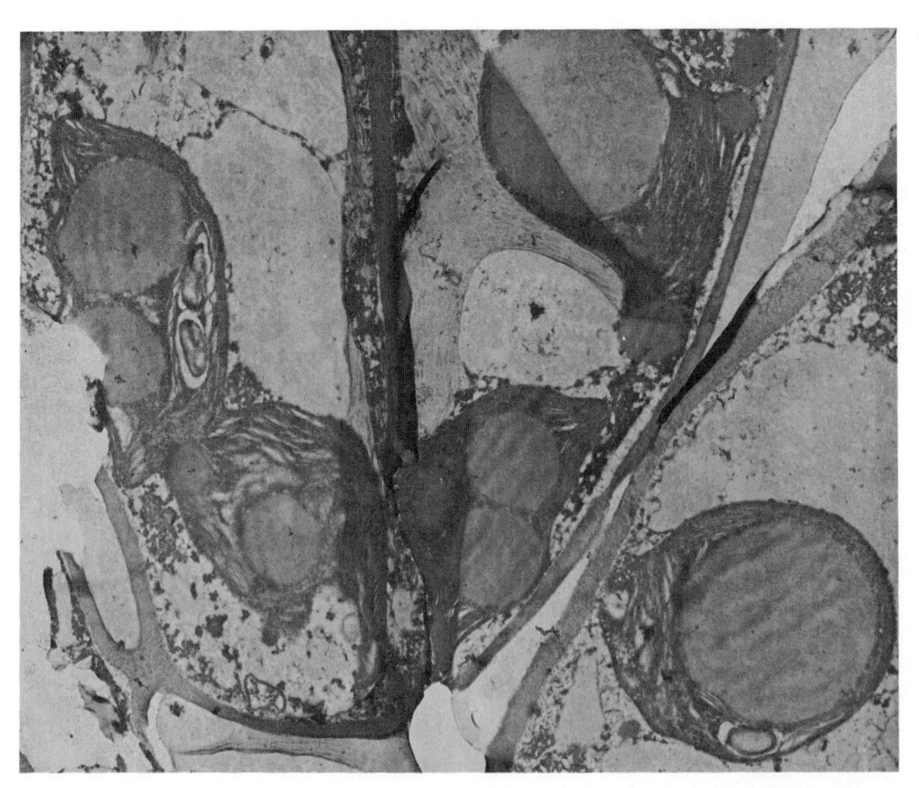

Fig. 11-13. Electron micrograph of leaf tissue of the angiosperm *Cercis canadensis* when the leaf had a bright yellow autumn coloration. Note large amorphous "vacuoles" within chloroplasts. Carotenoids are probably a major constituent of these vacuoles and so impart the yellow color to the leaf. Much of the chlorophyll has disappeared by this stage.

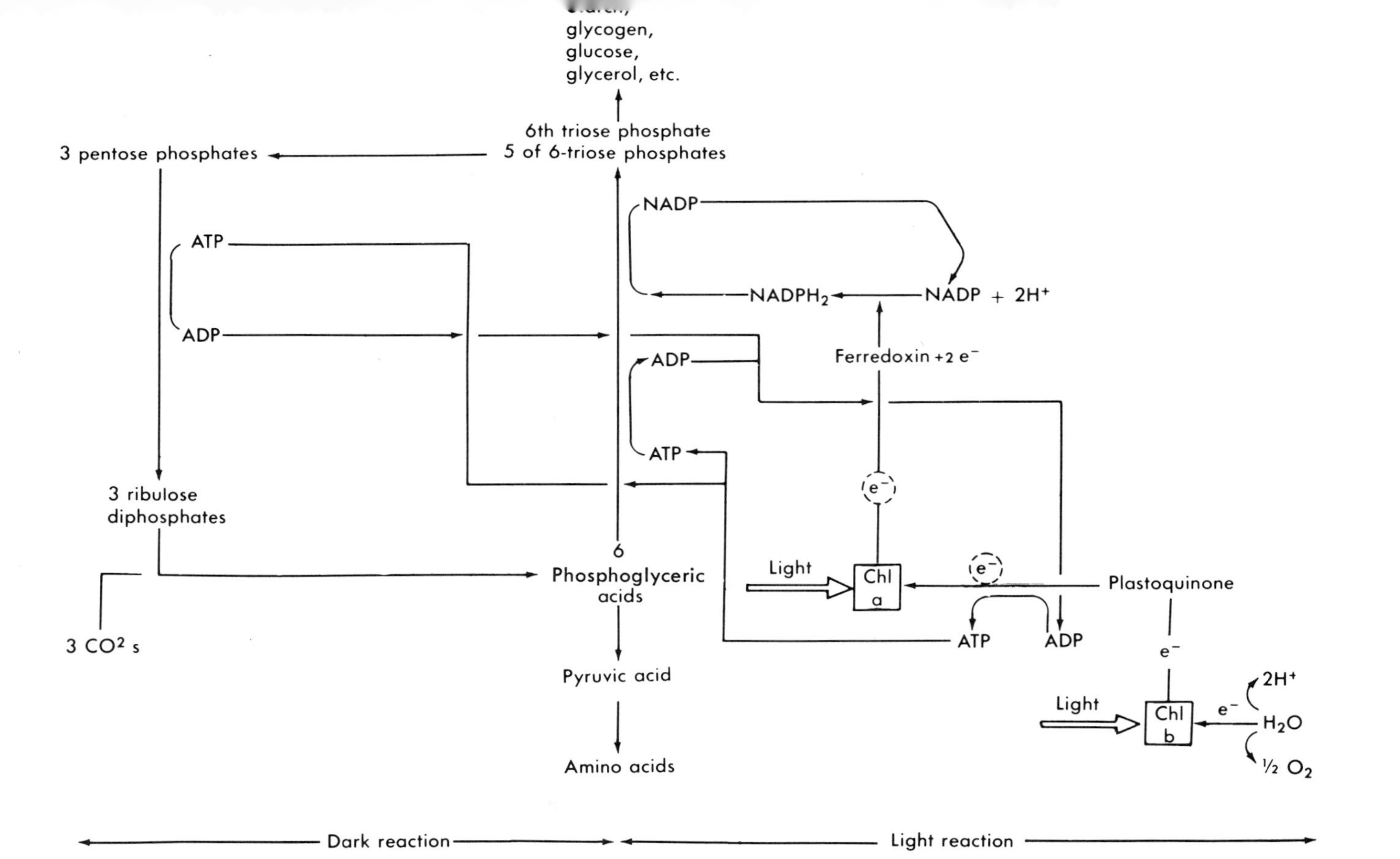

Fig. 11-14. A diagrammatic scheme of photosynthesis. Light reaction on right acquires electrons from water, and O_2 is produced. Chlorophyll, light, enzymes, cytochromes, and other electron-carrier molecules result in production of ATP and $NADPH_2$. These high-energy carriers and reducing power "run" the dark reaction so that CO_2 is reduced to CH_2O. The immediate products of photosynthesis are sugars or amino acids. These can be formed quickly into a wide variety of needed organic molecules by enzymatic intermediary metabolic pathways of the cell. Molecules of the photosynthetic process are arranged in photosynthetic membranes and, in land plants, quantasomes of the granal lamellae.

small vesicles in a maturing chloroplast or stromal or granal lamellar sacs of a mature chloroplast (Fig. 11-7, *inset*).

Mature chloroplasts also contain spherical lipid (probably carotenoid) droplets scattered or grouped between and among the stromal lamellae (Figs. 11-1, 11-3, 11-7). During chloroplast degeneration, as leaves die and produce autumn coloration, such lipid droplets become abundant and large as the membranes disappear (Fig. 11-13).

Chloroplast functions

Certainly, the primary function of the chloroplast is the conversion of light (photon) energy into molecular bond (electron) energy of ATP and $NADPH_2$, which are then utilized for the reduction of CO_2 to $[CH_2O]$, the light and dark reactions, respectively, of photosynthesis (Figs. 11-10 and 11-14) (Arnon, 1960). Calvin and others have worked out the details of a model of the dark reaction that involves the enzymatic synthesis of 3 pentose phosphates from 5 triose phosphates and the involvement of 3 ATP to change the 3 pentose phosphates to 3 ribulose diphosphates. The combination of these molecules with carbon dioxides and the immediate splitting of the 3 six-carbon transient molecules to produce 6 molecules of phosphoglyceric acid follows. One of these, the product molecule, may then proceed along many possible pathways: to starch, to amino acids, to protein, to lipids, or to any molecule the plastid or cell has the enzymes to synthesize. Certainly, enzymes for the intermediary metabolism to starch, amino acids, fatty acids, and many other molecules are present within the plastids. The remaining 5 phosphoglyceric acid molecules are reduced by ATP and $NADPH_2$ to 5 triose molecules, which are used to continue the synthetic cycle (Fig. 11-14).

Another photosynthetic "dark reaction" scheme that is supported by considerable recent experimental evidence proposes that in some but not all flowering plants and all Kranz plants, pyruvate (3 carbons) may be phosphorylated and then carboxylated by phosphopyruvate carboxylase to four-carbon oxaloacetate and malate. By some unknown sequence 3-phosphoglycerate and sugar are then formed (Slack and Hatch, 1967). Ribulose 1,5-diphosphate and phosphoribulokinase also seem to be involved.

Kranz syndrome

Although most plants carry out dark reaction of photosynthesis by the C_3 (ribulose diphosphate-3,phosphoglyceric acid) Calvin cycle, it has been found recently that about half of all grass species, nearly 1,000 species of sedges, and some species in about six other angiospermous families employ an additional biochemical and cytological complexity. Thus radioactive carbon from $^{14}CO_2$ is first found in 4-carbon molecules (oxaloacetic, malic, and aspartic acids) rather than the 3-carbon 3-phosphoglyceric acid as in most plants.

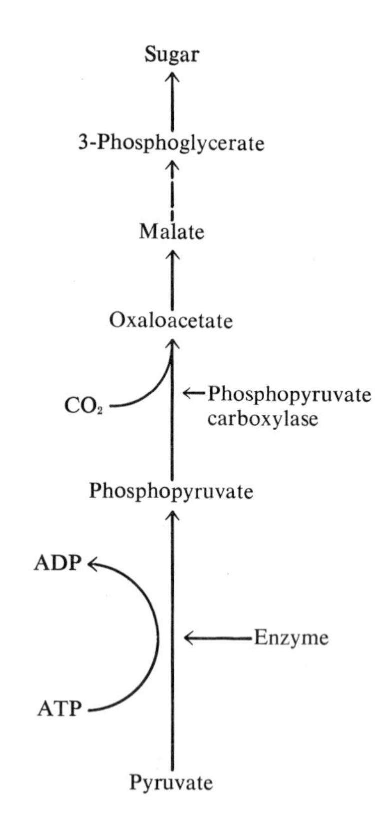

This more complex C_4 photosynthetic pathway was quickly related to a long-known form of leaf anatomy (Figs. 11-7 and 11-8) that has a sheath (kranz) of large thick-walled cells surrounding the vascular bundles of the leaves. Concentrically surrounding the kranz is the distinctive mesophyll of usually radiating cells, like spokes of a wheel. The inner ends of the radial mesophyll cells are connected to the kranz cells by numerous plasmodesmata (Brown, 1958). In nature starch is formed only in the kranz (parenchyma sheath) cells. This is called the *Kranz anatomy* and is always correlated with C_4 biochemistry.

Other cytological and physiological phenomena rapidly (since 1968) were correlated with the C_4 biochemistry and Kranz anatomy (Tregunna et al., 1970) to form a syndrome, called the *Kranz syndrome,* and plants having the syndrome are called Kranz or C_4 plants. Such plants, when confined, were found to reduce the carbon dioxide in their environment to about 5 ppm (parts per million), whereas non-Kranz plants cannot reduce the carbon dioxide in their confined environment below about 50 ppm (Downton and Tregunna, 1968). All plants reduce the amount of the stable ^{13}C isotope they take in from the air as carbon dioxide relative to the amount of ^{12}C (atmospheric CO_2: $^{12}C = 98.9\%$; $^{13}C = 1.1\%$), but non-Kranz plants get rid of more ^{13}C and have lower negative $^{13}C/^{12}C$ ratios (–22 to –38) than do Kranz plants, which have higher negative ratios (–8 to –16) (Smith and Epstein, 1971). When confined plants in the light have lights turned off, the non-Kranz plants give off a burst of carbon dioxide, but many Kranz plants do not (Brown and Gracen, 1972). Peroxysomes or microbodies are mostly limited to the kranz cells, whereas in non-Kranz plants they are generally distributed in the mesophyll (Frederick and Newcomb, 1971). Chloroplasts within the kranz cells are usually large and in some taxa (the panicoid grasses) have no grana (Figs. 11-7 and 11-8), whereas non-Kranz plants have no such agranal chloroplasts. The chloroplasts in the mesophyll of Kranz plants are unusually small.

In *Atriplex,* uniquely it is believed, both Kranz and non-Kranz species are known within one truly phylogenetic genus (Björkman et al., 1971). They can be hybridized, and F_2 and F_3 segregation has demonstrated that many independent genes are involved for Kranz anatomy and enzymes.

The Kranz syndrome C_4 dark reaction of photosynthesis is more complicated and more efficient than the non-Kranz process, at least in high-light and high-temperature environments. Instead of all aspects of photosynthesis occurring in each cell and chloroplast, certain reactions of the process are partitioned by segregation of certain enzymes within mesophyll or kranz cells but not both (Björkman et al., 1971). Molecular intermediates move back and forth between the two types of cells through the plasmodesmata. The thick walls of the kranz cells are assumed to be necessary impervious partitions to prevent interference among enzymes. The old Calvin cycle is still present and essential but is restricted to the kranz sheath cells. The new pyruvate-C_4 cycle is divided, partially in kranz cells, partially within mesophyll cells, but the first incorporation of carbon dioxide by phosphoenol pyruvate carboxylase occurs in the mesophyll cells. The reduction in amount of mesophyll per se results in the radial arrangement of mesophyll of Kranz species. Reduction in amount of mesophyll is apparently necessary to balance its activity against the biochemical functions of the limited amount of sheath.

The cellular arrangements among Kranz plants are variable. Dicotyledonous and grass species of the subfamilies Eragrostoideae and Panicoideae have a simple unicellular kranz sheath. The grass subfamily Aristiodoideae has two adacent and concentric parenchyma sheaths. In most Kranz

Cyperaceae the kranz sheath is surrounded by a layer of small, thick-walled cells that have no chloroplasts. The most complicated anatomy occurs in the tribe Fimbristylidae of the Cyperaceae. It consists of two concentric parenchyma sheaths with a layer of small, thick-walled cells between them. However, all these anatomies and chloroplast differences have essentially the same C_4 photosynthesis.

The two Kranz subfamilies of the grasses, Eragrostoideae and Panicoideae, differ remarkably for chloroplast structure and arrangement within the kranz or parenchyma sheath cells. In the Panicoideae the chloroplasts are completely or almost completely agranal, and the chloroplasts occupy the outer, centrifugal region of the cells. In the Eragrostoideae the chloroplasts have many large grana, and the plastids appear to be attached by one end to the inner, centripetal wall of the kranz cells. In the Aristidoideae the inner parenchyma sheath cells are like those of the Panicoideae, whereas the outer parenchyma sheath is like that of the Eragrostoideae (Brown, 1960).

Kranz plants occur in eight genera of Amaranthaceae, four genera of Compositae, one genus of Euphorbiaceae, two genera of Zygophyllaceae, seven genera of Chenopodiaceae, at least three genera of Nyctaginaceae, one genus of Portulacaceae, eighteen genera of Cyperaceae, 350 genera of Gramineae, and one or more of Aizoaceae. Thus it has evolved independently in ten families but is an uncommon condition except in grasses and sedges.

Many details of the light reaction, however, remain to be characterized. It is generally known that more than one quantum absorbed by different pigments (two types of chlorophyll) is required. The first photochemical process produces molecular oxygen and reducing (electron) power from water. The reducing power converts ADP to ATP. The second photochemical process produces reducing power in the form of $NADPH_2$. The ATP and $NADPH_2$ are then utilized in the dark reaction (Fig. 11-14). Of course, a number of cytochromes, quinones, and enzymes, are involved in the overall light reaction, some of which have been determined but not as completely as the model for oxidative phosphorylation and electron transport in mitochondria. It must be realized that the light reaction is probably the most complex and involved single biochemical cellular process so far evolved by life on earth.

Although the greatly simplified scheme of photosynthesis as diagrammed in Fig. 11-14 indicates extensive two-dimensional displacements of molecules, the actual movements of molecules or electrons is probably no more than from one enzyme, cytochrome, quinone, or chlorophyll to an adjacent molecule. This presupposes that the enzymes, etc., are all arranged in an exact and orderly array just as is proposed for similar functional molecules in or on the inner membrane of the mitochondrion (Lehninger, 1961). In the latter the functional arrays form structures known as *oxysomes.* In the membranes of chloroplasts, at least of grana, the structural-functional array forms the structural subunits called by some scientists *quantasomes* (Fig. 11-9).

Models of the likely arrangements of a few of the many molecules known to be involved in the light reaction have been proposed for granal lamellae based, to some extent, on the known number of chlorophyll, phospholipid, carotenoid, and other molecules per unit area of membrane. Arrangements of molecules within quantasomes have not even been attempted.

LITERATURE CITED

Arnon, D. I. 1960. The role of light in photosynthesis. Sci. Amer. **203:**105-118.

Arnon, D. I. 1967. Photosynthetic activity of isolated chloroplasts. Physiol. Rev. **47:**317-358.

Bassham, J. A. 1962. The path of carbon in photosynthesis. Sci. Amer. **206:**89-100.

Björkman, O., M. A. Nobs, R. W. Pearcy, and J. A. Berry. 1971. Hybrids between Atriplex species with and without β-carboxylation photosynthesis. Carnegie Inst. Wash. Year Book **69:**624-662.

Brown, D. L., and T. E. Weier. 1968. Chloroplast development and ultrastructure in the freshwater red alga Batrachospermum. J. Phycol. **4:**199-206.

Brown, R. H., and V. E. Gracen. 1972. Distribution of the post-illumination CO_2 burst among grasses. Crop Sci. **12:**30-33.

Brown, W. V. 1958. Leaf anatomy in grass systematics. Bot. Gaz. **119:**170-178.

Brown, W. V. 1960. A cytological difference between the Eupanicoideae and the Chloridoideae (Gramineae). Southwest. Nat. **5:**7-11.

Brown, W. V., H. Mollenhauer, and C. Johnson. 1962. An electron microscope study of silver nitrate reduction in leaf cells. Amer. J. Bot. **49:**57-63.

Downton, W. J. S., and E. B. Tregunna. 1968. Carbon dioxide compensation—its relation to photosynthetic carboxylation reactions, systematics of the Gramineae, and leaf anatomy. Canad. J. Bot. **46:**207-215.

Ellis, R. J. 1969. Chloroplast ribosomes: stereospecificity of inhibition by chloramphenicol. Science **163:**477-478.

Famintzin, A. 1907. Die Symbiose als Mittel der Synthese von Organismen. Biol. Centralblatt **27:**353-364.

Frederick, S. E., and E. H. Newcomb. 1971. Ultrastructure and distribution of microbodies in leaves of grasses with and without CO_2 photorespiration. Planta **96:**152-174.

Giraud, G. 1963. La structure, les pigments et les caracteristiques fonctionneles de l'appareil photosynthétique de diverses algues. Physiol. Vég. **1:**203-255.

Granick, S., and K. R. Porter. 1947. The structure of the spinach chloroplast as interpreted with the electron microscope. Amer. J. Bot. **34:**545-550.

Hall, W. T., and G. Claus. 1967. Ultrastructural studies on the cyanelles of Glaucocystis nostochinearum Itzigsohn. J. Phycol. **3:**37-51.

Heslop-Harrison, J. 1963. Structure and morphogenesis of lamellar systems in grana-containing chloroplasts. I. Membrane structure and lamellar architecture. Planta **60:**243-260.

Johnson, C., and W. V. Brown. 1964. An electron microscope study of the photosynthetic apparatus in plants, with special reference to the Gramineae. Unpublished Ph.D. dissertation of the senior author, University of Texas, Austin.

Lee, S. G., and W. R. Evans. 1971. Hybrid ribosome formation from *Escherichia coli* and chloroplast ribosome subunits. Science **173:** 241-242.

Lehninger, A. L. 1961. How cells transform energy. Sci. Amer. **205:**63-73.

Margulis, L. 1967. On the origin of mitosing cells. J. Theor. Biol. **14:**225-274.

McHale, J. T. 1965. The reduction of heavy metal salts by chloroplasts, with reference to ascorbic acid. Unpublished Ph.D. dissertation, University of Texas, Austin.

Mereschkowsky, C. 1905. Über Natur und Ursprung der Chromatophoren in Pflanzenreiche. Biol. Centralblatt **25:**593-604.

Paolillo, D. J., and R. H. Falk. 1966. The ultrastructure of grana in the mesophyll plastids of Zea mays. Amer. J. Bot. **53:**173-180.

Paolillo, D. J., and J. A. Reighard. 1967. On the relationship between mature structure and ontogeny in the grana of choloroplasts. Canad. J. Bot. **45:**773-782.

Park, R., and S. Epstein. 1961a. Carbon isotope fractionation during photosynthesis. Geochim. Chosmochim. Acta **21:**110-126.

Park, R., and S. Epstein. 1961b. Metabolic fractionation of C^{13} and C^{12} in plants. Plant Physiol. **36:**133-138.

Ris, H., and W. Plaut. 1962. Ultrastructure of DNA-containing areas in the chloroplast of Chlamydomonas. J. Cell Biol. **13:**383-391.

Schnepf, E., W. Koch, and G. Deichgraber. 1966. Zur Cytologie und taxonomischen Einordnung von Glaucocystis. Arch. Mikrobiol. **55:**149-174.

Slack, C. R., and M. D. Hatch. 1967. Comparative studies on the activity of carboxylase and other enzymes in relation to the new pathway of photosynthetic carbon dioxide fixation in tropical grasses. Biochem. J. **103:**660-665.

Smith, B. N., and S. Epstein. 1971. Two categories of $^{13}C/^{12}C$ ratios for higher plants. Plant Physiol. **47:**380-384.

Tregunna, E. B., B. N. Smith, J. A. Berry, and W. J. S. Downton. 1970. Some methods for studying the photosynthetic taxonomy of the angiosperms. Canad. J. Bot. **48:**1209-1214.

Wehrmeyer, W., and G. Röbbelen. 1965. Räumliche Aspekte zur Membranschichtung in den Chloroplasten einer *Arabidopsis-Mutante* unter Auswertung von Serienschnitten. III. Über Membranbildungsprozesse im Chloroplasten. Planta **64:**312-329.

Weier, T. E., and A. A. Benson. 1967. The molecular organization of chloroplast membranes. Amer. J. Bot. **54:**389-402.

Weier, T. H., A. H. P. Engelbrecht, A. Harrison, and E. B. Risley, 1965. Subunits in the membranes of chloroplasts of Phaseolus vulgaris, Pisum sativum, and Aspidistra sp. J. Ultrastruct. Res. **13:**92-111.

Weier, T. E., C. R. Stocking, and L. K. Shumway.

1966. The photosynthetic apparatus in chloroplasts of higher plants. Brookhaven Symp. Biol. **19**:353-374.

Whitfield, P. R., and D. Spencer. 1968. The biochemical and genetic autonomy of chloroplasts. In W. J. Peacock and R. D. Brock (editors). Replication and recombination of genetic material. Australian Academy of Science, Canberra.

Zelitch, I. 1967. Control of leaf stromata—their role in transpiration and photosynthesis. Amer. Sci. **55**:472-486.

CHAPTER 12

Lysosomes and related bodies

LYSOSOMES

Although the size of the lysosome (Figs. 10-1 and 12-1) is above the resolution of the light microscope, the development of the lysosome concept was the result of differential centrifugation analysis of cytoplasmic formed bodies. According to de Duve (1959), the development of the lysosome concept was based on a morphologically distinct entity defined by purely chemical data. Early work had shown that acid phosphatase activity was associated with the mitochondrial fraction and thereby led to the concept of the heterogeneity of mitochondria (Berthet and de Duve, 1951). On the other hand, the fraction containing acid phosphatase activity was localized in the microsomal fraction when studied by other investigators. For a time it was suggested that the distinction between microsomes and mitochondria was not real, that a continuous spectrum of cytoplasmic particles existed that represented the various stages in the life cycle of these particles (Chantrenne, 1947). Later work by de Duve and Berthet (1953) and Applemans et al. (1955) on the physical separation of cellular particles showed that the L (or light) fraction contained particles that were rich in acid phosphatase activity and that did not contain the cytochrome oxidase activity associated with mitochondria. This fraction also contained a number of other enzymes in significant concentractions such as β-glucuronidase, cathepsin, DNAase, and RNAase (de Duve et al., 1955; Gianetto and de Duve, 1955; Wattiaux et al., 1956). This fraction represented an intermediate class of cytoplasmic granules that were devoid of both mitochondrial and microsomal enzymes and therefore constituted a true component of the cytoplasm. The particles of this new class were named lysosomes (lytic bodies) because of their high concentration of hydrolytic enzymes. There are, for example, hundreds of lysosomes in each liver cell, as revealed by acridine staining and fluorescence microscopy (Allison, 1967).

After the identification of the lysosome in liver, other studies showed lysosomes to be present in the kidney, where they are referred to as kidney droplets, as well as in macrophages and nervous tissues (Becker and Sandbank, 1964). They have also been observed in cell cultures (Ogawa et al., 1961) and venom glands. In fact, they appear to be universally distributed in animals, from the Protozoa to vertebrates, as well as in some plant cells.

Morphology

Based on calculations derived from ultracentrifugation studies, the lysosome from the liver was shown to be approximately 0.4 μm in diameter and to have a density of

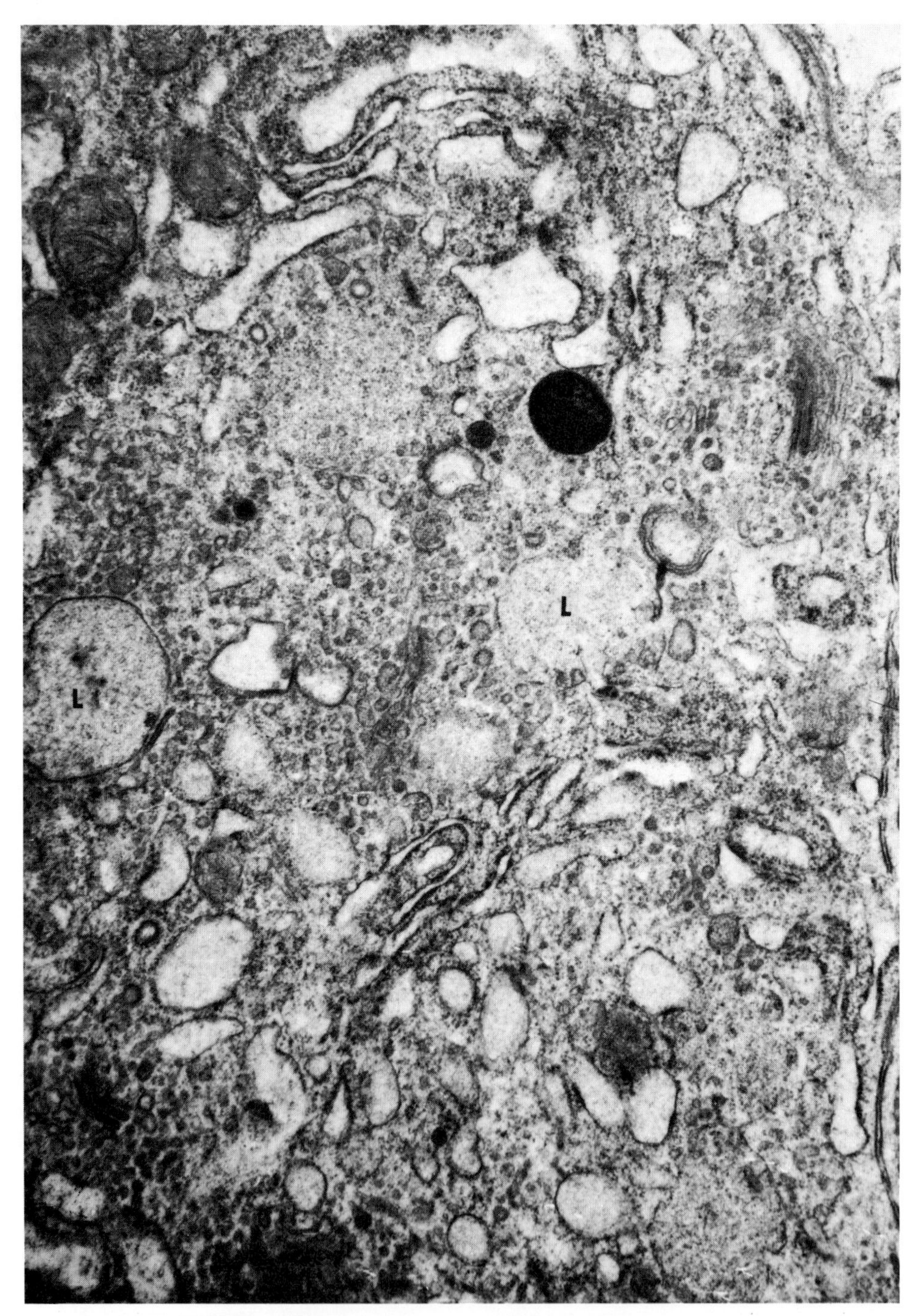

Fig. 12-1. Section of venom gland from the western diamondback rattlesnake *(Crotalus atrox)* showing two lysosomes, **L.** Lysosomal membrane on right is breaking down.

about 1.15. The range in size varies in other tissues from approximately 0.2 to about 0.8 μm. For example, the average size of the so-called kidney droplets is 0.5 μm. Lysosomes are also large in the macrophages, as for example, the von Kupffer cells of the liver.

The lysosome is relatively spherical in shape and is encompassed by a single lipoprotein membrane (Fig. 12-1). This membrane is considered to be similar to the unit membrane of Robertson. Within this membrane are the various hydrolases now known to be associated with the lysosome. One of the most important properties of this membrane is its high degree of stability within the cell. In isolated particles the amount of acid phosphatase activity in the medium is low when a substrate such as β-glycerophosphate is added. However, the acid phosphatase increases significantly when these particles are subjected to hypotonic solution or to a substance that acts on membranes such as Triton X. This treatment destroys the membranes, thereby releasing the enzymes contained within.

One of the problems of recent electron microscopic cytology has been identification of lysosomes on a purely morphological basis. This is due to the high degree of pleomorphism and varied appearances exhibited by this class of particles. The morphological pleomorphism, however, has been related to the physiological activities of the lysosome. The internal appearance varies from somewhat dense and homogeneous to one or more internal cavities lined with a dense layer. Others may show fine granular or flaky material of electron-dense material comparable to ferritin. In fact, the lysosomes of some animal tissues contain more ferritin than any other cytoplasmic fraction (de Duve, 1958).

Knowledge of the chemistry of the lysosome has made identification easier. Since acid phosphatase activity is high, its histochemical identification has offered an excellent tag for identification at both the light and electron microscope level (Essner and Novikoff, 1960a). Gomori's lead method has proved useful as a tag not only for light microscopy but even more so in studying lysosomes by electron microscopy. This is due to high electron scattering by the deposited lead. Other methods such as naphthol AS phosphate are also used for identification at the light microscope level. Nitroblue tetrazolium and neotetrazolium salts have been used for intravital staining of lysosomes (Koenig, 1965).

Chemistry

Much of the characterization of the lysosome is the result of the chemical studies

Table 12-1. Enzyme composition of lysosomes

Enzyme	Substrate	
Deoxyribonuclease	Deoxyribonucleic acid	
Ribonuclease	Ribonucleic acid	
Acid phosphatase	Phosphate esters and mononucleotides	
Phosphoprotein phosphatase	Phosphoproteins	
Cathepsin (A, B, and C?)	Proteins	
α-Glucosidase	α-Glucosides	
β-N-Acetylglucosaminidase	β-N-Acetylglucosaminides	Muco-poly-saccharides
β-Glucuronidase	β-Glucuronides	
α-Mannosidase	α-Mannosides	
Arylsulfatases (A and B)	Sulfate esters	

of the enzymes found within these membrane-bounded particles. After the identification of acid phosphatase other acid hydrolases were soon detected. At the present time the lysosome is known to contain about ten enzymes (Table 12-1). Examination of Table 12-1 shows that these enzymes, as a group, act on a wide range of substrates so that very few cellular compounds escape the activities of their concerted action. Recent studies (Canonico and Bird, 1970) have indicated that subgroups of lysosomal particles may exist. One group is characterized by containing 95% of cathepsin D and acid phosphatase activity and 75% of RNAase, β-glucuronidase, and arylsulfatase. The second group contains a higher proportion of arylsulfatase and β-glucuronidase.

As stated previously, these enzymes are contained within a liproprotein membrane, and when this membrane is disrupted by any means, as for example, the detergent Triton X-100, hypotonic medium, lecithinase, proteolytic enzymes, a Waring blender, or dimethyl sulfoxide, the enzymes are released simultaneously and become active.

Another characteristic of the lysosome is the lack of oxidative enzymes, which in part differentiates it physiologically from the mitochondrion.

Functions

It was stated earlier that the identification of lysosomes on a purely morphological basis is difficult because of their polymorphism. Much of this pleomorphism is conditioned by a variety of digestive activities and a wide array of contained substances in various tissues and stages. It is the contents that determine their morphological characteristics (de Duve, 1963). For convenience the various types of lysosomes can be classified as *storage vacuoles, digestive vacuoles, autophagic vacuoles* (which will be discussed in the section on cytolysomes), and *residual bodies.*

The *storage vacuole* represents the original or virgin lysosome. The lysosome appears homogeneous throughout and gives a positive acid phosphatase reaction. The storage vacuole is not engaged in any intracellular digestive process (Fig. 12-1).

The *digestive vacuole* results partly from the phagocytotic and pinocytotic processes of the cell. By these processes foreign proteins and large particles can be engulfed by the cell, referred to in this context as *endocytosis.* The engulfed particle is enclosed by a membrane derived from the plasma membrane. The resulting vacuole is called the *phagosome.* The phagosome and a lysosome approach each other, and the membranes of the two fuse to form a single large vacuole. Digestion then proceeds within this vacuole, which is now known as the digestive vacuole.

Evidence of the relationship between phagocytosis and lysosomes in forming a digestive vacuole was shown by Strauss (1964). Horseradish peroxidase blue with benzidine was injected into animal tissues. After the injection, phagosomes were formed, and fusion with lysosomes could be traced by the peroxidase reaction, which can be considered a protein marker. This indicates that there is fusion of the phagosome with a lysosome.

After enzymatic digestion within the digestive vacuole the resulting products diffuse through the membrane into the cytoplasm. However, some of the material that cannot be digested remains within the vacuole as undigestible material. This vacuole is now referred to as the *residual body.* In Protozoa such as amebas and *Paramecium,* as well as in a number of metazoan cells, the residual body is eliminated by a process comparable to reversed endocytosis, or *cellular defication.* In higher animal tissues such as liver, cellular defication proceeds very slowly or may be absent; that is, the residual bodies remain within the cell. The same digestive vacuole may then be repeatedly or continuously active, and the accumulation of indigestible material may play a role in the process of aging (de Duve, 1963). Many of the diverse hepatocellular pigments, such as occur in lipopathic jaundice, may represent residual bodies (Essner and Novikoff, 1960b). These same bodies exhibit acid phosphatase activity. Similarly, the pigment bodies found in nerve cells may represent residual bodies.

An interesting example of the role of lysosomes in phagocytosis is the actions of white blood cells during an inflammatory response such as results from bacterial infection. The white blood cells, particularly the neutrophils, contain numerous enzyme-containing granules that correspond to the lysosomes. When the bacteria become engulfed by the white blood cells, the granules can be seen to disappear and the cells are filled with vacuoles containing the bacteria or other particulate matter in various stages of digestion. The white cells apparently do not recover but soon die.

Evidence also exists that lysosomes can be discharged to the outside of the cell. The enzymes are released to destroy material near the cell (de Duve, 1963). The mechanism of bone erosion by the action of the osteoclast may be the result of such a release of lysosomes. The fragments of bone and other constituents may then be taken into these same or other cells, which digest them in their lysosomes. The osteoclast is a multinucleated cell that causes erosion of the bone during internal reorganization of bone tissue. It is formed by the fusion of stromal cells from the marrow cavity and also by fusion of osteoblasts or osteocytes.

Evidence also suggests that lysosomes may play an important role in morphological remodeling of tissue during metamorphosis. Weber (1957) has shown that during metamorphosis of the frog *Xenopus laevis,* in which there is regression of the tadpole tail, cathepsin (a lysosomal enzyme) increases in concentration, whereas the total or absolute amount of the enzyme remains constant. Similarly, with the increased formation of proteins there is a decrease of cathepsin.

Becker and Sandbank (1964) have shown a relationship between the neuronal Golgi apparatus and lysosomes in neonatal rats. Both are located predominantly in the apical dendrites of neurons comprising the fetal neonatal cerebral cortex. This relationship suggests that both Golgi and lysosomes may play an important role in propelling synthesized cytoplasmic materials into the growing dendrites.

Although autophagic activity is localized by the limiting membranes of the lysosome, there are times when the lysosome ruptures within the cell and releases all the hydrolytic enzymes. Autodissolution of the cells is the result. Probably many of the postmortem changes encountered may be the result of such action, and necrosis may be attributed, at least in part, to lysosomal activity. Lysosomes have been seen in electron micrographs of the petals of the plant *Tradescantia,* which undergo autodissolution into a liquid mass a few hours after the flower has opened.

Toxins that enter the cell may produce changes in the membrane structures of these particles, causing them to rupture and thereby release all the contained enzymes. An additional factor causing or possibly influencing membrane changes may be low oxygen tension in the cell. Anoxia may affect the lysosomal membrane in several ways. The integrity of the lysosomal membrane may depend on its being in the oxidized state; the low oxygen tension prevailing at the time prevents this condition, which then results in ruptured membranes. A corollary may be that the anoxia may be responsible for the release of one or more enzymes that are capable of breaking down the membrane itself (de Duve, 1958).

As suggested by de Duve (1963), if toxins influence the lysosome, would it not be possible to use drugs to control the release of lysosomal enzymes, to cause the rupturing of the membrane (to form "suicide bags"), or to prevent the rupturing of lysosomes? Drugs could be used to stabilize the membrane during a critical stage of infections, or drugs could be added to cause selective rupturing of the lysosomes to destroy the cell, as in the case of neoplasm management. For example, cortisone and hydrocortisone appear to have a stabilizing effect on the lysosomal membrane; on the other hand, excess vitamin A may have an opposite effect.

Origin of lysosomes

Early views suggested the Golgi complex as the site of lysosome formation. Both de Duve (1963) and Essner and Novikoff (1962) suggested that the enzymes associated with the lysosomes are produced by certain ribosomes associated with the ER and are then transported to the Golgi apparatus, where the lysosomes are formed. The acid hydrolases associated with the lysosomes would be contained within the Golgi vesicles that separate from the Golgi complex or dictyosome cisternae. Acid phosphatase was localized in the Golgi region. Moe et al. (1965), using undifferentiated epithelial cells of the intestinal crypt, have indicated that the pure lysosome or "virgin lysosome" is produced by the Golgi complex. The ER in close apposition with the Golgi complex may take part in lysosome formation, particularly in the early stage.

Studies by Brandes (1965) combining histochemistry and electron microscopy have shown that lysosomal formation may take place in two locations, depending on the type of ER, that is, rough or smooth.

In cells such as those found in the rat prostate gland or seminal vesicles, in which rough ER predominates, the lysosome and most of the enzymes associated with the lysosome are probably formed in the hyaloplasm of the cytoplasm, as was indicated by a positive acid phosphatase reaction. These areas appear to be localized in ogival dilations of the cytoplasm and have a tendency to be arranged in rows (Fig. 12-2). Evidence of acid phosphatase activity varies

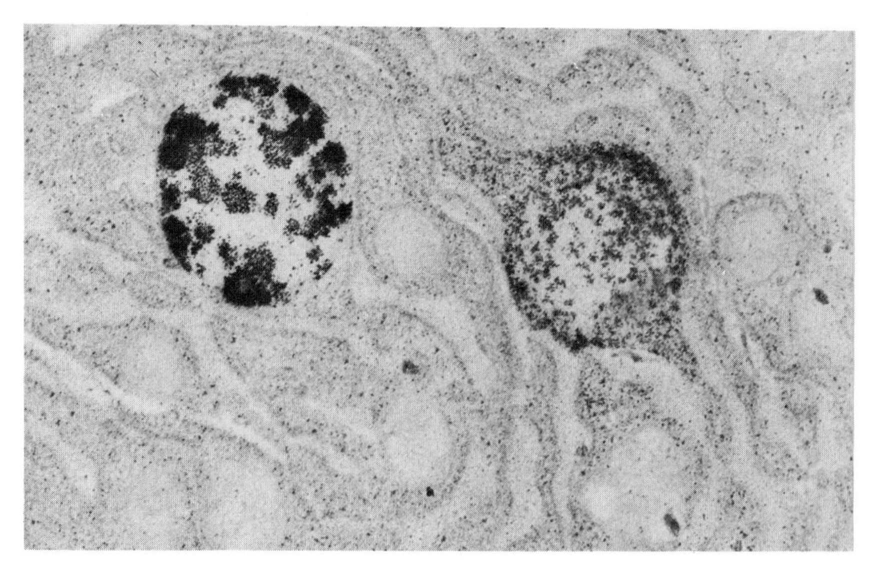

Fig. 12-2. Electron micrograph of rat prostatic epithelium after acid phosphatase reaction. Note accumulation of reaction products in ogival dilations in cytoplasm, suggesting that the origin of lysosomes in cells with a rough ER takes place in the hyaloplasm. No limiting membranes are observable. (From Brandes, D. 1965. J. Ultrastruct. Res. **12:**63-80.)

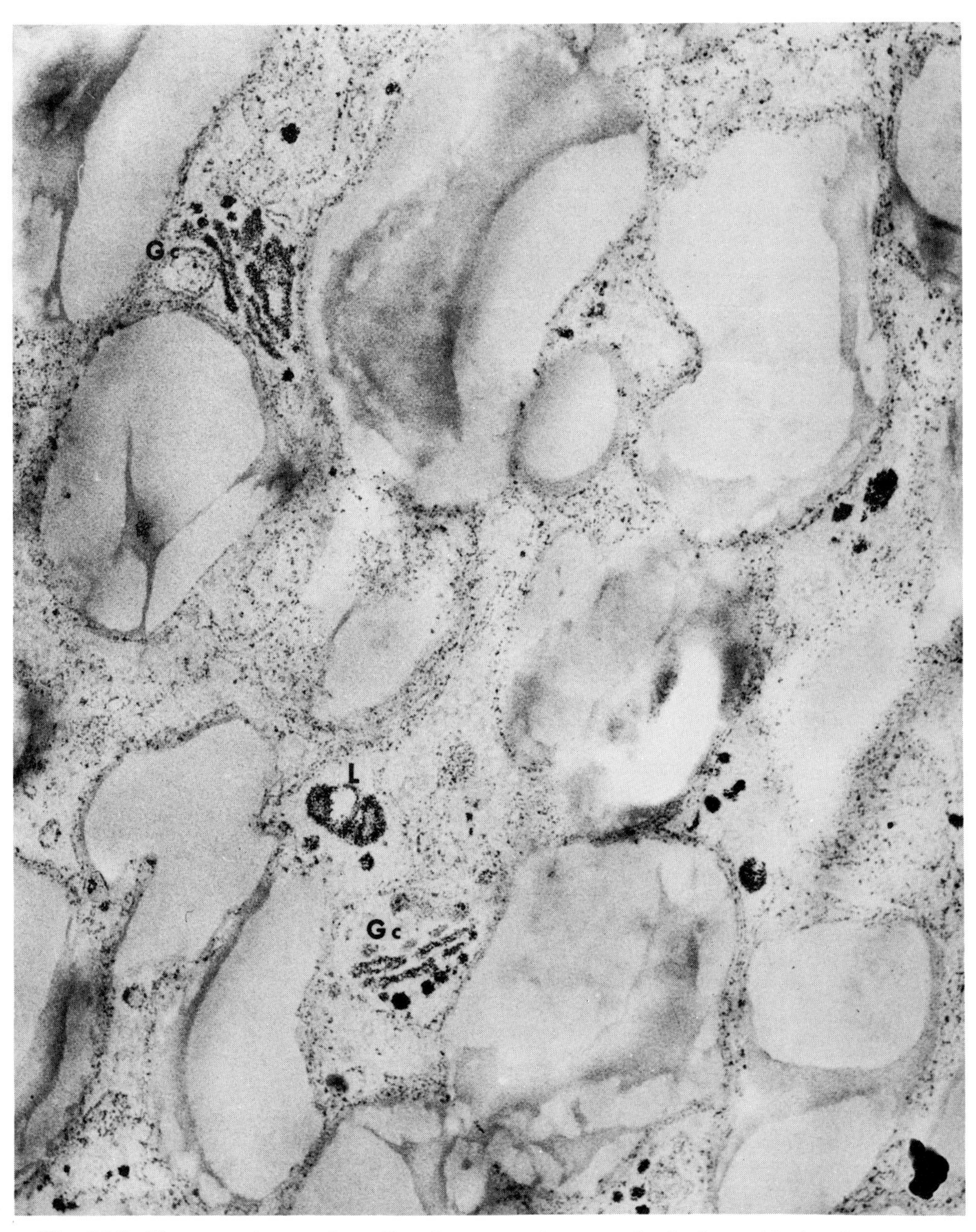

Fig. 12-3. Electron micrograph section from rat sebaceous gland after acid phosphatase reaction. Reaction is concentrated in Golgi cisternae and associated vesicles, **Gc.** A large acid phosphatase–positive body, **L,** is located just above the lower Golgi complex. (See text for explanation.) (From Brandes, D. 1965. J. Ultrastruct. Res. **12:**63-80.)

from mere aggregates of foci, which apparently lie free in the hyaloplasm, to membrane-bounded bodies. During this time, the Golgi vesicles appeared negative for acid phosphatase activity.

On the other hand, in cells such as were obtained from the sebaceous gland or from the protozoan *Euglena* the ERs are almost exclusively of the smooth variety. These cells have a well-developed Golgi complex. In these forms the acid phosphatase activity is positive in the Golgi region (Fig. 12-3). In the sebaceous gland the reaction is seen in small granules and large vacuoles that are similar to the Golgi vesicles; the flattened ER cisternae show minimal activity. In *Euglena* the acid phosphatase is observed in the flattened cisternae, saccular dilations, and vacuoles.

In the cells where the lysosomes are formed in the cytoplasmic matrix, no membrane is present at first and no evidence of hydrolytic activity was noted. This may be because the macromolecules (enzymes) and nonenzyme proteins are conjugated to acidic glycolipids by ionic, covalent, or other bonds so that they are inactive in this condition (Koenig, 1962).

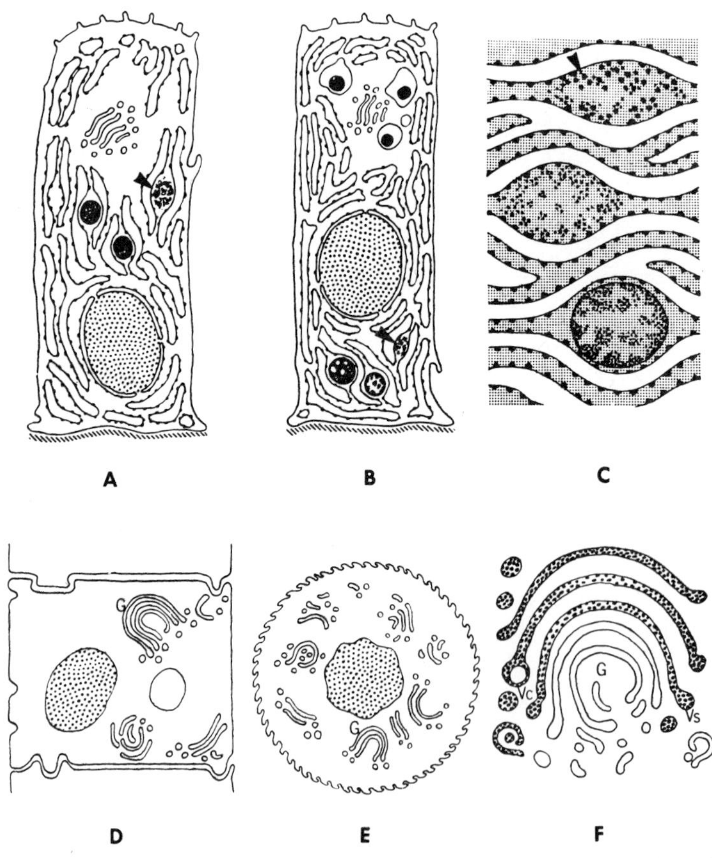

Fig. 12-4. Drawing depicting two possible mechanisms in lysosome formation. **A** represents cell with a rough ER. **B,** Lysosomes appear to originate in dilated areas of cytoplasm (arrow). **C,** Stages in formation of lysosomes. In such cells as a sebaceous epithelial cell, **D,** and *Euglena,* **E,** where smooth ER predominates, lysosomal enzymes appear to be concentrated in the Golgi apparatus, **F.** Lysosomes pinch off from Golgi cisterna. (From Brandes, D. 1965. J. Ultrastruct. Res. **12:**63-80.)

In fact, as suggested by Koenig, release or activation of the hydrolases from lysosomes themselves may be visualized as a cleavage of the glycoprotein-enzyme bond. This could be achieved by the methods described previously as causing lysosomal activity, that is, a hypotonic medium, surface activant, etc.

Summary

Evidence based on work by Brandes (1965) indicates that lysosomes are formed in the cytoplasmic matrix of cells that have a predominantly rough or granular ER but by the Golgi in those cells in which the ER is of the smooth or agranular variety (compare diagrams in Fig. 12-4).

Studies have demonstrated lysosome involvement in mitosis, the human lung diseases asbestosis and silicosis, skin sensitization to light, fertilization, stimulating or turning certain repressed ribosomes *on,* certain types of cancer, chromosome (DNA Watson-Crick double helix) breakage, hormone and drug action, gout, and inflammation (Allison, 1967). Thus the proteolytic enzymes contained within lysosomes have a great many "good" and essential actions as well as "bad" disease-producing actions within the cells themselves when the membrane is made resistant to breakage (as by cortisones) or weakened to the breakage point by numerous intrinsic and extrinsic factors.

CYTOLYSOMES

Cytolysomes, or autophagic vacuoles, are membrane-bounded intracellular bodies that contain mitochondria and other cellular material in varying degrees of degeneration. Like the lysosome the cytolysome also exhibits a positive acid phosphatase reaction. Cytolysomes differ from lysosomes per se in that they are usually larger, ranging in size from approximately 0.8 to 1.6 μm in diameter, as compared to 0.4 to 0.8 μm for lysosomes (Novikoff and Essner, 1962).

Cytolysomes were probably first encountered in cells from the proximal convoluted tubules of the newborn mouse (Clark, 1957). Since that time, however, they have been encountered in several diverse cells. More often, however, they have been observed in such tissue as the kidneys and livers of animals subjected to various vigorous procedures such as ligation of the ureter (Novikoff and Essner, 1962), treatment with glucagon, which has a catabolic effect (Ashford and Porter, 1962), or starvation. Since they were primarily associated with pathological cells undergoing cytolysis, these intracellular bodies were called cytolysomes by Novikoff. In addition to pathological tissues such as those just cited, cytolysomes have also been encountered in a number of cells not undergoing cytolytic processes. For example, the segregation apparatus during the maturation of erythrocytes in a number of urodele amphibians, which appears as clusters of granules in the cytoplasm under the light microscope, has been described as being cytolysomes when studied under the electron microscope. They appear as vacuolar bodies of approximately 0.5 to 4 μm in diameter and contain cell organelles such as mitochondria (Beams and Anderson, 1960; Tooze and Davies, 1965). It is believed that the cytolysomes are involved in degradation of cell organelles during the maturation process.

Cytolysomes have also been observed in the brown adipose cells that were rapidly mobilizing lipids (Napolitano, 1963). It is probable that the brown fat cells were reorientated in such a way that the lipolytic activity was greater than lipogenesis, as was evident by the increase in hydrolytic enzymes. Thus when nearly all the lipids were utilized, the enzymes still remained in the cytoplasm, and the cytolysomes arose in these regions to delimit the enzymes. As a result, there was also the incorporation of mitochondria and other cellular structures within the membranes of the cytolysome. According to Napolitano (1963), the formation of the cytolysomes around the foci of hydrolytic enzymes reorientated the cell back to a normal metabolism.

Cytolysomes may also be involved in the formation of protein granules (Locke and Collins, 1965) and of senility bodies in aging cells.

Origin and formation of cytolysomes

Two methods of origin have been proposed for the cytolysome. The first, originally proposed by Novikoff and Essner (1962) and later confirmed by electron microscopy by Locke and Collins (1965), is that cytolysomes are derived from the pinching off of Golgi cisternae. The second method of origin proposed is by de novo membrane formation around the sites that are physiologically active (Napolitano, 1963). This concept was based on the observation that the brown fat cells studied contained a paucity of membranes.

The sequence of stages in the formation of the cytolysome was shown in an electron microscopic study of the formation of protein granules in the fat bodies of the butterfly *Calpodes ethlius* (Locke and Collins, 1965) (Fig. 12-5). During the formation of RNA protein granules, Golgi vesicles flatten and fold back to invest a somewhat spherical mass of ER within a two-layered shell. Consequently, the entrapped ER bodies become isolated from the rest of the cell by a layer of material resulting from the fused Golgi vesicles (Fig. 12-6). These paired membranes are referred to as *isolation membranes*. Further changes consist of several ER bodies coming together with confluence of their outer membranes (Fig. 12-7); the inner membrane breaks down. In a sense, then, the ER is set free within the remaining membrane. The ER within the vacuole undergoes progressive degeneration in which the vacuoles between the ribosomes become filled with a dense and finely granular material. In the final stage the granules are very dense, and the ribosomes still maintain their identity but can be seen only with difficulty. Fig. 12-5 is a summary of the events leading to the formation of the granule.

Similarly, mitochondria may be isolated by an isolation membrane that is also derived from the Golgi complex; the sequences involved are similar to those just described. The mitochondria undergo progressive de-

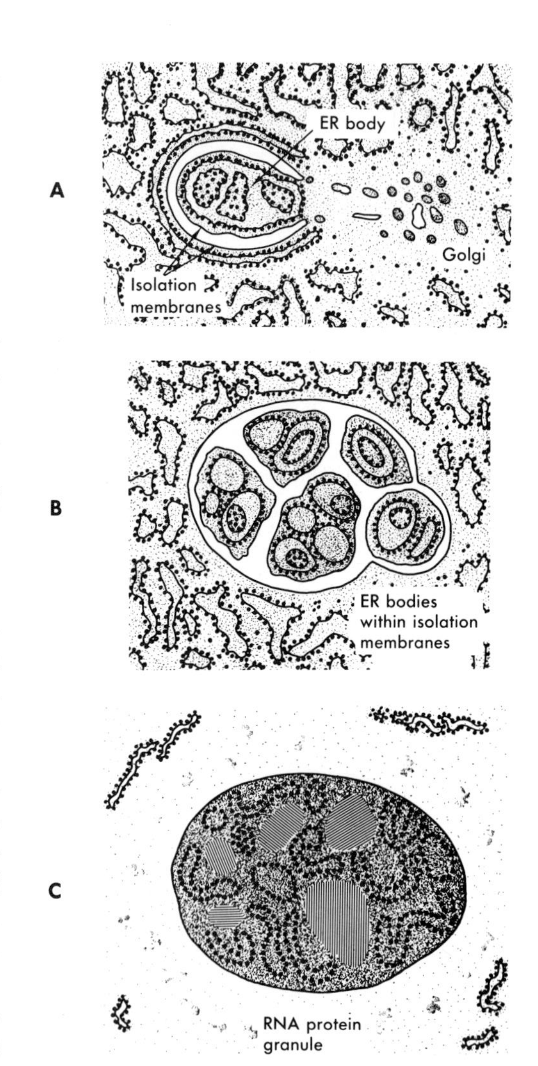

Fig. 12-5. Diagrammatic summary leading to formation of RNA protein body. **A,** Formation of ER body by isolation membranes. **B,** Aggregation of several ER bodies within outer membranes. **C,** Inner membranes are lost, and ribosomes and protein are condensed into a rather dense and partly crystalline granule. (From Locke, M., and J. V. Collins. 1965. J. Cell Biol. **26:**857-868.)

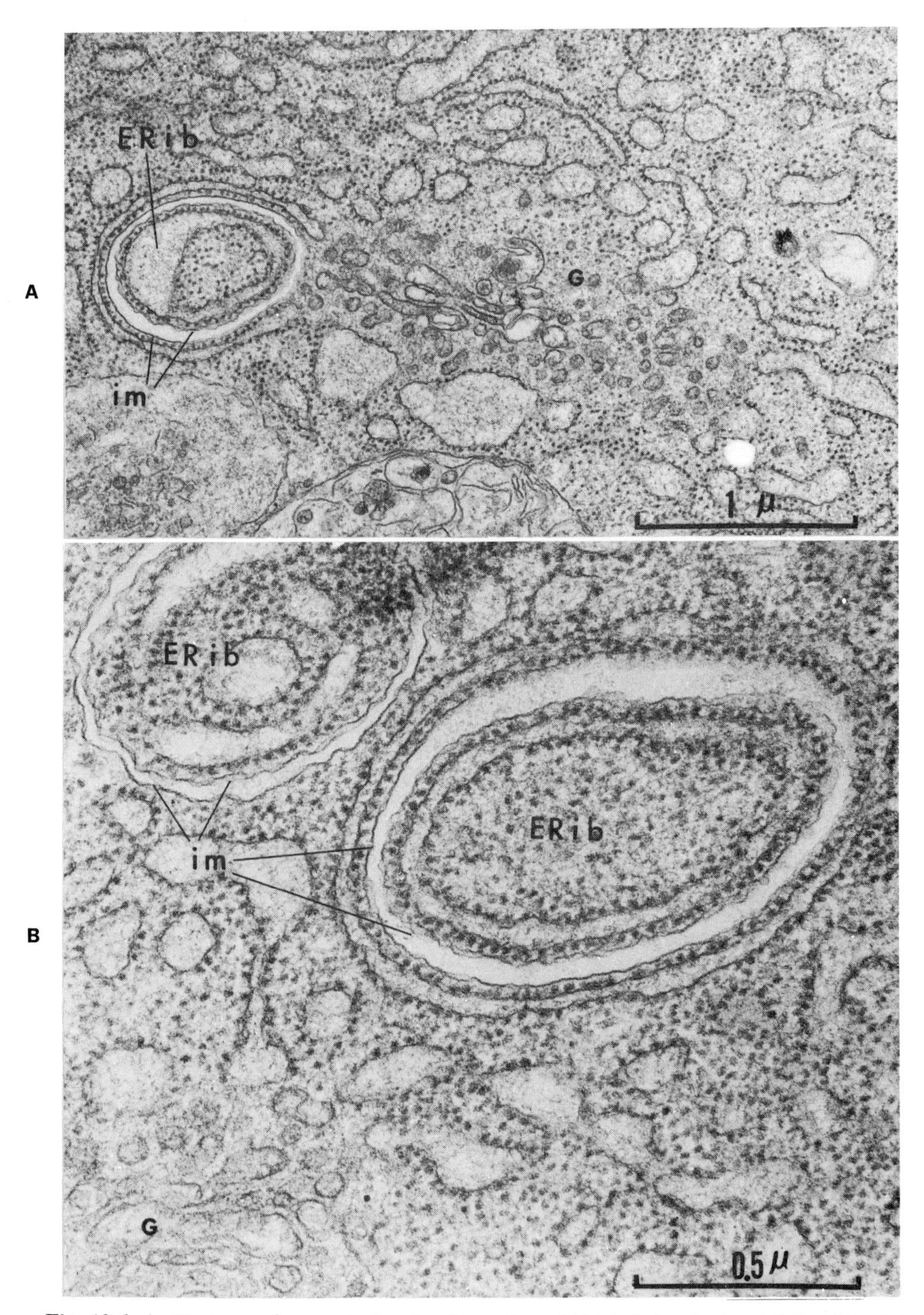

Fig. 12-6. A, Electron micrograph showing formation of ER isolation body. Golgi vesicles join to isolate a region of the ER, **ER ib. im,** Isolation membrane. **B,** Section showing two ER bodies. Note that isolation membranes do not contain ribosomes. **G,** Golgi apparatus. (From Locke, M., and J. V. Collins. 1965. J. Cell Biol. **26:**857-868.)

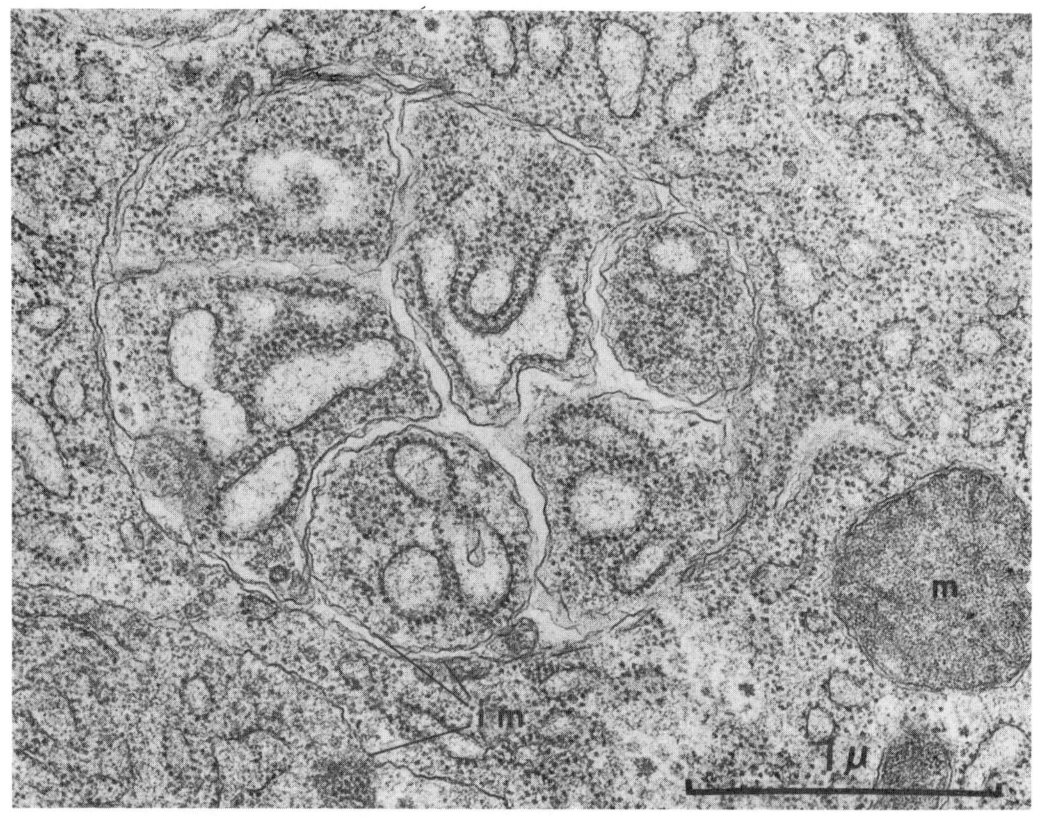

Fig. 12-7. Aggregation of several ER bodies. Outer membranes have fused. (From Locke, M., and J. V. Collins. 1965. J. Cell Biol. **26:**857-868.)

generation until the vacuoles contain a few mitochondrial membranes only, and these ultimately disappear (Fig. 12-8). Thus there is present within the cell a means whereby membranes derived from the Golgi complex can isolate organelles from the rest of the cell (Locke and Collins, 1965). The isolation of the aggregated ribosomes from the rest of the protoplasm by a membrane has been reported in spores of a bacterium.

Studies by Locke (1966) have also shown that isolation membranes may arise from the rough ER (for example, in epidermal cells) as well as from smooth ER in oenocytes, in addition to originating from the Golgi apparatus as just described.

In retrospect it appears that the cytolysome represents a distinct morphological entity from the lysosome. The presence of a positive acid phosphatase reaction in both merely indicates that they are biochemically similar.

PEROXISOMES

"Peroxisome" is a term proposed for certain microbodies observed in many cells of plants and animals. Morphologically, peroxisomes are round to oval bodies that have a diameter ranging between 0.1 and 0.5 μm and are limited by a single membrane. The contents of these bodies are somewhat granular. In addition, many species contain a dense core, which often appears striate. This core is presumably made up of tubules, the arrangement of which tends to be hexagonal (de Duve and Baudhuin, 1966). At times this dense material may assume a more complicated configuration in which the

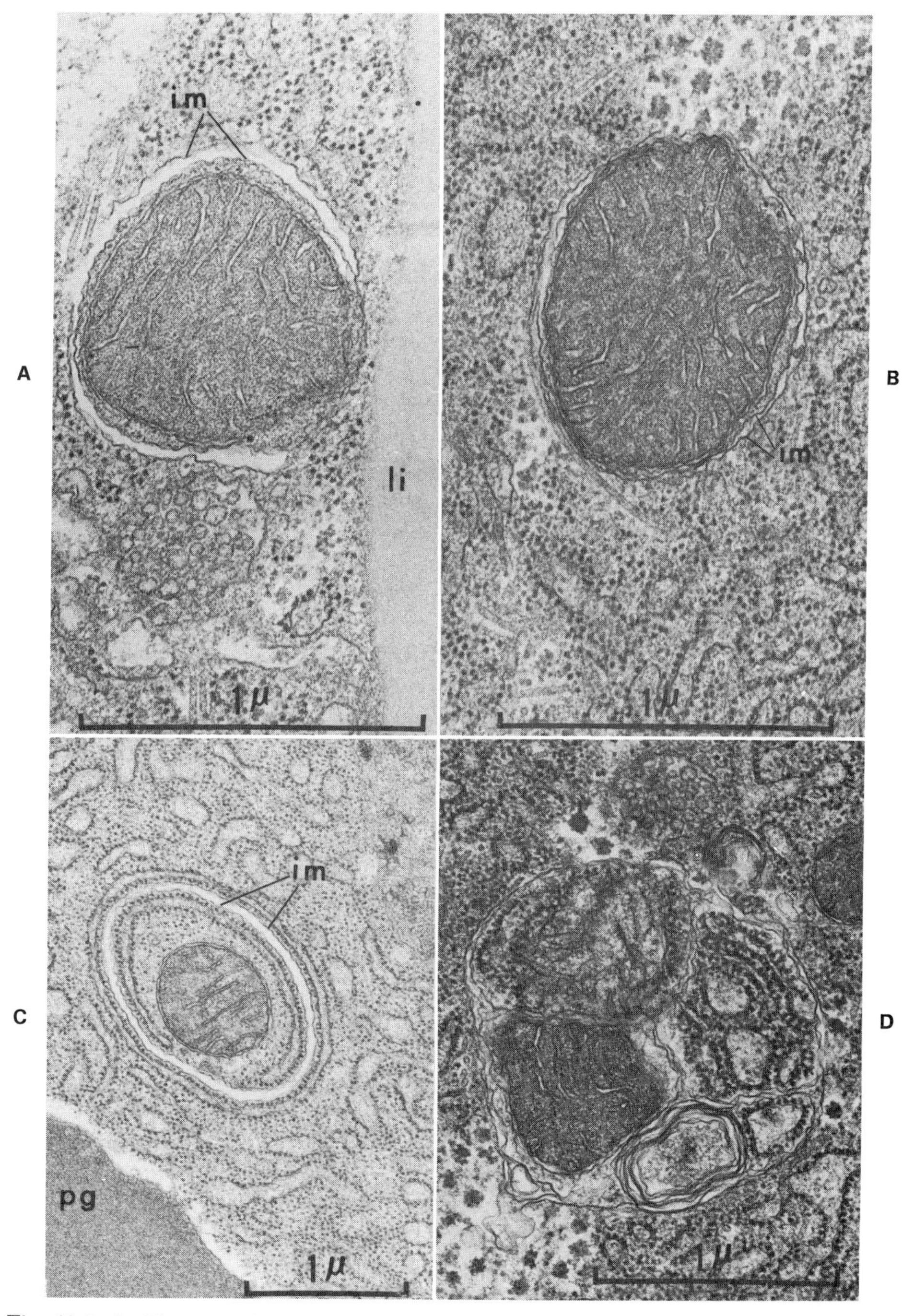

Fig. 12-8. A, Electron micrograph showing isolation membrane, **im,** which partly surrounds a mitochondrion. **li,** Lipid. **B,** Later stage in which isolation membrane has completely surrounded the mitochondrion. **C,** Electron micrograph of mixed isolation body containing a mitochondrion and ER. **pg,** Protein granule. **D,** Mixed isolation body containing three ER bodies, a mitochondrion, and a partly lysed mitochondrion. (From Locke, M., and J. V. Collins. 1965. J. Cell Biol. **26:**857-868.)

tubules appear to be linked side by side in a palisade fashion (Baudhuin, 1969).

Historically, their characterization was linked to that of the lysosome. Cell fractionation studies indicated that urate oxidase appeared to sediment along with acid phosphatase and therefore appeared to be lysosomal in origin. Later, catalase was detected (Thomson and Klipfel, 1957) as well as D-amino oxidase (Paigen, 1954). Further studies indicated that these two enzymes and urate oxidase belonged not to the lysosome but to another component that became known as peroxisomes because of the accumulation of hydrogen peroxide and its metabolism by catalase. The morphological identification came some time later (de Duve, 1965; Baudhuin et al., 1965).

Biochemistry

As far as is known, all peroxisomes contain the enzyme catalase. In addition, with few exceptions all contain D-amino acid oxidase, urate oxidase, and L-hydroxyacid oxidase. At the present time peroxisomes have been reported to contain about twenty-six different enzymes as follows.

Enzymes present in peroxisomes (glyoxysomes)*

Alanine: glyoxylate transaminase
Allantoinase
D-Amino acid oxidase
L-Amino acid oxidase
Catalase (also G)†
Enoyl-CoA hydratase
L-α-hydroxy acid oxidase
β-Hydroxyacyl-CoA dehydrogenase (NAD)
Isocitric dehydrogenase (NADP)
Glycerate dehydrogenase (NADP)
Glycolate oxidase
Glutamate: glyoxylate transaminase
Glutamate: hydroxypyruvate transaminase
Glutamate: pyruvic transaminase
Glyoxylate oxidase (also G)
Glyoxylate reductase (NADP)
Malate dehydrogenase
Urate oxidase (also G)
Xanthine dehydrogenase (NAD)

Enzymes present only in glyoxysomes

Aconitase
Acyl-CoA oxidase
Citric synthase
Crotonase
Isocitrate lyase
Glutamate oxaloacetate transaminase
Malate synthase

*Data from various authors: In J. F. Hogg and C. de Duve (editors). 1969. The nature and function of peroxisomes (microbodies, glyoxysomes). Ann. N. Y. Acad. Sci. **168**(2):209-381.
†Also present in glyoxysomes.

Function

The physiological role played by peroxisomes is difficult to assess. In Protozoa (Hogg, 1969; Muller, 1969) and in plants (Tolbert and Yamazaki, 1969) peroxisomes appear to function in gluconeogenesis. Therefore many reactions that are catalyzed by peroxisomes are for α-keto acids, which are the main components of gluconeogenesis. Additionally, it offers an accessory pathway for reoxidation of NADH by means of electron carriers such as lactate. In leaves, peroxisomes function in photorespiration and are involved in the oxidation of glycolates made photosynthetically in chloroplasts. The glyoxylate formed can be converted to serine in mitochondria and to glycerate back in the peroxisome, thus forming a type of shuttle system (Tolbert and Yamazaki, 1969). Peroxisomes from avian and amphibian livers and kidneys may play a role in the catabolism of purines (Scott et al., 1969). The presence of urate oxidase found in peroxisomes from mammalian liver appears to support this contention (de Duve and Baudhuin, 1966). Thus all the enzymes necessary for this degradation should be present. In addition, the catalase may play a role in protecting the cells against high concentrations of H_2O_2 (Baudhuin, 1969).

Glyoxysomes

Glyoxysomes (Fig. 12-9) comprise a subgroup of peroxisomes found in the endosperm of germinating seeds. They are characterized by containing the enzymes isocitrate lyase and malate synthase.

The function of glyoxysomes is glyconeogenesis. They differ from general peroxi-

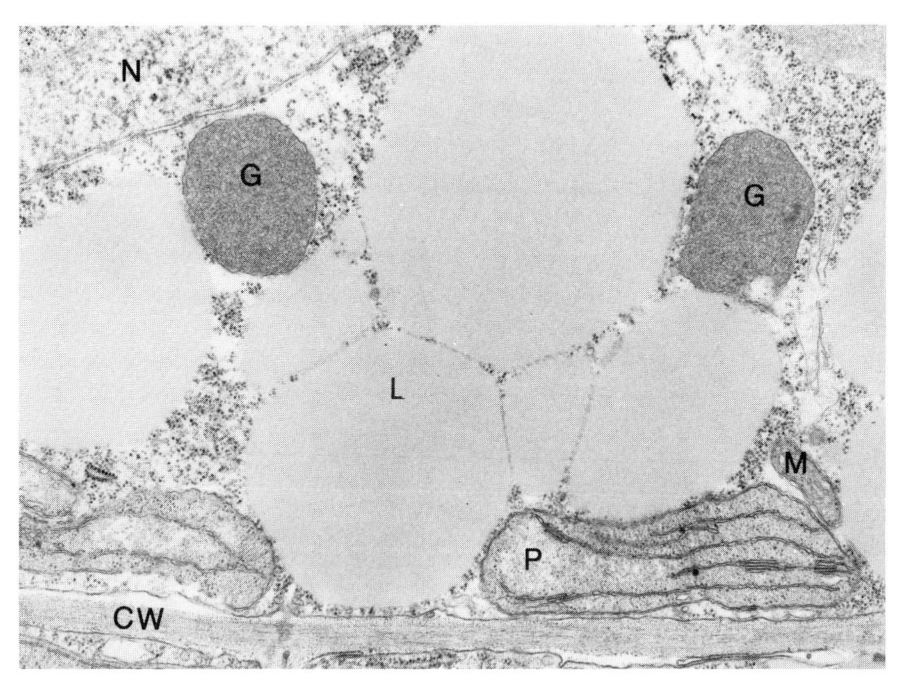

Fig. 12-9. Electron micrograph of a portion of a cotyledon cell from a 3-day-old cucumber *(Cucumis sativus)* seedling. Note the single membrane limiting the glyoxysomes, **G,** as compared to two membranes limiting the nucleus, **N,** plastids, **P,** and mitochondrion, **M.** Glyoxysomes are distributed among storage lipid bodies, **L,** as shown. **CW,** the cell wall. (Courtesy Dr. R. N. Trelease, Department of Botany-Microbiology, Arizona State University, Tempe, Ariz.)

somes in that the glyoxysome can convert triglycerides into carbohydrates. The presence of the glyoxylate cycle allows the conversion to oxaloacetate, and isocitrate lyase and malate synthase (Beevers, 1969) are the two key enzymes of the cycle. It is interesting to note that the level of these two enzymes rises from zero in ungerminated seeds to a maximum peak at the time of most rapid fat breakdown. These enzymes disappear when the process is completed.

At the present time there is little available in formation as to the origin of the peroxisome. Electron micrographs, particularly of liver tissue, show the peroxisome to be associated with the ER and, at times, in contact with it. From this information it is assumed that the peroxisome is derived from the ER.

Since the glyoxysome contains catalase, it can be considered to be a peroxisome, but the presence of the enzymes isocitrate lyase and malate synthase separates the glyoxysome from the typical peroxisome. Thus the glyoxysome considered can be a peroxisome, but the converse cannot hold; that is, a peroxisome is not a glyoxysome.

The histochemical identification of the peroxisome is the detection of catalase by 3-3′-diaminobenzidine (DAB). For the glyoxysome the presence of malate synthase is characterized by copper ferrocyanide formation (Trelease and Becker, 1972).

SPHEROSOMES

Spherosomes are small (usually 0.8 to 1 μm), spherical, cytoplasmic organelles that are abundant in many plant cells and are often the most conspicuous bodies present in the cytoplasm. They are of high refractive index (high density), flow rapidly in the cyclosis of the protoplasm, and are easily observed in brownian movement. They were first described by Hanstein in 1880 as "microsomes," but since that term is now applied to biochemical structures (pieces of rough ER in the form of vesicles), the term now accepted is "spherosomes."

Spherosomes are somewhat similar to small fat droplets (Holcomb et al., 1967), and in fact, it has been both proposed (Frey-Wyssling et al., 1963) and denied (Sorokin, 1967) that fat droplets develop from spherosomes. According to some researchers, small spherosomes first appear as membrane-bounded vesicles that bud off from the ER. They contain proteinaceous stroma, some of which is probably the enzyme acid phosphatase. This enzyme removes the phosphates from glycerol phosphate and links, through ester bonds, the glycerol to fatty acids to form lipid. According to this concept, typical spherosomes are supposed to contain within the unit membrane about 40% lipid.

In many cells that condition and size are supposed to be the end of spherosome differentiation, and as such 1 μm, highly refractive spheres they are abundantly present in many plant cells. They are easily seen in living plant cells under the optical microscope, especially with dark-field illumination, moving in the streaming protoplasm as tiny bright or dark spots smaller than mitochondria. In certain cells and tissues, however, the spherosomes are supposed to continue to synthesize lipid, enlarge, lose their protein, and become large fat droplets.

Sorokin (1967) and others, however, found that oil droplets do not have a bounding membrane and that spherosomes do not become oil droplets, that they never find intermediate conditions, that spherosomes and fat droplets react differently to stains, and that they do not contain neutral fat. Spherosomes never are found much larger or smaller than about 0.8 to 1 μm, whereas oil droplets range from the limit of optical microscopic resolution to as much as 150 μm. Walek-Czernecka (1965) found several hydrolytic enzymes in spherosomes, as have others (Holcomb et al., 1967), and concluded that they are probably involved in processes of intracellular hydrolysis but not in fat synthesis. At present it is not known whether triglycerides are formed by spherosomes or mitochondria.

Contents of hydrolytic enzymes such as acid phosphatase, acid ribonuclease, acid protease, and nonspecific esterase would seem to relate spherosomes to lysosomes (Matile et al., 1965).

LITERATURE CITED

Allison, A. 1967. Lysosomes and disease. Sci. Amer. **217:**62-72.

Applemans, F., R. Wattiaux, and C. de Duve. 1955. Tissue fractionation studies. V. The association of acid phosphatase with a special class of cytoplasmic granules in rat liver. Biochem. J. **59:**438-448.

Ashford, T. P., and K. R. Porter. 1962. Cytoplasmic components in hepatic cell lysosomes. J. Cell Biol. **12:**198-202.

Baudhuin, P. 1969. Liver peroxisomes, cytology and function. In The nature and function of peroxisomes (microbodies, glyoxysomes). Ann. N. Y. Acad. Sci. **168:**214-228.

Beams, H. W., and E. Anderson. 1960. Fine structure of the so-called segregation apparatus in the erythrocytes of Necturus. Exp. Cell Res. **20:**604-607.

Becker, N. H., and U. Sandbank. 1964. Neuronal Golgi apparatus and lysosomes in neonatal rats. J. Histochem. Cytochem. **12:**483-485.

Beevers, H. 1969. Glyoxysomes of caster bean endosperm and their relation to gluconeogenesis. In D. E. Green (editor). The nature and function of peroxisomes (microbodies, glyoxysomes). Ann. N. Y. Acad. Sci. **168:**313-324.

Berthet, J., and C. de Duve. 1951. Tissue fractionation studies. I. The existence of a mitochondrial linked enzymatically inactive form of acid phosphatase in rat liver tissue. Biochem. J. **50:**174-181.

Brandes, D. 1965. Observation on the apparent mode of formation of "pure" lysosomes. J. Ultrastruct. Res. **12:**63-80.

Chantrenne, H. 1947. Hétérogénéité des granules due foie de souris. Biochim. Biophys. Acta **1:** 437-448.

Clark, S. L. 1957. Cellular differentiation on the kidneys of newborn mice studied with the electron microscope. J. Biophys. Biochem. Cytol. **3:**349-360.

Canonico, P. G., and J. W. C. Bird. 1970. Lysosomes in skeletal muscle tissue: zone centrifugation evidence for multiple cellular source. J. Cell Biol. **45**:321-333.

de Duve, C. 1958. Lysosomes, a new group of cytoplasmic particles. In T. Hayashi (editor). Sub-cellular particles. The Ronald Press Co., New York.

de Duve, C. 1959. The function of intracellular hydrolases. Exp. Cell Res. **7**(supp.):169-182.

de Duve, C. 1963. The lysosome. Sci. Amer. **208:** 64-72.

de Duve, C. 1965. The function of microbodies (peroxisomes). J. Cell Biol. **27**:25A-26A.

de Duve, C., and Berthet, J. 1953. Reproducibility of differential centrifugation experiments in tissue fraction. Nature (London) **172**:1142.

de Duve, C., and P. Baudhuin. 1966. Peroxisomes (microbodies and related particles). Physiol. Rev. **46**:323-357.

de Duve, C., B. C. Presman, R. Gianetto, R. Wattiaux, and F. Applemans, 1955. Tissue fractionation studies. VI. Intracellular distribution patterns of enzymes in rat liver tissue. Biochem. J. **60**:604-617.

Essner, E., and A. B. Novikoff. 1960a. Acid phosphatase activity in hepatic lysosomes: electron microscopic demonstration of its reaction product. J. Histochem. Cytochem. **8**:318.

Essner, E., and A. B. Novikoff. 1960b. Human hepatocellular pigments and lysosomes. J. Ultrastruct. Res. **3**:374-391.

Essner, E., and A. B. Novikoff. 1962. Cytological studies on two functional hepatomas: interrelations of endoplasmic reticulum, Golgi apparatus, and lysosomes. J. Cell Biol. **15**:289-312.

Frey-Wyssling, A., E. Grieshaber, and K. Mühlethaler. 1963. Origin of spherosomes in plant cells. J. Ultrastruct. Res. **8**:506-516.

Gianetto, R., and C. de Duve. 1955. Tissue fraction studies. IV. Comparative study of the binding of acid phosphatase, β-glucuronidase, and cathepsin by rat liver tissue. Biochem. J. **59:** 433-438.

Hogg, J. F. 1969. Peroxisomes in Tetrahymena and their relation to gluconeogenesis. In J. F. Hogg and C. de Duve (editors). The nature and function of peroxisomes (microbodies, glyoxysomes). Ann. N. Y. Acad. Sci. **168**:281-291.

Holcomb, G. E., A. C. Hildebrandt, and R. F. Evert. 1967. Staining and acid phosphatase reactions of spherosomes in plant tissue culture cells. Amer. J. Bot. **54**:1204-1209.

Koenig, H. 1962. Histological distribution of brain gangliosides: lysosomes as glycoprotein granules. Nature (London) **195**:782-784.

Koenig, H. 1965. Intravital staining of lysosomes and mast cell granules by tetrazolium salts. J. Histochem. Cytochem. **13**:411-413.

Locke, M. 1966. Isolation membranes in insect cells at metamorphosis. J. Cell. Biol. **31**:132A.

Locke, M., and J. V. Collins. 1965. The structure and formation of protein granules in the fat body of an insect. J. Cell Biol. **26**:857-868.

Matile, P., P. P. Balz, E. Semadeni, and M. Jost. 1965. Isolation of spherosomes with lysosome characteristics from seedlings. Z. Naturforsch. **20b**:693-698.

Moe, H. J., J. Rostgaard, and O. Behnke. 1965. On the morphology and origin of virgin lysosomes in the intestinal epithelium of the rat. J. Ultrastruct. Res. **12**:396-403.

Muller, M. 1969. Peroxisomes of Protozoa. In D. E. Green (editor). The nature and function of peroxisomes (microbodies, glyoxysomes). Ann. N. Y. Acad. Sci. **168**:292-301.

Napolitano, L. 1963. Cytolysomes in metabolically active cells. J. Cell Biol. **18**:478-480.

Novikoff, A. B., and E. Essner. 1962. Cytolysomes and mitochondrial degeneration. J. Cell Biol. **15**:140-146.

Ogawa, K., N. Mizuno, and M. Okamoto. 1961. Lysosomes in cultured cells. J. Histochem. Cytochem. **9**:202.

Paigen, K. 1954. The occurrence of several biochemically distinct types of mitochondria in rat liver. J. Biol. Chem. **206**:945-957.

Scott, P. J., L. P. Visentin, and J. M. Allen. 1969. The enzymatic characterization of peroxisomes of amphibian and avian liver and kidney. In J. F. Hogg and C. de Duve (editors). The nature and function of peroxisomes (microbodies, glyoxysomes). Ann. N. Y. Acad. Sci. **168**:244-264.

Sorokin, H. P. 1967. The spherosomes and the reserve fat in plant cells. Amer. J. Bot. **54**:1008-1016.

Straus, W. 1964. Factors affecting the state of injected horseradish peroxidase in animal tissues and procedures for the study of phagosomes and phago-lysosomes. J. Histochem. Cytochem. **12**:470-480.

Thomson, J. F., and F. J. Klipfel. 1957. Further studies on cytoplasmic particles isolated by gradient centrifugation. Arch. Biochem. **70:** 224-238.

Tolbert, N. E., and R. K. Yamazaki. 1969. Leaf peroxisomes and their relation to photorespiration and photosynthesis. In J. F. Hogg and C. de Duve (editors). The nature and function of peroxisomes (microbodies, glyoxysomes). Ann. N. Y. Acad. Sci. **168**:325-341.

Tooze, J., and H. G. Davies. 1965. Cytolysomes

in amphibian erythrocytes. J. Cell Biol. **24:**146-150.

Trelease, R. N., and W. M. Becker. 1972. Cytochemical localization of malate synthase in glyoxysomes. J. Cell Biol. **55:**262A.

Walek-Czernecka, A. 1965. Histochemical demonstration of some hydrolytic enzymes in the spherosomes of plant cells. Acta Soc. Bot. Poloniae **34:**573-598.

Wattiaux, R., P. Baundhuin, A. M. Berliner, and C. de Duve. 1956. Tissue fraction studies. VIII. Cellular localization of bound enzymes. Biochem. J. **63:**608-612.

Weber, R. 1957. On the biological function of cathepsin in tail tissues of Xenopus larvae. Experientia **13:**153-155.

GENERAL REFERENCES

Baudhuin, P., H. Beaufay, and C. de Duve. 1965. Combined biochemical and morphological study of particulate fractions from rat liver. J. Cell Biol. **26:**219-243.

Berthet, J., L. Berthet, F. Applemans, and C. de Duve. 1961. Tissue fractionation studies. II. The nature of the linkage between acid phosphatase and mitochondria in rat liver tissue. Biochem. J. **50:**182-189.

Diengdoh, J. V. 1964. The demonstration of lysosomes in muscle and skin. Quart. J. Micr. Sci. **195:**73-78.

Gordis, L., and H. M. Nitowsky. 1965. Lysosomes in human cell culture: kinetics of enzyme release from injured particles. Exp. Cell Res. **38:**556-569.

Kerr, D. N. S., and A. R. Muir. 1960. A demonstration of the structure and disposition of ferritin in the human liver cell. J. Ultrastruct. Res. **3:**313-319.

Misch, D. W. 1965. The penetration of lysosomes by dimethyl-sulfoxide. J. Cell Biol. **27:**67A.

Reuck, A. V. S., and M. P. Cameron. 1963. Lysosomes. Ciba Foundation Symposium. Little, Brown & Co., Boston.

Wattiaux, R., and C. de Duve. 1956. Tissue fractionation studies. VII. Release of bound hydrolases by means of Triton X-100. Biochem. J. **63:**606-608.

CHAPTER 13

Cilia and flagella

Cilia and flagella (Chapters 14 and 19) are fine hairlike structures found on the free surfaces of many types of cells (Figs. 13-1 and 13-2). Their function is the creation of relative movement of fluid or the cell. If the cell or organism possessing cilia or flagella is small and free, the movement of these organelles produces locomotion of the organism through the liquid environment. On the other hand, if the cells are stationary, such as those of the epithelial lining of the human trachea or the gills of a clam, ciliary and flagellary action causes movement of fluids over the cell surfaces. The differences between cilia and flagella are trivial; both show similar ultrastructure. However, from a purely morphological view some distinctions can be made. In general, cilia are smaller in diameter and considerably shorter than flagella. However, in some ciliates cilia can be compounded to produce ciliary structures much thicker and longer than flagella. Another distinction between cilia and flagella is that generally cilia are more numerous than flagella, often hundreds per cell. However, several Protozoa, for example, *Polymastigina,* contain a large number of flagella, and several ciliates contain only a small number of cilia.

Functionally, at the midpoint of the beat of a cilium, movement of fluid is at right angles to the long axes of the cilium. The flagellum, on the other hand, produces a movement more or less along the flagellar axis.

Cilia and flagella are widely distributed in the animal kingdom and algae. In Protozoa they occur typically in two large classes—the Ciliata and Flagellata. In the multicellular animals, the Metazoa, they serve a wide range of functions, participating in locomotion, digestion, excretion, respiration, circulation, and reproduction, as well as being receptors for several sensory systems in modified form. In addition to serving as locomotary structures in the Protozoa they also act as organs of locomotion in some of the Platyhelminthes, annelids, some molluscs, and some primitive chordates. In Ctenophora, Aschelminthes, some annelids, and Echinodermata they serve or participate in digestion; these organelles aid in the transport of food through the digestive tract. They function in excretion in many of the invertebrate animals. In Platyhelminthes, for example, flagella are present in flame cells; in Annelida, cilia are present surrounding the nephrostome. Celomic circulation is mediated by ciliary structures in some Annelida, Echinodermata, and some forms of Mollusca. In some vertebrates the presence of cilia in the ventricles of the central nervous system no doubt contributes to the circulation of the cerebrospinal fluid. In vertebrates, cilia line the respiratory system, where they serve as

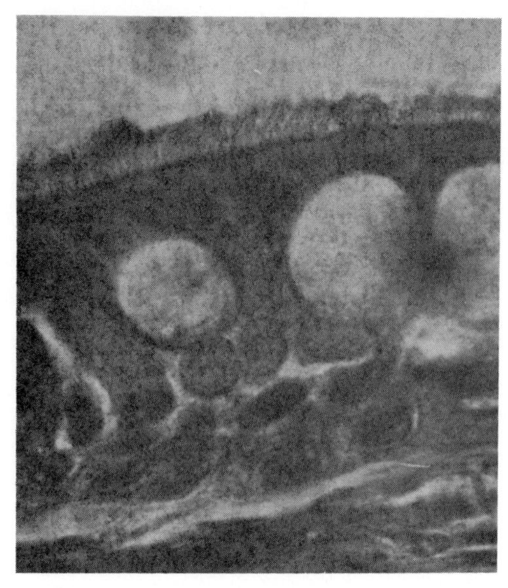

Fig. 13-1. Photomicrograph of ciliated epithelium from larynx of rat. There are many cilia on the free (upper) surface of each cell.

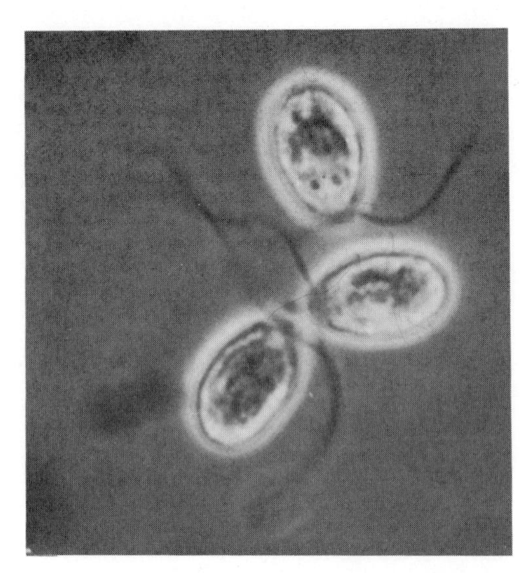

Fig. 13-2. Two living paired gametes (and a third party) of the unicellular alga *Chlamydomonas moewusii* photographed under strobe light with phase contrast. It shows the two flagella of each organism and the use of flagella as copulatory organs. The first act of gametic union is the pairing of flagella evident here. (Courtesy Dr. R. M. Brown, Dr. H. C. Bold, and Dr. C. Johnson, University of Texas Cell Research Institute, Austin, Texas.)

a protective mechanism by eliminating foreign materials that may have been inhaled and by beating liquids upward away from the lungs. Cilia are also present in the sinus cavities and in the reproductive system. In the female they line the oviducts and participated in the movement of the ovum. With few exceptions the male gametes are flagellated throughout the animal kingdom. There is also evidence that cilia may be present in the hypophysis (Rivera, 1962). Cilia have also been found in the fetal esophagus of human beings, but they disappear during subsequent development. The tails of most sperm are modified flagella.

The cilia mentioned so far are motile; yet some specialized types are nonmotile. Those found on the free surfaces of the cells of the epididymis are nonmotile, as are those having sensory function such as the cilia found in the organ of Corti, the organs involved in equilibrium, the photosensitive elements of the retina, the pineal body of lower chordates, and the electric organ.

Cilia and flagella are not limited to the animal kingdom, however, but are also found in the plant and fungal kingdoms. They serve as organs of locomotion and copulation in many small algae and fungi (Fig. 13-2) as well as performing functions of a sensory nature. As in the case of animals, flagella serve and propel the male gametes in the algae and some fungi as well as in the lower vascular plants (Chapters 14 and 19).

Structure

Examination of ciliary structures by means of the light microscope long ago demonstrated the ciliary apparatus to be composed of (1) the shaft, (2) the basal body, and (3) the rootlets. In many plants and Protozoa, electron microscopy has revealed an associated system of microtubules.

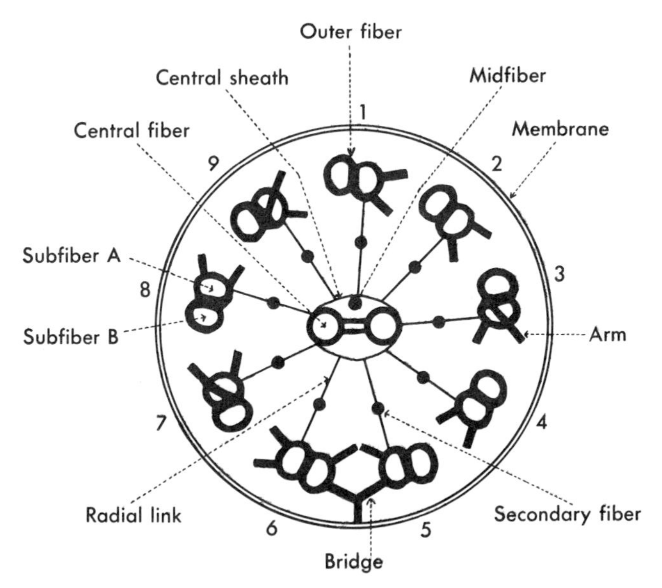

Fig. 13-3. Diagrammatic cross section of cilium shaft. (From Gibbons, I. R. 1961. J. Biophys. Biochem. Cytol. **11:**179-204.)

Shaft. The shaft is a fine protoplasmic projection from the free surface of the cell. It is of uniform diameter throughout its length but tapers near the distal end. Its thickness varies from about 0.15 to 0.3 μm, which is at or close to the limit of resolution of the light microscope. The length of the cilium varies from about 5 μm in man to about 12 μm in *Paramecium* (Sedar and Porter, 1955). The flagellum is similar to the cilium in width, but its length ranges from about 55 μm in the sperm tail of the genus *Homo* (Sleigh, 1962) to about 3,000 μm in the comb plate of the genus *Mneniopsis*. Because of the extreme thinness of these structures (at the limit of resolution of the light microscope), the cilium and flagellum were regarded as internally structureless on the basis of light microscopy observations. Some observations, however, did indicate that internal structures may be present.

Although evidence was available from light microscopic studies of the possible presence of fibrils in cilia and flagella, it was not until the development of the electron microscope that the fine structure was definitely established and characterized. Numerous studies of the ultrastructure of these organelles, from both plants and animals, have shown that cilia and flagella are constructed on a common plan. This minimum basic fibrillar shaft pattern consists of the plasma membrane, cytoplasmic matrix, and an axoneme composed of eleven longitudinal fibrils arranged in an outer ring of nine with two in the center.

Axoneme. Studies (Gibbons and Grimstone, 1960; Gibbons, 1961) show that the fibrils of the axoneme run longitudinally the length of the shaft. Generally the two central fibrils end basally before reaching the basal body; the remaining nine continue downward into the basal body. Cross-sectional studies show that two of the eleven fibrils (or fibers) are central and nine are arranged peripherally in a circular arrangement about the central pair (Figs. 13-3 and 14-2). The two central fibrils are circular in cross section and average about 240 Å in diameter. They are parallel and about 300 Å apart, which is their center-to-center spacing. These central fibrils have an electron-dense outer region about 45 Å thick and a central region of less dense material. The two central fibrils may be enclosed by a *central sheath* which appears to arise from each fiber, curving around to join the other. Longitudinal sections indicate that this sheath appears as slanting lines that run across the fibers. It was suggested that this central sheath may consist of one or several extremely thin filaments coiled around the central pair of fibers. The two central fibers are now considered examples of somewhat modified microtubules.

The nine outer fibers are each composed of two subfibers, each of which is a microtubule. Each outer fiber is a doublet measuring about 300 to 350 Å in diameter and lies about 250 Å in from the sheath membrane. As in the case of the central fibrils, the nine peripheral fibrils are composed of a circular electron-dense region about 45 Å thick. It has been shown that the plane determined by the two longitudinal axes of each doublet is oriented from 5 to 10 degrees to the tangent of the axoneme. This would then place one of the subfibers of the doublet closer to the center than the other.

In many cilia and flagella two short extensions called *arms* arise from one of the subfibers of each of the nine peripheral doublets. Each arm is about 50 Å thick and 150 Å long. They are pointed in the same directions on all fibers in a clockwise direction. Gibbons and Grimstone called the subfiber containing the projections or arms *subfiber A,* and the other subfiber of the doublet they called *subfiber B.* Subfiber A is somewhat more dense than subfiber B, is slightly smaller, and lies closer to the center. In the gill cilia of the lamellibranch Mollusca, Gibbons (1961) observed that two of the outer fibers are joined by a bridge that results when arms from subfiber B, which in these cilia does have two arms, meet the adjacent A subfibers. Occasionally, a link exists between the center of the bridge to the ciliary membrane (Fig. 13-3).

In longitudinal section the arms have a rectangular aspect, measuring about 150 Å long and 50 Å thick. The center-to-center spacing is approximately 130 Å.

Longitudinal sections through the central fibers indicate the presence of additional substructural arrangements (Gibbons and Grimstone, 1960) (Fig. 13-4). Electron micrographs show what appear to be cross striations running obliquely along the width of these fibers. These diagonal striations suggest the possibility that the central fibers may consist of coiled filaments that form a helical configuration. The periodicity of the substructure is about 130 Å. Later studies in which negative staining

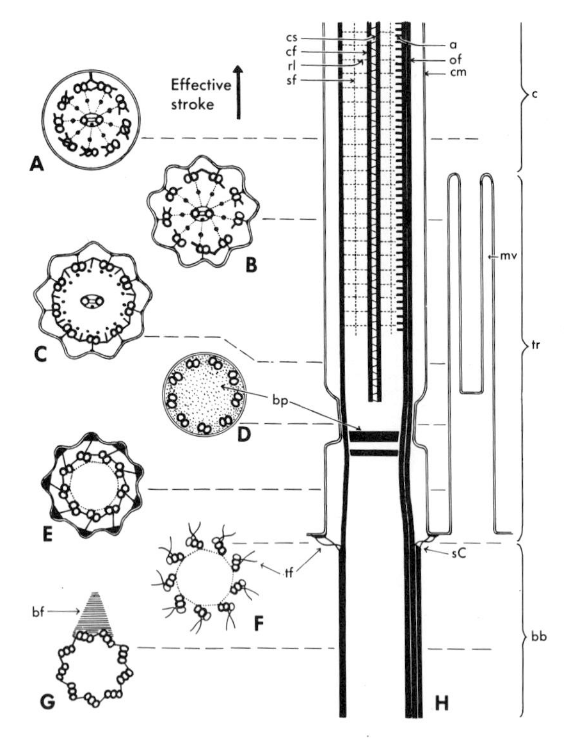

Fig. 13-4. Reconstruction of flagellum and basal body from the protozoan *Pseudotrichonympha.* These are transverse sections at the various levels indicated. **a,** Arms; **bp,** basal plate; **cf,** central fiber; **cm,** cell membrane; **of,** outer fiber; **p,** proximal region of basal body; **bb,** basal body; **tr,** transition region; **c,** cilium; **mv,** microvillus. (From Gibbons, I. R., and A. V. Grimstone. 1960. J. Biophys. Biochem. Cytol. **11:**179-204.)

Fig. 13-5. Electron micrograph of group of outer fibers of flagella from the protozoan *Trichonympha.* Negative staining shows them to be composed of several longitudinal filaments, presumably microtubules. Also note beaded appearance of these filaments. (From Grimstone, A. V., and A. Klug. 1966. J. Cell Sci. **1**:351-362.)

techniques were employed have shown that the flagellar fibers of at least some species appear to be composed of a number of short, longitudinally oriented subfilaments that form the walls of the hollow fibers (Grimstone and Klug, 1966), additional evidence of their microtubular nature. These longitudinally oriented filaments have a center-to-center spacing of about 40 to 50 Å and appear to have heads (Figs. 13-5 and 14-3). The heads of subunits give rise to an axial repeat along the filament of 40 Å and a basic lattice of 40 to 50 Å. Additional longitudinal periodicities were also observed, appearing as 80 and 160 Å repeats. These long spacings are believed to arise as departures in the arrangement of the subunits, perhaps similar to the repeats of collagen.

Another concept of flagellar fibers is that the walls are composed of rings of about thirteen globular proteins (Figs. 14-2 and 14-3) rather than longitudinal or spiral fibers.

A third set of fibers called secondary fibrils (Fig. 13-3) can also be seen in cilia and flagella. There are nine secondary fibrils that appear as dots, lines, or additional microtubules. They are located between the central fibers and each of the outer fibers, usually closer to subfiber A than to subfiber B. These secondary fibers are about 50 Å wide. In longitudinal sections each appears as a rather sinuous line. In addition, lines of lesser density that represent radial links from the secondary fibrils to the outer fibers and from the secondary fiber to the central sheath are sometimes visible (Gibbons, 1961).

In addition to the fibrils just described, cilia from the lamellibranch Mollusca (Gibbons, 1961) show a dense dot of about the same diameter as the secondary fibrils located just inside the central sheath. This structure is referred to as the *midfiber* (Fig. 13-3). In addition, a pair of dense lines bridge the space between the two central fibers. Unfortunately, longitudinal sections do not show these structures sufficiently for identification.

It is evident that cilia and flagella from different species and from different kinds of cells vary considerably with respect to these secondary structures of the shaft. They all have in common, however, the primary 9 + 2 fiber plan of the axoneme.

The shaft of the cilium and flagellum is bounded by a plasma membrane that is continuous with the plasma membrane of the cell. It appears as a trilaminar membrane about 90 Å thick.

From the evidence obtained it is presumed that the fibers of the axoneme somehow are bound or linked together because they retain their relative position with respect to one another.

Fig. 13-6. Electron micrograph of cross sections of many cilia from celomic lining of *Tomopteris* showing numerous cilia (arrows) with an extra filament. Its pattern is 1 + 9 + 2. (From Afzelius, B. 1963. J. Ultrastruct. Res. **9:**381-392.)

Near the tip of a cilium or flagellum the arms and secondary fibers begin to drop out, and the outer fibers approach one another. At about this same level the paired central fibers seem to lose their central position. More distally, the doublets of the outer fibers become single and finally terminate near the tip.

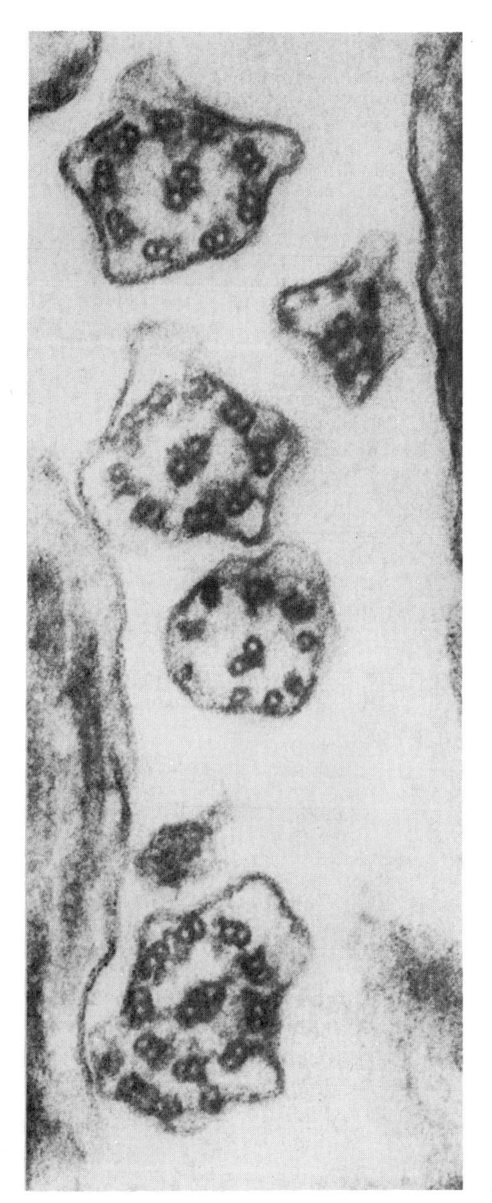

Fig. 13-7. Cilia from gills of the mussel *Mytilus edulus.* Cilium at bottom shows supernumerary filaments, whereas the smaller profile just above shows a reduced number. The latter is probably a section near the distal tip. (From Afzelius, B. 1963. J. Ultrastruct. Res. **9:**381-392.)

Abnormal forms may often be seen within a population of cilia or flagella. They may show supernumerary peripheral filaments (Figs. 13-6 and 13-7), supernumerary central filaments, or reduced peripheral filaments (Fig. 13-7) or lack central filaments. Thus the following abnormal patterns can be observed: 1 + 9 + 2, 2 + 9 + 2, 2 + 9 + 2, 5 + 8 + 2, 6 + 2, 7 + 0, 9 + 4, and 10 + 4 (Afzelius, 1963). Since these descriptions were obtained from cross sections, it is not known whether the accompanying basal body is also changed or is normal.

Basal body. At the base of the shaft of a cilium or flagellum but within the cell itself is the basal body (Chapters 14 and 19). This structure is called the *kinetosome* by protozoologists or the *blepharoplast* by some phycologists. In light microscope sections basal bodies have been variously described as being roughly spherical or short rod-shaped structures located just beneath the cell surface. In electron micrographs (Figs. 13-4 and 17-2) these structures vary from 120 to 170 nm in diameter (a few may be as wide as 250 nm, Sleigh, 1961) and from 200 to 500 nm or much more in length. They have an electron-dense periphery formed by the nine outer fibers (Gibbons and Grimstone, 1960) that surrounds an electron-lucent center. In most cases this central cavity contains homogeneous material. In others small osmiophilic granules called *intrablepharoplastic granules* have been described as well as axial granules that are formed by the termination of the central pair of fibers at the level of the *basal plate* (Noirot-Timothee, 1958).

In basal bodies each of the nine outer fibers appears triple instead of double, as seen in the flagellar shafts (Fig. 13-4). The axes of the triplets are inclined more tangentially, but in the same direction as the shaft doublets, to the extent of 30 to 50 degrees, thus forming a "pinwheel" pattern (Figs. 13-4, *F* and *G*) (Gibbons and Grimstone, 1960). The innermost fiber of the triplet corresponds to subfiber A, the middle fiber is B, and the outermost fiber is C. The last does not extend into the flagellar shaft.

In ciliates the basal bodies are cylindrical structures in which the top, the *distal end,* is enclosed by the basal plate and the bottom, the *proximal end,* is open to the cytoplasm. In multicellular forms the structure is essentially similar except that a second plate that "closes" the lower end may be present. Various curvatures and external processes are present among species and tissues that are characteristic; they are tissue or species specific. For example, in the intestinal epithelia of the freshwater mussel a knoblike process of about 100 nm projects backward toward the next basal body in the same row. In the amphibian the upper or distal portion is cylindrical, but the lower or proximal portion has a blunt tip that curves backward and is parallel to the free surface (Fawcett and Porter, 1954). Additional modifications are mentioned in Chapter 19; see also Fig. 14-5.

Rootlets. Additional structures that extend into the cytoplasm often arise from the basal body. These elongate, radiating fibers, called *rootlets,* are found in many ciliary structures. Functionally, they serve to anchor and provide mechanical support for the basal body and cilium. One or more rootlets may arise from the proximal end of the basal body. According to the numerous studies made, the number of rootlets is constant in a species or tissue. Microtubular and other systems are often present in flagellated plant cells (Chapter 19).

Specialized cilia and flagella

In the preceding discussion it was noted that cilia and flagella have essentially the same structural arrangement. They all possess a basal body and shaft, and the structural arrangement of the axoneme of the shaft is the 9 + 2 fibril plan. Some motile cilia and flagella, although still maintaining a 9 + 2 plan, may have additional fibrous components located along the periphery of the eleven longitudinal fibers. Other motile forms may develop specialization along the surface of the flagellum. It is these modifications that may alter the movement of the organelles and increase their efficiency during activity. Such modifications are especially common in sperm tails (Chapter 19).

On the other hand, flagella that are nonmotile may be modified in such a way that there is either loss of the two axial fibers or extensive modification of them.

Motile forms. In several flagellates such as the chrysomonads the flagella contain lateral hairlike processes known as *mastigonemes* when viewed with a light microscope (Fig. 13-8). These structures appear as fine uniform projections at right angles from the shaft. At times mastigonemes near the distal end may become somewhat shorter and the angle more acute, the angle be-

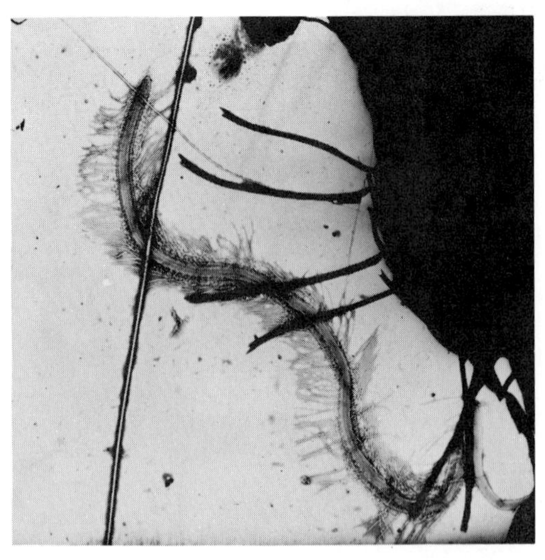

Fig. 13-8. Negatively stained flimmer flagellum of *Mallomonopsis paxillata* showing hairlike structures (mastigonemes) along the flagellar shaft. (From Bradley, D. E. 1966. Exp. Cell Res. **41:** 162-173.)

ing directed toward the free tip. Bradley (1966), using a negative staining technique, studied the "flimmer" flagella of *Mallomonopsis paxillata* (a chrysomonad). The mastigonemes of this species appeared to be composed of loosely wound helices extending along the length and penetrating the flagellar membrane to join the axoneme (Fig. 13-9). Each mastigoneme is a tube about 80 Å in diameter with an external spirally wound layer, making a total thickness of 400 Å. At the tips are five filaments about 40 Å in diameter. The relationship between the mastigonemes and the shaft is elusive. They may be branches of the flagellar fibers, or they may be attached to them.

In addition to the mastigonemes, Bradley (1966) also observed scales along the flagellar surface (Fig. 13-10). These scales were flat and annular in form, having a diameter of about 1,350 Å with a 500 Å "hole" in the center.

Specializations of various types have been observed in the flagella of sperm, including mammalian sperm (Randall and Friedlander, 1950). For example, while retaining the 9 + 2 fibrillar arrangement of typical flagella, the tails of mammalian sperm also have a *fibrous sheath,* or cortical helix, that consists of a helical fiber or fibers tightly wound about the periphery of the axoneme of the flagellum (Fig. 13-11).

Fig. 13-9. Higher magnification of mastigonemes shown in Fig. 13-8. Note penetration of mastigonemes into shaft of flagellum to join the axoneme. (From Bradley, D. E. 1966. Exp. Cell Res. **41:**162-173.)

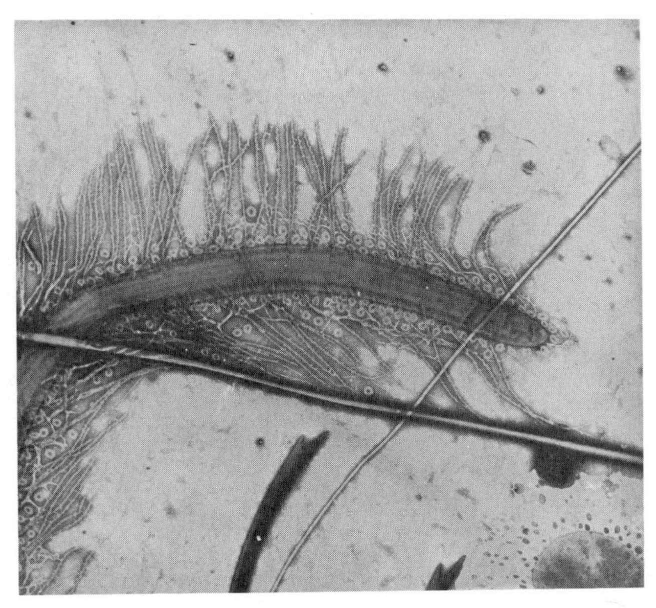

Fig. 13-10. Higher magnification of mastigonemes shown in Figs. 13-8 and 13-9. Note scales associated with flagellum. These scales have a diameter of 1,350 Å with a 500 Å "hole." Also note presence of fine terminal fibril at the ends of the mastigonemes. (From Bradley, D. E. 1966. Exp. Cell Res. **41**:162-173.)

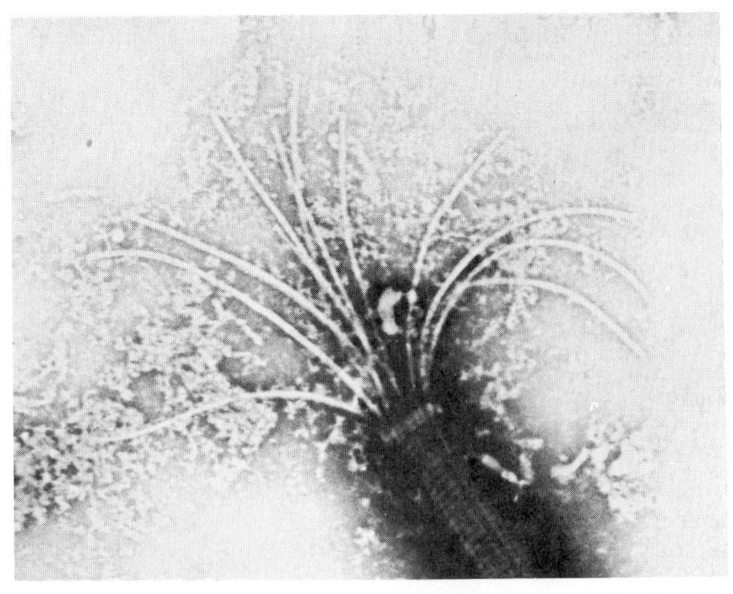

Fig. 13-11. Negatively stained flagellum of sperm cell from Sundervall's (Natal) gartersnake *(Elapsoidea sundervallii)*. At distal end of flagellum the eleven flagellar fibers lie free. Note helical spiral around axoneme. (Courtesy Dr. M. J. Fouquette, Department of Zoology, Arizona State University, Tempe, Ariz.)

In the kinocilia of sensory cells found in the inner ear and fish lateral line system there are three arms attached to the outer fibers of the cilium. Two of the arms are positioned clockwise, as found in other cilia, but the third arm is directed radially toward the ciliary membrane (Flock and DuVall, 1966).

Undulating membranes also illustrate a modification of flagella in which a membrane extends out from the side of the body, and an axoneme borders the outer margin. The axoneme, or *axial filament,* is composed of nine peripheral fibers and two central fibers. When the membrane vibrates, it shows a characteristic undulating movement. Undulation membranes are found in the tails of sperm of amphibians and in a number of protozoan flagellates as, for example, in the parasitic Mastigophora such as *Trypanosoma* and *Trichomonas.*

The "flagella" of bacteria, although they do not represent modified flagella, are certainly of simpler structure and possibly a more primitive form. *Bacterial flagella* (Figs. 4-8 and 13-12) have been described as simple filaments of the protein flagellin (Emerson et al., 1970). Starr and Williams (1952) observed the flagellar structure of a motile diphtheroid as being composed of

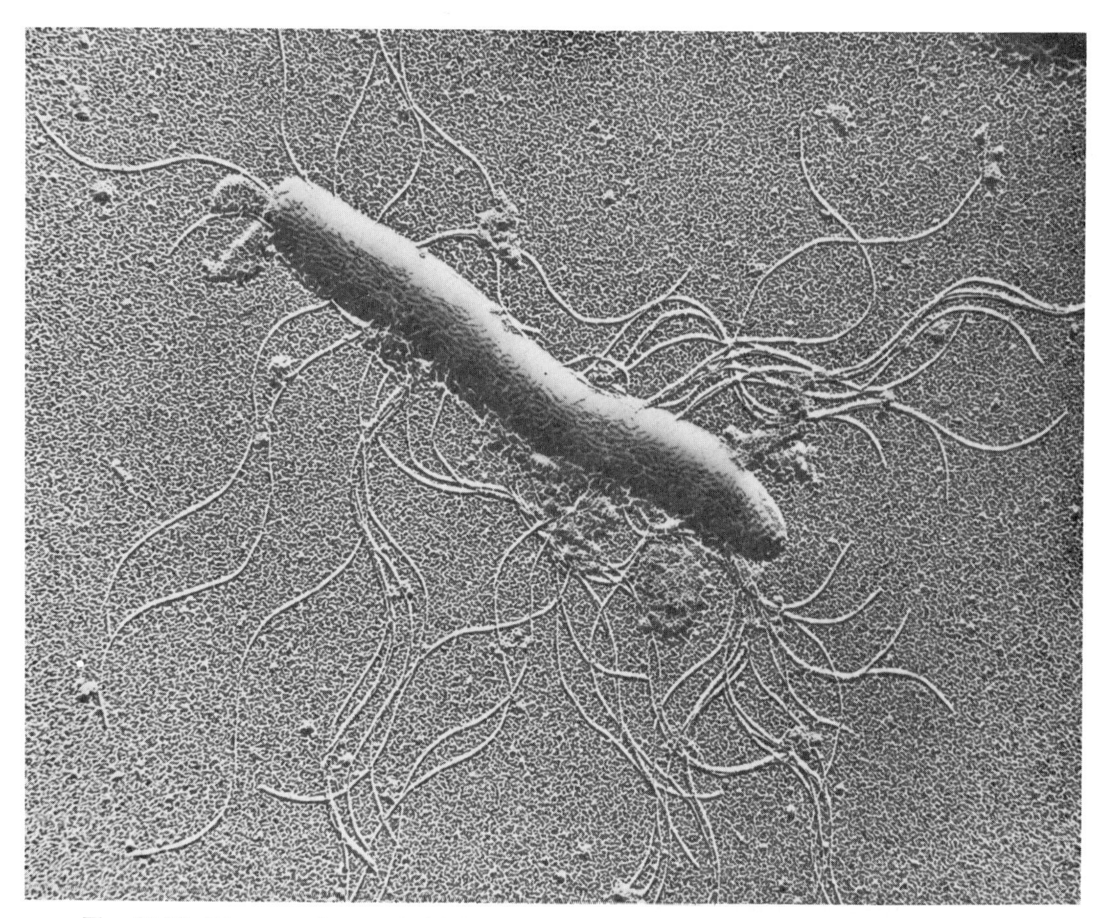

Fig. 13-12. Electron micrograph of flagellated *Bacillus.* This specimen was shadowed with gold. Bacterial flagella are obvious. (Courtesy Dr. J. Swafford, Laboratory of Electron Microscopy, Arizona State University, Tempe, Ariz.)

a helical structure that has the form of a triple-thread screw. The direction of the helical turns are most often that of a left-handed screw. The period or the distance for one complete turn is constant throughout the flagellum. The flagella apparently grow by polymerization of flagellin at the tip, not at the cell surface (Emerson et al., 1970).

Nonmotile forms. Most of the nonmotile cilia are sensory in nature. The olfactory sinus cilia from frogs may be 200 μm long and arise from bipolar neurons. At the base the cilium shows the typical 9 + 2 arrangement with double peripheral fibers, but distally, toward the tip, there are only single fibers. In this transition there is loss of fibers: the doublets become singlets and the loss of one central fiber occurs. This loss is accompanied by a decrease in diameter. The axial fibers end just short of the tip. A number of vesicles arise along the length of the shaft. From a functional point of view it is proposed that these ciliary structures are loci where electrical excitation in the olfactory organ is initiated by contact with an odorous substance (Reese, 1965).

Electron microscopic studies of rods and cones from the eyes of vertebrates show that each of these is composed of two segments (Sjöstrand, 1953a,b). The *outer segment* is connected to the *inner segment* by a slender stalk. This stalk contains nine

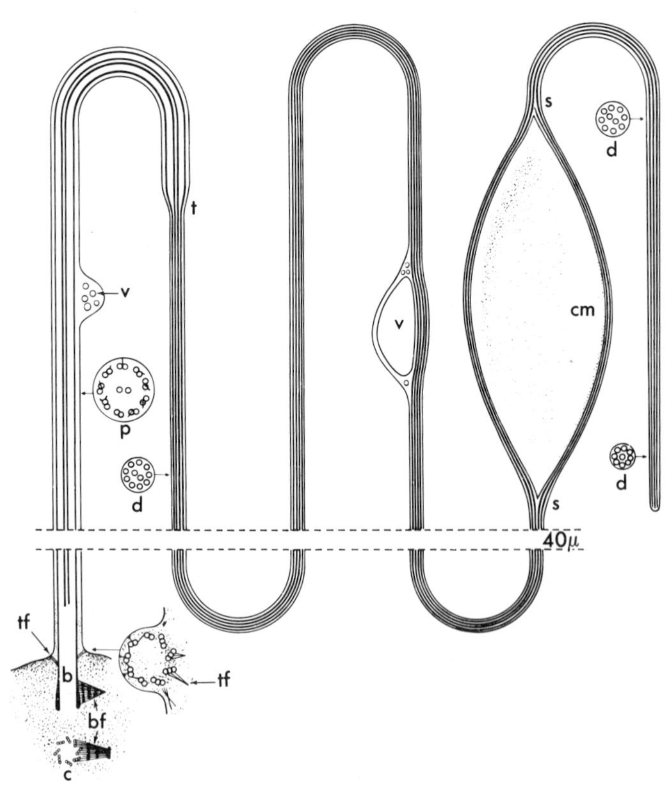

Fig. 13-13. Diagram of olfactory cilium from dendrite of frog's neuron. In the natural state the cilium would be extended. Note conventional ciliary pattern of proximal segment, **p,** and loss of the doublet arrangement in distal segment, **d.** Splits in the fiber array are bridged by a double fold of the ciliary membrane, **cm.** This arrangement occurs in about one tenth of the olfactory cilia. **v,** Vesicles; **b,** basal body; **tf,** transitional fibers; **bf,** basal foot; **c,** centriole; **t,** transition between the proximal and distal segment. (From Reese, T. S. 1965. J. Cell Biol. **25:**209-230.)

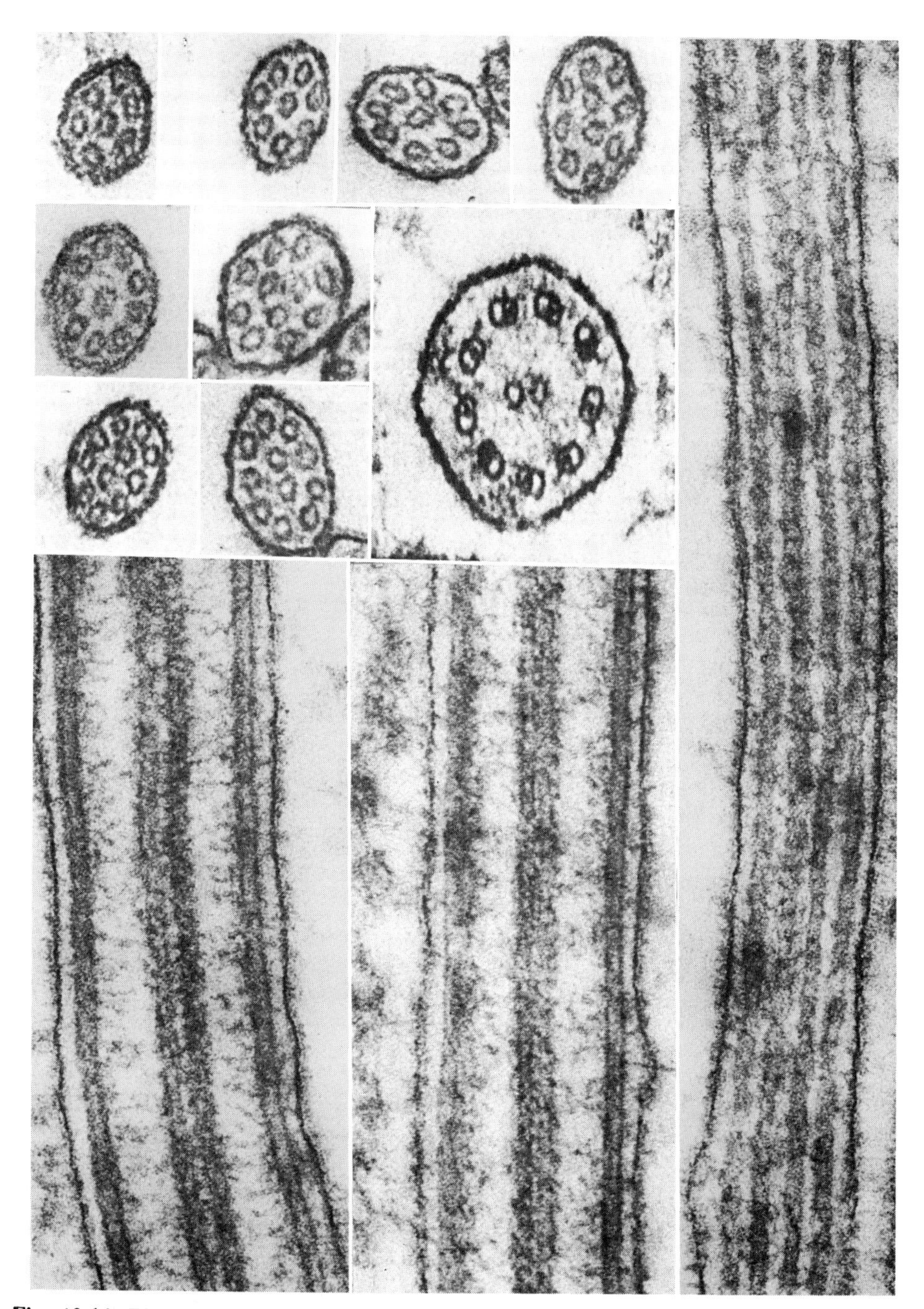

Fig. 13-14. Electron micrographs of cross and longitudinal sections through distal segments of frog's olfactory cilia. Note the nine single fibers surrounding the central pair. Those with less than eleven fibers presumably occur at or very near the tips of the cilia. (From Reese, T. S. 1965. J. Cell Biol. **25:**209-230.)

doublet fibers but lacks the central pair. The fibers have their origin in the basal body found in the inner segment. The ciliary stalk most likely conducts the impulses from the receptor, which is the outer segment, to the inner segment.

Subsequent studies on the morphogenesis of rods and cones show that the outer segment could develop from an abortive cilium (Fawcett, 1961). The axoneme is probably a functionless remnant of a former motile cilium.

Other modified cilia having a sensory function are those on the crown cells in the *saccus vasculosus* of the brains of fish. The cilia contain the nine doublets located around the periphery but lack the paired central fibers. The base contains the basal body; however, at the distal ends the tips are expanded and contain a mass of small vesicles (Bargman and Knoop, 1955).

Cnidocils located on the nematocysts of Coelenterata (Cnidaria) contain a rather dense core of nine uniformly spaced peripheral ridges. A basal body is located at the base of the modified cilium (Chapman and Tilney, 1959). The cnidocil functions as a trigger to cause the discharge of the nematocyst used by these animals for protection and foodgetting.

In fact, all sensory structures of invertebrates and most sensory structures of vertebrates are cilia.

It is interesting to note that in these cilia modified for sensory function there is a characteristic lack of the central pair of fibers or, as in the case of the frog's olfactory cell, a loss of one central fiber (Figs. 13-13 and 13-14).

Chemical composition

One of the difficulties encountered in studying the chemical composition of cilia and flagella has been the problem of isolation of these organelles. In the past it was not known with certainty how much of the organelle was lost in the preparation or how much contaminant of cellular origin was present. Yet, despite these difficulties, some analyses were performed. As would be suspected, the analyses showed cilia or flagella to be composed essentially of protein and some lipids. The latter were presumably derived from the membranes and sheaths. Tibbs (1957, 1958) studied the chemical composition of sperm flagella of several fish and algal flagella from the genus *Polytoma*. In addition to protein his results indicated that carbohydrates comprise a small and variable amount ranging from 0.6% to 6.2%. Hexosamines were also present but appeared to be negligible. Tibbs (1957) and Watson et al. (1961) found RNA in the cilia and flagella but noticeably lacking in sperm flagella. In a later study Tibbs (1958) believed that the RNA observed in flagella of *Polytoma* was probably due to contamination.

Enzymes such as acetylcholinesterase have been found in the tails of trout and perch sperm (Tibbs, 1960). It was suggested that the acetylcholine-acetylcholinesterase system is probably associated with the control of wave propagation and with rotation rather than with the contraction-relaxation cycle. Tibbs (1958) also found ATPase in flagella.

Gibbons (1963) and Gibbons and Rowe (1965), using a density gradient technique for separation, obtained a protein called *dynein* (*dyne*, "force"; *ein*, "protein") from the cilia of *Tetrahymena pyriformis* that had ATPase activity. This protein forms the arms located on the outer fiber. Density gradient separation yielded two proteins, each of which has ATPase activity. One fraction was 14s and the other 32s. The 14s fraction can be considered as the monomeric form, which has a molecular weight calculated to be about 600,000 ± 100,000. The polymeric 32s fraction had a molecular weight of about 5,404,000.

A starch-gel electrophoretic method yielded a fibrillar protein subunit with a molecular weight of 40,000, which is near the molecular weight of globular proteins revealed by electron microscopy in the fibers. It was suggested that there exists a 1:1 relationship between the chemical and morphological subunits in cilia (Watson and Hynes, 1966). Available data indicate that cells contain a chemical pool of ciliary precursors. In addition, chemicals crucial to their regeneration can be synthesized on demand or can be obtained from resorbed cilia (Rannestad, 1972).

When ciliated animal cells are treated with 60% glycerol (Gibbons, 1965), a suspension of cilia of high purity is obtained. When these isolated cilia are treated with ATP, they show a vigorous bending movement that is propagated along the length of the cilium, from its basal end toward the free surface. It was shown that these cilia have a frequency of 2 to 3 waves per second. Undulating motion is most often seen at the beginning and near the base, becoming more lashing toward the tip. No movement can be obtained in the absence of ATP.

Physiology of ciliary action

Early attempts to describe ciliary activity were hampered by the rapidity with which the cilia move. However, Valentine (ca. 1842) in a series of observations described four types of ciliary activity. These included (1) pendulum or pendicular motion, (2) an uncinate or hooklike motion, (3) an undulatory motion, and (4) an infundibular motion. In the pendicular type of motion the cilium remains essentially rigid, except at the base, throughout the effective stroke of its beat, there being little curvature. The uncinate type of motion is characterized by the cilium undergoing a bending that progresses from the tip to the base; thus a hooklike configuration is assumed. In general, the pendicular and uncinate types of ciliary activity are seen in the cilia of Metazoa. The undulatory motion is characteristic of flagellates; the wavelike contractions progress from the origin to the distal tip. At times a sinusoidal type of wave ensues.

In early attempts to determine the frequency of the ciliary beat the rates at which particles such as carbon or carmine would move along the surface of ciliated tissue were measured. Unfortunately, these early methods produced highly variable results because of the various particle sizes used as well as the tendency for these particles to clump together along the ciliated epithelium. On the other hand, valuable and reproducible results can be obtained with the use of more recently available stroboscopic (Fig. 13-2) or cinematographic methods. Using the cinematographic method, the frequency of the ciliary cycle for gill epithelium of lamellibranchs was found to range from 500 to 1,000 per minute (Fawcett, 1961).

Ciliary reversal or changes in the direction of beat occur in a number of ciliated Protozoa. In *Paramecium* and *Opalina,* for example, reversal of ciliary beat is apparently normal and controllable. In Metazoa, however, ciliary reversals are rare; once the direction of beat is established it cannot be reversed. Evidence of temporary reversal of cilia has been shown to exist in the sea anemone *Metridium.* This reversal is required in feeding and removal of detritus. Normally, cilia beat outward, but bathing them with glycogen or mussel extract causes ciliary reversal (Parker, 1928; Parker and Marks, 1928).

Ciliary reversal can also be attained by electric currents. Ludloff has shown that the direction of the ciliary beat on the surface of the *Paramecium* nearest the cathode can be reversed when the electric circuit is closed. Jahn (1961) "explained" the Ludloff phenomenon by assuming the *Paramecium* to be a core conductor. By utilizing the laws of polarizing currents, one can then explain reversal of ciliary beat as well as the activation of an immobilized animal by the effects of the current on the membrane potential of the animal.

Mechanism of ciliary action

Knowledge of the ultrastructure of cilia provided Bradfield (1955) with the basis

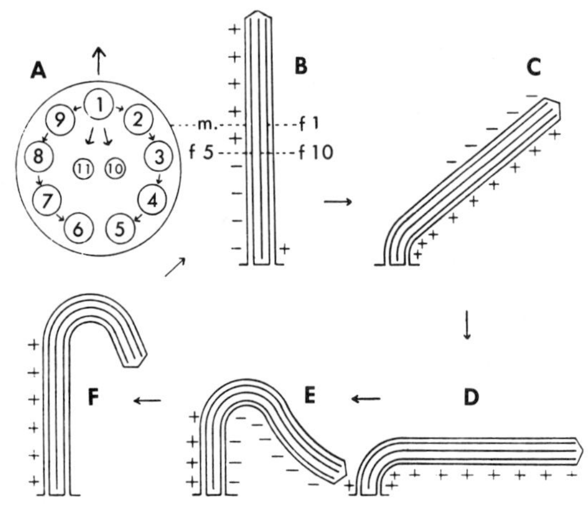

Fig. 13-15. Possible mechanism for ciliary movement as postulated by Bradfield. It is assumed that the impulse originates under fiber 1 and spreads radially around the cilium and to the central pair. (See text for explanation.) (From Bradfield, J. R. G. 1955. Sympos. Soc. Exp. Biol. **9:** 306-334.)

for a scheme of ciliary motion of unknown validity. In proposing this model it was *assumed* that (1) the basal body initiates the beat, (2) the nine peripheral fibers are capable of propagating the impulse as well as contracting locally, (3) the central pair of fibers are specialized for conduction and are not attached to the basal plate, and (4) the matrix comprising the interfibrillar space imparts stiffness to the cilium.

The beat of a cilium begins in the basal body, where the impulse arises under fiber 1 (Fig. 13-15). This impulse initiates a propagated contraction radially, where it fires off fibers 2 and 9. The impulse is also picked up by central fibers 10 and 11 and is rapidly conveyed by them throughout the entire length of the cilium, thus stimulating all points along fibers 1, 2, 9, 3, and 8 to cause the cilium to bend as a soft rod. This is the effective stroke. In the meantime the impulse spreads radially, firing off fibers 4, 7, 5, and 6. The contraction spreads upward at a natural speed of propagation (fibers 10 and 11 do not stimulate fibers 4, 7, 5, and 6 because the former are refactory at this time). Contraction of these fibers tends to pull the cilium into a vertical position through a series of curves—the recovery stroke.

All of Bradfield's assumptions are unproved and highly questionable, but this is still a useful hypothesis.

A more recent model of ciliary bending has been proposed by Brokaw (1972). It assumes, as most students of microtubules assume, that microtubules are *not* contractile. This model proposes that such semirigid rods are closely associated and "tied" together not too tightly, as are adjacent outer doublet fibers of the axoneme. Bending of the cilium is produced when such adjacent doublets of microtubules slide longitudinally relative to one another. Such sliding is assumed to be similar to the relative sliding of thick and thin filaments of striated muscle (Chapter 7), and the arms extending from doublets are assumed to be somewhat comparable to the myosin bridges extending from striated muscle thick filaments. When the cilium is stimulated, certain pairs of doublets within the axoneme slide relatively past each other, and this causes bending of the ciliary shaft locally or along its whole length.

Coordination of ciliary beat

When all cilia are beating together and, in general, are in the same phase of contraction at the same time, the so-called *isochronal rhythm* is produced. On the other hand, cilia on a surface may exhibit *metachronal rhythm,* in which successive cilia in each row start their beat in sequence so that each cilium is more advanced in its phase of contraction than the preceding one. This type of rhythmical contraction produces waves that move over the surface of the organism or epithelium. Such coordination of ciliary activity suggests that a regulatory coordinating mechanism is involved. In fact, Engelmann proposed the *neuroid theory* in which he postulated a

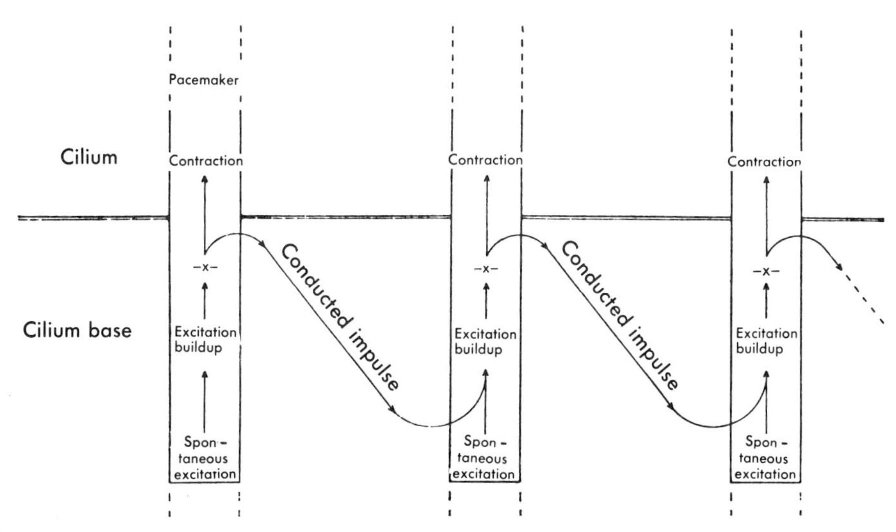

Fig. 13-16. Theory of metachronal coordination as proposed by Sleigh. Spontaneous buildup in the pacemaker cilium will determine the frequency of the ciliary beat. (From Sleigh, M. A. 1957. J. Exp. Biol. **34:**106-115.)

nervelike impulse was responsible for this coordination. The "silver line" system observed in *Paramecium* was thought to have the function of impulse conduction (Sleigh, 1962). Electron microscopy shows that these fibers do not connect one basal body to another. Verworn (ca. 1890) proposed a different concept that he called the *mechanical theory,* according to which the movement of a cilium stimulates the next to beat.

Sleigh (1956, 1957) proposed the pacemaker and transmission concept of metachronal contractions. This is a two-step process consisting of (1) *intraciliary excitation* and (2) *interciliary conduction.* The intraciliary process consists of the building up of an excitatory state. The discharge of the excitatory state would set off not only the contraction of that cilium but also influence the next cilium to an excitatory state, and so on (Fig. 13-16). The buildup of excitation in the pacemaker determines the frequency of beat of that cilium and other cilia at constant intervals (Sleigh, 1962).

LITERATURE CITED

Afzelius, B. A. 1963. Cilia and flagella that do not conform to the 9 + 2 pattern. J. Ultrastruct. Res. **9:**381-392.

Bargman, W., and A. Knoop. 1955. Electronmikroskopische Untersuchungen der Knonchenzellen des Saccus vasculosus. Z. Zellforsch. **43:** 184-194.

Bradfield, J. R. G. 1955. Fibre patterns in animal flagella and cilia. Sympos. Soc. Exp. Biol. **9:** 306-334.

Bradley, D. E. 1966. The ultrastructure of the flagella of the chrysomonads with particular reference to the mastigonemes. Exp. Cell Res. **41:**162-173.

Brokaw, C. J. 1972. Flagellar movement: a sliding filament model. Science **178:**455-462.

Chapman, G. B., and L. G. Tilney. 1959. Cytological studies on the nematocysts of Hydra. J. Biophys. Biochem. Cytol. **5:**69-84.

Emerson, S. U., K. Tokuyasu, and M. I. Simon. 1970. Bacterial flagella: polarity of elongation. Science **169:**190-192.

Fawcett, D. W., and K. R. Porter. 1954. A study of the fine structure of ciliated epithelia. J. Morph. **94:**221-281.

Fawcett, D. W. 1961. Cilia and flagella. In J. Brachet and A. E. Mirsky (editors). The cell. Vol. 2. Academic Press, Inc., New York.

Flock, A., and A. J. DuVall. 1966. The ultrastructure of the kinocilium of the sensory cells

in the middle ear and lateral line system. J. Cell Biol. **25**:1-8.
Gibbons, I. R. 1961. The relationship between fine structure and direction of beat in gill cilia of a lamellibranch mollusc. J. Biophys. Biochem. Cytol. **11**:179-204.
Gibbons, I. R. 1963. Studies on the protein components of cilia from Tetrahymena pyriformis. Proc. Nat. Acad. Sci. U.S.A. **50**:1002-1010.
Gibbons, I. R. 1965. Reactivation of glycerinated cilia from Tetrahymena pyriformis. J. Cell Biol. **25**:400-402.
Gibbons, I. R., and A. V. Grimstone. 1960. On the flagellar structure in certain flagellates. J. Biophys. Biochem. Cytol. **7**:179-204.
Gibbons, I. R., and A. J. Rowe. 1965. Dynein, a protein with adenosinetriphosphatase activity. Science **149**:424-426.
Grimstone, A. V., and A. Klug. 1966. Observations on the substructure of flagellar fibres. J. Cell Sci. **1**:351-362.
Jahn, T. L. 1961. The mechanism of ciliary movement. I. Ciliary reversal and activation by electric current; the Ludloff phenomenon in terms of core and volume conductors. J. Protozool. **8**:369-380.
Noirot-Timothee, C. 1958. L'ultrastructure du blepharaplaste des infusoires cilies. C. R. Acad. Sci. (Paris) **246**:2293-2295.
Parker, G. H. 1928. Glycogen as a means of ciliary reversal. Proc. Nat. Acad. Sci. U.S.A. **14**:713-714.
Parker, G. H., and A. P. Marks. 1928. Ciliary reversal in the sea anemone Metridium. J. Exp. Zool. **52**:1-6.
Randall, J. T., and M. H. G. Friedlander. 1950. The microstructure of ram spermatozoa. Exp. Cell Res. **1**:1-29.
Rannestad, J. 1972. Cilia regeneration in partially deciliated Tetrahymena. J. Cell Biol. **55**:210A.
Reese, T. S. 1965. Olfactory cilia in the frog. J. Cell Biol. **25**:209-230.
Rivera, J. A. 1962. Cilia, ciliated epithelium, and ciliary activities. Pergamon Press, Inc., New York.
Sedar, A. W., and K. R. Porter. 1955. The fine structure of the cortical components of Paramecium multimicronucleatum. J. Biophys. Biochem. Cytol. **1**:583-602.
Sjöstrand, F. S. 1953a. The ultrastructure of the outer segments of rods and cones of the eye as revealed by the electron microscope. J. Cell. Comp. Physiol. **42**:15-44.
Sjöstrand, F. S. 1953b. The ultrastructure of the inner segment of the retinal rods of the guinea pig eye as revealed by electron microscopy. J. Cell. Comp. Physiol. **42**:45-77.
Sleigh, M. A. 1956. Metachronism and frequency of beat in the peristomal cilia of Stentor. J. Exp. Biol. **33**:15-28.
Sleigh, M. A. 1957. Further observation on the coordination and the determination of frequency in the peristomal cilia of Stentor. J. Exp. Biol. **34**:106-115.
Sleigh, M. A. 1960. The form and beat in cilia of Stentor and opalines. J. Exp. Biol. **37**:1-10.
Sleigh, M. A. 1961. An example of mechanical coordination of cilia. Nature (London) **191**: 931-932.
Sleigh, M. A. 1962. The biology of cilia and flagella. The Macmillan Co., New York.
Starr, M. P., and R. C. Williams. 1952. Helical fine structure of flagella of a motile diphtheroid. J. Bact. **63**:701-706.
Tibbs, J. 1957. The nature of algal and related flagella. Biochim. Biophys. Acta **23**:275-288.
Tibbs, J. 1958. The properties of algal and sperm flagella obtained from sedimentation. Biochim. Biophys. Acta **28**:636-637.
Tibbs, J. 1960. Acetylcholinesterase in flagellar systems. Biochim. Biophys. Acta **41**:115-122.
Watson, M. R., J. M. Hopkins, and J. T. Randall. 1961. Isolated cilia from Tetrahymena pyriformis. Exp. Cell Res. **23**:629-631.
Watson, M. R., and R. D. Hynes. 1966. Starch-gel electrophoresis of the cilia of Tetrahymena pyriformis. Exp. Cell Res. **42**:384-386.

CHAPTER 14

Microtubules, vacuoles, and crystals

MICROTUBULES

Microtubules were first characterized as a genus of common cytoplasmic organelles by Slautterback (1963) and by Ledbetter and Porter (1963, 1964). They had been observed earlier by numerous electron microscopists, such as the tubules of Protozoa, in cilia and flagella, in the spindles of dividing cells, and in axons of neurons. They have been reported subsequently in a wide variety of plant (Newcomb, 1969) and animal (Behnke and Forer, 1966) cells, usually in the cytoplasm but occasionally in nuclei, and in some bacteria. Since spindle fibers of dividing eukaryotic cells are microtubules (Figs. 17-4 to 17-6), it seems that all eukaryotic cells can produce the protein subunits and assemble them into one or other form of microtubule. Cells can also break them down again into subunits.

Microtubules (Figs. 14-1 to 14-3) are proteinaceous; have a "clear" center in cross-sectional and longitudinal view; are long (up to 10 μm or more); are almost always straight or gently curved; have varying outside diameters but generally about 250 Å; vary from semipermanent (as in cilia) to evanescent (spindle fibers); consist of globular protein subunits arranged in parallel or spiraled longitudinal rows in a 70 Å thick circle of eight to thirteen subunits around the clear center; and associated tubules can share common subunits (Fig. 14-2, *B*). They are rigid, as indicated by the fact that they usually break or kink and form sharp angles rather than curves when bent (Fig. 14-1), as in extracted and concentrated fractions (Burton, 1966). This rigidity of microtubules may be their most important characteristic, permitting them to function, as a cytoskeleton for the maintenance of unstable form. They can curve in vivo, as when flagella bend, or in the circumference of the flat mammalian erythrocyte. They are typically present in unstable (*very* different from spherical) forms of cells or parts of cells such as flattened, stellate, and long narrow cells (erythrocytes, melanocytes, neurons, smooth muscle, eye lens) or cellular extensions (cilia and flagella, root hairs, undulating membranes, axopodia [Fig. 14-4]). In such elongate cells or extensions of cells the microtubules extend parallel to the long axis (Fig. 14-4). They can attach to other organelles such as basal bodies and chromosomes.

It now appears that the cell produces the globular subunits, of molecular weight about 60,000 daltons and a half-life of about 4 days (Bensch et al., 1969), which are then formed into tubules at specific times and places within the cell. The cell can also disassemble the microtubules into the constituent subunits, such as spindle fibers at telophase. Similar but experimentally produced reversible disassembly has been achieved by

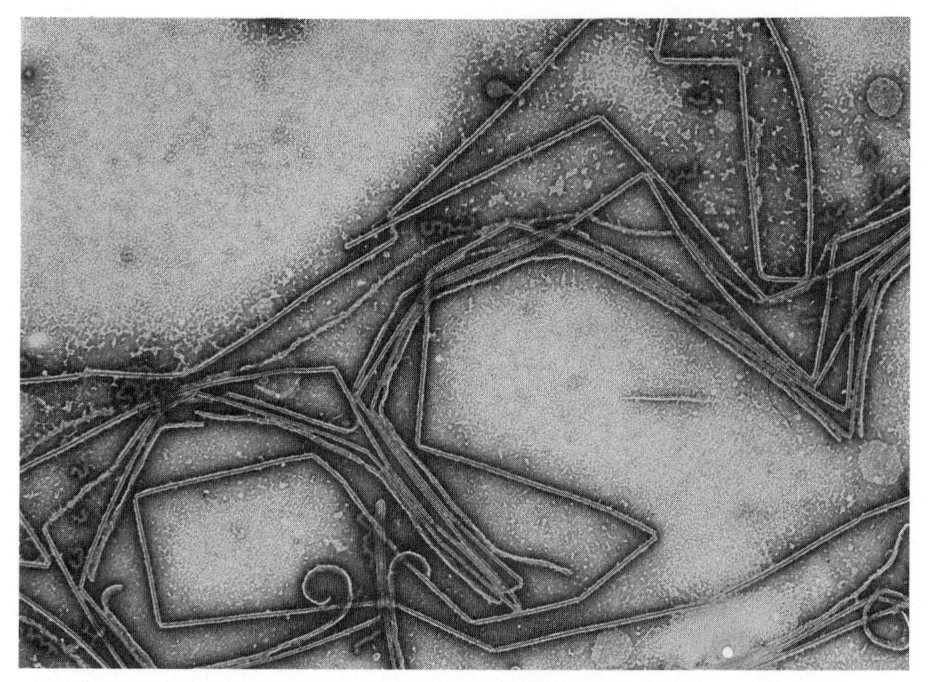

Fig. 14-1. Negatively stained singlet microtubules from disrupted lungfluke spermatozoa. The treatment has bent them, and they generally break or kink at an angle. This is evidence that they are rigid organelles. (About ×30,000.) (From Burton, P. R. 1966. Science **154:**903-905. Copyright 1966 by the American Association for the Advancement of Science.)

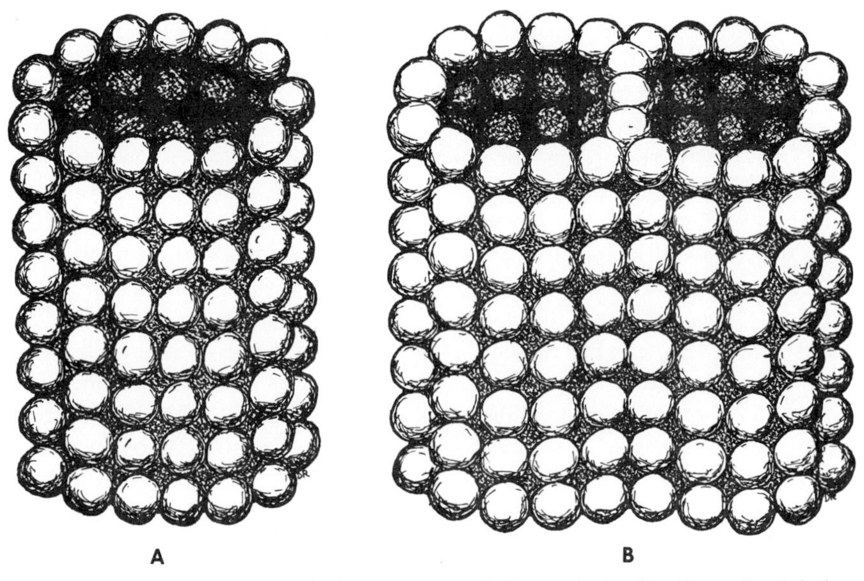

Fig. 14-2. Hypothetical models of the structure of **A,** a single flagellar microtubule, and **B,** a flagellar doublet. In cross section, **A** is assumed to consist of a ring of thirteen 45 Å subunits. In **B** the doublet shares three subunits, the three being common to both tubules. These interpretations probably considerably oversimplify details of the actual structures. (From Ringo, D. L. 1967. J. Ultrastruct. Res. **17:**266-277.)

high pressure, by low (0° to 5° C) temperature (Tilney and Porter, 1967), and by the drugs colchicine (Tilney and Gibbins, 1969, and many others) and the *Vinca* alkaloids vinblastine and vincristine (Bensch et al., 1969). In fact, the specific reversible breakdown of microtubules by colchicine is a practical and adequate proof of microtubules, being comparable to the possibly specific and reversible breakdown of microfilaments by cytochalasin B (Wessels et al., 1971) (see later in this chapter). As a cytoskeleton, microtubules form as a cell or part of a cell elongates and remain during the existence of the unstable elongate condition. If they are destroyed naturally or experimentally, the elongate condition cannot usually persist. It is still uncertain, however,

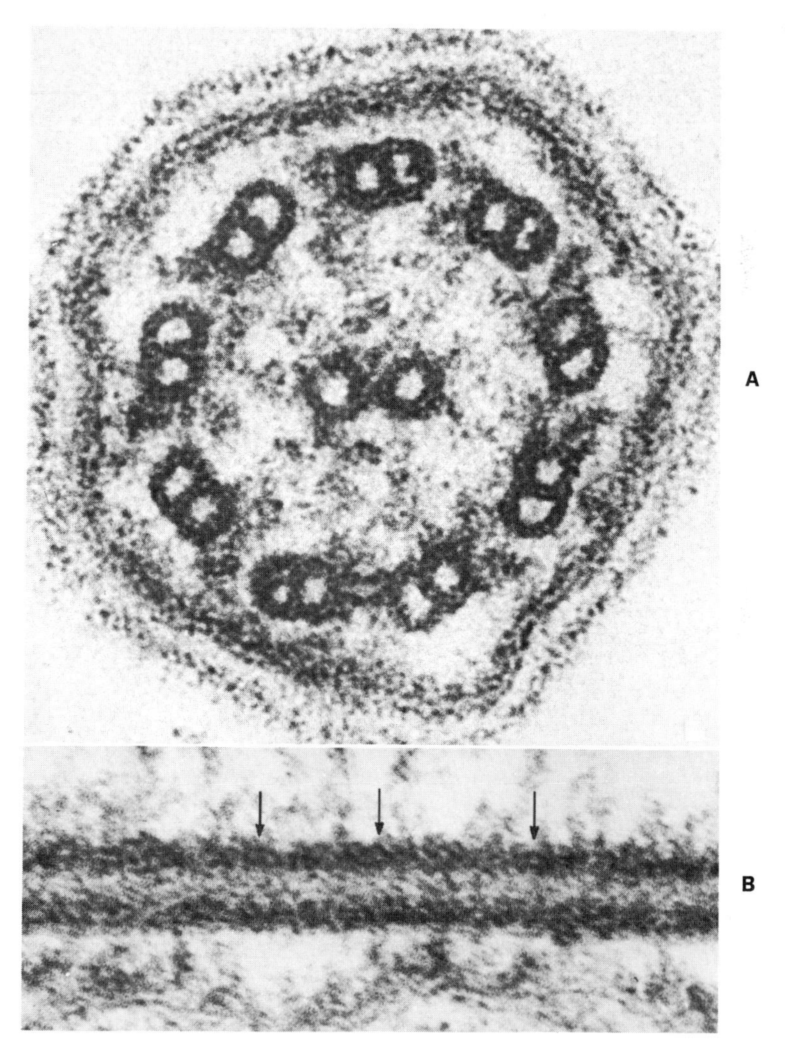

Fig. 14-3. A, Electron micrograph cross section of a flagellum of *Chlamydomonas reinhardi* showing 40 to 50 Å subunits in both central and peripheral fibers. **B,** Median longitudinal section through peripheral flagellar subfiber that also shows 40 to 50 Å subunits. The interpretation therefore is that the subunits are round, as they certainly appear to be. (See Fig. 14-2.) (From Ringo, D. L. 1967. J. Ultrastruct. Res. **17:**266-277.)

A

B

C

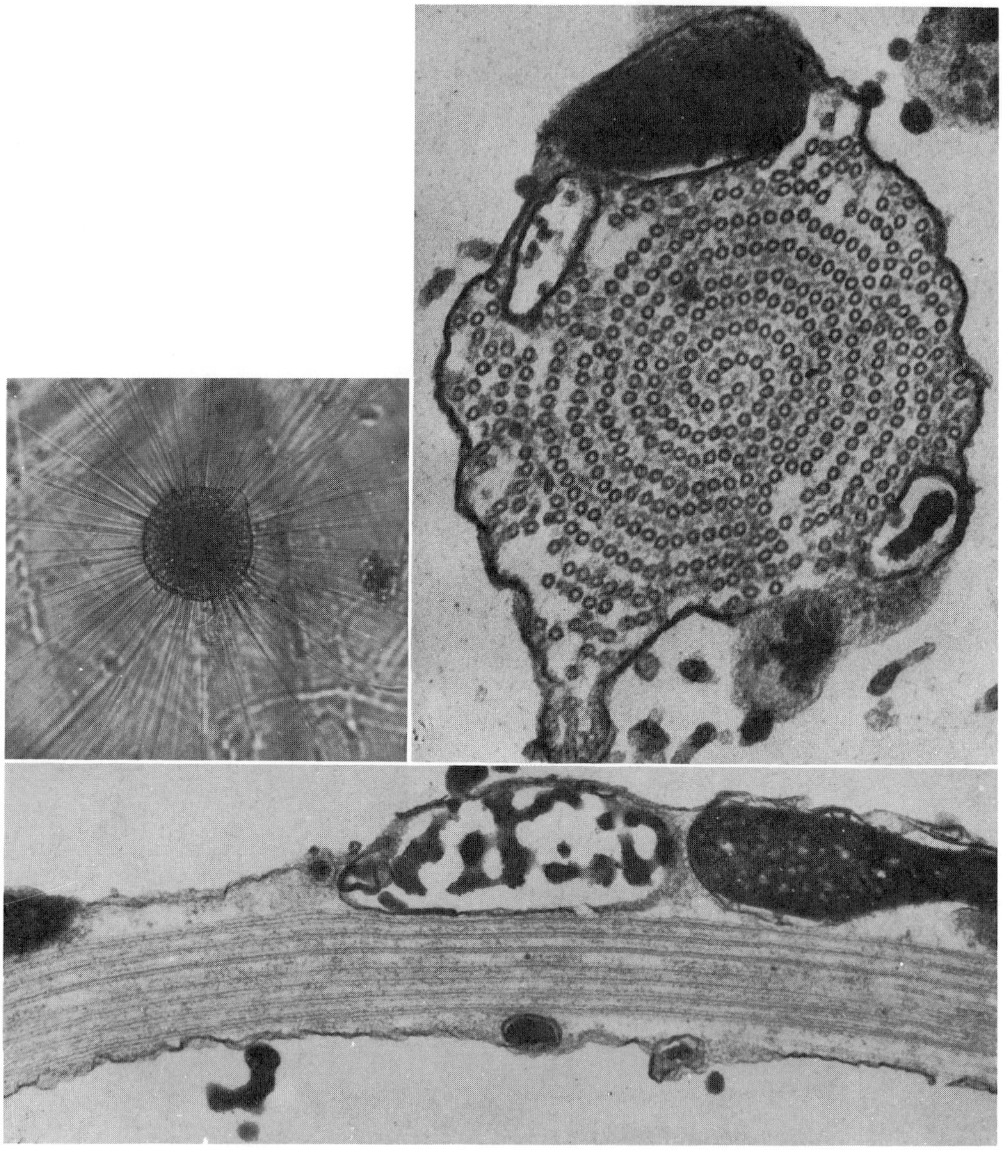

Fig. 14-4. A, Light micrograph of the freshwater heliozoan *Actinosphaerium nucleofilum* showing radiating needlelike axopodia. Outer cytosome (main body) is the cortical region with a contractile vacuole shown as a bump; the darker and denser central part of the cytosome is the medullary region in which the bases of the skeleton are embedded. **B,** Electron micrograph cross section of axopod showing the skeleton of two rows of microtubules, which form an interlocking double spiral. **C,** Longitudinal section of an axopod showing microtubules, which are very long, and protoplasm flowing on the outside of the skeleton, including a mitochondrion and an opaque granule and an outer plasma membrane. (From Tilney, L. G., Y. Hiramoto, and D. Marshland. 1966. J. Cell Biol. **29:**77-95.)

whether microtubules are actually involved in the elongation process itself, but they are certainly often essential to its persistence.

Gibbins et al. (1969) concluded from a study of the development of the mesenchyme of *Arbacia* that, "microtubules are a morphological expression of framework which operates to shape cells." (Microfilaments will be discussed later.)

They rarely, if ever, actually make contact with other structures such as the plasma membrane, nuclear envelope, centromeres, centrioles, or basal bodies of cilia; yet they often come close to them. Whatever "attachment" means at this macromolecular level, they may be functionally "attached" to these other structures through intervening molecules.

Microtubules have been correlated with movement, but intracellular movement itself is so general that there may actually be no cause-and-effect relationship. They are often described as forming a cytoskeleton. This is hardly necessary in plant cells that have walls, although they probably are skeletal in cilia, flagella, sperm, the axopodia of Heliozoa, erythrocytes and Protozoa. In the nonuniform deposition of certain plant cell wall thickenings they have been related to the deposition and arrangement of cellulose micelles. It has been proposed that they form a cytoskeletal intracellular brace for the basal ends of flagella. Their arrangement in the excretory apparatus of *Paramecium* has suggested their involvement in the contraction of the vacuole and opening or closing of the pore. Actually, these and other claims are hypotheses based on suggestive arrangements, positions, or correlations; none has been proved. The chief difficulty with ascribing motive power to them is that they are straight, rigid (they break rather than bend), and smooth. No evidence exists at all that they are contractile or undulate, since their diameter always seems to remain constant and they always appear as straight as the confines of the cell or protoplasmic extension permit.

There is now a considerable body of convincing evidence that microtubules do act as guides for the movement of protoplasmic bodies such as many kinds of small vesicles, chromosomes, and whole nuclei. It has not been determined whether the microtubules when functioning as guides are completely passive, acting merely as tracks to direct the structures to a particular region of the cell, or whether they also somehow provide all or some of the force required to propel the organelles along their lengths. It has often been claimed that the microtubules are passive—that it is the associated microfilaments that provide the (contractile) force. Others have proposed that it is interaction between microtubules and microfilaments or between thick and thin microfilaments (like thick and thin filaments of striated muscle) that provides the force. One of the clearest cases of such movement is the association of synaptic vesicles with the microtubules in axons (Smith et al., 1970), although the authors could not determine if the microtubules provided the force. There is also a questionable concept that microtubules can break down into subunits, which can then reassociate into microfilaments (discussed later). But it seems likely that the structure and amino acid composition of the two types of subunits are different (Davison, 1970).

Although microtubules are often more or less isolated from one another, as in smooth muscle cells, neurons, and pollen grains, nevertheless, there are numerous examples of definite associations and arrangements of few or many tubules. The 9 + 2 arrangement of the axoneme of cilia and flagella as well as the 9 + 0 of centrioles and retinal rod cell connecting segments are discussed elsewhere. In certain insect sperm tails they form a spiral of typical microtubules around the 9 + 2 arrangement of modified tubules. In the axopodia of Heliozoa they form two concentric spirals that constitute a skeleton, on the outside of which the protoplasm streams outward on one side and inward on the other (Fig.

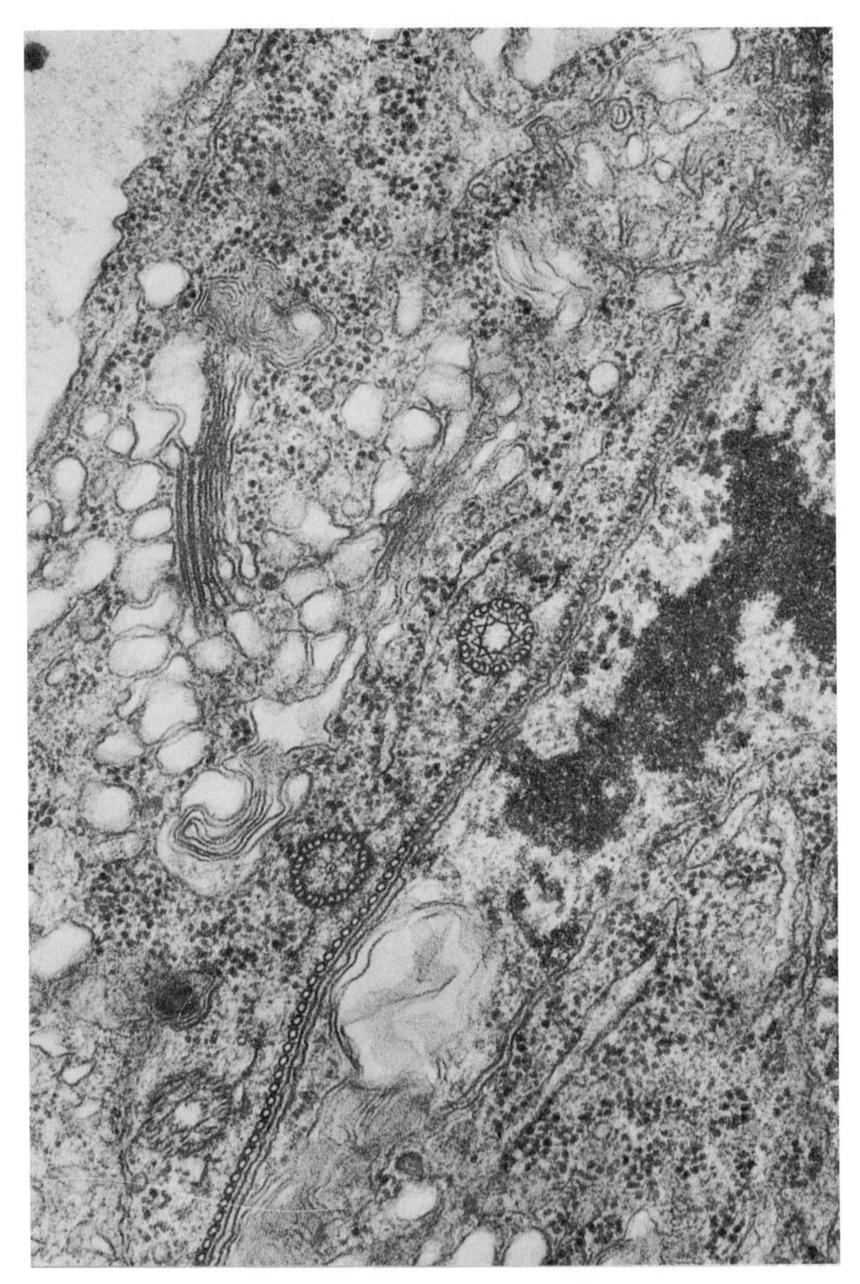

Fig. 14-5. Electron micrograph of some basal bodies, a layer of microtubules, and other cytoplasmic organelles of sperm of the plant *Equisetum*. Of the three sections of basal bodies, one shows the star arrangement, one the cartwheel arrangement, and the third, the most distal, a hollow center. The first two show the nine triple tubular fibers of a basal body. The layer of parallel microtubules probably forms part of the cytoskeleton of the spermatid. (Courtesy Dr. F. R. Turner, University of Texas Cell Research Institute, Austin, Texas.)

14-4). In the protoplasmic projections of Suctoria (Protozoa) the microtubules form two concentric circles of subgroups. The inner circle consists of seven groups of four, the outer circle consists of seven groups of three, and then one single tubule occurs outside of that. These form the skeleton of the hollow tube used for "sucking" in food. There are numerous groupings, often of large numbers, in various Protozoa (for example, the "muscle-like exocotyl," an internal organelle of certain symbionts of termites). In the sperm of mosses, *Equisetum,* and cycads there is a microtubular band consisting of numerous modified tubules running in close parallel the length of the sperm, perhaps as a "backbone" cytoskeleton (Fig. 14-5) from which mitochondria and nucleus are "suspended." Microtubules are scattered in the cytoplasm of smooth muscle cells. Many plant flagella have several microtubules "attached" to the basal body that extend far downward into the cytoplasm, often close to the outer surface of the nucleus or close to the plasma membrane. Thus they form a supporting framework for the wide dissipation in the cell of the reaction to the flagellar motion.

Unmodified or modified microtubules are common among Protozoa (including motile unicellular algae). Pitelka (1963) stated in a study of the electron microscopy of Protozoa that "If there is anything unique in the ultrastructural organization of Protozoa, it may be the extent to which they have utilized fibrous materials in the construction of cytoplasmic organelles and organelle systems. A bewildering profusion of fibrous structures has been described, including some in each protozoon class." These fibers are probably mostly unmodified or modified microtubules ranging in diameter from about 150 to 300 Å.

For example, the pellicle of trypanosomes and other zooflagellates probably consists of a layer of 250 Å tubules, having clear centers just below the plasma membrane, and others of 200 Å extend from the basal body, whereas the "cystostomal tube" is lined by them. The "axostyle" is limited by a sheet of 140 Å tubules, whereas in *Pyrsonympha* the axostyle consists of fourteen to seventy-four sheets of 230 Å tubules. Among fresh-water ciliates the contractile vacuolar membrane is backed by sheets of microtubules; each kinetodesma consists of a few hundred 200 Å tubular fibrils; and the cytoplasm around the esophagus is loaded with bundles of 150 Å tubules. These are only a few examples of the abundant use made by flagellates and ciliates of microtubules other than in spindles and in the flagella and cilia themselves. Nowhere among groups of organisms are tubules so abundant or so variously utilized.

In summary, microtubules, either of the evanescent types such as spindle fibers or modified and more permanent ones, are typical of eucells in general and of nuclear division, of long narrow protoplasm, and of protoplasmic movement in particular. However, proof of functions is circumstantial, based on correlated presence or logical deduction. They do constitute a temporary or permanent structural component of cytoplasm in general.

MICROFILAMENTS

In many cells that have movement or asymmetrical growth, often in addition to microtubules, there may be fine long filaments, at least some of which are composed of actinlike protein. Commonly these microfilaments are about 50 Å thick, but the thrombosthenin filaments of blood platelets are 80 to 100 Å, and neurofilaments, which may or may not be in this family of contractile microfilaments, are about 100 Å thick (Wessells et al., 1971). These microfilaments are frequently associated in large numbers into bundles or networks. They are commonly found in animal cells that are changing shape during morphogenesis (Wessells et al., 1971), in smooth muscle and in striated muscle if the filaments belong in this family, and in plant cells having cyclosis (O'Brien and Thimann, 1966; Nagai and Rebhun, 1966). (See Wessells et al., 1971, for other cell types containing microfilaments.)

It is now possible to separate microfilaments into two subclasses: (1) those broken down by the drug cytochalasin B and (2) those not so affected (Wessells et al., 1971). Microfilaments from some cell types have been characterized as actinlike and, in vitro, will contract in the presence of calcium ions and ATP. The hypothetical generalization is that microfilaments are contractile and are responsible somehow for most protoplasmic movement. Baker and Schroeder (1967) and others subsequently (Wessells et al., 1971) reported that embryonic tissue invagination can be achieved by formation of rings of microfilaments around the external ends of the cylindrical cells contracting to reduce the circumference and diameter of that end of each cell, like a "purse string." These adjacent cells become cone shaped, and the tissue perforce invaginates as the outer area only decreases without change of the area occupied by the inner ends. In the growth of axons, microfilaments are involved along with microtubules.

At the present time microfilaments, seen or postulated, are generally considered the producers of all protoplasmic motion at the ultimate macromolecular level. This includes cyclosis in plant cells, contraction of smooth and striated muscle, movements of cilia and flagella, prometaphase and anaphase movement of chromosomes, and movements of such other cellular organelles as mitochondria, plastids, and nuclei. Experiments with cytochalasin B should greatly add to knowledge of microfilaments and protoplasmic movement in the future.

VACUOLES

One of the most obvious parts of a typical mature plant cell is the voluminous vacuole (Figs. 11-1 and 11-8). The contents of the vacuole are not protoplasmic but mostly water, which contains a variety of solutes (Zirkle, 1937). In some cells the vacuole may constitute more than nine tenths of the volume contained within the plasma membrane. Essentially all mature cells of land plants and many fungi and algae (but not procells) have vacuoles; yet the youngest meristematic cells of plants and most animal cells have apparently none.

Efforts to study the origins of plant vacuoles began more than a hundred years ago, and vacuoles were traced backward through smaller and smaller sizes to numerous tiny ones. At that point they became indistinguishable from other tiny structures, especially mitochondria and plastid primordia. Resulting (and conflicting) hypotheses proposed that vacuoles arise de novo, that they do not, that mitochondria, plastids, and vacuoles have a common precursor structure, etc. For example, de Vries proposed in 1885 that vacuoles arose from individualized bodies in the cytoplasm of meristematic cells. These tiny bodies or granules he called *tonoplasts*. As the tonoplast enlarged by secreting water within itself, the original tonoplast became the vacuolar membrane, the meaning of the term today.

At about 1920, special staining methods did reveal that tiny vacuoles of meristematic cells are distinct from mitochondria and plastid primordia and that they are often connected like beads on a string or form a reticulum of strands and swellings. The appearance of the beginning vacuolar system naturally led to the assumption that it is related to certain forms of the Golgi apparatus in animal cells.

In hindsight it is evident that the beaded and reticulate forms of very young vacuolar systems are obviously similar to the endoplasmic reticulum as now revealed by phase-contrast microscopy and electron microscopy. It now seems likely that the beginning of a vacuolar system is a specialization of part of the ER system of a cell, the beads (the tonoplasts of de Vries) being derived from enlarging cisternae of the ER (Buvat, 1961). Thus the vacuolar membrane may not arise de novo but may derive from the ER. As the tiny vacuoles take up more and more water, the strands enlarge and flow together until there may be, at cell maturity and maximum enlargement, only one very large vacuole. This ER origin of the vacuolar membrane (tonoplast) explains why it is a single rather than a double membrane.

The earliest phases of a vacuolar system are described as containing a highly concentrated colloidal solution that becomes more and more dilute as it enlarges. Presumably, the concentrated colloid is produced by the differentiating part of the ER and functions, in part, in the uptake of water by the vacuolar system. The result is the significant enlargement of the plant cell with little increase in amount of protoplasm. That method of cell enlargement is typical of plant growth and development. Studies of vacuolar osmotic concentration have shown that it is 5 atmospheres or more above that of the environmental liquid. Therefore the vacuole and cytoplasm are generally under internal pressure against the cell wall. This positive pressure condition of plant cells is referred to as the cell (or tissue) being *turgid*. If water is lost from the cell by drying or by putting cells or tissues in a liquid of higher osmotic pressure, the vacuole decreases in volume and so must the protoplast as a whole. This condition is called *plasmolysis*. Often the plasmolyzed protoplast shrinks away from the wall smoothly, but sometimes certain areas of the protoplast stick to the wall, producing an irregular plasmolyzed protoplast. Aspects of turgidity and plasmolysis are important in experimental work on cells of plants, and the osmotic concentration of outside liquid is equally important in experimental work with animals cells, although the latter, lacking walls, do not plasmolyze. If a cell loses or gains too much water, its protoplasmic equilibrium is upset and abnormal changes occur; consequently, what may be observed by optical or electron microscopy may not be normal but an artifact. Furthermore, death of the cell may result.

The content of vacuoles is mostly water, salts, acids, and soluble proteins, but some contain particular solutes and others seem to accumulate protein. The blue, red, and intermediate colors of flower petals and the redness of many young leaves and other plant parts are due to the specific accumulation within the vacuoles of special pigment molecules of various anthocyanins, often in mixtures. These are determined by hereditary factors. In most seeds certain cells produce specific vacuoles that accumulate protein, which becomes solid and granular. Such reserve deposits of protein in vacuoles, which are often enzymes, are called *aleurone gains*. In barely, for example, these enzymes are used by the beer industry in the conversion of starch to sugar. Electron microscopy has demonstrated, at least in one species, the ER origin of aleurone vacuoles.

The yeast vacuole may not be comparable or homologous to that of plants. Isolated yeast vacuoles have been found to contain proteases, enzymes characteristic of lysosomes. Whether Matile's conclusion that the yeast vacuole is a lysosome is valid or not is difficult to judge and depends on concepts. Is any vesicle (if the yeast vacuole is a vesicle) containing certain sorts of enzymes to be considered a lysosome, or must a vesicle containing hydrolase enzymes originate from a dictyosome to be a lysosome? Can a sac as large as a yeast vacuole be properly classified as a lysosome? Does the yeast vacuole achieve what a typical lysosome accomplishes?

Contractile vacuoles

Many freshwater Protozoa and reproductive cells of some algae and aquatic fungi possess a vacuolar system that apparently functions in excretion of excess water from the protoplasm. Salt-water, parasitic, and symbiotic unicellular organisms and certain unicells of multicellular organisms (amebocytes and leukocytes) generally do not have contractile vacuoles, probably because their environment is almost isotonic with their protoplasm. Apparently, in freshwater ameboid cells small vacuoles appear in a particular region or, depending on the species, anywhere within the cytoplasm, increase in size, and fuse into one large vacuole, which then breaks through any part of the plasma membrane to discharge its contents to the exterior. There is a constant sequence of variously sized vacuoles in different phases of the cycle somewhere in the cytoplasm. Flagellates usually have one or two contractile vacuoles and Sarcodina (the ameboid Protozoa) can have many contractile vacuoles (CV) located in the endoplasm. Most ciliates have, in addition to the CV itself, one or more canals radiating from the contractile vacuole to form a system. For example, there is one canal in *Stentor,* about six in *Paramecium,* and many in some other species. Furthermore, there may be one CV (in the posterior region), two CV (one posterior and one anterior as in *Paramecium*), or more such systems. Even some marine and symbiotic ciliates have CVs, although they pulsate more slowly than do those of freshwater forms, probably eliminating only the water taken in with the food. The CV and its associated canals are fixed in position (in the inner ectoplasm), and the permanent CV itself is often attached by a permanent canal to the exterior by a tube through the pellicle. The collecting canals are also permanent and accumulate liquid, which is then periodically discharged into the large CV. The rhythm of filling and discharge of the CV

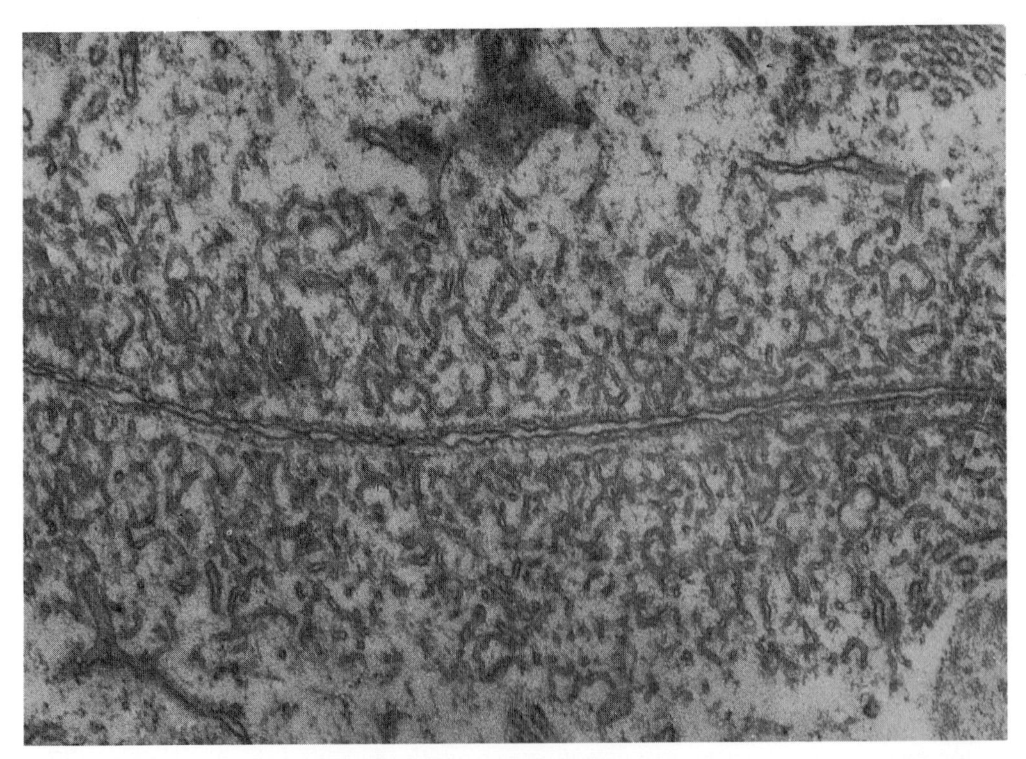

Fig. 14-6. Electron micrograph of contractile vacuole canal of *Paramecium* surrounded by modified ER, which probably extracts excretory material from the protoplasm and passes it into the canal. (From Schneider, L. 1960. J. Protozool. **7**:82-98.)

is related to the amount of excess water in the protoplasm of the region of the collecting canals.

In all types of CVs there is a region of modified ER around the vacuole or the radial canals that seems to function in removal of water from the cytoplasm (Fig. 14-6). In the simple, ameboid type the smallest vacuoles seem to be enlarged ER cisternae. In ciliates, however, the radial canals, CV, and discharge tube are all permanent, differentiated organelles of considerable complexity, involving microtubules, which presumably by controlled action, seem to open and close the ducts leading from the radial canals into the CV and the discharge tube leading from the CV to the exterior. Around each radial canal there are permanently modified ER tubules connected on the exterior to typical ER and on the interior to the radial canals.

Because the amount of water discharged by CVs may equal the volume of the cell in 10 to 15 minutes, there must be some mechanism for holding back innumerable water-soluble molecules in the protoplasm, probably the ER membrane. Since all evidence indicates that the CV itself is noncontractile and that discharge is accomplished by protoplasmic pressure, it has been proposed that "water expulsion vesicle" would be a better designation.

Therefore it seems that both plant vacuoles and at least some parts of the CV system of Protozoa are constructed of more or less modified parts of ER system. Hence it has been proposed that at least one function of the ER is related to osmoregulation.

Food vacuoles*

Protozoa and other cells that ingest solid particles of food do so by confining the particle and some liquid in a temporary, membrane-bounded vacuole called a food vacuole (Fig. 14-7). In general, when a spot of the plasma membrane senses the close presence of "food," tiny pseudopodia are extended around it until they meet outside the particle. Thus a part of the plasma membrane becomes the membrane of the food vacuole. The food vacuole contains both solid food and some of the environmental liquid. It is likely that lysosomes may produce the enzymes, which are then secreted into the liquid of the food vacuole to digest the solid food. Undigested material is then egested either through a special area of the pellicle of the protozoan or through any region of the surface.

In addition to most ciliates and Sarcodina probably all animals have such eating cells with food vacuoles. Sponges, Coelenterata, flatworms, and most Mollusca rely largely on such intracellular digestion. These phyla and all other animal phyla have ameboid cells such as leukocytes that, themselves, eat bacteria and naturally degenerating cells of the body.

Pinocytotic vacuoles

It seems that a great many animal and plant cells take in masses of purely liquid environment by invagination of the plasma membrane; when these droplets separate from the surface membrane, they become small vacuoles within the cytoplasm (Chapter 6). Because of their superficial origin, they are distinct from most other vesicles of the cell that are formed within the protoplasm itself. Thus food vacuoles and pinocytotic vacuoles differ from other vacuoles by having membranes derived from the plasma membrane rather than from the ER.

Nucleolar vacuole

It has been observed that nucleoli of plant, fungi, and animal cells contain canals and/or a vacuole (Figs. 15-7 and 18-21). Furthermore, this vacuole, which is probably *not* a permanent, membrane-bounded structure, often enlarges by accumulation of water and solutes and then discharges into the nucleoplasm. There are conflicting opinions as to whether the solutes are RNA

---
*Refer to Chapter 12 for further discussion.

and/or protein. Also, insufficient observations have been made to establish whether such nucleolar vacuoles are ubiquitous, merely common, or rather rare among plant and/or animal species or even among tissues of one organism.

Gas vacuoles

Although vacuoles are uncommon in the Prokaryota there are numerous species that form gas vacuoles typically or under specific conditions. They are characterized by having a unique proteniaceous membrane that

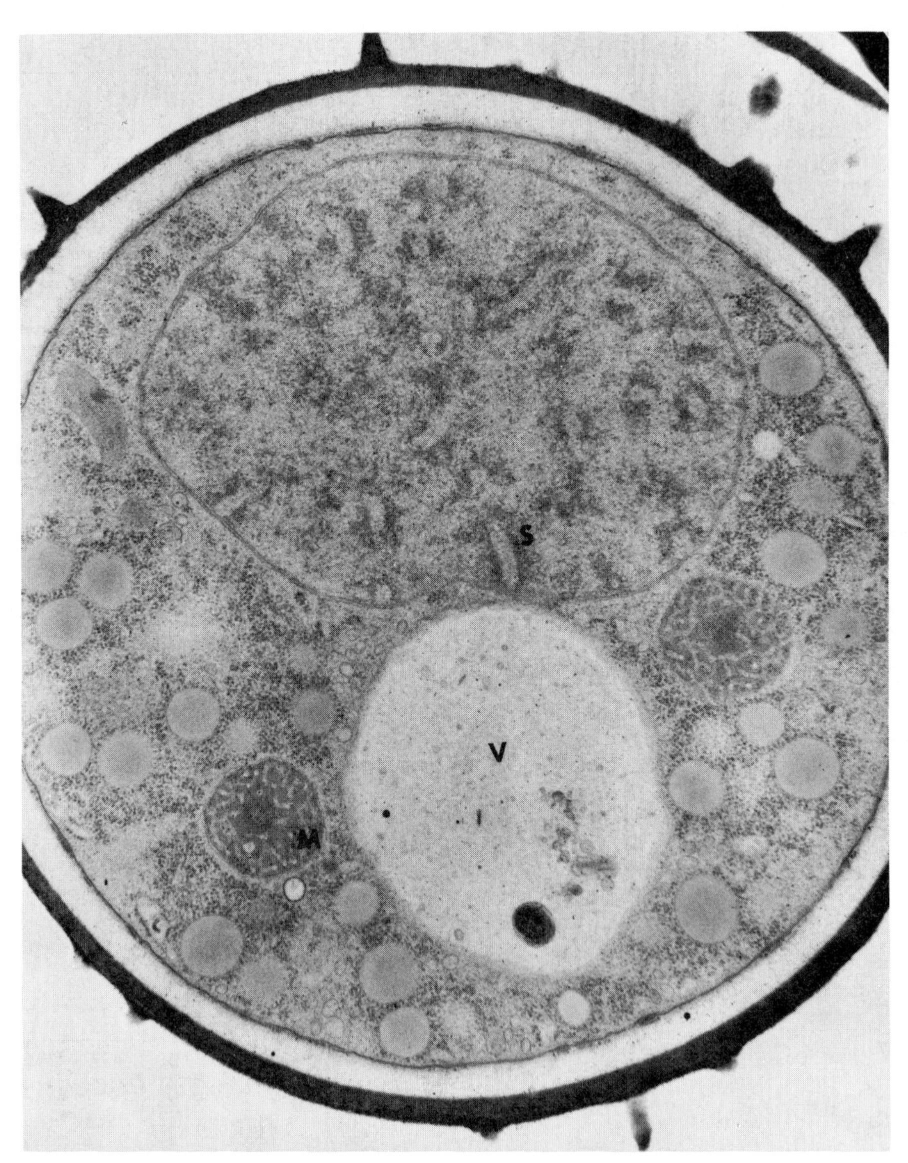

Fig. 14-7. Spore of the myxomycete *Physarum flavicomum* showing mitochondria, **M,** with central DNA region and tubular cristae; a large lightly stained food vacuole, **V;** and nucleus with double membrane and sections of synaptinemal complex, **S,** often abutting at right angles to the nuclear envelope as though attached. (Courtesy Dr. H. C. Aldrich, Department of Botany, University of Florida, Gainesville, Fla.)

lacks lipids and is transversely banded. For example, the blue-green alga *Nostoc muscorum,* when placed into distilled water, forms gas vacuoles that cause the filaments to rise to the surface of the water (Waaland and Branton, 1969). These particular gas vacuoles form de novo, are pointed at the ends, have the banded appearance, and probably add subunits and grow in length at about the middle.

CRYSTALS

Biologically active subcellular structures are not typically crystalline, but crystals of one sort or another do occur in cells of animals and plants. They can be roughly grouped into those that are largely of protein and those that are of oxalate.

Probably most intracellular crystals of animals are proteinaceous, although they often contain iron, probably in a prosthetic group. Such crystals have been reported within nuclei of echinoderm phagocytes, within distended cisternae of the ER of salamander liver cell cytoplasm, within the membrane-bounded yolk platelets of amphibians, insects, and other lower animals, and within lysosome-like granules of the eosinophilic leukocytes of most mammals. Hemoglobin may crystallize within erythrocytes, and crystals are often found within the cytoplasm of human testis interstitial cells, called *crystals of Reinke* after their discoverer (1896). Certain bacterial or viral parasites of certain insect larvae when they form endospores or virions also form protein crystals outside the endospore or capsid (Fig. 4-3), the protein of which is toxic for the insect. In plants certain vacuoles of specific endosperm cells of seeds typically contain in the cytoplasm proteinaceous crystals (enzymes) called *aleurone grains,* which seem to become functional for the digestion of the endosperm carbohydrate during seed germination. Plant (Fig. 14-8) and animal (Fig. 10-8) protein crystals have also been found in mitochondria, in the prokaryon of blue-green algae, in the nuclei and ER of eucells, and apparently free in the cytoplasm.

These proteinaceous crystals consist of orderly arrays of macromolecular spherical units of structure ranging from 60 to 300 Å in diameter. They are arranged in much the same way as smaller molecules in inorganic crystals. Of course, some cells may contain crystals, the structural units of which are viral particles. They would not be typical of normal cells but only of cells infected with the virus.

Inorganic intracellular crystals, calcium salts of carbonate, oxalate, or phosphate, are rather common in particular plants cells but are less common in animal cells. These are usually crystals of calcium oxalate, which form in vacuoles. Probably the commonest form consists of a bundle of needle-shaped crystals, known as *raphides* (Fig. 14-9), which are found in leaves, roots, fruits, etc. More or less spherical, but echinate, crystals are called *druses* (Fig. 14-10). Other forms are stellate or prismatic in shape. Electron microscopy has clarified the vague description of E. L. Smith in 1923 that although the crystals (raphides in this case) form in vacuoles they are, nevertheless, associated with the protoplasm.

Fig. 14-11 is an electron micrograph of a cross section of a bundle of raphides in a vacuole of a root cell of *Eichhornia.* Each crystal is surrounded by a membrane, and between adjacent membranes there are other protoplasmic structures. Actually, the membranes form before the crystals; the membranes produce and determine the form of the crystals. Fig. 14-12 is a diagrammatic interpretation of the membranous structures that produce these raphides. The crystals form in the long, narrow, square chambers. The tubes on the outsides of the chambers are abundant, are composed of unit membranes, have swollen regions at certain levels of the chambers, and extend to the vacuolar membrane (Arnott, 1966).

It has been concluded that the gross shapes of crystals are generally determined by the cell and not by mere physical fac-

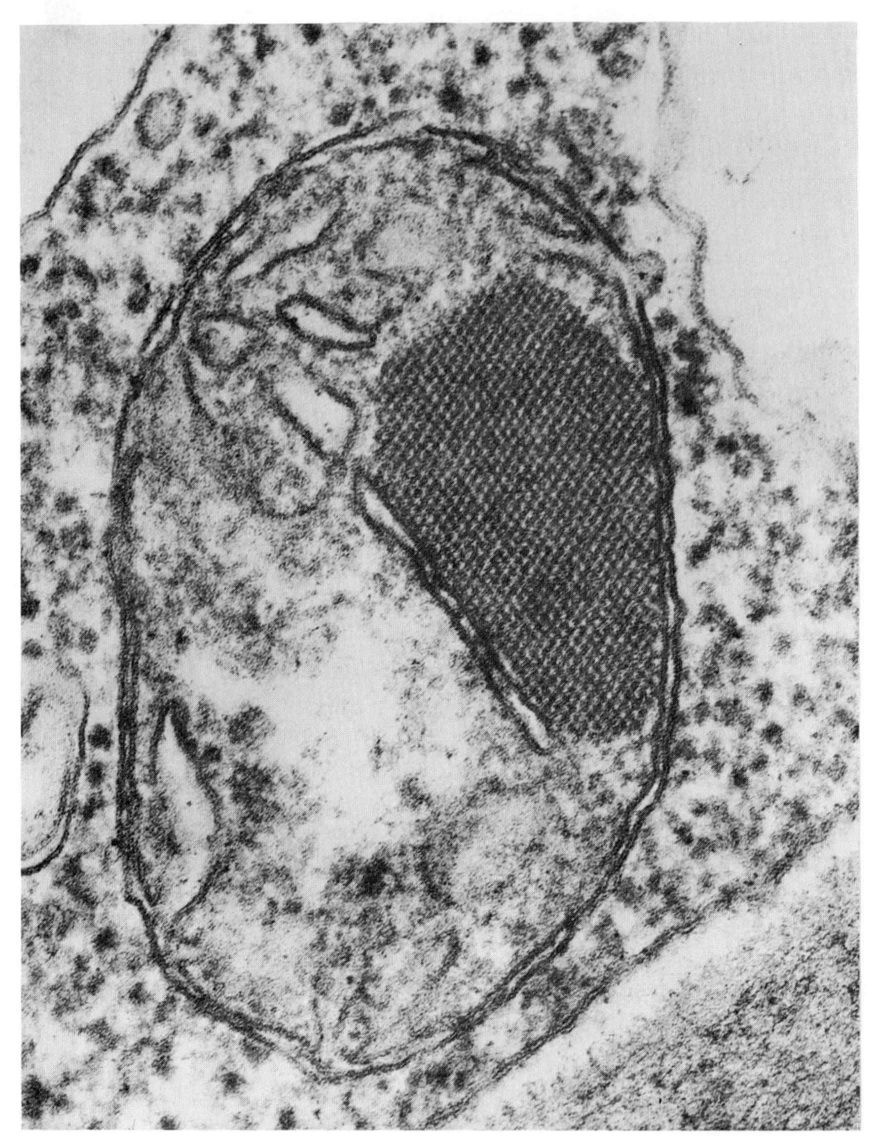

Fig. 14-8. A crystal, probably of protein, in a mitochondrion of the plant *Malpighia glabra.* (Courtesy Dr. H. Arnott, University of Texas Cell Research Institute, Austin, Texas.)

tors of crystallization out of a solution. This applies also to extracellular crystals; for example, hydroxyapatite is crystallized in the bone of mammals as tiny crystals, whereas in the same organism the crystals of teeth are much larger. In plants the crystalline forms of oxalate are various but are always determined by the cell producing them. Thus the shape is biologically controlled and takes place in certain specific cells as an aspect of their differentiation. In root tips forming raphides, in certain rows of cells only, the chambers develop as soon as mitosis in that row stops; all the cells of that row form crystals. It is possible that the structural units of "protein" crystals may be deter-

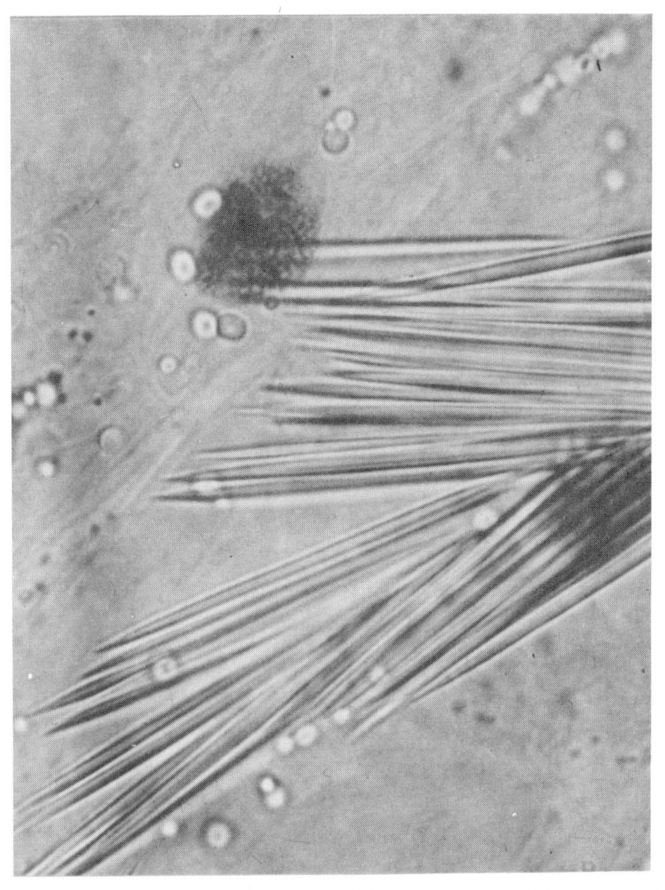

Fig. 14-9. Photomicrograph of a bundle of raphides from one cell of an anther of *Rhoeo discolor*. They have been somewhat spread apart in the squash preparation.

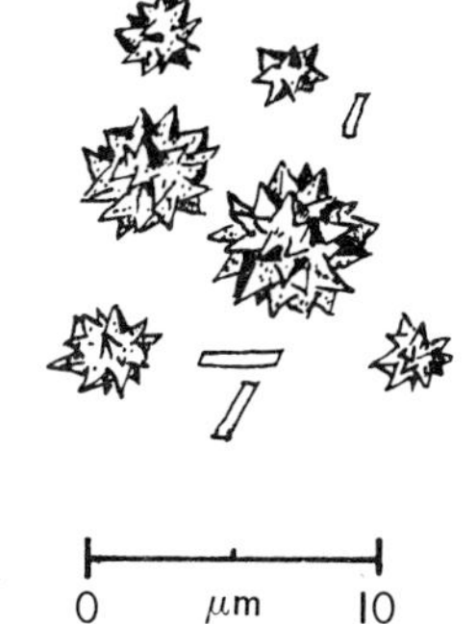

Fig. 14-10. Druses, a common form of irregular calcium oxalate crystals of plants. These are from florets of *Haplopappus gracilis*.

mined as to size and spacing by a membrane that forms the particles, whether ER or cristae of mitochondria. On the other hand, the formation of protein crystals in the vacuoles of aleurone cells of plants or the yolk platelets of animals seems to be more like crystallization out of solution, since there is amorphous material (liquid?) surrounding the crystal and filling the space between the crystal and the membrane.

Spicules of sponges, formed by special cells called scleroblasts, may be classified as crystals, especially the limy and silicious spicules. Such crystals range from needle shaped (two rayed) up to six rayed. The number of rays is determined in part by the number of nuclei formed by the scleroblast. If the scleroblast contains one or two nuclei as it starts to form the spicule internally, a needle-shaped spicule is determined. As the crystal becomes longer than

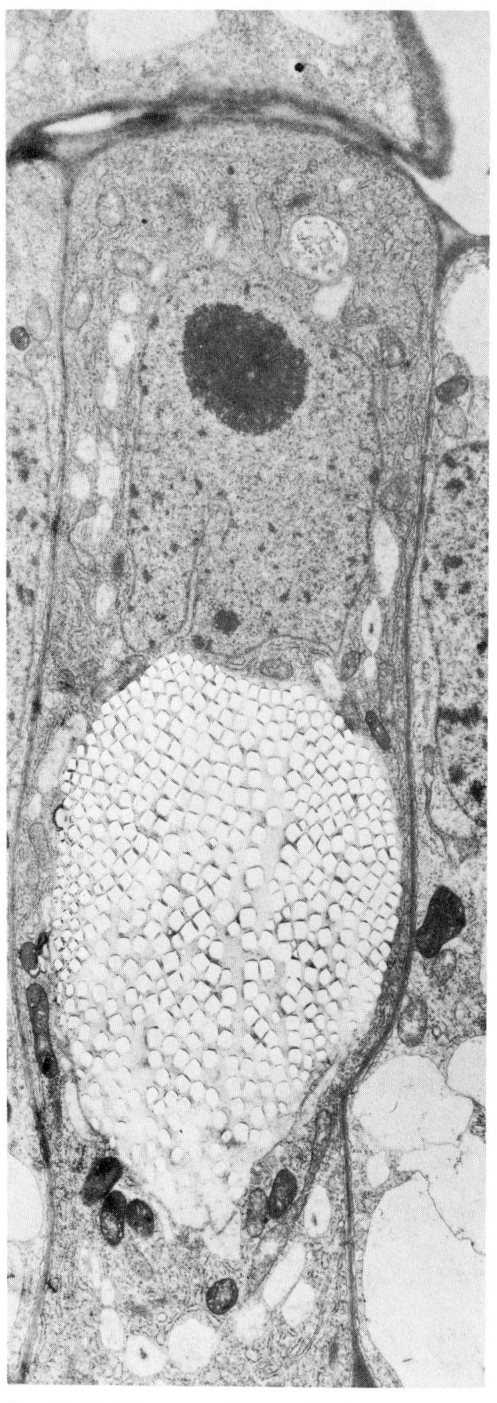

Fig. 14-11. Electron micrograph of cross sections of raphides (the mass of clear, square profiles) in a root tip cell of *Eichhornia.* They are all packed into a "vacuole," which has a vacuolar membrane called a tonoplast. (From Arnott, H., and F. G. E. Pautard. 1970. Calcification in plants. In Schraer, H. [editor]. Biological calcification: cellular and molecular aspects. Appleton-Century-Crofts, New York.)

the cell, each nucleus and about one half of the cytoplasm move out onto the lengthening crystal. Eventually, the two masses of cytoplasm separate with one cell at each growing tip. In this way long spicules can be formed. A triradiate spicule would be formed in a scleroblast (syncytium) of three nuclei, a six-rayed spicule in a syncytial scleroblast of six nuclei, etc. In each case the syncytium eventually divides into uninucleate cells, one at the tip of each growing ray.

Crystals of carotenoids are formed by many plants (Fig. 14-13). These yellow to red crystals are formed within differentiated plastids called chromoplasts. They are typical of nearly all yellow or orange plant parts such as carrots, flower petals, fruits, and stems. They are discussed in Chapter 11.

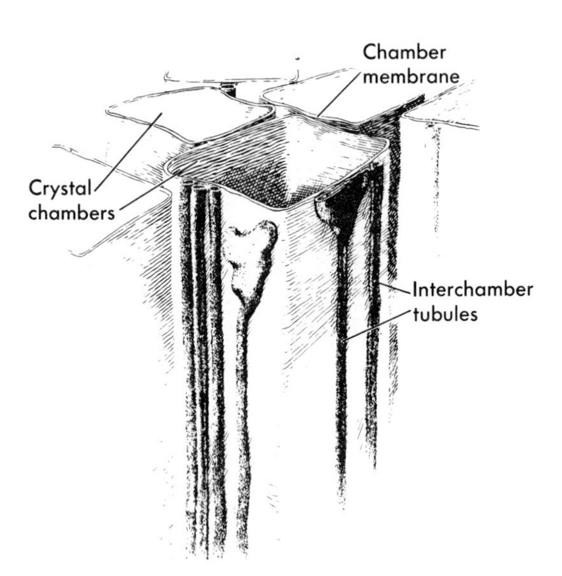

Fig. 14-12. Interpretative drawing of membranous chamber within which a raphide crystal appears to be formed. Associated externally with the chamber membrane are longitudinal *interchamber tubules* that seem to extend through the vacuolar membrane into the cytoplasm, thereby perhaps acting as channels for the movement of crystal material from cytoplasm to chambers. (From Arnott, H., and F. G. E. Pautard. 1970. Calcification in plants. In Schraer, H. [editor]. Biological calcification: cellular and molecular aspects. Appleton-Century-Crofts, New York.)

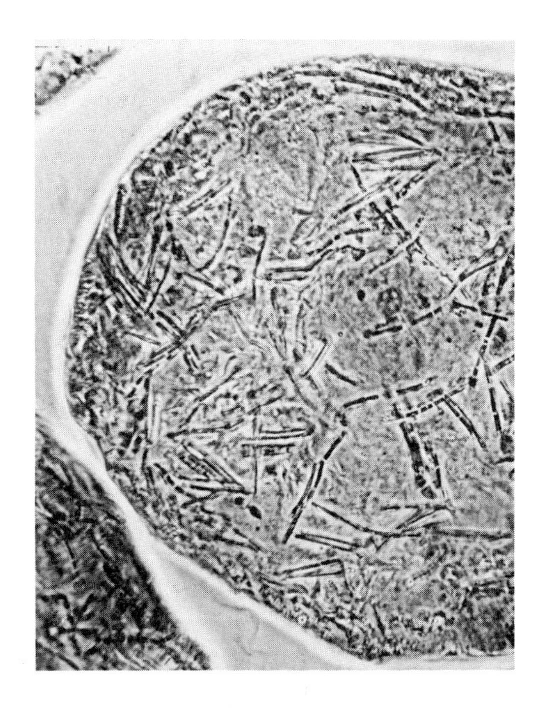

Fig. 14-13. Carotenoid crystals of a ripe tomato fruit in a squash preparation photographed by phase contrast. Each crystal was formed within a plastid as it changed from a chloroplast to a chromoplast. In general, the crystalline form is needle shaped, but flat sheets, rolled sheets, and triangles also occur commonly. (Courtesy Dr. S. W. Rosso, University of Texas Cell Research Institute, Austin, Texas.)

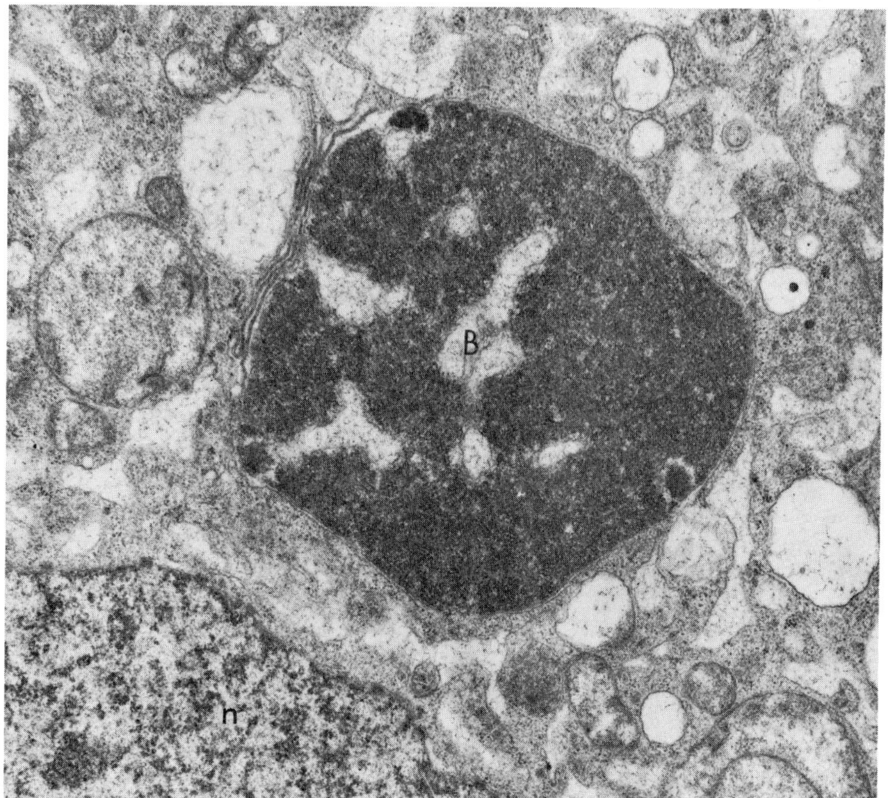

Fig. 14-14. Feulgen-positive, cytoplasmic, membrane-bounded body, **B,** which appears in the tetrad (microspore) cells near the nucleus, **n,** after the second meiotic division in pollen mother cells of *Hippeastrum belladonna.* (Courtesy Dr. D. A. Larson, University of Texas Cell Research Institute, Austin, Texas.)

CYTOPLASMIC DNA

Cytoplasmic DNA, or at least Feulgen-positive and DNAase-removable material, other than normal mitochondrial and plastid DNA, is known in plants and animals. In plants such granules (Fig. 14-14) have been reported in microsporocytes during prophase I in numerous plants (Sparrow and Hammond, 1947) and in the embryonic apical meristematic cells of *Stellaria media* (Pritchard, 1964). Such granules range from about 0.3 to 7 μm in diameter.

DNA granules have also been reported to pass from tapetal cells into microsporocytes in a number of plants (Cooper, 1952), but this observation needs confirmation before being accepted. Painter (1953) has pointed out that the numerous nurse cells of *Drosophila* and the tapetal cells of plant anthers generally become endopolyploid (increase their content of DNA) and then break down as nutrient for developing ova or pollen grains. At that time granules containing DNA might get into the cytoplasm of such cells.

Cytoplasmic nucleic acid, or chromatin, has long been known to accumulate in animal ova. For example, in amphibians the large egg contains 300 to 500 times as much DNA as a diploid somatic cell. Fish and sea urchin eggs have about fifty times as much as a diploid cell. In the fern *Pteridium aquilinum* the egg has considerably more DNA than a somatic cell, as is true also of *Drosophila* and many other organisms.

In the amphibian, Brachet and Quertier (1963) found that DNA increased close to the nucleus during the late diplotene and proposed that the DNA came from the nucleus. Dawid (1966), however, found that at least two thirds and possibly all of the cytoplasmic DNA of the frog egg (*Rana pipiens* and *Xenopus*) is located in the mitochondria, and it is similar to mitochondrial DNA.

Furthermore, Muckenthaler and Mahowald (1966) found cytoplasmic DNA in the egg of *Drosophila,* and Bell and Mühlethaler (1964) reported cytoplasmic DNA in the egg of the plant *Pteridium aquilinum* to be all or mostly mitochondrial and, in the latter species, proplastid also. Presumably, the mitochondria (and in plants, plastids also) increase in number, and each organelle possesses a larger amount of DNA. Such great increase in cytoplasmic DNA is as much or more for rapid organelle reproduction than for nuclear (chromosomal) increase during subsequent rapid cleavage.

Cytoplasmic DNA as *informational* DNA (I-DNA) in tiny particles called *I-somes* is claimed by Bell (1969, 1971) to be perhaps intermediate in the synthesis of mRNA. Presumably, chromosomal DNA or genes form small units of the I-DNA (of 7s), which, associated with protein, appear in the cytoplasm as I-somes of 16s. These "particles" then synthesize the mRNA for specific protein synthesis. Some evidence exists for an even more complicated pathway from gene to mRNA such as nuclear DNA (structural genes), which produces a type of nuclear RNA. The latter then synthesizes forms of I-DNA in the cytoplasm, and the I-DNA produces the mRNA.

LITERATURE CITED

Arnott, H. J. 1966. Studies of calcification in plants. Third European Symposium on Calcified Tissues. Springer-Verlag New York, Inc., New York.

Baker, P. C., and T. E. Schroeder. 1967. Cytoplasmic filaments and morphogenetic movement in the amphibian neural tube. Develop. Biol. **15:**432-450.

Behnke, O., and A. Forer. 1966. Intranuclear microtubules. Science **153:**1536-1537.

Bell, E. 1969. I-DNA: its packaging into I-somes and its relation to protein synthesis during differentiation. Nature (London) **224:**326-328.

Bell, E. 1971. Informational DNA synthesis distinguished from that of nuclear DNA by inhibitors of DNA synthesis. Science **174:**603-606.

Bell, P. R., and K. Mühlethaler. 1964. Evidence for the presence of deoxyribonucleic acid in the organelles of the egg cells of Pteridium aquilinum. J. Molec. Biol. **8:**853-862.

Bensch, K. G., R. Marantz, H. Wisniewski, and M. Shelanski. 1969. Induction in vitro of microtubular crystals by Vinca alkaloids. Science **165:**495-496.

Brachet, J., and J. Quertier. 1963. Cytochemical detection of cytoplasmic deoxyribonucleic acid (DNA) in amphibian oocytes. Exp. Cell Res. **32:**410-413.

Burton, P. R. 1966. Substructure of certain cytoplasmic microtubules: an electron microscopic study. Science **154:**903-905.

Buvat, R. 1961. Le reticulum endoplasmique des cellules végétales. Deutsch. Bot. Gesell. Ber. **74:**261-267.

Cooper, D. C. 1952. The transfer of DNA from the tapetum to the microsporocyte at the onset of meiosis. Amer. Nat. **86:**219-227.

Davison, P. S. 1970. Microtubules and microfilaments. In Biochemistry of simple neuronal models. Raven Press, New York.

Dawid, I. B. 1966. Evidence for the mitochondrial origin of frog egg cytoplasmic DNA. Proc. Nat. Acad. Sci. U.S.A. **56:**269-270.

Gibbins, J. R., L. G. Tilney, and K. R. Porter. 1969. Microtubules in the formation and development of the primary mesenchyme in Arbacea punctulata. I. The distribution of microtubules. J. Cell Biol. **41:**201-226.

Ledbetter, M. C., and K. R. Porter. 1963. A "microtubule" in plant cell fine structure. J. Cell Biol. **19:**239-250.

Ledbetter, M. C., and K. R. Porter. 1964. Morphology of microtubules of plant cells. Science **144:**872-874.

Muckenthaler, F. A., and A. P. Mahowald. 1966. DNA synthesis in ooplasm of Drosophila melanogaster. J. Cell Biol. **28:**199-207.

Nagai, R., and L. I. Rebhun. 1966. Cytoplasmic microfilaments in streaming Nitella cells. J. Ultrastruct. Res. **14:**571-589.

Newcomb, E. H. 1969. Plant microtubules. Ann. Rev. Plant Physiol. **20:**253-288.

O'Brien, T. P., and K. V. Thimann. 1966. Intracellular fibers in oat coleoptile cells and their possible significance in cytoplasmic streaming. Proc. Nat. Acad. Sci. U.S.A. **56:**888-894.

Painter, T. S. 1953. Some cytological aspects of the nucleic acid problem. Texas Rep. Biol. Med. **11:**709-714.

Pitelka, D. R. 1963. Electron-microscopic structure of Protozoa. The Macmillan Co., New York.

Pritchard, H. N. 1964. A cytochemical study of embryo development in Stellaria media. Amer. J. Bot. **51:**472-479.

Smith, D. S., U. Järlfors, and R. Beránek. 1970. The organization of synaptic axoplasm in the lamprey (Petromyzon marinus) central nervous system. J. Cell Biol. **46:**199-219.

Slautterback, D. B. 1963. Cytoplasmic microtubules. I. Hydra. J. Cell Biol. **18:**367.

Sparrow, A. H., and M. R. Hammond. 1947. Cytological evidence for the transfer of desoxyribose nucleic acid from nucleus to cytoplasm in certain plant cells. Amer. J. Bot. **34:**439-445.

de Thé, G. 1964. Cytoplasmic microtubules in different animal cells. J. Cell Biol. **23:**265.

Tilney, L. G., and J. R. Gibbins. 1969. Microtubules in the formation and development of the primary mesenchyme in Arbacea punctulata. J. Cell Biol. **41:**227-250.

Tilney, L. G., Y. Hiramoto, and D. Marsland. 1966. III. Studies on the microtubules in Heliozoa. J. Cell Biol. **29:**77-95.

Tilney, L. G., and K. R. Porter. 1967. Studies on the microtubules in Heliozoa. II. The effect of low temperature on the structures in the formation and maintenance of axopodia. J. Cell Biol. **34:**327-343.

Waaland, J. R., and D. Branton. 1969. Gas vacuole development in a blue-green alga. Science **163:**1339-1341.

Wessells, N. K., et al. 1971. Microfilaments in cellular and developmental processes. Science **171:**135-143.

Zirkle, C. 1937. The plant vacuole. Bot. Rev. **3:**1-30.

CHAPTER 15

The nucleus

Because of its large size, the nucleus was one of the first cellular bodies seen by early microscopists in the cells of higher plants and animals. As early as 1831 it was possible for Robert Brown to propose that the nucleus is a structure that is probably present in all cells. Subsequent studies revealed the truth of that generalization except in bacteria, actinomycetes, blue-green algae—the group now known as the Prokaryota. It was not until about 1960, by use of electron microscopy, that the true nature of the central "nucleus" of these prokaryotic organisms was revealed.

If one defines the term "nucleus" to include the DNA-containing regions of the Prokaryota, as is the practice among microbiologists and many cytologists, a classification of "nuclei" such as the following is possible:

A. Prokaryotic nucleus
    1. Prokaryota (Chapter 4)
    2. Plastids (Chapter 11)
    3. Mitochondria (Chapter 10)
B. Eukaryotic nucleus (in all other organisms)

This classification is possible because it has now been demonstrated that plastids and mitochondria have DNA, RNA, active genes, and some self-sufficient protein synthesis. Some mitochondria (Figs. 10-9 and 17-4) seem to have, according to electron micrographs, as much of a "nucleus" as a bacterium (Figs. 15-1, 3-1, and 10-19). Loop or circular chromosomes similar to those of bacteria have been isolated (Fig. 10-10). Also, division of plastids and mitochondria is similar to division typical of Prokaryota. Thus the symbolic hypothesis of the origins of these intracellular bodies has been greatly strengthened during the past few years.

The "nucleus" of the Prokaryota has been discussed in an earlier section as the "prokaryon," since it is so different from the nucleus of eukaryotic cells, to which the term "nucleus" was originally ascribed. Therefore the discussion here will be limited to the nucleus as it occurs in eukaryotic cells.

This nucleus mostly exists in complete cells as a membrane-bounded body except when distributing its chromosomes, as during mitosis and meiosis (Fig. 3-1). There is generally one nucleus, but two or more are not uncommon (in plasmodia and syncytia, for example). Furthermore, nuclei may vary considerably in chromosome content, from haploid to the more common diploid condition to highly complex conditions of polyploidy, endopolyploidy, and polyteny. They may also vary in size and shape among cells and tissues of a single multicellular organism and seem to have the ability to move autonomously and to assume definite positions within particular cells. They are of great importance in differentiation and may somehow determine the orientation of the spindle at division. They are, of course, completely dependent on the surrounding cytoplasm, which, in turn, is ultimately dependent for continued functioning and survival on the nucleus.

GENETIC ACTIVITY

In the typical eukaryotic interphase nucleus—and there seem to be exceptions as in the dinoflagellate algae (Dodge, 1963, 1964a) and perhaps fungi—the chromosomes are diffuse. It is in this extended condition only (except for certain exceptional

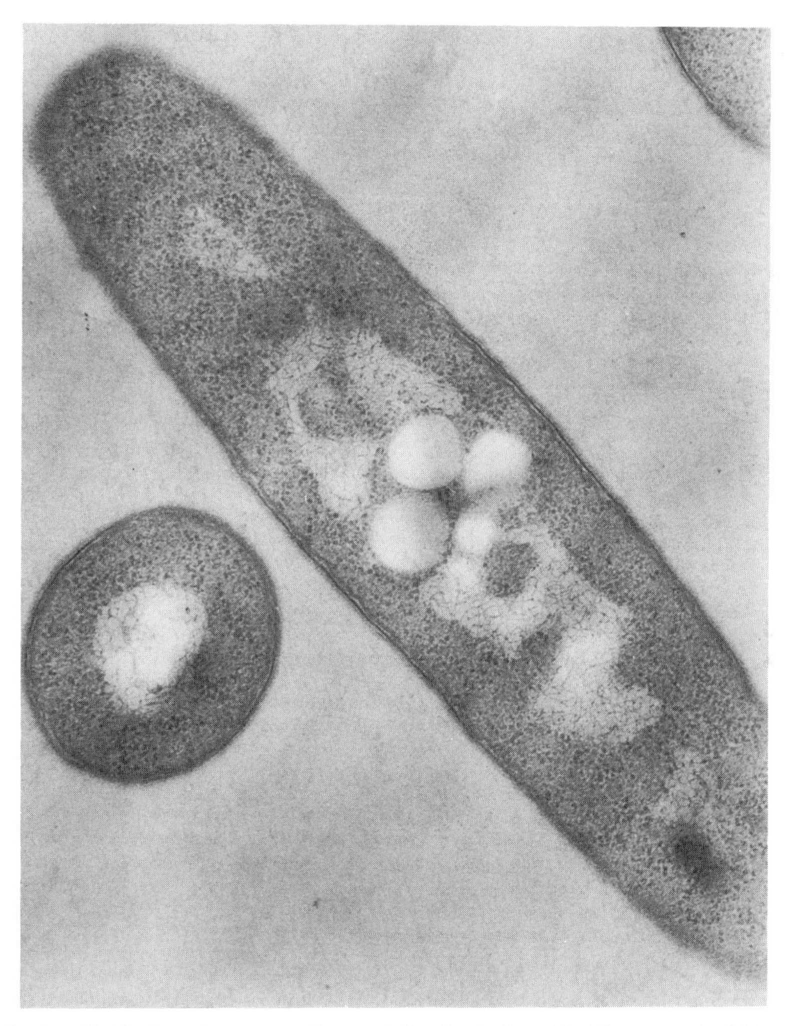

Fig. 15-1. Longitudinal and cross sections of the bacterium *Bacillus aneurinolyticus* showing the wall, procytoplasm containing many ribosomes but no other cytoplasmic organelles, and the much lighter stained prokaryon, which is of irregular shape and not membrane-bounded. The large, clear, spherical granules probably contained the not uncommon bacterial reserve polyester of β-hydroxybutyric acid monomers called *poly β-hydroxybutyric acid.* (Courtesy Dr. J. L. Wittliff, Dr. J. F. Smith, and Dr. R. L. Airth, University of Texas Cell Research Institute, Austin, Texas.)

Protista and fungi) that the DNA can replicate and transcription of various RNAs occurs. Thus it is in the interphase nucleus, or the equivalent *postmitotic* condition, that genetic activity occurs.

Fundamentally, the genetic activities of the nucleus are both the replication of the hereditary DNA and transcription of various RNAs. In ciliate Protozoa, however, there are two nuclei: The *macronucleus* seems to be specialized for RNA transcription and the *micronucleus* for hereditary DNA replication. Gene actions are the transcription of mRNA, tRNA, ribosomal RNA, and repressor substances. These genetic activities are now known to be far more complex than the aphorism "one gene—one enzyme," common about 1940, would imply. It is now known that several genes may be required to produce one enzyme. Some genes do not seem ultimately to produce metabolic enzymes at all but substances (RNA, protein, or nucleoprotein) that affect other genes, or else it is the RNA itself (tRNA and ribosomal RNA) that is functional. Genes that affect other genes (regulatory genes) induce or inhibit them, turn them "on" or "off." Thus at least three categories of genes are specified in Jacob and Monod's (1961) model of gene action. Far more complex systems of gene regulation have been proposed recently (Britten and Davidson, 1969).

Gene actions of these sorts seem limited to the nonmitotic condition of the nucleus. A mitotic division may interrupt the action but probably has little effect on the nuclear differentiation, and metabolism in the cytoplasm continues because the lifetime of mRNA and enzymes is usually longer than a mitotic division. Genetic differentiation in the cells of the germ line of animals is probably slight.

Energic nucleus

The energic nucleus, a term coined and justified by Berrill and Huskins (1936), is a nonmitotic nucleus, one not in division. As they emphasized, however, the term "energic" emphasizes the physiological activity of the nonmitotic nucleus. In addition to the biochemical activities of the energic nucleus, the authors contended that it is "responsible for the maintenance of certain kinds of cytoplasmic structures," and they cited references to the effect that generally when division occurs in ciliated cells of Protozoa and Metazoa, the cilia are resorbed and then re-formed after division. Hemoglobin content disappears from erythrocytes of *Triton* with the onset of mitosis. Glycogen and fat disappear from the cytoplasm of liver cells in mitotic division. Secretory granules in intestinal epithelial cells of the frog tend to disappear completely during mitosis. Cartilage cells during division do not form the intercellular matrix. Cells rarely differentiate until they become postmitotic and so possess an energic nucleus.

Thus there are two nuclear conditions in cells, the nondividing "energic" nucleus and the "kinetic" nucleus, which is in the process of mitotic division. It is also possible to subdivide energic nuclei into *intermitotic* or *interphase* nuclei, which will divide again, and *postmitotic* nuclei, which normally will never divide again. There are differences between these.

Nondividing nuclei

The interphase (or postmitotic or nonmitotic) nucleus is of great biological significance, as demonstrated by biochemists and others. Yet, cytologically, it is unexciting. The chromosomes can hardly be seen or studied, and the nucleus just sits there, as observably inactive as a sleeping dog and as static as the old term for this nuclear condition, "resting stage," indicates. Gradually, however, biochemistry and histochemistry have constructed a concept of the real activities and biological significance of this indispensable and certainly not "resting" cellular structure. It warrants extended treatment in a cytology text.

The chemistry, at least the gross chemical

categories, of a nonmitotic nucleus is quite well known because nuclei are rather easily isolated from the rest of the cell in large numbers. They certainly contain DNA, RNA, basic proteins (histones), acid and neutral proteins (some or all of which are enzymes), probably some lipid other than in the nuclear envelope, considerable calcium and magnesium, and, of course, water. Much of the DNA and RNA is probably complexed with various proteins as nucleoprotein. Some of the enzymes are functionally and structurally part of the chromosomes, but some are probably in the nucleoplasm and concerned with the glycolytic pathway.

The nucleus, like the cell itself, is an "open system" into which numerous kinds of molecules pass from the cytoplasm and out of which others move into the cytoplasm. Therefore, as is well known, the nucleus and cytoplasm constitute an integrated system, neither able to survive without the other. More specific chemical characterization will be made of the constituent parts of the nucleus: the nucleoplasm, nuclear envelope, nucleolus, and chromosomes.

MORPHOLOGY

The morphology of nuclei is variable not only among cells but even within one cell at different times. Nuclei range in size from the tiny nuclei (1 to 5 μm) of most fungi to the large nuclei of many oocytes and salivary gland cells. Mostly, however, nuclei have a diameter of 5 to 30 μm. Various reproductive nuclei tend to be large, such as those of meiocytes, ova, and zygotes. In general, nuclei of somatic cells of an organism are constant in size, except that nuclei of dividing (interphase) cells are larger than those of nondividing (postmitotic) cells. Nuclei also vary more or less proportionally to the amount of contained DNA. Salamander cell nuclei, high in DNA, are large for vertebrate cells. The nuclei containing giant chromosomes (salivary gland cells of Diptera) are very large (Figs. 17-15 and 17-16). Nuclei of polyploid species are somewhat larger than nuclei of comparable cells of related diploid species. Nuclei of actively synthesizing cells are often larger than those in less active cells.

Shapes

Nuclear shapes vary less than size. Nuclei are generally spherical or oblate spheroids. Nevertheless, in long, narrow cells such as developing fiber cells of plants they may be elongate, or when appressed against the membrane in a thin layer of cytoplasm, they may have a disk shape. In some plant and animal cells, however, the shape may be slightly to very irregular, described as polymorphic. The irregular nuclei in cells of the spinning glands of butterflies have long been known (Fig. 15-2). In at least some species of plants the tube nucleus in the pollen grain is equally polymorphic or even more so (Fig. 15-3). The irregular nuclei in many white blood cells of vertebrates are often highly lobed (Fig. 15-10), as they may be in certain plant cells of roots and stems (Fig. 15-4). Nuclei of sperm heads of animals are of various shapes, those of insects being almost as long (and narrow) as the sperm itself. Among some dinoflagellate algae the interphase nucleus is U shaped, being curved around the nucleous-like extranuclear central body. Among ciliate Protozoa the macronuclei assume many shapes characteristic of the species. In *Stentor,*

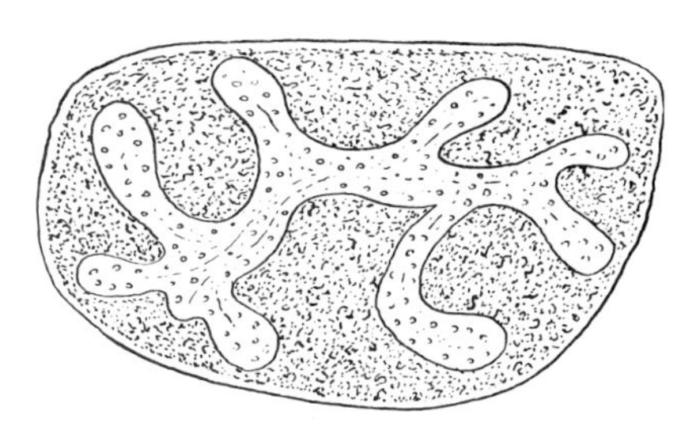

Fig. 15-2. Cell of spinning gland of butterfly larva. This is an extreme example of polymorphic nucleus (light-colored area), a condition often associated with high cellular protein synthetic activity. (After Karschett, 1897.)

for example, the macronucleus is like a string of beads.

In the guard cells of grasses each nucleus is drawn out into a thin thread through the pore of the central region, but at each end of the cell the nucleus is enlarged. Thus an elongate dumbbell-shaped nucleus results. This form is probably imposed by the unusual dumbbell shape of the protoplast itself. The irregular shape, as seen in the spinning glands of some insects (Fig. 15-2), is correlated with high metabolic activity, especially synthesis of protein and all that it implies.

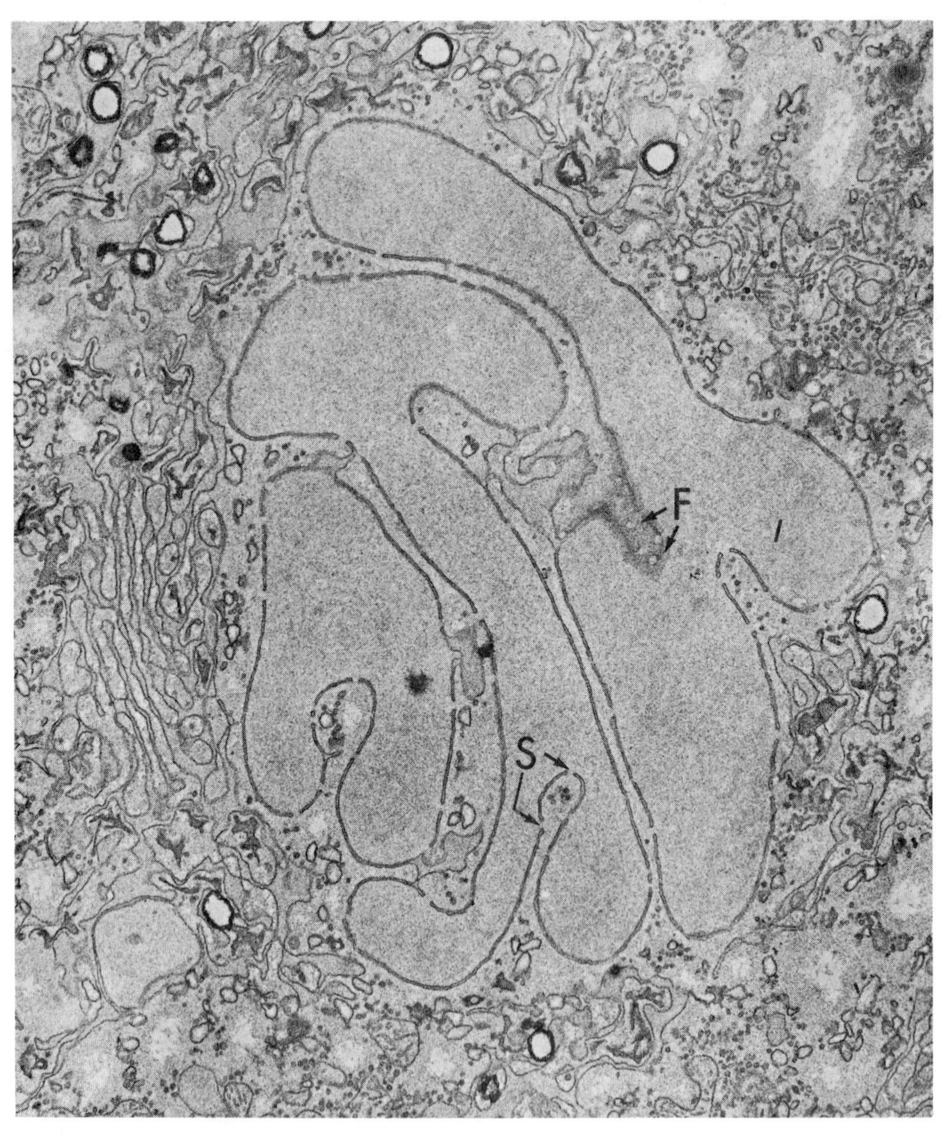

Fig. 15-3. Cross section of highly polymorphic tube nucleus in pollen grain of *Prosopis* (mesquite). Pores in nuclear envelope are evident both in face, **F,** and sectional, **S,** view. Note also unions of outer nuclear membranes where two or three portions of the nucleus lie close together. (Courtesy Dr. D. A. Larson, University of Texas Cell Research Institute, Austin, Texas.)

The most extreme form of nuclei is probably the threadlike nuclei reported by Molisch (1901) in the juice of leaves of the commonly cultivated spider lily *(Lycoris radiata)*. Some of these nuclei were 1,500 μm long and 0.2 μm thick, that is, 1.5 mm long. Nuclei in some insect sperm are also millimeters long.

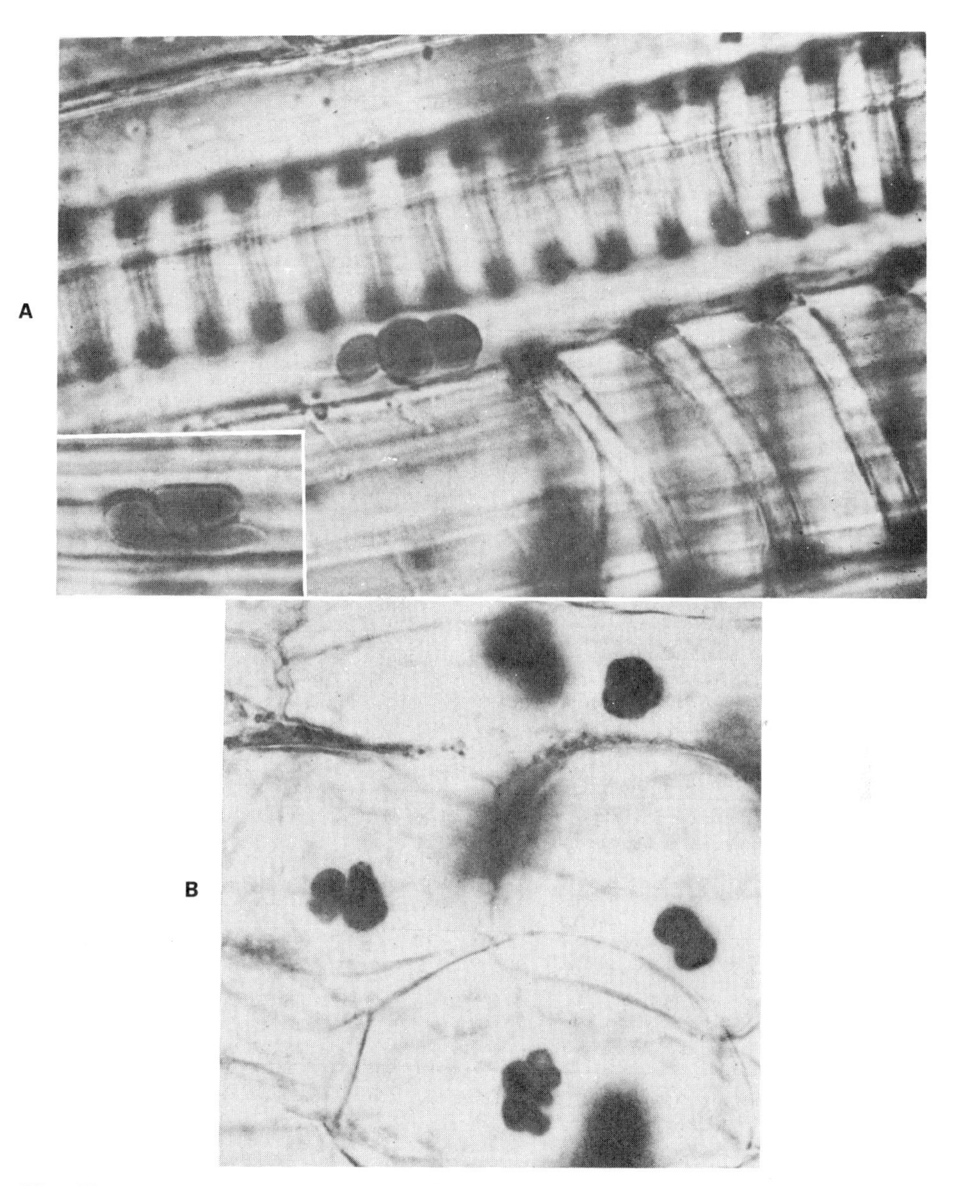

Fig. 15-4. Polymorphic nuclei in stem, **A,** and root, **B,** of *Tradescantia.* In **A** and in insert two polymorphic postmitotic nuclei are shown in narrow xylem cells (between two vessels in **A**). Vessel below nucleus has a spiral thickening, the one above has annular (ring-shaped) thickenings. **B,** Polymorphic nuclei in root tip cells close to the epidermis, back of the region of division, and in the region of cell enlargement. Such nuclei can be interpreted (perhaps wrongly) as evidence of amitosis.

Structure

Structure is evident in the nonmitotic nucleus. The largest and most obvious organelle, seen as early as the 18th century, is the nucleolus, or nucleoli if there are two or more (discussed later). It has also been known for many years that the nucleus is double membrane bounded, except perhaps

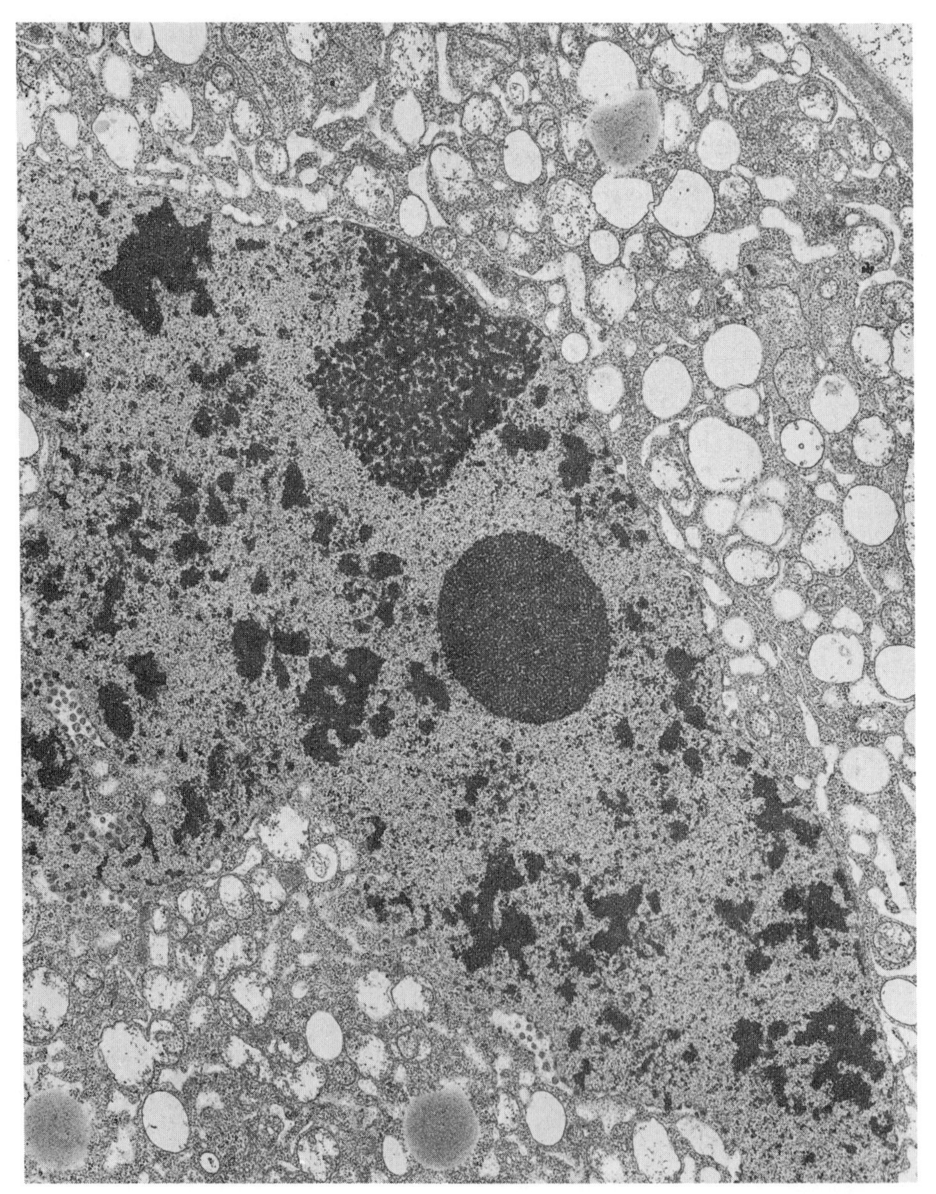

Fig. 15-5. Electron micrograph showing two separate sorts of nucleolar material in *Hippeastrum belladonna,* one of which is appressed against the nuclear envelope, a common nucleolar position in organisms at pachytene. Also note patches of pores in nuclear envelope along the lower left nuclear surface. (Courtesy Dr. D. A. Larson, University of Texas Cell Research Institute, Austin, Texas.)

in some dinoflagellates and some insect sperm (Chapter 7). Other structures are less obvious, but in stained nuclei numerous small to large, irregularly shaped masses of chromatin that indicate the presence of chromosomes can usually be seen (Figs. 3-1, 15-5, and 15-9). The nucleolus and chromosomes are suspended within the membrane in a nearly structureless fluid called *nucleoplasm*.

Nuclear envelope. The nuclear envelope (Chapter 7), as revealed by electron microscopy, is a *double* membrane system and for that reason is called an envelope rather than a membrane. Pores having diameters from 500 to 1,000 Å are typically present in the nuclear envelopes of animal (Chapter 7) and plant cells (Fig. 15-3 and 15-5). Breaks often appear in the nuclear envelopes of plants, varying from many small to one or a few large interruptions. These are probably artifacts caused by contraction of a large spherical surface. Some, however, may represent breaks that existed in vivo. That they may be real is indicated by the megasporocyte nucleus of *Ginkgo,* which always has a large break in the same position (Stewart and Gifford, 1967). Such a large break may represent from one tenth to one fifth of the nuclear circumference. These breaks have no pore complexes of any sort; they are just simple interruptions through which, if they occur in vivo, molecules, ions, or solid masses should pass freely. Formation of external vesicles by the double membrane may constitute a third mechanism of transport in addition to movement through pores and the membrane itself.

On the inside, chromosomes probably always and nucleoli sometimes are intimately associated with the nuclear envelope except just under the pores (Figs. 15-5, 15-9, 18-5, and 18-10). These associations may be important functionally as, for example, in prometaphase movements of chromosomes in mitosis and meiosis.

Origin of nuclear envelope. The origin of the nuclear envelope (a new one is formed at each cell division in most higher Eukaryota) is revealed by light and electron microscopy (Fig. 17-17). It forms at telophase, either by the membrane being formed de novo by the chromosomes themselves (Kater, 1927, 1928) or by pieces of ER or old pieces of prophase nuclear membrane approaching and making intimate contact with telophase chromosome surfaces. Either interpretation is possible from static electron micrographs (Brinkley, 1965; Pickett-Heaps and Northcote, 1966; Robbins and Gonatas, 1964). Of the two, the origin from existing pieces of ER or old nuclear membrane fits the accepted generalization that membranes do not form de novo, but only from preexisting template membrane. Certainly the earliest membrane pieces at telophase already have pores.

Cleveland (1953), however, reported that in certain Protozoa a new nuclear envelope forms around the chromosomes while they are still within the old nuclear envelope and isolated from the ER. Be that as it may, at telophase the exposed parts of chromosomes such as ends of arms and centromere regions are seen to have pieces of membrane closely associated on their surfaces. Either these pieces grow in area and make contact among themselves or more pieces from the cytoplasm continue to be added until the membrane is complete. It is likely that the associations of centromere and telomere regions of chromosome arms with the nuclear envelope persist throughout interphase. In some lower Eukaryota (some algae, protozoa, and fungi) the nuclear envelope persists intact or opens at the polar ends during mitosis (Figs. 17-4 and 17-5). In at least some of these the old envelope unquestionably forms the basis for the two new ones.

Micronuclei. Micronuclei are tiny nuclei that occur in addition to the two typical large ones at telophase. They usually form around a chromosome that "lags" at the metaphase plate at anaphase and does not become included in either telophase nucleus

(Fig. 15-6). Micronuclei generally do not persist long, but neither does the cell in which they form, since the regular nucleus is deficient in all the genes included in the micronucleus. Micronuclei generally appear at meiosis in unbalanced hybrids or in mitotic or meiotic cells subjected to x rays, certain chemicals, heat, and other conditions that partially upset anaphase.

Karyomeres. Karyomeres are rather like micronuclei except that they are normal and become associated to form a "compound" nucleus. At telophase, instead of one nuclear envelope surrounding all of the chromo-

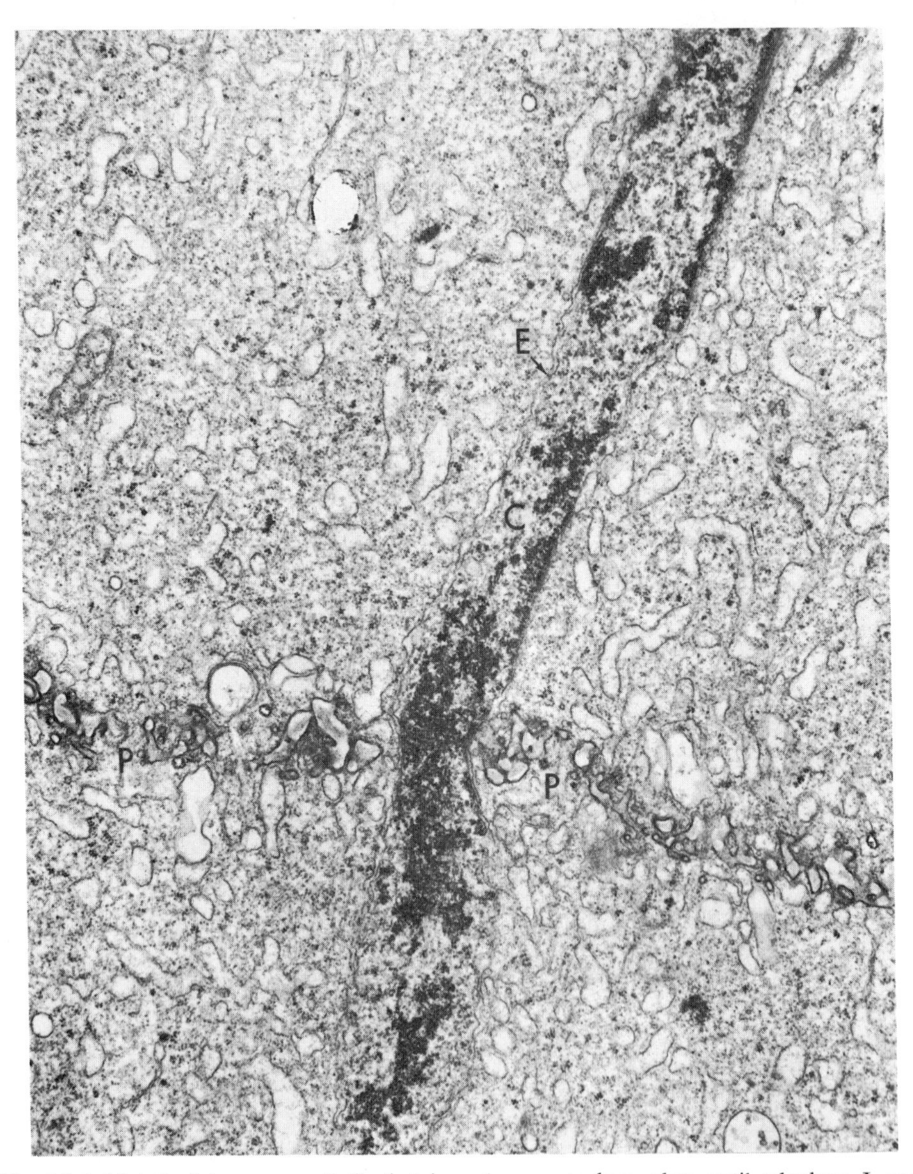

Fig. 15-6. Meiotic "chromosome," **C,** that lagged on metaphase plate until telophase I, produced its own nuclear envelope, **E,** and is caught lying across the developing cell plate, **P,** in *Hippeastrum belladonna.* (Courtesy Dr. D. A. Larson, University of Texas Cell Research Institute, Austin, Texas.)

somes, a "nuclear" envelope forms around each chromosome because of a divergent spindle that disperses the chromosomes at late anaphase. Karyomeres that form at telophase in the spermatogonia of some grasshoppers become partially fused, as do the karyomeres of *Fundulus* and *Crepidula.* In the blastomeres of the mite *Pediculopsis graminum* the four chromosomes form four distinct karyomeres that persist as separate nuclei until the next prophase and each forms a separate spindle, all of which lie parallel at the time of metaphase. In *Zea mays* a gene for "divergent spindle" produces a few small nuclei at each pole, each containing one or more chromosomes. These could be called either micronuclei or karyomeres, and if a telophase group contains a full haploid chromosome complement, the second meiotic division has multiple spindles but the microspore division may be normal. Formation of micronuclei has demonstrated that any chromosome can form a nuclear envelope, but it has also indicated that all chromosomes of the set do not produce nucleolar material or cannot form nucleoli at telophase because nucleoli appear only in the micronuclei containing the chromosomes possessing nucleolus organizers (see later discussion).

Restitution nuclei. Restitution nuclei are formed when anaphase separation is inhibited (as by genes, irregular anaphase as in hybrids, colchicine, and podophyllin) or is incomplete so that the two "anaphase" groups of chromosomes are not completely separated and become enclosed by one nuclear envelope instead of two. It is one manner in which polyploid nuclei arise naturally or artificially.

In all of these unusual nuclei as well as in typical nuclei the particular results are inevitable because of the manner of formation of the new nuclear envelope. That is, the first parts to form at telophase, regardless of how, appear on the exposed parts of chromosomes, the parts most exposed to the surrounding cytoplasm (Fig. 17-17). Later the gaps are filled in. If chromosomes are widely separated, micronuclei or karyomeres will form. If at telophase some chromosomes are scattered along the spindle more or less continuously between the main telophase groups, a single dumbbell-shaped nucleus must be formed that will round up into a restitution nucleus by interphase.

Nucleolus. The nucleolus (or nucleoli), being present in all nuclei of eukaryotic cells except in nuclei of some sperm, pollen tubes, cleavage cells of amphibians, and some algae, would seem to be of vital importance to the cell. This conclusion now seems to have been proved. Cells or embryos lacking nucleoli do not live long, and mitotic cells cannot complete mitosis without a nucleolus.

Nucleoli are unique organelles because they generally do not arise from preexisting nucleoli by division, are very dense (40% dry matter), are not membrane bounded, and come and go in most cells that are in cycles of division. That is, during metaphase and anaphase most cells do not have nucleoli, and they are formed de novo at each telophase. Otherwise, however, they are permanent and obvious nuclear organelles of intermitotic or postmitotic cells.

Nucleoli often consist of two regions. The center, the "core," is described as fibrillar *(pars fibrosa)* and contains, in part, the diffuse 100 Å chromatin filaments of the nucleolus organizer. The exterior portion, the "cortex," is granular *(pars granulosa)* and consists of 200 Å ribonucleoprotein particles that have similarities to ribosomes. There is evidence that the nucleolar RNA (nRNA) is transcribed in the pars fibrosa and protein is synthesized during the movement outward into the pars granulosa. The subsequent changes and movements of the nucleolar granules to cytoplasmic ribosomes are unclear, but the two are certainly not identical; that is, each of the redundant nucleolus organizer cistrons (rDNA) produces a linear nRNA strand about 0.33 μm long with a molecular weight of 40s. At some time and place (or times and places) this strand is "cut" into three portions: The first (28s) becomes the rRNA of the large part of the ribosome, the second (18s) becomes the rRNA of the small part of the ribosome, and the third is degraded. This probably occurs while the RNA is complexed with protein as ribonucleoprotein.

Recently the formation of the nRNA as it is being transcribed by the transcriptase (RNA polymerase) enzymes along the rDNA cistrons has been photographed by electron microscopy (Miller and Beatty, 1969). The nRNA polymers are shown in various stages of completion along each cistron. Presumably, they are detached when complete and leave the chromatin. Miller et al. (1970) have shown bacterial rDNA in action, producing RNA for ribosomes but not within nucleoli. The nucleoli used by Miller and Beatty were produced in amphibian oocytes by replicated nucleolus organizers separating from the chromosomes and forming about 1,000 such extra chromosomal nucleoli within the oocyte nucleus, the germinal vesicle.

The terms "karyosome," "endosome," and "central body" are applied to nucleolus-like nuclear organelles that are permanent structures. They divide or are divided into two parts at mitosis or meiosis by a pinching in of the metaphase plate at metaphase or anaphase. Karyosomes are probably permanent nucleoli that undergo division and are found in numerous algae, Protozoa, and some fungi, although no nucleolus has been seen by either light or electron microscopy in the dinoflagellate *Prorocentrum* (Dodge, 1963). In *Gonyaulax* the nucleolus-like central body lies outside the nucleus (Dodge, 1964b). If it is considered that these Protista represent primitive evolutionary forms, it can be assumed that the disappearance and re-formation of nucleoli are characters acquired by the "higher," more recent types of organisms. Evidence for this assumption is that in many flowering plants, and probably mammals too, some nucleolar material often does persist to metaphase or later and does divide, often at metaphase, into two parts that somehow move or are moved toward the spindle poles. Such persistent nucleolar remnants may or may not be included in the new telophase nuclei.

The nucleolus is now known to be a non-membrane-bounded body "attached" to two or more chromosomes at their nucleolus organizer segments (Figs. 16-1, 16-3, and 16-7) and composed mostly of ribonucleoprotein. Crosby (1957) found in wheat that only those chromosomes having nucleolar organizers (I, X, XIV, and XVIII) could produce nucleoli when present in a micronucleus and that an X isochromosome for the short arm (having two nucleolar organizers) produced twice as much nucleolar material as the normal X chromosome. With radioactive amino acids or nucleotides (for example, uracil) in the cell's environment it is evident by radioautography that RNA and protein are synthesized in the nucleolus. If DNA is detected in the nucleolus (for example, the DNA body or chromatin filaments), it is considered to represent that part of the chromosome known as the "nucleolus organizer" (Chapter 16). The best concept seems to be that the nucleoprotein is present as tiny, 150 Å particles similar to ribosomes (Fig. 15-5). In fact, the nucleolus is the site of initial ribosome precursor formation (Chapter 9). Since all cellular synthesis requires ribosomes for construction of necessary enzymes, ribosome formation is certainly an essential and vital activity. Numerous biochemical studies have indicated the similarity of nucleolar ribonucleic acid and protein to the same constituents of cytoplasmic ribosomes, and some electron micrographs have been interpreted as showing "ribosomes" passing from the nucleolus through pores in the nuclear envelope and into the adjacent cytoplasm. Involvement of the nucleolus in mRNA has been proposed but is less convincing.

The essential nature of the nucleolus and that it is a product of gene action is demonstrated in the South African "clawed toad" *Xenopus laevis* (Brown and Gurdon, 1965). A simple mutation exists in which the chromosome carrying the mutation lacks the nucleolus-organizing constriction and produces no nucleolus. The normal toad is 2-mu, having two nucleolar constrictions and two nucleoli. The heterozygote is 1-mu, having one nucleolar constriction and one nucleolus. The homozygous recessive (mutant) is 0-mu, having no nucleolar constriction and no nucleolus but only numerous small nucleolar blobs. This latter condition becomes lethal when the tadpole begins to swim, but sublethal effects appear earlier. Presumably, the 0-mu embryos "get along" on ribosomes produced earlier in the diploid oocyte of the heterozygous female parent and cannot produce any ribosomal RNA themselves. It has been proposed that the mutation is a deletion of all or most of the nucleolus organizer, which prevents the synthesis of both the 28s and 18s ribosomal RNA, as if these two are produced by one continuous cistron. Prevention of ribosomal RNA synthesis inhibits the formation of a nucleolus at that site. Thus the nucleolus is secondary and reflects the genetic activity of that section of a chromosome called the nucleolus organizer, where ribosomal RNA is transcribed. This region probably represents about 0.3% of the nuclear DNA and must include thousands of gene loci. It is estimated that there are about 900 rRNA-producing cistrons in this region in *Xenopus,* each capable of producing both the 28s and 18s rRNA, that is, 900 duplicate cistrons. The *Drosophila melanogaster* nucleolus organizer has about 130 duplicate cistrons, the bacterium *E. coli* has about five, and the chick about 100. This knowledge certainly relates nucleoli to ribosomes, but the nucleolus is possibly not so much a primary synthetic organelle as an accumulation of rRNA with secondary synthetic ability.

The "diffuse nucleoli" of the 0-mu *Xenopus* embryo are nonfunctional, but there are some Protista (yeasts, for example) that normally have their nucleolar material scattered in small blobs that are probably functional.

Canals and *vacuoles* (Fig. 18-21) are also often seen with optical and electron microscopy. Sometimes crystals or filaments are seen in such nucleolar vacuoles; the latter are called *nucleolini.* Reports by histochemists that RNA and/or protein is present in these spaces is still debated, especially whether or not there is a special RNA. Whether these canals and vacuoles contain nucleoplasm or have distinctive contents (nucleolar sap) or whether, for that matter, all are the same in content is unknown. However, time-lapse cinematography of living nucleoli of tobacco cells grown in culture has clearly shown that a probably temporary vacuole forms within the nucleolus, enlarges, and then discharges through a temporary canal into the nucleoplasm (Das et al., 1966; Johnson and Jones, 1967) (Fig. 15-7). If this observation is generalized, it seems that some liquid, perhaps just water, passes outward from the interior of the nucleolus in a quantity sufficient to require permanent or temporary passages. There is some supportive evidence to this effect. When canals are numerous and branched, this part of the nucleolus appears as a mass of coarse, anastomosing strands, a network of strands composed of 150 Å ribosome-like granules. A more definite fiber of a nucleolus or the nucleolar material through which numerous canals run is called the *nucleolonema.* One or numerous regions composed of smaller granules having a lower density, containing no canals, and with an amorphous appearance, called the *pars amorpha,* may also be present.

Nucleolar activity, like nuclear activity, is correlated with size. Actively synthesizing cells and meristematic cells have large nuclei and large nucleoli. The single nucleus of the large cell that constitutes the whole *Acetabularia* alga possesses during the active growth period a group of sausage-shaped nucleoli that form a mass about 80

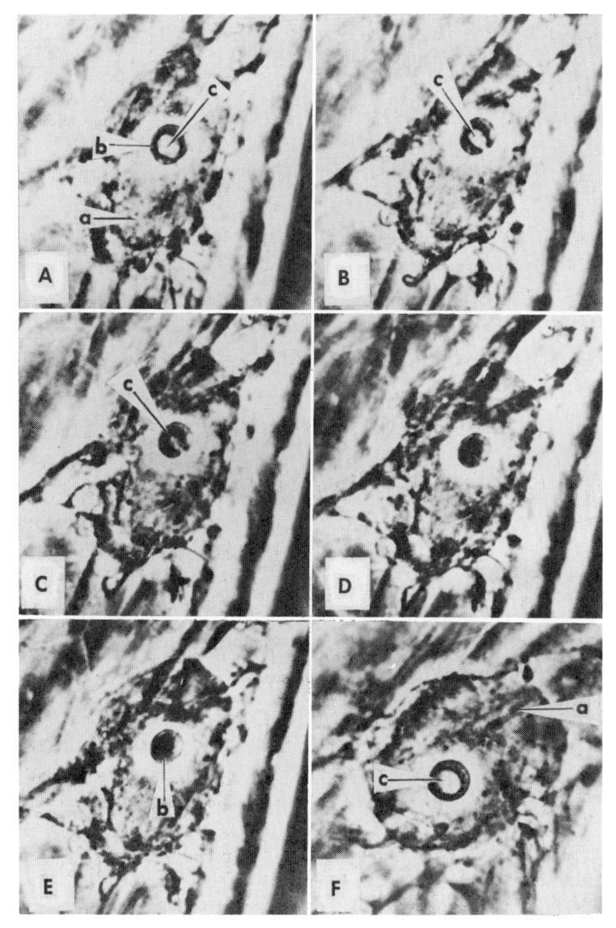

Fig. 15-7. Phase-contrast, time-lapse photomicrographs of nucleolar activity in a living tobacco cell grown in culture showing internal vacuole that discharges to the outside. Total time from **A** to **E** was 2 minutes, but it required 2 hours to refill from **E** to **F.** (From Johnson, J. M., and L. E. Jones. Amer. J. Bot. **54:**189-198.)

μm in diameter. The same cell at a later time when it is much less metabolically active has much smaller nucleoli. Thus nucleoli are certainly involved in rRNA and protein synthesis, probably as the necessary source of ribosomes. Some experimental evidence suggests that nucleoli which are unattached to chromosomes can somehow synthesize RNA, and nucleoli have been found to have enzymes, some of which are known to function in nucleotide synthesis.

Nucleoli are sometimes associated intimately with the nuclear envelope during interphase and also during prophase I of meiosis. In some plant and fungus meiocytes such as *Haplopappus* and *Neottiella* (Figs. 18-5, 18-10, and 18-24), during prophase I the nucleolus is flattened broadly over a wide area of the nuclear envelope so that it has a crescent shape. At leptotene in mammalian primary spermatocytes the nucleolus appears as a cap on a transient leptotene "structure" called the "chromatophore" or "chromatin nucleolus," which is appressed to the inner nuclear envelope and within which the ends of the "bouquet" stage, synaptinemal complex chromosomes are embedded.

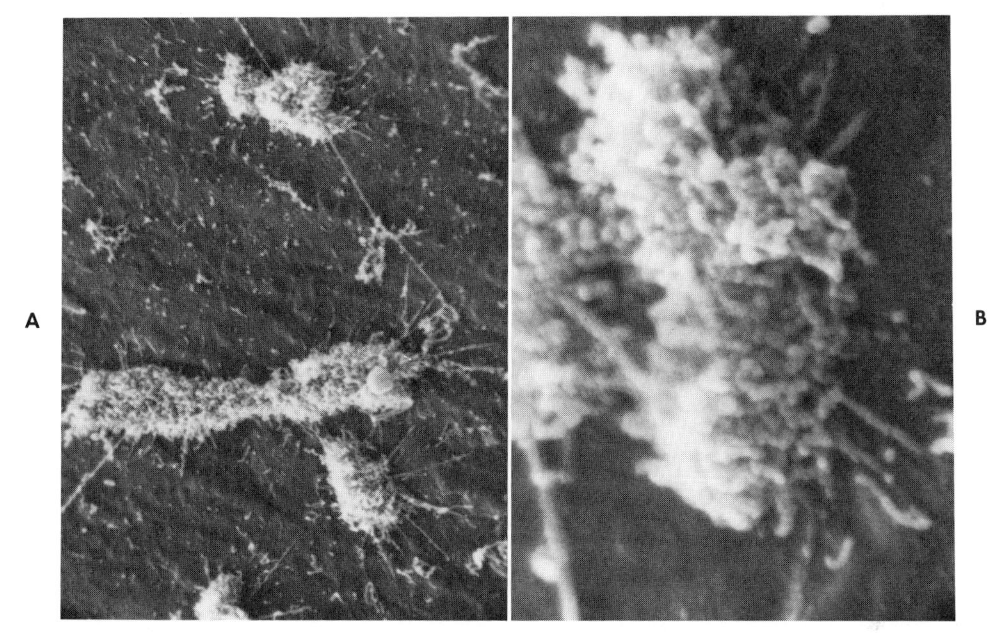

Fig. 15-8. Scanning microscope representation of human metaphase chromosomes. **A,** A group of chromosomes showing the fibrous nature and fibers extending outward from the chromosomes. **B,** A much higher power representation showing the looped, coiled, or folded organization of the chromatin fibers of the chromosome. (**A,** ×6,700; **B,** ×28,000.) (From Golomb, H. M., and G. E. Bahr. 1971. Science **171:**1024-1026. Copyright 1971 by the American Association for the Advancement of Science.)

Chromatin

The term "chromatin" originated during the last two or three decades of the 19th century as the unspecified material of mitotic and meiotic chromosomes that stains with basic dyes. It was not supposed to be generally present during the interphase but to form or accumulate on or in the chromosomes during prophase and leave them during telophase. For example, Rabl stated in 1885 that out of the resting nucleus the chromosomes again came into view due to the chromatic substance "flowing" back along predetermined paths into the primary chromosome bodies. It is unspecified chemically even today but is not just DNA. Since mitotic chromosomes contain both kinds of nucleic acids, basic and acidic proteins, and possibly some sorts of lipid, the staining characteristic could be due to any one or any combination of these or to the so-called chromosomal *matrix* or *kalymma.* Perhaps chromatin and chromosome matrix are the same thing, if matrix actually exists. It might in some way result from the physical condensation of the chromosomes at nuclear division and so be a physical rather than a chemical concept. For a long time it was generally assumed that chromatin came from the disappearing nucleolus during prophase and went back into the new nucleoli at telophase.

Chromatin is now considered to be the 250 Å (reported as 230 to 500 Å) filaments that are revealed by electron microscopy as composing both the condensed meiotic and mitotic chromosomes and the "chromosomes" in the nondividing nucleus (Fig. 15-8). Thus the chromatin seen in the light microscope is the aggregation of the chromatin filaments revealed by the electron microscope. (The fine structure of chromosomes, the chromatin, will be discussed later.)

Heterochromatin

In 1882 Flemming noticed stained nodes in the network of resting nuclei. This is one of the first records of chromatin present during interphase. In 1892 Rosen considered that there were often two sorts of nucleoli; the one or more large nucleoli he called "eunucleoli," and numerous smaller ones were named "pseudonucleoli." These latter corresponded to the nodes of Flemming. Rosenberg in 1904 was the first to conclude that these pseudonucleoli, or nodes, represented chromosomes or parts of chromosomes. In 1905 Overton called them *prochromosomes,* and 3 years later Bacarini called them *chromocenters.* Both of these names are still used, although the term "prochromosome" is generally used if the number is exactly correlated with the number of chromosomes (Fig. 15-9), and the term "chromocenter," or *"heterochromatic body,"* is used if there is no such exact correlation or if the number varies among nuclei of the same organism. By 1910 it was well established that prochro-

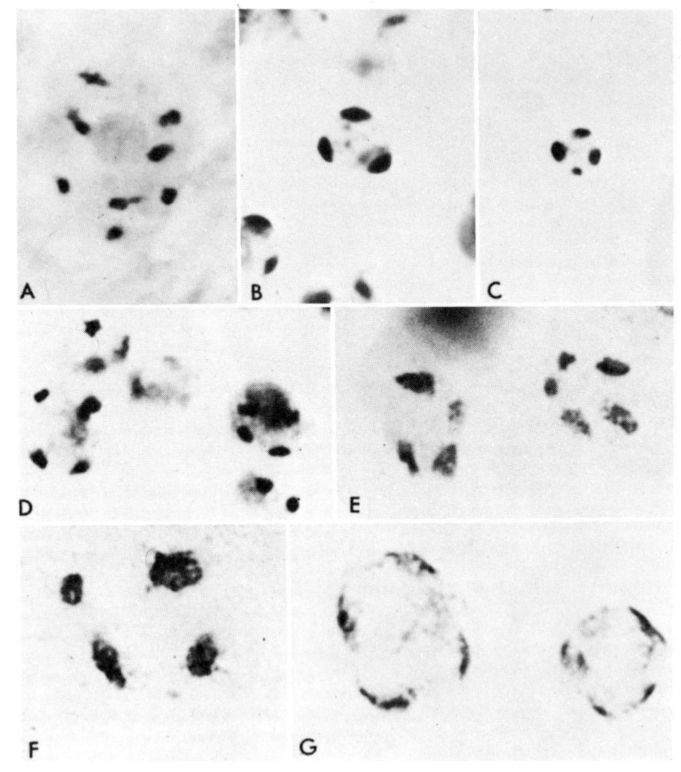

Fig. 15-9. Prochromosomes in interphase nuclei of *Plantago ovata* (2n = 8). **A,** The eight prochromosomes in each cell correspond to the eight distinct chromosomes in root tip nuclei. **B,** In somatic cells of the flower bud, homologous prochromosomes have paired so intimately that there are only four in each nucleus, three of which are visible in the optical plane of the photomicrograph. **C** to **G,** During the interphase just before meiosis in the sporogenous cells of anthers, the four dense, paired prochromosomes, **C,** become more, **D** and **E,** and more, **F** and **G,** diffuse. They increase in size as the nuclei, **C** to **G,** and cells increase in size preparatory to meiosis. (Courtesy S. M. Stack, University of Texas Cell Research Institute, Austin, Texas.)

mosomes (or chromocenters) were definitely related to chromosomes, often, but certainly not always, equaling the chromosomes in number.

Heitz renewed interest in chromatin during the late 1920s. He called chromocenters *heterochromatin* in contrast to the normal chromatin, or *euchromatin,* which "disappears" at telophase. Gregoire had noticed in 1907, as have others since, that prochromosomes seemed to represent the permanently stained regions of the chromosomes adjacent to the centromere. Overton in 1909 concluded, and subsequent workers have confirmed the observation, that during prophase the chromatin appears to spread outward from the prochromosome along the *linin threads* (euchromatin) until the fully stained late prophase chromosome is produced. He also noticed, as did Doutraligne (1939) and Vanderlyn (1948), that in some plants during early prophase the prochromosomes are intimately associated with the inner nuclear membrane surface (Fig. 15-9). This observation may eventually prove to be highly significant for the action of heterochromatin and even of nuclei. Electron microscopy does reveal that some chromosomal matter is closely appressed to the inner surface of the nuclear envelope, often as large irregular globs, and may represent heterochromatin.

During the 1930s, Heitz concluded that the meta-anaphase morphological characteristics of chromocenters are not lost during telophase as they are for euchromatin, that any correspondence between the number of chromocenters and the chromosomes is purely coincidental, and that prochromosomes do not represent centers of formation of chromosomes, but that heterochromatin is really different from euchromatin and behaves differently during the mitotic cycle. Thus it was established that the heterochromatin of chromocenters and prochromosomes is different from euchromatin, possibly because it has a different cycle, remains coiled, and/or has more or less DNA or other material present. Heitz also designated a number of types of heterochromatin, and White in 1935 proposed positive and negative heterochromatin; the former is stainable *(positively pyknotic)* when the euchromatin is not, as during interphase, and the latter is not stainable *(negatively pyknotic)* when the euchromatin does stain, as during mitosis and/or meiosis.

In 1935 Heitz concluded that heterochromatin is genetically inert, a generalization that is still considered to be true (with some known exceptions such as in *Drosophila, Zea mays,* and some other organisms), although Darlington (1942) concluded that "genes in heterochromatin are not, indeed, inert but rather nonspecific in their activity." Thus the concept of the importance of heterochromatin in gene action, at least for certain sorts of heterochromatin, was introduced. In 1948 Huskins and Steinetz proposed that heterochromatin plays a part in cellular differentiation.

In some organisms heterochromatin has been related definitely to gene action. If certain mosses lack heterochromatin, they die (Lobeer, 1961; Heitz, 1942). The gene action of the *strigens* complex of *Oenothera* is determined by the heterochromatin present (Japha, 1939). Fernandes (1943) concluded that a dominant gene was necessary for the heterochromaticity of a supernumerary chromosome in *Narcissus.* Longley reported a negative correlation between B chromosomes and number of chromosome knobs (both consisting of heterochromatin) in corn varieties, perhaps indicating that knobs and B chromosomes may play some interchangeable role. Plaut (1953) reported an effect on variegated pericarp (in corn) by B chromosomes that had previously been found to be largely heterochromatic (McClintock, 1933) and genetically inactive. Thus there seems to be adequate evidence for the hypothesis that heterochromatin may function in gene action (or suppression). Heterochromatin is found in all cells and as a large or small part of all chromosomes.

Additional information indicates further differences between euchromatin and heterochromatin. A biochemical difference, probably reflecting a significant functional aspect, is that euchromatin, functioning during interphase, takes up acetic acid (via acetyl-CoA) on its histone, whereas heterochromatin does not become acetylated.

A second difference between the two chromatins, which seems to be generally true, is that during the synthetic phase of DNA replication, euchromatin replicates during the early S phase, whereas heterochromatin is *late replicating*—at the end of the S phase. Excellent correlation between the locations of heterochromatin on the various human chromosomes and late DNA replication of those same sites has been established (Fig. 15-12). Furthermore, there seems to be no variation among cells of a wide variety of tissues. The same is true of onion root tip chromosomes, late replication being evident on both sides of the centromeres, at telomeres, and the nucleolus organizer constrictions. There seem to be constant differences of sites of late replication among chromosomes of different onion species. Furthermore, the heterochromatic polar cap and the chromocenters at the opposite pole of the onion interphase nucleus also show late DNA replication.

In a mammal at the beginning of cleavage in female embryonic development the two X chromosomes are not late replicating. In the few-celled cleavage stage one arm of each X chromosome becomes early replicating. At a later stage three of the four arms are late replicating (heterochromatic). Still later, all four arms become late replicating; that is, both X chromosomes are completely late replicating and remain so in all subsequent somatic cells.

Supernumerary chromosomes, which have been recorded in hundreds of species of plants and in a few insects, are generally composed of heterochromatin and are largely genetically inert. Certainly, the most thoroughly studied supernumerary chromosomes (or *B chromosomes*), those of corn, consist almost entirely of heterochromatin. On normal chromosomes the ends of the arms are supposed to terminate in heterochromatic *telomeres;* various *knobs* scattered along the euchromatin are heterochromatic; the *nucleolus organizer* is supposed to be heterochromatic; and the chromosome arms near the centromere are heterochromatic. The chromomers, present as spherical "beads" of various sizes on some chromonemata, are probably small heterochromatic regions. Sex chromosomes of many animals and some plants consist, more or less, of heterochromatin; at least they are heteropyknotic.

Caspersson could find little or no nucleic acid or protein difference between euchromatin and heterochromatin and agreed with Heitz that they are two different states of the same thing and not two different substances. Coleman (1941) concluded that heterochromatin is euchromatin "protected" by a thick layer of something that inhibits gene action. Certainly, heterochromatin can affect adjacent euchromatin and, in turn, is affected by temperature, sex, age of parents, neighborhood of the centromere, presence of additional Y chromosomes, and the direction of the cross (Prokofyeva-Belgovskaya, 1948). Thus heterochromatin is more labile than euchromatin and is affected by a variety of factors in its environment.

The amount, position, activity, and necessity of heterochromatin may vary. In corn the number and positions of the heterochromatic knobs vary considerably among strains. Heterochromatic supernumerary chromosomes of plants may be eliminated during embryogenesis from cells giving rise to roots but not from cells producing stems. The numbers and sizes of heterochromatic bodies during interphase may vary among tissues of a plant. Heterochromatic supernumerary chromosomes in many plants fail to disjoin at anaphase of the first *(Tradescantia)* or second (corn) pollen grain division but at no other division. In many vertebrates (from mice to man) one of the X chromosomes in females, but only one of the two, persists in the interphase nucleus against the nuclear envelope as the Barr body (Fig. 15-10) and drumstick. Since two Barr bodies appear in females with three X chromosomes (three if there are four X chromosomes), it seems that only one X chromosome does not form a Barr body. Apparently, Barr bodies are sometimes the X chromosome from the mother; in other nuclei they are the X chromosome from the father. They are genetically inactive.

Probably the most fantastic story of heterochromatin comes from coccid (mealy bugs and scale insects) cytology (White, 1954). Among the numerous variations reported for these cytologically unusual organisms, the simplest is as follows. Throughout development in the female all the chromosomes of both sets, one of which came from the father and the other from the mother, behave normally during interphase and during mitosis and meiosis. In the male, however, during the blastula stage of embryogeny, exactly half of the chromosomes begin to remain heterochromatic during interphase, in a clump, but divide normally at anaphase. During meiosis in the male the heterochromatic chromosomes divide mitotically during the first division. During anaphase of the second division the "heterochromatic" chromosomes all pass together to one pole, whereas the euchromatic chromosomes pass to the other pole. There is really no meiosis at all, no pairing or genetic exchange—a case of *apomeiosis.* Thus two of the four nuclei produced contain only "heterochromatic" chromosomes, the other two only euchromatic chromosomes. The latter two produce sperm cells, the former two disintegrate. Therefore at fertilization the zygote receives two sets of euchromatic chromosomes, a set from each parent.

It has been established by x-ray treatment of either a male or a female parent that the complete set of chromosomes received from the male parent becomes heterochromatized during embryogeny in the male. If a female parent was x-rayed, aberrations were found only in the euchromatic chromosomes of the progeny. If a male parent was x-rayed, it was the heterochromatic chromosomes that were found to be modified. Furthermore, no matter how badly the paternal chromosomes were affected by x rays, there was no genetic effect on the progeny, a fact which demonstrated that the heterochromatic chromosomes are genetically inert, except that a rather specific mass of heterochromatin is necessary for survival (severe x-raying of fathers did produce sterility in the sons), and a set of heterochromosomes from a male parent of another species resulted in larval death.

In another kind of coccid only one of the six chromosomes ($2n = 6$) is heterochromatic at meiosis, but in different parts of the testis it may be any one of the different chromosomes. Since sex is apparently not chromosomally determined in these insects (males and females are genetically identical), the random heterochromatization of individual chromosomes is inexplicable except that somehow it is genetically determined. Certain genes must be affected by some nongenetic aspects of the egg or maternal parent. Thus whole chromosomes may be converted from euchromatin to heterochromatin; of two genetically identical chromosomes within one nucleus, one may be euchromatic and genetically active, whereas the other may be heterochromatic and genetically inactive.

Heterochromatin has been proposed as a significant controller of the action of the structural genes of the euchromatin (Schultz, Mather, McClintock, and Brink). Brink (1960) has proposed that heterochromatin may be actually very important in differentiation. Accumulated evidence makes this likely, especially since it is probable that all chromosomes, or at least all chromosome sets of all species of organisms, seem to have some heterochromatin. It is often concentrated on each side of the centromere and may function there in part to hold prophase and metaphase chromatids together until anaphase by its stickiness. During prophase of meiosis in such plants as the potato, tomato, and the Onagraceae and during mitosis also in *Plantago* (Hyde, 1953), dark-staining material appears to spread from the region of the centromere toward the distal ends of the chromosome arms. The fact that chromosomes stain poorly, if at all, with certain dyes except between middle prophase and telophase is further evidence that chemical or physical changes occur within chromosomes during mitosis and meiosis which may be related to heterochromatin.

Recently the knowledge, staining techniques, and terminology of heterochromatin have had a significant burst of progress. There are now considered to be two sorts of heterochromatin that differ for type of genetic content and for permanence. *Facultative heterochromatin* is merely euchromatin that, for some reason, remains condensed in certain nondividing nuclei and has the typical sorts of unique and regulatory genes. In other nuclei of the organism the same chromatin may be in the diffuse euchromatic condition. An example of facultative heterochromatin is the "sex chromatin body" of female humans and many other animals (Fig. 15-10). In the typical human female nucleus there are two X chromosomes, one of which is not stained and is in the euchromatic condition. The other X chromosome, in some nuclei at least, is condensed as facultative heterochromatin against the nuclear envelope. The chromatin and genetic content of the two X chromosomes is the same, but one may remain condensed as facultative heterochromatin. It is clear that the condensed condition of facultative heterochromatin is determined by genetic action, which can be reversed.

Constitutive heterochromatin, on the other hand, is chromatin that is always condensed in all nuclei and consists of highly redundant chromatin; that is, within a region of constitutive heterochromatin there are many segments of DNA with the same sequences of nucleotides. Whether such regions should be described as genes or containing genes is unknown. The function(s)

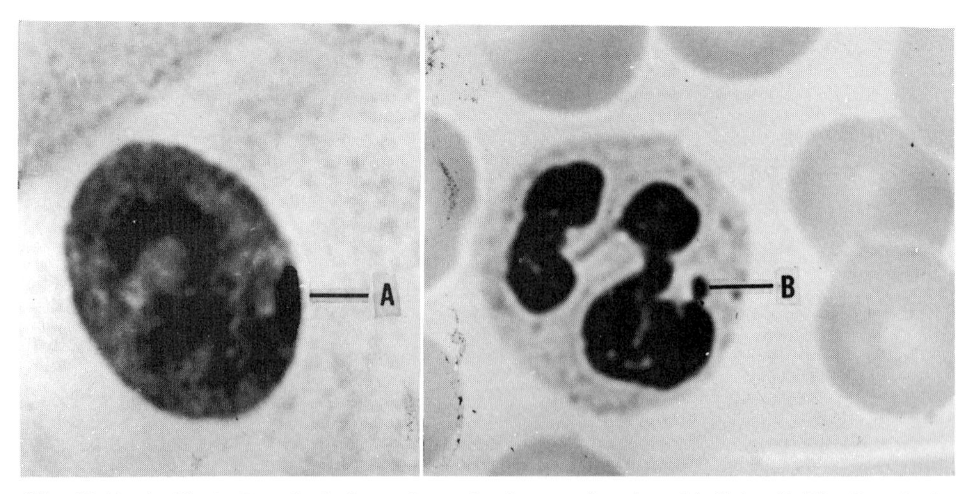

Fig. 15-10. A, Single Barr body in nucleus of a human female epithelial cell. The Barr body (named for Dr. Barr) is supposed to be one of the two X chromosomes of the female. **B,** Drumstick on polymorphic nucleus of a certain type of human leukocyte of the female. This, too, is a heterochromatic X chromosome; it remains condensed during interphase and appressed against the nuclear envelope. (Courtesy Carolina Biological Supply Co., Burlington, N. C.)

of this redundant DNA is unknown, but the redundancy may reach 1 million similar segments. Examples of constitutive heterochromatin are the heterochromatic regions often observed adjacent to the centromere (Figs. 15-9 and 18-9) and in other regions of the arms of chromosomes, including the tips of arms of some chromosomes (Figs. 15-13 and 16-14).

It is the redundancy of constitutive heterochromatin that permits its differential "staining" by various techniques, all of which involve the denaturing of the DNA (separation of the two strands). The prepreparation is then treated to permit some reassociation of complementary strands. Presumably such annealing occurs only in the highly repetitive constitutive heterochromatin, not in the nonrepetitive euchromatin. The stains used are fluorescent quinacrine mustard or Giemsa, and these bind only to the regions of constitutive heterochromatin. The technique often produces banded chromosome arms, staining on each side of the centromere, and staining only at arm ends. This makes it possible to distinguish between nonhomologous chromosomes that are otherwise nearly identical (Yunis and Yasmineh, 1971).

Euchromatin therefore describes the condition of a part of a chromosome arm (usually the distal half or so of each arm) that stains faintly, if at all, during interphase but stains darkly during middle and late mitosis or meiosis and seems to be the location of active genes. Heterochromatin, on the other hand, seems to represent small or large parts of chromosomes that probably have a different cycle of activity than euchromatin and contain genes that have a different function than genes of euchromatin.

Chromosomes. "Chromosomes" of nonmitotic nuclei are difficult to study cytologically. During telophase the chromosomes so clearly visible during metaphase and anaphase seem to disappear into the interphase, only to reappear at any later prophase that may occur. Just what the physical condition of a nonmitotic "chromosome" is, even if such exists, is almost impossible to determine. The chromosome is not simply a mass of chromatin but, rather, a structure periodically chromatic. The morphological identity of the chromosome has not been lost; a different kind of organization has been assumed.

It is known that during an interphase between telophase and prophase the amounts of DNA and histone double together, and other proteins and RNA increase in amount. The constancy of genetic linkage groups through many mitotic divisions is interpreted as indicating that the linear sequences of genes (that is, the genonemata of the chromosomes) remain essentially and perpetually intact structures. The constancy of the morphological (cytological) set of chromosomes with their peculiarities of arm lengths and ratios, of centromere locations, of secondary, nucleolar, and other constrictions, and of chromomere and knob arrangements all indicate indirectly the physical continuity of individual genonemata and therefore their presence as intact structures in some form or other in the interphase nucleus. It is certain that the "chromosome" during interphase is different structurally, functionally, and chemically from the metaphase-anaphase chromosome, and therefore clear thinking might require a distinct term for the interphase condition. "Genonema" and "chromonema" are useful terms for the interphase nucleoprotein.

Many interphase nuclei show, when stained, variously sized blobs of heterochromatin called chromomeres, prochromosomes, and chromocenters (Fig. 15-9). In some cells of some species of plants, supernumerary chromosomes may appear as such heterochromatic blobs. In some animal cells for example (human females) one of the X chromosomes is late DNA replicating and is functionally inactivated, called *lyonization* (Lyon, 1962). It appears in the nonmitotic nucleus as a blob against the nuclear envelope called the *sex chromatin body,* which takes the form of a Barr body or drumstick (Fig. 15-10).

The paired condition of prochromosomes in somatic and sporogenous premeiotic cells (Fig. 15-9) is an indication of premeiotic pairing of homologous chromosomes (Chapter 18) and has been reported in corn, *Drosophila,* and a few other plants also.

According to descriptions of nonmitotic nuclei up to at least 30 years ago, the telophase chromosomes elongated, spread apart internally, lost their matrix, and gave rise to very fine threads. Later, *anastomoses* grew out from these threads and made contact with others. Thus was formed the *reticulum* of the interphase nucleus. In one hypothetical description of the reticulum the strands were thought to consist of chromatic *chromomeres* (tiny bodies of chromatin) and connecting strands of achromatic *linin.* In a contrasting hypothesis the strands consisted of only one sort of material called *karyotin* (chromatin). Presumably, each telophase chromosome produced one zigzag or spiral filament of karyotin, which is at least the permanent and continuous DNA strand of that chromosome, often called the *chromonema.*

Furthermore, the concept had been expressed by van Beneden in 1883 and Rabl in 1885 that the centromere regions of chromosomes remain grouped close to the centriole during interphase as they were at telophase and that a line drawn from the centriole through the center of the nucleus determined the axis of the cell and nucleus. The point on the nuclear surface closest to the centriole (if there is one) or where the centromeres are clustered is the *pole* of the nucleus; the opposite point is the *antipole.* Vanderlyn in 1948 pointed out that the "chromosomes" during interphase are attached to the nuclear envelope in the regions of their centromeres and telomeres, and one pole is indicated by the aggregated heterochromatic centromeric regions of the chromosomes where they are attached to the nuclear envelope. However, in *Plantago* root-tip cells the centromeric prochromosomes are not grouped but spread uniformly around the nucleus (Fig. 15-9, *A*).

If the term "chromosome" continues to be used as originally intended (and for a long time by many cytologists) to specify the prophase-anaphase structures, chromosomes do not exist during interphase and a term such as "reticulum" or "genonema" is appropriate. It is likely that one telophase chromosome produces one segment of the total reticulum. What anastomoses are is still uncertain; some 19th century cytologists said that they arose as pseudopodia from the chromatic filaments, or they may be fixation artifacts.

As the telophase chromosomes decondense, they expand, and this expansion of chromosomes and development of nucleoli cause the enlargement of the nucleus. It is questionable if a nondividing nucleus contains any material that cannot be defined as chromosomes and nucleoli.

Electron microscopy has provided some new knowledge of the gross or fine structure of the nonmitotic chromosome. It has confirmed, as light microscopists had concluded (Fig. 17-1, parts 2 and 3), that chromatin is often associated with the inner nuclear envelope membrane and the nucleolus. It has indicated that the chromatin is variously distributed throughout the nucleus (Figs. 3-1, 15-5, and 15-9). Otherwise electron microscopy has provided little new knowledge of the gross structure of the "chromosomes" such as how many chromonemata are there per chromosome? Or, if a chromosome consists of two or more chromonemata, are they twisted around each other or not?

Fine structure. For a long time cytologists have been attempting to acquire knowledge of chromosome fine structure, that is, the number, diameter, variety, and organization of "strands" within an interphase or mitotic metaphase or anaphase chromosome. Light microscopy revealed little more than that the anaphase chromosome *may* consist of two strands *possibly* twisted around one another. Hypothetical models, however, some based on observations of chromatid or chromosome breaks after x-ray treatments, were also constructed with four, eight, sixteen, and more "strands" called chromonemata.

It was expected and hoped that the higher resolution of the electron microscope would reveal the major and minor strand structure of the chromosome during all phases. Unfortunately, the problem has not been resolved, although new models are still being proposed and "structures" much finer than one half or one quarter of the diameter of an anaphase chromosome have been seen in sectioned embedded material, in shadowed isolated chromosomes, and in chromosomes from burst cells.

The problem is about as follows: Biochemical and genetic analyses indicate that the DNA in a chromosome should compose a continuous linear DNA strand several centimeters or decimeters in length. Even during interphase no chromosome is that long, and during mitosis the equivalent of a strand of centimeter proportion must be confined within a chromosome having a length of a few microns. That is, about 50,000 μm of length must be confined within a 5 μm chromosome, a reduction in length of 10,000 times. This order of magnitude of packing does exist in bacteria and viruses. In the T-even phage a 60 μm DNA strand is confined within a 0.06 μm space, and the 1,100 μm "chromosome" is confined within the 1 or 2 μm bacterium *E. coli.* When the mechanism and arrangement by which the prokaryotic chromosome is aggregated into a tiny space and the mechanism of "chromosome" separation in bacteria are known, cytologists may have some clues to strand packing in eukaryotic chromosomes.

Present electron microscopic evidence indicates that a eukaryotic metaphase chromosome (Chapter 16) consists of a large number of about 200 Å thick "strands" that seem to be oriented parallel with the long axis of the major strand, the chromatid as seen by light microscopy (Fig. 18-7); that is, these parallel strands *may* follow a helical path from one end of the chromosome to the other. On the other hand, there is little evidence that the mitotic chromosome is helically coiled (for example, see Fig. 16-3), and some electron microscopic evidence indicates that the strands run parallel with the long axis of the chromosome itself. Each chromosome is perhaps like a sheaf of wheat straws. Just how to relate these many fine strands of an interphase chromosome to the single genetic sequence *(genonema)* clearly demonstrated by the logic of genetic linkage is one of the major problems of comprehending chromosome structure. The most obvious conclusion from electron microscopic observation is that the genonema should run repeatedly back and forth, from one end of the interphase chromosome to the other. But it is difficult to conceive how such a chromosome could separate, and separate semiconservatively (Meselson and Stahl, 1958) with respect to DNA, into two distinct chromatids by late metaphase.

The most reliable model of the fine structure of a chromosome is the "folded fiber" model of DuPraw (1970). This model is derived partly from electron microscopic study of isolated chromosomes from exploded cells. There is one chromatin fiber of 230 to 500 Å thickness per chromatid (two side-by-side sister chromatids attached at the centromere compose one metaphase chromosome). Presumably, this fiber has two ends and is approximately 500 μm in length. Within it is a coiled (or coiled coil) of Watson-Crick DNA double helix of about 5 cm in length. The fiber also contains proteins and RNA and is the chromatin.

This 500 μm fiber, in a metaphase chromatid (Fig. 15-8), is folded back and forth *across* the chromatid and also runs from end to end several times to produce the folded fiber model of a chromatid of about 5 μm in length and less than 1 μm in width. Thus 50,000 μm of DNA double helix are confined within 500 μm of fiber, and that within the 5 μm metaphase chromatid length. A number of such 230 Å fibers run across the centromeric region between the arms of each chromatid. The loci within the chromatid of the two ends of the fiber are unknown, but they do not seem to be at the ends of the arms of the chromatid.

There are also 230 Å fibers extending between the two sister chromatids, especially near the centromere, and it is known that the chromosomes in nondividing nuclei are attached by many fibers to the nuclear envelope. There are also numerous observations of such fibers connecting ends of nonhomologous chromosomes. Whether these connecting fibers regularly break during mitosis is unknown, but in preparations they seem to be broken.

It is not known whether these connecting fibers are part of the genome fiber or are fibers additional to the "gene string" that have the function, perhaps the only function, of interconnecting. If the latter is true, it is conceivable that the redundant constitutive heterochromatin is made up of these connecting fibers in whole or in part.

Electron micrographs of exploded nondividing nuclei show a tangle of these 230 Å fibers extending in apparent disorder (Fig. 15-8) with many fiber ends attached to the inner surface of the nuclear envelope, especially near annuli (DuPraw, 1970). It can be assumed in the intact living nucleus, however, that the fibers of each diffuse chromosome occupy exclusively a particular region of the nucleus that corresponds in form to the mitotic chromosome expanded in volume during telophase. The fibers of such diffuse chromosomes that occupy adjacent regions will often be in contact or very close together. This permits breaks and reunions to form inversions and translocations.

It is inconceivable at this time how such an apparently tangle interphase chromosome can double itself and then separate into two neat, side-by-side chromatids, unless the prophase condensation process itself pulls the two sister fibers into the two folded fiber chromatid arrangement. It is clear that the organization of the interphase chromosome is not now fully known.

Another problem arises from the known fact that there seems to be only slight correlation of the amount of DNA per nucleus with the probable number of genes (Table 15-1). For example, the salamander *Amphiuma* has about twenty-three times as much DNA as a toad (and a toad as much as a man), but the number of genes per nucleus is probably of the same order of magnitude in both amphibians. Following are other examples of variation in amount of DNA between related organisms. The leguminous plant *Vicia faba* has ten times the DNA of *Lupinus albus* (Sunderland and McLeish, 1961); the amphibian *Necturus* has more than ten times that of *Rana pipiens* (Gall, cited by Callan, 1967). Variations within the same genera include the following: The amphipod *Gammarus pulex* has three times the DNA of *G. chevreuxi,* and the planarian *Mesostoma ehrenbergi* has eleven times that of *M. lingua;* in both n = 4 (Keyl, cited by Callan, 1967). The general opinion, with considerable dissent, is that a species like *Amphiuma* may have a large number of parallel identical genonemata per chromosome. That is, the *Amphiuma* chromosome is *polyneme;* in a sense it is polytene. Perhaps, then, the toad chromosome is also polyneme, merely less so than the salamander, and it is seriously proposed that perhaps all chromosomes are more or less polyneme. If such is the case, the difficulty of understanding chromosome fine structure is so much greater. For example, what sort of structural and genetic rearrangement takes place in a chromosome with a diffuse centromere such as the plant *Luzula* (Fig. 16-6) when a chromosome is broken by irradiation, yet each "fragment" continues to act subsequently as a "normal" chromosome in agmatoploidy? Presumably, one

Table 15-1. Amounts of primary hereditary material in some viruses and organisms

Viruses	μg	Nucleotides and nucleotide pairs
Single strand (RNA)		
A tobacco virus	0.5×10^{-12}	1,000
F2	1.5×10^{-12}	3,000
TMV	3.0×10^{-12}	6,000
Single strand (DNA)		
$\phi \times 174$	2.6×10^{-12}	5,000
Double strand (DNA)		
Polyoma	2.6×10^{-12}	5,000
T2	2.0×10^{-10}	1.9×10^{5}
Organisms		
Bacteria (general)	2 to 25 $\times 10^{-9}$	1.9×10^{6} to 3×10^{7}
E. coli	4.0×10^{-9}	1.0×10^{7}
Fungi		
Yeast	0.07×10^{-6}	7.0×10^{7}
Neurospora	n = 0.02×10^{-6}	1.9×10^{7}
Aspergillus	n = 0.043×10^{-6}	4.0×10^{7}
Invertebrates (2n)		
Jellyfish	0.033×10^{-6}	0.3×10^{9}
Sea urchin	0.09×10^{-6}	0.8×10^{9}
Drosophila	0.16×10^{-6}	8.0×10^{9}
Vertebrates (2n)		
Lung fish	100×10^{-6}	
Shad	1.8×10^{-6}	
Carp	3.3×10^{-6}	
Necturus	48.5×10^{-6}	
Amphiuma	168×10^{-6}	6.8×10^{10}
Toad	7.4×10^{-6}	
Frog	15.0×10^{-6}	
Turtle	5.0×10^{-6}	
Water snake	5.2×10^{-6}	
Black snake	2.9×10^{-6}	
Alligator	5.0×10^{-6}	
Chicken	2.3×10^{-6}	2.1×10^{9}
Duck	2.6×10^{-6}	
Goose	2.9×10^{-6}	
A marsupial	9.0×10^{-6}	
Mouse	5.0×10^{-6}	4.7×10^{9}
Dog	5.5×10^{-6}	
Man	6.5×10^{-6}	2.9×10^{9}
Rat	6.8×10^{-6}	
Plants (2n)		
Chlorella (alga)	n = 0.050×10^{-6}	4.0×10^{7}
Corn	0.17×10^{-5}	7.0×10^{9}
Aquilegia hybrid	0.13×10^{-5}	
Anemone (three species)	2.1×10^{-5}	
Hepatica acutiloba	3.9×10^{-5}	
Anemone tetrasepala	5.25×10^{-5}	

chromosome break would involve numerous breaks in the longitudinally and repeatedly folded genonemata and many more if the chromosome is polyneme. The opposite idea is that the excessive amount of DNA is inserted as duplications in a single (unineme) genonema (Whitehouse, 1967) or as "slave" DNA duplication (Callan, 1967).

Perhaps, aside from any possible polyteny, there is not one continuous genonema within the chromosome no matter how it might be coiled or folded. That is, perhaps the nucleoprotein of each "gene," operon, or cistron is a short strand separate from all other similar units of structure. Such a model is presently inconceivable in the light of the demonstrated permanence of genetic linkage sequences and chromosome morphology.

Models of genonema. Models of the genonema have been published through the years since Weismann (1885) proposed its physical and hereditary continuity. During the early cytogenetic studies of the 20th century, Janssens (1909) proposed that a genetic crossover results from a break and reunion between adjacent genes, and Darlington (1935) made that concept of crossing-over generally acceptable. Belling (1931, 1933), however, rejected the break-and-reunion concept and proposed that chromomeres are important replicative units and that crossing-over occurs during duplication of genonemata by growth of interchromomeric connections to "old strand" or "new strand" chromomeres after duplication of the chromomeres themselves.

During the 1950s, the biochemical and genetic studies of viruses and especially bacteria permitted Lederberg (1955) to propose the copying-choice concept of simultaneous DNA and structural replication and crossing-over. Radioautography of eukaryotic chromosomal replication led to the concept of the semiconservative nature of replication (Taylor, 1957). Other models of that period were proposed by Schwartz (1955, 1960) and Freese (1958).

When it became evident that replication of one continuous DNA genonema from a centimeter to a meter in length would have to be far too slow to occur in one S phase and that the viruses and Prokaryota have circular genophores, models having protein "linkers" between adjacent genes or groups of genes (short DNA strands alternating with protein) discussed by Freese (1958) and Ris (1961) became popular. The likely presence of nonhistone protein linkers is indicated by the breakup of genonemata when treated with proteolytic enzymes. A genonema of short DNA strands alternating with linkers would permit the more or less simultaneous replication of all genes; that is, all DNA strands could replicate simultaneously, each from a linker at one end to the linker at the other. A modification of this scheme is that each short DNA strand is a loop (as in Prokaryota) with both "ends" attached to one linker and the middle of the loop attached to the next linker (Stahl, 1961). Various compound linkers have also been proposed.

To confine enough DNA for a strand a few centimeters long into an interphase chromosome of a few microns length, lateral linkers in two parallel rows with the DNA strands running crosswise have often seemed necessary (Taylor, 1963). This produces a wider genonema but does permit confining a great deal of DNA and many genes in a limited length. An alternative to the double strand of linkers with DNA between is the proposal of a central axis of linkers with the DNA looped out on both sides (Painter, 1964).

There are also three hypothetical alternatives with respect to genetic duplication. There is (1) a single genonema (the *unineme* concept), which is most acceptable to genetic analysis, the semiconservative distribution of replicated DNA, etc.; (2) from two to a few (Peacock, 1963) to as many as sixty-four (Ris, 1961) parallel polyneme strands; or (3) there is permanent or temporary (Whitehouse, 1967) "cycloid" linear duplication. In the last model mentioned the replicated cycloids would be temporarily detachable by crossing-over, leaving only one "master copy" during crossing-over among genes. Later the cycloid could re-enter the DNA strand by another crossover. Callan's (1967) "master" and "slave" genes, with genetic crossing-over only involving the master gene, is another linear unineme concept. The proposal of Uhl (1965) is, according to its author, adaptable to either unineme or polyneme structure. It involves more or less random distribution of linkers to either of the separated nucleotide (Watson-Crick) sequences, followed by formation of new linkers and complementary nucleotide sequences between old or new linkers. If polytene, many strands would separate into two groups, with one linker for each group of strands. A few other models worthy of mention are those of Whitehouse (1963, 1965), Lindegren (1964), who combines Belling's ideas (nonbreakage) with Darlington's twist and breakage-reunion, and De (1964).

There is a concept in biology that when all conceivably possible hypotheses exist simultaneously about some phenomenon, it is excellent proof of freewheeling, logical, imaginative speculation based on grossly inadequate evidence, and since, as someone once said, "logic is a way of being wrong with confidence" and because logic (hypothesis) usually proves wrong when tested by observation, it is suggested here that none of these hypotheses be taken at all seriously as representing the reality of macromolecular structure, structural replication, and/or crossing-over. As *hypotheses,* they may prove useful in indicating research. Linkers are now out of favor.

None of the models of the 20 to 500 Å double-helix or filament fine structure is helpful in creation of a model of the interior of the interphase chromosome or the metaphase chromatid or chromosome. But until a reliable model of chromosome fine and gross structure is achieved, there is little hope of understanding the events of synapsis and crossing-over at meiosis. Fibrils ranging from 30 to 200 Å and even 500 Å have been seen by various electron microscopists in chromosomes during interphase and mitosis, and there are reports that fibrils actually change in thickness during mitosis and among species, perhaps due to some polyteny. Some evidence has indicated a helical orientation of these fine fibrils; other evidence indicates that they are not so disposed. All things considered, it must be made clear that the fine structure of both interphase and mitotic chromosomes is not at all understood, and furthermore, there is no satisfactory model of even the gross structure of the interphase chromosome.

Perhaps the best concept of the structure of the early interphase chromosome is that it maintains the position and overall internal configuration of the condensed early telophase chromosome but that it expands or decondenses greatly in length and thickness, accompanied by loss of any matrical material that may be present during division. It may be compared to some extent to the stretching of a helical spring or the blowing up of a rubber balloon. The tightly compacted gyres, folds, or whatever arrangement it is that produces the compacted chromosomes during division opens up into much more widely spaced filaments. Such expansion of all the chromosomes during telophase results in the enlargement of the irregularly shaped early telophase nucleus into the larger and more or less spherical interphase nucleus. Concurrent enlargement of the nucleoli also increases the volume of the nucleus. The portions of chromosome arms that decondense only slightly appear during interphase as variably sized irregular masses of chromatin (Fig. 3-1, *B,* and 15-9). Whether there is any or much nucleoplasm between such expanded chromosomes is unknown. It may be that most nucleoplasm exists between and among the chromatin fibers of the chromosome and is, therefore, in a sense within the chromosomes. Contact between genetically similar segments of homologous chromosomes probably permits somatic crossing-over and recombination in this extended and diffuse condition of interphase chromatin. Translocations and inversions are similarly produced.

Electron microscopy of exploded interphase nuclei (DuPraw, 1968, 1970, for example) reveals a myriad of 200 to 250 Å thick fibers of chromatin. Such fibers are assumed to be composed of a once or twice coiled 25 Å DNA double helix plus associated proteins. This is assumed to be the fine structure of chromatin when it can replicate and transcribe RNAs. Some of the fibers seem to be attached to the inner surface of the nuclear envelope between pores. In contrast, the chromatin of the nucleolus organizer is within the nucleolus but in the form of 25 Å filaments, not 250 Å fibers.

Kuroiwa and Tanaka (1971) detected differences of interphase and postmitotic nuclei in root tips of *Crepis capillaris* by light and electron microscopy. They recognized five classes, of which Classes 4 and 5 were postmitotic, in the region of cell elongation. Class 1 was composed of the G_1 interphases with large chromatin masses and 200 Å fibers. Class 2 consisted of nuclei during the S (synthetic) phase. There were very few and small chromatic masses, as though the masses were being reduced for replication. Class 3 included nuclei in the G_2 period of interphase. The nuclei were larger and packed with thick (2,300 Å) filaments that were visible in the light micro-

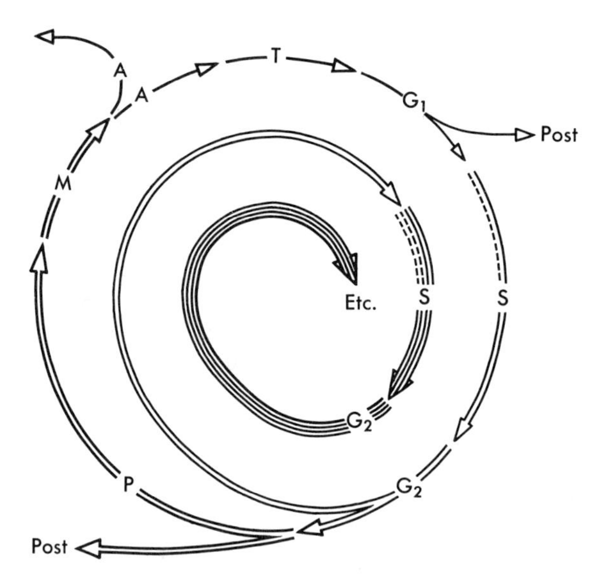

Fig. 15-11. Diploid mitotic cycle. Single arrows = 2C, double arrows = 4C, quadruple arrows = 8C, etc. G_1 extends from telophase to the beginning of the synthetic phase, the nucleus and cell having the 2C amount of DNA. It is likely that most cells in the 2C condition become postmitotic from G_1. Synthetic phase, **S**, is characterized by the gradual doubling of DNA to the 4C amount. Histone protein also doubles during that phase. G_2 is characterized by no DNA or histone synthesis but other proteins and RNA increase. In the G_2 phase a cell *may* become postmitotic and differentiate at the 4C level, although some investigators believe differentiation *always* occurs at the 2C level, or the cell may undergo one to many further DNA doublings without nuclear division, as occurs in polytene and endomitotic cells. G_2 may terminate at the beginning of the prophase of another division and pass through metaphase, **M,** and anaphase, **A,** to another telophase. Haploid mitosis, as occurs in plant gametophytes, has 1C telophase and 2C prophase; otherwise, it is comparable to diploid mitosis.

scope. Class 4 (postmitotic) consisted of small dense nuclei with small nucleoli in the elongating epidermal cells and root cap. Class 5 nuclei of the elongation region of both cortex and the central cylinder of the root tip were large, but the nucleolus was small and irregular in shape. There were a few small chromatin masses. Classes 4 and 5 probably formed from G_1 nuclei without DNA replication.

There is considerably more knowledge of "chromosome" structure in those interphase nuclei of flies containing giant chromosomes (the salivary gland nuclei, for example). Details of these are discussed in Chapter 16, but it must be remembered that these magnificent "chromosomes" are really modified interphase "chromosomes" and are not mitotic. However, their mere existence further supports the assumption that there is structural continuity of "chromosomes" during interphase.

REPLICATION

"Replication" is the term applied to the quantitative and sometimes to the structural doubling of the DNA during interphase. In fact, interphase has been subdivided with reference to replication (Fig. 15-11 and Table 17-1). Immediately following telophase the amount of DNA in a diploid cell is designated as 2C and the period as G_1 (G for gap). During the G_1 period, there is no detectable change in the 2n amount of DNA or any synthesis of it. Abruptly, DNA starts to synthesize itself and to increase in amount, and that event marks the beginning of the *synthetic period,* designated the S period, and ends when the amount of DNA reaches the 4C or 4n quantity.

The synthetic period is sometimes completed considerably before the beginning of mitotic prophase, but in the premeiotic interphase, replication continues into prophase I. Between the end of the S period and the beginning of mitotic prophase the DNA remains constant at 4C, and the period is designated as the G_2 period. In two experimental examples of interphase subdivided in this manner, G_1 is indicated as 4 hours, S as 8.5 hours, and G_2 as about 4 hours; in Ehrlich's acites tumor culture cells, G_1 is considered as 6 to 8 hours, S as 13 to 15 hours, G_2 as 6 hours, and mitosis as 0.75 hour. Since mitotic interphases vary considerably, as illustrated, these serve merely as examples. There also seems to be considerable variation in the time the S period begins and ends. The S period may begin in some cells types as early as mitotic telophase, and in others it may terminate in prophase.

At present, knowledge of structural changes that may occur during these periods is almost completely lacking. There is no unanimity of competent opinion as to the structure of the telophase chromosome (before the synthetic phase) nor of the chromosome at the very beginning of mitotic prophase (after the G_2 phase). Certainly, during or before prophase a chromosome of two observable chromatids is somehow achieved, but what structural changes at any and all levels of fibrillar diameters lead to this result are unknown. Evans and Savage (1963) and Wolff and Luippold (1964) have demonstrated by x rays and incorporation experiments on *Vicia* root tips that probable structural doubling occurs at late G_1 or early S phase.

After the last mitotic division in a cell lineage some nuclei may not pass through a synthetic period; the G_1 period may last until the cell dies. Few cells, however, stop in a permanent G_2 phase. In the case of a human neuron the postmitotic period at the G_1 or G_2 level might be 100 years or more. There is evidence that nuclei following the last telophase may remain in a G_2 or G_1 condition or undergo endopolyploidy or polyteny (DNA replication without mitosis) to achieve high levels of DNA content, a condition that may be significant in cellular differentiation.

It has also been well established that there is a doubling of the basic protein of the chromosome, the histone, during the S period in most nuclei. DNA and histone retain a constant quantitative relationship to each other in nearly all cells, but changes in DNA/histone ratios may be significant in differentiation. Other proteins and the RNA of the chromosomes, however, seem to increase independently of DNA and histone.

There is one differentiation in DNA synthesis—the DNA of heterochromatin often may replicate significantly later than the euchromatin of the same chromosome or chromosome set (Fig. 15-12). Presumably, the replication of the heterochromatic DNA would mark the latter part of the synthetic period. For example, one of the X chromosomes of the human female replicates early, the other late. This fact is probably related to the presence of only one heterochromatic X chromosome as the Barr body or "drumstick" in certain cells of the body (Fig. 15-10). Heterochromatin probably changes to euchromatin before it can replicate, either all at once or a little at a time.

Replication in nuclei having polyteny or some types of endopolyploidy does not lead to mitosis after the S or G_2 period, but rather directly to the next G_1 or S period. The G_2 and the following G_1 phase probably overlap, become the same or do not exist.

OTHER NUCLEAR INCLUSIONS

Other nuclear inclusions are reported in light and electron microscopic studies of various kinds of cells. Membrane-bounded

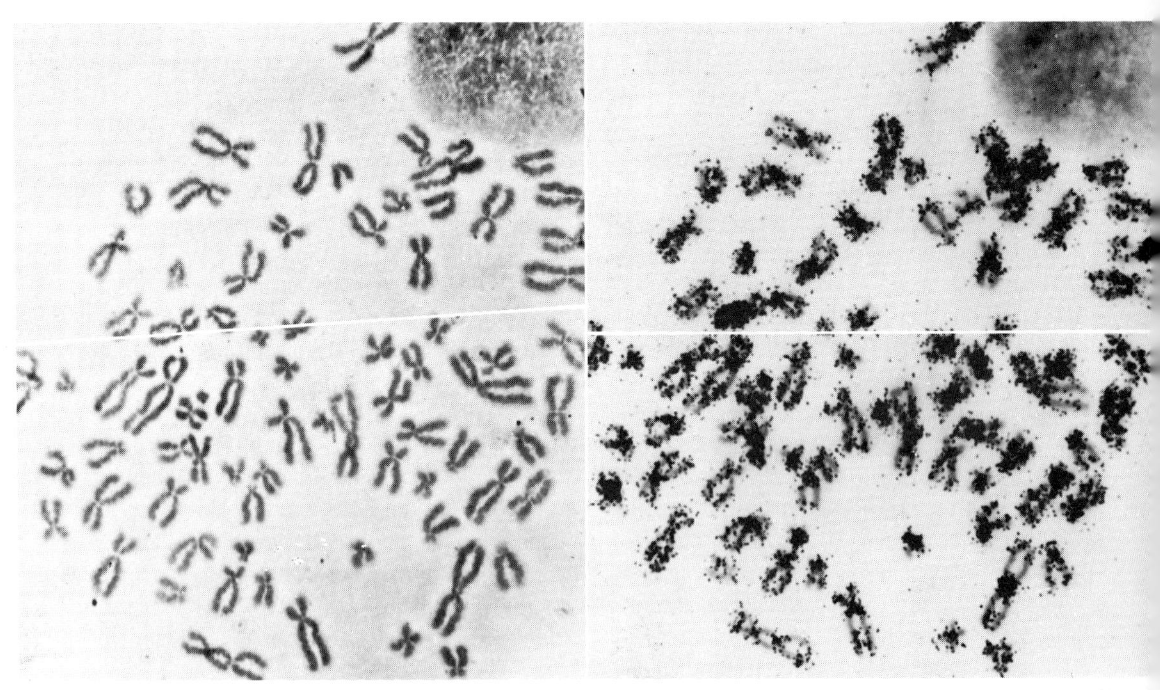

A B

Fig. 15-12. Metaphase in monolayer culture of aneuploid (77 chromosomes) human cancer cells, HE_p2. **A,** Chromosomes after removal of the photographic silver particles. **B,** Radioautograph of the same chromosomes that were fixed 6 hours after labeling with ^{3}H-thymidine. Thus they were labeled late in the S phase and therefore show late DNA replication, which is correlated with heterochromatic regions of the chromosomes. Notice that only parts of chromosomes or certain chromosomes are covered by silver grains, indicating earlier incorporation of radioactive thymidine. (Courtesy Dr. A. Zweidler, University of Texas Cell Research Institute, Austin, Texas.)

vesicles of 1 μm dimensions have been reported in "young" acinar cell nuclei of human salivary glands. Fine filaments and granules are often seen in the nucleoplasm but are of unknown function. Some granules are compared to nucleolar granules, and it is often claimed that they are ribosomal precursors passing from the nucleolus to the pores in the nuclear envelope. Virus or virus-related "nuclear bodies" are often seen as fibrous structures of whorls. At leptotene in primary spermatocytes of some mammals there is a transient "structure" called the *chromoplast* or *chromatin nucleolus.* This is a diffuse, nonmembrane-bounded mass slightly more electron dense than the nucleoplasm lying against the inner nuclear envelope, with the true nucleolus forming a cap on the inner side. Thus with the light microscope it would look and stain like both chromatin and nucleolus. Within the chromatin part can be seen profiles of the synaptinemal complex, which is the locus of the chromosome ends during the bouquet phase of early meiotic prophase. The chromatin part of this mass probably consists of the DNA-containing diffuse material surrounding typical synaptinemal complexes, and within the mass is probably located the nucleolus-organizing region of a pair of chromosomes; therefore the nucleolus must inevitably be located adjacent to the DNA-containing part of the "chromoplast."

During interphase in *Amoeba* and in some other organisms electron microscopic–revealed helical structures are produced in DNA regions of the nucleus. These filaments may be double, with a diameter of about 300 Å, a helix of about 600 to 700 Å width, and a few thousand Ångstroms long. They are probably ribonucleoprotein, probably contain no DNA, and have been seen "passing" out through pores in the nuclear envelope. They are probably related to ribosome formation somehow.

Temporary or permanent (yeast) microtubules are seen in nuclei that undergo mitotic (numerous Protista) or nonmitotic (yeast) nuclear division within permanent nuclear envelopes. In yeast (Figs. 17-9 and 17-10) the permanent intranuclear tubules attach to two "centriolar plaques," each of which appears as a thickened, electron-dense, 1,500 Å diameter disk filling a large pore of the nuclear envelope; a parallel disk in the cytoplasm lies a few hundred Ångstroms away. One of these plaques lies deeply "within" the nucleus, but actually at the end of a long, tubular, cytoplasmic invagination of the nuclear envelope (Fig. 17-10).

Crystals of protein and of other materials have occasionally been seen lying within the nucleoplasm. On the whole, however, nuclei contain fewer specialized and unusual modifications and structures than does the cytoplasm. (See the discussion of the DNA body later in this chapter.)

ESSENTIAL NATURE OF THE NUCLEUS

The essential nature of the nucleus is obvious, since it is the carrier of heredity and the informational source for synthesis of all proteins of the cell. No cell can persist indefinitely nor divide without a nucleus except enucleate echinoderm eggs. When activated, they may divide, but echinoderm eggs are peculiar and far from typical cells. Anucleate cells may persist for some length of time but eventually die. While still alive, they obviously differ from comparable cells with nuclei. Several cells have been observed after removal of nuclei, and normally anucleate or enucleate cells (mammalian erythrocytes and angiosperm sieve elements) do not survive long. However, many nucleate cells do not live long either, such as skin cells, taste bud cells, and the cells of intestinal villi.

Transplant experiments wherein nuclei of one variety or species are introduced into a cell or egg of a different variety or species that had been previously made anucleate have shown that the nucleus is very sensitive to its environmental cytoplasm. The nucleus of one species of the ciliate *Stentor* in the cytoplasm of another species produced an inviable combination, whereas a nucleus of *Amoeba proteus* in cytoplasm of *A. discoides* has produced a clone that survived for more than 6 years. Some characters of the individuals of this clone are determined by the cytoplasm (division rate and nuclear diameter); types of antigens are determined by the nucleus, whereas the shape of the cell when migrating is intermediate.

In the unicellular marine green alga *Acetabularia,* which can survive for weeks in an anucleate condition, Haemmerling (1965) has shown that a nucleus of the species. *A. mediterranea* in the cytoplasm of *A. crenulata* produces a *mediterranea* form of cap, whereas the reciprocal forms a *crenulata* cap; that is, the differentiation of the cap is determined by the single nucleus in the cell, the cytoplasm being indifferent. Cells containing one or two nuclei of each species are alike and intermediate; 1 *cren:*2 *med* or 2 *cren:*4 *med* are more like *mediterranea;* whereas 2 *cren:*1 *med,* 4 *cren:*2 *med,* or 3 *cren:*1 *med* are more like *crenulata.* Such "hybrids," however, are sterile, but the morphology of the cell is determined by the ratios of the nuclei.

DIFFERENTIATION

Differentiation of nuclei is illustrated by nuclear transfers made by King and Briggs (1965) between various embryonic cells and enucleate eggs of the frog *Rana pipiens.* If a nucleus of almost any cell of a *young* gastrula or earlier stage is introduced into an activated and enucleate egg, the egg will develop into a normal or nearly normal larva. It is assumed that up to and including the young gastrula stage the nuclei of all cells are "totipotent" or undifferentiated. However, if various randomly sampled nuclei are taken from the endoderm of an *old* gastrula and transplanted into enucleate eggs, some eggs develop into almost normal larvae but most into abnormal forms that often do not progress beyond the gastrula stage. It is assumed that the endoderm of the late gastrula contains some undifferentiated nuclei but also some that have differentiated and can no longer produce complete and normal larvae.

That this nuclear differentiation is permanent is demonstrated by repeating this transplantation for a number of generations. In such cases development continued to stop at about the same stages as it did in the first transplant generation. It is possible to "explain" this nuclear differentiation by applying the Jacob and Monod (1961) type of gene control by intrinsic and extrinsic co-repressors that permanently turn "on" and "off" various operator genes in the nucleus. Of course, this type of control may be only partially responsible for such nuclear differentiation.

Differentiated cells, those that have stopped division and have specialized somehow, can sometimes dedifferentiate "back" into dividing cells that are no longer specialized. An example is the mature cartilage cells of 10-day-old chicks that, when separated from one another and their cartilage matrix and grown in Carrel flasks with a plasma clot, started to divide and after a few transfers could no longer form chondroitin sulfate, a cartilage material (Holtzer, et al., 1965). Similarly separated chondrocytes but organ cultured (large or small masses of cells) on nutrient agar retained their chondrocyte appearance, did not divide, and produced chondroitin sulfate; that is, with this latter technique the cells did not dedifferentiate. Similar dedifferentiation has been reported for retina, muscle, liver, and other differentiated vertebrate cells that lost their specialized ability to form myosin, etc.

At the present time it is unknown what the change is when differentiated cells dedifferentiate—whether cytoplasmic, nuclear, or both. It seems likely, however, that the nucleus is probably involved to a major extent.

PREMEIOTIC INTERPHASE

Premeiotic interphase, preprophase, or preleptotene is the period and condition of the meiocyte after the last premeiotic telophase and before prophase I begins. It is assumed to be basically similar to a mitotic interphase, but it has some distinctive and significant differences involving chromosomes, nuclei, cytoplasm, and, in plants, cell walls. Premeiotic meiocytes also have a cellular environment that differs from that of mitotic interphase cells. That is, they are generally more or less surrounded by specialized cells such as the *Sertoli cells* around mammalian spermatocytes, the *nurse cells* around animal oocytes, and the *tapetal cells* surrounding the archesporial cells and microsporocytes in anthers of the flowering plants. Such accessory cells are often highly specialized themselves, both physiologically and cytologically, and are essential for the meiotic process.

The premeiotic interphase of meiocytes is, like the mitotic interphase, divided into metabolically different phases. The G_1 phase extends from the last premeiotic telophase to the S phase. The S phase is that period during which DNA, histones to same extent, and other chromosomal proteins are synthesized so that by the end of the S phase most of them have doubled quantitatively. In mitotic interphase the S phase is followed by the long or short G_2 phase, which ends at the beginning of prophase.

Present analyses indicate that in meiocytic interphase there is either no G_2 phase or there is no such thing as leptotene, since the S phase continues up to or into early prophase I, and some DNA synthesis may occur even during zygotene (Taylor, 1959). Thus the early stages of the first meiotic division (preleptotene, leptotene, zygotene, and pachytene) can be considered as more like a modified G_2 phase than a modified mitotic prophase.

Another difference between mitotic and meiocytic interphase is that many interphase meiocytes, especially animal oocytes, increase considerably in volume. In fact, a great deal of oocyte enlargement and cytoplasmic differentiation may precede the leptotene stage of meiosis. Other premeiotic meiocytes enlarge only slightly, such as the so-called megasporocytes of angiospermous plants. These last, however, are certainly different chemically from mitotic interphase cells, since their cytoplasm stains differently, probably due to accumulated RNA and protein. In *Ginkgo,* for example, as the megasporocyte develops during premeiotic interphase, *all* of the mitochondria and plastids become segregated at one end of the cell, the nucleus lies in the middle, and considerable but not all ER appears on the other side of the nucleus at the other end of the cell (Stewart and Gifford, 1967).

The chromosomal condition is essentially unknown in any interphase, especially in premeiotic interphase, but if pairing of homologues has occurred during the premeiotic mitosis (Fig. 18-13), and if the paired condition persists during meiocyte preprophase, as seems likely (Brown and Stack, 1968), then chromosome arrangement within meiocytic interphase is different from mitotic interphase. The presence of paired prochromosomes during the premeiotic interphase, as in *Plantago ovata* (Fig. 15-9) and in some other plants and animals, does indeed indicate or prove that homologues are paired in premeiotic meiocytes (Stack and Brown, 1969).

Indication that there is no sharp demarcation between premeiotic interphase and the beginning of prophase I is the use of the term "preleptotene" as a phase of first meiotic prophase. That concept may be equivalent to all of premeiotic interphase or only the last part, just before leptotene.

It is possible that the synaptinemal complex may begin to form much earlier than leptotene. Whatever that structural system eventually turns out to be and to be for, it is likely that earliest indications will be found during the premeiotic interphase, perhaps even quite early.

Thus it seems best at present to consider preprophase as much different from a mitotic interphase as meiotic prophase is from the early stage of mitosis. Preprophase becomes part of meiosis, and if pairing of homologous chromosomes really does occur during one or more of the premeiotic mitoses (Brown and Stack, 1968), "meiosis" as a process extends continuously through at least three divisions and two intervening periods.

SATELLITE DNA

Satellite DNA has received this designation because in analysis of cellular DNA in a density gradient it forms a small "satellite" peak somewhat removed from the large peak that represents the normal nuclear DNA. The position of the satellite peak usually indicates a lighter form of DNA that correlates with the low C-G (cytosine-guanine) content of satellite DNA. For example, the nuclear DNA of the myxomycete *Physarum polycephalum* has a C-G content of 41%, whereas the C-G content of the satellite DNA from the same organism is only 25%. Satellite DNA generally comes from certain cytoplasmic organelles, mitochondria, plastids, and less ubiquitous structures such as the "kappa" trait of *Paramecium* and the carbon dioxide factor of *Drosophila.* Heavy satellite DNA has been reported to "replace" most of the normal DNA in spores of *Bacillus subtilis* (up to 95%), and the satellite DNA will not hybridize with normal mRNA. Infective virus or bacteria would also produce satellite DNA. It is generally present as short strands that are often closed circles, and because the enzyme exonuclease I (which is specific for single-stranded DNA) will not affect it, satellite DNA is considered to be double stranded. It is therefore a miscellaneous category.

EPISOMES

Episomes (Campbell, 1962, 1969), somewhat like satellite DNA, are genetic "factors" additional to the regular genome. The lambda bacteriophage can be an episome when its "chromosome" integrates in or on a particular segment of the host bacterial chromosome, where it recombines and replicates with it. The "F factor" of *E. coli* is an episome. Bacteria with the factor can act as donor (male) cells and transfer the whole or part of their "chromosome," along with the F factor, to a host or recipient cell, thereby making the host cell diploid for that much of a chromosome. The kappa (killer) trait of *Paramecium* and the sigma (carbon dioxide sensitivity) factor of *Drosophila* may be considered to be episomes as well as satellite DNA. Perhaps at least some supernumerary chromosomes so common in flowering plants can be considered to be episomes as well as satellite DNA, especially if they contain genes for their own survival. Since both mitochondria and plastids contain genes that can mutate, they also can be considered to be episomes. Episomes, by definition, are genetic and are studied by some geneticists. In many cases, such as plastid inheritance, not only are the effects of plastid mutations sometimes obvious, but mutations of nuclear genes can also affect plastid characters, such as failure of chlorophyll to form and electron microscope–revealed abnormalities of internal membranes.

Mutations of mitochondrial DNA can produce obvious phenotypes such as the "petites" of yeast and the "pokey" of *Neurospora* (Wagner, 1969). Different mutant forms of mitochondria can even produce "hereditary" differences between identical twins, and hybrid vigor can now be "explained" by different sorts of mitochondria.

DNA BODY

The DNA body (Lima-de-Faria and Moses, 1966), which has been reported in oogonia of *Tipula, Pales* (Diptera), and *Dytiscus* (Coleoptera), lies within the nucleus, often occupying much of the nuclear volume and more than half of the nuclear

DNA. It also contains histone and therefore chemically resembles chromosomes. It surrounds the nucleolus and is functionally related to it.

In female *Tipula oleracea* the DNA body appears in four oogonial divisions before the oocyte; small ones occur in some nurse cells. It is formed in contact with the sex chromosomes and follows one anaphase group to a spindle pole. The other telophase nucleus becomes a nurse cell nucleus. The body grows rapidly during interphases but synthesizes DNA at a different time than the chromosome. At late diplotene it disintegrates, releasing the DNA into the nucleoplasm and cytoplasm.

In the oocyte the DNA body is appressed against the nuclear envelope but is separated on the interior surface from the inner chromosomes by a layer of ribosome-sized particles and a 0.5 μm layer high in RNA. Electron micrographs reveal that the body is composed of a tight mass of intertwined fibrils.

The assumption is that only the *nucleolus organizer cistrons* become highly polytene (like salivary gland chromosomes); the rest of the chromosomal arms do not. The hundreds of thousands of nucleolus organizer DNA strands form the bulk of this body and probably are highly active in the manufacture of nucleolar material. This activity is compared to the formation of many small DNA-containing "nucleoli" by the lampbrush chromosomes of *Triturus* oocytes during diplotene.

In *Cyclops* (Crustacea) it has been reported that Feulgen-positive bodies are released from the chromosomes and that they are found in the spindles. Such bodies can also be considered as DNA bodies.

In a hemipteran insect, extrusion of Feulgen-positive droplets from certain nuclei appeared to be used as material for the growing egg. Thus there seems to be a connection between DNA bodies of the nucleus and Feulgen-positive bodies in the cytoplasm (Fig. 14-14). These productions of extra DNA by specific regions of chromosomes, but not by all the nuclear DNA, are called *DNA amplification* (Pavan and da Cunha, 1969).

CELL HYBRIDIZATION

"Cell hybridization" (Ephrussi, 1972) is the term applied to the union of somatic animal cells in culture that was discovered in 1960. The union of cells is often followed by union of nuclear contents so that the cell, somewhat like a zygote, may produce a line of cells or clone that has chromosomes and genes of the two "parent" cells. Such union of cells is a naturally rare event in cultures, but it can be greatly increased by treatment of the cell mixture with the ultraviolet-inactivated hemagglutinizing virus of Japan (Sendai virus). The inactivated virus brings the plasma membranes into contact by agglutination, and the membranes in contact break down so that the cytoplasms become confluent and a binucleate or multinucleate cell results (Harris et al., 1966). Later, perhaps during simultaneous division of the two nuclei, the chromosome sets are united.

Out of the tens of thousands of parental cells used a very few truly hybrid cells, which include only one set of chromosomes from each parental culture, are formed, and of these some are viable enough to produce (after many cell generations) a hybrid cell culture. In such a culture between fairly closely related parents, such as mouse cells × rat cells or mouse cells × hamster cells, there is a loss of about 15% of chromosomes equally from both parents. But when the species that provided the cells are distant, such as mouse cells × human cells or hamster and human, the chromosomes of one species, in these cases always the human chromosomes, are quickly and preferentially reduced during a few divisions to only two to fifteen, but eventually to only one to three. The chromosome set of the other species culture remains intact (Ephrussi and Weiss, 1969). Therefore in a culture of cells containing a single and identifiable human chromosome any human gene, such as for a particular enzyme, can be assigned to the identified chromosome.

Numerous mouse-human (Harris and Watkins, 1965), hen erythrocyte–human HeLa (Harris, 1967), etc., cell hybrids have been produced. The hybrid cells of such mouse-human derivation generally have an increased number of mouse chromosomes but a decreased number of human chromosomes (Matsuya and Green, 1969). Since all mouse chromosomes are telocentric (Fig. 15-13), whereas only a few human chromosomes are acrocentric (Fig. 15-12), most human and mouse chromosomes are recognizable as to origin. Pontecorvo (1971) generalized that the chromosomes of one "parent" or the other of a cell hybrid are

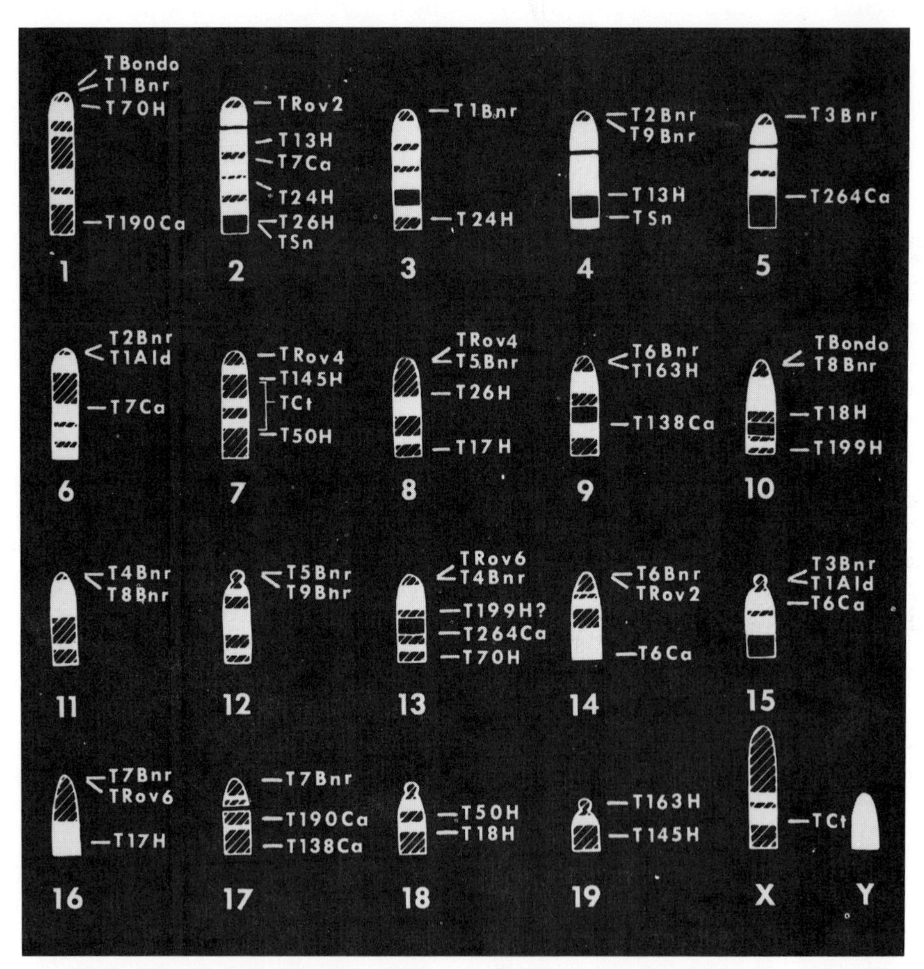

Fig. 15-13. Idiogram of the banding patterns of the mouse, *Mus musculus,* as determined by quinacrine fluorescence. Centromeres are all at the upper (rounded) ends of the chromosomes. The white bands are the fluorescent and, presumably, constitutive heterochromatic regions. The various designations are of known translocation break points of the chromosomes. For example, T163H involved chromosomes 9 and 19. It is evident that there is at least one translocation at the centromeric (upper) end of each chromosome. The constrictions indicated on chromosomes 12, 15, 18, and 19 represent secondary constrictions (nucleolus organizers) in the long (only) arm. (From Miller, D. A., and O. J. Miller. 1972. Science **178:**949-955. Copyright 1972 by the American Society for the Advancement of Science.)

usually gradually lost over successive divisions and that if one parent cell had been irradiated, its chromosomes would be lost.

By selecting clonal lines of cells having certain enzyme mutants, combining them by cell hybridization, raising selected clonal lines of cells in culture, making cytological examination of chromosomal content, and testing for presence or absence of enzyme production by the hybrid cell line, various conclusions can be made. For example, hybrid cells from a mouse line deficient for the enzyme dipeptidase-2 and a human line that produces dipeptidase-A (electrophoretically different enzymes) produced the dipeptidase-2 enzyme. It was concluded by the authors (Shows et al., 1972) that the inhibition of production of dipeptidase-2 in the original mouse line was due, not to mutation of a regulatory gene, but to mutation of a structural gene.

It is questionable if such cell hybridizations can occur within organisms, since they have cell and tissue rejection mechanisms. Hybridizations can occur in cell cultures where such mechanisms do not occur. As a cytogenetic technique, it is providing a great deal of significant information in the field of human genetics.

It has also been established that if one of the nuclei is differentiated, even as much as a hen erythrocyte, but the other is active in either DNA or RNA synthesis, the differentiated nucleus will dedifferentiate and begin to produce the same sort of nucleic acid (RNA or DNA) that the active nucleus is producing. Furthermore, if both nuclei synthesize DNA, they can undergo mitosis synchronously, spindles fuse, and truly hybrid nuclei form that may divide again. Apparently, the taxonomic or tissue differences possible to hybridize depend only on the sorts of cells the particular virus will adsorb onto.

LITERATURE CITED

Belling, J. 1931. Chiasmas in flowering plants. Calif. Univ. Publ. Bot. **16**:313-321.

Belling, J. 1933. Crossing over and gene rearrangement in flowering plants. Genetics **18**:388-413.

Berrill, N. J., and C. L. Huskins. 1936. The "resting" nucleus. Amer. Nat. **70**:257-261.

Brink, R. A. 1960. Paramutation and chromosome organization. Quart. Rev. Biol. **35**:120-137.

Brinkley, B. R. 1965. The fine structure of the nucleolus in mitotic divisions of Chinese hamster cells in vitro. J. Cell Biol. **27**:411-422.

Britten, R. J., and E. H. Davidson. 1969. Gene regulation for higher cells: a theory. Science **165**:349-357.

Brown, D. D., and J. B. Gurdon. 1965. Absence of ribosomal RNA synthesis in the anucleate mutant of Xenopus laevis. In E. Bell (editor). Molecular and cellular aspects of development. Harper & Row, Publishers, New York.

Brown, W. V. 1972. Textbook of cytogenetics. The C. V. Mosby Co. St. Louis.

Brown, W. V., and S. M. Stack. 1968. Somatic pairing as a preliminary to meiosis. Bull. Torrey Bot. Club **95**:369-378.

Callan, H. G. 1967. The organization of genetic units in chromosomes. J. Cell Sci. **2**:1-7.

Campbell, A. M. 1962. Episomes. Adv. Genet. **11**:101-145.

Campbell, A. M. 1969. Episomes. Harper & Row, Publishers, New York.

Cleveland, L. R. 1953. Studies on chromosomes and nuclear division. III. Pairing, segregation, and crossing-over. Trans. Amer. Phil. Soc. (n.s.) **43**(pt. 3):809-869.

Coleman, L. C. 1941. The relation of chromocenters to the differential segments in Rhoeo discolor Hance. Amer. J. Bot. **28**:742-748.

Crosby, A. R. 1957. Nucleolar activity of lagging chromosomes in wheat. Amer. J. Bot. **44**:813-822.

Darlington, C. D. 1935. The time, place, and action of crossing-over. J. Genet. **31**:185-212.

Darlington, C. D. 1942. Chromosome chemistry and gene action. Nature (London) **149**:66-69.

Das, T. M., A. C. Hildebrandt, and A. J. Riker. 1966. Cinephotomicrography of low temperature effects on cytoplasmic streaming, nucleolar activity and mitosis in single tobacco cells in microculture. Amer. J. Bot. **53**:253-259.

De, D. N. 1964. A new chromosome model. Nature (London) **203**:343-346.

Dodge, J. D. 1963. The nucleus and nuclear division in the Dinophyceae. Arch. Protista **106**: 442-452.

Dodge, J. D. 1964a. Chromosome structure in Dinophyceae. II. Cytochemical studies. Arch. Mikrobiol. **48**:66-80.

Dodge, J. D. 1964b. Nuclear division in the dinoflagellate Gonyaulax tamarensis. J. Gen. Microbiol. **36**:269-276.

DuPraw, E. J. 1968. Cell and molecular biology. Academic Press, Inc., New York.

DuPraw, E. J. 1970. DNA and chromosomes. Holt, Rinehart & Winston, Inc., New York.

Ephrussi, B. 1972. Hybridization of somatic cells. Princeton University Press, Princeton, N. J.

Ephrussi, B., and M. Weiss. 1969. Hybrid somatic cells. Sci. Amer. **220:**26-35.

Evans, H. J., and J. R. K. Savage. 1963. The relation between DNA synthesis and chromosome structure as resolved by x-ray damage. J. Cell Biol. **18:**525-540.

Fernandes, A. 1943. Sur l'origine des chromosomes surnumeraries heterochromatique chez Narcissus bulbocodium. L. Bol. Soc. Brot. **17** (2): 251-266.

Freese, E. 1958. The arrangement of DNA in the chromosomes. Cold Spring Harb. Symp. Quant. Biol. **23:**13-18.

Haemmerling, J. 1965. The role of the nucleus in differentiation, especially in Acetabularia. In E. Bell (editor). Molecular and cellular aspects of development. Harper & Row, Publishers, New York.

Harris, H. 1967. The reactivation of the red cell nucleus. J. Cell Sci. **2:**23-32.

Harris, H., and J. F. Watkins. 1965. Hybrid cells derived from mouse and man: artificial heterokaryons of mammalian cells from different species. Nature (London) **205:**640-646.

Harris, H., J. F. Watkins, C. E. Ford, and G. I. Schoefl. 1966. Artificial heterokaryons of animal cells from different species. J. Cell Sci. **1:**1-30.

Heitz, E. 1942. Über mutative Intersexualität und Sexualität und Geschlechtsumwandlung bei den Lebermoosen *Pellia neesiana* und *Sphaerocarpus donnellii.* Naturwissenschaften **30:**751.

Holtzer, H., J. Abbott, J. W. Lash, and S. Holtzer. 1965. The loss of phenotypic traits by differentiated cells in vitro. I. De-differentiation of cartilage cells. In E. Bell (editor). Molecular and cellular aspects of development. Harper & Row, Publishers, New York.

Hyde, B. B. 1953. Differentiated chromosomes in Plantago ovata. Amer. J. Bot. **40:**809-815.

Jacob, F., and J. Monod, 1961. Genetic regulatory mechanisms in the synthesis of proteins. J. Molec. Biol. **3:**318-356.

Janssens, F. A. 1909. La théorie de la chiasmatypie: Nouvells interpretation des cinéses de maturation. Cellule **22:**387-411.

Japha, G. 1939. II. Die Meiosis von Oenothera. Z. Bot. **34:**321-369.

Johnson, J. M., and L. E. Jones. 1967. Behavior of nucleoli and contracting nucleolar vacuoles in tobacco cells growing in microculture. Amer. J. Bot. **54:**189-198.

King, T. J., and R. Briggs. 1965. Serial transplantation of embryonic nuclei. In E. Bell (editor). Molecular and cellular aspects of development. Harper & Row, Publishers, New York.

Kuroiwa, T., and N. Tanaka. 1971. Fine structure of interphase nuclei. I. The morphological classification of nuclei in interphase of Crepis capillaris. Cytologia (Tokyo) **36:**143-160.

Lederberg, J. 1955. Recombination mechanisms in bacteria. J. Cell. Comp. Physiol. **45:**75-91.

Lima-de-Faria, A., and M. J. Moses. 1966. Ultrastructure and cytochemistary of metabolic DNA in Tipula. J. Cell Biol. **30:**177-192.

Lindegren, C. C. 1964. A new theory to explain crossing-over between genes on chromosomes. Nature (London) **204:**322-324.

Lobeer, G. 1961. Strukur und Inhalt der Geschlechtschromosomen. Ber. Dtsch. Bot. Ges. **59:** 369-375.

Lyon, M. F. 1962. Sex chromatin and gene action in the mammalian x-chromosome. Amer. J. Hum. Genet. **14:**135-148.

Matsuya, Y., and H. Green. 1969. Somatic cell hybrid between the established human line D98 (presumptive HeLa) and 3T3. Science **163:**697-698.

McClintock, B. 1933. The association of nonhomologous parts of chromosomes in the midprophase of meiosis in Zea mays. Z. Zellforsch. **19:**191-237.

Meselson, M., and F. W. Stahl. 1958. The replication of DNA in Escherichia coli. Proc. Nat. Acad. Sci. U.S.A. **44:**671-682.

Miller, D. A., and O. J. Miller. 1972. Chromosome mapping in tthe mouse. Fluorescence banding techniques permit assignment of most genetic linkage groups. Science **178:**949-955.

Miller, O. L., and B. R. Beatty. 1969. Visualization of nucleolar genes. Science **164:**955-957.

Miller, O. L., B. R. Beatty, B. A. Hamkalo, and C. A. Thomas. 1970. Electron microscope visualization of transcription. Cold Spring. Harb. Symp. Quant. Biol. **35:**505-515.

Molisch, H. 1901. Studien über der Milchsaft und Schleimsaft der Pflanzen. Gustav Fischer, Jena.

Painter, T. S. 1964. Fundamental chromosome structure. Proc. Nat. Acad. Sci. U.S.A. **51:** 1282-1285.

Pavan, C., and A. B. da Cunha. 1969. Gene amplification in ontogeny and phylogeny of animals. Genetics **61:**(supp.)289-304.

Peacock, W. J. 1963. Chromosome duplication and structure as determined by autoradiography. Proc. Nat. Acad. Sci. U.S.A. **49:**793-801.

Pickett-Heaps, J. D., and D. H. Northcote. 1966. Cell division in the formation of the stomatal complex of the young leaves of wheat. J. Cell Sci. **1**:121-128.

Plaut, W. S. 1953. The effect of B-chromosomes on the variegated pericarp phenotype in maize. Amer. J. Bot. **40**:344-348.

Pontecorvo, G. 1971. Induction of directional chromosome elimination in somatic cell hybrids. Nature (London) **230**:367-369.

Prokofyeva-Belgovskaya, A. A. 1948. Heterochromatization as a change of chromosome cycle. J. Genet. **48**:80-98.

Ris, H. 1961. Ultrastructure and molecular orgaization of genetic systems. Canad. J. Cytol. **3**: 95-120.

Ritossa, F. M., and S. Spiegelman. 1965. Localization of DNA complementary to ribosomal RNA in the nucleolus organizer of Drosophila melanogaster. Proc. Nat. Acad. Sci. U.S.A. **53**: 737-745.

Robbins, E., and N. K. Gonatas. 1964. The ultrastructure of a mammalian cell during the mitotic cycle. J. Cell Biol. **21**:429-463.

Schwartz, D. 1955. Studies on crossing over in maize and Drosophila. J. Cell. Comp. Physiol. **45**(supp.2):171-188.

Schwartz, D. 1960. Deoxyribonucleic acid and chromosome structure. In J. S. Mitchell (editor). The cell nucleus. Academic Press, Inc., New York.

Shows, T. B., J. May, and L. Haley. 1972. Human-mouse cell hybrids: a suggestion of structural mutation for dipeptidase-2 deficiency in mouse cells. Science **178**:58-60.

Stack, S. M., and W. V. Brown. 1969. Somatic and premeiotic pairing of homologues in Plantago ovata. Bull. Torrey Bot. Club **96**: 143-149.

Stahl, F. W. 1961. A chain model for chromosomes. J. Chem. Phys. **58**:1072-1077.

Stewart, K. D., and E. M. Gifford. 1967. Ultrastructure of the developing megaspore mother cell of Ginkgo biloba. Amer. J. Bot. **54**:375-383.

Sunderland, N., and J. McLeish. 1961. Nucleic acid content and concentration in root cells of higher plants. Exp. Cell Res. **24**:541-554.

Taylor, J. H. 1957. The time and mode of duplication of chromosomes. Amer. Nat. **91**:209-221.

Taylor, J. H. 1959. Autoradiographic studies of nucleic acids and proteins during meiosis in Lilium longifolium. Amer. J. Bot. **46**:477-484.

Taylor, J. H. 1963. The replication and organization of DNA in chromosomes. In J. H. Taylor (editor). Molecular genetics. Academic Press, Inc., New York.

Uhl, C. H. 1965. Chromosome structure and crossing-over. Genetics **51**:191-207.

Vanderlyn, L. 1948. Somatic mitosis in the root tip of Allium cepa—a review and a reorientation. Bot. Rev. **14**:270-318.

Wagner, R. P. 1969. Genetics and phenogenetics of mitochondria. Science **163**:1026-1031.

Weismann, A. 1885. Die Kontinutät des Keimplasmas, als Grundlage einer Theorie der Vererbung. Gustav Fischer, Jena.

White, M. J. D. 1954. Animal cytology and evolution. Cambridge University Press, New York.

Whitehouse, H. L. K. 1963. A theory of crossing-over by means of hybrid deoxyribonucleic acid. Nature (London) **199**:1034-1040.

Whitehouse, H. L. K. 1965. Crossing-over. Sci. Progr. (London) **53**:285-296.

Whitehouse, H. L. K. 1967. A cycloid model for the chromosome. J. Cell Sci. **2**:9-22.

Wolff, S., and H. E. Luippold. 1964. Chromosome splitting as revealed by combined x-ray and labelling experiments. Exp. Cell Res. **34**: 548-556.

Yunis, J. J., and W. G. Yasmineh. 1971. Heterochromatin, satellite DNA, and cell function. Science **174**:1200-1205.

CHAPTER 16

Metaphase chromosomes and sets

By the time mitosis (Chapter 17) has proceeded to metaphase the chromosomes have almost reached their maximum shortening. They have also become distinct bodies of characteristic form. In general, when chromosomes are referred to, the metaphase form is implied; meiotic, interphase, prophase, anaphase, telophase, etc., chromosomes are usually so specified. There is an extensive literature on metaphase chromosomes from most groups of plant and animals and a few fungi. Thus comparisons of size, form, structure, number, and variations from the typical can be made. Metaphase chromosomes have been studied extensively since first seen by Hofmeister in the 1840s and especially since staining techniques were developed during the 1870s. The typical metaphase chromosome consists of two chromatids held together tightly or loosely; they are attached to each other at only one limited region, the region of the centromere. The remainder of the chromatids are often quite independent of one another, often twisted loosely about each other (Figs. 16-1 to 16-3).

It is evident that among the Eukaryota there are numerous sorts of chromosomes (Darlington, 1937, 1956; White, 1950). The vast majority are of the ordinary or typical sort and will be called *autosomes* here. Another common but much less numerous category of chromosome is the *sex chromosome* generally present in animals but much less common in the plant kingdom. A third and rather different, less common, but not rare type of chromosome in plants is the *supernumerary chromosome.* These three distinct types will be discussed in considerable detail in this chapter. Whether or not the tiny *m chromosomes* so common in mosses are supernumerary has not been demonstrated one way or the other. The E and S chromosomes of the Cecidomyiidae (gall midges) and the "limited chromosomes" of *Sciara* are probably best regarded as subtypes of autosomes. The long germ line chromosomes of the parasitic roundworm *Parascaris equorum* may each be considered as a compound chromosome consisting of a large number of small autosomes attached end to end and having one heterochromatic acentric "chromosome" attached at each of the two extremities of each "chromosome." Among yeasts, dinoflagellate algae, and some Protozoa the "chromosomes" seem to remain in much the same condition during interphase and "mitosis," and there is no typical mitosis, metaphase, or metaphase chromosome (Kubai and Ris, 1969). The ordinary or autosomal chromosome (Schrader, 1953) will be discussed first.

AUTOSOMAL CHROMOSOMES

Chromatid structure

A chromatid is an obvious longitudinal subdivision of a chromosome (Figs. 16-1 to

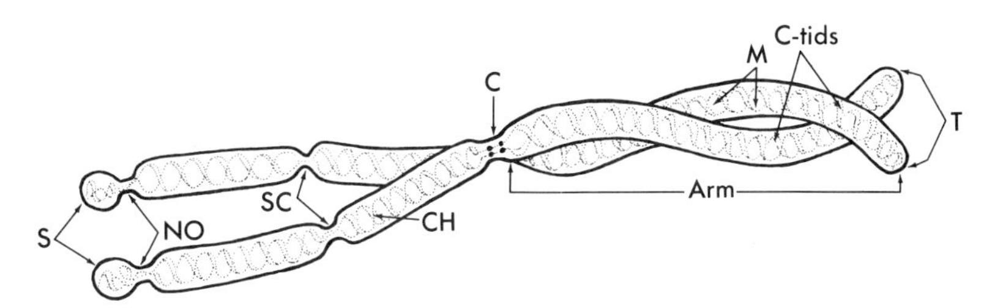

Fig. 16-1. Diagram of mitotic metaphase chromosome of two chromatids, **C-tids. C,** Centromere, or primary constriction; **CH,** chromonema; **M,** matrix; **T,** telomeres, one at the end of each arm of each chromatid; **SC,** secondary constrictions, which are often absent; **NO,** nucleolus organizer constriction, sometimes referred to as a secondary constriction; **S,** satellites, which are short segments distal to the nucleolus organizer constrictions. (Compare with Fig. 16-3.)

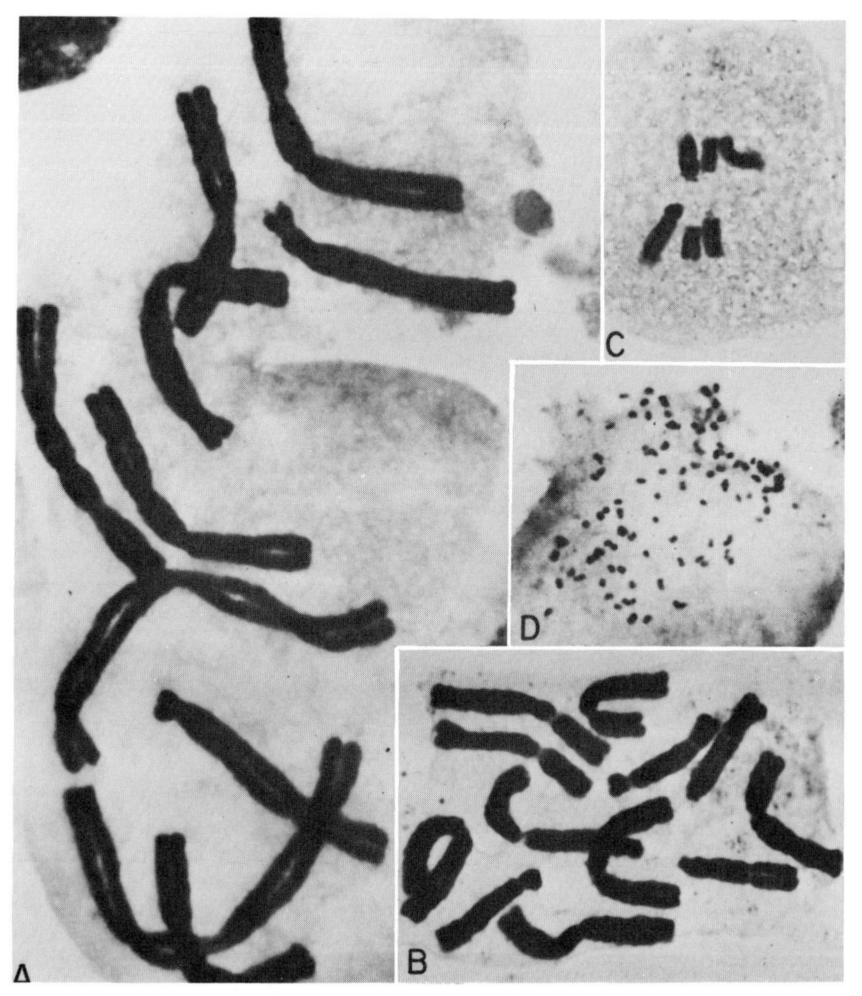

Fig. 16-2. A variety of sizes of mitotic metaphase chromosomes. **A,** Those of *Trillium erectum* are the largest known, approximately 30 μm. **B,** Chromosomes of *Podophyllum peltatum* are large. **C,** Chromosomes of *Crepis capillaris* are of about average size for organisms as a whole, approximately 5 μm. **D,** Tiny chromosomes of *Sedum rupidragum* (2n = 136). (From Sparrow, A. H., et al. 1965. Radiat. Biol. **5**(supp.):101-132.)

16-3). The generalized concept of a metaphase chromatid is that of a coiled *chromonema,* which is a single or multiple nucleoprotein strand of linearly arranged "genes"; its internal structure is presently unknown. Based on light microscopy, by 1950 it had been concluded that the metaphase chromosome, or chromatid, had some sort of "chromatin" surrounding the chromonema called the *matrix,* which produced the smooth contour of the chromosome or chromatid. Additionally, many light microscopists proposed that the outer surface of the matrix constituted some sort of membrane, which they called the *pellicle.* Since 1950, however, no definite membranous pellicle has been found with electron microscopy, and the existence of matrix is even in question. With respect to matrix, however, since electron microscopy is unable to distinguish between as many different kinds of molecules as light microscopy, it is possible that the matrix does exist as a particular sort of protein (with or without RNA) and possibly some lipid, and that the "pellicle" is merely the interface between this material and the different protoplasm of the nucleoplasm surrounding the chromosome. Cer-

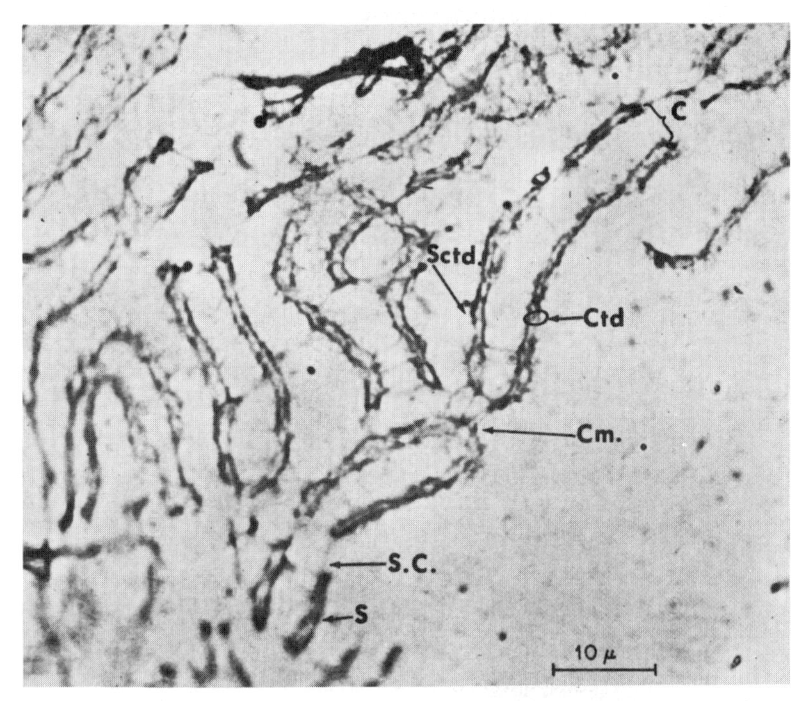

Fig. 16-3. An example of revealed metaphase chromosome structure. Mitotic metaphase chromosomes of *Vicia faba* were removed from the cell, spread on a slide, treated with trypsin to remove proteins, and Feulgen stained to reveal DNA. Notice especially the long M chromosome extended diagonally from lower left to upper right. The centromere, **Cm.,** is at the center as a constriction. The nucleolus organizer constriction, **S.C.,** is in the lower arm with the distal region of that arm, the satellite, **S.** The parts of the upper arm are labeled. The whole chromosome, **C,** consists of two widely spaced chromatids, **Ctd.,** and each chromatid of two subchromatids, **Sctd.** Details below that level are of unknown significance, such as the strands across the centromere, the strands connecting chromatids and subchromatids, and the strands connecting different chromosomes. There is no evidence of coiling and only a small amount of twisting in these mitotic chromosomes. (Compare with the set as usually prepared in Fig. 16-9, *E.* Chromosomes prepared in this way are four times as long as when prepared by other methods.) (From Trosko, J. E., and D. S. Wolff. 1965. J. Cell Biol. **26:**130-135.)

tainly, light microscopy does indicate that as prophase progresses, there is chemical change as well as physical compaction. The term "matrix" is still widely used, for example, to describe the ribonucleoprotein of the meiotic prophase lampbrush chromosomes.

Chromatid composition

An example of the composition of metaphase chromosomes extracted from cells, human HeLa cell chromosomes (Huberman and Attardi, 1966), and others, is 2 mg of acid-soluble protein, 2.7 mg acid-insoluble protein, and 0.64 to 1 mg of mostly ribosomal RNA for each milligram of DNA.

An argument that indicates the presence of matrix (or of great and unknown variation in internal composition and structure among chromosomes) is the spectacular variation in total metaphase chromosome volume among species (Fig. 16-2). For example, the metaphase chromosomes of *Trillium erectum* and *Scirpus californicus* (a 5-foot long bulrush) can be compared to the total chromosome volume. The haploid chromosome number of *Trillium* is n = 5, with an average length of 28 μm and a diameter of 1.5 μm. Thus the haploid volume of somatic metaphase chromosomes is about 210 μm^3. In *Scirpus californicus* there are no more than fifty tiny chromosomes of maximum dimensions of 1 $\times$ 0.5 μm, producing a total volume of less than 10 μm^3 and, compared to *Trillium,* about 5% the chromatic volume. It is probably a safe assumption that as many genes are necessary to determine a *Scirpus* as a *Trillium* plant and its life cycle. It can be supposed, logically, that the greater volume of *Trillium* chromosomes might be the result of a large amount of "padding" material, which can be called matrix. On the other hand, it is probable that *Trillium* actually does have twenty times the amount of DNA as does *Scirpus. Scirpus* probably has about the same amount of DNA per haploid cell as *Sedum alfredi* (5.6×10^9 nucleotides), whereas *Trillium luteum* has 1.3×10^{11} or twenty-five times the DNA of *Sedum* (Fig.16-2, *D*). Furthermore, a large *Trillium* chromosome has 300 times as much DNA as a tiny *Sedum* (or *Scirpus*) chromosome (Sparrow et al., 1972). These authors list amounts of DNA per cell and per chromosome of many species of animals, plants, Protozoa, bacteria, and viruses and discuss considerations of evolution of DNA amounts and chromosomes. All chromosomes may be somewhat polytene, some much more than others. According to this hypothesis, small chromosomes consist of very few genonemata (DNA strands), whereas large chromosomes consist of many parallel strands. This interesting problem, like so many others of chromosome structure, has not been resolved.

In the Droseraceae a bulk difference of 1,000 times has been reported (Behre, 1929). It is hardly likely that *Drosophyllum* has 1,000 times as many genes or perhaps 1,000 times as much DNA as the related genus *Drosera.* Actually, there is only a DNA amount difference of about seventy-five times between *Drosophyllum* and *Drosera* (Rothfels and Heimburger, 1968). In most species, however, bulk chromosomal differences among species, as seen in the light microscope, do correspond with DNA amount differences. Furthermore, there is some evidence that the sizes of all chromosomes (the amount of matrix or density of compaction of the chromatin fibers) of a set is under genetic control, that chromosomes of polyploids are generally smaller than those of the diploid ancestors, and that chromosomes of different tissues of the same organism may be of different sizes. The behavior of the heteropyknotic X chromosome of short-horned grasshoppers and crickets during spermatogonial and first meiotic divisions is best explained by variations in amount of matrix. Sometimes they are thin and pale (negatively pyknotic) and at other times large and darkly stained (positively pyknotic) compared to autosomes; yet the amount of DNA probably remains the same. The hypothesis that there is some material called matrix, then, is a reasonable possibility. (Compare Fig. 16-2, *B,* with Fig. 16-3.)

Centromere

The centromere is the topological reference point of a metaphase chromosome. It is a single structural modification of a typical chromosome to which the half spindle fibers are "attached" (Figs. 16-1 and 16-3). It is structurally and functionally distinct from the remainder of the chromosome (Brinkley and Stubblefield, 1970). The fact that it is functional during division when the rest of the chromosome is genetically inactive (it may be the locus of some of the genes for mitotic and meiotic activity) requires that it have a different DNA cycle from the chromosome *arms,* which are the regions of the chromosome from the centromere to the two ends.

The centromere as such is not generally seen in mitotic chromosomes, but its location is often evident as an apparent constriction of the chromosome (Figs. 16-1 to 16-4). This constriction associated with the centromere is often loosely called the centromere, or *kinetochore,* but more exactly it is the *primary constriction.* With proper preparation it has been revealed that each "typical" chromosome has one primary constriction which has a definite position in each particular chromosome. However, among chromosomes in general, primary constrictions, and therefore centromeres, may be located anywhere along the length of a chromosome (Fig. 16-4). If the centromere (and therefore the primary constriction) is near an end of a chromosome, the chromosome is described by zoologists as *acrocentric* and the primary constriction is described by botanists as *subterminal.* If the centromere is at or very near the center so that the chromosome arms are equal or nearly so, the chromosome is described as *metacentric* and the centromere as *median.* If the centromere is not as distal as the subterminal position nor at the center so that one arm is obviously shorter than the other, the chromosome is described as *submetacentric* and the primary constriction is *submedian.* Occasionally, in experimental plant and animal materials and, possibly or probably, in a few wild types of organisms the centromere has been "broken" crosswise, producing two chromosomes, each with a *terminal centromere.* Such *telocentric* chromosomes are possibly unstable or produce genetic unbalance and so may not persist long in nature. Marks (1957), however, has defended the concept that some species of Protozoa, plants, and mammals do have naturally occurring and persistent, truly telocentric chromosomes (Fig. 16-10). His argument is based not only on observations of claimed telocentric chromosomes in Protozoa and mammals but also on the appearance within a species or in two closely related species of a pair of rod-shaped, apparently telocentric chromosomes in place of one metacentric chromosome, as in two species of the onionlike plant *Nothoscordum,* some species of *Allium* (the onion), *Miersia chilensis, Campanula,* the sex chromosomes of hops, *Oxalis dispar,* wheat, and *Phleum echinatum.* Electron micrographs of certain mammalian chromosomes indicate that they may be truly telocentric. Some chromosome evolutionists consider such natural

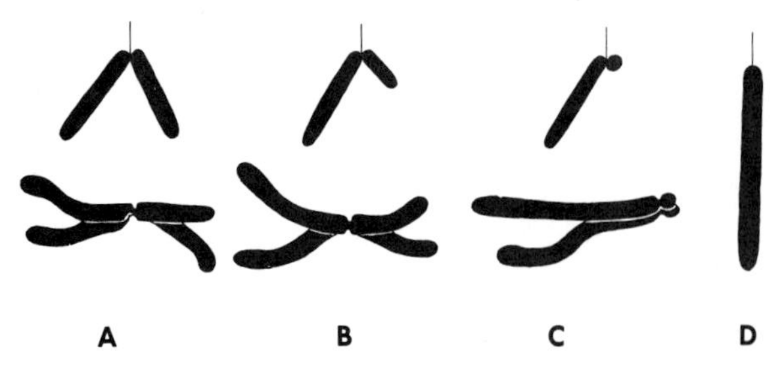

Fig. 16-4. Diagrammatic representations of, from **A** to **D,** metacentric, submetacentric, acrocentric, and telocentric chromosomes. Positions of the centromeres are median, submedian, subterminal, and terminal.

breakage as one process by which chromosome number may be increased without, however, necessarily increasing genetic content. It seems likely that rather rarely or quite often truly telocentric chromosomes may occur and persist in nature. All or nearly all mouse chromosomes are telocentric, at least in some varieties.

The centromere itself was named by light microscopists as a clear unstained gap in the chromosome. During the 1940s and 1950s more detail was achieved, often by special pretreatments, and darkly stained granules of about 0.5 μm were described. By 1950 (Tjio and Levan) it was generally established that in the two-chromatid metaphase chromosome there are four such granules, called *centromeric chromomeres,* arranged in a square within the otherwise unstained centromere (Fig. 16-1). At anaphase only two such chromomere granules are evident, two in each chromatid, a fact that would relate these centromeric chromomeres to lateral structures with which associated spindle fibers are seen by electron microscopy.

Apparently, by metaphase the chromonemata of the two chromatids have already separated (Fig. 16-3), but whether the clear part of the centromere (if it really is a structure at all) has divided or not is unknown. The electron microscope interpretation is that the centromere is a region of the chromonema that is in an extended condition, in contrast to the arms of the chromosome, which are much more compacted. Centromeric chromomeres are specializations of the region for spindle fiber attachment and perhaps spindle fiber formation (Fig. 16-5). There is adequate evidence, however, that spindle fibers do terminate at or near the centromere and extend poleward from there. A number of spindle fibers are associated with each lateral half of the centromere or kinetochore and extend toward the nearer spindle pole.

Recent terminology specifies the *centromere* as the primary constriction region of

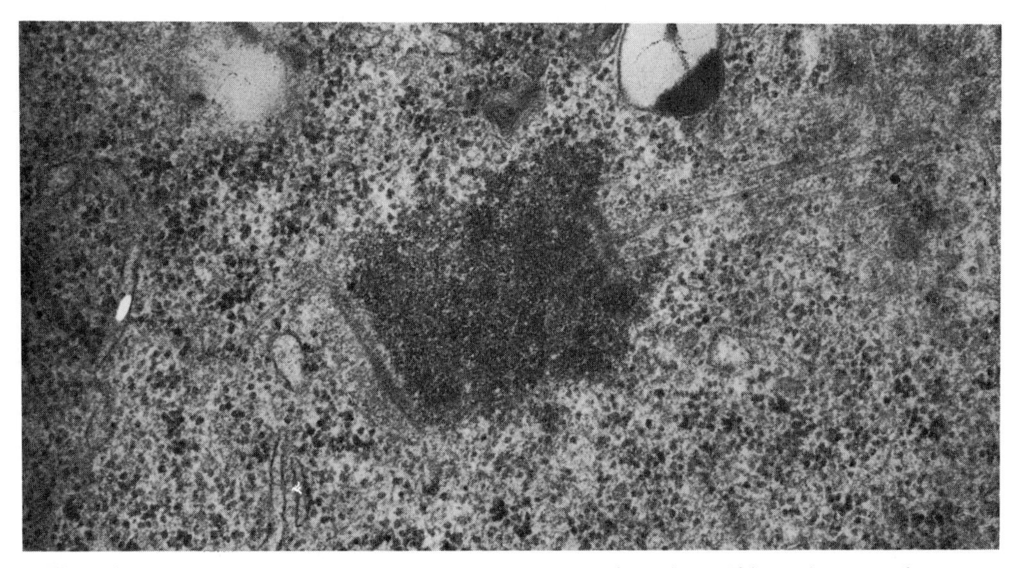

Fig. 16-5. Electron micrograph of centromere at metaphase in a Chinese hamster chromosome. "Centromere" seems to consist of two plates, one on each side of the chromosome. Such plates or comparable structures are often called "kinetochores." Microtubular spindle fibers extend outward from each plate of the centromere. (From Brinkley, B. R., and E. Stubblefield. Chromosoma **19:**28-43.)

the chromosome and specifies the temporarily formed structures to which the spindle fibers are attached as *kinetochores* (Fig. 16-5). Electron microscopy has revealed what seems to be several different structures at or even composing the centromeres of different species of organisms. It would be anticipated that all centromeres would be of the same structure, but that may not be true.

It has also been proposed that the two chromatids are not held together until anaphase by the centromere per se but by special region on each side of the centromere that have a special cycle of activity or that consist of heterochromatin, which sticks the two chromatids together until anaphase separation. Nevertheless, the time when centromere duplication and separation occur during typical mitosis and meiosis is still not established.

It was stated earlier that each typical chromosome has only one such specialized and localized centromere. There are, however, natural and artificially produced exceptional conditions. Among naturally occurring exceptions found in a few animals and plants are the so-called *diffuse* centromeres or *polycentric* or *holocentric chromosomes* (Braselton, 1971; Comings and Okada, 1972). There are some data available on the structures implied by these two concepts—of many centromeres on each chromosome or of a "diffuse" centromere spread out from one end of the chromosome to the other. These are not merely two ways of describing the same unknown condition. The observations that have given rise to these concepts, however, are fairly clear.

Electron microscopy of such holocentric chromosomes seems to indicate that each

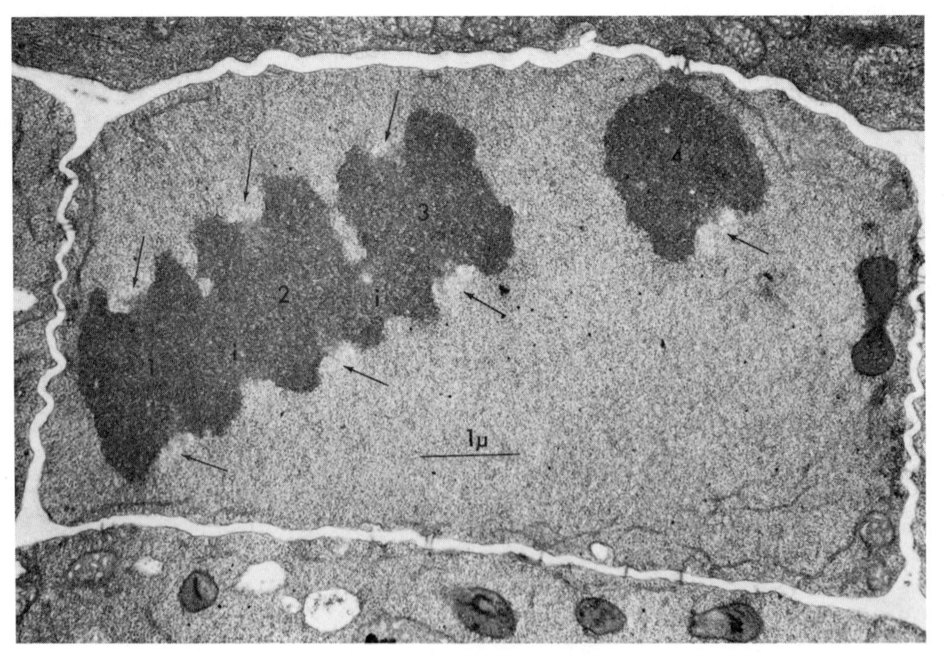

Fig. 16-6. Cross sections of four (**1, 2, 3,** and **4**) of the six polycentric (holocentric) mitotic metaphase chromosomes in a root tip cell of *Luzula purpurea.* Kinetochore regions are recognized by the electron-translucent halos (arrows). Chromosomes **1, 2,** and **3** are somewhat united by interchromosomal connections **(i).** (×24,000.) (Courtesy Dr. J. P. Braselton, Ohio University, Athens, Ohio.)

small chromosome (and most holocentric chromosomes are small, about 1 to 2 μm long) is comparable to a centromere, as in the plant *Cyperus* (Braselton, 1971), the insect *Rhodnius* (Buck, 1967), and the insect *Oncopeltus* (Comings and Okada, 1972). The kinetochores of these insects cover 75% to 100% of each side of the length of the chromosome. In *Luzula purpurea* the chromosomes are remarkably long (about 10 μm) for holocentric chromosomes, and they appear more polycentric, having several rather distinctly separated centric regions. There appear to be no typical kinetochores; rather, regions of electron-translucent material occupy depressions on each side of the chromosome (Fig. 16-6).

Chromosomes with diffuse centromeres have been observed in a number of dinoflagellate and euglenoid algae, in insects of the orders Lepidoptera, Homoptera, and Hemiptera, in a scorpion, in the genus *Luzula* (White, 1954; Malheiros and de Castro, 1947; Nordenskiold, 1951), in the sedges and rushes, and in the parasitic roundworm *Ascaris (Parascaris)* of cytological fame.

At "metaphase" in the dinoflagellates and euglenoid algae the two-chromatid chromosomes are arranged parallel to one another, but uniquely, they lie parallel (rather than perpendicular) to the axis of the spindle (Dodge, 1964). At anaphase the two chromatids of each chromosome slide past each other in opposite directions with no evident point of spindle fiber attachment. Actually, there may be no spindle! Furthermore, if the chromosomes of these organisms are fragmented by x rays, all of the fragments move normally at anaphase, which is impossible for fragments of "normal" monocentric chromosomes. Perhaps these chromosomes and the "chromosomes" of procells should be described as *acentric,* a term usually reserved, however, for fragments of monocentric chromosomes that lack centromeres. Whether the chromosomes of *Parascaris, Luzula,* the scorpion *Tityus bahiensis,* the Homoptera, and the Hemiptera should be described as acentric or as having a diffuse centromere is uncertain. Certainly, they have somewhat observable centromeres (Fig. 16-6).

During early cleavage cell divisions of *Parascaris equorum* (*Ascaris megalocephala* var. *univalens*) embryo, the chromosomes fragment in the cells destined to produce the somatic tissues (White, 1954). The four heterochromatic end segments of the two chromosomes are lost (have no centromeres?), but the fifty to seventy-five "fragments" of the rest of the two chromosomes persist as so many small chromosomes (which they probably are), as though each is a tiny centric chromosome. Among the germ line cells of the embryo destined to form the reproductive cells of the gonads, the two long zigzag chromosomes remain intact. The same series of events occurs in the four-chromosome variety. Thus the two large chromosomes of the zygote and germ line are described as being polycentric. In *Ascaris lumbricoides,* which has forty-three chromosomes in the male and forty-eight in the female, the same casting off of chromosome ends occurs, but the central regions do not fragment. In this species the chromosomes seem to be monocentric.

In the scorpion *Tityus bahiensis,* the genus *Luzula,* and the insects of the orders Hemiptera and Homoptera the sister chromatids of metaphase chromosomes lies parallel to one another and parallel to the metaphase plate, and adjacent chromosomes are often united laterally by chromatin (Fig. 16-6). At anaphase they move away from each other, either remaining parallel or with the two ends leading slightly, as though the numerous spindle fibers are attached to the chromatids from one end to the other. In contrast to the perhaps acentric chromosomes of the algae just discussed, there definitely are spindles and spindle fibers in these latter cell divisions, and their chromosomes may have diffuse centromeres, whatever that may eventually mean.

Dicentric chromosomes are occasionally produced, for example, when certain structurally different homologous chromosomes pair during meiotic prophase or as a result of certain translocations. If the two centromeres of one chromosome move to different poles during anaphase, a bridge is produced, which eventually breaks.

Unusual additional secondary or *neocentric* "centromeres" have appeared in cultures of *Zea mays* (corn) (Rhoades and Vilkomerson, 1942) and *Secale* (rye). In corn the presence of an "abnormal" chromosome 10 causes the ends of all chromosomes to move poleward ahead of the normal centromeres; the condition seems to be genetically controlled. In rye the terminal *neocentromeres* definitely have spindle fibers associated with them. There is no satisfactory hypothesis for this phenomenon of terminal neocentromeres.

It seems that centromeres are not necessary for "chromosome" movement and separation in procells and some eucells, and that in a number of unrelated organisms the unusual condition of diffuse centromeres has evolved which, nevertheless, works. In most eucells, however, the monocentric chromosome is typical. The poleward movement of persistent nucleoli during metaphase or anaphase, structures that lack centromeres, is still unexplained but does raise the question of whether centromeres are absolutely necessary for poleward movement during mitosis.

Chromosome arms

The arms of a metaphase chromosome are the portions from the centromere to the ends (Figs. 16-1 to 16-3). These vary greatly among different chromosomes in length and width and in structural modifications. Since the length of the centromere is short, total chromosome length is represented by the sum of the lengths of the two arms. Probably the longest chromosomes are those of *Trillium,* the longest of which is about 30 μm. The shortest chromosomes, such as those of fungi, some sedges, and rushes, for example, are often less than 1 μm in length at metaphase. The seven spherical to elliptical mitotic metaphase chromosomes of *Neurospora crassa* (McClintock, 1945) range from 1.25 to 0.45 μm in length, and in an unidentified basidiomycete the four chromosomes range from 1×0.45 μm to 0.7×0.35 μm. In some species of *Carex, Scirpus,* and *Juncus* all chromosomes are 1 μm or less in length.

Some monocotyledonous plants with large chromosomes that have been studied a great deal are *Trillium, Tradescantia, Lilium, Secale,* and *Allium. Paeonia* and *Podophyllum* are exceptional among dicotyledonous plants for large chromosomes, as are the grasshoppers and salamanders unique for large chromosomes among animals. Chromosomes between 5 and 8 μm are of about average length for all organisms. Human chromosomes ranging from 2 to 10 μm in length are therefore typical (Figs. 15-12, 16-12, and 16-13).

As far as is known, chromosomes are longer than wide, although the short arm of an acrocentric chromosome may be shorter than wide. The chromosome arm consists of a compacted, possibly or sometimes coiled (Manton, 1950) (Fig. 16-10) chromonema, with what appears to be some additional material called matrix. Not only do chromosomes vary among themselves but essentially homologous chromosomes in various species or races may be observably different, and the same chromosome in different cells or organs of one organism may differ in size.

Woodard (1948), for example, reported that the chromosomes from the root tip of the same plant of *Medeola* at all phases of mitosis are as much as 50% longer and thinner than the same chromosomes at the same phases from shoot tips. Other similar cases of intraindividual variation in chromosome form are known among animals. Chromosomes of rapidly dividing tissues of the early blastula stage of certain marine invertebrates are often smaller than chromosomes of older tissues that are dividing less rapidly. Intraspecies variation in chromosome size has been found among plants of the grass *Lolium perenne,* and the "Snowflake" variety of the cultivated plant *Matthiola* has chromosomes 55% longer and half as thick as chromosomes of all other varieties (Lesley and Frost, 1927). This condition is controlled by a single recessive gene mutation that appears again in the F_2 generation. It affects shape but not volume. Interspecies differences of presumably comparable chromosomes are known among numerous animal and plant genera; for example, the homologous chromosomes of *Ambrosia trifida* are obviously larger than those of *A. elatior* (Jones, 1943). The size difference was evident even in the hybrid at mitosis and meiosis. Even more spectacular chromosome differences appeared in *Luzula,* a hybrid of *L. campestris* (n = 6 large) and *L. sudetica* (n = 24), the latter being an agmatoploid species (Nordenskiold, 1951). In the fly species *Chironomus thumii* the variety *thumii* has 27% more DNA than the variety *piger,* most of which occurs in particular bands of the salivary chromosomes where it is exactly two, four, eight, or sixteen times the amount in comparable bands of *piger.* The chromosomes of *Allium porrum* (2n = 16) are about half the size of the chromosomes of *A. sativum* (also 2n = 16). Similar examples are known from animal hybrids of fish, crustaceans, and echinoderms.

Stack (1971) found in *Ornithogalum virens* (2n = 6) that chromosome size, shape, arrangement on the metaphase plate, and somatic pairing vary during development of the plant, especially within the flower parts in contrast to shoot apices and root tips.

Within the thoroughly studied genus *Crepis* there seems to have been an evolutionary reduction in chromosome number, size, and total chromosome bulk (Fig. 16-16). There are, of course, great differences in chromosome size among genera of some plant families such as between the festucoid and panicoid grasses, the Commelinaceae, the Droseraceae, and many others. The chromosomes of *Trillium* are said to be 100 times the size of chromosomes of the related genus *Medeola.* In the Droseraceae the chromosome bulk in the genus *Drosophyllum* is estimated to be 1,000 times the bulk of the chromosomes in the related genus *Drosera.*

Chromosomes within a single nucleus may almost all be the same size and shape (for example, *Tradescantia*), or considerable variation may occur (for example, in the plant species of the *Yucca* group, birds, lizards, and many insects). A species with all chromosomes of about the same size (Fig. 16-18) is said to have a *symmetrical karyotype,* whereas a species with chromosomes of two different sizes is described as having an *asymmetrical karyotype* if the chromosome sizes fall into two distinct classes (Fig. 16-11) or if there is a gradual gradient from longest to shortest (Figs. 16-13 and 19-14).

Modifications. The arms of chromosomes not only vary in length but some have localized modifications. Arms of some chromosomes, apparently common in Arctic plants but also reported in some other plants and animals that have large chromosomes, may show one or more *secondary constrictions.* Such secondary constrictions are not nucleolus organizer constrictions, although some cytologists do refer to the nucleolus organizer as the secondary constriction (Figs. 16-1 to 16-3). These truly secondary constrictions appear somewhat like primary constrictions but differ from them in that they are not sites of centromeres. What they do represent is unknown, although their locations are constant. It has been proposed that they may mark sites of breakage and subsequent fusion or sites deficient in nucleic acid or matrix, a deficiency that is often revealed by low temperature. Certainly, metaphase chromosomes of *Trillium* (Bailey, 1952), of *Paris* (Darlington and LaCour, 1940), and of some other plants when subjected to temperatures close to 0° C for many hours, and of the amphibians *Ambystoma* and *Triturus* (Callan, 1942) when cold treated, do consist of alternating stained and unstained bands, but it is doubtful if these really correspond to secondary constrictions. The chromatin of the unstained bands is called *allocyclic.*

Telomere. Chromosome arms are not always uniform from primary constriction to end. There is a theoretical uniqueness at the tip of each arm called the telomere, which represents more of a chemical or ultrastructure difference from the rest of the arm than a morphological one. Its existence is assumed because normal chromosome ends do not stick together or unite, whereas two newly created "ends," produced by breakage within arms, do fuse. Neither will a telomere unite with a broken end; it takes two broken ends to recombine, although broken ends from different chromosomes can and do unite, probably as easily as the reunion of two broken ends of one chromosome. Chromosome ends, and therefore telomeres, are often heterochromatic (Fig. 16-14).

Telomeres may be important as regions specially modified for attachment to the nuclear envelope. It does seem to be true that chromosome ends are usually or always associated with the nuclear envelope from telophase into prophase. Furthermore, other parts such as the centromere regions and also "inactive" chromatin of inactive cells also are "attached" to the inner surface of the nuclear envelope.

Nucleolus organizer. Another common or probably universal local modification of at least one arm of one certain chromosome of the haploid set, so that there are two or more per diploid set in most cells, is the nucleolus organizer (Figs. 16-1, 16-3, and 16-7). These have been reported in a great many plants, some insects, the fungus *Neurospora, Drosophila,* toads, the axolotl, and some fish. In such organisms, and perhaps in most, each cell has at least two chromosomes (a pair of homologous chromosomes) possessing this significant modification in one of its arms, not always but usually a short arm, for some unknown reason (Longwell and Svihla, 1960). This region is not evident in metaphase karyotypes of all plants or animals, especially of species having small chromosomes. It has been reported generally in species possessing large or very large chromosomes. At metaphase it generally appears in light microscopy as a short, long, or very long constriction near the end of a particular pair of chromosomes. Usually, the terminal piece of chromosome arm beyond this wide "constriction" is small enough to be merely a sphere, and often this sphere is so small that its diameter is much less than that of the chromosome arm. Such spherical structures are called *satellites* and mark the location of the nucleolus organizer (Figs. 16-1 and 16-7). A chromosome with a satellite is called a *SAT chromosome.* Sometimes at prophase of mitosis or meiosis, when the nucleolus is still evident, the nucleolus organizers can be seen appressed to the surface of the nucleolus and satellites as small spheres adjacent to the nucleolus (Fig. 16-7). Since there are at least two such chromosomes in each diploid nucleus, two nucleolus organizers and two satellites are evident. There may

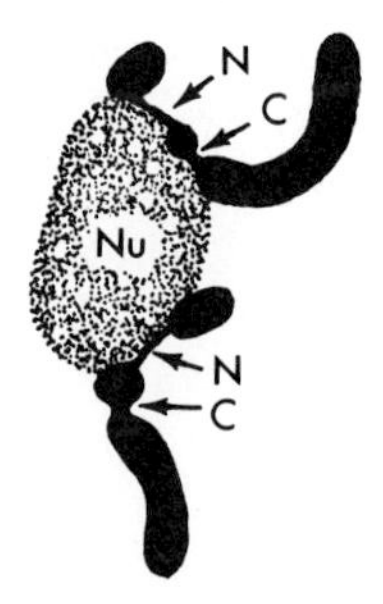

Fig. 16-7. Nucleolus organizers of a pair of homologous chromosomes, the G chromosomes, associated with one nucleolus in late mitotic prophase of the plant *Medeola.* **Nu,** Nucleolus; **C,** centromeres; **N,** nucleolus organizer constrictions. (From Stewart, R. M., and R. Bamford. 1942. Amer. J. Bot. **29:**301-303.)

be two nucleoli, one for each nucleolus organizer, or one nucleolus with both nucleolus organizers attached to it. In polyploid plants and cells and in some diploids the number of organizers and nucleoli may be greater; hexaploid wheat, for example, should have six pairs (Crosby, 1957), two pairs probably from two of its *Aegilops* diploid ancestors. Many polyploid species seem to have only two SAT chromosomes.

Smith (1933) studied the nucleolar organizer from the middle prophase of mitosis to telophase. During prophase the constriction is long; it is shorter during metaphase but lengthens during anaphase. Whether these changes reflect functional and real changes or merely represent alteration imposed by adjacent condensation is unknown.

Present evidence indicates that the nucleolus organizer is necessary for the formation of a nucleolus. It has been proposed in the past that the new nucleolar material comes from the protoplasm in which the chromosomes are suspended, from the chromosomal matrix of all chromosomes going back into the telophase nucleolus or that the material of the nucleolus is synthesized by all of the chromosomes of the set, only by the whole chromosome possessing the nucleolus organizer, or by the organizer alone. The best present evidence, however, is that probably the genes of only the organizer somehow synthesize some aspect of the nucleolus (at least ribosomal RNA), and the nucleolus also synthesizes part of itself. Crosby (1957) found that in wheat a single chromosome micronucleus containing any nonnucleolar chromosome produced no nucleolus but that any of the four nucleolar chromosomes, if present by itself in a micronucleus, did form a nucleolus. If an isochromosome formed of two short arms of chromosome X (therefore containing two nucleolus organizers) was present by itself in a micronucleus, a double-sized nucleolus was produced. Furthermore, micronuclei containing a single nonnucleolar chromosome lost their matrix at telophase, condensed, and divided at meiosis II, all without any observable nucleolus, although within a cell containing a nucleolus in the large normal nucleus.

In both *Zea mays* (Lin, 1955) and wheat (Longwell and Svihla, 1960) the presence of an extra nucleolus organizer (in a trisomic) produced about three halves as much nucleolar material as the normal diploid cell. That is, the amount of nucleolar material is proportional to the number of nucleolar chromosomes (or organizers) rather than the number of chromosome sets, since in corn the amount of nucleolus was the same in the trisomic for the nucleolar organizer chromosome as in the triploid. Reliable evidence indicates that the nucleolus organizer probably both produces some nucleolar material and keeps the mass associated with itself, somewhat comparable to the temporary accumulation of ribonucleoprotein—synthesized material on the lampbrush chromosome loop or salivary chromosome puff that produces it. In fact, electron microscopy indicates 100 Å loops, like small lampbrush loops, in the nonconstricted, distinctive electron-dense material of the nucleolus.

It has been estimated that the nucleolus organizer represents about 0.3% of the nuclear DNA and therefore many hundreds of gene loci. Research has characterized it in part as a region of many duplicate cistrons for production of both 28s and 18s rRNA. Duplications run into the hundreds, 100 in chick, 130 in *Drosophila melanogaster* (Ritossa and Spiegelman, 1965), and about 450 in the clawed toad *(Xenopus)*. It is likely that this region of the contracted chromosome is not contracted and is therefore active during nuclear division. Rattenbury and Serra (1952) have reported the first appearance of new nuclear material in the nucleolus organizer of *Vicia* as early as metaphase. Electron microscopy and radioautography indicate that this is true in the kangaroo *(Potorous tridactyla)*.

An interesting example of a tendency of polyploid species to lose all but two nucleolus organizers is wheat (Longwell and Svihla, 1960). This species is hexaploid, having six sets of chromosomes derived from three diploid ancestral species. It has two pairs of dominant nucleolus organizers, normally the only four to function; but if these are missing, the other, weaker nucleolar organizers do function in experimental material as though they are gradually losing their former ability and there has been a sort of survival of the fittest.

Some taxonomists have proposed basic chromosome numbers within genera on the assumption that a diploid species has only one pair of nucleolus organizers. For example, Hair (1962) found that the New Zealand composite species *Cotula coronopifolia* has 2n = 20 chromosomes. Because he found that there are four well-marked nucleolar (satellited) chromosomes, he proposed that the species is tetraploid and that the subgenus to which it belongs has the basic number x = 5.

This conclusion is based on the assumption that diploid species have only one pair of SAT chromosomes. That assumption may be generally true, but species that are undoubtedly diploid which have two pairs of SAT chromosomes are known. Jain (1966) has reported two pairs in the diploid grass species *Lolium perenne* (n = 7); *Plantago ovata* and *P. insularis* (both n = 4) have two pairs of SAT chromosomes (Stebbins and Day, 1967); and Riley et al. (1958) found four undoubtedly diploid (n = 7) species of the grass genus *Aegilops* that had two pairs of SAT chromosomes each. *Homo sapiens,* as far as is known a diploid species, has five pairs of SAT chromosomes. In the Chinese hamster, nucleolus organizers seem to be terminal on a number of chromosomes and so produce numerous small nucleoli. Such terminal nucleolus organizers may be common among animals. Therefore cytotaxonomists should apply this assumption with caution.

The nucleolus organizer seems to be necessary for cellular life, as has been demonstrated in a few plants and animals. Evidence of the function and significance of the nucleolus organizer comes from a certain "mutant" of the South African clawed toad *(Xenopus laevis),* the "mutation" being either the structural or genetically controlled loss of the nucleolus organizer (called in this case the secondary constriction). The normal toad (the homozygous normal) has two nucleolus organizers, one on each of the two particular chromosomes. Such cells usually have two nucleoli. The heterozygote has only one nucleolus organizer and one nucleolus in each cell, and the homozygous mutant has no "secondary constrictions" and no typical nucleoli. In place of one or two nucleoli this last form has numerous small nucleolar "blobs"; that is, no nucleolus is organized. Functionally, too, this anucleolar homozygous mutant is deficient. Not only is there less nuclear and cytoplasmic RNA but development is retarded immediately after hatching, and the embryos die as tadpoles. It seems that although the anucleolar cells have some nucleolar material (in a diffuse condition, however), they are incapable of synthesis of ribosomes and ribosomal RNA, either because of a deletion, the structural loss of the nucleolus organizer, or a mutation of the necessary operator gene that controls the 450 duplicate genes of the nucleolus organizer region. In corn it is known that a plant homozygous for deletion of the nucleolus organizer region does die. It now seems that an organized nucleolus is necessary for survival.

Acentric fragments. Occasionally in nature but especially in experimental material a chromosome may be broken without reunion. Since each typical chromosome possesses only one centromere, one of these pieces will lack the centromere and is called an acentric fragment. Such a fragment of a chromosome is incapable of anaphase movement and is not included in either telophase nucleus. However, the genetic deficiency produced by such loss from the karyotype and genome will generally produce lethality when the deficient centric chromosome is included in a haploid nucleus after meiosis or in the gametophytic generation of plants. Acentric fragments are most commonly observed during meiosis of hybrids, as discussed in Chapter 18.

Chromosome fine structure

By about 1950 there was general agreement among light microscopists that the metaphase chromosome consists of two chromatids and that each chromatid arm consists of one or more helically coiled chromonemata embedded in a material called matrix. There was some evidence that the outer layer of matrix formed a membrane, the pellicle, although the existence of a pellicle was not completely accepted as proved. There was also disagreement as to the number of linearly arranged strings of genes *(genonemata)* and/or cytological strands *(chromonemata)* in each chromosome. The numbers suggested ranged from two to thirty-two to very many. Furthermore, some of the structural models were influenced by the generally accepted assumption up to that time that protein is the basic, self-reproducing, hereditary material. Darlington and Lewis (1966) and Valencia and Grell (1965) report recent findings about chromosome structure.

During the last 30 years, however, electron microscopic and biochemical studies have completely or partially destroyed all of these earlier models of chromosomal structure, and so far the folded fiber model

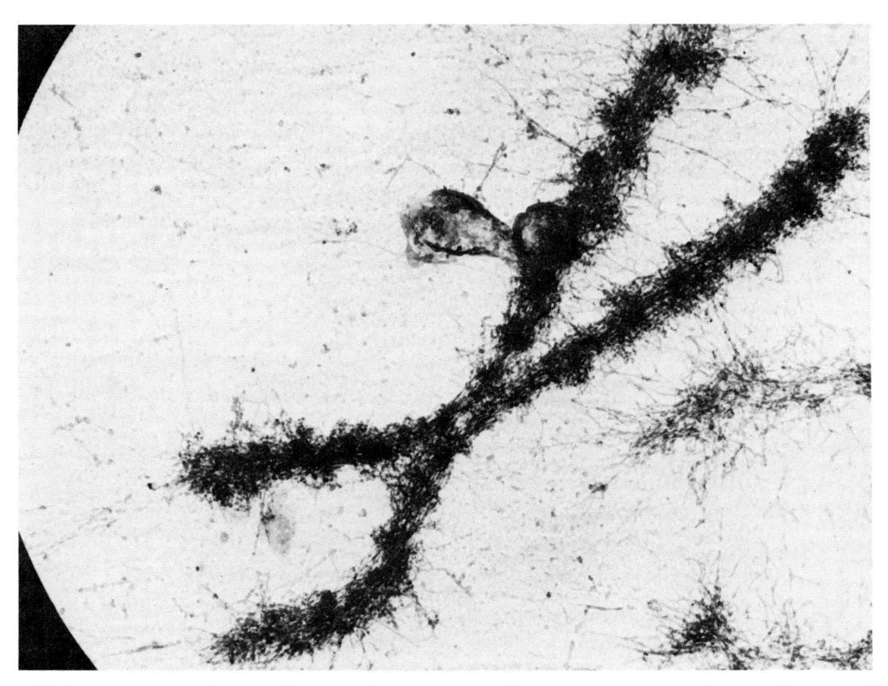

Fig. 16-8. Electron micrograph of a human metaphase chromosome from a burst cell. It shows the 250 Å chromatin fibers and fiber connections between sister chromatids and adjacent chromosomes. The sister chromatids are associated in the centromeric region. There may be a slight loss of detail because of reprinting from the original letterpress journal. (Compare with Fig. 15-8.) (×23,300.) (From Abuelo, J. G., and D. E. Moore. 1969. J. Cell Biol. **41:**73-90.)

of DuPraw (Chapter 15) is the best that has been suggested (Fig. 16-8). DNA is now accepted as the hereditary, coded, self-replicating material. The pellicle can now be considered as no more than a possible interface between chromosomal and non-chromosomal material. Matrix of some sort is likely, but a different concept of the term is necessary. The helical coiling, folding, or convoluting of something within the metaphase chromosome still seems real, but what it represents is uncertain. What the term "chromonema" should connote in electron microscopy is unknown. The problem of the number of linear subunits has been reduced to near meaninglessness by electron microscopy.

The present picture of metaphase chromosome ultrastructure is that of a vast number of very thin 30 to 500 Å filaments forming vague whorls that can be interpreted as a spiral chromonema or strand, which itself forms a helix, such as that visible by optical microscopy. Perhaps a metaphase chromatid contains two such strands (Fig. 16-3) or only one; it is difficult to decide.

The major conceptual problem at this time is to construct a model of how a strand of hundreds of nucleoprotein fibrils that form a twisted strand can replicate the DNA and yet at mitosis separate sideways into two chromatids, one of old DNA and the other of newly synthesized DNA, as the radioautographic studies of Taylor have shown probably does occur. This problem is part of the problem of the DNA ultrastructure of the interphase "chromosome." It seems evident that the total length of genes in a cell must be many thousands of times the total length of the interphase chromosomes. Therefore models of zigzag or cross-linked genes have been proposed within the interphase chromosome (Chapter 15), but so far it has been impossible to relate these hypothetical arrangements to the structure of a more or less twisted strand of hundreds of tiny filaments revealed by electron microscopy.

Thus at this time there is no model that adequately interrelates biochemical genetic, light microscopic, and electron microscopic knowledge of chromosome structure and ultrastructure.

Biochemical evidence strongly suggests that when a chromonema is uncondensed, it is synthetically active, but in the compacted condition occurring from prophase to telophase it is unable to transcribe. This appears to be true also of parts of chromonemata. During mitosis and meiosis the centromere (and perhaps the nucleolus organizer) is extended and therefore is possibly an active region of an otherwise inactive chromosome. On the other hand, chromocenters may represent regions of interphase chromonemata that remain compacted and biochemically inactive that are called *heterochromatin.*

A probable exception to this generalization is found in certain algae (*Euglena* and its relatives and the dinoflagellates) and some Protozoa, in which the telophase chromosomes do not uncoil or at most only slightly. The chromosomes are compacted all of the time. Since they must be functionally active during interphase, they must transcribe RNA in a partially compacted condition. They also divide structurally in the coiled condition, as demonstrated by both light and electron microscopy. Cleveland (1947) considers that the chromosomes of the flagellates he studied are in a prophase condition during interphase of the cell.

The problem of differences in metaphase chromosome bulk has not been resolved (Figs. 16-2 and 16-9). One hypothesis is that differences are due to different amounts of chromosomal matrix. A second hypothesis assumes that all chromosomes are more or less polytene; that is, each chromosome consists of several parallel duplicate genonemata. Small metaphase chromosomes are assumed to consist of a few strands, medium-sized chromosomes consist of more numerous strands (are more polytene), and large chromosomes are highly polytene. Species with large chromosomes such as the urodeles should have much more DNA than those vertebrates with much smaller chromosomes, and that is true, although the number of different genes may be greater in man than in the salamander. A third hypothesis is that large chromosomes have

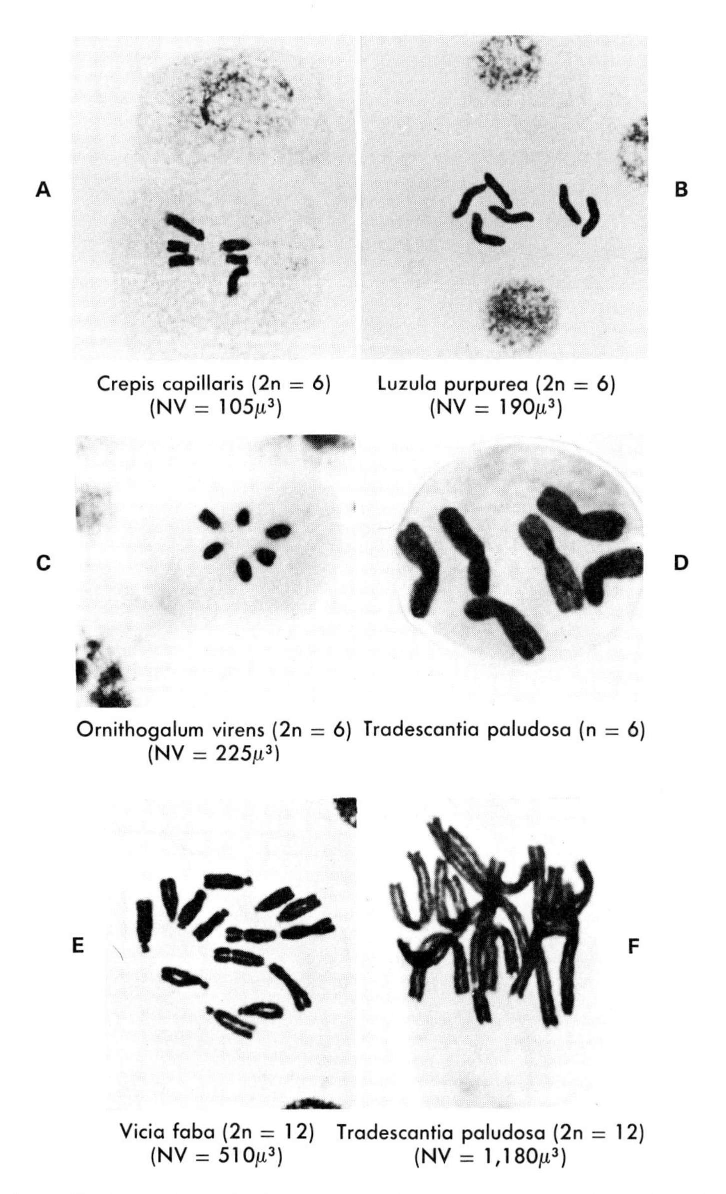

Fig. 16-9. A to **F,** A variety of chromosome sizes among some flowering plants having similar chromosome numbers and different nuclear volumes. (×2,000.) All are diploid mitotic metaphase sets except **D,** which is a haploid mitotic metaphase set at the first pollen grain division. In **E** the two longest chromosomes, lying side by side at right center, have a secondary constriction in addition to the long median centromere constriction. (From Evans, H. J., and A. H. Sparrow. 1961. Brookhaven Symp. Biol. **14:**101-127.)

much more heterochromatin than small chromosomes, although the amounts of euchromatin might be nearly the same.

In Chapter 15 the nature, techniques for revealing, and distribution of constitutive heterochromatin in chromosomes was discussed. These techniques reveal internal chromatin differences that make possible the exact specifications of the various chromosomes of the set or karyotype. In the mouse, for example, all chromosomes are telocentric, and there are only slight differences in lengths (Fig. 15-13). Nevertheless, the fluorescent bands are so different among the chromosomes that exact specification of each is possible. Exact identification as well as individual differences (polymorphisms) among human chromosomes are possible with these techniques.

The transverse banding implies that specific regions of a metaphase chromosome are possibly all euchromatin or all heterochromatin. This means, with respect to DuPraw's folded fiber model of chromosome structure, that the continuous chromatin fiber must have alternating regions of heterochromatin and euchromatin in tandem. But if the chromatin fiber extends from end to end of a chromosome several times, as well as being folded laterally, a number of different segments of heterochromatin must correspond or overlap in each band of heterochromatin along the metaphase chromosome. Of course, the uniformity of chromosome size, relative arm lengths, banding pattern, and so on do demonstrate that the chromosome structure is not altered at all for many cell generations and at each prophase the details of condensation are the same.

CHROMOSOME SETS

Ever since chromosomes were first seen by microscopists more than 100 years ago, it has been evident that a cell contains more than one chromosome, and since the 1880s, it has been known with increasing certainty that each species is characterized by a rather definite number, a set. Furthermore, it soon became evident that the chromosomes of a set might not all have the same morphology—there might be differences of size and/or shape. Also, a set might contain two or three different kinds of chromosomes such as autosomes and sex chromosomes or typical chromosomes and supernumerary chromosomes. Furthermore, it was discovered that closely related species might have very different sets and that sets might be different in the somatic cells and the germ line, or that males and females may have different sets. More recently, numerous exceptions to some of these generalizations have been reported and increasing extremes of numbers, sizes, and morphologies have been discovered. In this discussion the term "chromosomes" refers to those appearing in the metaphase condition of mitosis or meiosis, the condition most easily studied and that shows the constant morphology.

As stated earlier in this chapter, mitotic chromosome sizes vary from less than 1 μm to about 30 μm in length, the commonest length being about 5 μm. Mitotic metaphase chromosome widths vary from a fraction of a micron to almost 2 μm. It was also stated that the centromere might be located anywhere from the middle to the end of a chromosome, thereby producing metacentric, submetacentric, acrocentric, and, rarely, telocentric chromosomes (Fig. 16-10). A chromosome set may consist of various combinations of such sizes and shapes.

Chromosome numbers

Chromosome sets also vary widely in the number of chromosomes included at the haploid level (Table 16-1). If the probably compound single chromosome of *Parascaris equorum univalens* is excluded as atypical (having only two "chromosomes" in the germ line and gonia), the lowest chromosome number known among the Eukaryota is n = 2. The fungus (Basidiomycetes) *Tolyposporium christensenii* has n = 2 (Raghunath, 1967), as does the flowering plant *Haplopappus gracilis* (Jackson, 1957); some termite-inhabiting flagellates such as *Holomastigotoides* (Cleveland, 1947); the polychete annelid *Ophryotrocha puerilis* (Makino, 1951); numerous rhabdocoel flatworms such as some species of *Mesostoma* and *Phaenocora* and all species of *Dalyellia;* and the species of the scale in-

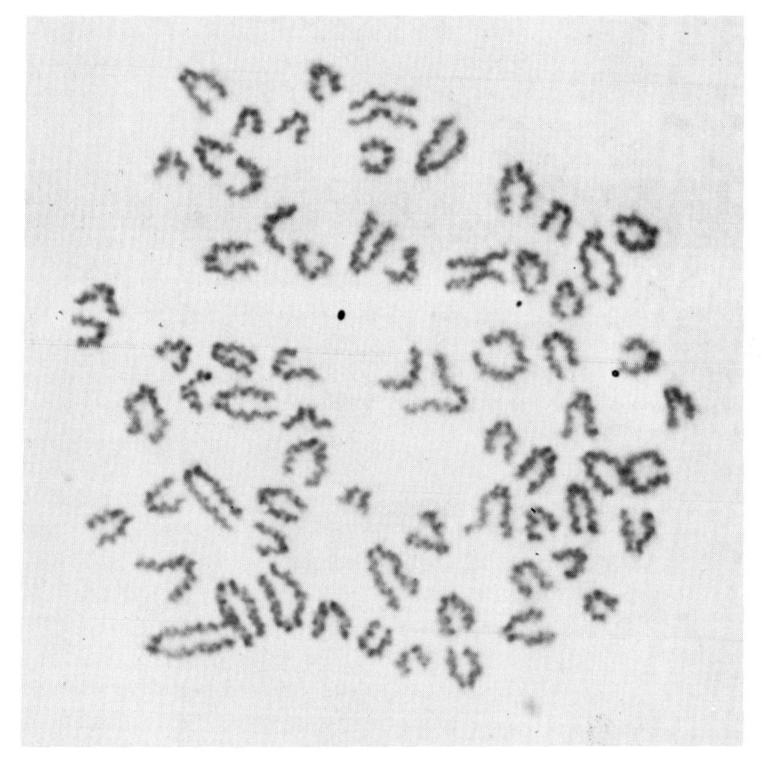

Fig. 16-10. Metaphase chromosomes of the Indian hog deer. The helical chromatids, which are often observed in mammalian chromosomes, man included, are evident. Dr. Wurster considers these chromosomes as excellent examples of the difficulty of determining the difference between truly telocentrics and acrocentrics with extremely small short arms. (Courtesy Dr. D. H. Wurster, Dartmouth Medical School, Hanover, N. H.)

Table 16-1. Haploid chromosome numbers of some animals and plants

Miscellaneous animals			
Some flatworms	2	A rodent *(Cricitus)*	11
Iceryine scale insects	2	Rat	21
Some flatworms	3	Man	23
Some scorpions	3	Primates	17-36
Few Heteroptera	3	Dog	39
Few *Drosophila*	3	Chicken	39
Numerous *Drosophila*	4	Crayfish	98
A kangaroo *(Potorous tridactyla)*	6	A moth	112
An insectivore *(Elephantulus)*	7	Hermit crab	127
A deer *(Muntiacus muntjak)*	6, 7	A butterfly *(Lysandra)*	191
Miscellaneous plants			
Haplopappus gracilis	2	Wheats	7, 14, 21
Crepis capillaris	3	*Zea mays*	10
Ornithogalum virens	3	Lilies	12
Crocus spp.	3, 4	Rice	12
Plantago ovata	4	Cattails	15
Numerous Compositae	4	Pine trees	12
Trillium species	5	Palms	16
Tradescantia species	6	*Yucca*	30, 60
Onion	7, 8	*Galium grande*	110

sect tribe Iceryini. In the last group the females are 2n = 4, but males are haploid (n = 2) (White, 1954). From that rare chromosome number of n = 2, which is the lowest, the number of species having each successive chromosome number increases rapidly above n = 4 to a maximum near n = 12 to 15. Among higher plants rather few species or genera have nonpolyploid chromosome sets containing more than fifteen chromosomes, but haploid numbers up to about n = 50 are not uncommon among animals. Extremely high chromosome sets in animals are just over n = 100, the highest known being the hermit crab *(Eupagurus ochotensis),* with n = 127. There are some cryptogamic land plants having n = 400 to over 600 (Table 16-2). These last are probably extant derivatives of ancient polyploids and/or products of some sort of chromosomal instability, since the chromosome number often varies so considerably within a single species.

The number of species of angiosperm plants having low chromosome numbers (n = 2 to 5) is unexpectedly large. From published lists it is evident that there are 574 species in 145 genera of forty-one families with such low numbers; that is, about 1.4% of the approximately 40,000 species of known chromosome number have low numbers. Two species are n = 2, twenty-six are n = 3, 242 are n = 4, and 298 are n = 5.

In general, related species, genera, tribes, and often families or classes tend to have chromosome sets containing chromosome numbers of about the same order of magnitude (White, 1954). Pulmonate Mollusca have mostly n = 17 to 30, rhabdocoel flatworms 2 to 8, trematodes 6 to 11, orthopterous insects 8 to 16, Hymenoptera 6 to

Table 16-2. Some examples of high chromosome numbers (haploid numbers) in cryptogamic vascular plants*

Equisetum (14 spp.)	108
Psilotum nudum	52, 104, 210
Psilotum triquetrum	93, 95, 102, 104
Tmesipteris (4 spp.)	102, 107
Tmesipteris (3 spp.)	204, 210
Lycopodium (9 spp.)	24, 34, 132, 165, 170
Helminthostachys (1 sp.)	94
Schizaea robusta	96
Schizaea pusilla	103
Schizaea fistulosa	270
Schizaea dichotoma	540
Pteris ensiformis	19-88 (n similar)
Adiantum capillus-veneris	9-70 (n = 30)
Botrychium (16 spp.)	45
Botrychium (13 spp.)	90
Ophioglossum (17 spp.)	120-630
Ophioglossum vulgatum	250, 340, 385-390, 410, 420, 465, 475, 480, 515, 520, 570
Ophioglossum reticulatum	435, 450, 480, 495, 570, 630

*Many numbers are approximate but close.

12, coccid insects 2 to 10, corixid insects 12, pentatomid insects 6 to 8, dragonflies 12 to 14, scorpion flies 12, beetles 6 to 19 (mostly 9 to 11), Lepidoptera 19 to 32 (11 to 112, but mostly 27 to 31), flies 3 to 7, mammals 12 to 39 (mostly 19 to 30), marsupials 6 to 15, teleost fish 21 to 25 (but also 9 to 52), birds 38 to 41, turtles 25 to 32, amphibians mostly 11 to 14. These figures do not always include the atypical extremes but, rather, the commonest for the groups.

Among plants (excluding polyploidy) "ancient" types of grasses have n = 12, the temperate, arctic, and alpine Festucoideae have n = 7, and the tropical Panicoideae have n = 9 and 10. Trees usually have about n = 12 or more in the haploid set.

Among higher organisms the chromosome set must include at least one centromere and two telomeres on each chromosome and at least one nucleolus organizer in each set. There is some evidence that each chromosome also contains some heterochromatin in addition to the euchromatin where the "typical" genes are located. It has also been proposed that each chromosome is an organized organelle so that the order of genes is more or less important. Certainly, the chromosome set is of such a nature that the loss of about one tenth of one chromosome (if homozygous) is often lethal.

Nevertheless, exchanges of pieces between nonhomologous chromosomes (translocations) often occur without serious effects on the cell but do produce a reconstruction of the chromosome set. The extreme of this sort occurs in those permanent complex heterozygotes such as *Oenothera* and *Rhoeo* in which there are no homologous chromosomes, only homologous terminal arm segments (Chapter 19). One of the interesting cytological results of bringing two slightly different chromosome sets together in the same cell, as occurs in interspecies hybrids, is the often (but not always) great upset of meiosis and even of chromosomes and spindles. There are numerous reports of the chromosomes fragmenting and forming numerous anaphase I bridges (Walters, 1950), asynapsis, irregular anaphase separation, and multiple spindle poles. It is to be anticipated that each gametic set from two closely related species, closely enough related to hybridize, would contribute essentially the same genes for these phenomena. It is difficult to account for upsets of spindles, chromosome fragmentation, and more numerous anaphase bridges than inversion heterozygosis would likely produce by slight genetic imbalance or slight interspecies chromosome segmental rearrangements.

Chromosomes in two different species that are homologous enough to pair may be different in length and thickness (*Ambrosia*—Jones, 1943); those in two varieties of one species may show simple mendelian segregation for chromosome length and thickness (*Matthiola*—Lesley and Frost, 1927); or chromosomes in root tips may be longer and thinner than those from shoot apices (*Mediola*—Woodard, 1948). Geitler (1938) discusses such cases of interindividual and intraindividual variations in chromosomal form.

Symmetry

Another form of chromosome set variation is the inclusion of different sorts of chromosomes in the same set. There are some species, genera, and even higher taxonomic categories in which all chromosomes are indistinguishable from one another in length and morphology. But because chromosome sets have evolved, it is to be expected in some genera and families and even orders that sets may have arisen which contain both extremes of chromosome size, that is, some large *(macrochromosomes)* and some tiny *(microchromosomes)* (Fig. 16-11). Such a set consisting of macrochromosomes and microchromosomes is described as an *asymmetrical karyotype.* Whether microchromosomes are in any way fundamentally different from

Fig. 16-11. Mitotic metaphase from root tip of *Yucca arkansana* showing the typical asymmetrical karyotype of ten large and fifty small chromosomes from the *Yucca-Agave* group. As in animals, large chromosomes are distributed around the periphery of the metaphase plate.

macrochromosomes is uncertain. It is not unlikely that some microchromosomes are really different. Bt that as it may, extremely asymmetrical karyotypes consisting of some large and some tiny chromosomes are common among animals but rare among plants. Many species of *Drosophila* have one pair of tiny chromosomes; many amphibians, birds, reptiles, long-horned grasshoppers, and Hemiptera have few to many small chromosomes and numerous considerably larger ones. Except in the *Yucca-Agave* group of flowering plants (Fig. 16-11), most plant species have symmetrical karyotypes (that is, all chromosomes of a set are about the same in size) or else they have asymmetrical karyotypes in which there is more or less of a gradation in size from large to small (Figs. 16-13 and 19-14).

Ploidy

Among some insects, *Parascaris,* and other organisms the chromosome set in the germ line is different from the set in the somatic cells, usually by elimination of some chromosomes during embryogenesis from the somatic cells. In such forms the extra chromosomes seem necessary for the meiotic process.

Among some insects such as the bee, wasps, all of the Hymenoptera, a few coccid

Homoptera, one beetle, and a number of Thysanoptera, and a number of mites the males are typically haploid, having only one set of chromosomes, in contrast to the diploid females that have two sets; that is, male germ line cells are haploid, but somatic cells may be endopolyploid.

In most plants there is such an alternation of generations that the sporophyte generation is diploid with two sets of chromosomes in each cell, whereas the gametophytes are haploid (Fig. 19-15). Some algae and Protozoa are always haploid; others are diploid only as the "zygote" after fertilization or autogamy. Haploids of normally diploid life states such as haploid plant sporophytes are usually small and weak, indicating that a haploid set of chromosomes is inadequate physiologically for such organisms.

Polyploidy is another condition wherein cells have a chromosome set different from the typical diploid set. Since aneuploidy, including the trisomic condition, is almost always a temporary and nonpersisting condition, the discussion here will be limited mostly to euploidy.

"Euploidy" is the term used to refer to cells or organisms possessing an exact multiple of some gametic chromosome number; that is, they have multiple sets. The chromosome number of the gamete of an organism or of an organism itself with the basic number is called *monoploid* or *haploid.* The zygote and the organism derived from it is said to be *diploid* (2n), since it has two sets of chromosomes. An organism with three complete sets of chromosomes is *triploid* (3n), one with four sets is described as *tetraploid* (4n), one with five sets is a *pentaploid* (5n), one with six sets is a *hexaploid* (6n), one with eight sets is an *octoploid* (8n), one with ten sets is a *10-ploid,* one with twelve sets is a *12-ploid,* etc.

The term "polyploid" refers to any organism having three or more sets. Organisms that are diploid, triploid, tetraploid, pentaploid, hexaploid, octoploid, etc., that is, having exact multiples of some gametic chromosome number, are said to be *euploid.* Any of these that have a few extra chromosomes or lack a few chromosomes so that the number is not an exact multiple of the gametic number is described as *aneuploid* and can be indicated as 3n + 2 or 6n – 3, etc. A *trisomic* diploid organism having one extra chromosome would be 2n + 1. A diploid or a certain kind of polyploid organism lacking one chromosome (2n – 1 or 6n – 1) is called *monosomic.* Wheat, which is hexaploid (2n = 42), has been manipulated so that all possible twenty-one trisomics and all possible monosomics have been produced and utilized in numerous experiments and breeding projects. Such terminology does not apply, however, to species within a genus in which there has been an evolutionary change of the gametic chromosome number, for example, in *Crepis* (Fig. 16-16). Aneuploidy produces abnormal phenotypes such as the trisomics of man (Table 19-1) and *Datura* (Blakeslee, 1934). The diploid set is a balanced system of genes. The addition or subtraction of one or more chromosomes upsets the balance.

Basic number

The term "basic number" (x) is sometimes applicable to genera or even families. For example, most grasses of arctic, cold temperate, and alpine regions belong to the subfamily Festucoideae. The chromosome number of nearly all diploid species of that group is 2n = 14 and the basic number is x = 7. In the plant family Compositae, on the other hand (*Crepis* is one example), diploid species even within a single genus may vary. *Crepis* species have n = 6, 5, 4, and 3 (Fig. 16-16). In such a genus or larger taxonomic category there is either no basic number, except perhaps a hypothetical or determined one, or the genus may be considered to be *multibasic* with respect to whole sets of chromosomes. The grass tribe Paniceae is dibasic, since it has numerous genera with x = 10 and others with x = 9. Therefore species that are euploid have multiple sets of chromosomes in each cell. The sets generally are not exactly homologous, since they have been derived from two or more species that hybridized to form the polyploid.

A true, secondary basic number can be formed at a polyploid (euploid or aneuploid) level. In the grass genus *Hilaria* the lowest chromosome number known is 2n = 36. Yet this genus exists in a group of genera having a basic number x = 9. The dying out of all true diploid species may leave such a genus with a higher, secondarily derived basic number. It is likely that most plant genera with very high basic numbers (Table 16-2) have achieved that condition through repeated polyploidy followed by extinction of diploid and low-level polyploid species during a long evolutionary existence.

During evolution at the polyploid level the duplicate or nearly duplicate sets become one large true set, a process called "diploidization," the best example of which was observed directly by Gillis and Randolph (1951) on a strain of autotetraploid *Zea mays.* Cytological comparison of meiosis in anthers of the original and the eleventh generation after 10 years of selection for vigor and fertility revealed a significant change toward bivalent rather than multivalent pairing and more regular segregation at meiosis; that is, pairs of homeologous chromosomes were beginning to form. Part of the diploidization of allohexaploid wheat (2n = 42) is due to genes for bivalent pairing in the 5A, 5B, and 5D chromosomes of the A, B, and D genomes from each of the three parental species. It is remarkable that either fewer or more than the two normal 5B chromosomes permit the breakdown of bivalent pairing (Feldman, 1966). No 5B long arms (in the nullisomic) permitted pairing of homologues *and* homeologues, and multivalents resulted. There was a strong pairing "force." When six 5B long arms were present, there was about 50% loss of directed pairing of homologues or homeologues so that there were equal chances of either type of pairing, but in 50% of cells neither occurred and univalents were present. Little or no pairing "force" was supposed to be acting. The 5A and 5D pairing genes were considered to be weak. Thus that aspect of diploidization in wheat is the result of a balanced set of mutations that are supposed to act on premeiotic pairing and not synapsis directly.

During diploidization the four homologues of each chromosome of an autotetraploid become pairs of homeologous chromosomes, and the pairs of homeologous chromosomes from the two parental species of allotetraploids are no longer even homeologous. The final result is assured bivalent pairing, as regularly as in a diploid, and such old, diploidized polyploids are therefore called *amphidiploids.*

Among plants certain evidently old cryptogamic vascular plant genera have high chromosome numbers and are probably such "diploidized" descendants of high polyploids (Table 16-2). For example, the "fern" genus *Ophioglossum* has had seventeen species examined and the n numbers range from 120, as in *O. polyphyllum,* to n = 630 in *O. reticulatum.* Nine species of *Equisetum* have n = 108. Four species of *Tmesipteris* have 102 (or 107), whereas three others have n = 204; the related genus *Psilotum* has species with chromosome numbers ranging from n = 52 to 104. Many other genera of cryptogamic vascular plants have basic numbers ranging from 50 to 500.

Ancient types of animals, however, do not show high basic numbers. Coelenterates and sponges have a chromosome number of about 2n = 15 to 30 (Makino, 1951). A horseshoe crab of Asia, *Trachyplens tridentatus,* has 2n = 16; a species of *Peripatus* has 2n = 28; *Tingula anatina* (a brachiopod) has probably 2n = 16; and two Bryozoa have 2n = 11 and 2n = 6 or

7. This is probably because polyploidy is rare in animals and when found, is usually associated with parthenogenesis, as in the small crustacean *Artemia salina* of high salinity waters; an isopod, *Trichoniscus;* a few other Crustacea such as a race of *Daphnia pulex;* a mollusc, *Paludestrina;* some Lepidoptera; a species of *Drosophila;* some weevils; numerous "earthworms"; a large wingless grasshopper; and numerous others. There are also a few known cases of apparent polyploidy in normal sexually reproducing animal species. But compared to the plants, polyploidy is rare among animals, probably because of the sex chromosomal mechanism. Doubling of sex chromosomes would result in males producing gametes of a variety of X and Y chromosomes, and consequently the progeny would consist of various sorts of females, intersexes, males, supermales, superfemales, and others.

Karyotype

The chromosome set of an individual or species is called the karyotype and may consist entirely of metacentric chromosomes (as in *Trillium* or *Tradescantia*), of only acrocentric chromosomes (as in some grasshoppers or the plant *Ornithogalum virens*), or mixtures of these as well as submetacentric chromosomes (as in the chromosome set of man, with a range from 2 to 10 μm) (Fig. 16-12). It should be stated, however, that the location of the centromere is frequently undeterminable in tiny chromo-

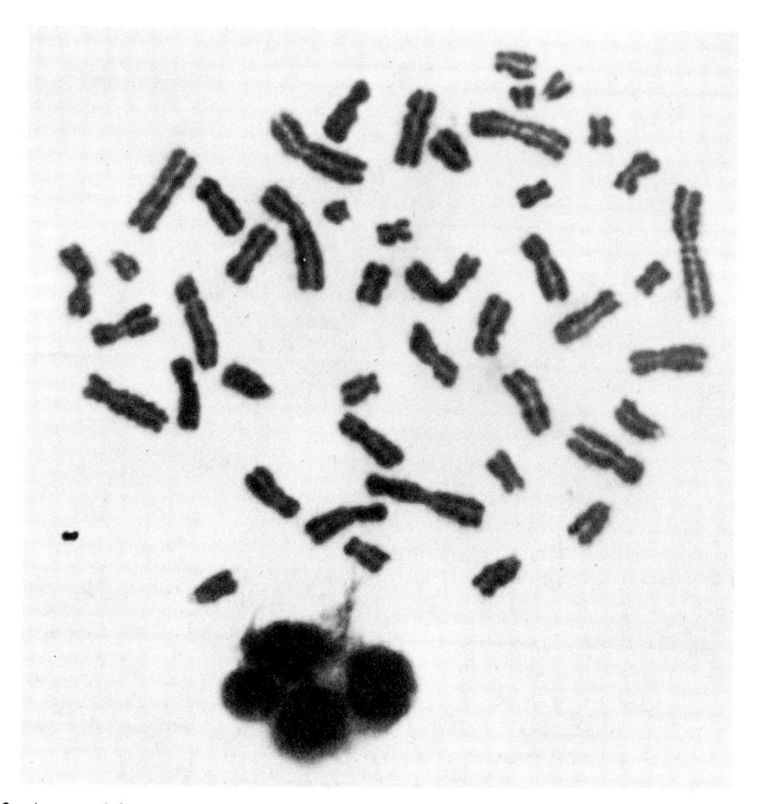

Fig. 16-12. A set of human female mitotic metaphase chromosomes showing their doubleness, primary (centromere) constrictions, and variety of sizes. Those of medium length are about average size for chromosomes in general, approximately 5 μm long. (Courtesy Carolina Biological Supply Co., Burlington, N. C.)

somes. Even in merely small chromosomes the exact location of the centromere may be best determined during meiotic prophase (diplotene), as in corn or in the very large, atypical salivary gland chromosomes of *Drosophila, Sciara,* and other flies.

If all the chromosomes of a set are of the same length and all have the same location of their centromeres, it is essentially impossible to recognize particular chromosomes of the set. But if, as is often the case, there are differences in length as well as differences in number or position of satellites, heterochromatin, and centromeres, the different chromosomes can often be recognized and specified. For example, the twenty-three metaphase chromosomes of man can be placed in a number of distinct groups, although exact designation within groups is difficult. When identification is possible, the chromosomes of the haploid set can be represented by a diagram in which they are arranged in a decreasing series by length, with the locations of the centromeres of each chromosome indicated and the satellite and secondary constrictions represented (Figs. 16-10 and 16-13). Such a schematic representation of the karyotype is called an *idiogram,* and idiograms of different species or genera can be compared.

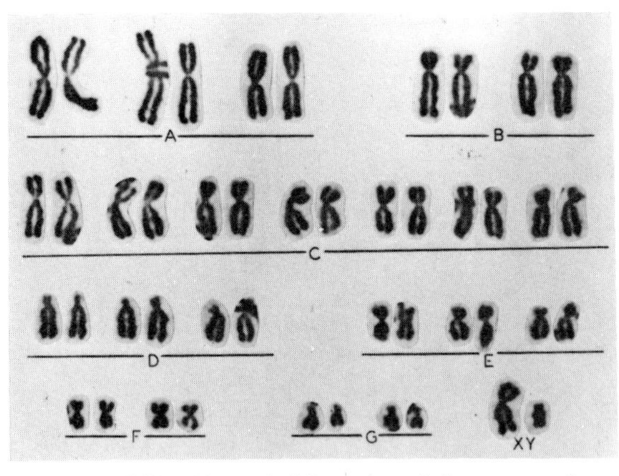

Fig. 16-13. Normal idiogram of human male chromosomes from a lymphocyte. The twenty-six chromosomes are arranged according to length and grouped according to a generally accepted scheme of nomenclature. They are numbered from 1 (the longest) to 22 (the shortest), plus X and Y. The X may be included at the beginning of group **C** and the Y at the end of group **G.** In length they range from 2 to 10 μm. A few chromosomes have others overlapping as they lay in the original smear (numbers 2, 4, 6, 11, 15, etc.) (Courtesy S. Tomb, Department of Botany, University of Texas, Austin, Texas.)

Analysis of idiograms has become much more exact with development of recent techniques to reveal the distribution of blocks of heterochromatin along arms of metaphase chromosomes (see also heterochromatin in Chapter 17). Such alternation of variously sized blocks of euchromatin and heterochromatin along arms in different chromosomes permits distinguishing specific chromosomes of the set from one another. Fig. 17-13 shows the diagrammatic fluorescence banding patterns of the nineteen autosomes and the X chromosome of the mouse when treated with quinacrine (Miller and Miller, 1972). This method has contributed greatly to the assignment of genetic linkage groups to specific chromosomes. These same techniques have also contributed greatly to the field of human cytogenetics and are applicable in other species. Different banding patterns in comparable human chromosomes have indicated polymorphisms within the species (Craig-Holmes and Shaw, 1971).

Karyotype changes of an evolutionary sort are known within families, genera, and even species, and a number of such examples have been well documented. Changes are of two sorts. Frequently among plants but rarely among animals a common change is the exact doubling of the sets, usually in hybrids, to produce polyploids. That type of chromosome set change has been discussed. A second sort of change in the chromosome set, common in animals and plants, occurs at the diploid level by changes of chromosome morphology and/or changes of chromosome number by only one or two at a time, called *dysploidy.* White's "principle of homologous change" holds that one chromosome after another undergoes the same type of change in the same evolutionary line of descent. This type of change is the basic type of chromosomal evolution in both animals and plants, it having been stated that karyotype change at the diploid level is the evolution of genera and families (as well as species), whereas polyploidy is little more than one sort of short-term evolution of species within a genus.

Changes of the basic chromosome number within a genus or family of plants or animals can be either upward or downward, more or less one chromosome at a time. The better documented examples are downward changes. This is accomplished by what is sometimes called "centric fusions." That is, essentially all of the genetic chromatin of one chromosome is broken away from the centromere and proximal heterochromatin and attached to an arm of another nonhomologous chromosome. The subsequent loss of the original centromere and later the duplication of the new, larger chromosome will have reduced the haploid by one chromosome. Navashin's 1932 "dislocation hypothesis" of the evolution of chromosome numbers states that there must be an increase or decrease of centromeres if chromosome numbers are to change. An example of such chromosome number reduction is the change within the plant genus *Crepis,* often called *descending aneuploidy* or *descending dysploidy.*

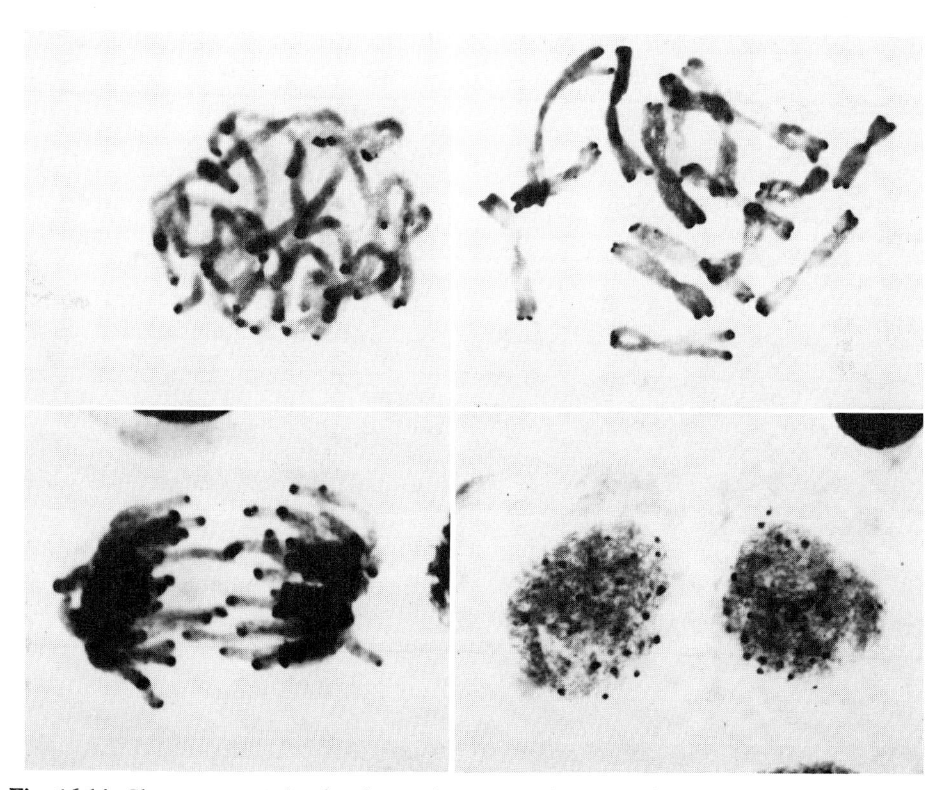

Fig. 16-14. Chromosomes of onion in prophase, metaphase, anaphase, and interphase prepared and stained by a technique to reveal some constitutive heterochromatin, in this case telomeres. During interphase, telomeres (prochromosomes) are located mostly in one half of the nucleus somewhat as they were disposed during anaphase. (Courtesy Dr. Stephen M. Stack, Department of Botany and Plant Pathology, Colorado State University, Ft. Collins, Colo.)

Detailed study of most species of *Crepis* has indicated that the ancient chromosomal constitution, as represented at present by *C. kashmirica,* was n = 6 for long chromosomes, each having a submedian centromere (Babcock, 1947). Chromosome evolution has "progressed" by centromere loss to n = 5, n = 4, and finally, to n = 3 (Fig. 16-16). An example of how n = 4 became n = 3 has resulted from the study of meiosis in both parents and in the hybrid between *C. neglecta* (n = 4) and *C. fuliginosa* (n = 3) (Tobgy, 1943). The four chromosomes of *C. neglecta* were designated A^n, B^n, C^n, and D^n; it was noted that the chromosome C^n is nearly all heterochromatic except for the distal end of one arm, which is euchromatic and presumably contains necessary genes. In *C. fuliginosa* (n = 3) there is no chromosome anything like C^n. The chromosomes of *C. fuliginosa* can be designated as A^f, B^f, and D^f. During meiosis in the anthers of hybrid plants, A^n pairs with A^f and D^n with D^f. However, B^f pairs sometimes with B^n, sometimes with C^n, and sometimes with B^n *and* C^n. The conclusion reached was that the euchromatic part of C^n had been added onto one arm of B^n, with the subsequent loss of the C^n centromere and its (unneeded) heterochromatin. Thus B^n plus some of C^n has become B^f, and the haploid chromosome number was reduced from n = 4 to n = 3. Of course, additional mutations and even additional chromosomal exchanges occurred before the present-day n = 3 species *C. fuliginosa* had fully evolved from the original n = 3 "mutant" of *C. neglecta.* More recent evidence has indicated that the probable original basic number in *Crepis* was n = 5 (Babcock, 1949).

Similar translocations probably produced n = 3 *Haplopappus gracilis* ("tribivalens") and finally n = 2 *H. gracilis* from the original n = 4 *H. ravenii* (Jackson, 1965). Several similar analyses have demonstrated this as a common method for reduction in basic chromosome number in other plant and animal genera. Such translocations of parts from one chromosome to another change the forms of chromosomes also. If a chromosome set consists of all metacentric chromosomes, and if two of these exchange pieces, a long piece for a short piece, one metacentric chromosome may become acrocentric and the other submetacentric.

White (1954) considered that the original karyotype for the short-horned grasshoppers (Acrididae) was in the male 2n = 23, all acrocentric chromosomes. By "centric fusions," the translocation of a long arm of one chromosome onto the short arm of another, called also an asymmetrical interchange, and the subsequent loss of the almost denuded centromere, one long metacentric chromosome was formed from two acrocentric chromosomes, with an eventual diploid chromosome number reduction of two. This was repeated a few times to produce finally the 2n = 12 mostly metacentric chromosomes of the most highly evolved grasshoppers. The number of long arms, however, has remained about the same. Such changes conform to Robertson's law (1916), which states that in certain groups of organisms the number of chromosome arms remains constant by centric fusions (or fissions), although the number of chromosomes varies accordingly.

Something of the same sort seems to have occurred in the genus *Drosophila.* The original *Drosophila* idiogram is conceived as having consisted of five "rod" acrocentric chromosomes and a dot chromosome. Centric fusions formed fewer but metacentric chromosomes to produce the most common number of n = 4 and a few species with n = 3. Additional and contemporary changes were translocations and pericentric inversions. The latter consists of an inversion including the centromere, but the inverted segment is asymmetrical, with one long and one short arm. The position of the centromere is changed and the lengths of the arms greatly altered by such an internal alteration.

There is only circumstantial evidence for the increase of basic chromosome numbers; yet it seems inevitable that it has occurred. If, for example, the basic number of the most primitive species of a genus and other genera of a family is x = 7 (as in the North American wild onions of the genus *Allium* and other Liliaceae), whereas the Eurasian species of *Allium* have n = 8, then an increase in basic chromosome number has probably occurred. The one n = 7 species of *Drosophila* is assumed to have arisen by chromosome increase, which is often called *ascending aneuploidy* or *ascending dysploidy.*

Just how an increase is achieved is rather difficult to observe or prove. The process must include the addition of a new centromere. Two methods have been proposed. One supposes that a centromere undergoes a transverse rather than the normal longitudinal division at some mitotic or meiotic division (Fig. 16-15) (White, 1954). There is good evidence from corn that each half centromere can function as a normal centromere. One possible result would be two telocentric chromosomes (which questionably occur) and therefore an increase in chromosome and centromere number, or two *isochromosomes* would be formed. That is, each of the two chromosomes produced would have two morphologically and genetically identical arms formed by their two chromatids opening out after transverse division of the centromere. If both of these two isochromosomes should move to the same spindle pole, the nucleus produced would have one extra chromosome. At a subsequent meiotic division, segregation of the two isochromosomes to one pole and the one original type chromosome to the other would produce gametes with the extra chromosome. The union of two such gametes would produce an individual homozygous for the extra chromosome. Subsequent evolution of the chromosomes would change each isochromosome to one having genetically different arms.

A second proposed method for increasing the basic chromosome number utilizes supernumerary chromosomes (see later in this chapter). It is a well-established fact that supernumerary chromosomes are fairly common among plants but rare among animal species, except grasshoppers, bedbugs, and a few other animal species, even though their mode of origin is not known. It is assumed that the centromere and heterochromatin of a supernumerary chromosome has been, in turn, derived somehow from a

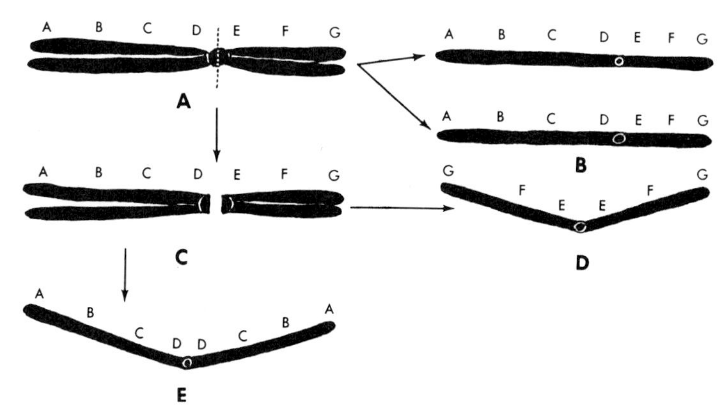

Fig. 16-15. Origin of isochromosomes. **A** and **B,** Formation of two normal sister chromatids. Transverse division of the centromere of **A,** however, along the dotted line produces two chromosomes, **C,** which when they straighten out, have two identical or duplicate arms, **D** and **E,** and are called isochromosomes.

more typical autosome. Given a supernumerary chromosome in an organism as the source of the new centromere and a translocation of a piece of a normal chromosome onto it (such a translocation has occurred in corn—Roman, 1947, 1948), then a new chromosome has been "produced" and could become homozygous at fertilization.

Perhaps a simple mechanism for the increase of a centromere and a whole chromosome is nondisjunction, an irregular mitotic or meiotic division such that two sister chromatids (or chromosomes) move to the same pole at anaphase. The result is one nucleus deficient for that chromosome. Such a cell would die if haploid, as when produced by meiosis, but it would survive if produced by a mitotic nondisjunction. The other nucleus, if produced during meiosis, would have two of one kind of chromosome or three if produced by mitosis. Such trisomic organisms have been found. In fact, in the plant species *Datura stramonium* (n = 12) all twelve possible trisomics have been found (Blakeslee, 1934); they were originally selected as genetic mutants (Blakeslee, 1921). All twenty-one trisomics of wheat have been produced (Sears, 1954). Trisomics could lead to an increase in basic number by the two pairs of homologues evolving differently for mutations and structural rearrangements.

Evolutionary changes in total chromosome length (and bulk) are also known. In *Crepis* (Fig. 16-16) if the n = 6 long chromosomes of *C. kashmirica* represent a total length of 100, the n = 4 very short chromosomes of *C. suffreniana* equal only 21, and the n = 3 chromosomes of *C. fuliginosa* equal 22. Thus the total lengths in these last two species are only about one fifth the total chromosome length of *C. kashmirica* (Babcock, 1947). There is probably little actual loss of genes during such rather common evolutionary shortening of chromosomes. Rather, there may have been a decrease in polyteny or a decrease in amount of heterochromatin, matrix, gene duplications, or combinations of these, any one of which could permit tighter coiling, shorter length, or other change that might result in shorter chromosomes.

If evolutionary reduction in chromosome basic number and length were universal, all extant species should have low base numbers and small chromosomes. Such is far from the case. There may be mechanisms both for increasing chromosome number as well as for increasing chromosome length, the latter perhaps by the accumulation of duplicate segments or increase in amount of heterochromatin.

Agmatoploidy

An unusual mechanism for the increase in chromosome number and change of the chromosome set called agmatoploidy exists in the genus *Luzula* (Fig. 16-6). This genus is characterized by the so-called diffuse centromere, and thus at anaphase the chromosomes remain parallel as they move away from each other. The lowest chromosome number occurs in *L. purpurea* (2n = 6), and the chromosomes are about 5 μm long. Most species have 2n = 12, with chromosomes 2 μm long, as though the six chromosomes of *L. purpurea* had broken in half. From 2n = 12 as a base there are normal polyploid-produced species (or varieties) with 2n = 24 and 2n = 48, and the chromosomes remain about 2 μm long. There is, however, another group of species showing such agmatoploidy that with each doubling of the set the chromosomes become half as long. There is no change in amount of DNA or chromatin, only in number of chromosomes (Nordenskiold, 1951). Thus agmatoploid plants with 2n = 24 have chromosomes 1 μm long, and plants with 2n = 48 have chromosomes only about 0.5 μm long. Furthermore, there may be such doubling of only one or a few chromosomes of the set to produce 2n = 14, 2n = 16, 2n = 18, etc. In bedbugs there seems to be agmatoploidy of the X chromosome only, producing four to eleven tiny X chromosomes. In each such case two small chromosomes replace one larger one. Evidently, this form of chromosome number increase is produced by fragmentation of chromosomes, and it is possible and able to persist because of the diffuse centromeres.

DNA content of nucleus

Another form of chromosome set evolution is change in total DNA content per nucleus. It has been well established that the average DNA of representatives of different major taxonomic groups may vary considerably. Thus within the Amphibia the salamanders have many times the cellular DNA content of the Aneura. Such a difference supports the conclusion that these two groups may be only distantly related.

Among the reptiles those most closely related to the birds have a comparably low DNA content, but those more closely re-

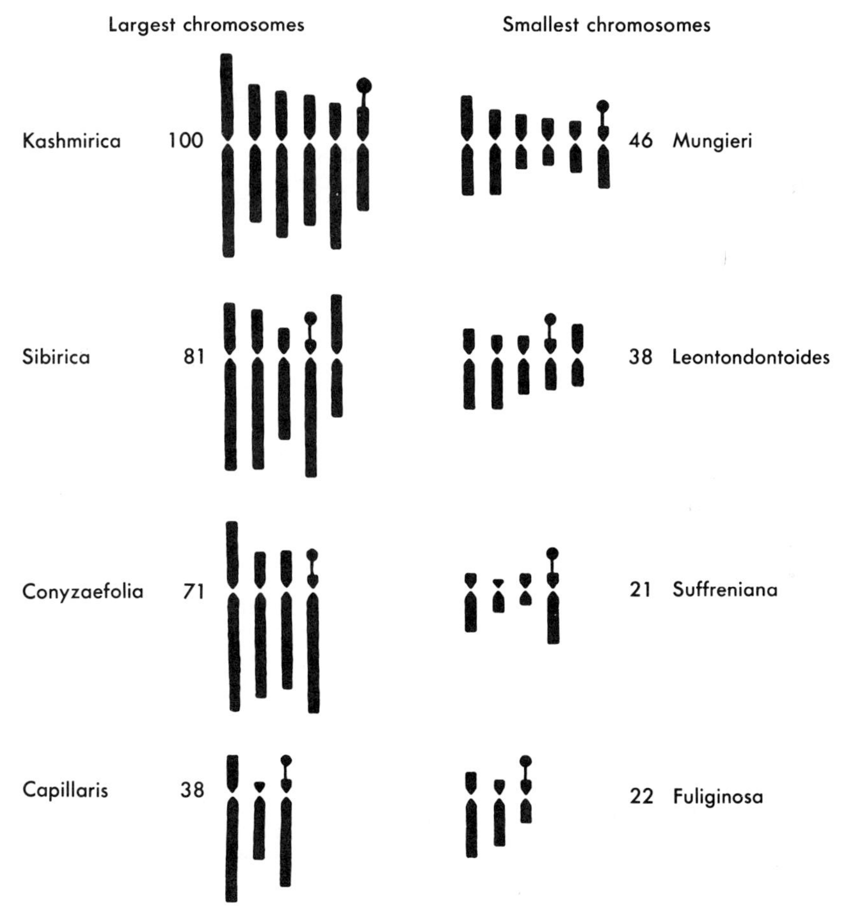

Fig. 16-16. Idiograms of species with longest and shortest total chromosome length in each of the four number classes n = 6, 5, 4, and 3. Reduction in symmetry is emphasized by placing the spindle fiber constrictions on a common base line in each number class. Using the total length of the somatic chromosomes in *C. kashmirica* as a base of 100, the proportional total length of each idiogram is shown by the number between the name of the species and its idiogram. With respect to the absolute size of the individual chromosomes these idiograms are accurate only to a degree sufficient for the purposes of the present discussion. (From Babcock, E. B. 1947. The genus Crepis. University of California Press, Berkeley.)

lated to mammals have a DNA content range almost as high as do the mammals. The most primitive fish have a DNA content much higher than the more modern fish, reptiles, or mammals.

Rothfels et al. (1966) reported that even within families and genera the amount of DNA may be detectably different among diploid species, as within the Ranunculaceae and even within one of its genera, *Anemone*. They reported the DNA content in grams and *total chromosome length* (TCL) of a chromosome set in some diploid species of some genera of Ranunculaceae to be as follows:

Aquilegia hybrid	n=7	0.13×10^{-11}gm	20 μm TCL
Pulsatilla occidentalis	n=8	1.22×10^{-11}gm	125 μm TCL
Anemone (average of 3 spp.)	n=8	2.1×10^{-11}gm	102-170 μm TCL
Hepatica acutiloba	n=7	3.9×10^{-11}gm	177 μm TCL
Anemone tetrasepala	n=7	5.25×10^{-11}gm	202 μm TCL

Reported relative differences in DNA content among three species of *Bufo* (Ullerich, 1966) are *B. calamita* (2n = 22), relative DNA content of 1; *B. bufo* (2n = 22), relative DNA content of 1.07; and *B. viridis* (2n = 22), relative DNA content of 1.49. That is, *B. viridis* has 50% more DNA than do the other two species.

These examples indicate ranges of DNA content per chromosome set among species, differences that probably are not correlated with the number of different genes. What such DNA differences among diploid species do reflect is really unknown. Some sort of linear or lateral duplication of genonemata are usually invoked to "explain" such observed differences.

Summary

It is evident that the numbers of the basic type of chromosomes may change greatly as a genus or species evolves and that individual chromosomes within the set may change in size and form. Thus chromosome sets evolve. Occasionally, diffuse centromeres may evolve from typical monocentric chromosomes.

The chromosome set of a species is an evolved and balanced genome of organized chromosomes that is frequently readjusted by chromosomal aberrations. Many such changes are detrimental, since they rearrange blocks of genes; alter position effects by breaking established ones and forming new ones; and affect crossing-over, producing meiotic irregularities, deletions, inversions, translocations, etc. Natural selection, however, permits any advantageous new arrangements to persist, and so chromosome sets evolve like any other phenotypic expression.

In some genera there is no detectable evidence of chromosome set evolution, as in *Sagittaria* (Fig. 19-14). In others such as *Drosophila* there has been a great deal of chromosome set change. Some of these will be discussed later as useful data in the field of cytogenetics and cytotaxonomy (Chapter 19).

SEX CHROMOSOMES

Sex chromosomes (Mittwoch, 1967), as the name implies, carry specific genes that determine the sex of the organism, which develops from the zygote or spore if, as in many kinds of organisms, such an organism can indeed be described as having sex. The case of sex is clear for animals generally but is confusing among many plants, the fungi, and many Protozoa. Sex, that is, maleness or femaleness, implies morphological and functional differences. When such is lacking, as in fungi, many small algae, and Protozoa, only two subtile types are required for union, described as plus (+) and minus (−) strains rather than sexes.

Furthermore, most vascular plants, many "lower" plants, and some animals are, in the diploid phase of the life cycle, simultaneously or sequentially both male and female; that is, they may have male gamete-producing and female gamete-producing organs in the same body. Among animals such as earthworms and flatworms this condition is called *hermaphroditic;* in higher plants it is called either *perfect* or *monoecious.* A single flower that has both anthers and pistil is called perfect, the common condition. Many plants, however, such as oak trees have staminate flowers distinct from the pistillate flowers on the same tree and are called monoecious. The few species such as grape and willow where there are some completely staminate and some completely pistillate individuals are called *dioecious.* It is only in dioecious species that sex chromosomes may occur in the sporophyte.

In most higher plants (the sporophytes) and such animal groups as the ctenophores, flatworms, ectoprocts, earthworms, leeches, a group of molluscs, and tunicates, hermaphroditism is the rule and there are no sex chromosomes. There are also bisexual animal species in which there is no direct genetic chromosomal control of sex determination. In two species of the worm genus *Bonellia,* and in parasitic isopod *Ione thoracica* chemical substances in the environment are effective in determining sex. In some other species sex is somehow determined by some condition of the egg cytoplasma. Among the insects of the order Hymenoptera, haploid eggs (determined by controlled nonfertilization) develop into males. In some terrestrial isopods there are two or three kinds of females—some are *gynogenic* and produce only females, others are *androgenic* and produce only males, whereas still others are *amphogenic* and produce both males and females. Such a condition is probably produced by several alleles, various combinations producing the different sexes.

There are numerous dioecious flowering plant species, some of which have recognizable sex chromosomes. The genetic system affects the flowers of the sporophyte so that "males" (staminate plants) have the gynoecia aborted, whereas pistillate "female" plants have the anthers aborted. However, the sexual dimorphism of the gametophytes (the female being the embryo sac and the male being the pollen grain) is not determined by sex chromosomes.

Among the mosses, on the other hand, there are species in which the sexuality of the haploid gametophyte is determined by recognizable heteromorphic sex chromosomes.

By definition a sex chromosome is one that by its mere presence (some Ys) or because it contains one or more specific genes (Xs and most Ys), plays a part in determining the sex of an individual. It may also be recognizably distinct from the autosomes in various ways, but it need not be. Frequently there are two distinctive kinds of sex chromosomes that are homologous enough to pair at meiosis, the Xs and the Ys. In some plants and animals there are three or more sex chromosomes, two or more of which pair with different arms of the third.

In all cases of distinct sexes and of plus and minus strains the two sexes or strains must be genetically different for at least one gene (some mosquitoes) and therefore for one chromosome so that at meiosis two genetic and chromosomal sorts of nuclei are produced, at least in one of the sexes or strains.

The term "sex chromosomes" is usually restricted in cytology to observably distinct chromosomes that are different from the nonsex chromosomes (autosomes), and if there are two sorts of sex chromosomes, they differ from each other. The general condition is that one sex has a pair of *heteromorphic* chromosomes (obviously of different sizes), whereas the other sex has two of one type of heteromorphic chromosomes. Additional terminology is that the sex having two of one sort of sex chromosome is said to be *homogametic,* producing only one sort of gamete with respect to sex

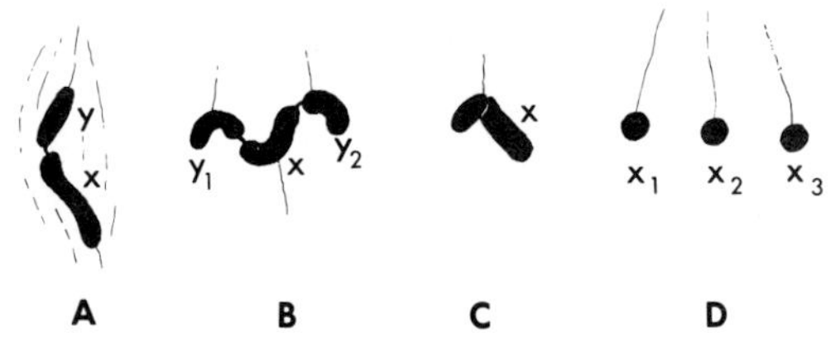

Fig. 16-17. Diagrammatic representations of metaphase I sex chromosome configurations in the heterogametic sex. **A,** Example of XY bivalent chromosomes. **B,** Tripartite XY_1Y_2 (or reversed, could be an X_1X_2Y trivalent) configuration illustrating alternate disjunction. **C,** Univalent X chromosome of the XO scheme. **D,** Three Xs of the $X_1X_2X_3O$ type, all somehow going to the same pole of the spindle.

chromosomes; the sex having two sorts of sex chromosomes is described as *heterogametic.* This condition is called the XX-XY type, usually with the male being XY, although XY females are known, especially in birds (Fig. 16-17). Another possibility, typical of grasshoppers and some other species, is the "loss" of the Y chromosome to produce XX females but XO males. In many XY species the Y contains no sex genes, possibly only genes for pairing with X, as in *Drosophila.* In other species the Y *is* the sex-determining chromosome, as in man and the plant *Melandrium dioecum.* A third but much rarer condition is two Ys that always move to the same pole at anaphase I and produce the $XX\text{-}XY_1Y_2$ condition of the Japanese hop plant, *Rumex acetosa,* and some crickets. The opposite condition X_1X_2Y, occurs in mantids, some crickets, and the plant *Atriplex.* White also lists $X_1X_2X_3Y$, X_1X_2O, $X_1X_2X_3X_4Y$, and many other known heterogametic sex chromosome conditions among insects.

Plants

As far as known, there are no morphologically recognizable sex chromosomes in algae or fungi. In the bryophytes (mosses and liverworts) they have been well documented. The bryophyte gametophyte generation is haploid relative to the sporophyte and is either monoecious (both antheridia and archegonia on the same gametophyte) or dioecious (some gametophytes bear only antheridia and are male, others only archegonia and are female). In general, species with a low chromosome number are dioecious, whereas "polyploid" species are usually monoecious. This same condition can be duplicated by making diploid gametophytes asexually from sporophyte tissue.

In 1945 Allen listed forty-six species of dioecious bryophytes in twenty-one genera of six orders that were known to have sex chromosomes, but also forty-four species in twenty-eight genera of four orders of dioecious bryophytes without recognizable sex chromosomes. Among the second group study has revealed that segregation for sex from the spores is the same as in the first group so that the species of the second group without doubt contain perfectly good genetic but cytologically undetectable sex chromosomes.

In most dioecious species of bryophytes the X chromosome is larger than the Y chromosome, in a few species the Y is the larger, and in two an XO scheme has been reported. Experimental work has demonstrated that a gametophyte with one or more X chromosomes is purely female (produces only archegonia and eggs), whereas a gametophyte containing only Y chromosomes is male (produces only antheridia and sperm). There is no evidence that genes for sex determination are present on any autosomes, as is true of *Drosophila.* A gametophyte of such a dioecious species containing (experimentally) both X and Y chromosomes in any proportion is monoecious but is almost always sterile. It is likely that the polyploid monoecious bryophytes have been derived from diploid dioecious species and, at least originally, contained both X and Y chromosomes.

Allen in 1945 discussed the m (minute) and M (large minute) chromosomes often present in mosses as possible sex chromosomes (see later in this chapter). He pointed out that they are often heteropyknotic, but at present it is questioned whether heteropyknosis of such tiny chromosomes could be detected, and there is slight evidence that they really are sex chromosomes.

The bryophytes are unique in that the sex chromosomes function in the haploid phase. This points up a fundamental difference between animals and plants—that the sexual phase of plants is the haploid phase, the gametophytes, which produce the eggs and sperm. The zygote develops into the diploid sporophyte, which is not really sexual. Nevertheless, there are plant species that have sporophytes that produce only female or male gametophytes, some of which have sex chromosomes that function in the diploid phase of the life cycle (as in animals) and that are also called dioecious species.

Among the angiosperms it is assumed that the fundamental condition of sporophytes is for them to have perfect flowers; that is, if they can be referred to in sexual terms, they are hermaphroditic. Therefore species of angiosperms that are dioecious have become so rather recently and are unrelated to other dioecious species in other families. In 1940 Allen reported genetically dioecious species of two categories: sixty-nine species in thirty genera of twenty-six families in which cytologically distinguishable sex chromosomes had been reported and forty-six species in thirty-two genera of twenty-five families in which sex chromosomes, if present, were not discernible as such.

Most angiosperm species having sex chromosomes are of the XX "female," XY "male" type. A few such as *Humulus japonicus* and *Rumex acetosa* (and seven closely related species) are XX-XY_1Y_2. *Humulus lupulus* is $2X_12X_2$-$X_1X_2Y_1Y_2$; *Phoradendron flavescens* has no Xs (the male has one Y and so has one chromosome more than the female); and there are a few other sex chromosome mechanisms known. As in animals, a male of XY_1Y_2 constitution has a sex trivalent at metaphase I; the two Ys synapse, one on each arm of the X. The two Ys have spindle fibers to the same pole, whereas the X moves to the opposite pole. The Xs or Ys are not homologous and so are designated as X_1X_2 or Y_1Y_2. Each has one arm more or less homologous with a different arm of the third element, and after synapsis they form a chain of three, the central element moving to one pole at anaphase I and the two terminal elements moving to the opposite pole. The cultivated hop is a dioecious species and has four sex chromosomes; the staminate (male) plant (sporophyte) is $X_1X_2Y_1Y_2$, and at meoisis a chain of four chromosomes is formed. These are examples of *alternate disjunction* when, in a chain of three or more chromosomes, every other chromosome goes to the same pole at anaphase I.

Among some dioecious plants polyploidy seems to occur for the autosomes but not for the sex chromosomes. For example, *Rumex hastatulus* has 2n = 8 (6A, 2X) in the female but 2n = 9 (6A, XY_1Y_2) in the male, whereas *R. acetosa* has 2n = 14 (12A, 2X) in the female and 2n = 15 (12A, XY_1Y_2) in the male, as though only the six autosomes of *R. hastatulus* had doubled in number to produce *R. acetosa*.

With respect to determination of the sex of the sporophyte it has been determined in *Melandrium dioecum,* in which the Y is larger than the X, that the ratio of X to Y determines the sex (XYY, XY, XXY, and XXXY are male; XXXXY is a hermaphrodite; and XX is a female) Warmke, 1946). In *R. acetosa,* on the other hand, sex is determined by the X/A ratio (as in *Drosophila*), the Y being inert, 2A, XX being female, and 2A, X being male regardless of Ys.

The X and Y chromosomes are generally different in form (they often constitute a *heteromorphic pair* when synapsed) and composition (the Y, if present, is more heterochromatic), but they generally have sufficient homology to synapse at meiotic prophase and remain together, usually end to end, until anaphase I. Nevertheless, as in *Drosophila* males and some other heterogametic individuals, although synapsis (or at least pairing) occurs, there may be no actual crossing-over between the X and the Y chromosomes.

The X chromosome generally is more like an autosome and a bearer of many genes, whereas the Y is more frequently largely heterochromatic and a carrier of few genes. However, the X chromosome of the XO orthopterous insects seems to be inert except for sex-determining genes.

Animals

The chromosomal mechanisms for the determination of sex in bisexual animal species is highly variable and not only of the two types XY and XO (see lengthy discussion by White, 1954). Certainly, the XY type is typical of eutherian mammals, some insects, and species in numerous other animal phyla, classes, orders, and families. Of course, the typically hermaphroditic animals—Mesozoa, ctenophores, flatworms, gastrotichs, ectoprocts, earthworms, leeches, opisthobranch and pulmonate snails, chaetognaths, and tunicates; some sponges, coelenterates, entoprocts, oysters and scallops, polychete annelids, and echinoderms; and a few crustaceans, echinoderms, cephalopods, brachiopods, coccids, flies, and fish—do not have sex chromosomes. All culicid mosquitoes have sexes determined by a single gene. Males are heterozygous Mm, whereas females are homozygous recessive, mm. But certainly the numerical majority of animal species do have separate sexes and usually chromosomal mechanisms for their determination (Mittwoch, 1967).

In most dioecious species of animals there is a chromosomal mechanism for the production of two genotypic kinds of gametes in one sex or the other. There are only a few cases known in which no such mechanism is evident, such as the chemical control of sex determination in the worm *Bonellia* and various egg determinations as in Hymenoptera, the tribe Iceryini of scale insects, etc., in which haploid parthenogenesis produces males; *Sciara* and terrestrial isopods in which sex is determined by possibly genetic differences among females; the scale insect *Pseudococcus,* in which it seems that the age of the female and/or environmental conditions determine sex; and the worm *Dinophilus,* which lays two kinds of eggs, the larger of which develop into females, the small ones into dwarf males, the egg character being determined long before meiosis.

In most animal species the male is heterogametic, being XY or, in grasshoppers and other insects, XO or some more complex system. In the Lepidoptera, Trichoptera, birds, and some fish it is the female that is heterogametic, often symbolically represented by female ZW and male ZZ. Among insects especially there are numerous cases of multiple sex chromosomes that either synapse and then segregate at first or second anaphase to produce two sorts of gametes or do not synapse but, nevertheless, segregate properly to produce the heterogametes. For example, in the male heteropteran *Oncopeltus* the X and Y do not synapse at prophase I but divide equationally. They pair by metaphase II and separate reductionally at anaphase II.

At least two mammals have rather distinctive sex chromosome mechanisms. The rodent *Microtus oregoni* has not only different chromosome numbers in the germ line and soma (it is a *gonosomic mosaic*), but the male differs from the female in chromosome number and sex chromosome composition.

The male soma has sixteen autosomes plus XY; the male germ line has sixteen autosomes plus OY because of loss of the X by selective nondisjunction. The male produces two sorts of sperm, Y-containing and O-containing. The female soma has seventeen chromosomes, sixteen autosomes plus X; the female germ line has sixteen autosomes plus two Xs. Thus XY zygotes produce males and XO zygotes females. It is proposed that female germ line cells acquire the second X chromosome by a type of selective nondisjunction which is the reverse of that in the male.

The small Indian mongoose *Herpestes auropunctatus,* a carnivore, is characterized by the male having thirty-five chromosomes and the female thirty-six. The male is XO, the female XX. At meiosis in the male the end of the single X associates with one end of only one autosome of a particular synapsed pair. It has been proposed that there was once a Y chromosome, but its X-pairing and male-determining part was translocated to an autosome and the remaining centromere and heterochromatin of the Y were lost. Presumably, the male maintains the heterozygosity of this autosome pair, one with and one without the terminal Y segment, in spite of crossing-over between the centromere and the Y-containing end. This could be considered a special case of a Y_1Y_2X male. Reports of other mammals having a sex mechanism other than the XX-XY are inconclusive, but such exceptions doubtless exist in addition to the cases mentioned.

In many species the sex chromosomes (or some of them) are heteropyknotic, and the Y is typically heterochromatic. In male grasshoppers (XO) the X chromosome is negatively heteropyknotic during spermatogonial and meiotic metaphases. In human females one of the two Xs is condensed and heteropyknotic as the sex *chromatin body* during interphase of many tissues, appearing as a dark blob, the Barr body, (Fig. 15-10) against the inner surface of the nuclear envelope in some mucosa cells or as a nuclear projection on the polymorphic nucleus of certain white blood cells, the drumstick (Fig. 15-10). The number of Barr bodies equals one less than the number of X chromosomes in the nucleus. Males (XY) have no Barr body. Normal females (XX) have one Barr body, but abnormal females such as XXX and XXXX have two and three Barr bodies, respectively. Why this is so is unknown, except that the heterochromatic X has late DNA replication.

Sex chromosomes are variously modified typical chromosomes. Therefore by translocation of part of a Y, for example, with part of an autosome the homologue of the latter may be converted into an additional X set chromosomes, since it will then synapse with part of the Y. That seems to be the origin of some multiple Xs such as $X_1X_2X_3Y$. Many Ys have become heterochromatic to the point of containing few if any necessary genes. Their loss would then give rise to the XO condition. Even X chromosomes are often heteropyknotic and in some insects behave unusually, such as passing to a spindle pole at metaphase I, lagging behind the autosomes, or being eliminated during cleavage. Many probable sex chromosomes are not cytologically distinguishable because the X and Y are of equal size and shape and behave as regularly as the autosomes that they resemble, except for genetic differences between the X and Y.

There are, of course, genetic implications of the sex chromosome mechanism. The heterogametic sex is haploid for genes on the X and Y, whereas the homogametic sex lacks any genes that might be on the Y but is diploid for the genes on the X, unless one of the X chromosomes becomes heterochromatic and so, presumably, genetically nonfunctional, as in at least certain cells of the human body (Barr bodies and drumsticks).

SUPERNUMERARY CHROMOSOMES

The chromosomes discussed up to this point have been the typical chromosomes, (the autosomes) and the more unusual sex chromosomes. The latter often consist in whole or in part of heterochromatin but are genetically important. Another class of chromosomes is of a very different type: they are unnecessary genetically and occur in addition to the typical set of the species. Although other terms are applied to them, the term "supernumerary" connotes that they are additional and not very important. Many kinds of supernumerary chromosomes can be distinguished on the basis of size, chromatin, genetic content, activity, numbers, and distribution among individuals of a species. They occur more often in plants than in animals. Perhaps the one thing they have in common is that they do not synapse with the autosomes or sex chromosomes but do synapse among themselves. Their variability is to some extent reflected in the variety of terms that have been applied to them. In 1964 Battaglia listed more than fifteen terms for these unusual chromosomes, of which "B chromosomes" and "accessory chromosomes" are most widely used next to "supernumerary." Cytologists studying them seem to have personal preferences as to terminology, but they are completely interchangeable terms. In 1928 Randolph categorized the typical chromosomes of *Zea mays,* the autosomes, as "A chromosomes" and the supernumeraries as "B chromosomes." Battaglia briefly considered using the terms "primary" and "secondary" chromosomes for As and Bs.

Such chromosomes are unnecessary to the organism or cell in which they occur; they are not homologous with any of the normal chromosomes; they are often smaller than the normal chromosomes; they are present in some individuals of a species or population but not in others; in small numbers they do not generally affect the phenotype of the individuals possessing them; often they vary in number among individuals possessing them or even among cells of an organism; in many species they do not disjoin during certain divisions of the reproductive process and/or during mitotic divisions; they occur only in the germ line in one known animal and stem of some plants; and they are mostly heterochromatic.

It is obvious that supernumerary chromosomes as thus defined (Muntzing, 1966) are distinct from ordinary (autosomal) chromosomes. In fact, Ostergren (1947) has seriously proposed that they are parasites possessing genes for their own survival. White, on the other hand, believes that they are adaptive in the natural conditions under which they developed. It has been proposed that they may play a part in evolution by providing additional centromeres for an increase in chromosome number by translocation with an autosome. They increase variation in rye. How they originate is essentially unknown.

The term "supernumerary" means "in addition to the normal complement." However, in the strict definition of the word given previously certain "extra" chromosomes are excluded, although they probably are often reported as supernumerary. This excluded type is often merely an extra autosome, a *trisomic* chromosome, such that the organism would be $2n + 1$ and have three rather than two of a particular autosomal chromosome of its set. Such a chromosome would not fit most of the defined characteristics of a supernumerary chromosome and, as in human beings (Table 19-1), the plant *Datura,* and other organisms, trisomic organisms are very different phenotypically from the diploid.

Among animals supernumeraries have been reported in fifty-two species (according to White, 1954)—two flatworms and fifty insects. White listed insects with supernumeraries from six orders and seventeen families, but more than half (twenty-nine) of these are short-horned grasshoppers of the family Acrididae.

Among plants nearly all reports are from the angiosperms. By 1959 at least 200 species in eighty-eight genera had been reported to have supernumeraries; during the subsequent years, dozens of other species have been added. By 1967 supernumerary chromosomes had been reported in at least 460 species of 163 genera classified in forty-two families of angiosperms. Most species with supernumeraries are outbreeders. As White stated in regard to the Acrididae, if enough individuals of enough populations of almost any angiosperm species were examined, one might expect to find supernumeraries in at least some individuals. This also points out one of the characteristics of supernumeraries—they are present in only some individuals of a species, and in them the number may vary.

As an example, a species of *Tradescantia* was found to contain one individual with supernumeraries. Subsequent examination by Anderson in 1954 of many plants in seventeen other related species revealed a few individuals in some species with them. In seven of the ten species in which from seventeen to 116 individuals were examined, one to three individuals were found to have supernumeraries. Among the eight species in which only sixteen or fewer individuals were studied, no plant was found with supernumeraries. Thus the presence of supernumeraries in a species was more or less correlated with the number of individuals examined, but in any species the number of individuals having supernumeraries was small. One species studied by Anderson was *T. edwardsiana.* He examined seventeen individuals of two populations from near Austin, Texas, none of which had supernumeraries. Some years later a population, also near Austin, was found in which all individuals in one part of the population had from one to four supernumeraries (Brown, 1960) (Fig. 16-18). It is not unlikely that there are some plants, somewhere, in each of the species of the Virginiana group of *Tradescantia* having supernumerary chromosomes. However, the proportion is low. Anderson found about 2% of plants (ten in 485) to contain supernumerary chromosomes.

Such an expectation that some individuals in many species have supernumeraries probably does not hold true in animals or even in most insects. It is likely, however, in the grasshoppers, and White believes that perhaps a fifth of all species of Acrididae might possess them. On the other hand, the

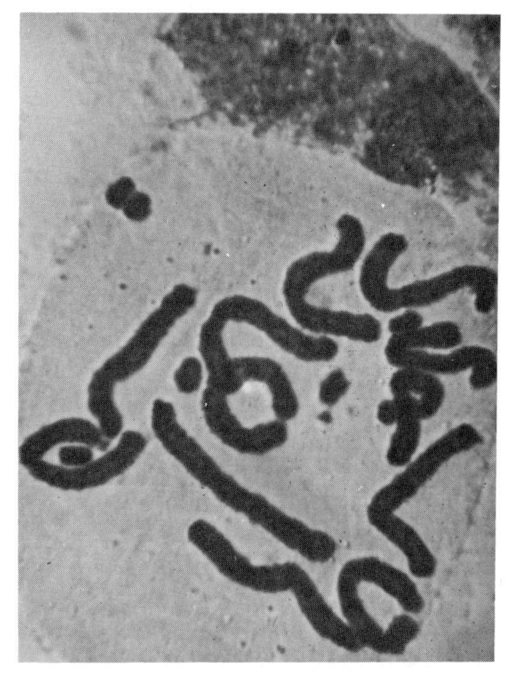

Fig. 16-18. Squash of root tip cell of *Tradescantia edwardsiana* showing twelve somatic and five small supernumerary chromosomes, one of the latter being clearly double. One normal and one supernumerary have satellites evident.

genus *Drosophila,* which has been well studied cytologically, has yielded no individuals with supernumeraries.

The usual number of supernumeraries in a nucleus is one or two. Higher numbers, of course, are known (for example, in corn they vary in number from zero to about six in certain varieties). By appropriate crossing higher and higher numbers were accumulated (in corn the progeny tend to have a number of supernumeraries greater than the sum of the two parents), up to about thirty per nucleus. Above about fifteen supernumeraries per nucleus phenotypic effects of decreased vigor and fertility were noted, until with the maximum number of about thirty the plants were poor, had defective kernels, aborted pollen, and were sterile. In cultivated European rye there is an inverse correlation between kernel weight and number of supernumeraries, such that with six supernumeraries the kernel weight is 20% of that of plants with no supernumeraries (Muntzing, 1966). Yet Moss (1966) found that B chromosomes increase seed weight but delay germination. In *Tradescantia* (Figs. 16-18 and 16-20) and several other species decreased vigor and considerable pollen and seed sterility were produced by more than five or six supernumeraries per nucleus. In *Tradescantia edwardsiana* grown in pots in a greenhouse, plants with one to nine supernumeraries were less vigorous than plants with none. In the flatworm *Polycelis tenuis* individuals having supernumeraries did poorly under aquarium conditions. A single supernumerary in *Haplopappus gracilis* (Fig. 16-19), however, does perhaps affect achene pigmentation (Jackson and Newmark, 1960). Thus in medium to large numbers they do affect the phenotype, but in small natural numbers (one to four) they rarely do, as though natural selection keeps the numbers low.

Supernumerary chromosomes are described as being typically heterochromatic and genetically inert. The heterochromaticity shows up, at least in some species, as positive pyknosis in interphase (chromocenters). Negative pyknosis is evident during meiosis by light staining at metaphase I (Fig. 16-20). Such heterochromaticity is correlated with genetic inactivity, a general cytogenetic concept. In some grasshoppers they may associate with the equally heteropyknotic sex chromosome during meiosis, but rarely do they actually synapse with autosomes, although they do synapse with one another. If a plant has only one supernumerary, it seems to divide mitotically during both meiotic divisions.

In corn, translocations have been produced between supernumeraries and autosomes. Both centromeres and chromosomes seem normal, except that the chromosome with the large amount of supernumerary material showed preferential fertilization, getting into the egg considerably more often

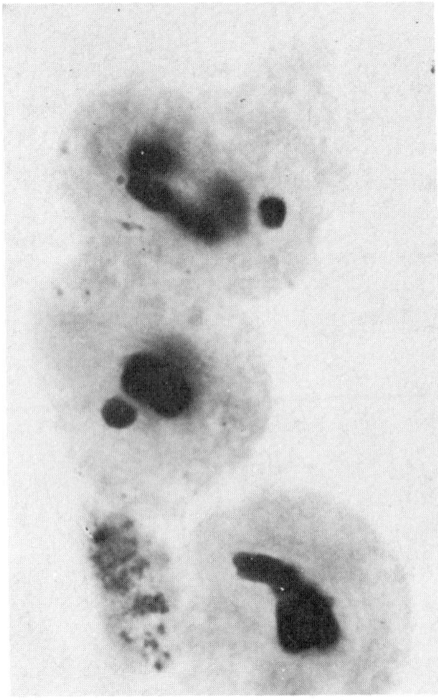

Fig. 16-19. Supernumerary chromosome in each cell of a plant of *Haplopappus gracilis* at meta-anaphase I.

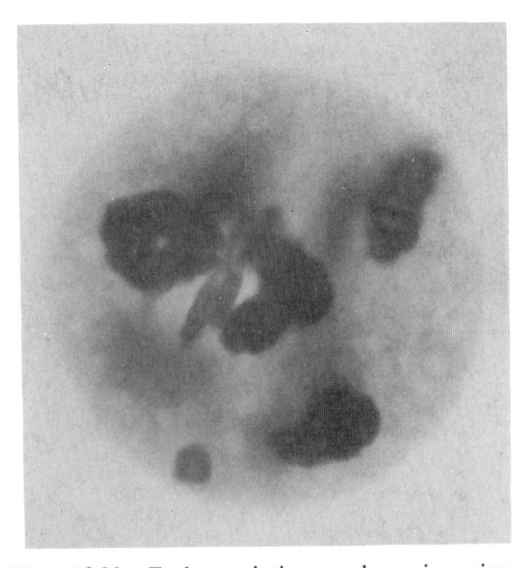

Fig. 16-20. Early meiotic anaphase in microsporocyte of *Tradescantia edwardsiana* with synapsed supernumeraries (the thinner, lightly stained chromosomes). One pair of spherical supernumeraries at bottom is somewhat out of focus.

than randomness would permit. Other so-called supernumeraries have been described as either partially or wholly euchromatic, additional evidence that supernumerary chromosomes are a miscellaneous category of chromosomes.

Supernumerary chromosomes are usually much smaller than the autosomes and, for that reason, have often been termed "fragment" chromosomes. This small size, presence of a centromere, and heterochromaticity have led to the assumption that a supernumerary represents little more than the centromere and adjacent heterochromatin of an autosome which has lost its euchromatic arms by translocation to other chromosomes. In truth, however, there is no reliable evidence indicating how supernumeraries originate or whether they are of recent or ancient origin or both.

One type or size of supernumerary can give rise to another. In corn there are various sizes, whereas in *Poa alpina* and *Allium porrum* there is a large common type that, according to Vosa (1966), has given rise to a much smaller and rarer type. He also reported that the higher the number of B chromosomes the more rapid is the germination, perhaps as a mechanism for their survival.

Probably the most unusual characteristic of supernumeraries, in a remarkably large number of species of plants and one animal, is their irregular distribution at particular cell divisions, as though they have genes that, in relation to the standard genome, affect themselves. These characteristics led Ostergren to propose the hypothesis that supernumeraries behave like parasites which have genes for their own survival. One of these peculiar actions results in the elimination of supernumeraries from certain tissues or organs. In plants such as *Sorghum purpureum-sericeum, Xanthisma texanum, Haplopappus gracilis,* and others, during early embryogenesis supernumeraries are eliminated from the roots but persist in the shoot. In *Poa alpina,* supernumeraries are eliminated from leaves and adventitious roots but persist in shoots and the primary root. In all such cases the supernumeraries do persist in the shoots, the organs that will pass them on to the next generation. A second type of peculiar action of supernumeraries is that they can increase in number in significant tissues or nuclei (Rutishauser and Rothlisberger, 1966). In three species of *Crepis* there is a doubling (from one to three to two to six supernumeraries) by two divisions of the supernumerary during one late mitotic division in those cells giving rise to the sporogenous tissue. More exactly, in a selection of *C. capillaris* essentially all cells of the seedlings had 1s (one supernumerary). In the stems and bracts of older plants nearly all cells had 1s, a few had 2s, and very few had 0s. In extremely young inflorescences, however, about one third had 2s, two thirds had 1s, and a few more had 0s; rarely, cells were found with 3s. The actual receptacles of the flower heads had about 80% cells with 2s, less than 20% cells with 1s, and 0s and 3s were about the same as in young inflorescences. But in the florets themselves almost 90% of cells had 2s; 0s and 1s were below 10% each. That is, the closer the cells were to reproductive parts (after the shoot apex changed from leaf producing to inflorescence producing) the higher was the number of cells possessing 2s and the fewer the number of cells with 1s, and there was a slight increase in the percentage of cells with 0s. Rutishauser and Rothlisberger concluded that cells with 1s could produce daughter cells by nondisjunction with 2s and 0s, but only after shoot apex transformation. The cells with 2s had such a great advantage that by the time actual flowers (florets) were formed, almost 90% of cells had achieved 2s by this nondisjunction-differential survival *boosting mechanism.*

The progressive increase of cells with 2s parallels the concept of "graduality" so obviously that the cause of gradual somatic pairing may be the cause of supernumerary increase in this species of *Crepis*.

In corn and numerous other species there is a nondisjunctive division of the supernumeraries in the developing pollen grain so that their number is doubled in the male gametes. A somewhat similar irregular division occurs in the egg mother cell of *Lilium callosum* and *Trillium grandiflorum*, by which in about two thirds of the anaphase I stages the single supernumerary passes preferentially to one particular nucleus so that it is eventually included in the egg of the embryo sac much more often than by random distribution.

A third peculiarity of supernumeraries which seems to indicate again that they have genes for their own survival is *preferential fertilization* in corn. This means that of the two male gametes in each pollen tube the gamete containing the supernumerary unites with the egg more often than expected statistically.

For example, such *directed nondisjunction* of the supernumeraries occurs in the first (rye) and second (corn) mitotic division in the pollen grain so that in rye and others the generative nucleus (which divides to form the two male gametes) receives twice the number, whereas the vegetative nucleus (which is not involved in sexuality) receives none. In corn the nondisjunction occurs in the division of the generative nucleus to form two male gametes so that one contains twice the number of supernumeraries and the other receives none. Subsequently, the male gamete with the supernumeraries unites with the egg cell sixty times to only forty times for the other gamete. This is called *directed fertilization*.

In the flatworm *Polycelis tenuis* there is an extra division of the supernumeraries in the ovary during meiosis, thereby increasing their number in the eggs of those individuals having supernumeraries.

Cases of what White calls "mitotic instability" occur in some animals. In the flatworm *Polycelis*, supernumeraries are eliminated from the somatic cells but remain in the germ line. In two species of grasshoppers different cysts of the testis often contain different numbers of supernumeraries.

One of the problems when studying supernumerary chromosomes in some species is to determine whether the extra chromosomes are really supernumerary or merely extra autosomes. Animal examples are the snail species *Triodopsis fraudulenta*, 2n = 58, but having individuals with 59, 60, 61, and 62; man with 2n = 47 or 48; or a grasshopper with one extra chromosome. These cases are probably examples of extra autosomes, but except in man, they just might be autosome-like supernumeraries. Homology and synapsis with autosomes are required as proof that they are autosomes, although in man the fact that the extra chromosomes do have genetic effects and morphological similarity to particular autosomes is adequate proof that these extras are autosomes.

Supernumerary chromosomes, it is clear, constitute a miscellaneous assortment of nonautosomal extra chromosomes. They range from being essentially indistinguishable from autosomes to more typical supernumeraries. They generally are morphologically different from autosomes, are usually smaller, are often genetically inert, are usually heterochromatic, often have abnormal behavior at meiosis and/or at certain mitotic division, lack homology with autosomes, and show numerical variability among individuals and among tissues of an individual. There are often two types in the same species, as in *Poa alpina* and *Allium porrum*. The smaller is rare and derived from the larger.

The mechanism of origin of supernumerary chromosomes is unknown, although it is generally assumed that they are derivatives of autosomes, consisting of a normal centromere and the proximal, genetically inert, heterochromatic regions of the two arms. Presumably, the distal, gene-containing, euchromatic regions of both arms have been lost. It is also not known whether they are of ancient or recent origin. For example, did the supernumerary chromosomes, present in about 2% of individuals of the various species of *Tradescantia,* all have one common origin, or have they arisen independently from time to time in the various species, or even more than once in the same species? Why are they common in grasshoppers but absent in *Drosophila?*

True supernumerary chromosomes are always smaller than the autosomes, except, perhaps, in species characterized by tiny autosomes. Presumably, and certainly in corn, each consists of a centromere, a small amount of heterochromatin, and probably a tiny amount of euchromatin. On the basis of size the tiny M chromosomes that are found in some individuals of so many species of mosses may be supernumeraries, although this has not been demonstrated.

About all that is known is that supernumerary chromosomes occur in plants more often than in animals and have enough characters in common to be considered as a type. Perhaps they are parasitic; perhaps they do have evolutionary significance. It is likely that they do have some effect on the genotype through the action of their heterochromatin.

CHROMOSOMAL INSTABILITY

Chromosomal instability refers to the uncommon, rather random condition of a species or individual possessing a variety of aneuploid individuals or cells. It does not refer to the euploidy of endopolyploid cells, a condition that is predictable. It does not include the common formation of an isolated polyploid cell in a root tip or stem tip of a plant. Nevertheless, when instability in chromosome number does occur, it is so obvious that it, the variation, is predictable.

Chromosome numbers of some cryptogamic vascular plants are listed in Table 16-2. *Equisetum* (the horsetails) show no somatic instability. Others such as species of *Psilatum, Tmesipteris,* and *Ophioglossum* demonstrate considerable intraspecies instability, whereas *Pteris* and *Adiantum* have many chromosome numbers among nuclei of the same root tip and, in *Pteris,* among sporocytes also.

Similar intraplant somatic instability has been found in angiosperms as well as cryptogams. In a population of plants derived from an intergeneric hybrid, *Agroelymus turneri* (2n = 28) (a natural hybrid of *Elymus inovatus* and a species of *Agropyron,* probably *A. dasystachyum*), chromosome numbers varied among root tip cells of each of a few selected plants (Nielsen and Nath, 1961). Numbers ranged from 2n = 4 to 80. Somewhat similar instability within single individuals has been reported in such plants as a cultivated variety of apple, a cultivated variety of *Rubus,* an *Aegilops* and *Triticum* hybrid, as well as "natural" plants of *Epilobium, Dioscorea,* and *Crinum.* In *Claytonia virginica,* chromosome numbers vary within plants and among plants from 2n = 12 to 190 in their natural habitats as well as those grown in New York City (Rothwell, 1959; Rothwell and Kump, 1965). Another interesting example was reported in plants of *Haplopappus gracilis* (2n = 4). Lima-de-Faria and Jaworska (1964) reported two plant *mosaics* that have some normally diploid somatic cells but others (77.4% in one plant and 1.5% in the other) haploid, with only two chromosomes. The plants were phenotypically normal.

Another extreme case in addition to *Claytonia virginica* is chromosomal instability in the grass *Poa pratensis.* Essentially, all 2n chromosome numbers from 2n = 28 to 2n = 142 have been reported. There does not seem to be instability within plants, however, and the variability within the species is permitted by both the polyploid condition and partial apomixis. Such partial apomixis and partial sexuality within a species and, in *P. pratensis,* within a single plant is called *facultative apomixis*. Instability in *P. pratensis* results from irregularities at meiosis in sexual reproduction, but because of polyploidy, aneuploid plants are often viable and can be perpetuated asexually by apomixis.

The cause or causes of intraplant chromosomal instability are unknown. It is so irregular that it is not comparable to the regularity of somatic nondisjunction of supernumerary chromosomes in some plants and a flatworm or of sex, L, and E chromosomes of various insects of the families Sciaridae and Cecidomyiidae or of sex chromosomes in male and female *Microtus oregoni*. Nondisjunction implies the failure of chromatid separation at anaphase, with both chromosomes passing to one nucleus. Intraplant chromosomal instability is certainly not typical of species but is common enough to be considered as a natural exception to the usual uniformity of species. Whether it plays much part in chromosomal evolution is debatable.

Chromosomal instability is also typical of most cell and tissue cultures, producing haploidy, polyploidy, and considerable aneuploidy among the cells of the culture. It is also common in cancerous growths.

OTHER CHROMOSOME TYPES

L chromosomes

Limited chromosomes, L chromosomes or Ls for short, are found in the dipterous family of Sciaridae, "L" referring to the fact that they are *large* chromosomes *limited* to the germ line of both males and females. They are eliminated during the fifth and sixth cleavage divisions from the nuclei destined to form the somatic tissues. Thus the somatic cells have three pairs of autosomes plus two Xs in the female, but one X in the male. In the germ line there is also usually one pair of L chromosomes (White, 1954).

During some mitotic division in the germ line of the male one of the L chromosomes is eliminated. Later one of the two sex chromosomes derived from the male parent is also eliminated. At anaphase I in the spermatocytes there is a unipolar spindle on which the maternal X chromosome, the remaining L chromosomes, and the autosomes derived from the maternal parent pass to the single pole. The X chromosome and the autosomes derived from the paternal parent are eliminated by moving away from the pole (a *very* unusual type of movement). The nucleus that forms at the pole divides at meiosis II by a typical bipolar spindle. However, the two Xs go to the same pole along with the haploid complement of autosomes and Ls. Only the single nucleus receiving the two Xs forms a sperm.

During oogenesis, meiosis is normal for all chromosomes, autosomes, Xs, and Ls so that the egg contains only the one X derived from its maternal parent. The sperm, as stated, receive two Xs derived from its maternal parent. Zygotes contain three Xs.

In *Sciara coprophila,* Ls may be present singly, in triplicate, or as a pair. The number does not seem to affect the phenotype and during some mitotic divisions and meiosis I they are heteropyknotic. Some species seem to have lost these inert heterochromatic chromosomes entirely. Although Ls have many characteristics of supernumerary chromosomes, because of their constancy in species having them and their large size they are not classified as supernumeraries.

S and E chromosomes

S and E chromosomes have been used to designate two types of chromosomes present in flies of the family of gall midges, the Cecidomyiidae, such as the genus *Miastor*. In this family, like the Sciaridae, the somatic cells have fewer chromosomes than are present in the germ line. The female *Miastor* has twelve chromosomes in somatic cells but forty-eight in the germ line. The male has six somatic chromosomes but, like the female, forty-eight in its germ line cells. Presumably, during cleavage the embryos eliminate during one or more mitotic divisions thirty-six chromosomes by the female and forty-two by the male. The chromosomes present in *both* soma *and* germ line have been designated S chromosomes and those eliminated from the somatic cells, E chromosomes.

During meiosis I in spermatocytes six S chromosomes pass to one pole, whereas thirty-six Es and six Ss remain on the spindle, forming a nucleus that eventually disintegrates. The nucleus with only the six Ss divides regularly at meiosis II and forms two sperm. During oogenesis the meiotic divisions are probably not regular, since each egg receives forty-two of the forty-eight chromosomes present in the germ line.

Similar chromosomal conditions (except numbers vary) and divisions occur in the other Cecidomyiidae. In all cases the zygote receives all of its E chromosomes from its maternal parent and half of its S chromosomes from each parent. S and E chromosomes of Cecidomyiidae are probably different genetically, and only the S chromosomes are heteropyknotic during interphases of spermatogonia and oogonia. In *Wachtliella persicariae* (Geyer-Duszynska, 1966) the somatic cells have 2n = 8 in the female, but 2n = 6 in the male. The germ line cells of both have about forty chromosomes. At the fourth cleavage division there is elimination of over thirty E chromosomes from the somatic nuclei, a process controlled by some stainable, extranuclear "pole plasm." Males or females having only six or eight chromosomes in the germ plasm develop normally, except that meiocytes during the pupal stage fail to form functional gametes.

S and E chromosomes have also been reported in the subfamily Orthocladiinae of the dipterous family Chironomidae. The extra chromosomes are eliminated during mitotic divisions of the early cleavage except in the germ line. In both oogonia and spermatogonia one set of Es is eliminated but is followed by irregular division so that one nucleus receives only the two sets of Ss, whereas the other nucleus receives two sets of both Ss and Es. The former become nurse cells or aberrant spermatocytes. All functional meiocytes have two sets of Ss and Es; meiosis and fertilization are regular.

m chromosomes

The m chromosomes are found in mosses and liverworts and some insects (Al-Aish and Anderson, 1960; Anderson and Al-Aish, 1963). Although they are called m chromosomes in both cases, it is doubtful that they are similar except for size. The m is a contraction for minute, which they certainly are, being only about 0.5 μm or less in diameter during meiosis. They do not occur in all species of bryophytes but have been seen in a few hundred species in nearly all groups and many genera (Fig. 16-21). They have been seen only occasionally during mitosis but are assumed to be present,

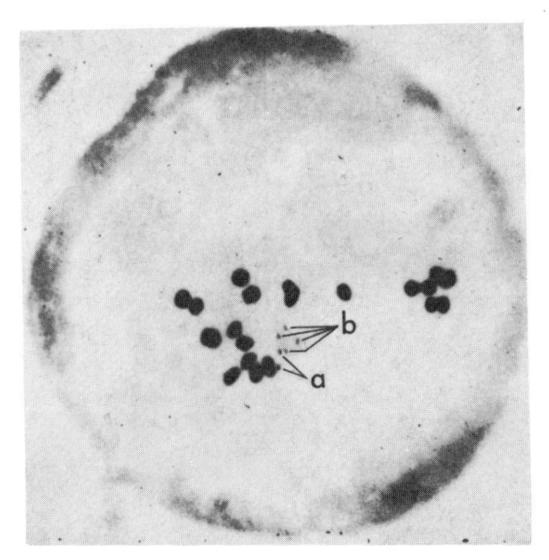

Fig. 16-21. Metaphase I in the moss *Sphagnum*. This photomicrograph is interpreted by the author as showing nineteen large bivalents and two tiny m chromosomes. Apparently, one of the m chromosomes consists of univalents, **a,** whereas the second m chromosome is a "quadripartite structure," **b.** It is clear, however, that m chromosomes occur and that they are very small. (From Bryan, V. S. 1955. Bryologist **58:**16-39.)

since for any particular species they seem to be constant in number, ranging from one to four or five, but usually there is one or two.

During meiosis, the behavior of m chromosomes is variable and unusual compared to the typical bryophyte chromosomes. They are known to contain DNA but stain lightly. Synapsis, or pairing at least, seems to occur, but they apparently separate precociously by metaphase I into two univalents or even a quadripartite assembly (Fig. 16-21). When the latter occurs, they form an open rectangle with faint connections between the adjacent chromatids. All m chromosomes in a sporocyte do not behave the same. If, for example, there are two m chromosomes in one sporocyte, one may separate into two univalents (or bivalents) at metaphase, whereas the other may compose a square of four interconnected chromatids. Therefore at anaphase I there may be three in each anaphase group. By anaphase II their distribution is evidently normal—one chromosome of each prophase I tetrad is distributed to each of the four spores.

Present evidence indicates that m chromosomes of bryophytes are not supernumerary chromosomes because of their constancy, nor are they sex chromosomes, since they are present in species having hermaphroditic gametophytes. If there are any genetic differences from the typical chromosomes, it is unknown at this time. It is assumed that they are regular, characteristic, but exceptional members of the chromosome set of the species possessing them.

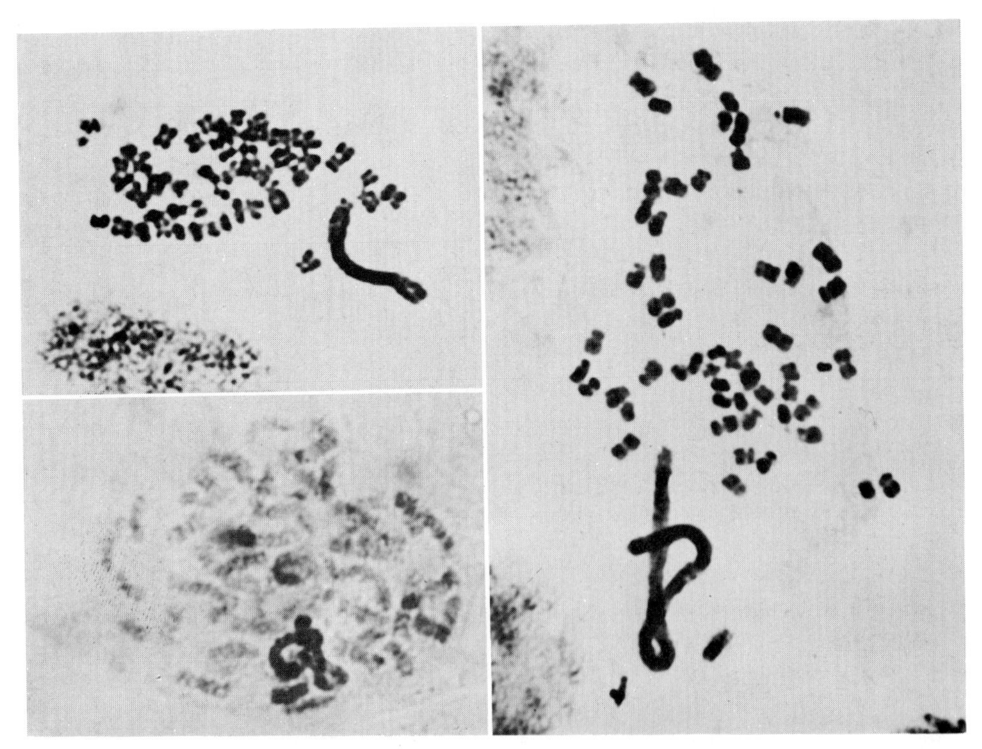

Fig. 16-22. Photomicrographs of megachromosomes and normal chromosomes at metaphase in derivatives of an interspecific *Nicotiana* hybrid. Two are at metaphase, and the third is at late prophase showing the heterochromatic character of this unusual chromosome type. (From Gerstel, D. U., and J. A. Burns. 1966. Chromosomes of unusual length in hybrids between two species of *Nicotiana*. In C. D. Darlington and K. R. Lewis [editors]. Chromosomes today, Plenum Press, Inc., New York.)

Some heteropterous insects of the family Coreidae, which have the XO scheme of sex determination, possess a pair of tiny m chromosomes. Unlike those of the bryophytes, they seem to behave rather typically during meiosis, although they apparently pair at prometaphase rather than earlier.

Megachromosomes

Megachromosomes have been reported in only a few species or hybrids and then in only a small minority of cells, for example, of certain plant hybrids of *Nicotiana tabacum* and *N. octophora* (Gerstel and Burns, 1966, 1967). Since these same plants also showed various examples of chromosomal fragmentation, it is assumed that there is a causal relationship between fragmentation and the presence of a block of heterochromatin from *N. octophora.* It was found that megachromosomes appeared in consecutive generations of certain lines, although they are not passed on as such by gametes. It was concluded that the ability to produce them is heritable. Megachromosomes occur only in plants possessing one or two other "abnormal" chromosomes that are characterized by large heterochromatic segments and satellites. Comparison indicated the likelihood that megachromosomes are greatly elongated in the long heterochromatic arm (Fig. 16-22). Generally there is only one megachromosome per cell, but two have been seen, and up to seven fragments have been seen in one nucleus. Actually, they are uncommon even in these plants, only about one cell in ninety-five had a megachromosome. The total number of chromosomes in a set containing one or more megachromosomes sometimes varied slightly above or below the number present in "normal" cells of the plant, and often so-called fragment chromosomes were present also. However, in such *Nicotiana* hybrids some chromosome instability of numbers and fragmentation is typical. The instability was also revealed by color variegation in the corolla.

These megachromosomes (Fig. 16-22) range up to fifteen times the length of normal chromosomes. There is considerable variation among them other than length. They may be dicentric, rings, or acentric. They seem to be largely heterochromatic and can be seen during prophase and anaphase. They are probably not passed on to daughter cells; that is, they form completely during one interphase and are not built up gradually during a number of divisions. At present there are only guesses as to how they are formed.

LITERATURE CITED

Al-Aish, M., and L. E. Anderson. 1960. Chromosome numbers of some Arizona mosses. Bryologist **63:**17-25.

Allen, C. E. 1935. The genetics of bryophytes. Bot. Rev. **1:**269-291.

Allen, C. E. 1940. The genotypic basis of sex-expression in angiosperms. Bot. Rev. **6:**227-299.

Allen, C. E. 1945. II. The genetics of bryophytes. Bot. Rev. **11:**260-287.

Anderson, E. 1954. Introgression; a series of papers on. Ann. Missouri Bot. Gard. **41:**305-327.

Anderson, L. E., and M. Al-Aish. 1963. Chromosome numbers of some mosses from North America. Bryologist **66:**165-178.

Babcock, E. B. 1947. The genus Crepis. I. The taxonomy, phylogeny, distribution, and evolution of Crepis. University of California Press, Berkeley, Calif.

Babcock, E. B. 1949. Supplementary notes on Crepis. II. Phylogeny, distribution, and Matthew's principle. Evolution **3:**374-376.

Bailey, P. C. 1952. Differential reactivity in six species of Trillium. Bull. Torrey Bot. Club **79:**451-458.

Battaglia, E. 1964. Cytogenetics of B-chromosomes. Caryologia **17:**245-299.

Behre, O. 1929. Physiologische und zytologische Untersuchungen über Drosera. Planta **7:**208-306.

Blakeslee, A. F. 1921. The "Globe," a simple trisomic mutant in Datura. Proc. Nat. Acad. Sci. U.S.A. **7:**148-152.

Blakeslee, A. F. 1934. New jimson weeds from old chromosomes. J. Hered. **25:**80-108.

Braselton, J. P. 1971. The ultrastructure of the non-localized kinetochore of Luzula and Cyperus. Chromosoma **36:**89-99.

Brink, R. A. 1960. Paramutation and chromosome organization. Quart. Rev. Biol. **35:**120-137.

Brinkley, B. R., and E. Stubblefield. 1970. Ultrastructure and interaction of the kinetochore and centriole in mitosis and meiosis. Adv. Cell Biol. **1:**119-186.

Brown, W. V. 1960. Supernumerary chromosomes in a population of Tradescantia edwardsiana. Southwest. Nat. **5:**49-60.

Bryan, V. S. 1955. Chromosome studies in the genus Sphagnum. Bryologist **58:**16-39.

Buck, R. C. 1967. Mitosis and meiosis in Rhodnius prolixus: the fine structure of the spindle and diffuse kinetochore. J. Ultrastruct. Res. **18:** 489-501.

Callan, H. G. 1942. Heterochromatin in Triton. Proc. Roy. Sci. [Biol.] **130:**324-335.

Cleveland, L. R. 1947. The origin and evolution of meiosis. Science **105:**287-289.

Coleman, L. C. 1941. The relation of chromocenters to the differential segments in Rhoeo discolor Hance. Amer. J. Bot. **28:**742-748.

Comings, D. E., and T. A. Okada. 1972. Holocentric chromosomes in Oncopeltus: kinetochore plates are present in mitosis but absent in meiosis. Chromosoma **37:**177-192.

Craig-Holmes, A. P., and M. W. Shaw. 1971. Polymorphism of human constitutive heterochromatin. Science **174:**702-704.

Crosby, A. R. 1957. Nucleolar activity of lagging chromosomes in wheat. Amer. J. Bot. **44:**813-822.

Darlington, C. D. 1937. Recent advances in cytology. Churchill, Ltd., London.

Darlington, C. D. 1942. Chromosome chemistry and gene action. Nature (London) **149:**66-69.

Darlington, C. D. 1956. Chromosome botany. George Allen & Unwin, London.

Darlington, C. D., and L. LaCour. 1940. Nucleic acid starvation of chromosomes of Trillium. J. Genet. **40:**185-213.

Darlington, C. D., and K. R. Lewis (editors). 1966. Chromosomes today. Plenum Press, Inc., New York.

Dodge, J. D. 1964. Nuclear division in the dinoflagellate Gonyaulax tamarensis. J. Gen. Microbiol. **36:**269-276.

Feldman, M. 1966. The effect of chromosomes 5B, 5D, and 5A on chromosomal pairing in Triticum aestivum. Proc. Nat. Acad. Sci. U.S.A. **55:**1447-1453.

Fernandes, A. 1943. Sur l'origine des chromosomes surnumeraries heterochromatique chez Narcissus bulbocodium. L. Bol. Soc. Brot. **17**(2):251-266.

Geitler, L. 1938. Chromosomenbau. Borntraeger. Berlin.

Gerstel, D. U., and J. A. Burns. 1966. Chromosomes of unusual length in hybrids between two species of Nicotiana. In C. D. Darlington and K. R. Lewis (editors). Chromosomes today. Plenum Press, Inc., New York.

Gerstel, D. U., and J. A. Burns. 1967. Phenotypic and chromosomal abnormalities associated with the introduction of heterochromatin from Nicotiana octophora into N. tabacum. Genetics **56:**483-502.

Geyer-Duszynska, J. 1966. Genetic factors in oogenesis and spermatogenesis in Cecidomyiidae. In C. D. Darlington and K. R. Lewis (editors). Chromosomes today. Plenum Press, Inc., New York.

Gillis, A., and L. F. Randolph. 1951. Reduction of quadrivalent frequency in autotetraploid maize during a period of 10 years. Amer. J. Bot. **38:**12-17.

Hair, J. B. 1962. Basic chromosome numbers in Cotula. Chromosome Information Service, Publication No. 3, p. 41.

Heitz, E. 1942. Uber mutative Intersexualität und Sexualität und Geschlechtsumwandlung bei den Lebermoosen Pellia neesiana und Sphaerocarpus donnellii Naturwissenschaften **30:**751-773.

Hsu, T. C., W. Schmid, and E. Stubblefield. 1964. In M. Locke (editor). The role of chromosomes in development. Academic Press, Inc., New York.

Huberman, J. A., and G. Attardi. 1966. Isolation of metaphase chromosomes from HeLa cells. J. Cell Biol. **31:**95-105.

Hyde, B. B. 1953. Differentiated chromosomes in Plantago ovata. Amer. J. Bot. **40:**809-815.

Jackson, R. C. 1957. New low chromosome number for plants. Science **126:**1115-1116.

Jackson, R. C. 1965. A cytogenetic study of a three-paired race of Haplopappus gracilis. Amer. J. Bot. **52:**946-953.

Jackson, R. C., and P. Newmark. 1960. Effects of supernumerary chromosomes on production of pigment in Haplopappus gracilis. Science **132:** 316.

Jain, H. K. 1966. Correlated synthetic activities of chromosomes. In C. D. Darlington and K. R. Lewis (editors). Chromosomes today. Plenum Press, Inc., New York.

Japha, G. 1939. II. Die Meiosis von Oenothera. Z. Bot. **34:**321-369.

Jones, K. L. 1943. Studies on Ambrosia. III. Pistillate Ambrosia elatior × A. trifida and its bearing on matroclinic sex inheritance. Bot. Gaz. **105:**226-232.

Kubai, D. F., and H. Ris. 1969. Division in the dinoflagellate Gyrodinium cohnii (Schiller): a new type of nuclear reproduction. J. Cell Biol. **40:**508-528.

Lesley, M. M., and H. B. Frost. 1927. Mendelian inheritance of chromosome shape in Matthiola. Genetics **12:**449-460.

Lima-de-Faria, A., and H. Jaworska. 1964. Haplo-diploid chimaeras in Haplopappus gracilis. Hereditas **52:**119-122.

Lin, M. 1955. Chromosomal control of nuclear composition in maize. Chromosoma **7:**340-370.

Lobeer, G. 1961. Struktur und Inhalt der Geschlechtschromosomen. Ber. Dtsch. Bot. Ges. **59:**369-375.

Longwell, A. C., and G. Svihla, 1960. Specific chromosomal control of the nucleolus and the cytoplasm in wheat. Exp. Cell Res. **20:**294-312.

Makino, S. 1951. An atlas of the chromosome numbers in animals. Iowa State University Press, Ames, Iowa.

Malheiros, N., and D. de Castro. 1947. Chromosome numbers and behavior in Luzula purpurea Link. Nature (London) **160:**156.

Manton, I. 1950. The spiral structure of chromosomes. Biol. Rev. **25:**486-508.

Marks, G. E. 1957. Telocentric chromosomes. Amer. Nat. **91:**223-232.

McClintock, B. 1933. The association of non-homologous parts of chromosomes in the mid-prophase of meiosis in Zea mays. Z. Zellforsch. **19:**191-237.

McClintock, B. 1945. Neurospora. I. Preliminary observations of the chromosomes of Neurospora crassa. Amer. J. Bot. **32:**671-678.

Miller, D. A., and O. J. Miller. 1972. Chromosome mapping in the mouse. Science **178:**949-955.

Mittwoch, U. 1967. Sex chromosomes. Academic Press, Inc., New York.

Moss, J. P. 1966. The adaptive significance of B-chromosomes in rye. In C. D. Darlington and K. R. Lewis (editors). Chromosomes today. Plenum Press, Inc., New York.

Muntzing, A. 1966. Some recent data on accessory chromosomes in Secale and Poa. In C. D. Darlington and K. R. Lewis (editors). Chromosomes today. Plenum Press, Inc., New York.

Navashin, M. S. 1932. The dislocation hypothesis of evolution of chromosome numbers. Z. Ind. Abst. Vererb. **63:**224-231.

Nielsen, E. L., and J. Nath. 1961. Somatic instability in derivatives from Agroelymus turneri resembling Agropyron repens. Amer. J. Bot. **48:**345-349.

Nordenskiold, H. 1951. I. Cyto-taxonomical studies in the genus Luzula. Hereditas **37:** 325-355.

Ostergren, G. 1947. Heterochromatic B-chromosomes in Anthoxanthum. Hereditas **33:**261-296.

Plaut, W. S. 1953. The effect of B-chromosomes on the variegated pericarp phenotype in maize. Amer. J. Bot. **40:**344-348.

Raghunath, T. 1967. Behavior of the diploid nucleus in germinating teliospores of Tolyposporium christensenii. Bull. Torrey Bot. Club **94:**191-193.

Randolph, L. F. 1928. Types of supernumerary chromosomes in maize. Anat. Rec. **41:**102.

Rattenbury, J. A., and J. A. Serra. 1952. Types of nucleolus reconstruction in telophase and the question of the "nucleolar organizer." Port. Acta Biol. ser. A **3:**239-260.

Rhoades, M. M., and H. Vilkomerson. 1942. On anaphase movement of chromosomes. Proc. Nat. Acad. Sci. U.S.A. **28:**433-436.

Riley, R., J. Unrau, and V. Chapman. 1958. Evidence on the origin of the B genome of wheat. J. Hered. **49:**91-98.

Ritossa, F. M., and S. Spiegelman. 1965. Localization of DNA complementary to ribosomal RNA in the nucleolus organizer region of Drosophila melanogaster. Proc. Nat. Acad. Sci. U.S.A. **53:** 737-745.

Roman, H. 1947. Mitotic nondisjunction in the case of interchanges involving the B-type chromosome in maize. Genetics **32:**391-409.

Roman, H. 1948. Directed fertilization in maize. Proc. Nat. Acad. Sci. U.S.A. **34:**36-42.

Rothfels, K., and M. Heimburger. 1968. Chromosome size and DNA values in sundews (Droseraceae). Chromosoma **25:**96-103.

Rothfels, K., E. Sexsmith, M. Heimburger, and M. Krause. 1966. Chromosome size and DNA content of species of Anemone L. and related genera (Ranunculaceae). Chromosoma **20:**54-74.

Rothwell, N. V. 1959. Aneuploidy in Claytonia virginica. Amer. J. Bot. **46:**353-360.

Rothwell, N. V., and J. G. Kump. 1965. Chromosome numbers in populations of Claytonia virginica from the New York metropolitan area. Amer. J. Bot. **52:**403-407.

Rutishauser, A., and E. Rothlisberger. 1966. Boosting mechanism of B-chromosomes in Crepis capillaris. In C. D. Darlington and K. R. Lewis (editors). Chromosomes today. Plenum Press, Inc., New York.

Schrader, F. 1953. Mitosis. Columbia University Press, New York.

Sears, E. 1954. The aneuploids of common wheat. Univ. Missouri Agric. Expt. Station Res. Bull. 572.

Smith, F. H. 1933. The relation of the satellites

to the nucleolus in Galtonia candicans. Amer. J. Bot. **20:**188-195.

Sparrow, A. H., H. J. Price, and A. G. Underbrink. 1972. A survey of DNA content per cell and per chromosome of prokaryotic and eukaryotic organisms: some evolutionary considerations. Brookhaven Symp. Biol. **23:**451-494.

Stack, S. M. 1971. Premeiotic changes in Ornithogalum virens. Bull. Torrey Bot. Club **98:**207-214.

Stebbins, G. L., and A. Day. 1967. Cytogenetic evidence for long continued stability in the genus Plantago. Evolution **21:**409-428.

Tjio, J. H., and A. Levan. 1950. Quadruple structure of the centromere. Nature (London) **165:** 368.

Tobgy, H. A. 1943. A cytological study of Crepis fuliginosa, C. neglecta, and their F_1 hybrid, and its bearing on the mechanism of phylogenetic reduction in chromosome number. J. Genet. **45:**67-111.

Ullerich, F. H. 1966. Karyotyp und DNS- Gehalt von Bufo bufo, B. viridis, B. bufo × B. viridis, und B. calamita. Chromosoma **18:**316-324.

Valencia, J. I., and R. F. Grell (editors). 1965. International symposium on genes and chromosomes: structure and function. Government Printing Office, Washington, D. C.

Vosa, C. G. 1966. Seed germination and B-chromosomes in the leek (Allium porrum). In C. D. Darlington and K. R. Lewis (editors). Chromosomes today. Plenum Press, Inc., New York.

Walters, M. S. 1950. Spontaneous breakage and reunion of meiotic chromosomes in the hybrid Bromus trinii × B. maritimus. Genetics **35:**11-37.

Warmke, H. E. 1946. Sex determination and sex balance in Melandrium. Amer. J. Bot. **33:**640-660.

White, M. J. D. 1950. The chromosomes. Methuen & Co., London.

White, M. J. D. 1954. Animal cytology and evolution. Cambridge University Press, New York.

Woodard, T. M. 1948. Difference in form and reaction to cold in root-tip and apical bud chromosomes of Mediola. Bull. Torrey Bot. Club **75:**250-255.

CHAPTER 17

Mitosis and its variations

Division is one of the ubiquitous characteristics of life. It must have been characteristic even of the hypothetical Eobiont, the first living organism on earth. Subsequent evolution among the numerous lines of descent has entailed a variety of processes and structures, all of which separate groups of genes into daughter cells. The fundamental requirement and usual accomplishment are some mechanism and action for providing each daughter cell with an exact copy of the genome present in the original cell. That is the genetic result of division in Prokaryota and most divisions in the Eukaryota.

At the cytological level of division the mechanism and sequence of events that accomplish the genetic result in the Prokaryota are unknown (Brown, 1972) (Fig. 4-7). Somehow, the probably naked, deoxyribonucleic acid, circular, daughter genophores that resulted from replication are spatially separated. The separation of one rather formless prokaryon into two appears to be casual, involving gradual irregular lengthening, gradual attenuation near the center, and finally separation into two polymorphic daughter prokaryons. The protoplasts are separated by a plasma membrane and wall that form a circular ingrowing furrow. According to the general cytological concept of mitotic division, this is not mitosis in any sense.

On the other hand, on the basis of the generally accepted scheme of mitosis, neither are the two divisions of meiosis in sexual Eukaryota mitotic divisions. The first division does not produce two daughter cells that are genetically equal to each other and to the mother cell. The second division is similar to a mitotic division, except that it is not preceded by DNA replication and the daughter cells are again not genetically equal.

Cellular divisions other than meiosis in the Eukaryota are considered to be mitotic, and except for unusual modifications that are often unique to a species, genus, tribe, family, or order, they do produce genetically equal daughter cells whether at the diploid or haploid level. But mitosis is a describably cellular process associated with observable structures; it is not a genetic result. It is increasingly evident that some of the mechanisms and procedures by which the genetic result is achieved by various eukaryotic cells are so different from the accepted model of mitosis that the term does not apply or the scheme is much too restrictive to include them. Even if the cytological scheme of mitosis is broadened considerably, a superhuman intellectual tour de force could not accommodate in one model the divisions, for example, of termite-inhabiting flagellates (Cleveland, 1953), of yeast cells (Robinow and Marak, 1966), and probably of many other fungi, of some dinoflagellates (Leadbeater and Dodge, 1967; Kubai and Ris, 1969), and of premeiotic divisions, described by Battaglia (1947) as "heterotypic," in at least many higher plants and animals (Smith, 1942).

In spite of the inadequacy of the term "mitosis" to cover all of these very different forms of division meaningfully, most will be discussed to a limited extent in this chapter.

Mitosis, as the term was originally used and as used by Schrader as late as 1953, referred to all cellular divisions. The first meiotic division was called the first meiotic mitosis, or *heterotypic mitosis*. The second meiotic division was designated the second meiotic mitosis, or *homeotypic mitosis*. However, common usage now restricts mitosis to somatic division of eukaryotic cells. But even with this limited definition there are exceptions to most of the generally accepted details of the process among the vast array of evolving plant, animal, and fungal species and among the organs, tissues, and cells of the various developmental stages of those species. Furthermore, modern biology is still unable to comprehend the cause or modus operandi of any of the various phenomena that together constitute the process in cells of higher plants and animals such as chromosomal movements, disappearance of the nucleolus, breakdown of the nuclear envelop, formation and significance of the achromatic figure (asters, centers, and spindle), etc. Schrader discusses the process with rigorous evaluations of hypotheses as of 1953. Mazia's discussion (1961) and different emphasis adds newly observed facts but demonstrates how little new understanding of the fundamental processes was achieved in the eight intervening years. Luykx (1970) has recently reviewed the subject with novel hypotheses.

As probably every college freshman knows, the mitotic event (Fig. 17-1) can be arbitrarily divided into four or five sequential phases. At the end of interphase the chromosomes begin to "appear" as they shorten and thicken, thereby marking the beginning of *prophase*. During *prometaphase,* also called "late prophase," the spindle forms, the nucleolus and nuclear envelop disappear, and the chromosomes move to the metaphase plate. *Metaphase* is characterized by the fact that the double chromosomes (each of two chromatids attached at the centromere) are in such a position that all centromeres lie in the spindle and on the metaphase plane; the latter is equidistant from the poles and perpendicular to the spindle axis drawn through the two poles. *Anaphase* begins when the centromeres divide and start to move toward opposite poles. This poleward movement, with each anaphase chromosome led by the centromere, characterizes anaphase. When movement ceases, *telophase* begins, a phase in which the reverse of prophase and prometaphase takes place. The chromosomes elongate and eventually disappear, the new nuclear envelope and nucleolus are formed, and the spindle and asters break down. In animals there are *centers* that lie just outside the nucleus and move to the poles during prophase as they produce the asters and some of the spindle. They mark the spindle poles and remain just outside the daughter nuclei after telophase. During telophase the cytoplasm is separated, and *cytokinesis* occurs (by furrowing in animals and by cell plate formation in plants). That, in brief, is what can be observed superficially to take place in most higher plants and animals and in that sequence. At least that much of mitosis had been worked out during the 1870s, almost 100 years ago, by a number of European cytologists.

If an attempt is made to define the term "mitosis" in higher organisms rather than describing it, difficulties are encountered, and it becomes evident that a wide variety of exceptions occur among organisms.

If one is satisfied with a genetic definition —that mitosis is any process which produces two genetically identical daughter cells, each

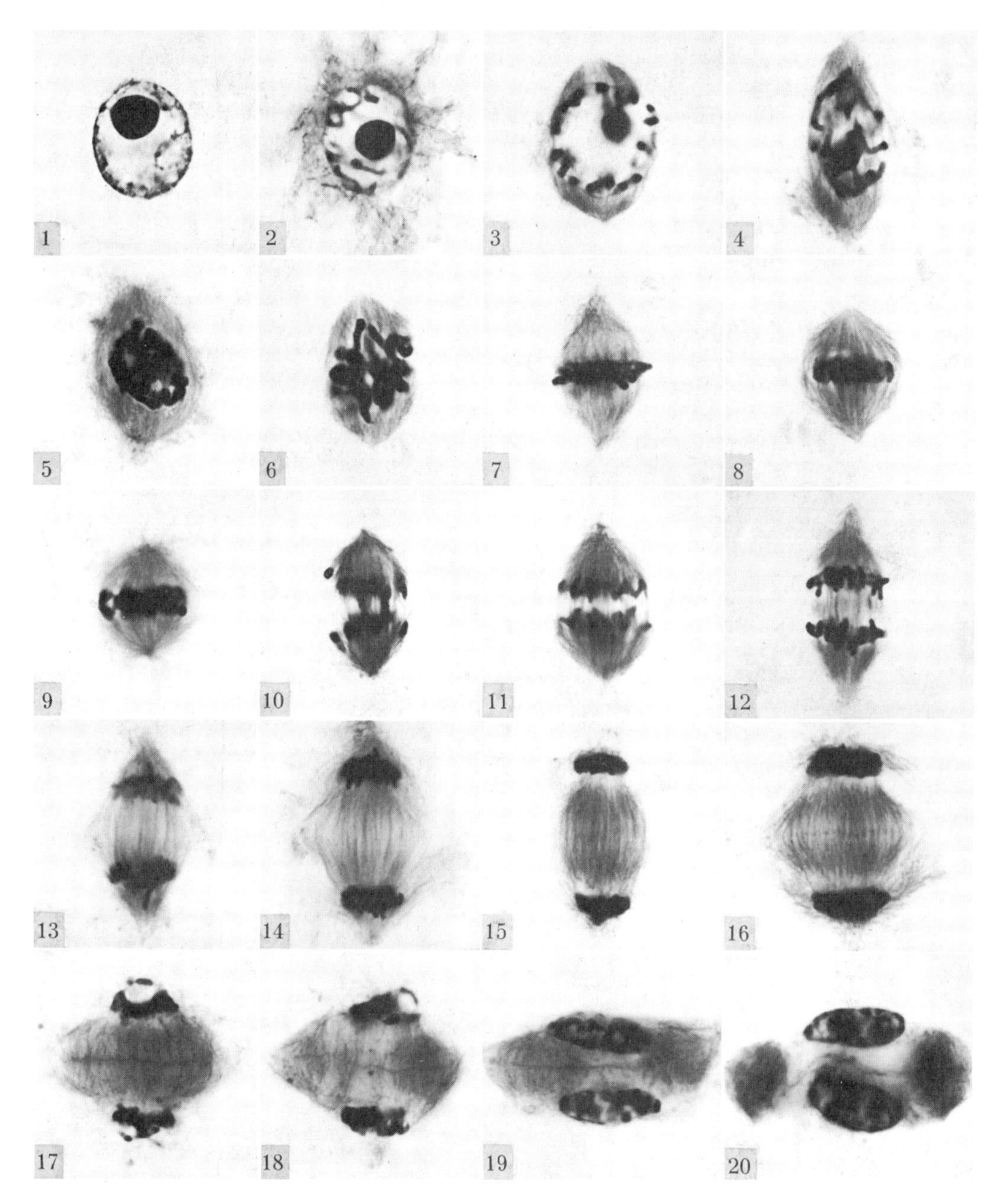

Fig. 17-1. Mitosis in maize endosperm. These divisions occurred in the late "plasmodial" stage of endosperm development and were isolated as whole spindles. **1,** Interphase. **2,** Early prophase with adhering, radially oriented fibrous material that is probably the beginning of extranuclear spindle fiber formation. **3,** Prophase with "polar caps," early spindle formation. In **1** to **3** notice that chromatin is mostly just inside or against the nuclear envelope. **4,** Prometaphase shortly after nuclear membrane breakdown. **5** and **6,** Prometaphase chromosome movement. **7,** Metaphase. **8** to **14,** Progress of anaphase showing progressive development and buildup of the phragmoplast (interzonal fibers). **15** to **20,** Progressive stages of telophase, especially of the phragmoplast and cell plate. **18** to **20,** Centrifugal formation of a ring of new fibers moving outward and extending the cell plate is demonstrated. These illustrations seem to support the contention of Esau and Gill (1965) that the phragmoplast is as much a distinct cell structure as the spindle and is distinct from the spindle. (From Duncan, R. E., and M. D. Persidsky. 1958. Amer. J. Bot. **45:**719-729.)

of which is genetically identical to the original cell—then all organisms, Prokaryota and Eukaryota, have mitosis. But that statement describes the genetic result only, and mitosis is a cytological process of structures. A definition of mitosis, if one is possible, must be in terms of structural changes (Sharp, 1934; Wilson, 1937; Levine, 1963).

It is well known that cytokinesis does not always follow karyokinesis immediately and that cytokinesis often occurs long after nuclear divisions, not at all, or even before nuclear division in the budding of yeasts. In many organisms, nucleoli do not disappear but divide along with the chromosomes. The same is true of the nuclear envelope; in many lower organisms the nuclear envelope remains intact, and thus the term "intranuclear division" is applied. There is now some evidence that at least in certain dinoflagellates the chromosomes do not condense during "prophase" because they are always condensed, even during interphase. In yeast there does not seem to be any chromosomal condensation at all, and the nucleolar material seems to consist of a large number of "fragments," which are divided more or less equally to the two daughter nuclei. It has been claimed that some dinoflagellates do not have a spindle. It is also evident that many fungi of the Ascomycetes and Basidiomycetes either do not have a spindle (yeast) or have an atypical "spindle" *(Neurospora, Coleosporium).* These same fungi do not have a metaphase plate, and anaphase may involve two sets of attached chromatids that may move past each other in opposite directions *on* a narrow, centrally located atypical "spindle." Of course, higher plants and perhaps some fungi do not have centrioles or asters as part of the mitotic process. Finally, the Prokaryota do not have any of these structures; even the string of genes (the genophore) is not a true chromosome.

It seems that a number of mechanisms have evolved, all of which are capable of achieving the same *genetic* result. Since the tendency in cytology is not to give distinct terms to all of the various modifications that have evolved, for example, to keep the cell concept in spite of plasmodia, syncytia, etc., it seems best to define mitosis as it occurs in higher plants and animals but to recognize that many variations exist. It does seem advisable to exclude the meiotic divisions, the divisions of the Prokaryota, and any proved cases of amitosis. It is still difficult, however, to include the division of yeasts as an example of mitosis, since few of the characteristic events occur.

Preparation for division

Mazia (1961) has subdivided the total division process differently from usual, considering the *interphase* as an essential part of the overall cellular activity called *cell division.* He treated interphase and prophase as a continuous period of *preparation for metakinesis;* anaphase and telophase he considered to blend into early interphase as the period of *division.* Metakinesis he defined as the movement of chromosomes into their metaphase positions.

During the period of preparation, the cell must replicate DNA and histone during the S period (as already discussed in Chapter 15) and synthesize the molecules for the achromatic figure, now known to consist of at least proteins, for the rapid construction of many microtubules that at anaphase may constitute 11% of the total protein of the cell. Also synthesized at that period are other cytoplasmic and nuclear compounds such as other proteins, RNAs, membrane precursor molecules, as well as an energy reservoir for the subsequent activities of movement and division. The simultaneous or wavelike progression of nuclear divisions in many plasmodia (as, for example, arthropod embryos, free nuclear endosperm of many angiosperms, and lactifers of some plants [Mahlberg and Sabharwal, 1967]), in many zygotes, and in binuclear cells produced by cell hybridization demonstrates that mitosis is a cellular process and not restricted to the nucleus.

Another aspect of the preparation period of mitosis, as discussed by Mazia, is cellular growth. Normally, a late telophase daughter cell, a product of one mitotic division, approximately doubles its volume before it divides again. This is true of cells of mitotically active mature tissues such as meristematic regions of vascular plants, of most Protista, and mitotically active tissues of adult Metazoa. It is *not* true, however, of all cells; exceptions are numerous. The cleavage and early embryonic divisions through the gastrula stage of essentially all multicellular animals are rapid, and little or no cellular growth occurs; the cells get smaller and smaller. There is little or no growth between the two meiotic divisions in animals and a few plants; telophase I often passes directly into prophase II. Among the diatoms there can be no growth, since each generation lives within a nonextensible glass wall of the previous generation. In fact, half of the population gets smaller each generation. When a cell of one of the Protista or an antheridial cell of a land plant divides into a large number of small gametes or spores (such as zoospores), there is no growth between nuclear divisions. In the largest of known plant cells, the green alga *Acetabularia,* there is only one nucleus during the growth period; but when growth is completed, that nucleus somehow produces hundreds of small nuclei, which migrate into the reproductive cysts at the other end of the 5 to 10 cm long cell. Cellular growth, not as a preparation for mitosis, often occurs as an aspect of postmitotic differentiation. Thus cellular growth and mitosis are not necessarily linked.

Just as there can be cell divisions without growth, there can also be nuclear and cytoplasmic divisions without DNA replication. The commonest example is the second meiotic division, which often lacks even the interphase in animals. In plants there is almost always an interphase but no DNA doubling. It has been found that polyploid nuclei (4n and 8n) reverted to the diploid (2n) condition in crown galls of plants. Mouse acites tumor cells treated with 5-fluorouracil divided so that each daughter nucleus had half the DNA present in the parent cell, but the chromosome number remained the same. There is also the classical example of the mosquito gut cells, which in the pupa reduce progressively from 96 to 6 chromosomes in four divisions.

The late preparation stage, which corresponds with prophase, starts with the separation and poleward movement of the centers in animals and algal cells.

Centrioles

Centers consist of specialized tiny structures called *centrioles* surrounded by a distinctive region of protoplasm called the *centrosphere,* the centriole and centrosphere composing the *centrosome* or center (Fig. 17-2). Centers are typical of animal and of algal cells. They are evidently present in fungi, although in slime molds and yeasts perhaps as evolutionary predecessors of true centrioles they are more like nuclear envelope thickenings associated with spindle fiber-like microtubules. Centrioles do not occur in land plants.

The centriole at anaphase is single but often doubles at telophase so that it is prepared for a cellular division at the previous telophase. At early prophase or later the center, which may be already double and which lies just outside the nucleus, "divides" as the two centrioles separate. At that time also each center causes the formation of microtubules, which radiate outward from the center in all directions, the *aster* (Fig. 17-3). The centers with their increasingly long astral fibers continue to move until they lie 180 degrees apart just outside the nuclear envelope and mark the poles of the spindle. Experimental displacement of centers and production of secondary spermatocytes without centrioles (Deitz, 1966) has "proved" that they are not necessary for spindle formation or anaphase movement of chromosomes. Their divisions and movements are merely for their own perpetuation and distribution to daughter cells so that in certain cells they will be available to form cilia or flagella. In early or late prophase there are some microtubules that extend from center to center and later will constitute part of the spindle; these are called

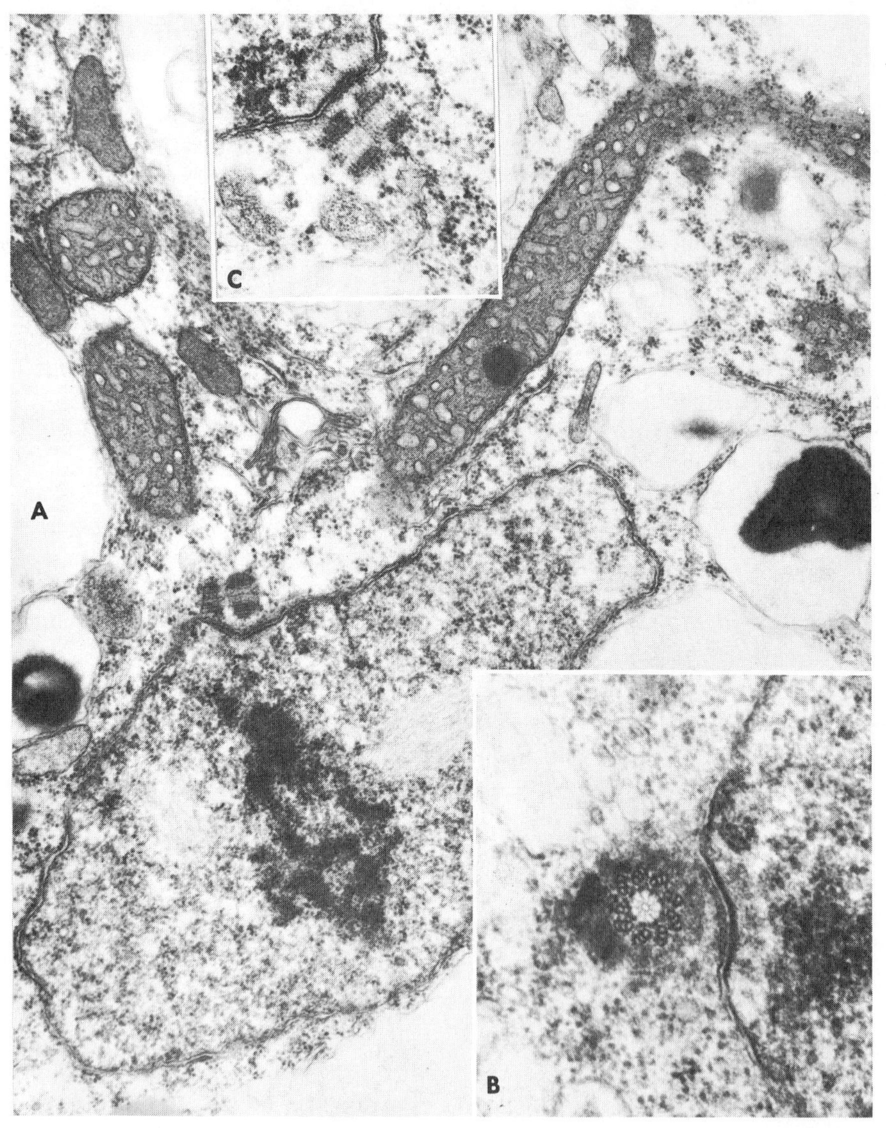

Fig. 17-2. A, Electron micrograph of a cell of the fungus *Achlya* showing tubular cristae typical of many lower organism mitochondria, nucleus, double membrane of the nuclear envelope, ribosomes, dictyosome, and centriole in longitudinal section. **B,** Cross section of a centriole of *Achlya* showing the nine triple fibers and cartwheel center. Nuclear envelope adjacent to centriole is modified inside and outside. **C,** Another longitudinal section of a centriole and modified nuclear envelope. The centriole seems to consist of two parts interrupted at the center. (Courtesy Dr. F. R. Turner, University of Texas Cell Research Institute, Austin, Texas.)

continuous fibers. They may be specifically for cytokinesis or subsequently used in that process (see later). All astral and spindle "fibers" are now known to be temporary microtubules about 200 Å in diameter, which is well below the resolving power of the light microscope. Therefore any light microscope photographs of spindle "fibers" (Fig. 17-3) must be really groups of associated tubules.

As is true of all movement of any protoplasm, the mechanism of motion of centers is unknown. How they "know" when to start, where to go, and when to stop are questions of even greater mystery. Do centers determine the orientation of the spindle and therefore of cellular divisions, or are they "told" where to take up positions? How can a center (perhaps only a centriole) cause microtubules to form at all, but especially in an orderly and organized system? Actually, how do centrioles themselves "reproduce"?

Centriole reproduction. Centriole reproduction has been known for a long time and also that this reproduction is not by "division." It has been described variously as "budding," as one "young" and one "old," as an unequal "division," as "parent" and "infant," and as "new" centrioles "growing from parents or from procentrioles." Obviously, centriole reproduction is not by fission in the manner that cells, mitochondria, and plastids divide. Furthermore, it is now known that centrioles can develop out of procentrioles and that procentrioles can be formed by a cell which completely lacks anything like a centriole, that is, de novo, as in gamete-forming cells of cryptogamic vascular plants (Chapter 19). Actually, many sorts of microtubules, including spindle fibers of dividing cells of land plants,

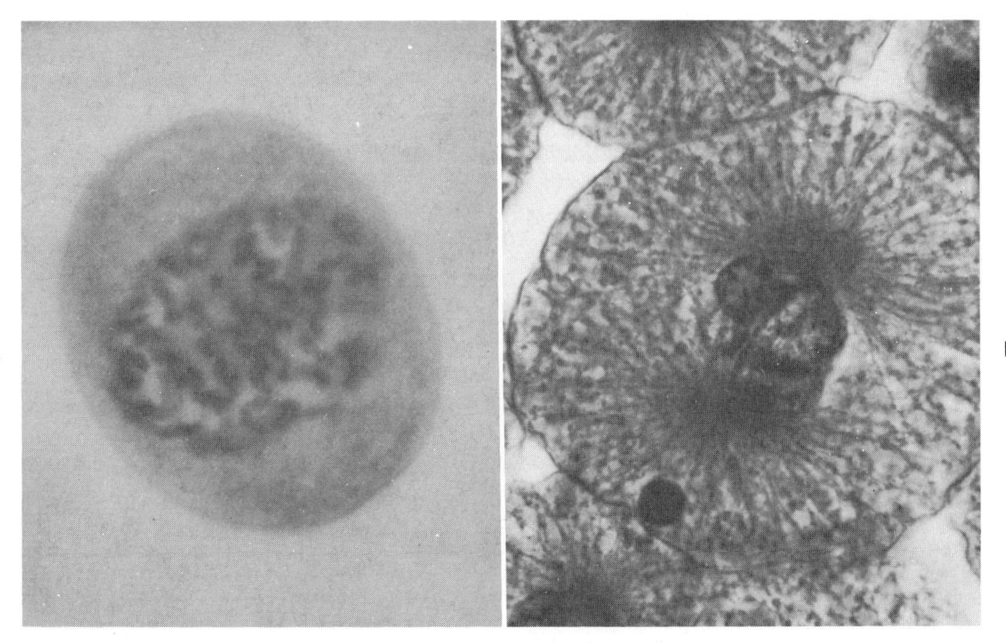

Fig. 17-3. A, Mitotic prophase in a pollen grain division of *Tradescantia.* Convolutions of the six shortening chromosomes are evident. **B,** Prophase of the first cleavage division in a whitefish zygote. The two dark polar centers composed mostly of radiating astral fibers are evident. The two gamete nuclei are still intact but pressed against each other to produce the lobed appearance. Paternal and maternal chromosomes get together at metaphase on the single spindle.

can be produced by cells without centrioles, and even centriolar basal bodies (mostly microtubular in structure) can be formed without preexisting centrioles.

It is also well established now that centrioles and basal bodies are microtubular in structure themselves and can cause the formation of additional microtubules; basal bodies form highly organized systems of microtubules, including the axoneme of cilia, flagella, and sperm tails. Perhaps, then, the most acceptable concept is that microtubules and microtubular structures are *always* formed de novo by cells. Therefore in cells possessing centrioles the procentriole also always forms de novo, adjacent to, at right angles to, and to some extent influenced by the preexisting centriole.

Electron microscopy indicates that, with few exceptions, in cells possessing a centriole there is a tendency for them to exist as a pair arranged at right angles to each other. Therefore, at least by telophase, the single centriole at each spindle pole becomes a pair by the formation of a new centriole. The first evidence of the formation of a new centriole is a blurry region in the cytoplasm near the proximal end of the existing centriole. Somewhat later this blurry region is somewhat longer than wide and extends outward at right angles from close to the surface of the old centriole. Later still the "creation" consists of short, 200 Å microtubules that lie parallel to each other in a ring. At this still somewhat blurry stage it can be called a procentriole. Later the procentriole grows in length and develops some "structure" such as the "cartwheel" center within the proximal end and becomes a centriole. It has been claimed that the proximal end of a centriole is the "reproductive" end, the distal end being able to produce axonemes and flagella. It has now been well established that each of the nine filaments of a centriole is triple (Fig. 17-2, *B*) and each of the twenty-seven tubules is formed of about thirteen or fewer subunits that are also tubular (Figs. 14-2 and 14-3). There are often obscure regions of protoplasm within, among, and just outside the nine triple tubules.

Centriolar structure. Centriolar structure has now been studied by electron microscopy in sufficient species to determine that they all have a common basic structure (Chapter 13). Except perhaps in some flagellate protozoans such as *Barbulanympha,* a centriole is a cylinder having a diameter of about 1,500 Å. Length varies considerably among species, but a typical centriole is about 5,000 Å long. The microtubules are arranged in a circle of nine triple fibers. The three tubules of each fiber are so intimately associated that when two are in contact, they share one to three subtubules in common. Of the three, the one closest to the central axis of the centriole is called the A tubule; the B tubule is slightly further away; and the C tubule is furthest away. The diameter of the A tubule is less than the others; the C tubule does not extend into the axoneme when the centriole becomes a basal body and forms a flagellum. Frequently, median longitudinal sections of centrioles reveal that the proximal third seems to have electron-dense material (cartwheel), whereas the distal end appears "hollow."

Prophase

Chromosomal condensation. Chromosomal condensation, the almost universal indication of mitotic prophase, is poorly understood either structurally or chemically (Fig. 17-3). It is certainly obvious that the prophase chromosomes become progressively shorter, thicker, and straighter. Structurally, this change has often been interpreted as being achieved by a helical coiling of the contained chromonemata. There is little doubt that the chromonemata of some mitotic chromosomes are coiled, but many recorded observations do not reveal real coiling. The conclusion that chromonemata of mitotic chromosomes are coiled is partly based on the assumption that mitotic chromosomal condensation is of the same nature as meiotic condensation, where coiling is indisputable. Certainly, electron microscopic evidence from isolated and shadowed metaphase chromosomes does not generally indicate coiling. It seems best to assume that chromonemata (if they actually exist at prophase) of mitotic chromosomes are not necessarily coiled but become progressively packed in some unknown manner into a shorter and shorter, but thicker and thicker chromosome.

Like all aspects of mitosis there are organisms such as some dinoflagellates and many fungi in which the chromosomes appear to be "condensed" all of the time, during interphase as well as mitosis. Such "condensation" is probably of a different structural and chemical sort that permits gene action in the condensed state.

Chemically, chromosomes add increasing amounts of RNA, protein, and probably phospholipid during prophase. This material can be considered as the *matrix* of the mitotic chromosome without trying to visualize any specific distribution of it relative to the DNA strands or chromonemata. The source of this RNA is unknown. Possibilities suggested are that this additional RNA of unknown function is (1) from the cytoplasm, (2) from the nucleolus, which at about this same time in higher plants and animals is declining, or (3) produced by the chromosome itself. Of these, the second has received considerable support. The correlation of chromosomal thickening and increased stainability with nucleolar dissipation was noted long ago and considered to be a functional relationship. That is, material (RNA?) from the nucleolus passes into the chromosomes during prophase and becomes matrix; then at telophase the reverse occurs. This hypothesis is still occasionally proposed, but somewhat stronger evidence for the telophase part of the concept indicates that nucleolar material is formed anew at each telophase by the nucleolus organizer alone.

As the chromosomes shorten, thicken, and become observable under the light microscope, it is evident that many parts of chromosomes are associated with the inner surface of the nuclear envelope. This association has been mentioned before and may have presently unknown importance to nuclear functions. Furthermore, the prophase chromosomes often appear to run parallel with each other. This reflects the parallel orientation of the previous anaphase persisting through interphase to prophase and has been claimed as evidence that chromosomes in the extended interphase condition do not move around (Fig. 16-14).

At some time, often during prophase but in other species not until metaphase, each chromosome becomes observably double—two *chromatids* held together at or near the centromere and often loosely twisted around each other. There are numerous reports that the doubleness of the mitotic chromosome is evident even as early as the previous telophase. Such telophase doubleness followed by interphase replication of both subunits is the scheme supported by some direct cytological observation (Fig. 16-3). Other schemes, of course, are possible.

DNA replication. There are three possible schemes of DNA replication that would perhaps become evident in different ways after treating nuclei during the synthetic period of one interphase with tritiated thymidine and then observing the next two metaphases by autoradiography.

According to the *dispersive scheme,* newly synthesized DNA material is mixed with old template DNA in each chromonema so that all subsequent chromosomes and chromatids would be radioactive but decreasingly so after each DNA replication. This scheme is not supported by theory or experimental observation and can be discarded.

The *conservative scheme* holds that when

a single DNA double helix replicates, one helix is old template (nonradioactive) and the other is all new and highly radioactive. If these two then form the two chromatids by metaphase, one chromatid of each chromosome would not be radioactive, the other would be. At subsequent divisions some whole chromatids would appear radioactive.

The *semiconservative scheme* (Delbruck and Stent, 1957) holds that when a Watson-Crick double helix replicates, each of the double helices resulting will be half old template and half new and radioactive. Thus when these two double helices form the two metaphase chromatids of each chromosome, both chromatids will be radioactive at that first metaphase, but at the next metaphase (with synthesis in cold thymidine during the second interphase) only one chromatid of each chromosome will be radioactive.

Of these schemes, present evidence generally indicates that DNA is replicated semiconservatively. Most such experiments show that both chromatids are radioactive at the first division but only one at the second division. There are, however, a few experiments in which only one chromatid was labeled at the first division, or there was a combination of unequal and equal distribution of radioactivity at that first division.

Complication arises in theory, however, if the chromosome is already two stranded or even polytene at telophase, as considerable cytological evidence indicates. With two or more strands during the G_1 period, the only possible explanation of the experimental results recorded is that after either conservative or semiconservative DNA replication there must be a sorting out of the multiple strands to give the observed results, unless groups of strands function as single strands (Uhl, 1965). But again, until a reasonably correct concept of the fine, medium, and gross structure of interphase and metaphase chromosomes is achieved, such schemes are largely guesswork and not to be accepted as reliable (Chapters 15 and 16).

Breakdown of nuclear envelope. Nuclear envelope breakdown occurs during the period often called prometaphase, but it is certainly a preparation for later mitotic actions. Nevertheless, prophasic or any breakdown at all is unnecessary, since many Protista and fungi (for example, yeast) have *intranuclear mitosis,* or in others the "ends" of the elongated nuclear envelope break open at late anaphase to let the chromosomes pass out to the telophase poles (Figs. 17-4 and 17-5). Be that as it may, in "higher" plants and animals, breakdown of the nuclear envelope does occur at all divisions. No mechanism to accomplish this act is known, but fragments with pores may be seen peripheral to the spindle at later stages by electron microscopy. Such fragments may persist and at telophase help to reconstitute the new envelopes, they may break down and disappear, or they may re-form as typical ER. What happens to them may be determined when the details of telophase formation of nuclear envelopes are understood.

Nucleolar dissolution. Nucleolar dissolution, like nuclear envelope breakdown, is not a universal phenomenon. Again, many Protista have permanent nucleoli that divide by pinching in half along with the chromosomes at metaphase or anaphase and furnish half-sized, already formed nucleoli to the telophase nuclei. Various terms such as "karyosome" or "endosome" in Protozoa and "central body" in some algae have been applied to these nucleoli or nucleolus-like bodies, but they are doubtless rather typical nucleoli.

Nucleoli do not occur in all eucells. They have not been detected in some Protista and yeast and are said to be absent from the well-studied cells of amphibians during cleavage. Nevertheless, they are essentially ubiquitous.

Just what occurs during nucleolar dissolution at prometaphase is unknown; they just "fade away." Study of persistent nucleoli in some angiosperms indicates the loss of RNA or ribonucleoprotein, leaving behind some sort of a more slowly dissolving proteinaceous "ghost." Furthermore, it has not been established yet what happens to the material of the nucleolus during late prophase and prometaphase. It has been proposed (and there is some proof) that at least some of the material of the nucleolus passes into or onto the condensing chromosomes. It doubtless also provides an opportunity for nucleolar material to pass into the cytoplasm; but that hardly seems necessary, since mature, postmitotic cells may

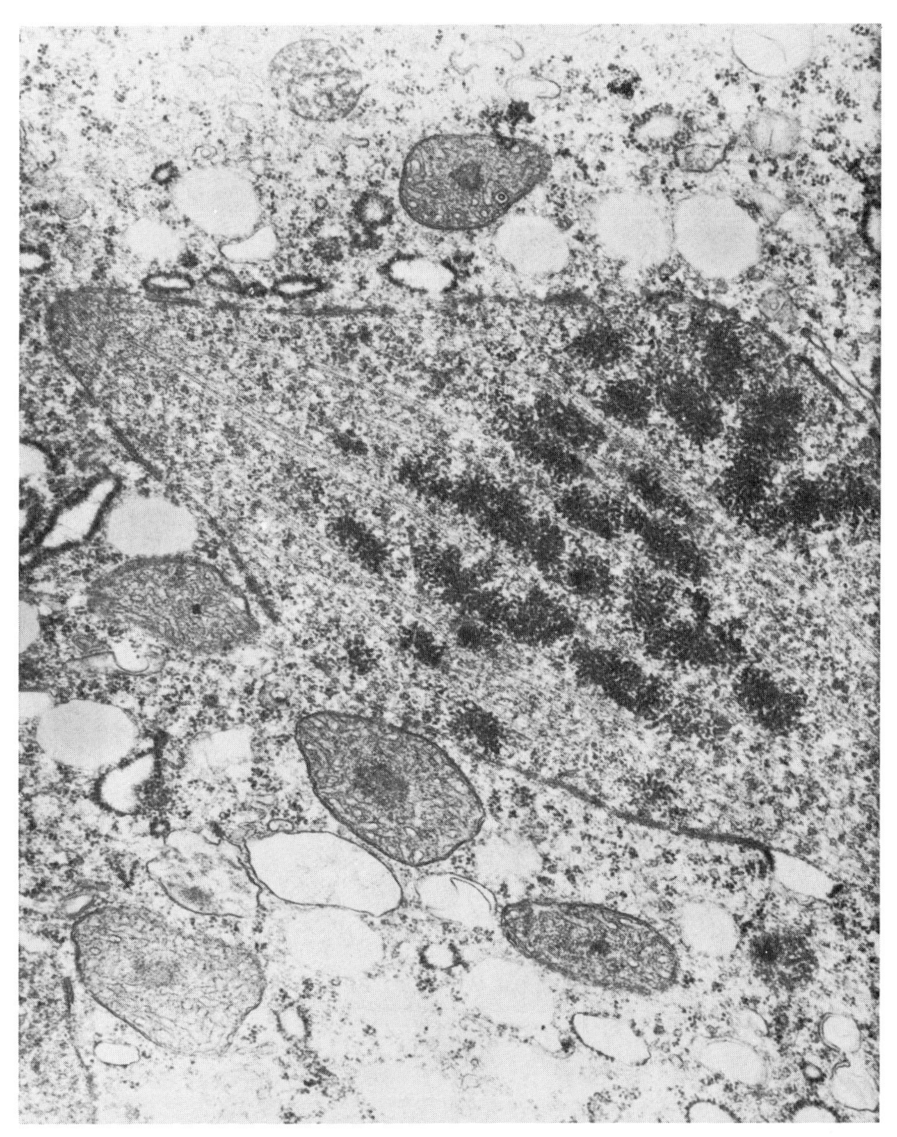

Fig. 17-4. Early anaphase of intranuclear mitosis in the slime mold sporangium of *Physarum flavicomum* showing microtubular spindle fibers. It seems as though the spindle fibers are elongating the nucleus. See Fig. 17-5 for a later stage when spindle fibers have burst through the nuclear envelope and extended into the cytoplasm. Also note the DNA centers of mitochondria, which also have tubular cristae. Polyribosomes are common. (Courtesy Dr. H. C. Aldrich, Department of Botany, University of Florida, Gainesville, Fla.)

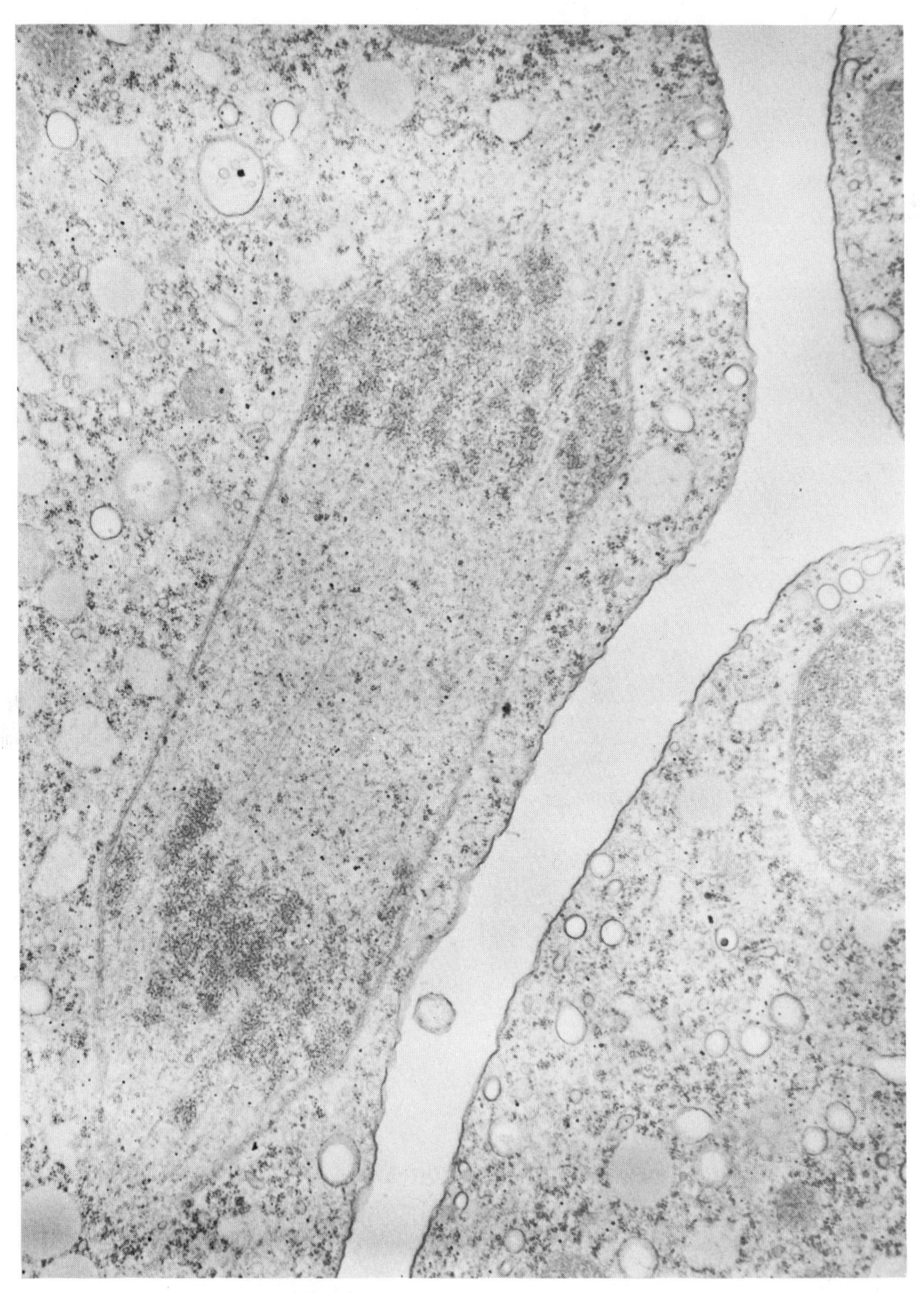

Fig. 17-5. Intranuclear late anaphase of the myxomycete *Physarum flavicomum* sporangium showing spindle fibers and opening of nuclear envelope at this stage of division. See Fig. 17-4 for an earlier stage of anaphase. (Courtesy Dr. H. C. Aldrich, Department of Botany, University of Florida, Gainesville, Fla.)

function for months or years without nuclear breakdown. One likely possibility is that during prophase the nucleolar genes of the nucleolus organizer are "turned off," and with no addition of new nucleolar ribonucleoprotein the normal turnover of nucleolar material and withdrawal of nucleolar DNA result in the prophase phasing out of the nucleolus.

The electron microscopic finding of a small amount of peristing nucleolar material passing into telophase nuclei at mammalian mitosis has, at present, no significance attached to it. Persistent nucleoli in angiosperms (Brown and Emery, 1957), really "ghosts" of nucleoli and probably devoid of RNA, are not included in telophase nuclei and dissolve usually by anaphase or telophase.

Achromatic figure. The achromatic figure (Figs. 17-1, 17-3, and 17-4) is a temporary system that occurs only at cell division. The cell produces the structure for chromosome segregation only, or perhaps it functions also in cytokinesis. It consists of at least a *spindle* but also of asters in those cells having centrioles. There seems to be no doubt that the centrioles "produce" the asters and sometimes part of the spindle, but in land plants and some algae that have no centrioles and no asters the spindle is determined otherwise. Some experimental evidence (Dietz, 1966) indicates that centrioles and asters are unnecessary during cell division but are merely being "carried along" for subsequent use in providing cilia or flagella for certain cells and sperm.

It has been said that the spindle forms suddenly out of the proteins synthesized previously, but that is probably not true of any cells. In most cells the formation of the spindle is correlated with nuclear envelope breakdown at prometaphase. Even some plant mitoses (free nuclear endosperm of the lily *Haemanthus* and in corn endosperm, Fig. 17-1) seem to have oriented fibrous material in a clear zone around the prophase nucleus, as revealed by ordinary and polarized light microscopy. Furthermore, "sudden" formation of structures by cells does not seem to be the manner of cellular activity; consequently, claims of "sudden formation" are suspect.

Spindles seem to consist of two parts, two sorts of fibers, that are intermingled by metaphase and that have two origins, times of origin, source of formation, and two different functions. These are the pole-to-pole fibers constituting the *central spindle* or *primary spindle* (Fig. 17-4) and the *chromosomal fibers* or *half spindle fibers* (Fig. 17-1, parts *10* and *11*). It is the primary spindle that may be formed by the centrioles or in "higher" plant cells forms around the nucleus during middle prophase. If there are centrioles, the primary spindle forms between them as they separate, or it may be responsible merely for centriolar separation outside the nuclear envelope.

Chromosomal movement. Whether formed outside or inside the nuclear envelope *(Cyclops),* the primary spindle seems to play little direct part in the movement of chromosomes. Such prometaphase or *metakinesis* movement to the metaphase plate and anaphase movement seem to be determined by the chromosome or *half spindle fibers* or *kinetochore fibers* that are "formed" by or at least "connected to" the centromere (Fig. 16-5) of the chromosome and extend to one of the poles (Fig. 17-6). They constitute the two *half spindles.* Apparently, the scattered prometaphase centromeres produce fibers perpendicular to the centromere, and these later extend to (grow toward) the pole most directly in line rather than to the nearest one. There can be loss and gain of fibers and even re-formation of fibers if the ones first formed are destroyed. It seems that the half spindle or chromosomal fibers are responsible for orienting the chromosomes on the *metaphase plate,* with the centromere of one chromatid directed toward and "connected" to one pole, whereas the centromere of the sister chromatid is directed toward and "connected"

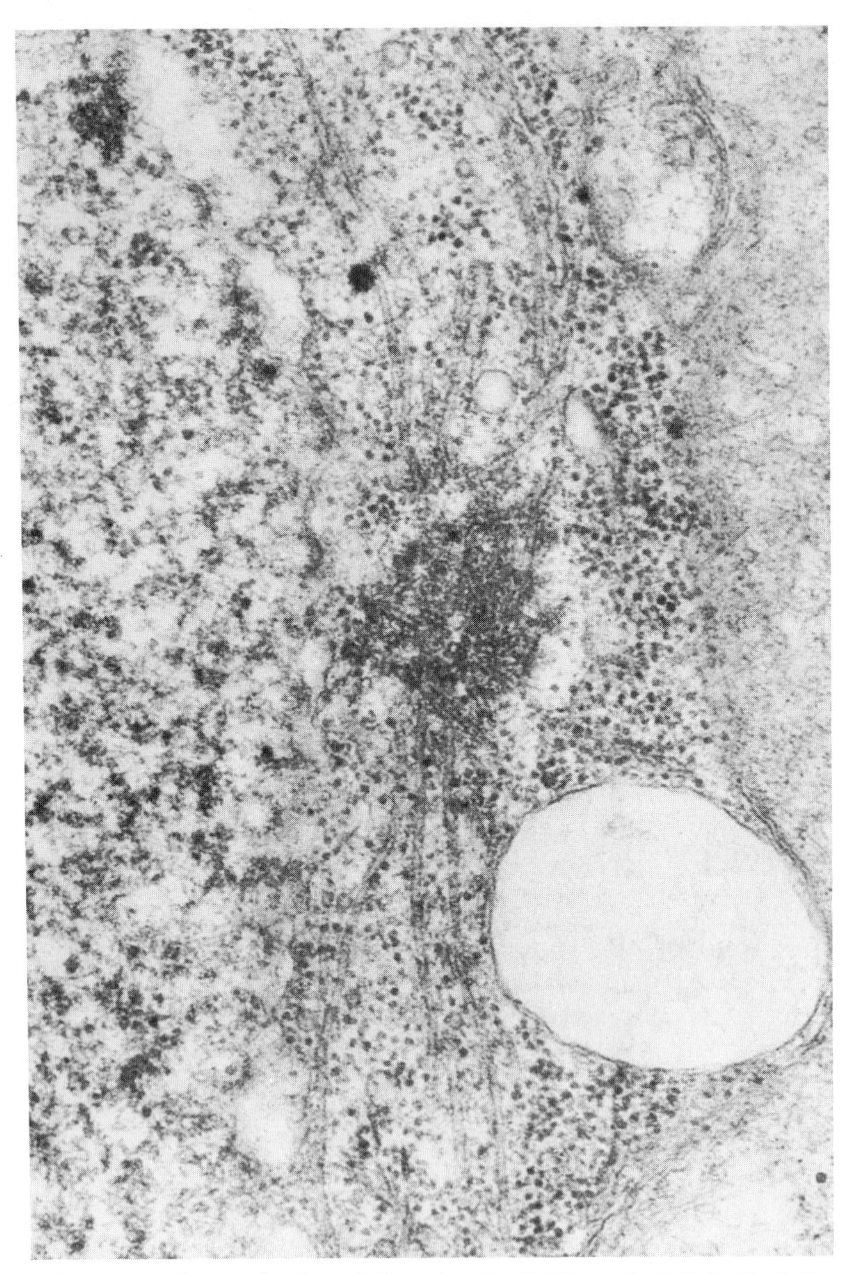

Fig. 17-6. Electron micrograph of a spindle pole of a dividing cell of *Reboulia* that was cut perpendicular to the spindle axis. Radiating microtubules are evident, but the structure, if any, of the central mass is not clear. (Courtesy Dr. F. R. Turner, University of Texas Cell Research Institute, Austin, Texas.)

to the other pole by the chromosomal fibers.

It is now known that spindle and astral fibers are microtubules (Figs. 17-4 to 17-6) with a diameter between 200 and 250 Å (Figs. 14-2 and 14-3); that is, they are typical microtubules representing quaternary protein structure. They are of micron length and are "attached" to centromeres and/or centrioles if the latter are present. They are far below the resolution of the light microscope, but because they often occur in bundles, it is the bundles or the optical density of a mass of fibers that makes them visible.

Since centromeres have never been reported in interphase nuclei but are fully formed by prometaphase, it seems that they form during prophase. The metaphase centromere often appears as a constriction in the chromosome, a region of uncondensed chromonema. Since there is good evidence that genes located in condensed mitotic chromosomes are temporarily nonfunctional, it would seem that the genes of the centromere may well be active during mitosis and thus somehow cause formation of kinetochores and microtubules.

The relationship between spindle fibers and chromosomal movement is presently unknown. There is good evidence of RNA and certainly proteins in spindles, but ATPase is low. There is no evidence that microtubules ever "contract"; yet evidence at prometaphase and anaphase indicates that the centromere is "pulled" toward the pole or poles, the arms of the chromosome apparently passively following along. The chromosome arms seem to be passive; the centromere *is* primarily involved somehow.

Considerable reported evidence of prometaphasic chromosome movement derives from observations of movements during prophase I of meiosis. It is not unlikely, however, that meiotic prophase and mitotic prophase movements may be very different. For example, the so-called *prometaphase stretch* during late prophase I of meiosis in some animal spermatocytes, during which the two centromeres of the synapsed bivalent move toward opposite poles and the chromosome arms between centromeres and terminal chiasmata are stretched, does not occur in mitosis. Here only mitotic movements are being discussed.

One of the arguments against the hypothesis that the chromosomes are "pulled" to the poles by the fibers is Newton's third law of motion, which states that for every action there is an opposite and equal reaction. Thus for spindle fibers to pull the chromosomes against considerable resistance through the protoplasm to the poles, the other ends of the fibers must be firmly anchored to some "immovable" body or structure. They probably are not, even in animal mitosis; but in higher plants there is no known attachment of the polar ends of spindle fibers.

Any hypothesis that does "explain" how the polar ends of the chromosomal fibers can be anchored against the resistance of large chromosomes moving through protoplasm must first assume that somehow the polar ends of the chromosomal fibers are "tied" to the polar ends of the continuous (pole-to-pole) fibers of the central spindle; then it must be assumed that if the central spindle is rigid enough, it will act as a brace to prevent equatorial movement of the poles as the chromosomes are pulled poleward during anaphase. Mitotic apparatuses with asters might satisfy the first assumption, but the anastral cells of land plants have no known firm association of the two kinds of spindle fibers at the poles. The second assumption is no more than an assumption; it is not known how rigid a cluster of microtubules can be. There are exceptions to this scheme such as the unipolar spindle of the fly *Sciara,* just as there are known exceptions to *every* scheme of mitotic movement of chromosomes (Schrader, 1953).

Perhaps fibers do not pull chromosomes. How do persistent nucleoli move toward spindle poles during metaphase since they presumably have no centromere and are not attached to fibers? Then why do acentric chromosomes and fragments not move rather than lag on the metaphase plate at anaphase? In some insects there is a unipolar spindle toward which some chromosomes move, led by the centromere. But other chromosomes, also attached by spindle fibers and with the centromere pointing toward the pole, *move in the opposite direction!* Such questions and many more and all of the extant hypotheses of chromosomal motion were discussed by Schrader in 1953. Then, as now, there was no acceptable hypothesis to account for all chromosomal movements. But that is true of all cases of protoplasmic motion. Cells and cell organelles do move; there is not the slightest doubt about that, but the movement cannot be explained, only described.

At the present time the generally accepted mechanism of any protoplasmic motion involves contractile protein as approximately 70 Å thick microfilaments that are myosinlike or actinlike. Electron microscopy often reveals sheaves of such filaments in known contractile regions of cells (Chapter 14). There have been some tentative reports of bundles of such filaments running parallel with and among the microtubules of the spindle. The presence of such contractile microfilaments must be a fact, unless chromosomes have some ability for autonomous movement of unknown nature. It is assumed that such contractile filaments working in association with the microtubules of the spindle and the centromeres of the chromosomes achieve chromosomal movements of prometaphase and anaphase. It is, of course, certain that numbers of spindle microtubules are connected to the kinetochores of the centromeres, although other spindle microtubules (the continuous fibers) run past and even through the chromosomes.

Chromosomes or pieces of chromosomes having no part of a centromere (called *acentric*) may move around but not specifically and directly toward one pole. A part of a centromere will function in chromosome movement about as well as one that is intact. Persistent nuclei, which lie within the spindle, move toward the poles. In some species the mitochondria arrange themselves relative to the spindle but outside of it and later separate into two groups by telophase. Modern evidence requires acceptance of the fact that pieces of nuclear membrane somehow move to make contact with telophase chromosomes.

The simplest but not necessarily correct hypothesis is that chromosomes move *autonomously* and are merely guided by spindle fibers. The pole-to-pole fibers could act as rails for guiding them longitudinally, whereas the chromosome fibers guide the two sister anaphase chromosomes to opposite poles. With the present lack of knowledge of mechanisms producing observed intracellular movement, this explanation is adequate and permits inclusion of all exceptional cases.

On the other hand, any autonomous movement must have some energy-expending, movement-creating mechanism, and no such equipment is known. Popular models of prometaphase and anaphase chromosomal movement implicate the visible microtubules and some largely invisible "force-generating elements" among the spindle microtubules, which are often equated to microfilaments (Luykx, 1970). In such models the microtubules guide the orientation of the "force-generating elements" parallel to the longitudinal axis of the spindle and to contact with the kinetochores. Actually, there has been little progress toward a reliable and generally acceptable model of the mechanism of mitotic and meiotic chromosomal movement since Schrader (1953) and Mazia (1961), except that microtubules (visible spindle fibers) do not apparently pull the kinetochores.

Metaphase

Metaphase (Figs. 17-1, part 7, and 17-7) is a period of dynamic stability during which the centromeres of the double chromosomes lie on the metaphase plate, one directed toward each pole. In electron microscopy (Fig. 16-5) the centromere appears as an electron-dense disk lying on the surface of a chromosome to which, or from which, a number of microtubules extend toward the pole that lies perpendicular to the disk and on the same side of the chromosome. Probably the centromere is double at metaphase, becoming so at the same time that the chromosome itself first consisted of two chromatids. The nature of the union of sister chromatids in the centromere region at metaphase is unknown, but at that time it is probably more like being stuck together by matrix material than doubling of the centromere, which is already double.

The structural nature of "diffuse centromeres" of the "polycentric" chromosomes of homopterous and hemipterous insects, the rush, *Luzula,* dinoflagellates, and others is unknown. Certainly, spindle fibers attach along one side of each chromatid, and the anaphase chromosomes move sideways toward each pole (Fig. 16-6).

Another interesting phenomenon of metaphase is the orderly arrangement of chromosomes sometimes seen at metaphase. In species having both large and small chromosomes the large ones almost always are peripheral and the small ones lie at the center (Fig. 16-11). Homologous chromosomes lie close to one another in all Diptera, forming pairs at metaphase (Fig. 17-14); this paired condition persists at all phases, even during interphase of salivary gland cells where they may be "synapsed" (Fig. 17-16). Pairing of homologous chromosomes, at least during the metaphase of premeiotic mitosis, which may not be a typical mitotic division (Fig. 18-13), has been reported in numerous classes and phyla of animals and plants (see later in this chapter).

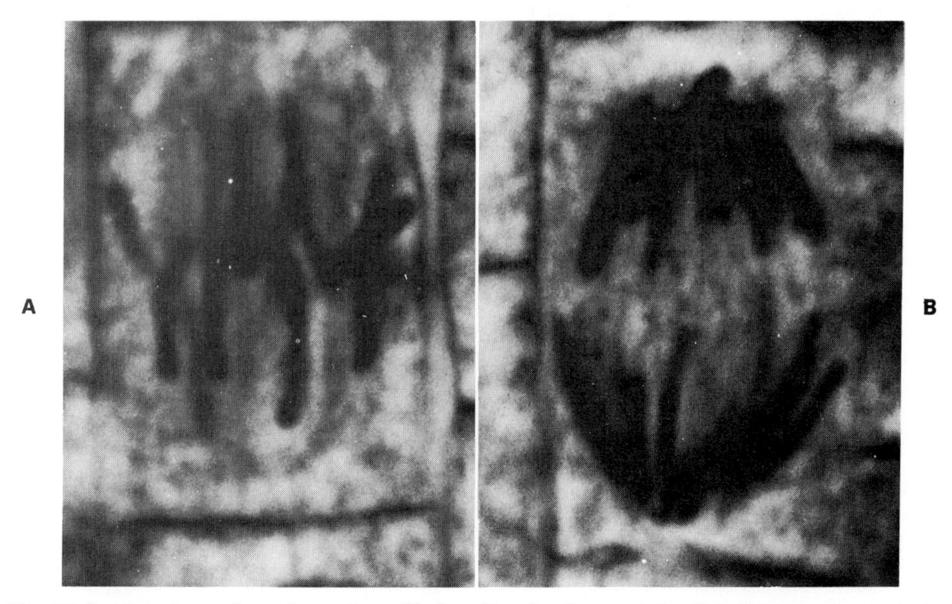

Fig. 17-7. Metaphase, **A,** and anaphase, **B,** in cells of onion root tip. Spindle axes are vertical; the poles are at the top and bottom of the figures. At metaphase the centromeres are all positioned on the metaphase plate, which extends horizontally about equidistant from the two poles or the end walls of the cell. The arms of the metaphase chromosomes extend away from the metaphase plate randomly, often toward the poles. At anaphase the centromeres move toward the poles; the arms appear to be dragged passively behind the centromeres so that at anaphase the arms have been reversed, extending backward toward the metaphase plate.

Anaphase

Anaphase (Figs. 17-1, parts *8* to *14,* and 17-7) begins when sister chromatids separate at the centromere. The cause of this separation is unknown, but because it happens to all the chromosomes at the same time and because most of the chromosomes may "wait" for one laggard, it seems to be determined by a condition in which the whole cell, all the chromosomes, or at least all the centromeres are involved. This is true also of first cleavage divisions having two separate spindles or in binucleate cells, even those produced by the insertion of an extra nucleus.

There are, of course, many hypotheses that attempt to "explain" anaphase chromosomal movements. There does seem to be considerable evidence that there are often two distinct causes, one of which is the lengthening of the spindle resulting from the polar centers moving further away from each other (or being "pushed" away from each other by longitudinal growth of spindle fibers, Figs. 17-4 and 17-5). But the cause or causes of the movement of chromosomes all the way to the poles is still unknown. Chromosomal fibers must decrease in length to nonexistence. It has been proposed that there are two sorts of chromosomal half spindle fibers: the visible microtubules that do not contract or pull the centromeres and some presently "unseen" but contractile fibers that, by contraction, do pull chromosomes toward the poles, at least part way.

Ideas about chromosomal movement, including anaphase, have been discussed.

Nondisjunction. Nondisjunction of chromosomes occurs sporadically or normally at anaphase; that is, the two sister chromatids reach the same pole. If that occurs to all of the chromosomes (probably really by formation of a restitution nucleus), a polyploid nucleus results. If it occurs to a single chromosome, it produces one daughter nucleus with one extra chromosome (a *trisomic*) and the other lacking one chromosome (a *monosomic*). Several plant and one animal species regularly lose their supernumerary chromosome in certain tissues and in other tissues double the number, presumably by gene-controlled nondisjunction. The nuclei receiving the nondisjoined supernumerary chromosomes are also predetermined. In the haploid microspore mitosis in developing pollen grains of such species the nondisjoined chromosomes always move to the generative nuclear pole. Gene-controlled (natural) nondisjunction is used to decrease or increase X chromosomes in some insects.

Atypical spindles. *Unipolar spindles,* that is, half spindles with only one pole, are regularly formed at certain divisions by some insects such as *Sciara coprophila* (White, 1954). This division is famous in cytology because of several unusual conditions. No definite metaphase occurs; some chromosomes (those from the maternal parent) move, centromere first, toward the pole. The chromosomes derived from the paternal parent have their centromeres "attached" to spindle fibers and are oriented with their centromeres directed toward the single pole, but they *back away* from it until stopped by the plasma membrane. This case confounds most hypotheses of anaphase movement. Also difficult to explain by spindle fiber "pulling" is anaphase movement of chromosomes all the way to the poles, such that fibers are reduced to zero length. One proposal was that spindle fibers shorten by losing molecules into the cytoplasm—they actually fade away to nothing.

The normal spindle in plants and animals converges more or less toward the pole or polar region. *Divergent spindles* form naturally in a few species and due to the effects of a single gene in corn, the fibers flairing outward rather than converging. The result is widely dispersed telophase chromosomes, often so widely separated that each chromosome forms a micronucleus. The typical convergent spindle jams the chromosomes together into an irregular mass at early telophase and so is an extremely important and essential structural arrangement in producing only one nucleus at each pole.

Telophase

Telophase phenomena (Figs. 17-8, 17-1, parts *16* to *20,* and 17-17) have been mentioned previously as, to some extent, the reverse of prophase. Since all nuclei in the cell, both daughter nuclei typically but also karyomeres and micro-nuclei if any exist, undergo the same changes at the same time, these reactions seem to be cellular. The same is doubtless true of all phases of mitosis. The nuclear envelope at telophase re-forms, probably by fragments of old nuclear envelope or ER "moving" against the exposed parts of chromosomes and then by growth linking up to form a continuous membrane and subsequently increasing in area as the late telophase nucleus expands (Fig. 17-17). Possibly, however, the chromosomes themselves determine the formation of new envelope. For what it is worth, Cleveland (1953) reported the formation of new "nuclear envelope" around the chromosomes within the still intact old "nuclear envelope" in certain termite-inhabiting flagellates. Perhaps the rRNA that gets onto prophase chromosomes functions at telophase to produce membrane.

Re-formation of nucleoli seems to be accomplished by the nucleolus organizer alone, which may have been functional as early as metaphase as an uncondensed region of a particular chromosome. As stated earlier, this chromosomal region seems to produce the rRNA or a precursor rRNA and is highly redundant because of cistron duplications. Apparently, the previous concepts that (1) the matrix "deposited" on the chromosomes at prophase came off at telophase to form the new nucleolus and (2) all chromosomes, some of them, or only the arms of the nucleolus organizer chromosome

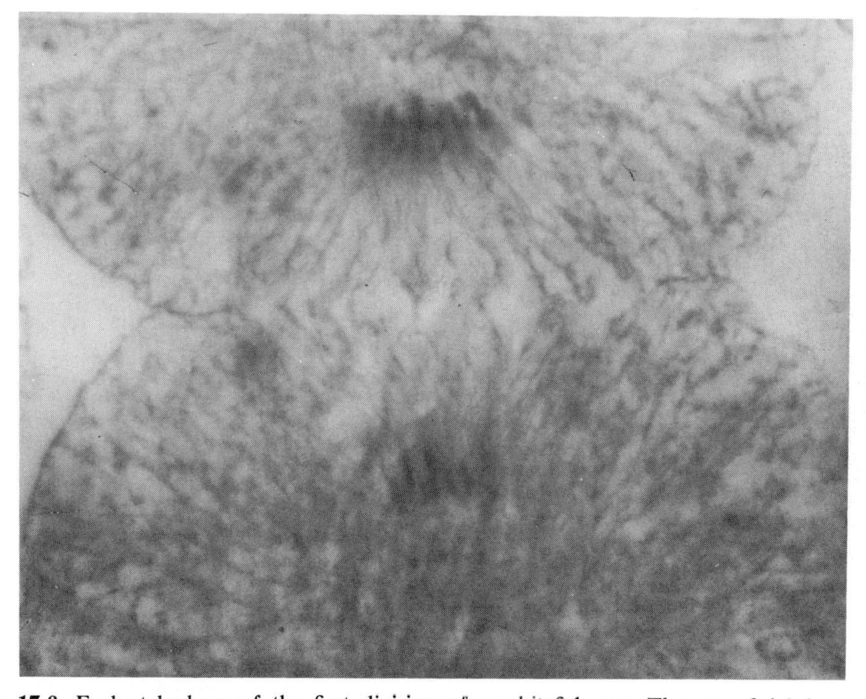

Fig. 17-8. Early telophase of the first division of a whitefish egg. The superficial furrow is evident, but interior equatorial details are not clear or well preserved. Groups of chromosomes at the poles of the spindle are obvious.

formed the new nucleolar material have been superseded.

In polyploids such as hexapliod wheat there are several chromosomes with nucleolus organizers. In hexaploid wheat (Longwell and Svihla, 1960) there are eight, the chromosomes I, X, XIV, and XVIII. Nonnucleolar chromosomes when present singly in micronuclei, form nucleoli in about 1.5% of micronuclei. Chromosome I in micronuclei formed nucleoli in 15%, chromosome X in 20%, chromosome XIV in 13%, and chromosome XVIII in 7%. When chromosome I or X is tetrasomic (4 rather than the usual 2), the average number of 1.5 nucleoli per nucleus is increased to 3; when chromosome XIV or XVIII is tetrasomic, there are only 2.1 or 2 nucleoli per nucleus. Therefore Longwell and Svihla concluded that the nucleolar organizers on chromosomes I and X are strong, but those on XIV and XVIII are weak. Furthermore, if both I or both X chromosomes are missing, the weak organizers can compensate for them with respect to nucleolar volume, dry mass, cytoplasmic dry mass, or cytoplasmic RNA content. Tetrasomic non-nucleolus organizer chromosomes do not affect those factors, but nucleoli in nuclei tetrasomic for the strong organizers on chromosomes I or X are 50% larger. Thus there can be strong and weak nucleoli in the same polyploid nucleus. Similarly, strong and weak nucleolus organizers have been reported among species of *Crepis;* polyploid species of *Nicotiana* seem to have no more nucleolar DNA than diploids; and *Drosophila,* having deletions of various amounts of the nucleolus organizers, seems to compensate to have about the same amount of nucleolar DNA.

Whether it is significant or not, Longwell and Svihla also noted that in plants, at least, nucleolar organizers are generally in short arms of chromosomes, hence there may be some value or necessity to such a location.

Telophase is also characterized by the dissolution of the achromatic figure and the organization of new centrioles. What happens to centromeres is unknown, although they probably change from an extended to a condensed heterochromatic condition. Of more significance is what happens to the chromosomes. Without doubt they resume the nonmitotic condition, which must involve the reverse of condensation. The matrix leaves the chromosomes, and the chromonemata uncoil, unfold, or whatever is required to achieve the interphase condition. Some reports indicate a "flow" of RNA (matrix? rRNA?) along the spindle from the region of the chromosomes toward the equator. If true, possibly this material functions in cytokinesis (discussed later in this chapter). Other hypotheses propose that the chromosomal matrix becomes new nucleolar material. It is certain that the telophase chromosomes do lose their smooth meta-anaphase contours and dark matrical staining; therefore chromonemata can be seen, although poorly, because the chromosomes are jammed together at early telophase. Nevertheless, many reports of two chromonemata per chromosome have been made and documented, indicating that double strandedness seems to be the gross structure of the telophase chromosomal condition. The fine structure, however, is still unknown.

It is evident from the chromatin condition during interphase and from theory that the whole lengths of the chromonemata do not become uncondensed at telophase. At least that is what *heterochromatin* is supposed to be. The portions of chromosomes that do become uncondensed are described as being *euchromatic.* Euchromatin becomes unobservable by late telophase, presumably because it represents chromonemata that have elongated and lost all of the matrical material. Cytogenetic evidence indicates that genes located in euchromatin can be functional but that genes located in heterochromatic regions, called *prochromosomes* or *chromocenters* during interphase (Fig. 15-9), are inactive. A chromosome region or whole chromosome may be largely euchromatic in one cell but facultatively heterochromatic in another.

Most chromosomes are heterochromatic on both sides of the centromere, at least during meiotic prophase; some sex chromosomes are often heterochromatic at all phases; chromomeres and knobs are short regions of heterochromatin; the stained disks of salivary gland giant chromosomes and the chromomeres of meiotic prophase lampbrush chromosomes are short regions of heterochromatin; most supernumerary chromosomes and some other unusual types of chromosomes are heterochromatic during all phases; and it seems likely that the nucleolus organizer is heterochromatic during pachytene of meiosis.

Since all nuclei of eukaryotic cells have some heterochromatin, and since some genetic work has indicated some aspects of its relationship to gene action (such as inhibition), it would seem that the heterochromatic condition, or the presence of some heterochromatin, is essential to nuclear activity. Its relationship to gene action has involved it in discussions of mechanisms of cellular differentiation.

Results of mitosis

The results of mitosis are cytological and genetic, but, of course, these are really two aspects of the same thing. Mitosis is a very regular process controlled by many genes, but like all biological events, errors occur. Such errors are the basic material of evolution. Almost without exception, then, nuclear division results in two nuclei, each of which is cytologically and genetically identical to the other and with the nucleus from which it was derived. This exact reproduction is of great biological significance.

"Rejuvenation" of the cell or prevention of aging is also claimed to be a result of cell division. Such a concept, mostly derived from studies of Protozoa, is not convincing. Certainly, there are tissues of multicellular animals in which the cells are short lived and are constantly renewed—the *Hydra,* skin, blood cells, various epithelia, etc. But there are other tissues characterized by long-lived cells with few or no divisions, insect larvae and adults, muscle and nerve tissues in other animals, and xylem parenchyma in plants, for example. The concept that divisions prevent senescence is reminiscent of the now discredited concept (also based on studies of Protozoa) that sexuality is necessary to prevent senescence. Of course, all life results from cell divisions, and growth and differentiation of tissues and organs ultimately require the multiplication of cells. Division is certainly characteristic of cells, but even actively metabolizing cells can adapt to a long postmitotic existence. There can be rapid molecular turnover without cellular replacement.

Other forms of nuclear division

Yeasts. Nuclear and cytoplasmic division in some yeasts (*Saccharomyces* and *Wickerhamia*) is very different from typical mitosis (Fig. 17-9). Cytoplasmic division has long been known as *budding* and mostly precedes the nuclear division. Considerable evidence indicates (Robinow and Marak, 1966) that the numerous chromosomes of yeasts change little if at all from the non-dividing nucleus during division, although chromosomes are evident in *Lipomyces.* The "interphase" nucleus has two "centriolar plaques" on opposite sides of the nucleus, on or in the envelope (Fig. 17-10). One lies in a shallow depression, the other in a deep depression so that it is near the center of the nucleus. A "gray crescent," possibly a diffuse nucleolus and chromatin, occupies one side of the nucleus. Extending from one centriolar plaque to the other are about twelve microtubules that form a short intranuclear fiber just visible in the light microscope. When the bud is about full size, the chromatin part of the nucleus becomes pale and the nucleus starts to squeeze into the bud, led by the centriolar plaque in the shallow depression. The microtubular fiber

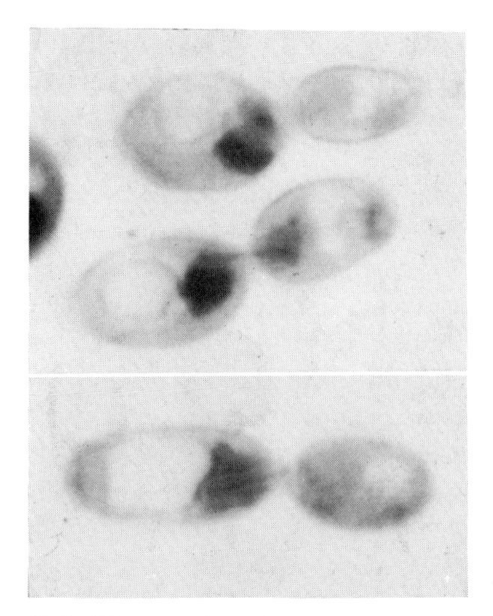

Fig. 17-9. Three stained budding yeast cells. The uppermost cell shows a rather typical nucleus; the lowermost cell shows a nucleus in division, with the rodlike "spindle" beginning to extend into the bud. In the central figure, division is further advanced. (From Robinow, C. F., and J. Marak. 1966. J. Cell Biol. **29:**129-151.)

elongates greatly within the intact nuclear envelope, extending from the original cell into the bud (Fig. 17-9). When about half of the nucleus has passed into the bud, the nucleus in the neck constricts, producing two daughter nuclei, one in each cell. Somehow an equal distribution of replicated "chromosomes" has been accomplished, and the crescent material distributes itself about equally to the bud and the original cell. The intranuclear fiber is not at this time considered to be a spindle nor, according to all competent investigators, a mechanism for elongating the nucleus when part of it extends into the bud. Some consider that the rodlike fibers provide rigidity to the self-elongating nucleus.

The "centriolar plaques" (Fig. 17-10) have little structure in common with centrioles, although it has been proposed that they are evolutionary predecessors of cen-

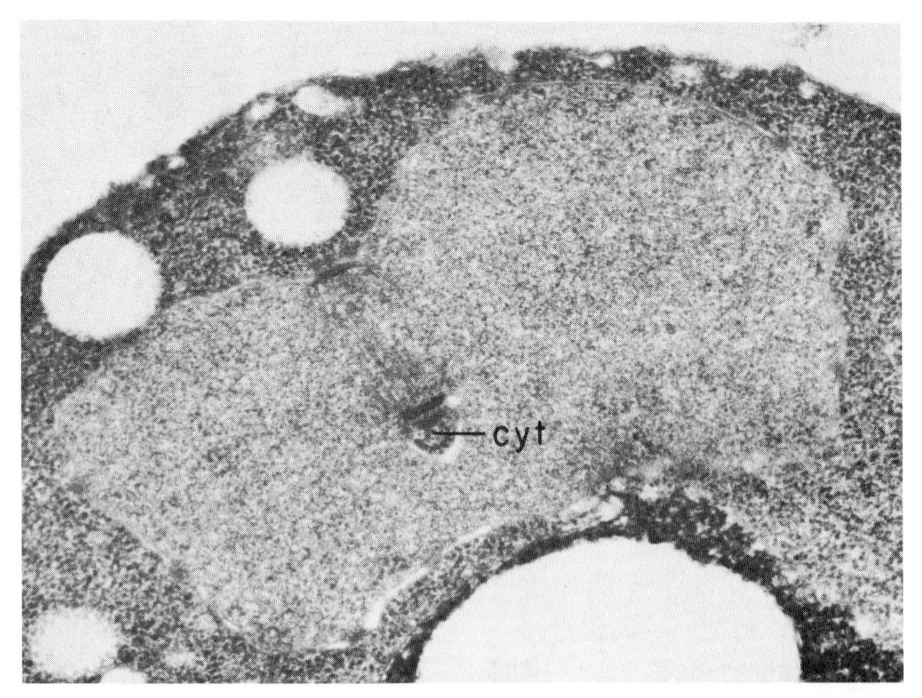

Fig. 17-10. Electron micrograph of a nondividing yeast cell showing the rodlike "spindle" of microtubules connecting two centriolar plaques. Both plaques are on the nuclear envelope, but the lower one is at the bottom of a deep, tubular cytoplasmic **(cyt)** invagination into the nucleus. (From Robinow, C. F., and J. Marak. 1966. J. Cell Biol. **29:**129-151.)

trioles. Each consists of an electron-dense plate, about 1,500 Å in diameter, positioned as though in a large pore of the nuclear membrane and a second parallel plate in the cytoplasm a few hundred Ångstroms away with possible interconnections. To a large extent the structures and the division process in yeasts are different from typical mitosis. There is no chromosomal condensation, no centers, no spindle, no nuclear envelope breakdown, no dissolution of nucleolus, and no metaphase or anaphase. Except for equal division of "chromosomes," this might be a good example of amitosis. Nuclear division in yeasts is more nonmitotic than in other fungi.

Fungi. Mitosis and meiosis (Figs. 17-11 and 17-12) in several Ascomycetes (other than yeasts) and in some Basidiomycetes have now been characterized as probably involving a microtubular fiber somewhat similar to that of yeast, although it may be much thicker, of many more tubules, and even like a thin spindle. The stage comparable to metaphase seems to show the condensed chromosomes or chromatids spread along the outside of this "spindle" (Fig. 17-11). There is evidence that there may be two rows of daughter chromosomes, the so-called railway track anaphase; those in each row are physically linked together end to end into a "compound chromosome." It is assumed that somehow one row (one compound chromosome) passes to one pole, the

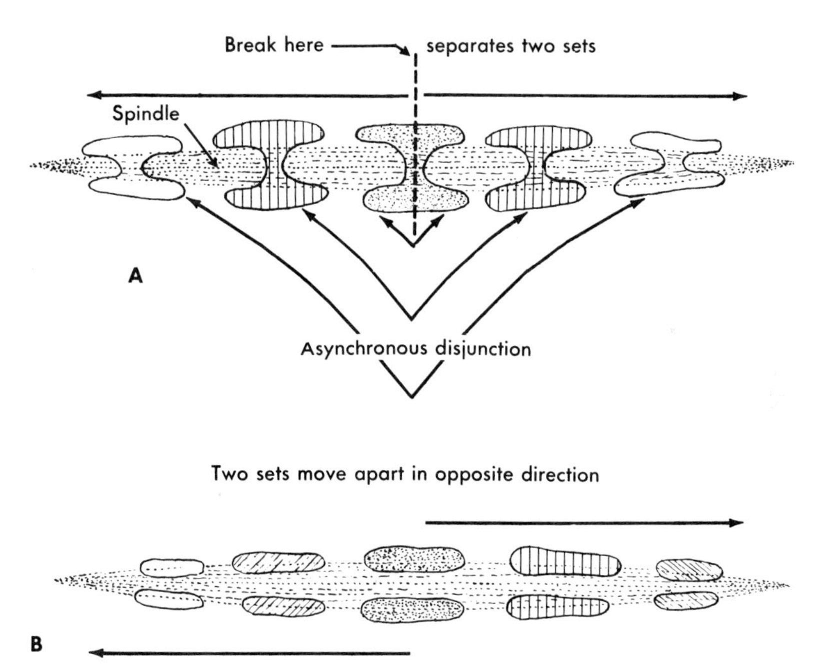

Fig. 17-11. Two tentative schemes for "metaphase-anaphase" separation of sister chromatids on the narrow spindle of at least some fungi—the "railway track" anaphase problem. **A** is the "asynchronous disjunction" scheme, according to which the chromosomes *in turn* and sequentially "get onto the spindle" at the equator and divide, and the two sisters move toward opposite poles, perhaps attached together as two "trains" moving in opposite directions from the equator. **B** represents the "synchronous disjunction" scheme, by which the double "metaphase" chromosomes "get onto the spindle" along its length, separate into sisters, perhaps attach to form two "trains," and these "trains" move in opposite directions along the spindle "railway track." (Based on sketches and personal correspondence from Dr. C. F. Robinow, University of Western Ontario, London, Ontario.)

other "chromosome" to the other pole. It has been proposed that only one chromosome in each compound chromosome may possess a centromere, and it leads the others to a pole. During anaphase the chromosomes gradually disappear from the "spindle" toward the poles, but often a thin filament, probably of aggregated spindle fiber material, links the dense telophase nuclei. Such "mitosis" has been reported in *Neurospora, Coleosporium, Aspergillus, Marasmius,* and *Helminthosporium.*

Much critical investigation of the difficult-to-study fungal nuclear division remains to be done before a clear integrated generalization can be synthesized. It is questionable that centrioles occur in Ascomycetes and Basidiomycetes; some seem to have intranuclear division, others do not; some have rather typical metaphase, others do not;

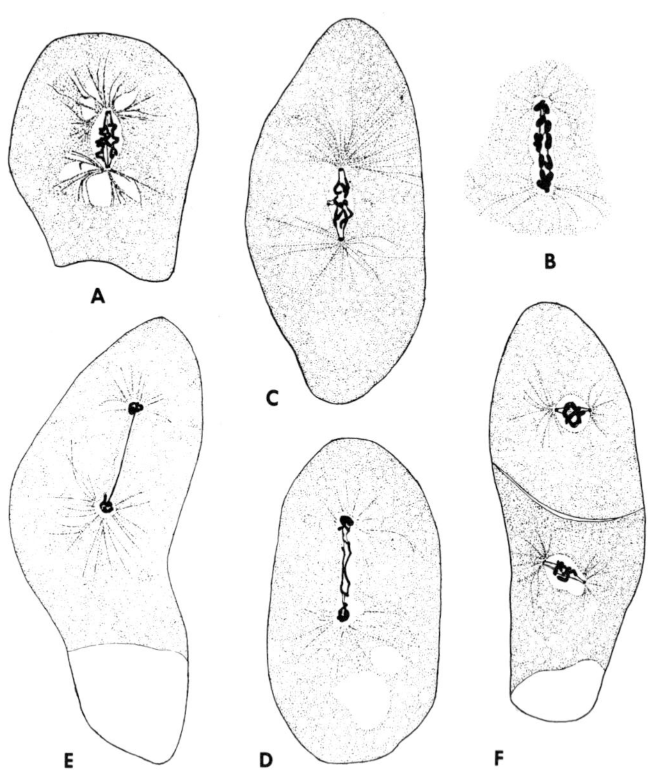

Fig. 17-12. Late stages of meiosis I in the rust fungus *Coleosporium vernoniae.* **A,** "Metaphase" as often seen in fungal divisions, both meiotic and mitotic. The spindle is narrow, almost a fiber, the chromosomes are arranged on its outside surface, the details of which are unknown, and there is no metaphase plate. **B,** Early anaphase. Chromosomes have disjoined simultaneously and are moving on the spindle, either all on one side (left side, for example) or interconnected, and are moving to one pole, whereas those on the other (right) side are moving toward the other; or disjunction has occurred successively near the middle of the spindle so that all those on the upper half of the spindle are moving toward the upper pole, whereas the rest are moving toward the lower pole. This is sometimes called "railway track" anaphase. **C,** Middle anaphase I. **D,** Later anaphase. **E,** Telophase, which typically has such a "fiber" connecting the two telophase groups of chromosomes. The "fiber" may be the disintegrating spindle. **F,** Metaphase II with the same sort of spindle and chromosomal arrangement. It is questionable if centrioles exist in ascomycetous and basidiomycetous fungi. (From Olive, L. S. 1949. Amer. J. Bot. **36:**41-50.)

spindles vary widely, from similar to those in yeast to rather typical ones; anaphase is often of the "railway track" type (Fig. 17-12) (whatever that means); in some yeasts there is no prophase contraction of chromosomes; etc. With respect to variation in fungal cytology it should be remembered that they may be polyphyletic and also that, like insects, the fungi are evolving rapidly and "trying" many cytological ways of getting along.

Flagellates. Dinoflagellate and euglenophyte "mitosis" is also so different from the classical scheme that the term hardly applies (Leadbeater and Dodge, 1967; Leedale, 1958; Kubai and Ris, 1969). In these organisms the histoneless chromosomes remain contracted during interphase; the chromosomes divide into sister chromatids progressively from one end; the nucleolus is permanent and divides; the nuclear envelope is permanent, achieving division by constricting at telophase; there is no typical or really any spindle; and there is no metaphase arrangement of chromosomes. In one dinoflagellate a few narrow tubular invaginations of the nuclear envelope form and extend into or completely through the nucleus. They run parallel to the direction of "anaphase" chromosome movement, and each contains several 180 Å microtubules. These cytoplasmic tubules, which can hardly be considered spindle fibers, are separated from any chromosomes present by the nuclear envelope walls of the invaginations. It is as likely that the microtubules are more related to the growth of the invaginations per se than to anaphase chromosome movement. Cytokinesis is by furrowing from one end of the organism, which is typical of many unicellular organisms.

Cytokinesis

Cytokinesis is said to be of two sorts in plants—furrowing in algae, fungi, and some microsporocyte divisions in vascular plants and cell plate formation in land plants, including the bryophytes. Thus furrowing is by far the typical mechanism among organisms in general, occurring in Prokaryota and all Eukaryota except land plants. Even in most land plants the separation of microspores is often accomplished by furrowing.

Furrowing. Furrowing in plants and fungi differs from that process in animals, primarily because the cell wall fills the furrow continuously as the furrow deepens. As far as is known, the furrowing process is largely the activity of the plasma membrane and/or the protoplasm just beneath it, under the control of evolved genetic systems. Thus where and when the furrow is formed varies in most organisms. For example, in a filamentous alga, vegetative division may regularly divide a cell into equal halves, but certain definite divisions are off center and produce two unequal daughter cells. Such *asymmetrical divisions* are often associated with production of cells for reproduction or special differentiation.

Furrowing is considered to be the general method of division of protoplasm into two parts. The name indicates that it is achieved by the plasma membrane in a band around the protoplast, in a definite and specified region, growing inward to produce a circumferential furrow. The furrow deepens progressively until it meets itself at the center, where the two membranes unite so that each daughter protoplast has a complete membrane. In some types of fungi (Ascomycetes and Basidiomycetes) and some algae, furrow growth may stop before it reaches the center. In Basidiomycetes the *dolipore septum* and *parenthesome* (Fig. 17-13) result. Thus a centrally located protoplasmic connection persists between adjacent cells. Among the Prokaryota, fungi, and algae, organisms having cell walls, the cell wall fills the furrow as it grows inward.

Furrowing seems to be the basic form of cytokinesis among organisms. Cell plate formation in land plants, however, is possibly an evolutionary replacement or alternative method and has been thought to be restricted to those plants. Furrowing occurs, at least in part, in all other groups, from Prokaryota to chordates.

Most attempts to study the mechanism of furrowing have been in the large zygotes of animals, amphibians, echinoderms, and others, that is, spherical cells which are essentially free and independent of other cells. Certainly, the observations made and conclusions drawn probably apply to such isolated cells, but division of cells deep within a tissue or even columnar epithelial cells (Kater, 1927, 1928) may be somewhat different, probably often by vacuole formation, where a dividing cell has extensive contact with closely appressed cells around it. Furthermore, a generally applicable scheme of furrowing must apply to all organisms except land plants; that is, it must apply to those with and without cell walls, with and without centrioles and asters, and even to the Prokaryota without spindles.

Numerous hypotheses have been proposed to explain the "pinching-in-half" type of furrowing in divisions of some large animal zygotes. Cytoplasmic currents flowing toward the equator near the surface from the two telophase poles and axial flow from the equatorial plane toward the two poles where the spindle had been was an early hypothesis. Presumably, the furrow grows inward parallel to the cytoplasmic flow in the equatorial plane. The idea of such currents, coupled to low-surface tension in the polar region and high tension in the equatorial surface, was a modification of the streaming hypothesis. Between 1915 and 1920 Heilbrunn and Chambers considered the possibility that the two polar asters are very viscous, whereas the equatorial region is highly fluid, and that

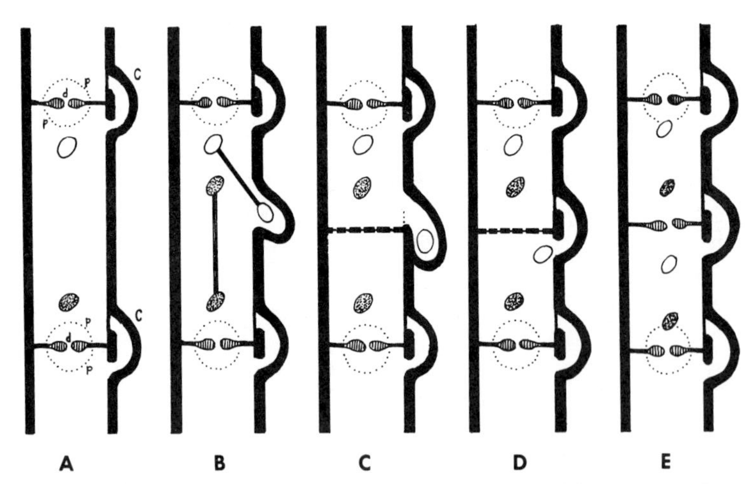

Fig. 17-13. Clamp connection development and function in Basidiomycetes. They perpetuate the dikaryophase in each cell, which includes one nucleus of each mating type. **A,** The mycelium at the start of division showing the two different nuclei and two old dolipore septa, **d,** with parenthesomes, **P,** and with old clamp connections, **C. B,** Beginning of new division. Tubular outgrowth appears on one side of the mycelium, and two nuclear divisions occur, one partly in the lateral tubular clamp connection and the other below and parallel to the mycelial axis. **C,** One daughter nucleus of each mating type is at the upper end of the dividing cell, one is in the tip of the developing clamp connection, and the fourth is near the bottom of the cell. **D,** Clamp connection is complete; it has discharged its nucleus into the lower end of the dividing cell; cross walls are forming, one at one end of the clamp connection; and a dolipore septum is forming across the mycelium at the level of the clamp connection. **E,** Division is complete, and each daughter cell is dikaryotic, having one nucleus of each mating type.

these contrasting conditions might induce the equatorial membrane to grow inward as a furrow (Fig. 17-8).

Some recent electron microscopic studies have indicated that a ring of microfilaments forms in the equatorial region around the telophase zygote just under the membrane. The contraction of this ring plays a part in constricting the cell to form the furrow.

More recently it has been shown that the plasma membrane of such isolated cells itself "flows" from the polar to the equatorial region and then inward as a furrow. Microscopic particles on the surface observed to move thus provided the evidence for this proposal. Such surface movement of cells in intimate contact and/or with cell walls, however, is difficult to conceive, and such mechanisms may not be the fundamental causes of more general furrowing. The budding of yeast, division by constriction in many unicellular algae, and formation of conidia and basidiospores in fungi are, if furrowing at all, extreme cases of loose "furrowing."

Cell plate formation. Cell plate formation is the usual mechanism of cytokinesis in land plants and is thought to be distinct from furrowing. After *karyokinesis* (division of the nucleus in mitosis), vesicles *(phragmosomes)* form in a plane that is genetically determined. Generally it is perpendicular to the spindle axis and equidistant from the two spindle poles (Fig. 17-17). Eventually these vesicles coalesce to form two new plasma membranes across the original cell and some material between them called the *middle lamella.* Subsequently, each new plasma membrane secretes material for two new primary walls against the new middle lamella, and cytokinesis is complete.

Electron microscopy seems to reveal the source of the vesicles to be dictyosomes and/or ER. It is also likely that the *continuous fibers* of the spindle (those that extend from pole to pole) are concerned with organizing or positioning the young cell plate (Fig. 17-1, parts *12* to *15*). Light microscopy has demonstrated that the cell plate starts near the center and grows outward in the plane toward the surrounding wall (Fig. 17-1, parts *16* to *20*). This *interzonal region* does contain continuous fibers of the spindle, and during early cell plate formation this region of spindle fibers, phragmosomes, ER, and dictyosomes has been called the *phragmoplast.* As the forming cell plate spreads laterally (Fig. 17-1, parts *17* to *20*), it invades the region lacking spindle fibers, but sometimes new short fibers perpendicular to the forming cell plate appear. Electron microscopy has now confirmed this (Fig. 17-17) and has demonstrated that the expanding circle contains a concentration of ER, dictyosomes, and vesicles. The latter, the vesicles that form the new plasma membranes and the middle lamella by fusion, have been called phragmosomes.

During the simultaneous cytokinesis after the second meiotic division in anthers of some plants, new chromosomeless spindles form and connect the four microspore nuclei. These special spindles act as phragmoplasts for the cytokinesis that produces the four microspores.

In the first pollen grain division and in the formation of subsidiary cells of the stomatal apparatus of grasses a curved, hemispheric cell plate is formed. In certain plant syncytia such as gymnosperm embryos and some endosperms, cell plates form among the scattered nuclei long after nuclear divisions that form the syncytia have been completed.

Cell plates, as they form, often have tubes of the ER running across. The cell plate leaves an opening around such ER tubes called a *plasmodesma* (Fig. 17-17). Certainly, such plasmodesmata often do have ER in each protoplast at their ends, but whether true ER runs through or not is still debated. Such plasmodesmata, if grouped and in certain types of cells, determine the loci of pit fields in primary walls and true pits in secondary walls. Other types of plasmodesmata that are not produced by cell plates exist in the lateral walls of certain types of endosperm.

Bajer (1965), on the basis of cinemicrographic analysis, and Esau and Gill (1965), on the basis of light and electron microscopy, proposed that the phragmoplast of plant cytokinesis is not just a dense region, nor is it a ring of dictyosomes around the spreading cell plate, nor does it consist of ER profiles oriented perpendicular to the long axis of the spindle, as others had proposed. Rather, it should be conceived as a discrete temporary entity, fully comparable to the mitotic spindle. It has its own microtubules, vesicles, and activity.

These authors propose that small vesicles form among the phragmoplast tubules, grow in size, and move, propelled by or guided by the tubules to the plane of the plate. There, it is assumed, the vesicles are positioned by tubules "pulling" on them in opposite directions, comparable to the spindle fibers positioning prometaphase chromosomes on the metaphase plate by "pulling" in opposite directions. In that position the vesicles fuse to form the cell plate.

This hypothesis does account for the exact location of the cell plate and seems to be a more valuable hypothesis than previous ones.

Thus cytokinesis by cell plate formation would seem to be entirely different from cytokinesis by furrowing and is a rather recent evolutionary process restricted to land plants.

Other forms of cytokinesis. Other forms of cytokinesis have been described over the years. One, which is probably common, especially in animals, is initiated by the formation of vacuoles among and between nuclei in plasmodia such as the plasmodial epithelium of a very young vertebrate embryo of *Mytilus* (Humphreys, 1964) and numerous fungal sporangia (Hohl and Hamamoto, 1967) as well as various nonplasmodial tissues of the rat (David, 1959; Buck, 1963). The vacuoles form, "position themselves" with respect to the nuclei, flatten, spread, and fuse to eventually cut off uninucleate cells. This form of cytokinesis can now be proposed as the probable enlargement of cisternae of the ER or of vesicles derived from ER or dictyosomes to become vacuoles, and the fused vacuolar membranes become two new regions of the plasma membranes.

Buck (1963) has demonstrated this sort of cytokinesis by electron microscopic work in rat erythroblasts of bone marrow, intestinal epithelium, and the regenerating liver and has shown that perhaps cell plate formation is not unique to land plants but may be typically a part of the furrowing process, at least in certain tissues of some animals. He reported the involvement of the continuous fibers of the spindle, a unique arrangement of the ER, and vacuole formation in rat cytokinesis as additional to the preliminary superficial furrowing. The portions of the continuous fibers where cytokinesis is to occur, that is, in the plane of the equator, become thickened to form the *midbody,* "stem body" of Belar, or "Flemming body," which has been seen in cytokinesis of other animals, including *Hydra* (Fawcett et al., 1959). At the same time the ER in what is to become the cytoplasms of the two daughter cells forms two separated sheets, parallel and close to the equator, and vesicles develop between them or are given off by them as a developing "cell plate." Eventual enlargement and fusion of vesicles form the two new continuous parts of the plasma membranes. The function of the continuous fibers and midbody is still unknown.

There are reports in the literature of membranes cutting cells out of a plasmodium in embryogeny of cycads, *Ephedra, Gnetum,* and other organisms and the formation of the membranes about the cells of the angiosperm embryo sac. If true, they also could be like cytokinesis by vacuoles, except that the two ER membranes do not separate far. It is also possible that such membranes are really somewhat modified cell plates.

Electron microscopy has now established that the cytokinesis of ascospores, in one species at least, is accomplished by the formation of special double membranes, one from the ER and the other from the nuclear envelope, that migrate and eventually surround and cut out the spores. The spore wall forms between the two membranes.

Thus in furrowing, some of the new plasma membranes are produced by increase of the existing surface membrane, whereas the new plasma membranes produced by vacuoles, membranes, and cell plates (phragmosomes) are derived from the ER or vesicles produced by ER or dictyosomes. These classes of cytokinesis, by membranes, vacuoles, and cell plates, seem to be the basic forms of cell division. In all cases, however, membrane probably does not arise de novo but from preexisting membranes. Robertson's unit membrane concept implies the basic similar structure and interconvertibility of the various sorts of membranes. Numerous observations seem to prove that vesicle and ER membrane can, indeed, become plasma membrane and vice versa.

General scheme. A general scheme of cytokinesis, at least for eukaryotic cells, seems to be that the continuous fibers of the spindle or specially formed microtubules function somehow in cytokinesis. Parts of the furrowing process and cell plate formation are similar in that the ER is involved and vesicles (phragmosomes in plants) are produced which enlarge, fuse, and form at least part of the new plasma membranes. The contents of the vesicles or phragmosomes become the new intercellular material (the middle lamella in plants). The difference between cytokinesis in animals and land plants seems to be that in animals furrowing is often the first apparent evidence of cytokinesis, with centrifugal "cell plate" formation and function of the midbody as the culminating process. In land plants, on the other hand, the midbody or phragmoplast is the first evidence of cytokinesis, and the phragmoplast does develop and function by centrifugal growth (Fig. 17-1). Thus the difference between higher plant and animal cytokinesis is only superficial, and among animals numerous variations with respect to the actual amount of furrowing and/or the actual amount of cytokinesis by cell plate formation in specific organisms and tissues is to be expected.

Cytokinesis in the Prokaryota seems to be accomplished entirely by the plasma membrane growing inward as a ring of growth until cytokinesis is complete. It is possible that in many algae and fungi also the inward-growing plasma membrane only, without vesicle formation, accomplishes division at telophase (Fig. 4-6).

Duration of mitosis

The duration of mitosis, especially if the interphase is included, varies considerably among species and tissues (Table 17-1). The few cases cited indicate a variation from 10 to 30 hours for a complete cycle. It is obvious, however, that the interphase is always much longer than division—about nine times as long. During division, prophase is considerably longer than any of the other phases, and anaphase is generally the shortest. Even anaphase usually lasts for 10 to 20 minutes; the actual rate of chromosomal movement is so slow that it is unobservable except by time-lapse photomicrography.

There are various methods of determining the time duration of mitosis and/or certain phases. Probably the most exact is direct observation of living cells by time-lapse photomicrography of animal culture cells or plant endosperm (Bajer, 1965) on a slide. Another method is to kill, embed, section, and stain a tissue, the cells of which are actively dividing, especially the meristematic region of a plant root tip. Counts are made of interphase and each mitotic phase nuclei. Such counts when reduced

Table 17-1. Duration of mitotic divisions in hours

	Interphase			Division				
	G_1	S	G_2	Pro-phase	Meta-phase	Ana-phase	Telo-phase	Total
Haplopappus	3.5	4	1.4	1.1	0.3	0.26 →		10.5
Tradescantia	4	10.8	2.7	1.6	0.3	0.6 →		20
Mouse	9.5	7.5	1 (approx.)	0.3	0.1	0.12	0.14	18.7
Vicia	12	6	8 →		4 →			30
Iris endosperm				0.75-1	0.16-0.5	0.2-0.4	0.75-1.25	
Pea endosperm				0.75	0.3	0.2	1.8	
Grasshopper				1.7	0.2	0.14	0.9	
Triton				0.27+	0.27-0.55	0.25-0.5	0.5	

to percentages give the percentages of time, the relative amounts of time nuclei spend in each phase. If a short pulse of tritium-labeled thymidine is given to living root tips and these are sampled at known time intervals after the pulse until metaphase chromosomes with label are detected, the beginning of the G_2 to metaphase period is determined. Samples taken later, when metaphase chromosomes cease to be labeled, give the end of the G_1 period. Much later samples, when metaphase chromosomes again appear labeled, give the next beginning of G_2, and thus the time for one whole cycle can be determined. Percentages of each phase can then be converted into time, and interphase can be divided into the already determined S phase. The time from the beginning of G_2 to metaphase, minus prophase, gives the duration of G_2. Total time minus S, G_2, and mitosis gives the duration of G_1.

Somatic pairing

"Somatic pairing" is a term applied to the close or loose association of homologous chromosomes during metaphase and/or anaphase of a mitotic division (Fig. 17-14). By about 1920 (Metz, 1916) it had been established that in probably all species of flies (Diptera) somatic pairing of homologues occurs during all mitotic divisions. The paired condition of giant (salivary gland) chromosomes (Fig. 17-16) is merely an example of this condition during interphase. The association of homologues as achiasmatic bivalents during meiosis in spermatocytes and genetic evidence of somatic crossing-over in male flies are other examples of this general condition in Diptera. Because pairing of "homologues" in salivary gland chromosomes varies so much among Diptera, within the genus *Drosophila*, and among *Drosophila* hybrids, Dobzhansky (1949) concluded that pairing of salivary gland chromosomes in *Drosophila* hybrids is influenced by genetic factors. It is as though in flies one or more genes for somatic pairing function all of the time or, conversely, that genes which prevent somatic pairing are turned off all of the time.

Fig. 17-14. Spermatogonial division of the fly *Calliphora vomitoria* showing the pairing or association of homologous chromosomes at metaphase of a mitotic division. (After Stevens, 1900.)

Among other types of organisms this

condition is less evident or does not occur. Diptera are therefore not good examples of general conditions of behavior of mitotic chromosomes in the Eukaryota, and generalizations related in any way to the phenomenon of somatic pairing should not be based on observations of Diptera alone. For example, Grell's concept of "dispersive pairing" in *Drosophila* (1965) may apply only to flies because it may be a case of "somatic" pairing during meiosis.

There are, however, many reports of somatic pairing in other kinds of organisms. One of the best known occurs at somatic metaphase in the genus *Yucca* and related genera, in which the basic chromosome set contains 5 large and 25 small chromosomes. Although homology has not been proved, numerous workers (for example, Watkins, 1935) have reported the association of similar large chromosomes around the periphery of the metaphase plate and loose pairing also of the small chromosomes. Therman (1951) has reported somatic pairing in the plant *Ornithogalum,* and Kitani (1963) has reported such pairing in *Vicia.* Boss (1955) has reviewed this subject after finding pairing of probably homologous chromosomes at anaphase in cultured newt cells (1954).

Somatic pairing seems to occur often in tissue or cell cultures, even though it does not in cells of the same species and tissue when part of a complete organism (Boss, 1954). Mitra and Steward (1961) reported not only pairing of definitely homologous chromosomes in culture of *Haplopappus gracilis* (n = 2) but also pseudochiasmata between the pairs. In normal root tips of this species there is no indication of somatic pairing. Revell (1953) has reported pseudochiasmata in *Vicia* root tips "produced" by a radiomimetic compound. Probably, somatic pairing, chiasma formation, and somatic reduction, somewhat similar to cases in cultured *Haplopappus* cells, are the basis of parasexuality in asexual fungi (Pontecorvo, 1958).

A special case of somatic pairing (see also following discussion of premeiotic mitosis and Chapter 18) is possibly a general feature of flower development (Brown and Stack, 1968). In 1947 Battaglia reported "heterotypic divisions" in somatic cells of the pistil of the flowering plant *Sambucus.* He claimed that homologues were paired by metaphase and that haploid anaphases resulted. Brown and Stack studied cell divisions in flower parts of *Haplopappus gracilis* because it has the extremely low chromosome number of 2n = 4. Therefore the type of division should be clearly evident and not obscured by a large number of chromosomes. Surprisingly, from 50% to 85% of divisions in the anther walls, pistil, and petals showed close somatic pairing of both pairs of homologues (Fig. 18-13), and in many of the other divisions one pair of homologues was closely associated. They also found evidence of ring pairing in somatic cells of flowers of the complex heterozygote *Rhoeo discolor* (Fig. 18-13), just as it should be if pairing of homologous ends does occur somatically.

Brown and Stack proposed that in such plants there may be a gradual and cumulative buildup of the paired condition more or less throughout the bud, as a general preliminary to meiosis occurring specifically in the sporogenous tissues. This slow accumulation of paired homologues they described as the process of *graduality,* in contrast to the concept of sudden pairing of homologues at zygotene of meiotic prophase. Graduality would also include such chromosomal changes during more than one premeiotic division, as have been reported by Rhoades (1961), Oksala (1944), and Tobias (1956) in other animals and plants (Chapter 18). Even the claim that reduction division occurs in the spermatogonia of lice (Rhoades, 1961) as much as six divisions before the spermatocyte may be a case of graduality because premeiotic pairing *does* in fact reduce the number of chromosomes. In *Haplopappus gracilis* the haploid chromosome number (n = 2) was evident in most somatic cells of the bud.

Brown and Stack did not claim that graduality occurs in all organisms, only that somatic pairing of homologues is accomplished before the premeiotic interphase. Pairing may occur rather suddenly, when the chromosomes are contracted just before premeiotic interphase. It is certain that graduality *cannot* occur in algae and fungi having zygotic meiosis. In many animals and plants also, pairing and reduction may occur suddenly, during the last premeiotic division only.

If somatic pairing of homologous chromosomes before premeiotic interphase does indeed occur typically as part of "meiosis," as seems likely, pairing of chromosomes in the contracted prometaphase-metaphase-anaphase condition, or possibly during prophase or even interphase, must be an effect of gene action that can be turned *on* or *off*. In the Diptera it is *on* all of the time; in other organisms cultural conditions are often able to turn it *on*. If somatic recombination is of evolutionary significance in asexual fungi (Pontecorvo, 1958), they, too, probably have genes for somatic pairing.

Evidence that the paired condition persists through somatic and premeiotic interphase is illustrated by the presence in most flower cells of *Plantago ovata* (2n = 8) of only four heterochromatic prochromosomes, whereas in root tip interphase nuclei there are eight, one for each chromosome (Fig. 15-9) (Stack and Brown, 1969). Janaki-Ammal (1932) had earlier reported similar paired prochromosomes in *Nicandra physaloides* (n = 10) floral cells, including cells of anthers.

Secondary association is probably related to somatic pairing but occurs during meiotic diakinesis and metaphase I (Lawrence, 1931). This phenomenon is evident as homeologous (similar genetically but not quite homologous) bivalent chromosomes lying close together but not in contact in a polyploid of ancient origin; that is, they are "paired at a distance," as are homologous chromosomes during somatic pairing. Just how homologous univalents during somatic pairing or homeologous bivalents during meiosis can "pair at a distance" is presently inexplicable.

As is discussed in more detail in the next section and in Chapter 18, it is likely that all species have genes for "somatic pairing" which are often turned *on* only during the condensed condition before premeiotic interphase.

Premeiotic mitosis

"Premeiotic mitosis" is the term applied to the last one or more mitotic divisions before the meiocytes form. In animals if there is only one such division, it would be the last gonial division and in higher plants, the last archesporial division. There is a considerable body of evidence that this is neither a typical mitotic nor meiotic division but of an intermediate or unique character, preparatory to meiosis (Fig. 18-13). It is discussed in detail in Chapter 18.

In 1942 Smith published an admittedly incomplete list of animal species in which various cytologists had reported that homologous chromosomes become closely paired during metaphase and/or anaphase of the last premeiotic mitosis. Naturally, many examples come from the Diptera (flies), since paired homologues are typical of all their divisions (Fig. 17-14). Nevertheless, there were examples from nearly all animal phyla. Watkins (1935) published a list of thirty-three plant species in which somatic pairing had been reported, and at least eight additional species have been reported since. Some of these are examples of somatic rather than premeiotic pairing.

In 1937 Atwood made a critical study of the last premeiotic division in the plant *Gaillardia* (2n = 72). He was trying to determine if anaphase chromosomes of that division are double and thus would be double going into meiosis. He did report a rather surprising doubling in late metaphase and assumed that each metaphase chromatid doubled at that time. On the other hand, he might have been seeing homologous pairing, but the large number of chromosomes prevented counting and critical observation.

Brown, one of the authors of this book, and Stack (1968) have seen many examples of closely paired homologues at metaphase and anaphase of this division in the ideal material, the plant species *Haplopappus gracilis* (Fig. 18-13), which was selected for the study because of its uniquely low number of typical chromosomes ($n = 2$). They also found end-to-end pairing of homologous ends in the somatic tissues of the complex heterozygote *Rhoeo discolor,* which they considered a rigorous test of their assumption based on *Haplopappus*. The implication is that the homologous chromosomes enter the premeiotic interphase already very closely paired, but not necessarily synapsed.

Rhoades (1961) has reported that corn chromosomes during the prophase of the last few premeiotic mitoses are longer than they are in typical mitotic divisions, as though the chromosomes are getting ready for meiosis.

Of course, so-called *somatic pairing,* of which this is probably an example, is common in Diptera and has been reported in cells of numerous tissue cultures of plant and animal materials. Even *somatic crossing-over* has been claimed by geneticists in male *Drosophila* and asexual fungi such as *Aspergillus,* and so-called *pseudochiasmata* have been seen between such paired somatic homologues. Therefore proposal of pairing of homologous chromosomes at premeiotic mitosis is not a wild unsupported claim of a unique condition; it is an alternative scheme to the more generally accepted dogma of zygotene pairing and is as equally well proved. It is a special case of somatic pairing in cells leading to meiosis and, as far as is known, is no different from somatic pairing in any other tissue of the organism where it may occur.

A number of cytogeneticists (Sachs, 1952; Feldman, 1966; Maguire, 1966; Grell, 1965) have already hypothecated premeiotic pairing of homologues, but based on indirect evidence. So it seems safe to propose at this time that premeiotic mitosis is a type of division; it is not a typical mitosis nor a typical meiotic division, and it is a regular preliminary to meiosis. It occurs also in somatic cells of some flower parts such as petals, receptacles, and stigmas but does not lead to meiosis. It is as though all the cells of the young flower bud are stimulated to change from typical mitosis to premeiotic mitosis, but only sporogenous cells lead to meiosis (Brown and Stack, 1968).

Pseudochiasmata

Pseudochiasmata are chiasmata or chiasma-like configurations between homologous chromosomes during normal or abnormal mitotic divisions.

It has long been known genetically that somatic crossing-over occurs in male *Drosophila* in which, apparently, no meiotic crossing-over occurs (Stern, 1936). Sturtevant and Dobzhansky (1930) reported a cross of four chromosomes regularly at *mitosis* in an interchange heterozygote of *Drosophila,* which must have involved somatic pairing between homologous segments. Somatic pairing and crossing-over must occur in such asexual fungi as *Aspergillus* (Pontecorvo, 1958).

Cytological observations of pseudochiasmata have been made of plant cells of root tips of *Vicia faba* treated with di-(2,3-epoxypropyl) ether (Revell, 1953) and in cells of *Haplopappus gracilis* grown in culture (Mitra and Steward, 1961). Revell concluded that homologous chromosomes were paired and then the chemical treatment caused breakage and reunion and that the breakage and reunion are in some way fostered by the act of pairing. Whether the pairing and formation of pseudochiasmata occurred during prophase or metaphase (observations were made of metaphase) is unknown, although Mitra and Steward illustrated a late prophase pseudochiasma that might have been produced at any other earlier stage, back to the previous metaphase.

Two sorts of pseudochiasmata are known. Those in mitotic cells may be either true chiasmata or a local association of two chromosomes that look like chiasmata. The latter may also occur during prophase of meiosis I in male flies (Cooper, 1944, 1949); the homologues stick together at a few "special pairing regions" but with no crossing-over or chiasmata.

This phenomenon of "true chiasmata" in somatic cells is related to somatic pairing and genetic recombination in at least asexual species.

Mitotic stimulators

Mitotic stimulators that can speed up divisions or restart them in postmitotic cells are known in both plants and animals. In plants they are simple molecules, but in animals they are mostly proteins and amino acid.

"Kinin" and "cytokinin" are terms that refer to certain natural or synthetic compounds, which at least under certain conditions, have the physiological activity of promoting cell divisions in plant and probably some animal tissues (Miller, 1961; Buckley et al., 1962; Skoog and Miller, 1965; Letham, 1967b). Haberlandt, as early as 1921, found good indirect evidence for some sort of a plant cell division hormone. During the 1950s Miller and others found further evidence for a cell division factor. Later still, a compound identified as 6-furfurylaminopurine (a derivative of adenine) was isolated from commercial DNA preparations and had properties of the natural factor (Miller et al., 1955a,b). The compound is called *kinetin.* Kinins, or *cytokinins,* are various 6-aminopurines, some of which are natural, such as zeatin, 6-(4-hydroxy-3-methylbut-*trans*-2-enyl)aminopurine, and 6-(3-methylbut-2-enyl)aminopurine, which have been detected in *Zea mays* and *Corynebacterium fascians,* respectively.

Jensen et al. (1964) reported that 1 ppm of kinetin inhibits RNA breakdown in rapidly elongating postmitotic cells after a few minutes. Several hours of exposure to the kinetin establishes an equilibrium above that of the control between RNA synthesis and breakdown. After 12 hours of exposure kinetin begins to inhibit DNA synthesis, and 48-hour exposure completely blocks all nucleic acid synthesis.

Since cytokinins are modified adenine, it is not surprising that at least some are incorporated into or found in hydrolyzates of certain animal, plant, and yeast transfer RNAs that typically contain a wide variety of substituted purines and pyrimidines. Cytokinins also inhibit certain enzymes, act as adenine antagonists, and may influence gene action by acting as gene de-repressors in the Jacob-Monod type of control (Letham, 1967a).

Auxin, the plant hormone (indolacetic acid, or IAA), also promotes cell divisions, alone or in association with a kinin. For example, auxin at the proper concentration can cause mitotic activity in mature pith cells that have ceased to divide. Actually, wounding alone, as by a pinprick or cutting, can directly or indirectly cause postmitotic cells to resume division. Auxin and kinetin together often increase mitotic activity more than either alone.

Skoog and Miller (1965) have pointed out that stimulation of nuclear division is only one effect of kinins and auxins. They also affect cell wall elongation, bud and root inhibition or stimulation, development of lateral roots, and other morphogenetic effects when applied in certain concentrations or combinations. Both are also probably involved in nucleic acid metabolism, including its synthesis (Jensen et al., 1964). Proper growth and development of plant parts seem to depend on a protoplasmic balance of kinis, auxin, adenine, and other organic and inorganic molecules, some of which appear to be antagonistic to one another.

Phytohemagglutinin is used widely in the preparation of vertebrate blood cells for chromosome studies. It not only agglutinates the red blood cells but it also starts the white cells, which normally divide rarely, toward mitotic divisions by turning on DNA replication and RNA transcription.

In animals certain growth factors that effect cell division have also been found (Cohen, 1965; Levi-Montalcini, 1965), but these are proteins. The "nerve growth factor" (NGF) causes increase in number and size of sensory and sympathetic nerve cells, and the "epidermal growth factor" (EGF) directly stimulates division of epidermal cells. Both have additional effects just as do the nonprotein growth factors of plants. Thyroxine, an amino acid, seems to raise the mitotic index as much as 600% in certain neurons when applied as a thyroid graft to tadpoles. Again, it is clear that stimulation of mitosis in certain brain and spinal cord cells is only one effect of thyroxine.

In all probability there are many other naturally occurring compounds in plants and animals that, at specific concentrations, stimulate mitotic divisions in certain cells as part of their overall effects on growth and development, of which cell division is a major aspect.

Supernumerary chromosomal reproductions

Supernumerary chromosomal reproductions was a phrase used by Lorz (1947) twenty-five years ago to include diverse mechanisms and results of increased chromosomal material in a nucleus, including formation of polytene chromosomes and the processes of endomitosis and polysomaty. An equivalent term is "endoreproduction." All of these are regular gene-determined cellular processes and not fortuitous "mistakes." Lorz even questioned whether the so-called random chromosome doubling so often reported in root tips of flowering plants is really a mistake. As the phrase indicates, all of these mechanisms produce nuclei with multiples of the zygotic chromosome number; that is, the chromosomes divide and multiply, but the nucleus does not. Therefore increase in chromosome number by nuclear fusion, as at syngamy and a few other known cases, is excluded. Since these supernumerary chromosomal reproductions are gene determined, they are regularly found in certain tissues of certain species or families or whole classes of plants and animals. It is immediately obvious that these phenomena are gene-directed modifications of typical cellular and mitotic divisions and therefore will be discussed in the order of increasing change from the typical cell division.

Multinucleate cells. Within anthers of flowering plants there is a layer of cells just outside the sporogenous cells, the *tapetum,* which is somehow important to the normal processes of meiosis and pollen grain development. It is probably true that all tapetal cells, about the time of meiosis of the adjacent microsporocytes, increase their chromosomal material one way or another. The simplest way this is accomplished, as in all grasses, tomato, and numerous other families, is a rather typical mitotic division without subsequent cytokinesis. This may be repeated, as in *Fuchsia, Chrysanthemum,* and *Galtonia,* to make four-nucleate tapetal cells. Some of these species also undergo endomitosis additionally. Thus each tapetal cell of such species shortly before it breaks down to provide material for development of the microspores is multinucleate and has two or four times the chromosomal material of ordinary diploid cells.

Polysomaty. Polysomaty is a nuclear process that is a somewhat more typical case of endoreproduction than a mere failure of cytokinesis. This is a true supernumerary chromosomal reproduction. Lorz, in his review, limited polysomaty to plants. In them it occurs regularly in tapetal cells of some species and in root tips and other tissues of many flowering plants. It is probably responsible for nearly all polyploid somatic cells of roots, stems, leaves, etc.

Although the details are unknown, it seems that each chromosome doubles structurally twice for one mitotic division. Doubling must occur twice in interphase and/or prophase because by metaphase there are twice as many two-chromatid chromosomes as is typical of mitotic divisions of the plant. Thus tapetal cells of *Haplopappus gracilis* ($2n = 4$) have $2n = 8$ and $2n = 16$ metaphase chromosomes as they undergo their last two divisions. In numerous species such as spinach, *Cannabis,* potato, onion, and beet, polysomaty occurs typically in root tips and in many species in shoot tips and leaves. In all cases, however, it is thought that polysomaty occurs in the last one or two divisions before division normally and finally stops in those cells, as the cell differentiates. This type of endomitosis is rather similar to the effects of colchicine and other mitotic poisons that destroy or prevent the spindle from forming and prevent anaphase. In the so-called C mitosis (for colchicine) the nuclear envelope breaks down, and sister chromosomes lie parallel to each other.

Endomitosis. The term "endomitosis" is generally used to include all cases of chromosomal reproductions, usually within a nuclear envelope, but especially with no effective anaphase separation. As originally used by Geitler (1937), the chromosomes do contract and pass through stages called *endoprophase, endometaphase,* and an ineffective *endoanaphase,* as in a few animal cells and the tapetal cells of tomato and spinach. As the *reconstitution nucleus* reverts to interphase, it has doubled the original number of chromosomes. This rather more modified mitotic division is perhaps the commonest form of endomitosis and results in an increased number of typical chromosomes. Geitler (1937) originally described this form of endomitosis in the water strider *(Gerris),* but that of tomato tapetum seems to be very similar (Brown, 1949). When the tomato microsporocytes are at leptotene (synizesis), the tapetal nucleus divides by a normal mitosis but no cytokinesis follows. During pachytene of the microsporocytes the paired nuclei of the tapetal cells simultaneously begin endomitosis. As far as prometaphase these divisions are similar to mitosis, and even prometaphase is similar in respect to the loss of nucleolus and nuclear envelope. However, no spindle seems to form, and consequently endometaphase is irregular and no movement of chromosomes occurs at endoanaphase, except that sister chromosomes do separate from one another. During endotelophase the double number of chromosomes (tetraploid in tomato) are included in each of the two nuclear envelopes of the resulting binucleate cell. Both nuclei proceed through these phases simultaneously. Endomitosis is repeated in both nuclei once more (octoploid) and rarely to the 16-ploid stage. It is possible that 32-ploid nuclei are sometimes formed in the binucleate tomato tapetal cells.

Endomitosis of this sort is essentially normal mitosis with a gene-determined lack of spindle formation. In some species, however, the nuclear envelope may persist throughout. A common form of endomitosis is characterized by chromosomal reproduction in a probable interphase, with no observable "mitotic" phases. As in polysomaty and the previously described form of endomitosis, the doubling can be repeated a number of times, always with an exact doubling of the previous "chromosome" number. Therefore, starting with a diploid number, tetraploid, octoploid, 16-ploid, up to 1,000-ploid or more are achieved in certain cells of particular species. In this form of endomitosis, after each interphase increase in chromosome number the daughter interphase chromosomes separate from each other so that *each chromosome is a typical interphase "chromosome."*

Since interphase chromosomes cannot be counted or directly observed as such, the determination of how many there are in an endomitotic nucleus depends on indirect determinations. The classical example of this method is the water bug *Gerris,* as worked out by Geitler. It is known that in each set of 20 autosomes of *Gerris* chromosomes from an XO-type male there is a heterochromatic X chromosome, which during interphase is contracted as an obvious blob. It was also determined that a tetraploid nucleus has two and an octoploid nucleus has four such obvious heterochromatic chromosomes. Therefore by counting X chromosomes in the nuclei of various tissues it was possible to determine the ploidy of male interphase nuclei, the ploidy being twice the number of visible Xs. Geitler found that muscle cells were tetraploid; midgut epidermal cells were 16-ploid; nuclei of the lining of the sperm duct were octoploid; of the seminal septum 16-ploid; of various portions of the malpighian tubules 16-, 32-, and 64-ploid; and in certain cells of the fat body 64- and 128-ploid. The highest grade of ploidy occurred in the highly pleomorphic resting nuclei of the salivary gland (1,024- and 2,048-ploid).

Another classical example of endomitosis occurs in the mosquito gut lining (Berger, 1938; Grell, 1946). The chromosome number of the species is 2n = 6. After the egg hatches there are no mitotic or cell divisions in this tissue, but the nuclei and cells enlarge greatly during larval life. In the pupa this tissue persists, and the nuclei divide. The first division usually has ninety-six chromosomes per metaphase group, indicating that there were four endomitotic divisions during larval life (6-12-24-48-96). The subsequent divisions are also classical. The 96 chromosomes of the first division are paired as 48 "bivalents," which separate as two anaphase groups of 48 each. During this anaphase the homologues again pair (synapse?) and remain paired; at the second division they form 24 bivalents. The 24-chromosome anaphase groups again form pairs of homologues and at the third metaphase there are 12 bivalents. At the fourth division there are 6 pairs, and each anaphase has the zygotic number. From then on there is only the loose pairing of homologues typical of all Diptera, no bivalents are formed, and each nucleus is diploid (2n = 6).

Similar analysis has revealed that the macronuclei of ciliates and nuclei of some other Protozoa are highly polyploid. The primary nucleus of the radiolarian *Aulacantha* is considered to be 1,028-ploid.

Polyteny. Polytene chromosomes are also formed by interphase divisions, but the daughter, granddaughter, etc., chromatids remain intimately associated. Thus whereas the 21 chromosomes of a male *Gerris* became 43,000 essentially typical interphase chromosomes in a huge pleomorphic nucleus, the n = X "synapsed" chromosomes of the very young salivary gland cell of a fly remain X even after nine or ten endomitotic divisions, but each eventually consists of a bundle of about 1,000 parallel interphase chromonemata. That is, the polytene chromosome, as the name connotes, consists of many parallel, united, indistinguishable strands. Polytene chromosomes are therefore unusually large and highly compound bundles of long chromonemata, although in corn endosperm (Duncan and Ross, 1950) the polytene chromosomes are probably only slightly larger than normal ones.

One usage of the term "polytene," or "polyneme," applies to "typical" chromosomes. From electron microscopic study of chromosomes several workers are convinced that a typical interphase chromosome may itself be constituted of a rather large number of parallel, genetically identical, fine (100 to 200 Å) filaments. However, this assumption is tentative and not to be accepted as a valid description of chromosome fine structure. This concept is employed, however, to "explain" the often considerable difference in chromosome diameter, volume, and amount of DNA between closely or distantly related species or even among cells of different tissues of an individual. For example, salamanders have more than ten times as much DNA per cell as do mammals or reptiles.

So-called polytene chromosomes, also called *giant interphase chromosomes* and *salivary chromosomes,* however, are probably of a different composition. They seem to be at least 100 times as long and up to 10,000 times the cross-sectional area of a typical interphase chromosome. They are typically banded transversely, although each band is really a disk of fused chromomeres, and often show their "synapsed" character by short or long splits down the center. They are generally present in the haploid number, and each half, or the whole, of the giant chromosome is a solid cylinder of about 1,000 chromonemata.

Giant interphase chromosomes. Such giant chromosomes seem to be limited to a variety of tissues of Diptera, a collembolan, and a few special cells (suspensors) of some plant embryos. They seem to be an alternate condition to endopolyploidy. The salivary glands and their giant chromosomes are broken down and destroyed in the pupa. In the mosquito the nuclei of the inner layer of the gut are endopolyploid, whereas the cells of the malpighian tubules are polytene. In most cecidomyids the one or two "super giant" cells of each salivary gland is *either* polytene *or* endopolyploid. But, uniquely, the "super giant" salivary gland cells of the cecidomyid *Lestodiplosis* have chromosomes that are *both* polytene *and* endopolyploid; that is, there are about twenty "small" giant polytene chromosomes of each of the basic set of four (White, 1954). There is considerable evidence that the size (extent of polyteny) varies with age of the larva and also among tissues; generally the salivary gland cells have the largest giant chromosomes. Furthermore, the sizes of salivary gland chromosomes vary among genera of flies, as does intimacy of "synapsis." In *Drosophila* and *Chironomus* the polytene homologues are tightly paired, whereas in *Simulium* they are loosely twisted about each other and attached at only a few points.

The *chromocenter* of many such nuclei is a fused mass of heterochromatin of all the chromosomes. In *Drosophila melanogaster* the heterochromatic regions of the chromosomes are adjacent to the centromeres so that in such salivary gland nuclei it appears as though the arms of all chromosomes radiate outward from the chromocenter. Chromocenters are not found in salivary gland nuclei of all genera. There is none in *Sciara, Bibio, Simulium,* the Chironomidae, and the Cecidomyidae.

Because there has been so much cytogenetic and structural study of polytene chromosomes of salivary glands of *Drosophila, Chironomus,* and others, the terms "giant interphase chromosomes" and "salivary gland chromosomes" are essentially interchangeable, and "salivary gland chromosome" is the more commonly used term even for similar polytene chromosomes of other tissues.

Salivary gland chromosomes. Salivary gland chromosomes, then, are large, "synapsed," banded, polytene, interphase chromosomes (Fig. 17-15). Because homol-

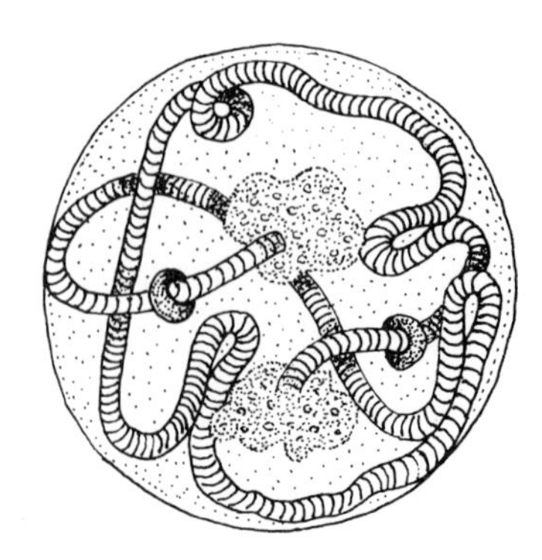

Fig. 17-15. "Permanent spireme nucleus" from the salivary gland cell of larva of the fly *Chironomus.* Two "Balbiani rings," now called "puffs," are evident. (After Balbiani, 1881.)

ogous chromosomes are paired (intimately in *Drosophila*), any heterozygous structural differences of the parents show up in the salivaries. Painter in 1933 first established this fact for hybrids of known structural rearrangements such as inversions and translocations. In such heterozygous salivaries the corresponding bands (fused chromomeres) were still paired, even though complicated configurations were required. In a loose sense, bands represent gene loci so that gene order, deletions, etc., show up visibly. However, metabolic activity, as represented by RNA synthesis, seems located in the interband regions. Actually, the bands are of variable thickness and spacing so that particular regions of particular chromosomes can be readily identified and recognized; therefore they have been valuable aids to cytogenetic study.

Some salivary gland chromosomes have, along their length, one or more diffuse, small or large swellings known as *puffs* (Fig. 17-16). Large puffs may be called *Balbiani rings* because Balbiani in 1881 drew them as rings around the chromosomes (Fig. 17-15). Modern study has indicated that a puff is formed by all or most of the chromonemata of a band extending out laterally and very locally as many loops. The hundreds of loops all formed at one locus (band?) produce a puff, a single loop of which can be more or less related to a loop of the lampbrush chromosome on a small scale; that is, a loop in a large puff may be about 5 μm in length, whereas a loop of a lampbrush chromosome is about 50 μm. In both cases, however, it is assumed that such a loop is a nucleoprotein strand in active metabolism, especially active in

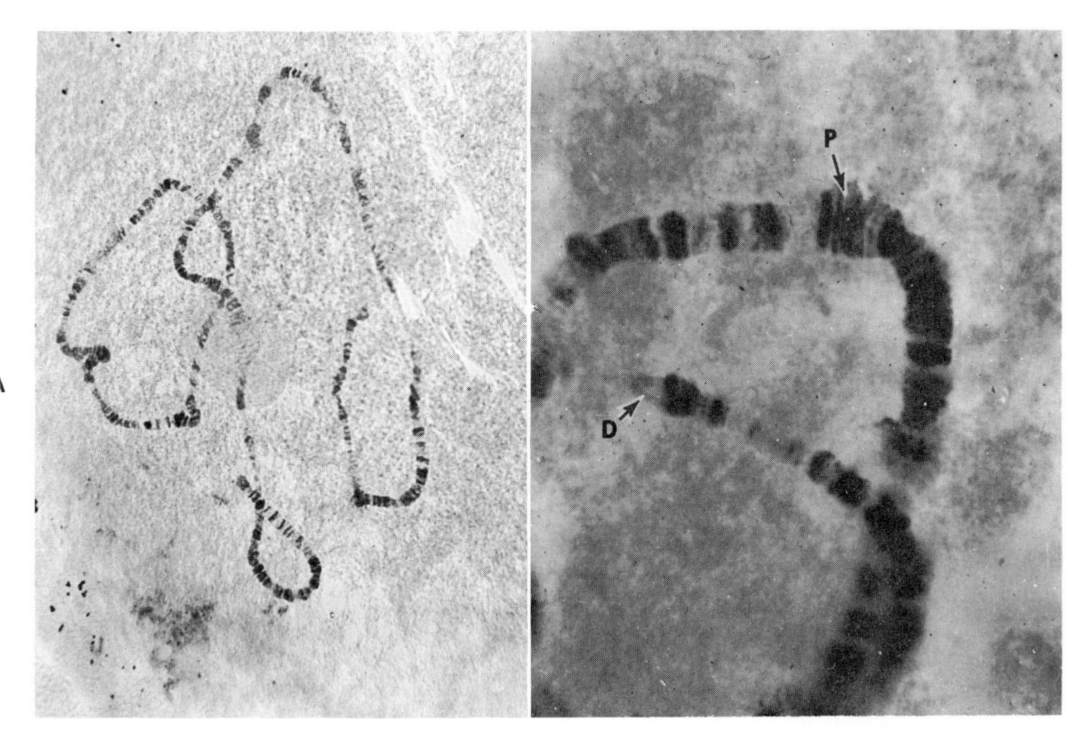

Fig. 17-16. Salivary gland chromosomes from an unidentified species of the fly *Chironomus*. **A,** Low-power photomicrograph of squashed cell showing all of the giant chromosomes. The low-contrast gray mass at the center may be the chromocenter. **B,** Higher magnification of part of one or more salivaries. At top right is a puff, **P.** The end of a chromosome, **D,** shows its doubleness. The bands are darkly stained; the interbands are unstained.

RNA synthesis. Experiments with puffs in different tissues of one organism, in different cells of one salivary gland, or in comparable cells at different times have demonstrated that they are not permanent, species specific, or random. Rather, they represent characteristic active sites correlated with the activity of the tissue or cell at a specific time (Beermann, 1963; Pavan, 1965; Bultmann and Clever, 1969). Each puff seems to represent a "gene," operon, or whatnot that has been induced to actively synthesize mRNA at a certain time for the production of some specific enzyme or proteinaceous glandular secretion. For example, the moulting hormone of insects, ecdysone, injected into a *Chironomus* larva produces a puff in a specific site on chromosome 1 in about 30 minutes. A second puff appears at a specific site on chromosome 4 about 30 minutes later. Since these responses always follow, it is assumed that the hormone acts directly as an inducer or is indirectly responsible by affecting the sodium pump of the plasma membrane and thereby the Na^+/K^+ ionic ratio of the protoplasm, which affects puffing of certain bands.

Thus salivary gland chromosomes have contributed considerably to cytogenetic knowledge of chromosome structure and now to cytological aspects of information transfer in differentiation. At least in this last area of research they will continue as unique subjects of great scientific value.

Amitosis

"Amitosis" is the term applied to cases (real and assumed) of an "interphase" nucleus pinching into two more or less equal halves without passing through any phases of mitosis.

During the nineteenth and early twentieth centuries many cases of amitosis were reported among plants and animals. It is now generally accepted that many of these were observations of polymorphic interphase nuclei or intranuclear divisions of a temporary dumbell shape, the observer interpreting the configuration as an apparent step in an amitotic division. Many other cases were apparently correct but of pathological conditions and so not applicable to normal healthy cells (Fig. 15-4).

True amitotic nuclear division does occur in the ciliate Protozoa but is restricted to the macronucleus, which is highly polytene as a result of numerous endomitotic divisions. Therefore an approximately equal or an unequal division of such a highly redundant macronucleus is certain to have many chromosomes of each kind in each approximate half. As an example, the ciliate *Stentor* has a macronucleus arranged like a string of about twelve beads. Transplantation of one such "bead," that is, one twelfth of the complete macronucleus, into an individual from which the whole macronucleus had been removed was sufficient for the requirement of continued existence and the function of producing RNA for protein synthesis.

Amitosis has been claimed as the mechanism of "nuclear" division in the Prokaryota. In a sense that is true, since the separation of the daughter genophores, probably in a fully extended condition, is in no sense mitotic. Nevertheless, it is somehow an exact distribution of whole chromosomes, or the one whole chromosome, by some unknown mechanism and not at all a pinching in half of a nucleus.

Amitosis, except in ciliates and some other Protozoa, is not a mechanism of nuclear division in normal healthy cells.

Cell synchrony

The term "synchrony" is usually applied to cultures of unicellular organisms (bacteria, algae, yeast, protozoa, etc.) in which large numbers of cells (or all cells) divide at the same time (Zeuthen, 1964; Cameron and Padillo, 1966). The condition is produced by various treatments that stop activity at a certain phase so all cells can "catch up" and reach that condition; then they are all released together. Such cul-

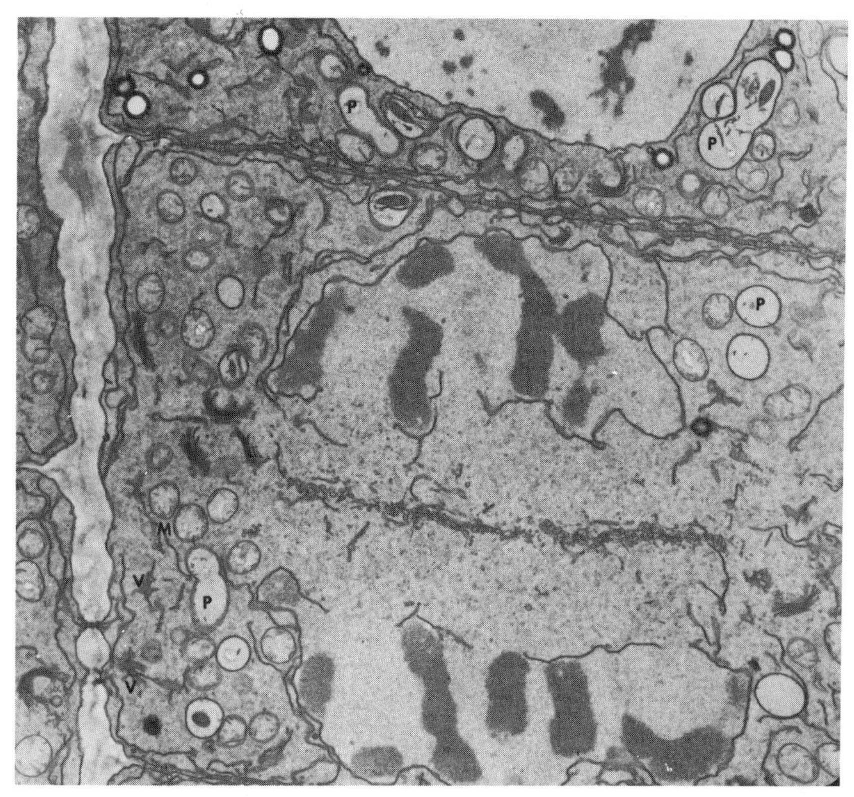

Fig. 17-17. Formation of nuclear envelope at telophase in corn root tip cells. Nuclear envelope forms as disconnected pieces of membrane in contact with exposed parts of chromosomes, but not with chromosomal surfaces within the telophase mass. It is likely that the chromosome-envelope contact remains until the next prophase. Also note developing cell plate of vesicles (phragmosomes), pieces of ER, and some dictyosomes near one end of the developing plate. Leukoplasts, **P,** mitochondria, **M,** and small vacuoles, **V,** are also evident. (Courtesy Dr. M. Dauwalder, University of Texas Cell Research Institute, Austin, Texas.)

tures are useful in studying biochemical changes that occur during division and for electron microscopy of division. Under natural conditions, however, cells, whether of a population of unicellular organisms or of a tissue of a multicellular organism, generally do not divide synchronously; rather, the cells are usually in all phases of mitosis and interphase at any instant of time. The nuclei of multinucleate cells, however, generally do divide simultaneously.

In plants most sporocytes in an anther or anther sac or a sporangium usually divide almost synchronously. Early divisions of endosperm in those angiosperm species having free nuclear endosperm in the embryo sacs divide synchronously. Numerous studies of divisions of cells in root tips have indicated in some species at least certain periods of the day or night when divisions are somewhat more numerous than at other times, but some divisions occur all the time. No true synchrony has been reported in root tips of any species.

In many animal species, groups of spermatogonia and spermatocytes divide synchronously and have protoplasmic bridges between adjacent cells (Fawcett et al., 1959). In arthropod eggs the nuclear divisions in the syncytium are synchronous at first, for five (32 cells) to twelve (4,000 cells) divisions. Then, as in free nuclear endosperm of plants, waves of division pass through the syncytium; that is, there is an orderly transition to asynchrony, which is achieved as plasma membranes form. All spermatogonia in each cyst of many arthropod testes divide synchronously, and there is radial synchrony of spermatogonial divisions in tubules of vertebrate testes. The cnidoblasts of *Hydra* are in groups of up to 16, and all cells of a group divide synchronously. In the flatworm *Plagiostomum girardi* the 10 to 12 eggs in a cocoon start to divide synchronously.

Thus cases of natural synchrony are known, but they generally involve nuclei derived from one original nucleus, either in a syncytium or a group of sister cells.

LITERATURE CITED

Atwood, S. 1937. The last premeiotic mitosis and its relation to meiosis in Gaillardia. Proc. Nat. Acad. Sci. U.S.A. **23:**1-5.

Bajer, A. 1965. Cine-micrographic analysis of cell plate formation in endosperm. Exp. Cell Res. **37:**376-398.

Battaglia, E. 1947. Divisione eterotypica in cellule somatiche di Sambucus ebulus L. Nuovo. G. Bot. Ital. **54:**724-733.

Battaglia, E. 1964. Cytogenetics of B-chromosomes. Caryologia **17:**245.

Beermann, W. 1963. Structure and function of interphase chromosomes. In S. J. Geerts (editor). Genetics today. Vol. 2. Pergamon Press, Inc., New York.

Berger, C. A. 1938. Multiplication and reduction of somatic chromosome groups as a regular developmental process in the mosquito, Culex pipiens. Contrib. Embryol. No. 167, pp. 210-232.

Boss, J. 1954. Mitosis in cultures of newt tissues. II. Chromosome pairing in anaphase. Exp. Cell Res. **7:**225-234.

Boss, J. 1955. The pairing of somatic chromosomes; a survey. Texas Rep. Biol. Med. **13:** 213-227.

Brown, S. W. 1949. Endomitosis in the tapetum of tomato. Amer. J. Bot. **36:**703-716.

Brown, W. V. 1972. Textbook of cytogenetics. The C. V. Mosby Co., St. Louis.

Brown, W. V., and W. H. P. Emery. 1957. Persistent nucleoli and grass systematics. Amer. J. Bot. **44:**585-590.

Brown, W. V., and S. M. Stack. 1968. Somatic pairing as a regular preliminary to meiosis. Bull. Torrey Bot. Club **95:**369-378.

Buck, R. C. 1963. The central spindle and the cleavage furrow. In L. Levine (editor). The cell in mitosis. Academic Press, Inc., New York.

Buckley, W. B., E. R. Witkus, and C. A. Berger. 1962. Kinetin, as a mitotic stimulant in Triturus viridescens. Nature (London) **194:**1200-1201.

Bultmann, H., and U. Clever. 1969. Chromosomal control of foot pad development in Sarcophaga bullata. I. The puffing pattern. Chromosoma **28:**120-135.

Cameron, I. L., and G. M. Padillo (editors). 1966. Cell synchrony. Academic Press, Inc., New York.

Cleveland, L. R. 1953. Studies on chromosomes and nuclear division. III. Pairing, segregation, and crossing-over. Trans. Amer. Phil. Soc. **43:** 809-869.

Cohen, S. 1965. Isolation and biological effects of an epidermal growth-stimulating protein. In E. Bell (editor). Molecular and cellular aspects of development. Harper & Row, Publishers, New York.

Cooper, K. W. 1944. Analysis of meiotic pairing in Olfersia and consideration of the reciprocal chiasmata hypothesis of sex chromosome conjugation in male Drosophila. Genetics **29:**537-568.

Cooper, K. W. 1949. The cytogenetics of meiosis in Drosophila. Mitotic and meiotic autosomal chiasmata without crossing over in the male. J. Morph. **84:**81-122.

David, H. 1959. Acta Biol. Med. Ger. **3:**330-337. (Cited by Buck, 1963.)

Delbruck, M., and G. Stent. 1957. On the mechanism of DNA replication. In W. D. McElroy, and B. Glass (editors). The chemical basis of heredity. The Johns Hopkins Press, Baltimore.

Dietz, R. 1966. The dispensability of the centrioles in the spermatocyte divisions of Pales ferruginea (Nematocera). In C. D. Darlington, and K. R. Lewis (editors). Chromosomes today. Plenum Press, Inc., New York.

Dobzhansky, T. 1949. Genetics and the origin of species. Columbia University Press, New York.

Dodge, J. D. 1963. The nucleus and nuclear division in the Dinophyceae Arch. Protistink. **106:** 442-452.

Duncan, R. E., and J. G. Ross. 1950. The nucleus in differentiation and development. III. Nuclei of maize endosperm. J. Hered. **41:**259-268.

Esau, K., and R. H. Gill. 1965. Observations on cytokinesis. Planta **67:**168-181.

Fawcett, D. W., S. Ito, and D. Slautterback. 1959. The occurrence of intercellular bridges in

groups of cells exhibiting synchronous differentiation. J. Biophys. Biochem. Cytol. **5**:453-460.
Feldman, M. 1966. The effect of pairing of chromosomes 5B, 5D, and 5A on chromosomal pairing in Triticum aestivum. Proc. Nat. Acad. Sci. U.S.A. **55**:1447.
Geitler, L. 1937. Die Analyse des Kernbaus and der Kernteilung der Wasserlaufer Gerris lateralis und Gerris lacustris und die Somadifferenzierung. Z. Zellforsch. **26**:641-698.
Grell, F. 1946. Cytological studies in Culex. I. Somatic reduction divisions. II. Diploid and meiotic divisions. Genetics **31**:60-94.
Grell, R. F. 1965. Chromosome pairing, crossing-over, and segregation in Drosophila melanogaster. In J. I. Valencia and R. F. Grell (editors). International symposium on genes and chromosomes: structure and function. Government Printing Office, Washington, D. C.
Hohl, H. R., and S. T. Hamamoto. 1967. Ultrastructural changes during zoospore formation in Phytophthora parasitica. Amer. J. Bot. **54**:1131-1139.
Humphreys, W. J. 1964. Electron microscope studies of the fertilized egg and two-cell stage of Mytilus edulis. J. Ultrastruct. Res. **10**:244-262.
Janaki-Ammal, E. K. 1932. Chromosome studies in Nicandra physaloides. Cellule **41**:87-110.
Jensen, W. A., E. G. Pollock, P. Healey, and M. Ashton. 1964. Kinetin and the nucleic acid content of onion root tips. Exp. Cell Res. **33**: 523-530.
Kater, J. M. 1927. Nuclear structure in active and hibernating frogs. Z. Zellforsch. **5**:263-277.
Kater, J. M. 1928. Nuclear structure and chromosomal individuality. Somatic and germ nuclei of the rat. Z. Zellforsch. **6**:587-610.
Kitani, Y. 1963. Orientation, arrangement, and association of somatic chromosomes. Jap. J. Hum. Genet. **38**:244-256.
Kubai, D. F., and H. Ris. 1969. Division in the dinoflagellate Gyrodinium cohnii (Schiller): a new type of nuclear reproduction. J. Cell Biol. **40**:508-528.
Lawrence, W. J. C. 1931. The secondary association of chromosomes. Cytologia **2**:352-384.
Leadbeater, B., and J. D. Dodge. 1967. An electron microscope study of nuclear and cell division in a dinoflagellate. Arch. Mikrobiol. **57**: 239-254.
Leedale, G. F. 1958. Nuclear structure and mitosis in the Euglenineae. Arch. Mikrobiol. **32**:32-64.
Letham, D. S. 1967a. Chemistry and physiology of kinetin-like compounds. Ann. Rev. Plant Physiol. **18**:349-364.
Letham, D. S. 1967b. Regulators of cell division in plant tissues. V. A comparison of the activities of zeatin and other cytokinins in five bioassays. Planta **74**:228-242.
Levi-Montalcini, R. 1965. Growth control of nerve cells by a protein factor and its antiserum. In E. Bell (editor). Molecular and cellular aspects of development. Harper & Row, Publishers, New York.
Levine, L. 1963. The cell in mitosis. Academic Press, Inc., New York.
Longwell, A. C., and G. Svihla. 1960. Specific chromosomal control of the nucleolus and of cytoplasm in wheat. Exp. Cell Res. **20**:294-312.
Lorz, A. P. 1947. Supernumerary chromosomal reproductions: polytene chromosomes, endomitosis, multiple chromosome complexes, polysomaty. Bot. Rev. **13**:597-624.
Luykx, P. 1970. Cellular mechanisms of chromosome distribtuion. Int. Rev. Cytol. Suppl. 2. Academic Press, Inc., New York.
Maguire, M. P. 1966. The relationship of crossing over to chromosome synapsis in a short paracentric inversion. Genetics **53**:1071-1077.
Mahlberg, P. G., and P. S. Sabharwal. 1967. Mitosis in the non-articulated lactifer of Euphorbia marginata. Amer. J. Bot. **54**:465-472.
Mazia, D. 1961. Mitosis and the physiology of cell division. In J. Brachet and A. E. Mirsky (editors). The cell. Vol. 3. Academic Press, Inc., New York.
Metz, C. W. 1916. Chromosome studies on the Diptera. II. The paired association of chromosomes in the Diptera, and its significance. J. Exp. Zool. **21**:213-236.
Miller, C. O. 1961. A kinin-like compound in maize. Proc. Nat. Acad. Sci. U.S.A. **47**:170-174.
Miller, C. O., F. Skoog, M. H. von Saltza, and F. M. Strong. 1955a. Kinetin, a cell division factor from deoxyribonucleic acid. J. Amer. Chem. Soc. **77**:1392-1394.
Miller, C. O., F. Skoog, F. S. Okumura, M. H. von Saltza, and F. M. Strong. 1955b. J. Amer. Chem. Soc. **78**:1375.
Mitra, J., and F. C. Steward. 1961. Growth induction in cultures of Haplopappus gracilis. II. The behavior of the nucleus. Amer. J. Bot. **48**:358-368.
Oksala, T. 1944. Ann. Acad. Sci. Fenn. ser. A. **4**(5):1. (Cited by Rhoades, 1961.)
Painter, T. S. 1933. A new method for the study of chromosome rearrangements and the plotting of chromosome maps. Science **78**:585-586.
Pavan, C. 1965. Chromosome differentiation. In J. I. Valencia and R. F. Grell (editors). International symposium on genes and chromosomes: structure and function. Government Printing Office, Washington, D. C.
Pontecorvo, G. 1958. Trends in genetic analysis. Columbia University Press, New York.

Revell, S. H. 1953. Chromosome breakage by x-rays and radiomimetic substances in Vicia. Heredity **6:**107-124.

Rhoades, M. M. 1961. Meiosis. In J. Brachet and A. E. Mirsky (editors). The cell. Vol. 3. Academic Press, Inc., New York.

Robinow, C. F., and J. Marak. 1966. A fiber apparatus in the nucleus of the yeast cell. J. Cell Biol. **29:**129-151.

Sachs, L. 1952. Chromosome mosaics in experimental amphidiploids in the Triticinae. Heredity **6:**157-170.

Schrader, I. 1953. Mitosis. Columbia University Press, New York.

Sharp, L. 1934. An introduction to cytology. 3rd ed. McGraw-Hill Book Co., New York.

Skoog, F., and C. O. Miller. 1965. Chemical regulation of growth and organ formation in plant tissue cultured in vitro. In E. Bell (editor). Molecular and cellular aspects of development. Harper & Row, Publishers, New York.

Smith, S. G. 1942. Polarization and progression in pairing. II. Premeiotic orientation and the initiation of pairing. Canad. J. Res. **20:**221-229.

Stack, S. M., and W. V. Brown. 1969. Somatic and premeiotic pairing of homologues in Plantago ovata. Bull. Torrey Bot. Club **96:**143-149.

Stern, C. 1936. Somatic crossing over and segregation in Drosophila melanogaster. Genetics **21:**625-630.

Sturtevant, A. H., and T. Dobzhansky. 1930. Reciprocal translocations in Drosophila and their bearing on Oenothera cytology and genetics. Proc. Nat. Acad. Sci. U.S.A. **16:**532-536.

Therman, E. 1951. Somatic and secondary pairing in Ornithogalum. Heredity **5:**253-269.

Tobias, P. V. 1956. Chromosomes, sex-cells, and evolution in a mammal. Percy Lund, Humphries, & Co., Ltd., London.

Uhl, C. H. 1965. Chromosome structure and crossing over. Genetics **51:**191-207.

Watkins, G. M. 1935. A study of chromosome pairing in Yucca rupicola. Bull. Torrey Bot. Club **62:**133-150.

White, M. J. D. 1954. Animal cytology and evolution. Cambridge University Press, New York.

Wilson, E. B. 1937. The cell in development and heredity. 3rd ed. The Macmillan Co., New York.

Zeuthen, E. (editor). 1964. Synchrony in cell division and growth. John Wiley & Sons, Inc., New York.

CHAPTER 18

Meiosis and related cytology

Meiosis (Rhoades, 1961) is a genetically controlled cellular act that is complementary to sexuality, the two having evolved simultaneously. That is, during any life cycle involving sexuality there must be meiosis in at least one sex somewhere during that cycle. Sexuality produces a diploid nucleus from two haploid nuclei; meiosis, which occurs in a *meiocyte,* produces haploid nuclei from a diploid. Sexuality always occurs in a life cycle at the creation of a zygote, but meiosis may occur anywhere else in the life cycle, from just after sexuality *(zygotic meiosis)* as in numerous fungi and unicellular algae, to quite remotely in the cycle as in most plants that have sporophyte and gametophyte generations, to just before sexuality *(gametic meiosis)* as in most animals. In animals, meiosis produces cells (spermatids and ootids) that become gametes; in most plants, meiosis produces cells that become spores, cells that do not act as gametes but grow by mitotic divisions into gametophytes or, in fungi, into the haploid phase of the life cycle.

It is possible to characterize organisms as amictic, mictic, or apomictic. *Amictic* organisms are those in whose ancestry there has never been sexuality, such as the Prokaryota, some unicellular algae, and some Protozoa. Of course, amictic organisms do not have meiosis either. *Mictic* organisms are sexual and have meiosis, either in its typical form or some, probably recent, adequate modification. *Apomictic* organisms are those (probably of recent origin) that have given up sexuality and, of course, meiosis also. Apomictic organisms (properly called *parthenogenetic* by zoologists) are commonest in the higher fungi (the so-called imperfect fungi), various insects and other animals, and flowering plants, especially the grasses. They have various modifications of or methods for bypassing both meiosis and sexuality and will be discussed later.

In most sexual species (multicellular animals and seed plants) meiosis occurs in two distinct organs. Both organs may occur in the same individual, called *hermaphroditic* (most plants and numerous animals), or in distinct individuals, called males and females if animals and dioecious if plant species. In animals these organs are called *testes* if they produce sperm and called *ovaries* if they produce ova (eggs). Meiosis produces microspores in the *microsporangia* of seed plants (the *anthers* of flowering plants) and in a few nonseed plants such as *Selaginella;* in the *megasporangia* (ovules of seed plants) it produces megaspores. Microspores develop into male gametophytes and megaspores into female gametophytes. In plants other than the seed plants (with few exceptions) and in fungi, meiosis occurs in only one general type of structure, called the *sporangium,* and only one type of spore is produced, except for mating types. Fundamentally, meiosis is the same in all of these various sorts of sexually reproducing organisms, but there are often minor differences, as between spermatogenesis and oogenesis. In some animals having modified meiosis the differences may be spectacular, and some cases will be discussed later.

In such an introductory text as this it is impossible to describe many of the unusual modifications of meiosis that are known to occur in animals and plants, especially in numerous insects. The student is referred to White (1954) for zoological and Stebbins (1950) for botanical details of these interesting modifications as examples of cellular evolution in progress. At this point the generalized meiotic process will be discussed.

Typical meiosis, as usually described, consists of two sequential, modified "mitotic" divisions, of which the first has a greatly modified prophase. There is some strong evidence, however, that at least the last *premeiotic mitosis* (the mitotic division just before the first meiotic one) shows some preliminary cytological modification in many organisms and perhaps should be considered as part of the overall meiotic

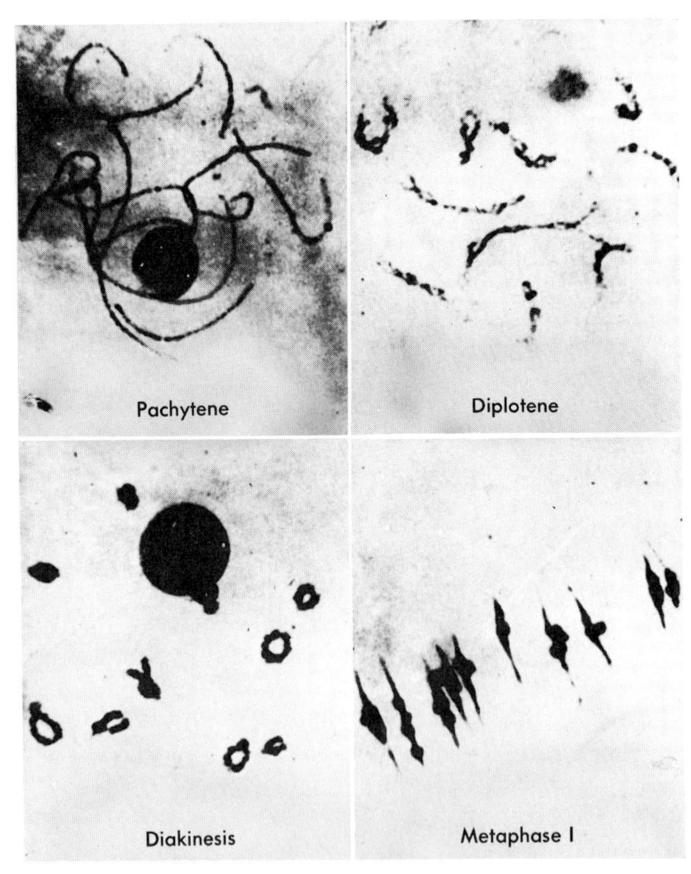

Fig. 18-1. Early stages of meiosis in maize. The paired nature of bivalents and chiasmata are evident at diplotene and diakinesis. Compare this photomicrograph of pachytene with the interpretation in Fig. 18-8. (From Rhoades, M. M. 1950. J. Hered. **41:**49-67.)

process (Smith, 1942; Boss, 1955; Rhoades, 1961; Brown and Stack, 1968).

The main nuclear difference between the first meiotic prophase and the prophase of mitosis is that pairing of homologous chromosomes occurs (or has already occurred) in the former, thereby producing *bivalent chromosomes* united by *chiasmata* and reducing the chromosome number to half. Associated with such pairing or *synapsis* in most organisms are a few exchanges between nonsister but homologous chromonemata at more or less random sites along the bivalents, producing the cytological *chiasmata* that are probably equivalent to the genetic *crossovers.* Subsequent events from prometaphase I through the rest of meiosis I and the second meiotic division (meiosis II) are similar to mitotic divisions, except that there is no DNA or structural doubling of chromosomes between telophase I and prophase II, and the two-chromatid metaphase II chromosomes have existed as such at least since anaphase I. In other words, during meiosis there is only one DNA doubling (during the interphase before prophase I) and one structural doubling (at least by midprophase I) for two nuclear or chromosomal divisions. The result (including pairing of homologous chromosomes and crossing-over) is the reduction by one half of the original diploid

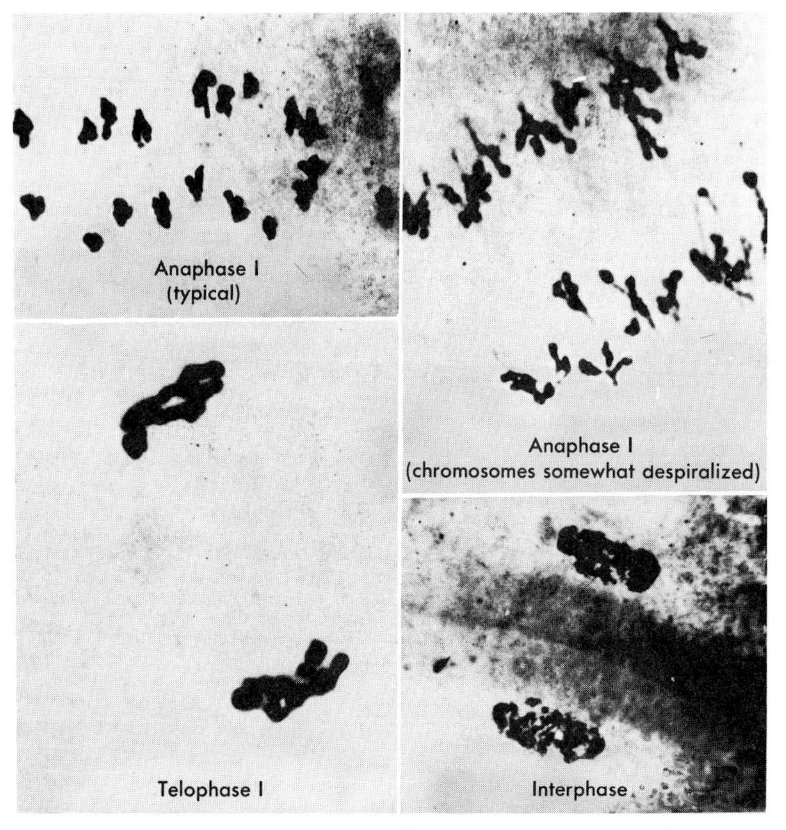

Fig. 18-2. Final stages of meiosis I in corn. These stages follow those shown in Fig. 18-1. Notice the odd, four-parted, X-shaped anaphase I chromosomes when despiralized. (From Rhoades, M. M. 1950. J. Hered. **41:**49-67.)

chromosome number and recombination of linked genes.

It is only recently that the designations "meiosis I" and "meiosis II" have been used. Previously, meiosis I was called the *heterotypic mitosis,* implying that it is an atypical mitosis, which it certainly is; meiosis II was called the *homeotypic mitosis,* implying that it is a fairly typical mitotic division, which it is. Actually, the same "phases" are recognized in both divisions of meiosis as in mitosis—prophase, prometaphase, metaphase, anaphase, and telophase —except that prophase I can be further subdivided into *leptotene* (or leptonema), *zygotene* (or zygonema), *pachytene* (or pachynema), *diplotene* (or diplonema), and *diakinesis,* which is then followed by prometaphase I (Figs. 18-1 to 18-3).

Premeiotic preparations

Before the first meiotic division begins some preparatory cellular changes of the cytoplasm and nucleus of the meiocyte take place. These changes, for example, changes of ER, mitochondria, ribosomes, and also at the biochemical and genetic levels, cause meiosis rather than just another mitotic division. These changes from mitosis are probably initiated in part by the interaction of the particular environment of the reproductive cells acting on certain genes. This environment generally includes special "nurse" cells, which, themselves, have become specialized also. It is still not known whether the chromonemata going into prophase I are any different from chromonemata going into a mitotic prophase, although there are numerous reports of

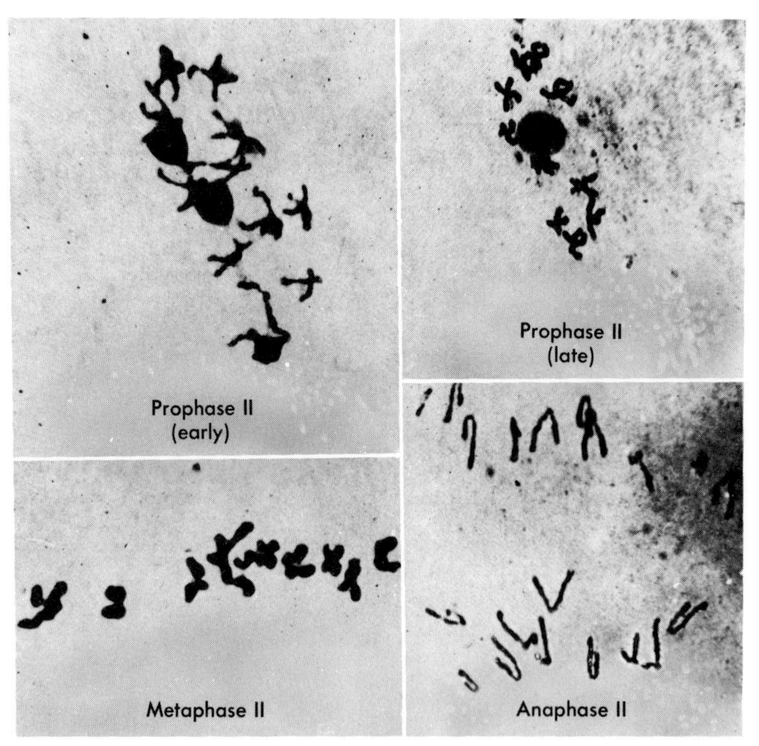

Fig. 18-3. Meiosis II in corn. These stages follow those shown in Fig. 18-2. Compare the X-shaped prophase II chromosomes with those of anaphase I. Each four-stranded diplotene chromosome has finally dispersed into four separate, single-stranded anaphase II chromosomes. (From Rhoades, M. M. 1950. J. Hered. **41**:49-67.)

animals and a few plants in which pairing is claimed to be accomplished during the premeiotic mitosis. There has been great indecision regarding the exact time, mechanism, and place of pairing. It has been proposed that meiotic chromonemata going into prophase are single, whereas chromonemata going into mitosis are already double; yet there are many reports of double chromosomes at premeiotic anaphase and telophase (Atwood, 1937). Tritium-labeled thymidine incorporation indicates that all or most DNA is replicated before leptotene. The x-raying of premeiotic interphase nuclei indicates, by chromatid rather than chromosome breaks at metaphase I, that chromosomes are also structurally double before leptotene (Mitra, 1958).

Prophase I

Preleptotene. Although the usual first stage of meiotic prophase I is leptotene, a previous stage of considerable chromosomal contraction, called preleptotene, has been described in several plants and probably animal species as the "Croft" clone of *Lilium longiflorum* (Walters, 1970, 1972). The contraction by spiralization of the chromosomes can be considerable, resembling late prophase of mitosis, although some microsporocytes in the same anthers contract less and some appear to pass directly from interphase into leptotene. It has been proposed that preleptotene may represent a condition of the chromosomes actually entering a mitotic prophase pathway, which is then halted by cellular control. The nucleus then reverts to the leptotene condition by the chromosome despiralizing. The cell enters the unique meiotic pathway characteristic of meiocytes. If this hypothesis is correct, it seems likely that in most species the false mitotic start of preleptotene does not occur, and the premeiotic interphase nuclei enter directly into the meiotic pathway at leptotene.

Leptotene. The chromonemata at earliest prophase of meiosis I, called leptotene, usually *appear* to be single (the observational evidence is difficult and poor) and, in contrast to mitosis, remain long, thin, and uncoiled (Gelei, 1921; Belling, 1933). From leptotene to pachytene each chromosome (whether single, double, or quadruple) may appear as a string of small beads of various sizes and spacing. Each "bead" is called a *chromomere* (see later in this chapter). In many animals and some plants the chromosomes are often "attached" to the nuclear envelope at leptotene. It has been reported that chromosome ends or only one end (McClung, 1927) is attached to the nuclear envelope in a limited area (closest to the centrosome in animals), whereas the rest of each chromosome forms a long loop within the nucleus (Fig. 18-4). It is possible also that the centromere regions are attached to the nuclear envelope elsewhere. Since in this configuration chromosome ends are attached to the nuclear envelope close together in the same region and the looped chromosomes extend inward from there, this configuration is called the *bouquet*. Actually, chromosome ends may always be "attached" to the nuclear envelope (except during division), which is

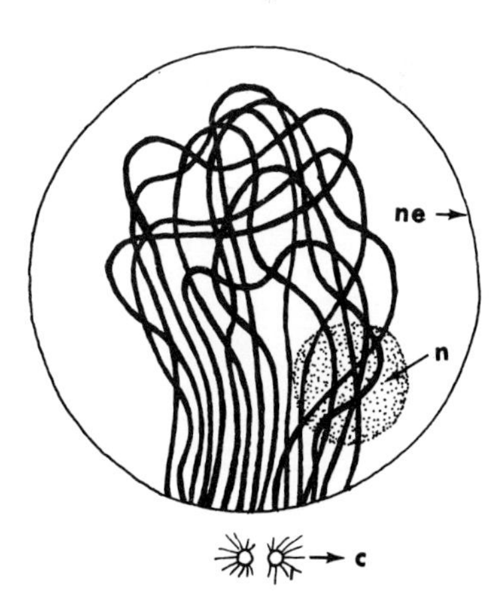

Fig. 18-4. Diagrammatic representation of bouquet stage of prophase I in animal gametocyte. Chromosome ends are in contact with nuclear envelope within a limited region and opposite to the centriole. **ne,** Nuclear envelope; **n,** nucleolus; **c,** centriole.

explicable since at telophase the new nuclear envelope forms in contact with the chromosomes (Barer et al., 1959), and this contact may persist between telomeres (chromosomal ends) and the envelope (Fig. 17-17).

In several organisms it has been shown by labeling experiments that synthesis of DNA does not stop before meiotic prophase begins, as it does in mitosis, but continues into leptotene. For this and other reasons it has been proposed that leptotene, zygotene, and pachytene might better be considered as constituting a unique G_2 period rather than being comparable to mitotic prophase (Brown, 1972). In fact, some DNA synthesis has been reported during pachytene (Hotta et al., 1966).

At this same leptotene stage in plants and some animals the chromosomes (perhaps as a fixation artifact) form a knot attached to the nucleolus. This dense chromosomal aggregate is called the *synizetic knot* (Fig. 18-5) and is thought by some cytologists to be comparable to the bouquet. Leptotene, which is difficult to study cytologically, gradually becomes the next phase, although some cytologists doubt that there is, in fact, a leptotene phase.

Zygotene. Zygotene, as the name implies, is thought to be the phase of pairing or synapsis (again, the observational evidence is difficult and poor) during which homologous chromosomes come slowly together gene for gene, often described as "zipper-like" (Fig. 18-6). On the other hand, Smith (1942) stated that "the pairing of homologues consummated at pachytene is initiated at the latest by the telophase of the last premitotic division," and he listed dozens of reports from most animal phyla to support the statement. Watkins (1935) cited reports of loose pairing of homologous

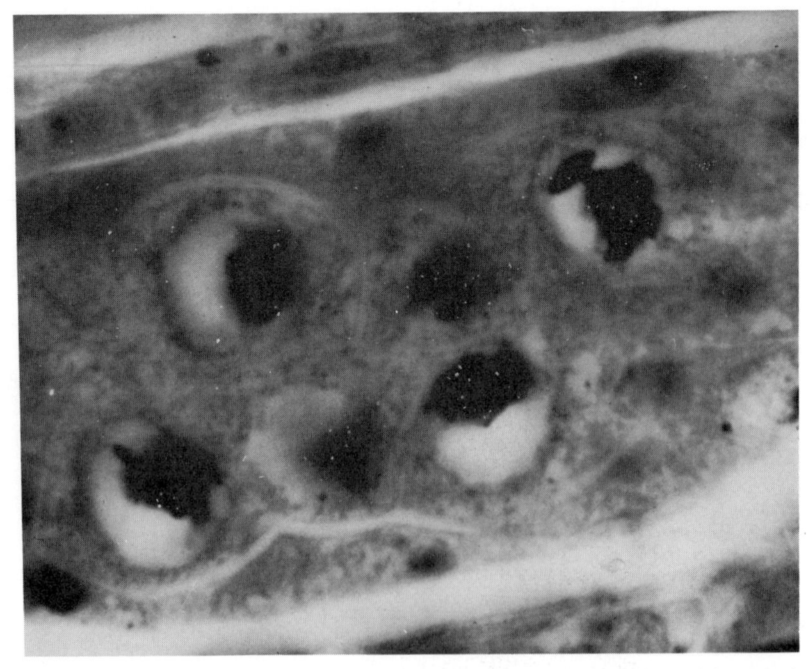

Fig. 18-5. Synizesis in *Haplopappus gracilis.* The chromosomes are collapsed into an irregular mass at one side of the nucleus, and the mass is connected to the nucleolus (cell at upper right). In that cell the nucleolus is lenticular and is appressed against the nuclear envelope, which is typical of first meiotic prophase in this and many other species.

chromosomes during root tip mitotic metaphase of thirty six species of seventeen families of angiosperms. He implied that such pairing may be a general tendency but not evident or actually occurring in many species. Pairing of homologues at premeiotic mitosis and association of chromosome ends and perhaps centromere regions with the nuclear envelope at definite regions could represent a mechanistic preparatory phase for the bouquet configuration and synapsis during early stages of meiosis (pp. 450 and 453). Another disagreement with the usual scheme of meiosis, in addition to McClung's (1927), is that of Moens (1964), who claimed that the first prophase I stage rather than leptotene is actually pachytene. The old zygotene does not rep-

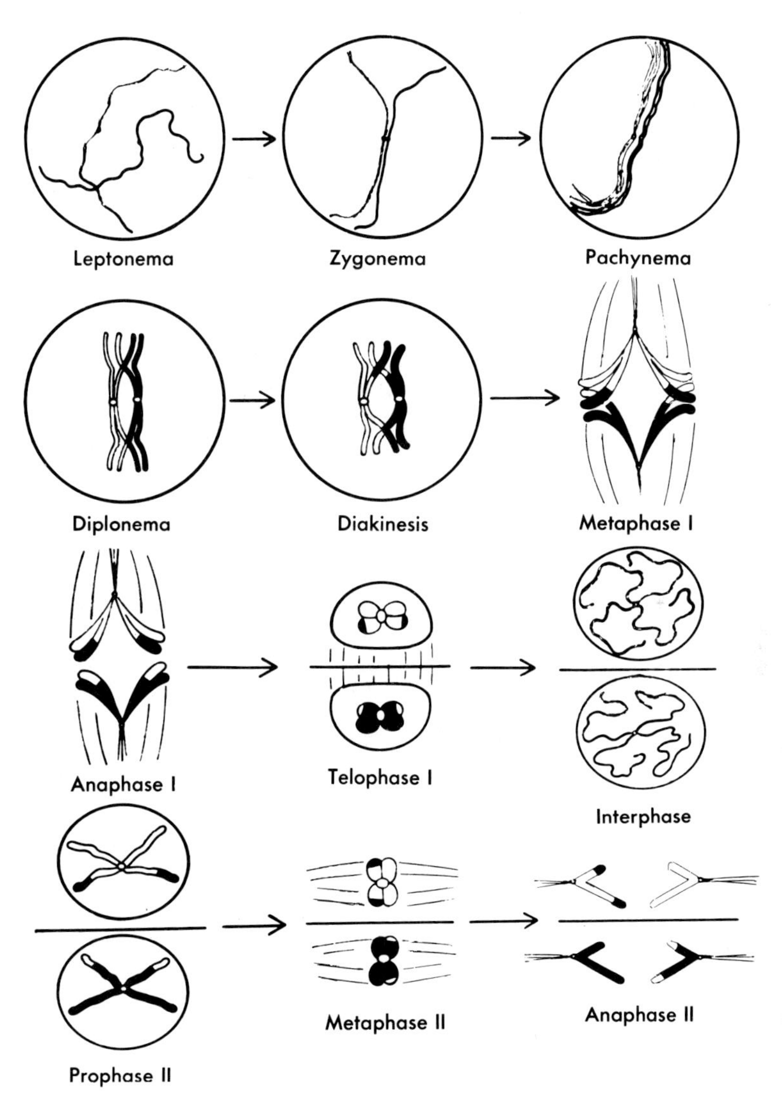

Fig. 18-6. Highly schematized diagram of stages of meiosis according to the popular concept, as though the cell had only one pair of chromosomes ($n = 1$). Notice doubleness of each chromosome from pachytene to metaphase II. (From Rhoades, M. M. 1950. J. Hered. **41:** 49-67.)

resent pairing, he concluded, but the beginning of opening out and should be called *schizotene.* Diplotene, diakinesis, and the other stages follow as generally accepted. This scheme *requires* premeiotic pairing and eliminates leptotene. Correlation of increasing anther lengths in lilies with meiotic stages, however, supports the classical scheme of leptotene, zygotene, and then pachytene (Moens, 1968).

Regardless of when pairing and synapsis actually occur and whether they may be

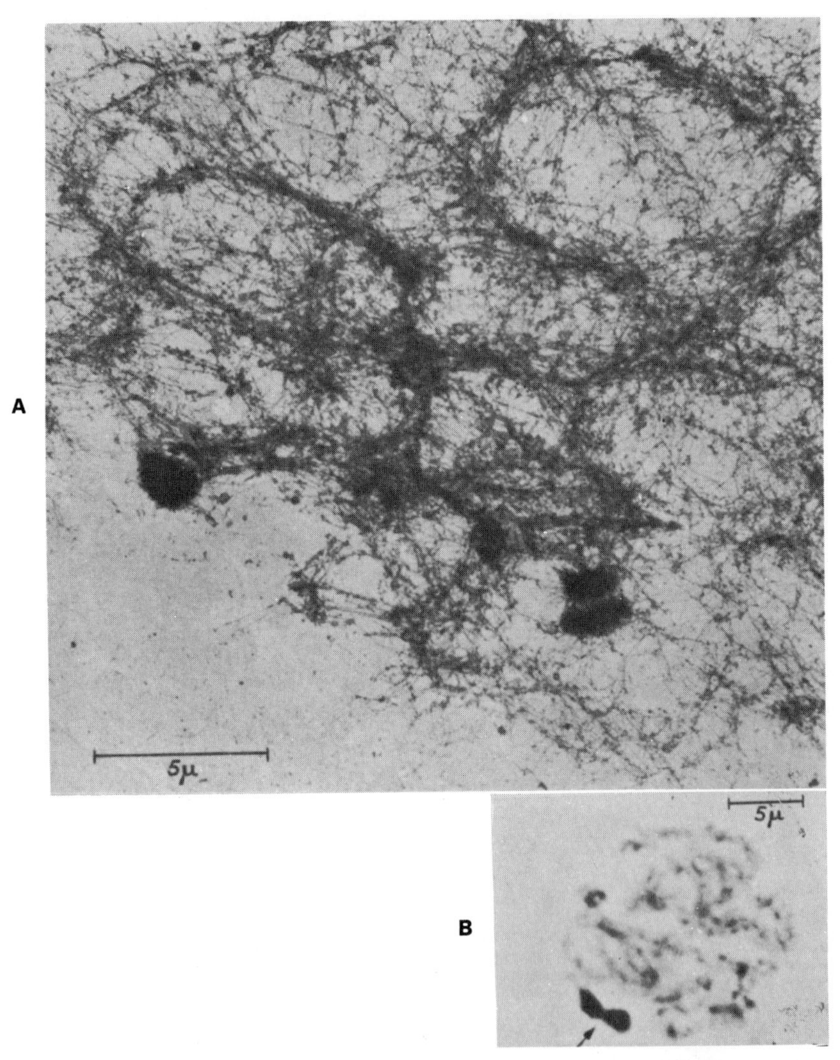

Fig. 18-7. A, Electron micrograph of zygotene chromosomes of the heteropteran insect *Oncopeltus fasciatus* after cells were burst, spread, and dehydrated. (×4,800.) **B,** Light micrograph of the same chromosomes, except an aceto-orcein squash was used. X and Y sex chromosomes are evident in **A** and are indicated by arrow in **B.** Other fibrous aggregates represent autosomes. Fibers are nucleoprotein and have a thickness of about 250 Å. Subsequent meiotic stages show increasing concentration of fibers. This technical method produces images of chromosomes that are quite unlike others. Where and what is synapsis? (From Wolfe, S. L., and B. John. 1965. Chromosoma **17:**85-103.)

different names for one act or distinct and separate acts, there are certainly important but inexplicable genetic and chromosome actions that are involved in synapsis, such as how can two specific homologous chromosomes (really their genes?) "recognize" one another at a distance among all the other nonhomologous chromosomes, as they seem to do, and then by some natural force "move" together, pair, and synapse so that only the same genes (or alleles) come together? Does the nuclear envelope during the bouquet stage or earlier have anything to do with sorting out and bringing together the homologous chromosomes? What is there about different genes that causes gene-for-gene synapsis only? Does gene-for-gene synapsis really occur or is synapsis restricted to a few short segments, *collochores,* that Pritchard (1960) called *effective pairing?* The most likely mechanism by which each gene can recognize its identical twin or allele is by its nucleotide sequence, somewhat like base pairing, but there is as yet no conceptual model for this. Perhaps the fact that metaphase chromosomes contain a large amount of "ribosomal" RNA (Huberman and Attardi, 1966) is a clue to the pairing phenomenon, although proteins are usually considered to be the pairing and recognition substance. What is the relationship between synapsis (or crossing-over) and the synaptinemal complex (discussed later in this chapter)? And how is crossing-over actually achieved (Fig. 18-7)?

It does seem evident, cytologically, that zygotene pairing, including synapsis, is a slow process and that it begins at the chromosome ends and/or the centromere or elsewhere and progresses along the two elongate homologous chromosomes. Furthermore, it is only rarely, and then in cells with long chromosomes, that two pairs of synapsing homologues become tangled so that one chromonema of each pair runs between the two chromonemata of the other pair to produce a pair of *interlocked chromosomes* (Fig. 18-20). Interlocking is now considered to be an aspect of partial homology (Davidson and Webster, 1966). By the end of zygotene, synapsis is probably completed, but the bouquet configuration may persist into the next phase.

In angiosperms there are numerous observations confirming that during meiosis in the anthers the cell walls between adjacent meiocytes are partially dissolved, leaving channels through which the protoplasts become confluent. This condition is called *cytomixis* (Fig. 18-29). Observations indicate that these channels in the walls arise de novo and are not expansions of preexisting plasmodesmata. They vary in size but are often easily visible in the light microscope. There are numerous reports from light and electron micrographs that organelles and chromosomes do indeed pass through from cell to cell. Cytomixis has been observed in anthers of so many species that it may be a general condition of late prophase I meiocytes.

Fawcett et al. (1959) have shown that a somewhat comparable condition occurs in many animals, from *Hydra* to vertebrates. That is, between adjacent spermatocytes and spermatids the plasma membranes are broadly incomplete so that the two (or more) protoplasts are confluent. Other observations indicate that cytomixis may be an artifact of preparation.

Pachytene. Pachytene is a phase of meiotic prophase that has contributed considerably to our present knowledge of cytogenetics, especially of corn, and chromosome structure (Figs. 18-1, 18-8, and 18-9). Compared to leptotene and zygotene, it is somewhat easier to observe since the synapsed chromosomes are generally shorter, thicker, easier to spread in preparation, and more widely spaced. Some cytologists believe that at early pachytene each bivalent consists of two synapsed chromonemata and that during this phase each splits longitudinally so that each bivalent chromosome becomes a packet of four long strands more or less intimately associated gene for gene.

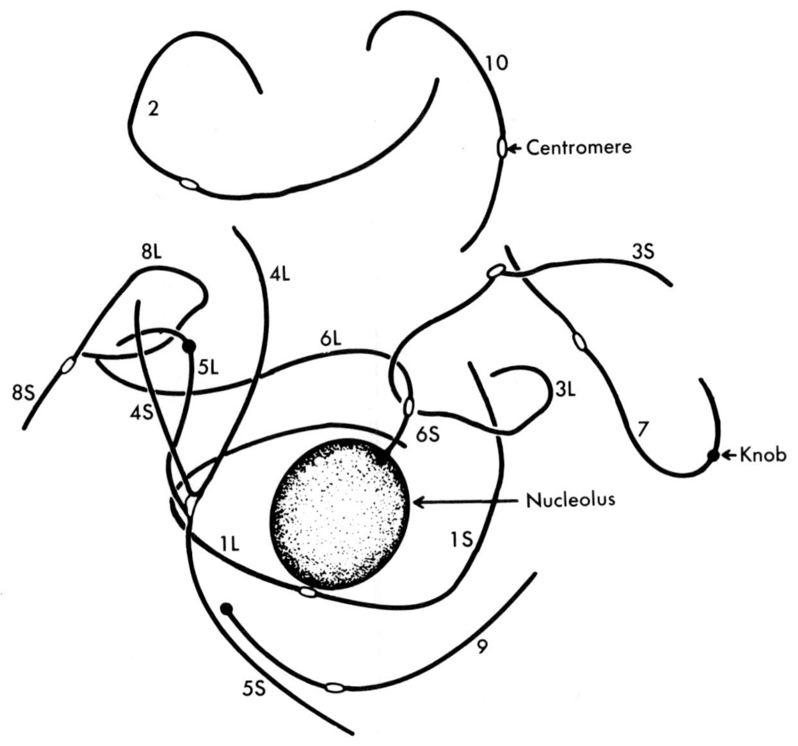

Fig. 18-8. Schematic diagram of pachytene chromosomes and nucleolus of *Zea mays* (corn). The ten tightly paired bivalents are numbered, and in some of the longer bivalents the long, **L**, and short, **S**, arms are labeled also. Centromeres, knobs, and the nucleolus organizer are also indicated. (From Rhoades, M. M. 1950. J. Hered. **41:**49-67.)

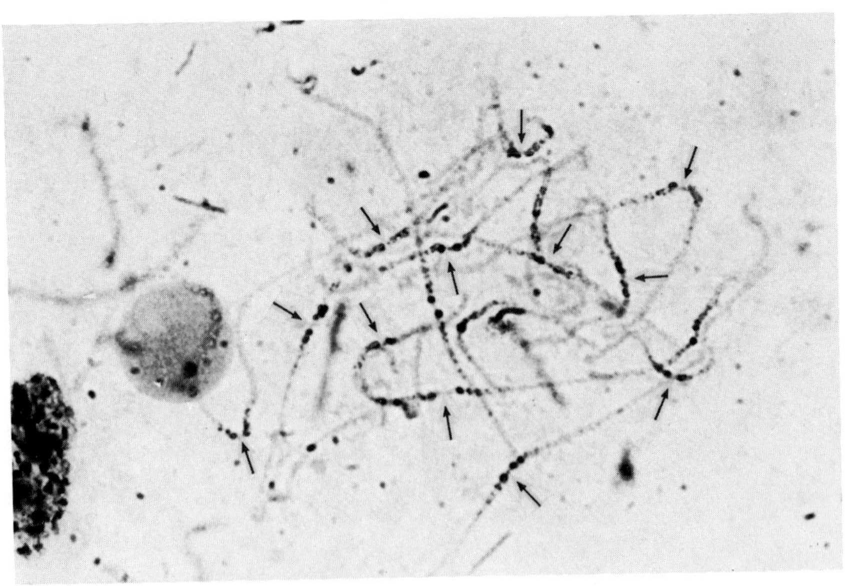

Fig. 18-9. Pachytene chromosomes of *Hibiscus cannabinus* showing darkly stained heterochromatin in central portions of chromosomes on each side of the centromeres (arrows). Nucleolus and heterochromatic nucleolus organizer (dark material on the nucleolus) are evident. (From Menzel, M. Y. 1966. Cytologia **31:**33-42.)

The distribution of heterochromatin along the chromosomes as the knobs of corn (Fig. 18-8) and nucleolus organizers (Figs. 18-8 and 18-9) and adjacent to the centromere (Fig. 18-9) is evident. In contrast to the uncondensed nucleolus organizer at mitotic prophase, during meiotic prophase it is condensed and inactive. This is also the phase of the synaptinemal complex and may be the beginning of lampbrush chromosomes, when chromosomes of most species first have an irregular woolly appearance that becomes more pronounced and evident in the next phase (p. 457). Perhaps the synaptinemal complex is an arrangement for crossing-over rather than for synapsis, since synapsis occurs during zygotene whereas crossing-over may occur and the completed synaptinemal complex does occur at pachytene. The synaptinemal complex may start to form much earlier.

As mentioned earlier, however, pachytene (Fig. 18-10) may be the first stage of prophase I rather than the third. If so, it is followed by schizotene (zygotene but opening rather than pairing), then leptotene (the diffuse stage), and then diplotene.

Diffuse stage. The diffuse stage follows pachytene and precedes diplotene. It has occasionally been referred to for many years by light microscopists (Moens, 1964) and more recently by electron microscopists studying prophase I of plants (Moens, 1968) and animals (Roth, 1966). Apparently by the beginning of the diffuse stage the chromosome bivalents have completed synapsis and recombination, and the synaptinemal complexes except for the stripped cores) have been eliminated. But instead of progressing directly by continued contraction from late pachytene to early diplotene, the "bivalents" elongate into a condition something like a fuzzy zygotene. That is, the chromosomes as observable individuals become obscure and spread throughout the nucleus. Later they do contract to produce early diplotene. This condition may or may not be typical of most species. Its functional significance is unknown.

Diplotene. Diplotene is the phase by which crossing-over has definitely occurred and in which there is an opening out or spreading apart of the two fuzzy two-

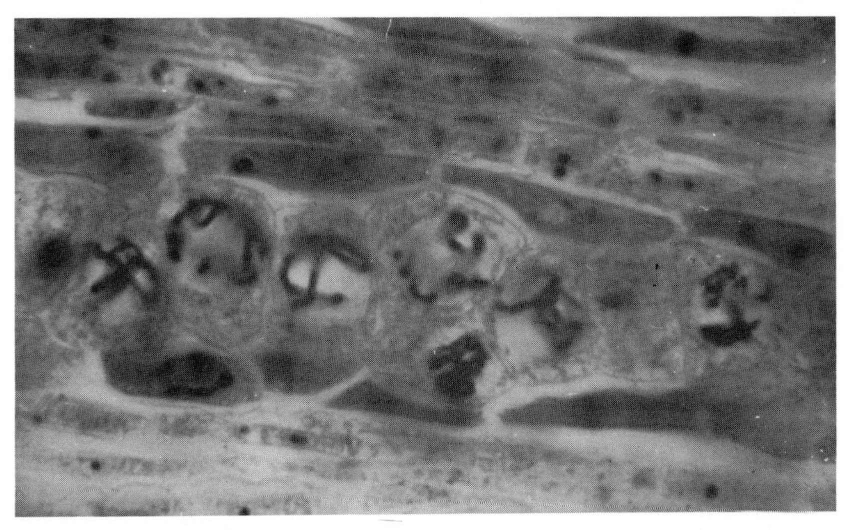

Fig. 18-10. Pachytene in PMCs of *Haplopappus gracilis* (sectioned material). Chromosomes are thick and convoluted. Thin cells on each side of PMCs are the tapetal cells.

chromonemal halves of each bivalent chromosome (Fig. 18-1). It looks as though there is a repulsion of each double strand by the other, but complete separation of chromosomes is prevented at one or more points by crossing-over of two nonsister chromonemata. Diplotene is the phase in oocytes of some animals when the lampbrush chromosomes are fully extended, fully developed, and active. Diplotene in such large oocytes may persist for weeks, months, or years (12 to 50 years in human females, from the fifth prenatal month on), whereas the oocyte and its nucleus may grow to a very large size. Such a long diplotene has been called *dictyotene*. Dictyotene oocyte nuclei that do not have lampbrush chromosomes often resemble interphase nuclei in chromosome structure. They transcribe RNA, whereas amphibian oocyte lampbrush chromosomes also replicate nucleolar DNA several times (called *gene amplification*). Such cells are far more active metabolically than cells that pass through diplotene quickly and uninterruptedly.

Crossing-over, the probable genetic equivalent of the cytological *chiasma*, has certainly taken place in diplotene by the time the two chromosome strands are opening out. Just how crossing-over occurs is another unsolved problem of meiosis. Genetically, it is known to be an exchange, *as though*, according to the most popular genetic model, "broken" ends were exchanged between only two nonsister chromatids of the four-stranded bivalent chromosome. The "break" is supposed to occur in the two nonsister strands at the same level, between or within the same two genes. The result is that the two double-stranded halves of the bivalent are "tied" together and remain so until anaphase. It is also certain that only one chiasma, between two homologous chromosomes, can occur at any one site. This is evident from study of meiosis in organisms having three or more homologous chromosomes. Three or more chromosomes can synapse, but only at different places along the arms.

There are other models of how crossing-over may occur, such as the "disproved" copying-choice model for bacteria and others that do or do not require actual breaks (Belling, 1931, 1933; Uhl, 1965). However, until the fine structure of chromosomes is much better known, such models are mere guesses and should be taken lightly.

Terminalization. There is considerable evidence that chiasmata can move away from the site of the crossover during and after diplotene. Since this movement is toward the ends of the bivalent arms, it is called terminalization. Actually, chiasmata may even slip off the ends so that the number of chiasmata per bivalent or per cell may decrease between diplotene and metaphase I. Thus the chiasma frequency per bivalent or per cell varies with time and phase of prophase I.

Chiasma frequency. The number of chiasmata, the chiasma frequency, produced per bivalent, per cell, or per chromosome arm varies somewhat among chromosomes. Generally, small or tiny chromosomes of good species have 1 per bivalent, never 0 or 2, and it is usually in the longer arm if there is only one chiasma. In somewhat longer chromosomes there may be up to 4 chiasmata per bivalent, but the number may vary in the same bivalent from cell to cell. In very long bivalents there may be as many as 10 chiasmata. They may form anywhere along either arm but probably they do not. In both corn and *Drosophila* (and probably most species), crossing-over is uncommon near the centromere, in the proximal heterochromatic region. Most crossing-over occurs in the distal, euchromatic regions of chromosome arms. There are, however, some species of grasshoppers in which chiasmata typically form close to the centromere and some in which there is usually a chiasma in the very short arm. Whether low frequencies of proximal crossing-over are due to influence of the centromere or to the fact that proximal regions of chromosomes are almost always heterochromatic is uncertain. Furthermore, according to White, crossing-over may occur at sites where a heterochromatic region is in contact with a region of euchromatin, the *frontier hypothesis.* It also seems that a second crossover cannot occur closer to the first than some minimal distance, as though one interferes with the formation of another, called *positive interference.*

Gene control. There is considerable evidence that crossing-over is under genetic control (Gowen, 1933; Fahmy, 1952). There is no crossing-over in male *Drosophila* and numerous other insects (Diptera, some mantids, grasshoppers, and Mecoptera), some flagellates, Foraminifera, gregariens, Heliozoa, some molluscs, worms, mites, copopods, coccids, and *Trillium kamtschaticum.* They are described as being *achiasmatic.* Some so-called *asynaptic* mutations perhaps prevent crossing-over rather than synapsis and are therefore often called *desynaptic* mutations. Perhaps pairing and synapsis are two different processes, synapsis or possibly crossing-over requiring the synaptinemal complex. Certainly, loose pairing occurs in the male *Drosophila* spermatocyte and perhaps synapsis occurs, but crossing-over does not and it is known that there is no synaptinemal complex.

Recombination. Another concept of prophase chromonemal doubling and crossover formation is described as *copying-choice* recombination (Lederberg, 1955). This hypothesis recently was "discredited" for bacteria and is based on genetic evidence from bacteria only but still has value. According to this concept, pairing of "single" homologous chromonemata must have occurred before the early interphase preceding meiotic prophase. Structural chromonemal doubling occurs at the same time as the quantitative DNA doubling, that is, during the S phase of middle and late premeiotic interphase (Fig. 18-11). The "new" synthesizing chromonemata form

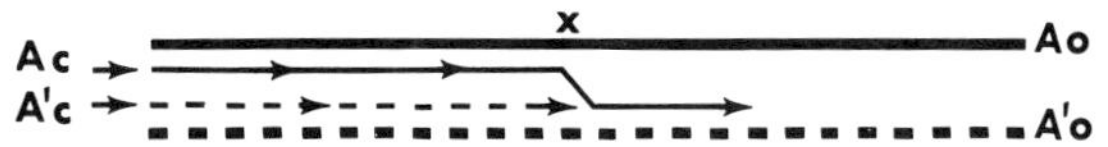

Fig. 18-11. Diagrammatic representation of copying-choice recombination and formation of a crossover at time of DNA quantitative doubling. Homologous chromosomes **Ao** and **A′o** have paired. New chromonemata are copying along them from left to right; **Ac** is copying from **Ao,** and **A′c** is copying from **A′o.** At **x, Ac** "chooses" to copy **A′o** rather than **Ao,** and thus **A′c** has to change its template from **A′o** to **Ao.** Thus a crossover is formed at **x.** Since DNA doubling has been accomplished just before leptotene, this hypothesis requires pairing, structural doubling, and formation of crossovers to be accomplished before prophase I begins.

progressively; they "copy" along the "old" paired, homologous chromonemata. At certain more or less random points, either of the lengthening, new copying chromonemata may suddenly "choose" to be formed by the other homologue, thus forcing the second copying chromonema to do the same at the same point. Thus pairing, chromonemal doubling, and chiasmata (recombination) have all occurred before prophase I of meiosis starts, and breakage and reunion are not required.

One weakness of this hypothesis is that there result two "old" and two "new" chromonemata, and recombination can occur only between the two new ones. This is not true; according to genetic analysis, any two nonsister chromonemata, old or new, seem able to recombine. Sister-strand exchanges *and* copying-choice between them could produce the types of recombination found, but there is no good evidence nor hypothetical mechanism for sister-strand exchange. Furthermore, copying-choice might occur in bacteria (Prokaryota) but not in the Eukaryota having "normal" meiosis or vice versa. Nevertheless, Grell and Chandley (1965) have established that DNA replication (by radioautography) and crossing-over (by heat treatment to increase the numbers of crossovers) occur simultaneously in *Drosophila melanogaster,* and since replication certainly occurs during interphase, so therefore, may crossing-over.

However, other experiments indicate that genetic replication and cytological crossing-over occur during pachytene, and that is the consensus among geneticists at this time (Church and Wimber, 1971).

Again, genetic speculation is ahead of reliable cytological knowledge of fundamental chromosome structure, time of pairing, details of chromonemal duplication, and time and mechanics of crossing-over. The logic of genetics, however, may be incapable of correctly describing the actual physical basis of recombination. At the present time there is great uncertainty about the time and mechanics of the events peculiar to meiosis, especially recombination.

• • •

Chiasmata typically hold the synapsed homologous "chromosomes" together as one bivalent chromosome until anaphase I. Nevertheless, homologous chromosomes can pair and remain paired until anaphase without chiasmata, as in male *Drosophila* and some other animals (Metz, 1916). In fact, pairing of homologous chromosomes is typical of all fly cell divisions (from anaphase to the next prophase), not only of the salivary gland cells and the gametocytes.

During diplotene the opened-out bivalents continue to shorten and thicken by helical coiling, the chiasmata being quite evident.

Diakinesis. Diakinesis, the next phase, is characterized by continued shortening, thickening, and smoothing out of the chromosome surfaces (Figs. 18-1 and 18-6). The chiasmata are most evident but are terminalizing and often decreasing in number. The nucleolus with its attached bivalent chromosome or chromosomes is still evident. What makes diakinesis excellent for observation in many organisms is the fact that the shortened bivalents are spread out and widely separated against the inner surface of the nuclear envelope, as though all chromosomes were "repelling" each other and all had moved away from each other as far as the confining nuclear envelope permits. Perhaps the nuclear envelope somehow accomplishes this spreading.

During diakinesis the bivalents and multivalents of three or more synapsed chromosomes are best analyzed microscopically. They appear as bivalent rods if there is only one terminal chiasma; as ring bivalents if there is a chiasma at each end; as two attached rings if there are three chiasmata, one at each end and one in the middle (interstitial); as a ring and two projecting ends if one chiasma is terminal and one interstitial; etc. Bivalents of tiny chromosomes generally appear as two attached spheres, but typical diakinesis does not seem to occur in all species; rather, diplotene seems to blend into prometaphase.

Prometaphase

Prometaphase is essentially the same as in mitosis; the nuclear membrane disappears, the spindle forms in plants or invades the nucleus in animals, the nucleolus generally disappears, and the chromosomes move or are moved about, ending up as bivalents on the metaphase plate. In some animals the two centromeres of each bivalent may move toward opposite poles, but the chiasmata hold them together even though the chromosomes are greatly stretched. This is called the *prometaphase stretch.*

Metaphase

The most obvious difference in *metaphase* I and a mitotic metaphase is that the two centromeres of each bivalent are separate, one lying "above" and one "below" the plane of the metaphase plate of the spindle rather than on the plate, as in mitotic metaphase. Also metaphase I chromosomes are obviously coiled in many species (Sax and Humphrey, 1934; Hillary, 1940). Metaphase I is widely analyzed for chromosome numbers, structure, and pairing.

At this stage, in a diploid species with good synapsis and crossing-over, the two double homologous chromosomes are held together by one or more chiasmata, which are often terminalized. The number of chiasmata is more or less proportional to the lengths of the chromosomes.

Although each homologue is known to be double, there is no visible evidence of doubleness during diakinesis, prometaphase, or metaphase I, although when the homologues have separated during early anaphase I, the two chromatids quickly separate widely except at the centromere.

At metaphase I unpaired chromosomes are called *univalents*. They often do not get on the metaphase plate but may range randomly along the spindle. Any chromosomes (univalents, bivalents, multivalents) that fail to get on the metaphase I plate are called *laggards,* and they may move to the nearer pole ahead or behind the chromosomes that behave normally at anaphase. Univalents actually consist of two chromatids and are thus like mitotic metaphase chromosomes. Like mitotic chromosomes they generally separate at anaphase I. There are numerous reports of univalents moving undivided to the poles at anaphase I but dividing at anaphase II. It is evident that they cannot divide twice because there is no DNA replication between anaphase I and II.

The diameters of metaphase I chromosomes are produced by large *major coils;* but the coils are themselves composed of coils, the *minor coils.* This double coiling produces the short and fat metaphase I chromosomes, which are shorter and fatter than the same chromosomes during mitotic metaphase.

Multivalent chromosomes at metaphase I result from the presence in the cell of more than two homologous chromosomes, or almost homologous, called *homeologous* chromosomes. If these synapse and form chiasmata so that three, four, or more homologues or homeologues are associated at various loci along their lengths, at metaphase I the configurations become complex. Somewhat similar multivalents result from translocations so that 4, 6, 8, 10, 12, 14, etc. chromosomes are associated end to end as rings or chains at metaphase I.

Anaphase

During anaphase I the two centromeres of each bivalent appear to be pulled strongly toward the opposite poles, against what appears to be strong resistance to final separation of the remaining chiasmata (Fig. 18-12). As a result, the chromosome arms

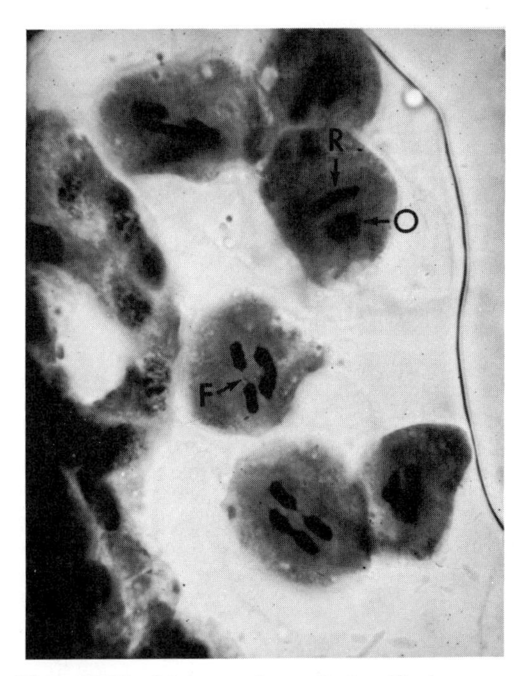

Fig. 18-12. Meta-anaphase I in *Haplopappus gracilis* ($n = 2$). In most cells one bivalent at late metaphase has one terminal chiasma and forms a rod bivalent, **R;** the other chromosome usually has two chiasmata, one in each arm, and thus forms a ring bivalent, **O.** The two chromosomes of the rod bivalent seem to move end first toward the poles at anaphase, with a thin connection of some sort, **F,** during the early stage.

between the centromere and the first chiasma appear thin and stretched, often well into anaphase and often almost to the pole if the chromosomes are very long. Eventually, however, the chiasmata all terminalize and slip off the ends, permitting the two double anaphase chromosomes to separate. Anaphase I also differs from mitotic anaphase because each chromosome obviously consists of two clearly separated chromatids. Typically, the two chromatids attached at the centromere have the arms spread apart, as Xs or Vs, depending on the location of the centromere (Figs. 18-2 and 18-6). Such obviously double anaphase chromosomes are not seen in mitosis. Anaphase I is often studied for inversions that form bridges and fragments at this stage and for other aberrations as in hybirds and after irradiation.

Telophase

Telophase I may be similar to mitotic telophase, or in many animals the chromosomes may not elongate much and pass directly into prophase II or even prometaphase II. In plants there is generally a distinct though short interphase characterized by diffuse chromosomes, new nuclear envelope, and nucleolus. There is, however, no DNA replication or structural doubling of the chromosomes (Fig. 18-2).

Meiosis II

Meiosis II is essentially a mitotic division (Figs. 18-3 and 18-6), except that the chromosomes go into it already double, as was clearly evident in anaphase I.

Many cytological phenomena of meiosis that are of genetic significance, such as inversions, deletions, and translocations are discussed elsewhere.

Other models or schemes

Other models or schemes of meiosis exist, one of which is rapidly acquiring support in contrast to the previously described and generally accepted model (Brown and Stack, 1968). Present evidence indicates that the meiotic process may include at least three rather than only two divisions (Smith, 1942) and that pairing is probably different from synapsis. The pairing of homologous chromosomes is merely an example of well-known somatic pairing (Huskins, 1948; Boss, 1954, 1955), but it occurs gradually and typically during prometaphase, metaphase, and anaphase of the premeiotic mitosis or a known equivalent in fungi (Rossen and Westergaard, 1966) when the chromosomes are contracted. It is assumed that this pairing persists throughout premeiotic interphase in a more or less loose or probably a very intimate form.

That pairing persists through the premeiotic interphase is indicated by the presence of paired heterochromatic regions during most of that period in *Plantago ovata* (Fig. 15-9) (Stack and Brown, 1969). These fused prochromosomes may become uncondensed for late replication in late S phase, but probably remain paired even then.

Synapsis, on the other hand, perhaps occurs at late interphase or during early prophase I as a process different from pairing but a culmination, a subsequent event to pairing. Synapsis is as different from pairing as the tightly "synapsed" salivary gland chromosomes of many Diptera are probably different from the loosely paired chromosomes of other somatic cells of flies. During middle and late premeiotic "interphase" the DNA doubles quantitatively, except in at least one ascomycete where replication occurs in the "gamete" nuclei (Rossen and Westergaard, 1966), and the synaptinemal complex probably forms slowly. The synaptinemal complex may be a structure necessary for forming crossovers rather than synapsis. The so-called first and second meiotic divisions then follow as really the second and third divisions.

This model of the meiotic process is based on cytogenetic and genetic demand and many observations of homologous pair-

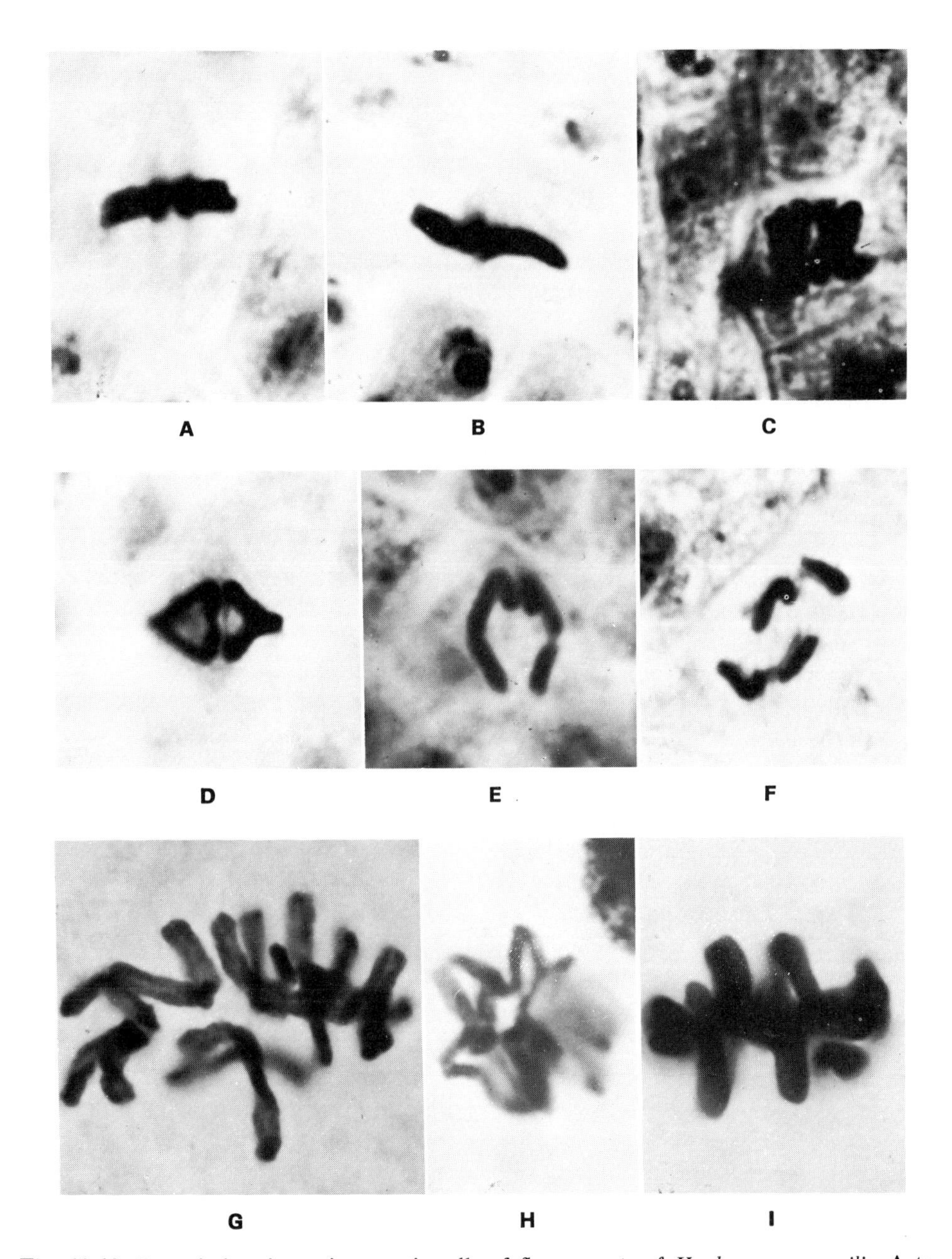

Fig. 18-13. Premeiotic mitoses in somatic cells of flower parts of *Haplopappus gracilis,* **A** to **F,** and *Rhoeo discolor,* **H** and **I. A** to **C,** Metaphase showing the haploid (n = 2) chromosome number. **C** shows the four-parted character of such chromosomes. **D** to **F,** Anaphase. In **D** the sticking of chromosome ends to form the "double triangle" appearance of early anaphase is evident. Spindles in **A** to **G** and **I** extend toward the top and bottom. In **E** the two paired "bivalents" have nearly separated. Although it looks as though the two chromosomes moving "up" are homologous, as are those moving "down," actually two nonhomologous "bivalents" are moving to each pole, as is evident at later anaphase in **F,** where doubleness of each anaphase chromosome is evident. **G,** Typical mitotic metaphase in *Rhoeo discolor.* **H,** Polar view and, **I,** side view of premeiotic metaphases showing pairing of chromosome ends. Such pairing in this complex heterozygote must (and does) occur if pairing of homologues occurs in divisions before meiosis. (Modified from Brown, W. V., and S. M. Stack. 1968. Bull. Torrey Bot. Club **95:**369-378.)

ing during mitotic divisions (Boss, 1955; Watkins, 1935) and at premeiotic mitosis in both animals and plants (Smith, 1942), and it avoids the difficult proposal of the moving together of very long chromosomes within the confines of a nuclear envelope at zygotene. Actually, there is no evidence that such long, extended, essentially interphase chromosomes ever "move," whereas there is no doubt about condensed mitotic chromosomes moving or being moved. It is supported by Moens' observations (1964) that pachytene (or a pachytene-like chromosomal condition) precedes zygotene (which he called *schizotene*) in the tomato; by McClung's observations (1927) that in some grasshoppers, pairing occurs at late telophase (his *diatene*) and is followed by bouquet formation (his *peritene*) and a sort of pachytene (his *pharanosome stage*) and only then seems to enter a sort of interphase (his *cryptosome stage*); by Grell and Chandley's observations (1965) that, in *Drosophila* at least, DNA replication and crossing-over are simultaneous phenomena; and others.

There are now sufficient observations of premeiotic pairing in animals (Smith, 1942) and plants (Battaglia, 1947; Brown and Stack, 1968) to warrant serious consideration that pairing (as distinct from synapsis) in preparation of meiosis is a special case of somatic pairing (Fig. 18-13). Perhaps sexual species have genes for somatic pairing that, except in Diptera, tissue culture, as a radiation effect, etc., are activated only in cells during certain premeiotic divisions.

The historical criticism of this concept is that organisms with zygotic meiosis, meiosis I being the first division after karyogamy (the union of gamete nuclei), have no premeiotic mitotic division when such pairing could occur. Such zygotic meiosis is characteristic of the Ascomycetes and Basidiomycetes as well as many algae.

Studies of karyogamy and meiosis in the ascomycetes *Neurospora* (McClintock, 1945; Singleton, 1953), *Neottiella* (Rossen and Westergaard, 1966), *Preussia* (Kowalski, 1965c, 1966), *Pycnidiophora* (Kowalski, 1964), *Melanospora* (Kowalski, 1965b), and *Didymocrea* (Kowalski, 1965a); and the basidiomycete *Coleosporium* (Olive, 1949) (Fig. 17-12) have demonstrated that the chromosomes in the two haploid (gamete) nuclei are contracted at the time of karyogamy just as are the chromosomes of higher organisms at premeiotic mitosis, and in this condition they probably pair. Subsequently, the chromosomes elongate (premeiotic interphase or "leptotene"?) and then shorten to pachytene with a synaptinemal complex, at least in *Neottiella*. Also in *Neottiella*, DNA replication takes place in the two haploid (gametic) nuclei before karyogamy (Fig. 18-14). This case provides evidence against the copying-choice scheme of replication and recombination.

Thus species without a premeiotic mitosis accomplish the same thing—chromosomal pairing, probably of homologues, in a contracted condition followed by elongation before the usually accepted meiosis begins.

The period of chromosomal elongation after pairing in these fungi does not suggest a premeiotic interphase. In fact, the so-called interphase before meiosis in organisms in general may be far more of a dynamic "preleptotene" stage of meiosis than a phase comparable to a mitotic interphase. This scheme, if true, greatly prolongs the meiotic process, backward to at least the prometaphase of the premeiotic mitosis and in at least some angiosperms backward many divisions into late or even early bud formation (Brown and Stack, 1968). It can also be assumed that other preparatory changes for this lengthy process occur even earlier than that.

The mysteries of pairing itself: why homologous chromosomes do pair meiotically or mitotically, whereas nonhomologous chromosomes do not; why homologous genes are paired so exactly at synapsis (if they really are); how and when crossovers are formed; what the synaptinemal complex does and how; and when structural doubling of the paired (or synapsed) chromonemata occurs remain to be worked out. Aside from cytochemical changes, it is not known what goes on chromosomally during premeiotic interphase and early prophase I. Leptotene and zygotene phases may actually not occur at all, since they are defined by conditions assumed by the most widely ac-

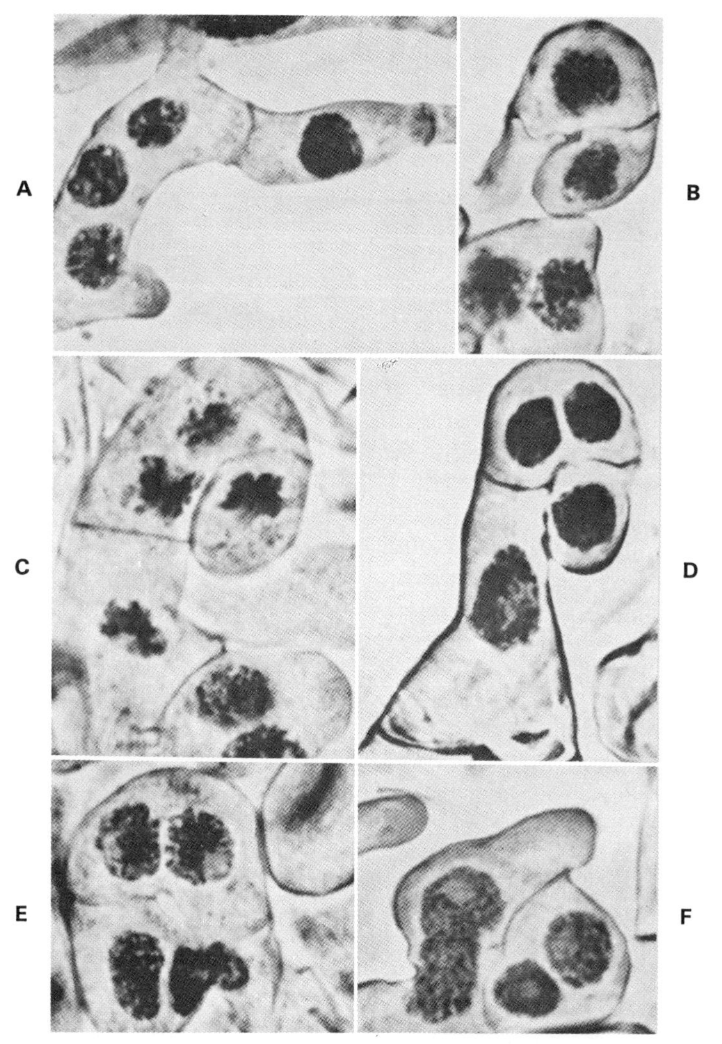

Fig. 18-14. Some stages in reproduction of the ascomycetous fungus *Neottiella (Peziza).* **A,** Ascogenous hyphae with nuclei in G_1 phase. **B,** Beginning of crozier formation as tip of hypha bends and a transverse wall forms between the two terminal nuclei. **C,** Anaphase and telophase of the two synchronized mitoses in the crozier. **D,** Crozier with stalk cell nucleus and terminal cell nucleus in S phase. Two nuclei in the penultimate cell are in the G_1 phase. **E,** Migration of stalk cell nucleus into terminal cell through a pore in the cell walls. **F,** Two prefusion nuclei at left are in the G_2 phase, and the ascus is beginning to grow out from the terminal cell. (From Rossen, J. M., and M. Westergaard. 1966. C. R. Trav. Lab. Carlsberg **35:**233-260.)

cepted, and possibly incorrect, largely genetic model of meiosis. The genetic model, for example, of Grell (1965), proposes that there is not only pairing of homologues accompanied by crossing-over, called *exchange pairing,* but a later pairing of previously unpaired homologues or nonhomologues, called *distributive pairing.*

Results of meiosis

The cytological results of meiosis are, whatever the actual sequence of events, that each of the four nuclei produced has received one of the four chromonemata that composed the metaphase I bivalent, and because of crossing-over, pieces of the *homologous* chromosomes have been exchanged; that is, recombination has occurred. The chromosome number has been reduced so that sexuality can be a part of the life cycle. Both sexuality and crossing-over increase the variability among the individuals of the species. Such high variability is essential for either average or unusually rapid evolutionary change and evolutionary survival in competition with other sexual species. It is questionable if sexuality is biologically necessary otherwise.

Although the main events of meiosis are generally the same in both sexes of animals, microsporangia and megasporangia of heterosporous plants, and the sporangia of lower plants and fungi, the cellular results are often different. In spermatogenesis of male animals and microsporogenesis of plants the four haploid nuclei produced are, except in a few species, contained in four equal cells, each of which then transforms into a sperm or microspore. In oogenesis of female animals (Fig. 18-15) and in megasporogenesis of most heterosporous plants, three of the haploid nuclei produced are not used. In oogenesis the first meiotic division occurs close to the nuclear envelope, and one of the nuclei produced moves into a small pouchlike expansion of the plasma membrane to form a *polar body,* a small cell consisting of the nucleus and very little cytoplasm. This nucleus may not divide again, or it may go through meiosis II to form two polar bodies; it may divide at meiosis II, still within the oocyte, the two

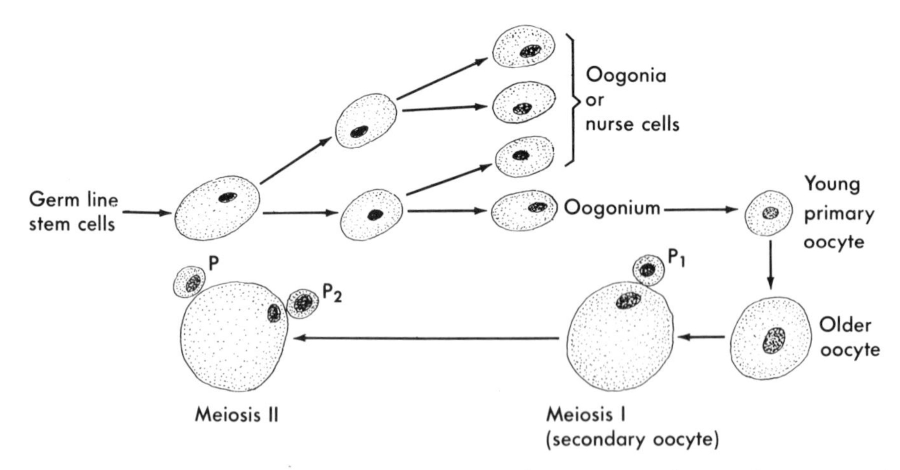

Fig. 18-15. Rather typical, female, animal, germ line sequence from primary oogonium through oocyte and meiosis to the ootid, or egg. The number of oogonial divisions between primary oogonium and oocyte varies. Some oogonia may differentiate into nurse cells. The large nucleus of an oocyte is called the germinal vesicle. At the end of meiosis I one nucleus is ejected as the first polar body. At the end of meiosis II a second polar body is generally formed. Nurse cells in females and Sertoli cells in male mammals are germ line cells that do not function as meiocytes.

daughter nuclei forming into two polar bodies only afterward. In any case the polar bodies have little cytoplasm, and they subsequently disintegrate. The other nucleus produced at meiosis I goes through meiosis II, and one of these daughter nuclei is also eliminated as a polar body. The one remaining haploid nucleus is the functional haploid egg nucleus. Meiosis in oogenesis sometimes occurs or is completed only after the male gamete nucleus has entered the oocyte; the sperm nucleus then waits for oocyte meiosis to occur before nuclear fusion occurs.

The fates of the four haploid nuclei produced by meiosis in the megasporocytes of plants are varied. In the gymnosperms and most angiosperms four definite, haploid megaspores are formed as a row of cells. Of these four cells, three degenerate and the fourth grows into the female gametophyte or embryo sac. In numerous angiosperms, however, there are variations of this sequence of events; probably the commonest exceptional condition is the four nuclei produced by the two meiotic divisions to remain in a single mass of protoplasm, not segregated into four cells. The four genetically different "microspore" nuclei actually function as the nuclei of the four-nucleate stage of the embryo sac. After one more (mitotic) division one of the eight nuclei transforms into the egg nucleus; the other nuclei form the three antipodal and two synergid cells as well as the two polar nuclei of the typical embryo sac.

Meiosis in at least some slime molds, as indicated by the presence of the synaptinemal complex, occurs in the spore; three of the four haploid cells produced apparently degenerate so that only one haploid cell emerges from each spore. Gametes arise from the haploid products of meiosis only after numerous divisions; gametic union follows. Thus the plasmodium is diploid.

Anomalous meiosis

Anomalous meiosis, which may, however, be normal for the particular species, is not uncommon among animals and plants. Some modification of meiosis is quite common, even though associated with sexuality or systems in which reduction fails to occur in permanently or temporarily asexual species. In animals this latter form of reproduction from eggs without fertilization is called *parthenogenesis.* Because plants have alternation of generations and meiosis is separated from egg cell formation by the gametophyte generation, such asexual reproduction is more complicated and the term *"apomixis"* (Stebbins, 1941; Gustaffson, 1946, 1947) is applied to the overall process, with special terms applied to the various portions of it, including parthenogenesis if an egg is actually formed.

Apomixis. Among the angiosperms the aberrant nuclear division that replaces normal meiosis I is called *apomeiosis.* It may start out as a fairly normal meiotic division as far as anaphase, but instead of forming two haploid nuclei, the chromosomes come back together within one nuclear envelope to form a diploid *restitution nucleus.* At the other extreme of apomeiotic divisions is a normal mitotic division. In any case the female gametophyte and the egg nucleus eventually formed are diploid, and the unfertilized egg develops into the embryo parthenogenetically. There are other examples in which neither megasporocytes (egg mother cells, or EMCs) nor megaspores are formed. This is called *apospory;* that is, embryo sacs form within the ovule from typically somatic cells. In numerous species of the citrus family, embryos form from somatic cells of the ovule external to any embryo sac, much like the formation of embryos in callus or on vegetative tissues such as leaves or stems. In such apomictic plants with anomalous meiosis in megasporocytes, there is generally more or less normal meiosis in the microsporocytes of the anthers, except for various aberrations imposed by hybridity and polyploidy. Pollen and pollination are usually required, at least for endosperm development.

Parthenogenesis. Parthenogenesis in animals, like apomixis in plants, occurs sporadically in many groups; in each such group it has arisen independently of other groups, and so differences are expected and found. White (1954) has subdivided parthenogenesis in animals into (1) *arrhenotoky,* which is associated with male haploidy and limited to that sex, as known in bees and essentially all other Hymenoptera, some Homoptera, one species of Coleoptera, some Thysanoptera, as well as many mites and several rotifers; and (2) *thelytoky,* in which diploid females are produced without meiosis or syngamy by *diploid parthenogenesis,* males not being necessary.

Arrhenotoky. Arrhenotoky, as in the haploid male Hymenoptera, does not and cannot involve chromosomal pairing or synapsis, and only a typical haploid mitotic division occurs. There is no second division, and two sperm are produced. Meiosis is normal in the females, since they are diploid and produce haploid eggs. The proportion of males is somehow controlled by failure of fertilization, and among such species the ratios of males to females fluctuates or varies widely, males often being rare. In the gall wasps there is generally an alternation of arrhenotoky with thelytoky.

The nuclear division in the male Iceryini (a tribe of coccid insects having a chromosome number of 2n = 4 and haploid males) is also a mitotic division producing two sperm. In one hermaphroditic species the embryo, until it is hatched, consists of diploid cells only. During later embryogeny, haploid nuclei arise somehow and produce a haploid testis that is surrounded by a diploid ovary. Self-fertilization occurs. This is an example of *somatic reduction,* which is accomplished by modified mitotic divisions, usually by nondisjunction of certain specific chromosomes at rather specific and genetically determined mitotic divisions.

The apomeiotic division in a haploid arrhenotokous male beetle consists of an abortive unipolar spindle with no division, followed by mitosis. Thus the apomeiotic divisions in males of arrhenotokous animal species consist generally of haploid mitotic divisions.

Thelytoky. Thelytokous parthenogenesis, in which males are unnecessary, may be subdivided into *complete parthenogenesis,* wherein males either do not occur or are very rare, and *cyclical parthenogenesis,* wherein some generations consist exclusively of females, reproducing parthenogenetically, and other generations are sexual with diploid males and females, with normal meiosis in both. In this latter, more common group are the aphids, gall wasps, many rotifers, *Cladocera,* and many parasitic worms.

Among thelytokous animals, meiosis may occur, called the *meiotic type,* or it may be replaced by a mitotic division, the *ameiotic type.* Of course, if meiosis does occur and haploid secondary oocyte or even ootid nuclei are produced, with sexuality *not* following, the diploid condition must be restored by some novel mechanism.

In most species having the meiotic type of parthenogenesis (all females, of course) the two haploid nuclei of the second meiotic division in the secondary oocyte reunite to form a diploid egg nucleus (called *autofertilization*). Another less common method of restoring diploidy without sexuality after meiosis is for two haploid nuclei to unite during some early embryonic division, as in some Lepidoptera. In some earthworms and flatworms, on the other hand, there is a doubling of the chromosome number to the tetraploid level just before meiosis, either during the premeiotic mitosis or during prophase I. Meiosis then produces a diploid egg nucleus by reduction, but sexuality does not follow.

• • •

There are also anomalous types of meiosis among normally sexual species. Some are produced by mutation, and others have been produced by chromosomal rearrangements. Some result from hybridization or polyploidy, and others are typical of the species, genus, or larger taxonomic category. The study of such atypical meiosis is generally characterized as the field of cytogenetics.

Lampbrush chromosomes

The so-called lampbrush chromosomes (probably "pipe-cleaner chromosomes" would be more meaningful in the age of electric lighting) have been known since Flemming first described them in an amphibian oocyte in 1882 and Rückert studied them in more detail in the oocytes of a shark in 1892 (Fig. 18-16). During the past 30 years they have become a popular subject of studies of various sorts and have contributed considerable knowledge concerning chromosome fine structure, gene function, and meiosis. They are, however, not ubiquitous concomitants of meiosis or even of synapsis, being restricted to those oocytes of vertebrate and invertebrate animals that grow greatly in cytoplasmic and nuclear volume during the prophase of the first meiotic division. Nevertheless, they have been reported in oocytes of the chaetognath *Sagitta,* the mollusc *Sepia,* the crustacean *Anilocra,* several insects, the echinoderm *Echinaster,* two species of sharks, and many amphibians, birds, and reptiles. It is only in certain vertebrate oocytes, however, that the *very* elongate form is found. The so-called lampbrush chromosome of the invertebrates are little more than "hairy" pachytene, diplotene, and/or diakinetic chromosomes of not unusual length.

More and more the synaptinemal complex, lampbrush chromosomes, the bouquet

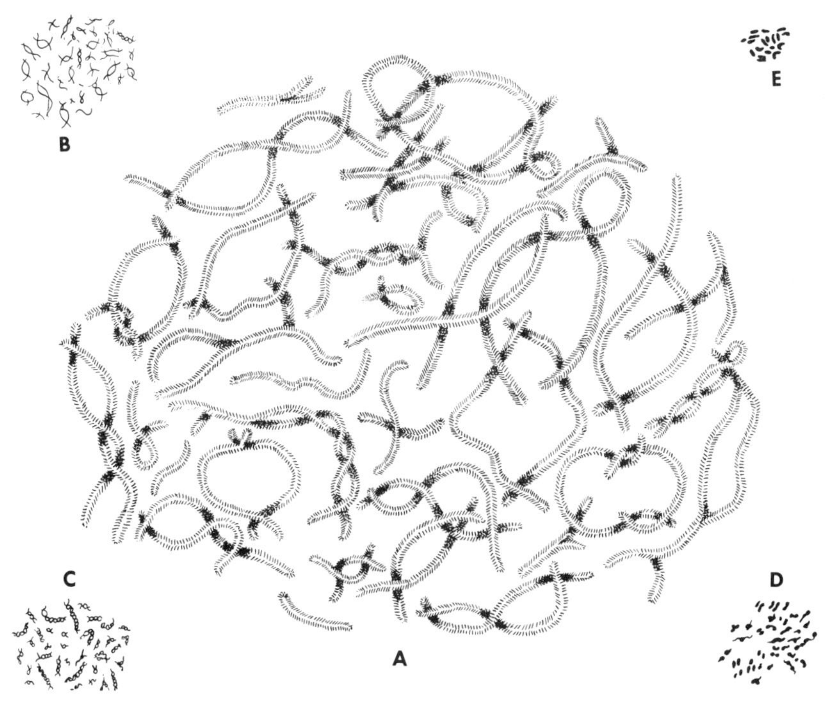

Fig. 18-16. Chromosomes during various stages of prophase I in the shark *Pristiurus* drawn to the same scale of magnification. **A,** Typical lampbrush chromosomes at maximum size during diplotene. **B,** Later diplotene when chromosomes have contracted greatly. **C,** End of diplotene. **D,** Diakinesis. **E,** Metaphase I. (Redrawn from Rückert, J. 1892. Anat. Anz. **7:**107-158.)

stage of animal meiosis, and synapsis are becoming related, lampbrush chromosomes probably being an extreme aspect of a general condition. Therefore the reports of lampbrushlike chromosomes in spermatocytes of grasshoppers and in the microsporocytes of a wild onion (Fig. 18-17) are not surprising.

The following discussion is based primarily on observations made with the light microscope, especially the phase-contrast microscope, and mostly from lampbrush chromosomes of the newt (Callan and Lloyd, 1961; Izawa et al., 1963), that is, of the true vertebrate type. Like the synaptinemal complex the lampbrush chromosome is a synapsed bivalent of 2 homologous chromosomes having chiasmata during early prophase I, but unlike the synaptinemal complex, the lampbrush chromosome is greatly extended in length, being 1 mm (1,000 μm) long or more in many organisms. Furthermore, they may be 20 μm or more wide. Such great extension can occur only in very large nuclei, those 150 μm in diameter or more.

The obvious structure of such a diplotene lampbrush chromosome (Figs. 18-18 and 18-19) is of two longitudinal strands, which make a few contacts, and all along their lengths there are fine loops extending laterally. Actually, there are four longitudinal strands, and the contacts are chiasmata. In fine structure the axis of the loop, which probably contains the DNA and protein, has a diameter of 60 to 80 Å and is covered variably with ribonucleoprotein matrix. An average lampbrush chromosome of the newt *Triturus* has about 1,000 pairs of loops, making a total of about 12,000 for the whole set of n = 12 chromosomes. Loops of newt lampbrush chromosomes average about 50 μm in length, but the longest may be 200 μm. An assumed structural gene, one producing mRNA, might consist of a sequence of 1,000 nucleotides to specify (on the basis of a triplet code) a protein of 333 amino acids. A 50 μm loop must therefore contain a linear DNA sequence much, much greater than one gene,—about 150 times as much. What the great excess per loop might be is unknown—whether a series of different genes, a series of like (duplicate) genes, essential but nonmessenger gene code, or some presently inconceivable DNA-RNA-protein functional structure.

Compared to ordinary chromosomes, lampbrush chromosomes contain about 800 times as much protein and about 100 times as much RNA to DNA. There may even be two or more times as much DNA as there is in a diploid somatic cell.

Each lampbrush (bivalent) chromosome

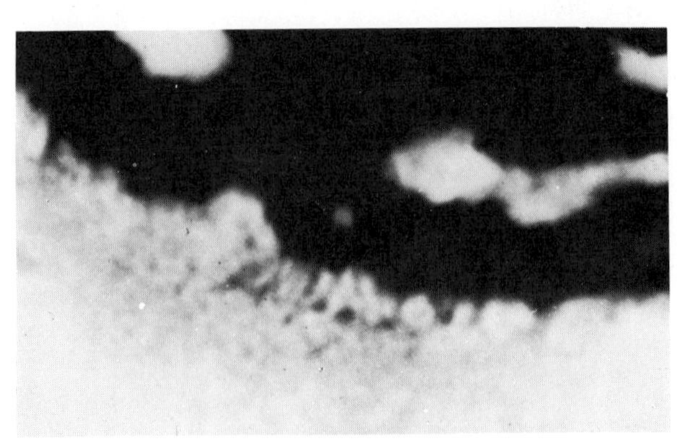

Fig. 18-17. Portion of diplotene chromosome of *Allium cernuum* showing lateral extensions that may be comparable to a lampbrush chromosome. (Courtesy Dr. P. Grunn, Pennsylvania State University, University Park, Pa.)

consists, according to present concepts, of a pair of continuous DNA filaments that are close together in spots, the chromomeres, which more or less alternate with thin filaments. At each chromomere the DNA filaments separate from each other and extend outward as two loops, a pair of loops; the filament then returns to the chromomere from which it originally separated (Fig. 18-19). This whole continuous DNA filament is "covered" with ribonucleoprotein, and the loops have so little DNA that it is unobservable by staining techniques. Its presence is revealed by the fact that the loops (and also the main axis) break up when treated with the enzyme DNAase and by surface-film, microcentrifugation electron microscope techniques (Miller, 1965).

On the loops, the thinnest being about 1 μm thick, the amount of ribonucleoprotein (called "matrix") varies considerably from loop to loop and also along a single loop of a chromosome. A loop may be very thin from one end to the other (symmetrical), or

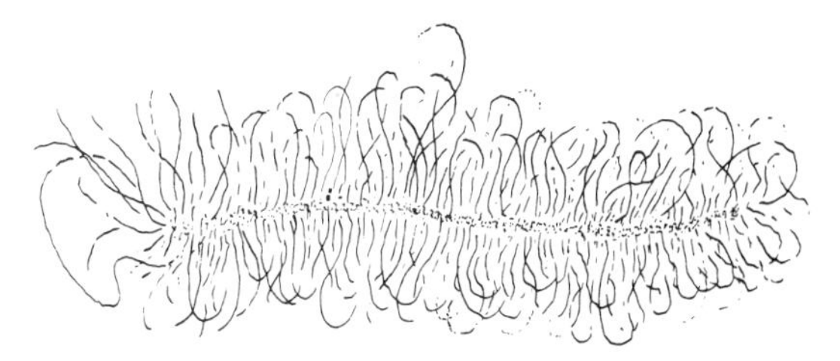

Fig. 18-18. Drawing of a lampbrush chromosome of the shark *Pristiurus*. Compare with Fig. 18-19. (From Rückert, J. 1892. Anat. Anz. **7:**107-158.)

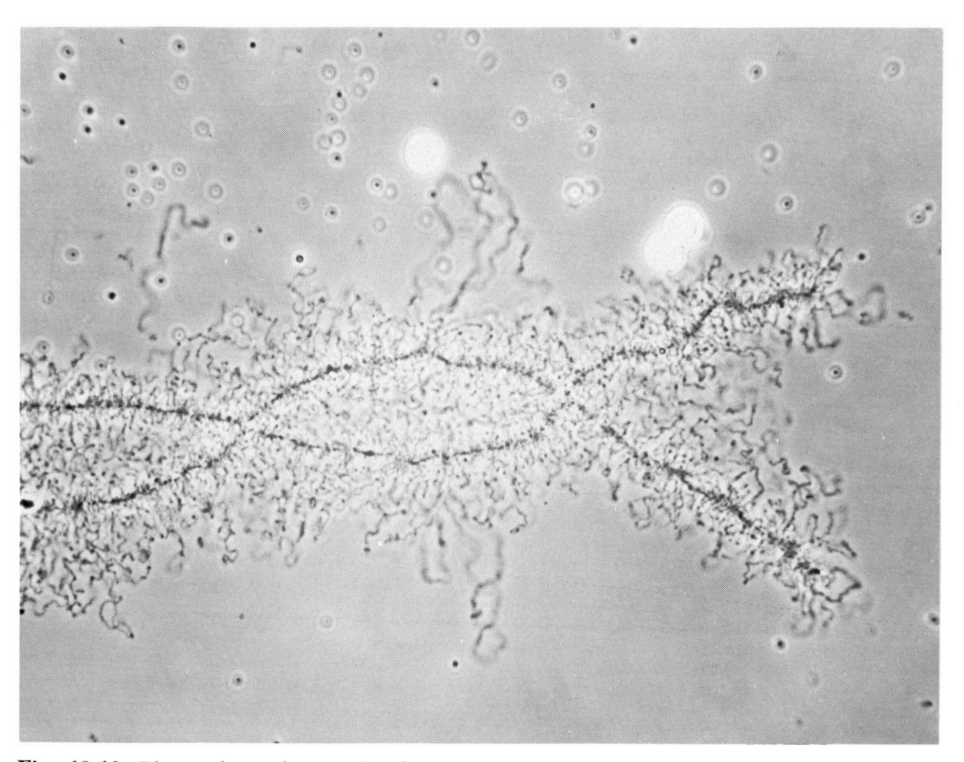

Fig. 18-19. Phase photomicrograph of part of a lampbrush chromosome of the amphibian *Triturus viridescens* showing the bivalent nature, chiasmata, axial strands, and lateral loops. Compare this with Fig. 18-18. (Courtesy Dr. J. Gall; from Taylor, J. H. 1963. The replication and organization of DNA in chromosomes. In J. H. Taylor (editor). Molecular genetics. Part I. Academic Press, Inc., New York.)

one part of the loop may be very thin and the other half thickened by matrix (asymmetrical), a little or a great deal. The patterns of symmetrical and asymmetrical loops vary in time as the early prophase progresses, and during that period various loops produce spherules of ribonucleoprotein that seem to drift off into the nucleoplasm and disappear. These droplets seem to be the product of loop activity (genetic activity). Numerous reports claim that these droplets also contain DNA. The period of the lampbrush condition and of synthetic activity is long, extending for many weeks in the newt oocyte.

Certainly the nucleolus organizers of these chromosomes do produce many nucleoli that separate from the chromosomes. Each such extrachromosomal nucleolus contains a replicated DNA copy of the nucleolus organizer. Thus such an oocyte nucleus contains about 1,000 copies of the nucleolus organizer in about 1,000 nucleoli, each of which is producing ribosomal material (Miller, et al., 1970). These authors also published illustrations of the DNA strands of lampbrush loops with attached RNA polymers of various lengths, that is, in various stages of formation. They called such illustrations "genes in action."

Small swellings without loops at the ends of the main axes of the lampbrush chromosomes are called telomeres, and a small spherical swelling on each bivalent, somewhat larger than the chromomeres, is called the centromere.

During late prophase the lampbrush chromosomes become smaller and smaller (Fig. 18-16). Starting on each side of the centromere and progressing toward the two ends of each chromosome, there is a gradual thickening of the axial filament as the loops regress, as if they are being withdrawn. Eventually, all loops disappear, the whole axis of the chromosome thickens, and the chromosome becomes greatly shortened. Such thickening of the late pachytene bivalent, starting on each side of the centromere and progressing toward the ends, is also evident in microsporocytes of a number of plants—potato, tomato, *Plantago*, numerous Onagraceae, and others.

It is assumed that the greatly extended condition of lampbrush chromosomes is a sort of unique "interphase during prophase," a period of active RNA synthesis by much of the DNA, correlated with a great deal of rapid protein synthesis that results in much cellular metabolism, thereby producing the large volume of a wide variety of molecules that constitute the large oocyte. When the egg is fertilized, this stored food provides the large mass of complex protoplasm necessary for embryogeny. In fact, it has been stated that almost the entire genome may be functioning during this chromosomal condition, a statement difficult to accept in the light of the many operons restricted to growth, development, differentiation, and reproduction after zygote formation. It is also likely that a less extreme form of chromosomal extension of low metabolic activity and with much shorter lateral loops is essential for the synaptic process, as evidenced by the synaptinemal complex.

Interlocking

Interlocking refers to a somewhat uncommon phenomenon described at meiotic metaphase I in species having long metaphase chromosomes such as *Trillium, Tradescantia,* and grasshoppers. When interlocking occurs, each of two bivalents has a half bivalent of the other passing between its half bivalents. The result is like two links of a chain (Fig. 18-20).

It has long been believed that such a configuration is a random accidental result of an "error" at zygotene synapsis, in which a univalent crossed or was caught between two long, thin pairing chromosomes. White (1954) did state that the rarity of such "accidents" argues in favor of a precise and far from random orientation of the chromosomes in the leptotene (or presynaptic)

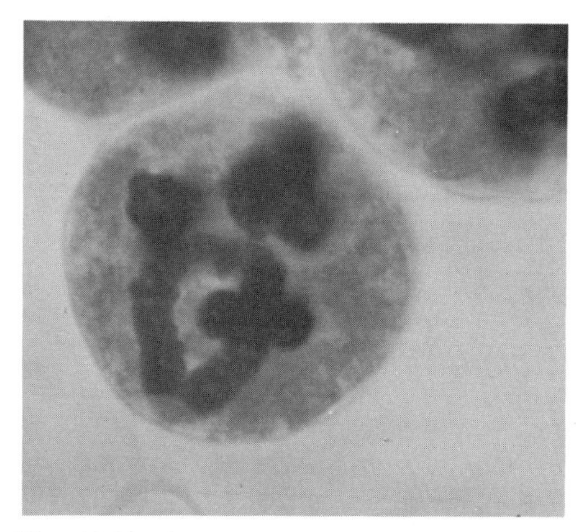

Fig. 18-20. An example of interlocking of bivalents at metaphase I in *Tradescantia gigantea* PMC. The two bivalents run through each other like two links of chain.

nucleus. Such orientation, nonoverlapping of nonhomologous chromosomes, must derive from side-by-side pairing at least by telophase of the premeiotic mitosis. Evidence by Davidson and Webster (1966) from *Tradescantia,* however, indicates that in a particular plant with a high rate of interlocking almost without exception the same two bivalents only were interlocked and that in a few pollen mother cells (PMCs) these same two bivalents were synapsed to form a quadrivalent. They have assumed that interlocking is not a random event at all but is caused by homologous segments associating, somewhat like a loose, achiasmatic "quadrivalent." Feldman (1966) (Chapter 17) considered interlocking, or lack of it, in wheat as evidence of premeiotic pairing.

The existence of interlocking as an error when zygotene chromosomes are sorting themselves out as homologous pairs used to be interpreted as circumstantial evidence for zygotene pairing. If interlocking is, on the contrary, always a result of homology (a generalization so far only indicated), the pairing of homologues is just so much more free of random interlocking error and is therefore a process that perhaps does not even permit interlocking between truly nonhomologous bivalents. That is, perhaps the chromosomes are already paired when "synapsis" begins. Interlocking between pairing, condensed, premeiotic metaphase chromosomes is far more unlikely than between long zygotene chromosomes.

Interlocking when one bivalent passes through *two* adjacent loops of another bivalent, "doubly interlocked" bivalents, has been used (Mather, 1933) as support for the concept (chiasma-type theory) that when diplotene bivalents begin to open out, it is always pairs of sister chromatids that separate from each other on each side of a chiasma rather than an alternative concept (classical theory), which assumes that a chiasma is formed where pairs of separating sister chromatids meet a pair of nonsister chromatids separating. Double interlocking, which is found rarely, cannot occur if the latter scheme represents the form of diplotene separation that actually occurs.

Synaptinemal complex

The synaptinemal complex (also called the *axial core, tripartite group, prophase complex, chromosomal axial complex,* and *chromosomal core*) was first reported in the electron microscopic literature in 1956, when Moses observed it in crayfish spermatocytes and Fawcett observed it in spermatocytes of pigeon, cat, and man. During the subsequent 17 years (Moses, 1968) it has been seen in at least forty-one species of animals (nine mammals, two birds, two amphibians, one fish, two decapod crustaceans, twenty-five species of insects [Fig. 18-23], one arachnid, three snails, and one roundworm), in nine species of monocotyledons and three dicotyledon species of the angiosperms, in one ascomycete fungus (Fig. 18-24), and in eight slime molds. Thus it can be assumed to be a general concomitant of synapsis and therefore of meiosis. Although it is generally considered limited to pachytene (or earlier) of prophase I (Fig. 18-21),

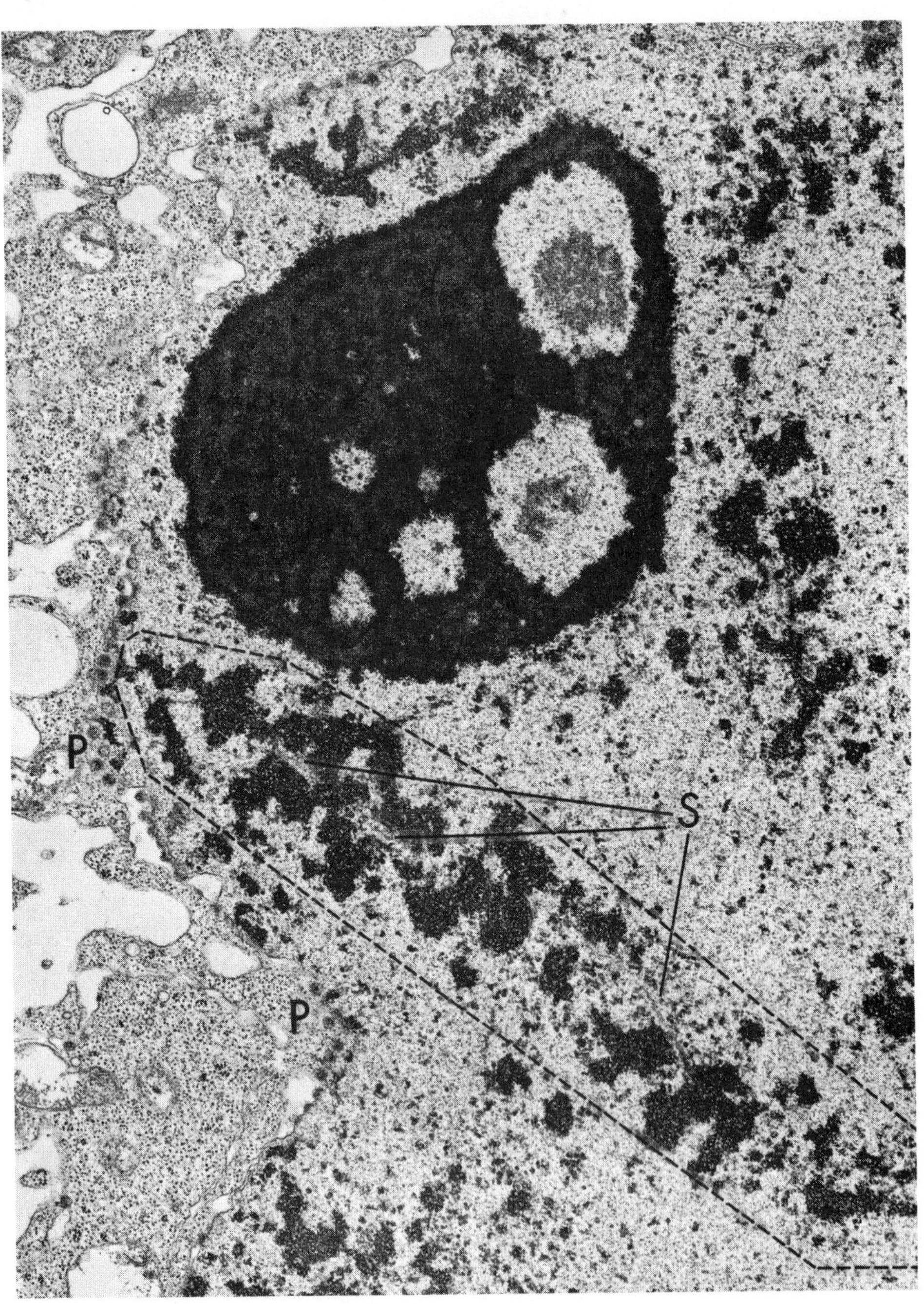

Fig. 18-21. Electron micrograph showing a probably synapsed bivalent (as marked) and the axial synaptinemal complex, **S,** in microsporocyte of *Hippeastrum belladonna.* The nucleolus is vacuolate. Note also pores, **P,** in nuclear envelope. (Courtesy Dr. D. A. Larson, University of Texas Cell Research Institute, Austin, Texas.)

it has been reported (although probably somewhat modified) in secondary spermatocytes, that is, after completion of meiosis I, and even in spermatids (after the second meiotic division) in three insects. Nothing like it has been reported in nonmeiotic nuclei except occasionally in nurse cells, but some specific meiotic nuclei do not have it. As the name implies, it is apparently a prophase I structural complex involving homologous chromosomes that is present at about the time synapsis is supposed to take place. That they are structural components in addition to the chromosomes is likely, but it seems certain that the chromosomes, when involved in the complex, are structurally different than at all other times.

The typical appearance of a mitotic interphase or early prophase chromosome in the electron microscopic cross section (Figs. 3-1, *B*, and 17-17) is a more or less circular, homogeneous, more darkly stained smear than the nuclear sap. In longitudinal section it would be an elongate homogeneous smear. According to present scanty evidence, it seems that before synapsis such homogeneous chromosomes "condense" at the center or on one side into a dense *axial element* surrounded or paralleled by less dense chromatin to form what is called the single axial element. Presumably, the large mass of less dense chromatin consists of radiating microfibrils extending outward from the axial filament as either free-ending or looped, 100 Å fibrils. One interpretation is that two such homologous single axial elements synapse at zygotene or early pachytene by the axial elements coming to lie close to one another and longitudinally parallel, as a *bipartite complex* (Fig. 18-23). The distance between axial filaments varies among organisms, but a range of 1,000 to 1,200 Å is typical. The axial filaments generally have a rather vague outer "surface," but diameters of 400 to 700 Å have been estimated. The axial filaments are parallel but may lie in one plane or be twisted loosely about each other, still always maintaining exactly their distance apart.

Uncommonly in cross section but often in longitudinal section a faint "line" can be detected parallel to the paired axial filaments and halfway between them. This line is thought to be formed by the contact of specific and homologous regions of chromatin, called the *"central pairing line"* or *medial component.* Often in longitudinal section numerous strands connecting the paired axial filaments, forming a ladderlike structure, can be seen. In cross sections of this "ladder" it is evident that each rung, as seen in long section, actually consists of several nearly parallel, 60 Å connecting strands, called *bridging filaments* or *internal strands* (Figs. 18-22 and 18-23). The two axial elements and the *"central pairing line"* form the *tripartite complex.*

Moens (1968) proposed the following terminology and ideas based in part on his study of *Lilium longiflorum.* The 1,600 to 2,400 Å wide *synaptinemal complex,* as seen at pachytene, consists of a pair of parallel 300 to 500 Å *lateral elements* spaced 1,000 to 1,200 Å apart and between which is a 100 to 300 Å wide *central element.* Many 600 Å long *transverse filaments* from each lateral element extend toward each other and overlap to form the central element. Before the complex is formed, as at leptotene and zygotene, each chromosome forms within itself a longitudinal *axial core,* which later becomes one lateral element of a complex. Lateral elements are not parts of chromosomes but are structures formed de novo by the chromosomes for some special purpose. After the complex has completed its function (by the end of pachytene) each lateral element is released from its chromosome and comes to lie in the nucleoplasm as a *stripped core.*

The large mass of chromatin external to the pachytene complex consists of 100 to 200 Å thick DNA-protein loops of gene copies or *slaves.* The 25 Å *master strands* (of the cycloid model of Whitehouse, 1967) are double, are of two 10 to 15 Å strands,

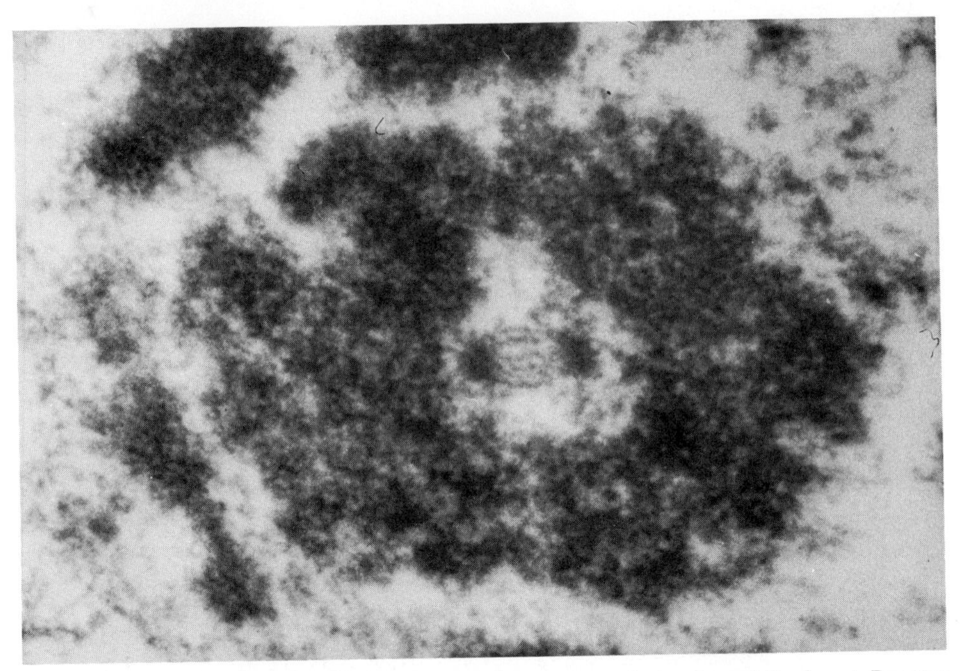

Fig. 18-22. Electron microscopy cross section of synaptinemal complex of the insect *Panorpa neptialis* surrounded by the thick ringlike chromosomal mass, which may consist of two more or less distinct halves, one behind and to the sides of each axial filament. The two large lateral filaments are connected by six internal strands, and each is connected to the chromosomal mass by vague external strands. (×108,000.) (Courtesy Dr. G. Gassner, formerly of the Zoology Department, University of Texas, Austin, Texas.)

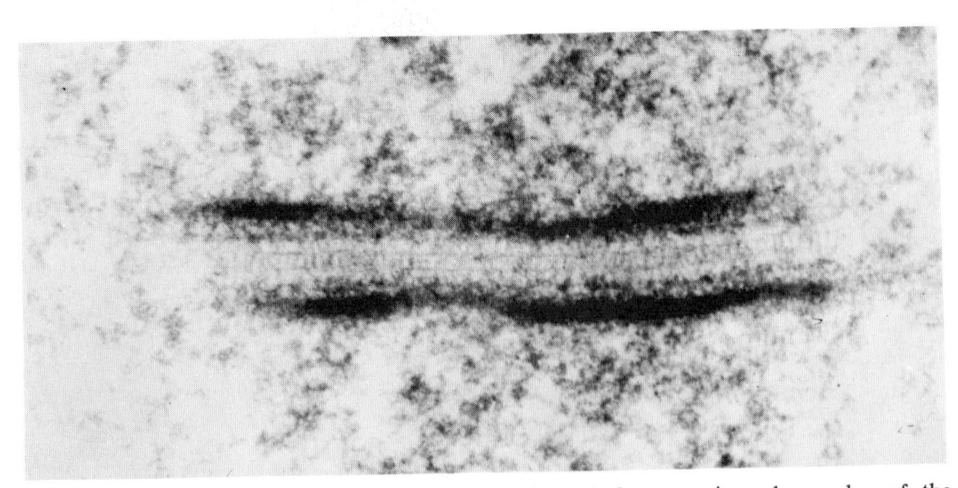

Fig. 18-23. Electron microscopy longitudinal section of the synaptinemal complex of the insect *Panorpa neptialis* showing the two heavy lateral filaments, the tripartite central pairing line peculiar to this species, and internal and external strands. (×108,000.) (Courtesy Dr. G. Gassner, formerly of the Zoology Department, University of Texas, Austin, Texas.)

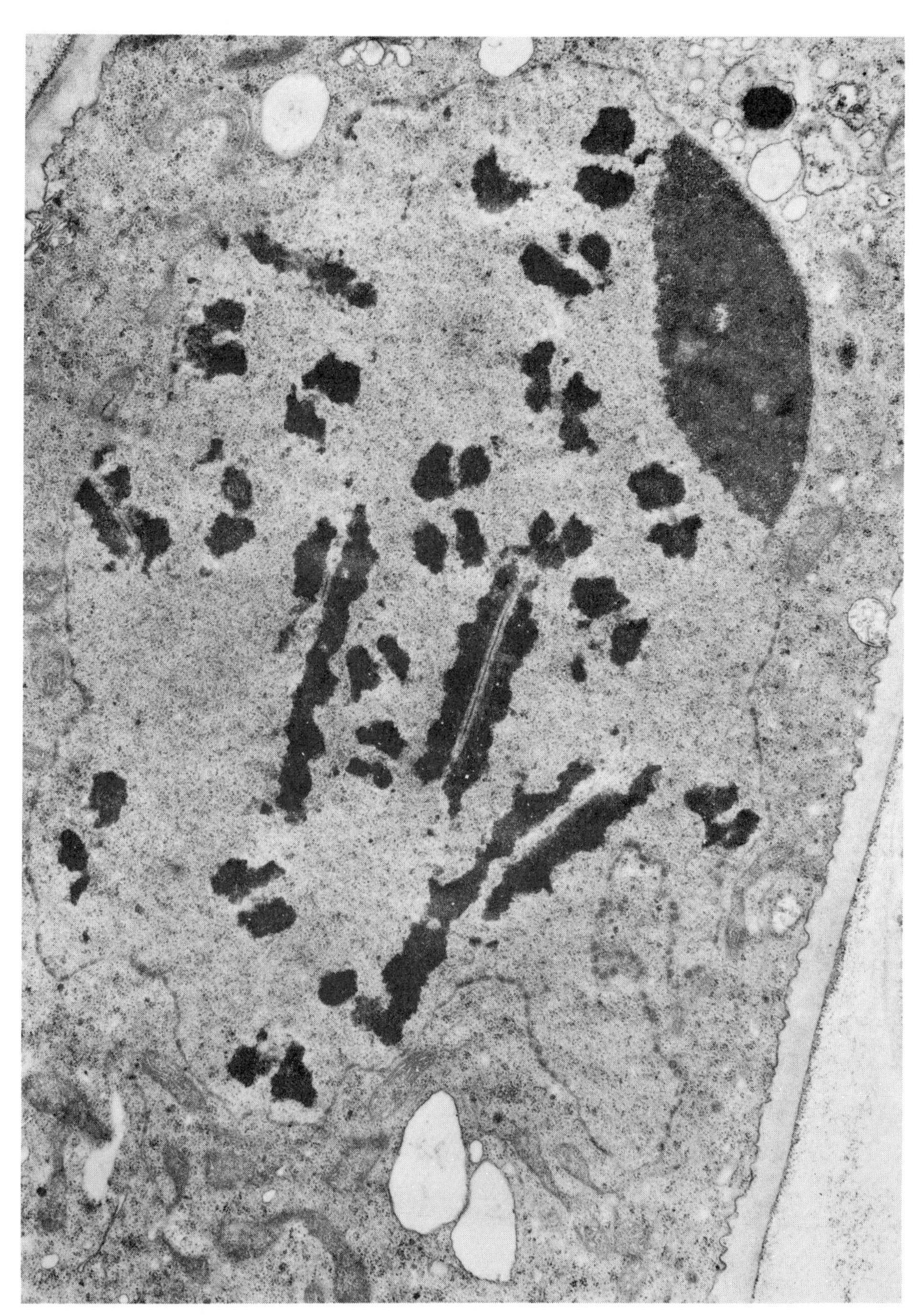

Fig. 18-24. Synaptinemal complexes in a fusion nucleus of *Neottiella.* Note also hemispheric nucleolus "pressed" against the nuclear envelope. In cross and longitudinal sections it seems as though homologous chromosomes are united by the synaptinemal complex that lies between them. The long, longitudinal section near the center of the nucleus is shown at higher magnification in Fig. 18-26. (Courtesy Dr. D. von Wettstein, University of Copenhagen, Copenhagen, Denmark.)

and are assumed to run parallel to and closely associated with the lateral elements. The association of master strand *and* axial core might produce a mechanism for exact homologous pairing not possessed by either alone. Crossing-over occurs only between subunits of the master strands of the two synapsed homologues.

In the best material of some organisms and at high magnification the central element may be resolved into three lines in long section, of which the middle is faintest and is the "true" line of contact. On each side of this interface line and between it and the lateral elements are two other lines of equal diameter. These lines, parallel to the lateral elements, may be composed of two series of granules on the *internal strands* or actual longitudinal filamentous bridges between adjacent strands. Since these longitudinal bridges (if that is what they are) have a greater diameter than the fine 60 Å internal strands, the transverse filaments, they appear as granules in cross section, and there are as many pairs of granules as there are internal strands (Figs. 18-22 and 18-23), at least in the insect *Panorpa,* which generally has six internal strands (Gassner, 1966).

In most illustrations of the synaptinemal complex the dense lateral elements blend into the less dense fibrous masses of radiating microfibrils on the side away from the contact of homologues (Fig. 18-24). In *Panorpa,* however, the lateral elements are somewhat separate from the fibrous masses but connected to them by *external strands,* which in this case may be the radiating bases of microfibrils that become looped and contorted further out. Also in *Panorpa* and some other species the fibrous masses of microfilaments may form an irregular ring (in cross section) around the synaptinemal complex (Figs. 18-22 and 18-23).

There are reports of lateral elements being double, two chromatids, perpendicular

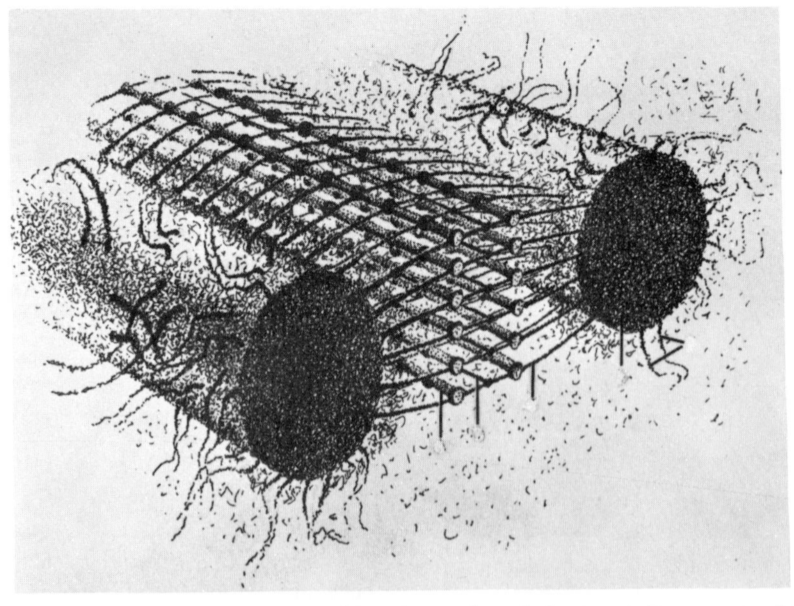

Fig. 18-25. Interpretive model of synaptinemal complex of the insect *Panorpa neptialis.* The two large strands are the lateral elements. In most organisms there is a single central pairing line. (Courtesy Dr. G. Gassner, formerly of the Zoology Department, University of Texas, Austin, Texas.)

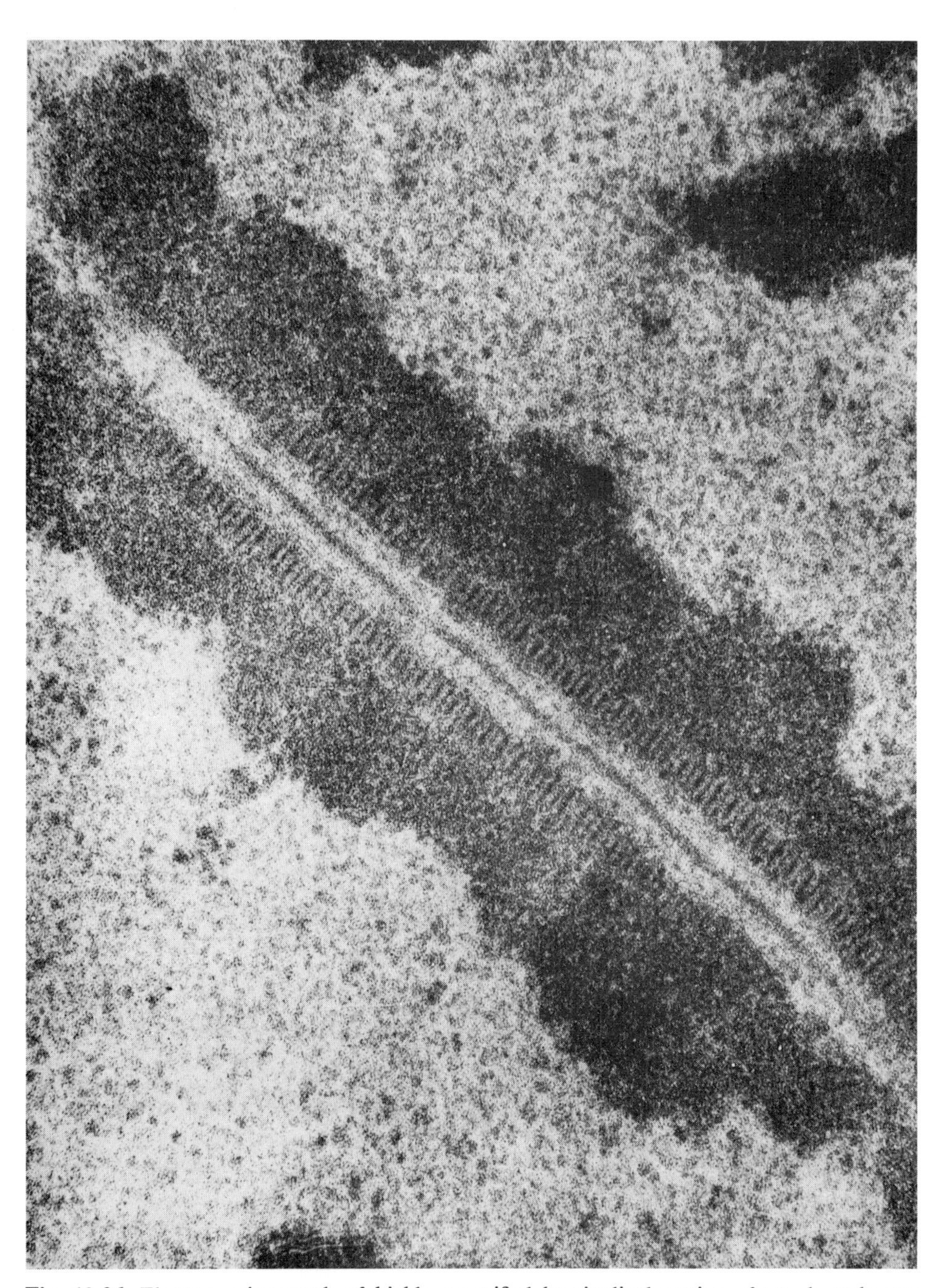

Fig. 18-26. Electron micrograph of highly magnified longitudinal section of two homologous chromosomes "united by," "held together by," or "in synapsis with" a synaptinemal complex of unusual structure in a fusion nucleus of the fungus *Neottiella*. The parallel band structure of the "lateral elements," which actually do occur in this material, is unknown in animals and plants. For interpretation see Fig. 18-27. (Courtesy Dr. D. von Wettstein, University of Copenhagen, Copenhagen, Denmark.)

to the internal strands. In *Panorpa* (Fig. 18-25) when the lateral elements are single, they are connected by five or occasionally six internal strands. When one or both lateral elements are double, each of the half filaments keeps three internal strands but "adds" another outside its three. Thus a pair of double lateral elements is connected by eight internal strands, as two groups of four, the outer of each group probably being different. In some organisms the lateral elements are reported as always double (crayfish) and in others as always single, in contrast to *Panorpa* and some others in which single and double conditions appear locally or late in pachytene.

The illustrations (Figs. 18-24 and 18-26) and interpretation (Fig. 18-27) of the synaptinemal complex in the ascomycete fungus *Neottiella* (Westergaard and von Wettstein, 1966) demonstrate a structural arrangement different from that of the insect *Panorpa*. Of the two, *Panorpa* is more typical, but there does seem to be considerable variation among organisms.

As far as is known, no local differences of the synaptinemal complex that might represent sites of crossing-over have been reported. Perhaps crossovers form at a later stage.

In *meiocytes* (cells in which meiosis I occurs) known to be young, a high proportion of single axial cores are reported in two species only. In later stages only the bipartite (paired lateral elements) complexes are usually observed. In still later stages of some animals, as late as secondary spermatocytes and even spermatids, some modified forms of the "complex" have been reported, called *residual complexes*. Since these cells are haploid and the complex involves paired homologues, it is obvious that they must be different.

Sotelo and Wettstein (1965) are not

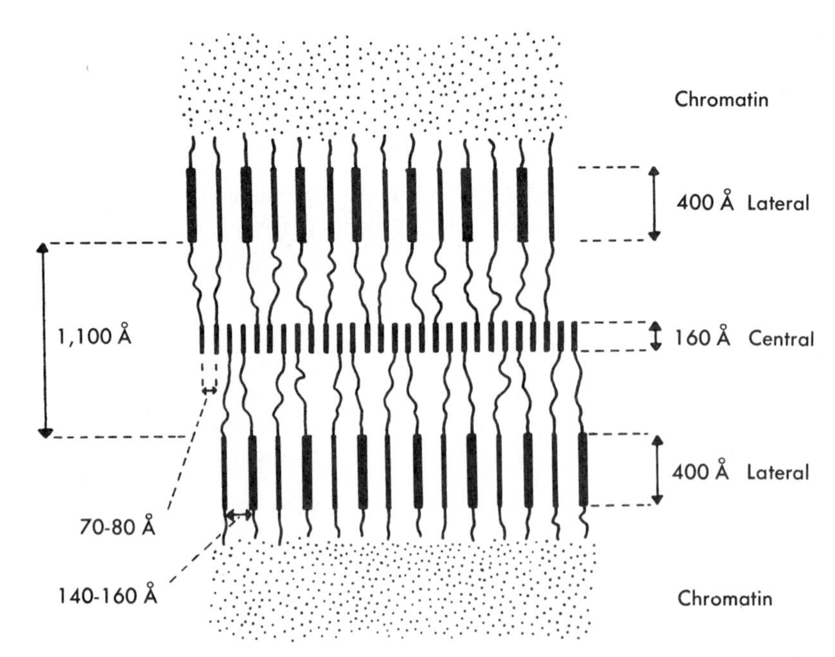

Fig. 18-27. Interpretation of fine structure of synaptinemal complex of *Neottiella* from electron micrographs such as those seen in Figs. 18-24 and 18-26. There are twice as many short transverse rods or fibers in the central band as in either lateral band. Transverse rods of the lateral bands are alternately thick and thin. Contrast this form of complex with that of the insect *Panorpa* in Figs. 18-23 and 18-25. (From Westergaard, M., and D. von Wettstein. 1966. C. R. Trav. Lab. Carlsberg **35**:261-286.)

convinced that the tripartite complex represents synapsed homologues because of failure to find the act of pairing. They are inclined to believe that each group forms the core of a single chromosome. Moens (1968) and others do claim to see the act of pairing in electron micrographs of the zygotene complex; that is, profiles show two axial cores that "approach" each other like two arms of a Y and then run parallel as a zipping-up synaptinemal complex, forming the base of the Y.

Just what all this means functionally is far from clear. The name, applied by Moses in 1956, implies a relation to synapsis, which is certainly a good guess. Others have proposed that it may not be so much a mechanism for synapsis as for crossing-over, a somewhat less reliable guess. Evidence from *Drosophila* supports at least a probable direct correlation with synapsis, crossing-over, or both.

Geneticists determined long ago that there is essentially no crossing-over between homologous chromosomes within spermatocytes of male individuals of *Drosophila.* The implication is that there may not be any synapsis either (as distinct from pairing). Meyer in 1960 found synaptinemal complexes in *Drosophila* oocytes; there synapsis and crossing-over do occur, but not in spermatocytes. Thus one would expect to find the complex only in meiocytes that have synapsis, crossing-over, or both. When seen, it can be assumed that meiosis I is occurring in that cell and can be used as evidence of the time of meiosis in those organisms where this stage of the life cycle is otherwise difficult to determine, such as myxomycetes. Few short pieces of synap-

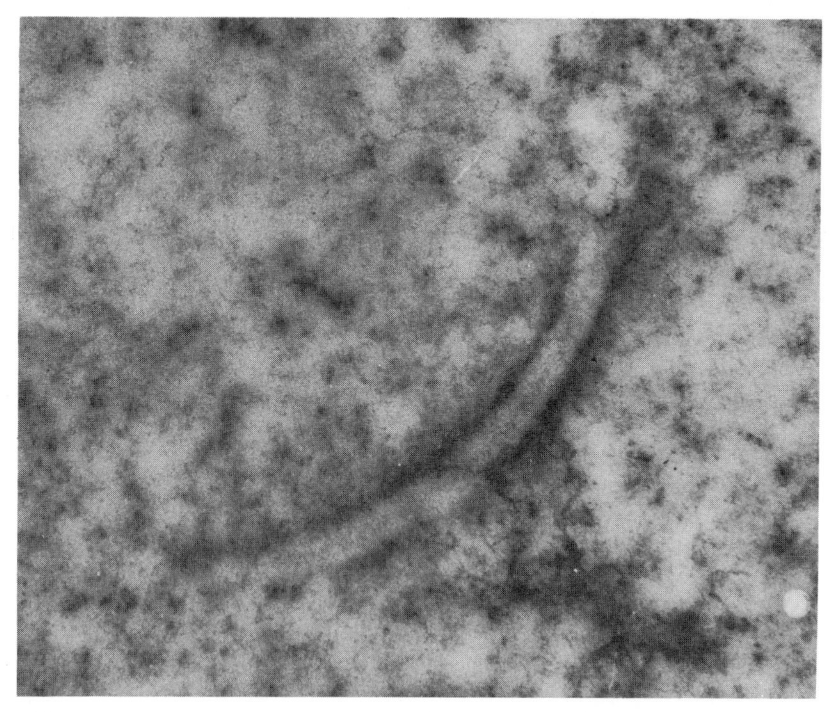

Fig. 18-28. An example of synaptinemal complex in tomato, but in a microsporocyte of a haploid plant. Such profiles were uncommon but did occur and probably represented synapsis between duplicated segments on the same or two different chromosomes. (From Menzel, M. Y., and J. M. Price. 1966. Amer. J. Bot. **53:**1079-1086.)

tinemal complex have been seen even in haploid tomato PMCs (Fig. 18-28), perhaps indicating some segmental homologies.

There seem to be enough observations of synapsed homologues with apparently normal synaptinemal complexes that, nevertheless, are followed by failure of chiasmata and recombination to conclude that "the synaptinemal complex is not in itself sufficient to assure the occurrence of crossing-over" (Stack, 1973). On the other hand, the intimate association of homologues in synapsis may require the presence and functioning of the complex.

If the microfibrils radiating outward from the lateral elements are really loops, synaptinemal complex chromosomes are morphologically related to and may be an early phase of the lampbrush chromosomes of certain diplotene oocytes, which in most meiocytes do not develop further.

Another function of the synaptinemal complex was proposed by Stack (1969) during a general discussion of coiling in chromosomes. The point had been made that evidence for coiling as typical of mitotic prophase, metaphase, and anaphase chromosomes is poor, whereas unquestionable coiling does occur in chromosomes of many species during meiosis I (Hillary, 1940; Sax and Humphrey, 1934). Since the synaptinemal complex is restricted to meiosis, and probably coiling also, Stack argued that perhaps the complex is a mechanism for producing coiling, which may be a necessary chromosomal form during this division.

Support for this hypothesis comes from the known formation of paired homologues in somatic cells and genetic crossing-over and cytological pseudochiasmata in somatic cells, especially during parasexuality in male *Drosophila* and such asexual fungi as *Aspergillus,* as far as is known, all without the synaptinemal complex. It is also supported (if one hypothesis is proper evidence for support of another) by the hypothesis of Cole (1962) that coiling of meiotic chromosomes is accomplished by "contraction" of a proteinaceous strand somewhat external to the chromosome. Stack merely proposes that the lateral elements of the synaptinemal complex are such strands. Brown (1972) has proposed that the transverse strands between the lateral elements may be contractile protein for pulling homologues close together.

Cole's hypothesis does seem to overemphasize the importance of meiotic chromosomal coiling, for which there are few claims of necessity (Janssens, 1909; Vejdovsky, 1912). On the other hand, since somatic pairing and parasexuality are so random and fortuitous, perhaps the synaptinemal complex is a special mechanism for guaranteeing crossovers and persistence of bivalents to anaphase I.

Thus there are at least nine probably unique chromosomal conditions during meiosis I: (1) the synaptinemal complex; (2) possible premeiotic pairing; (3) synapsis of the already paired homologues; (4) crossing-over; (5) the bouquet or synizetic knot; (6) true chromomeres; (7) possibly no G_2 phase (DNA replication may extend into prophase); (8) no DNA replication during interphase between meiosis I and II, and (9) coiling. It is not unlikely that these are all interrelated, and they must all be considered and integrated in any model of the cytology of meiosis I. Meiosis may have evolved from mitosis, but it, including two "interphases," is probably different from mitotic division and somatic interphase. Moses (1968) has recently reviewed the synaptinemal complex.

Cytomixis

"Cytomixis" is a botanical term that refers to the passage of chromatin from one microsporocyte (pollen mother cell, or PMC) to another (Fig. 18-29). It was so named and defined by Gates in 1911, although Kornicke first described the condition in pollen mother cells of *Crocus sativus* in 1901. More generally, it applies to such movement from any cell to another, as in epidermis, root tips, etc. Such movement of chromosomes, nucleoli, and nuclear membrane requires a plasma canal through the two plasma membranes and the cell wall between adjacent cells. Such canals range up to a few microns in diameter; since they are regularly produced, at least in many species and hybrids, they must be the result of gene action. They have been recorded by both light and electron microscopy.

Somewhat similar protoplast confluence between reproductive cells were discussed in Chapter 17. There is no report of chromatin passing from cell to cell, however, in these examples in animals.

Most reports of cytomixis have been of such movement of nuclear material from one PMC to another during early prophase of meiosis, especially from leptotene to pachytene (Bopp-Hassenkamp, 1959), but also throughout the two divisions of meiosis. The phenomenon occurs in normal species, hybrids, and apomicts and is so widespread that one wonders if it is a general phenomenon (Kamra, 1960).

There can be no doubt that cytomixis occurs, but whether the cytological results attributed to it are equally real is questionable. The presence of binucleate (and anucleate) PMCs as well as both increase and decrease in chromosome number have been attributed to cytomixis. For example, in

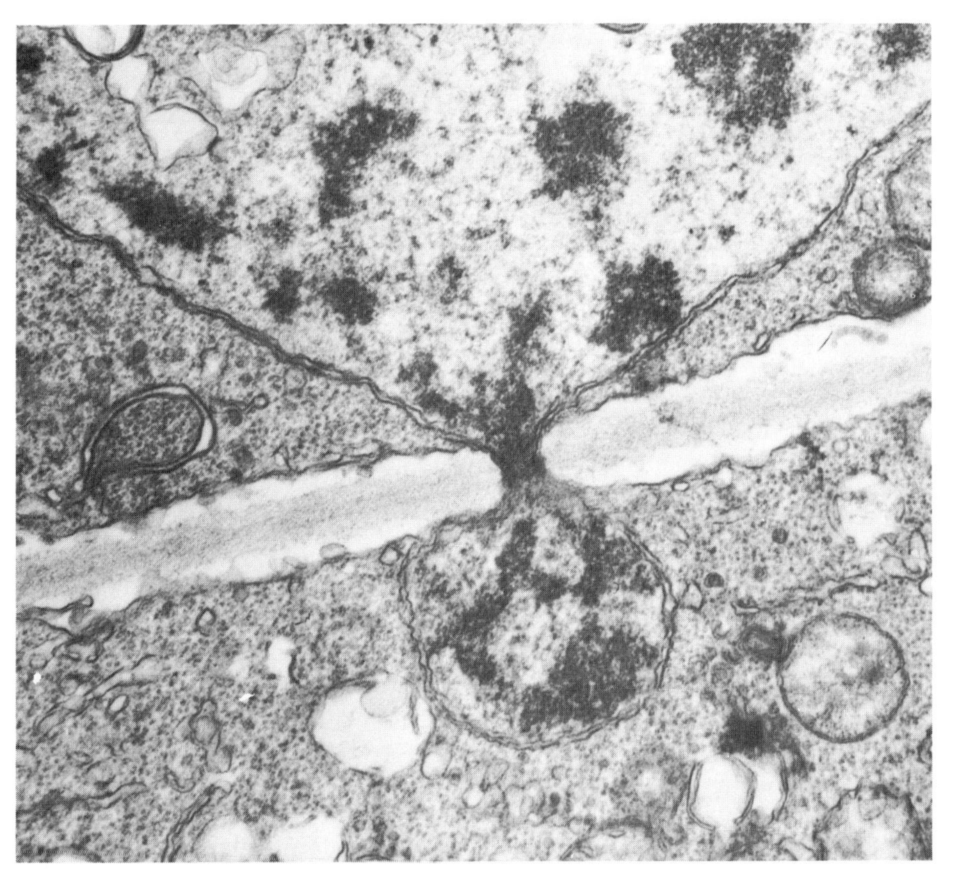

Fig. 18-29. Cytomixis in anther of *Haplopappus gracilis* showing part of a nucleus and contained chromatin of a meiocyte passing through a hole in a cell wall into an adjacent meiocyte. (Courtesy S. Stack, University of Texas Cell Research Institute, Austin, Texas.)

hybrid tetraploid cotton (2n = 52), Sarvella (1958) found from one to four cells in each of the chromosome number classes 1 to 11, 12 to 21, 22 to 31, 32 to 41, and over 63; twelve to eighteen cases of chromosome numbers between 42 to 51 and 53 to 62; and 700 cells with 2n = 52, the expected number. That is, about 3% of cells had more or less than the tetraploid number, ranging from 3 to 85. In a hexaploid hybrid (2n = 78), chromosome numbers per PMC ranged from 33 to 99, involving 11% of the 204 cells examined. He considered the aneuploid chromosome numbers were probably the result of cytomixis.

Heslop-Harrison (1964), from an electron microscope study of hemp anthers, stated that "communicating channels have been observed with sufficient frequency to indicate that any one meiocyte may be linked at some time with all contiguous ones. If this is so, the whole sporogenous mass is at one stage effectively a huge coenocyte."

Cases of aneuploidy in somatic tissues have been explained by recourse to cytomixis. Sharma and Majumdar found no constancy of chromosome number is root tip or sporogenous cells of the fern *Pteris ensiformis;* numbers ranged from 19 to 88, with 33 being the only number occurring in both. In another fern, *Adiantum capillus-veneris,* numbers in root tip cells ranged from 9 to 70. In this species, however, all sporogenous cells had n = 30. Somewhat similar aneuploid variations have also been reported in a variety of somatic tissues of several angiosperms. Irregular mitotic divisions might also produce such results without cytomixis.

Although the term has not been so applied, the concept of cytomixis holds also for characteristic processes in the fungus groups of the Ascomycetes and the Basidiomycetes. In the crozier of the ascomycetes, three cells are produced—the *stalk cell,* then the *penultimate cell,* and at the tip, the *terminal cell.* The penultimate cell is binucleate; the stalk and terminal cells are uninucleate. Later "cytomixis" occurs by a pore forming between the adjacent stalk and terminal cells so that either nucleus (but only one or the other) migrates into the other cell to produce a binucleate and an anucleate cell. An ascus develops from the binucleate stalk or terminal cell or the binucleate penultimate cell (Fig. 18-14).

In the Basidiomycetes, migration of one particular nucleus from one cell to the other occurs at division by way of the bypass structure called the *clamp connection.* Thus each cell produced by division contains two nuclei—one of the plus strain, the other of the minus strain—in the *dikaryotic phase.* Division, including the clamp connection, is a complicated process by which each daughter cell is guaranteed two nuclei, one of each parental strain (Fig. 17-12). Karyogamy finally occurs in the young basidium and just before meiosis, which is comparable to karyogamy and meiosis in the young ascus of the Ascomycetes.

The term "cytomixis" has also been applied, perhaps too loosely, to the mere breakdown of plasma membranes and walls between adjacent somatic cells. An example in *Yucca* roots is the dissolution of walls between adjacent cells in a row of crytal-containing cells (Fig. 14-11). This is really the formation of a syncytium, as occurs also in some animals such as the epidermal layer of Aschelminthes.

True cytomixis, as it occurs in PMCs, seems to be common, but its effects are poorly understood at present. Tarkowska (1965, 1966) considered all or most cytomixis as an artifact produced by pressure on the cell from which the nucleus moves.

Chromomeres

Chromomeres are small but variably sized, beadlike, stained swellings on certain extended chromonemata or chromosomes. Therefore they have been reported only in the most extended conditions of chromosomes, during interphase, early mitotic prophase, from leptotene to pachytene of prophase I of meiosis, in "salivary" chromosomes, and in lampbrush chromosomes. They are, however, rarely seen at interphase or during prophase of mitosis and may well be strictly meiotic. There are a few hundred of them on each chromosome and thus a few thousand in a chromosome set. It has been reported that the larger ones are constant in size, position, and number for each species, although the smallest vary considerably. Large chromomeres may consist of several fused small ones, the smallest being called "ultimate" chromomeres, each of which may represent the locus of a gene (Fig. 18-9).

In the older cytological literature (before 1950) chromomeres were considered to be real and significant structures of meiotic chromosomes quite different from the *interchromomere* region of the chromosome. For example, Belling (1931, 1933) in his scheme of recombination and chromosome structural duplication at meiosis proposed that the single-stranded homologous zygotene chromosomes synapsed chromomere to homologous chromomere. Each of the pair of chromomeres then duplicated itself, and not until then did the new chromomeres become linked into a linear series (with crossovers) by the formation of interchromomeric connections. Chromomeres have reentered theoretical considerations as replicative and synthetic units of genonemata (Pelling, 1966). Others have proposed that a pair of homologous chromomeres contain one unique antibody for the unique antigen of the other. Thus chromomere-for-chromomere and gene-for-gene pairing was "explained." Now homologous loci of homologues are generally considered uniquely *alike* rather than different, but it is still often proposed that chromomeres are important in synapsis.

As discussed elsewhere, each band of the giant chromosomes of Diptera is considered to be composed of hundreds of homologous chromomeres fused into a transverse disk (Fig. 17-16). Much of the study of chromomeres has been focused on the investigation of such giant chromosome bands and the heterochromatic chromocenters of the same nuclei. From such study it seems that chromomeres are related to heterochromatin. Perhaps each chromomere is a tiny bit of heterochromatin. This concept is either supported or derived from the study of lampbrush chromosome chromomeres, which are considered to be small loci of coiled or folded chromonema separated from each other by an interchromomeric region of extended (uncoiled or unfolded) chromonema. The concept of unextended chromonema is now the widely accepted concept of chromomeres in general and also of heterochromatin. In all probability the "knobs" of pachytene chromosomes of *Zea mays* (Fig. 18-8) are really large chromomeres of constant position for a particular strain of corn but varying among strains. In fact, it has been proposed that among strains of corn the amount of other heterochromatin and number of knobs vary inversely, the more of one the less of the other. Therefore chromomeres may constitute a special case of heterochromatin.

Sex differences

Diverse sex differences in characters of meiosis are known. The most outstanding and best known is the achiasmatic condition of one sex only, as in male *Drosophila* and the female silkworm. Less obvious but nonetheless common is a sex difference in chiasma frequency. Both chiasma frequency and crossing-over are higher in the female mouse than in the male (Slizynski, 1960). Chiasma frequency is higher in the female of the flatworm *Dendrocoelum* than in the male (Pastor and Callan, 1952) and higher in ovules of *Fritillaria, Lilium* (Fogwill, 1958), and several species of *Allium* (Brat, 1966) than in anthers. In newts such sex difference varies, being higher in the female of *Triturus helveticus* but higher in the male of *T. cristatus cristatus*. In the latter species of the newt, however, chiasmata are randomly distributed in the male but are nonrandomly proximal in the female. A similar sex difference in chiasmata distribution occurs in *Allium pallens* (Brat, 1966), where distribution is random in PMCs but mostly localized near the centromere in EMCs. The reverse has been found in *Fritillaria* (Fogwill, 1958), with random distribution in the ovules. In *Dendrocoelum* there is distal chiasma localization in males but random distribution in females.

In *Zea mays,* chromosome 5 chiasma frequency is equal in both sexes, except that the PMCs have a higher frequency in the proximal (centric) region (Rhoades, 1961). In chromosome 9 there is a higher crossing-over frequency in the PMCs than in EMCs (Nelson, 1964). In the presence of the asynaptic gene (Beadle, 1933), recombination is high in ovules but low in anthers. In general, it can be stated that most of the known cases of such sex differences in both animals and plants show higher crossing-over in the females. This may be related to the generalization among plant hybridizers that greater success is achieved when the more abnormal parent is the female (pistillate) parent.

There are, of course, other sex differences of meiosis in animals, such as lampbrush chromosomes in some oocytes, arrest of meiosis at some stage in females (dictyotene), polar body, no centrioles, and superficial division due in part to the large size of oocytes relative to spermatocytes, and different divisions among parthenogenetic species, haploid male Hymenoptera, various scale insects, etc. Among apomictic plants the apomeiotic division in the ovule may be very different from that in the anthers. Almost always in such plants the division in anthers is more meiotic than is the apomeiotic division in the EMCs. In the dog roses the EMC and PMC divisions are also quite different.

Such sex differences of meiosis are not surprising, since the environments in which the divisions occur are distinctive and the cellular products resulting, male as opposed to female gametes or microspores as opposed to macrospores, are also very different. They are no more exceptional than the sexual dimorphism that they accompany and the different kinds of gametes or gametophytes that are produced.

Another type of cytological sex difference, but not of meiosis, is the asynchronous labeling of replicating DNA in sex chromosomes. It has been established that heterochromatin replicates (is labeled by tritiated thymidine) at the end of the S phase and after the euchromatin has completed its replication. Sex chromosomes are or may be highly heterochromatic, for example, the lyonized Barr body X chromosome (an old hypothesis including gene action and dosage compensation used to explain the Barr body by Lyon in 1961 and 1962). In the Chinese hamster, Taylor (1960) found that in culture cells derived from a female animal one whole X chromosome, but only the long arm of the other, the homologous X, are late replicating, whereas in the cells derived from a male the Y chromosome and only the long arm of the single X are late replicating.

Parasexuality

"Parasexuality" is a term Pontecorvo (1958) applied to systems that do produce recombination in which plasmogamy, karyogamy, and haploidization take place (they do also in meiosis), but not at a specified time (meiosis) and at a unique and definite stage (fertilization) of the life cycle of the species.

Among such fungi as the asexual *Aspergillus nidulans,* in which it was first worked out, other Ascomycetes, Basidiomycetes, and some imperfect (asexual) fungi, step 1 involves formation of a haploid heterokaryon (a cell or coenocyte with two different haploid nuclei or types of haploid nuclei). During step 2 there is some fusion of pairs of these nuclei. These two steps are comparable to gametic union and fusion of gamete nuclei in sexual reproduction. Step 3 involves multiplication of such diploid nuclei with occasional somatic crossing-over in step 4, which may imply some somatic pairing also—a kind of somatic "meiosis." Apparently, there is some type of sorting out of such diploid nuclei so that some parts of the mycelium become largely diploid in step 5. At the same time there seems to occur, occasionally or rarely, the somatic haploidization of such diploid nuclei, again a somatic equivalent of meiotic reduction, constituting step 6. Steps 4 and 6 may be comparable to the somatic pairing and pseudochiasmata in diploid tissue culture cells of *Haplopappus gracilis,* followed by haploid anaphase groups and haploid daughter nuclei (Mitra and Steward, 1961). The last step in parasexuality (step 7) that can occur is a sorting out of such haploid nuclei containing genetic recombination so that progeny result having the recombination phenotypes.

Parasexuality certainly does occur in laboratories and may also occur in nature, but each step is occasional, haphazard, and far below sexuality and meiosis as a source of variability and rapid evolution.

Pontecorvo considers four novel systems in bacteria as other known examples of parasexuality.

1. *Transformation,* by which DNA of one strain of bacteria can enter individuals of another strain and genetically change it (Hotchkiss, 1955).
2. *Quasisexual reproduction* between (haploid) bacteria, a rare event, by which a donor individual unites with another and introduces some donor DNA into the recipient (which is then a *merozygote*). The descendants of the merozygote demonstrate recombination (Lederberg, 1947).
3. Bacteriophage-mediated *transduction,* during which a phage particle formed in one bacterium carries some of the DNA of that host bacterium into a new bacterium at infection and the transported DNA becomes part of the DNA system of the new viral host, with recombination (Zinder and Lederberg, 1952).
4. This type of perhaps questionable parasexuality is called *lysogenization* (Lwoff, 1953). It is now well known that in some viruses the nucleic acid merges with the genetic matter of the host bacterium. It becomes largely undetectable; does not severely affect the host, although it may change its physiology; it replicates along with replication of the host DNA; and it may persist in this state of lysogeny for endless bacterial generations (Jacob and Wollman, 1957).

By genetic recombination all of these parasexual systems do provide variability beyond mere mutation.

LITERATURE CITED

Atwood, S. 1937. The last premeiotic mitosis and its relation to meiosis in Gaillardia. Proc. Nat. Acad. Sci. U.S.A. **23:**1-5.

Barer, R., S. Joseph, and G. A. Meek. 1959. The origin of the nuclear membrane. Exp. Cell Res. **18:**179-182.

Battaglia, E. 1947. Divisione eterotypica in cellule somatiche di Sambucus ebulus L. Nuovo. G. Bot. Ital. **54:**724-733.

Beadle, G. W. 1933. Further studies on asynaptic maize. Cytologia. **4:**269-287.

Belling, J. 1931. Chiasmas in flowering plants. Calif. Univ. Publ. Bot. **16:**313-321.

Belling, J. 1933. Crossing over and gene rearrangement in flowering plants. Genetics **18:**388-413.

Bopp-Hassenkamp, G. 1959. "Cytomixis" im Elektronenmikroskopischen Bild. Exp. Cell Res. **18:** 182-184.

Boss, J. 1954. Mitosis in cultures of newt tissue. II. Chromosome pairing in anaphase. Exp. Cell Res. **7:**225-231.

Boss, J. M. N. 1955. The pairing of somatic chromosomes: a survey. Texas Rep. Biol. Med. **13:**212-221.

Brat, S. V. 1966. Genetic systems in Allium. II. Sex differences in meiosis. In C. D. Darlington and K. R. Lewis (editors). Chromosomes today. Plenum Press, Inc., New York.

Brown, W. V. 1972. Textbook of cytogenetics. The C. V. Mosby Co., St. Louis.
Brown, W. V., and S. M. Stack. 1968. Somatic pairing as a regular preliminary to meiosis. Bull. Torrey Bot. Club **95:**369-378.
Callan, H. G., and L. Lloyd. 1961. Lampbrush chromosomes of the crested newts Triturus cristatus (Laurenti). Roy. Soc. Phil. Trans. [Biol.] **243:**135-219.
Church, K., and D. Wimber. 1971. Meiosis in *Ornithogalum virens* (Liliaceae). Exp. Cell Res. **64:**119-124.
Cole, A. 1962. A molecular model for biological contractility: implications in chromosome structure and functions. Nature (London) **196:**211-214.
Davidson, D., and P. Webster. 1966. Interlocking and structural hybridity in Tradescantia. In Biological Research in Department of Biology, Western Reserve University, Cleveland. (Abstract.)
Fahmy, O. G. 1952. The cytology and genetics of Drosophila subobscura. VI. Maturation, fertilization, and cleavage in normal eggs and in presence of the cross-over suppressor gene. J. Genet. **50:**486-506.
Fawcett, D. W. 1956. The fine structure of chromosomes in the meiotic prophase of vertebrate spermatocytes. J. Biophys. Biochem. Cytol. **2:** 403-406.
Fawcett, D. W., S. Ito, and D. Slautterback. 1959. The occurrence of intercellular bridges in groups of cells exhibiting synchronous differentiation. J. Biophys. Biochem. Cytol. **5:**453-460.
Fogwill, M. 1958. Differences in crossing-over and chromosome size in the sex cells of Lilium and Fritillaria. Chromosoma **9:**493-504.
Gassner, G. 1966. A light and electron microscopy study of spermatogenesis in the scorpionfly Panorpa nuptialis G. and other Mecoptera. Ph.D. dissertation, University of Texas, Austin.
Gelei, J. 1921. Weitere Studien über die Oogenese des Dendrocoelum lacteum. Arch. Zellforsch. **16:**88-169.
Gowen, J. W. 1933. Meiosis as a genetic character in Drosophila melanogaster. J. Exp. Zool. **65:** 83-106.
Grell, R. F. 1965. Chromosome pairing, crossing-over, and segregation in Drosophila melanogaster. In J. I. Valencia and R. F. Grell (editors). International symposium on genes and chromosomes: structure and function. Government Printing Office, Washington, D. C.
Grell, R. F., and A. C. Chandley. 1965. Evidence bearing on the coincidence of exchange and DNA replication in the oocyte of Drosophila melanogaster. Proc. Nat. Acad. Sci. U.S.A. **53:**1340-1346.
Gustaffson, A. 1946. Apomixis in higher plants. I. The mechanism of apomixis. Lunds. Univ. Arsskrift **42:**1-67.
Gustaffson, A. 1947. Apomixis in higher plants. II. The casual aspect of apomixis. III. Biotype and species formation. Lunds. Univ. Arsskrift **43:**71-178; 179-370.
Heslop-Harrison, J. 1964. In H. P. Linskens (editor). Pollen physiology and fertilization. North Holland Publishing Co., Amsterdam.
Hillary, B. B. 1940. Use of the Feulgen reaction in cytology. II. New techniques and special applications. Bot. Gaz. **102:**225-235.
Hotchkiss, R. D. 1955. Bacterial transformation. J. Cell Comp. Physiol. **45:**1-22.
Hotta, Y., M. Ito, and H. Stern. 1966. Synthesis of DNA during meiosis. Proc. Nat. Acad. Sci. U.S.A. **56:**1184-1191.
Huberman, J. A., and G. Attardi. 1966. Isolation of metaphase chromosomes from HeLa cells. J. Cell Biol. **31:**95-105.
Huskins, C. L. 1948. Segregation and reduction in somatic tissues. J. Hered. **39:**311-325.
Izawa, M., V. G. Allfrey, and A. E. Mirsky. 1963. Composition of the nucleus and chromosomes in the lampbrush stage of the newt oocyte. Proc. Nat. Acad. Sci. U.S.A. **50:**811-817.
Jacob, F., and E. L. Wollman. 1957. Genetic aspects of lysogeny. In W. D. McElroy and B. Glass (editors). The chemical basis of heredity. The Johns Hopkins Press, Baltimore.
Janssens, F. A. 1909. La theorie de la chiasmatypie. Nouvelle interpretation des cineses de maturation. Cellule **25:**389-411.
Kamra, O. P. 1960. Chromatin extrusion and cytomixis in pollen mother cells of Hordeum. Hereditas **46:**592-600.
Kowalski, D. T. 1964. The development of cytology of Pycnidiophora dispersa. Amer. J. Bot. **51:**1076-1082.
Kowalski, D. T. 1965a. The development and cytology of Didymocrea sodasavanii. Mycologia **57:**404-416.
Kowalski, D. T. 1965b. The development and cytology of Melanospora tiffanii. Mycologia **57:** 279-290.
Kowalski, D. T. 1965c. Development and cytology of Preussia typharum. Bot. Gaz. **126:**123-130.
Kowalski, D. T. 1966. The morphology and cytology of Preussia funiculata. Amer. J. Bot. **53:**1036-1041.
Lederberg, J. 1947. Gene recombination and linked segregations in Escherichia coli. Genetics **32:**505-525.

Lederberg, J. 1955. Recombination mechanism in bacteria. J. Cell. Comp. Physiol. **45**(supp. 2):75.
Lwoff, A. 1953. Lysogeny. Bact. Rev. **17**:269-337.
Lyon, M. F. 1962. Sex chromatin and gene action in the mammalian X-chromosome. Amer. J. Hum. Genet. **14**:135-148.
McClintock, B. 1945. Neurospora. I. Preliminary observations of the chromosomes of Neurospora crassa. Amer. J. Bot. **32**:671-678.
McClung, C. E. 1927. Synapsis and related phenomena in Mecostethus and Leptysoma (Orthoptera). J. Morph. Physiol. **43**:181-252.
Mather, K. 1933. Interlocking as a demonstration of the occurrence of genetical crossing-over during chiasma formation. Amer. Nat. **67**:476-479.
Metz, C. W. 1916. Chromosome studies on the Diptera. II. The paired association of chromosomes in the Diptera, and its significance. J. Exp. Zool. **21**:213.
Meyer, G. F. 1960. The fine structure of spermatocyte nuclei of Drosophila melanogaster. Proc. Eur. Reg. Conf. E. M. **2**:951-954.
Miller, O. L. 1965. Fine structure of lampbrush chromosomes. In J. I. Valencia and R. F. Grell (editors). International symposium on genes and chromosomes: structure and function, Government Printing Office, Washington, D. C.
Miller, O. L., B. R. Beatty, B. A. Hamklo, and C. A. Thomas. 1970. Electron microscope visualization of transcription. Cold Spring Harbor Symp. Quant. Biol. **35**:505-515.
Mitra, S. 1958. Effects of x-rays on chromosomes of Lilium longiflorum during meiosis. Genetics **43**:771-789.
Mitra, J., and F. C. Steward. 1961. Growth induction in cultures of Haplopappus gracilis. II. The behavior of the nucleus. Amer. J. Bot. **48**:358-370.
Moens, P. B. 1964. A new interpretation of meiotic prophase in Lycopersicum esculentum (tomato). Chromosoma **15**:231-242.
Moens, P. B. 1968. The structure and function of the synaptinemal complex in Lilium longiflorum sporocytes. Chromosoma **23**:418-451.
Moses, M. J. 1956. Chromosomal structure in crayfish spermatocytes. J. Biophys. Biochem. Cytol. **2**:215-218.
Moses, M. J. 1968. Synaptinemal complex. Ann. Rev. Genet. **2**:363-412.
Nelson, O. 1964. Differential crossing-over in male and female gametes of plants heterozygous for Dp. 9. Maize Genet. Coop. News Letter **38**: 449-454.
Olive, L. S. 1949. Karyogamy and meiosis in the rust Coleosporium vernoniae. Amer. J. Bot. **36**:41-50.
Pastor, J. B., and H. G. Callan. 1952. Chiasma formation in spermatocytes of the turbellarian, Dendrocoelum lacteum. J. Genet. **50**:449-454.
Pelling, C. 1966. A replicative and synthetic chromosomal unit—the modern concept of the chromomere. Proc. Roy. Soc. [Biol.] **164**:279-289.
Pontecorvo, G. 1958. Trends in genetic analysis. Columbia University Press, New York.
Pritchard, R. H. 1960. The bearing of recombination analysis at high resolution of genetic fine structure in Aspergillus nidulans and the mechanism of recombination of higher organisms. Soc. Gen. Microbiol. 10th Symp., pp. 155-280.
Rhoades, M. M. 1950. Meiosis in maize. J. Hered. **41**:49-67.
Rhoades, M. M. 1955. The cytogenetics of maize. In G. F. Sprague (editor). Corn and corn improvement. Academic Press, Inc., New York.
Rhoades, M. M. 1961. Meiosis. In J. Brachet and A. E. Mirsky (editors). The cell. Vol. 2. Academic Press, Inc., New York.
Rossen, J. M., and M. Westergaard. 1966. Studies on the mechanism of crossing over. II. Meiosis and the time of meiotic chromosome replication in the ascomycete Neottiella rutilans (Fr) Dennis. C. R. Trav. Lab. Carlsberg **35**:233-260.
Roth, T. F. 1966. Changes in the synaptinemal complex during meiotic prophase in mosquito oocytes. Protoplasma **61**:346-386.
Rückert, J. 1892. Zur Entwicklungsgeschichte des Ovarialeies bei Selachiern. Anat. Anz. **7**:107-158.
Sarvella, P. 1958. Cytomixis and the loss of chromosomes in meiotic and somatic cells of Gossypium. Cytologia **23**:14-24.
Sax, K., and L. M. Humphrey. 1934. Structure of meiotic chromosomes in microsporogenesis of Tradescantia. Bot. Gaz. **96**:353-362.
Sharma, A. K., and A. Majumdar. 1956. Karyotypic variation in Pteridiophyta and their significance. Agron. Lusitana **18**:243-246.
Singleton, J. R. 1953. Chromosome morphology and the chromosome cycle in ascus of Neurospora crassa. Amer. J. Bot. **40**:124-144.
Slizynski, B. M. 1960. Sexual dimorphism in mouse gametogenesis. Genet. Res. **1**:477-486.
Smith, S. G. 1942. Polarization and progression and pairing. II. Premeiotic orientation and the initiation of pairing. Canad. J. Res. **20D**:221-229.
Sotelo, J. R., and R. Wettstein. 1965. Fine structure of meiotic chromosomes. In J. I. Valencia and R. F. Grell (editors). International symposium on genes and chromosomes: structure

and function. Government Printing Office, Washington, D. C.

Stack, S. 1973. The synaptinemal complex and the achiasmatic condition. J. Cell Sci. **13:**83-95.

Stack, S. M., and W. V. Brown. 1969. Somatic and premeiotic pairing of homologues in Plantago ovata. Bull. Torrey Bot. Club **96:**143-149.

Stebbins, G. L. 1941. Apomixis in the angiosperms. Bot. Rev. **7:**507-542.

Stebbins, G. L. 1950. Variation and evolution in plants. Columbia University Press, New York.

Tarkowska, J. 1965. Experimental analysis of the mechanism of cytomixis. I. Cytomixis in vegetative tissues. Acta Soc. Bot. Pol. **34:**27-44.

Tarkowska, J. 1966. Experimental analysis of the mechanism of cytomixis. II. Cytomixis in the pollen mother cells of the lily-Lilium candidum L. Acta Soc. Bot. Pol. **35:**25-40.

Taylor, J. H. 1960. Asynchronous duplication of chromosomes in cultured cells of Chinese hamster. J. Biophys. Biochem. Cytol. **7:**455-464.

Uhl, C. H. 1965. Chromosome structure and crossing over. Genetics **51:**191-207.

Vejdovsky, F. 1912. Zum Problem der Vererbungsträger. Böhm, Prague.

Walters, M. S. 1970. Evidence on the time of chromosome pairing from the preleptotene spiral stage in Lilium longiflorum "Croft." Chromosoma **29:**375-418.

Walters, M. S. 1972. Preleptotene chromosome contraction in Lilium longiflorum "Croft." Chromosoma **39:**311-332.

Watkins, G. M. 1935. A study of chromosome pairing in Yucca rupicola. Bull. Torrey Bot. Club **62:**133-150.

Westergaard, M., and D. von Wettstein. 1966. Studies on the mechanism of crossing over. III. On the ultrastructure of the chromosomes in Neottiella rutilans. C. R. Trav. Lab. Carlsberg **35:**261-286.

White, M. J. D. 1954. Animal cytology and evolution. Cambridge University Press, New York.

Whitehouse, H. L. K. 1967. A cycloid model for the chromosome. J. Cell Sci. **2:**9-22.

Zinder, N. D., and J. Lederberg. 1952. Genetic exchange in Salmonella. J. Bact. **64:**679-699.

CHAPTER 19

Cytogenetics and reproductive cells

CYTOGENETICS

Cytogenetics (see Brown, 1972, for extended treatment of this subject) is a field of research in which cytology contributes information and methods of analysis and provides physical systems to explain the logical conclusions of genetics. After Mendel's time and before 1900 there was speculation and some research that could be called genetics. Then in 1900 biological science caught up to Mendel; three biologists, de Vries, Correns, and Tschermak, almost simultaneously "rediscovered" Mendel's work and/or discovered by themselves the same statistical laws he had determined 35 years before. The year 1900 marks the official birth of the science of genetics, even though the *First International Congress of Genetics* was held in London the previous year.

Shortly after 1900 the results of cytogenetic studies began to appear in the scientific journals. In 1901 Montgomery presented a summary of the cytological phenomena necessary for a physical explanation of mendelism. In 1902 Sutton, another cytologist, related chromosomes, meiosis, and sexuality to mendelian theory, showing that mendelian genetic ratios of alleles are exactly the same as cytological ratios of homologous chromosomes. His special contribution was that the particular chromosomes of the set derived from the female parent do not segregate at anaphase I *as a group* from the set derived from the paternal parent. Rather, the spindle pole to which any particular maternal or paternal chromosome moves out of the bivalent at metaphase I is equally one or the other. Thus each anaphase I group of chromosomes is a random mixture of chromosomes derived from both parents. The random segregation of alleles is explained by the random segregation of chromosomes derived from the two parents. He also concluded that each chromosome contains several allelomorphs (different genes), thus implying linkage; each chromosome of the set contains many, but a distinct set of genes.

Throughout subsequent years linkage groups and the sequences of genes within each group (linkage maps) have been determined by geneticists in several various species, including a few viruses, bacteria, fungi, and higher plants and animals, but in most detail for the fruit fly *Drosophila melanogaster* and corn *(Zea mays)*. It was not, however, until about 1930 that cytogeneticists, using the salivary gland chromosomes of *Drosophila* and pachytene chromosomes of corn, were able to specify which linkage group belonged to which particular chromosome of the set, except that the sex chromosomes of *Drosophila* had been so specified because genetic analysis alone could logically relate a small linkage group to a small chromosome; likewise the minute chromosome 4 was assumed to have the smallest linkage group. Genetic linkage groups by the early 1930s were related to particular chromosomes when various chromosomal aberrations (such as translocations, inversions, deletions, monosomics, and trisomics) that produce genetic effects much like mutation and are linked to typical genes could also be identified cytologically. Thus if a genetic linkage group includes a structural chromosome aberration, and if the aberration can be identified as being on, for example, chromosome 9 of corn or chromosome 2 of *Drosophila,* all the genes of that linkage group are known immediately to be on that particular chromosome also.

Similar work involving two or more such cytological markers on one chromosome has permitted the determination of the exact sites of numerous genes on particular chromosomes. In this manner cytological maps of linkage groups have been prepared. Cytological maps involve physical distances along a chromosome, whereas genetic maps concern hypothetical (crossover) units; the two may correspond only in sequential order of the genes. Generally, cytogenetics locates genes nearer to the ends of chromosome arms than do genetic maps.

Chiasmata and recombination

In 1911 Morgan proposed, on the basis of cytological knowledge of meiosis, that many genes are linked. He demonstrated that the sex chromosome of *Drosophila* does carry a number of genes. He further proposed that the variable ratios found could be produced by a twisting of paired homologous chromosomes followed, essentially, by several internal breaks and reunions. Thus the further apart two genes might lie on a chromosome the greater would be the chance of their alleles becoming unlinked and segregating more like nonlinked genes (Fig. 19-1).

That was the first proposal of a sort of crossing-over to explain genetic results. Cytogenetic confirmation of the genetic assumption of crossing-over was achieved simultaneously in 1931 by Creighton and McClintock in corn and by Stern in *Drosophila.* In both cases chromosomes containing simultaneously several known genes and two cytological markers were employed. In corn a modified chromosome 9 was used that had the alleles *C* (colored aleurone) and *wx* (waxy endosperm), the former close to a terminal knob and the latter close to a translocation point of a piece of chromosome 8. The other homologue in the heterozygote had a normal knobless chromosome 9 and the alleles *c* (colorless aleurone) and *Wx* (starchy endosperm).

If crossing-over (or some equivalent process) did not occur, the knob-*C*-*wx*-translocation chromosome and the knobless-*c*-*Wx*-nontranslocation chromosome would always occur; there would be two classes of progeny that could be recognized genetically *and* cytologically. It was found

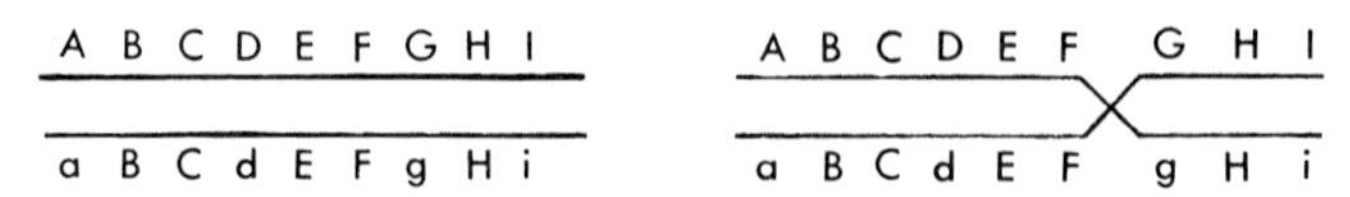

Fig. 19-1. Phenotypes are determined by linked alleles *ADGI* and *adgi.* When such alleles are brought together in the hybrid and the homologues have synapsed, the only types of progeny possible without crossing-over would be *ADGI* and *adgi.* But with crossing-over between *F* and *g* in some cells, phenotypes determined by *ADgi* and *adGI* would also be recovered. Furthermore, there is a greater chance that more cells would show *AI* being changed by a crossover to *Ai* than for *dg* being changed to *dG,* if there is always to be at least one crossover, but its location between *A* and *I* is random among all the cells undergoing meiosis.

however, that *four* genetic classes occurred, *C-wx, c-Wx, C-Wx,* and *c-wx*. Almost without exception any plant having *C* had an associated knob, any plant having *c* had a knobless chromosome 9, any *Wx* had no translocation, and any *wx* had an associated translocation. There were four cytological classes that also corresponded to the four genetic classes. Thus genetic crossing-over between the waxy and colored genes was accompanied by an exchange of associated chromosomal aberrations. Genetic crossing-over is therefore a physical exchange of some sort between two paired homologous chromosomes.

By the use of known, abnormal, specially prepared chromosomes of meiotic cells of known genetic composition, Bridges assumed in 1916 that the meiotic bivalent chromosome is probably a tetrad of four chromatids when crossing-over occurs. That assumption was required to explain what was determined genetically, the involvement of three or four strands in a pair of crossovers, the so-called two-strand, three-strand, and four-strand doubles (Fig. 19-2). In 1925 Bridges and Anderson demonstrated that at any one point or crossover of a bivalent only two of the four chromatids can exchange segments. In 1953, by the use of a plant heterozygous for a ring-shaped and a normal chromosome 6 in corn, Schwartz concluded, indirectly, from a complex cytological study of anaphase I and II single and double bridges that crossing-over does occur also between sister strands, between an old and its genetically identical newly formed chromonema. Sister-strand crossing-over is essentially impossible to detect genetically and so is of little significance in genetic studies. It is of theoretical significance in cytological concepts of chromosome doubling and formation of chiasmata during meiosis. Cytogeneticists are still unconvinced (although open-minded) that sister-strand crossing-over occurs regularly during meiosis.

In 1927 Muller (then at the University of Texas) and in 1928 Stadler (of the University of Missouri) reported that x rays produced genetic mutations. In 1933 Painter (of the University of Texas and a colleague in cytology of the geneticist Muller) was able to relate gene loci and chromosomal rearrangements to particular sites of *Drosophila* salivary gland (synapsed, polytene) chromosomes. Thus in an individual fly heterozygous for a genetic deletion of a small piece of a chromosome the salivary gland chromosome containing the deletion would have a small piece of a few bands missing on one half at a certain locus.

This configuration results because a salivary gland chromosome originates from a pair of synapsed, homologous, interphase, somatic chromosome strands. Essentially the same chromosomal relationships are seen in the pachytene chromosomes of corn (Rhoades, 1955), tomato, and other plants and animals (Fig. 19-3).

Deletions

Deletions at the cytological level are lost pieces of chromosomes long enough to be detected when paired to a normal homologue as in salivary or pachytene

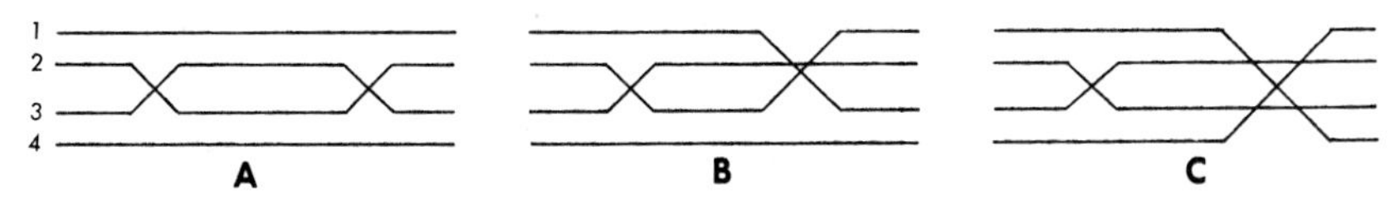

Fig. 19-2. Four-stranded condition of a pair of synapsed homologous chromosomes at the time of crossing-over. **A,** "Two-strand double" crossover; that is, there are two crossovers but only two strands (**2** and **3**) are involved. **B,** "Three-strand double" crossover; strands **1, 2,** and **3** are involved, and one strand, **3,** is involved in both. **C,** Case of "four-strand double" crossover; all four strands are involved, once each. Sister-strand crossing-over would occur between strands **1** and **2** or **3** and **4.**

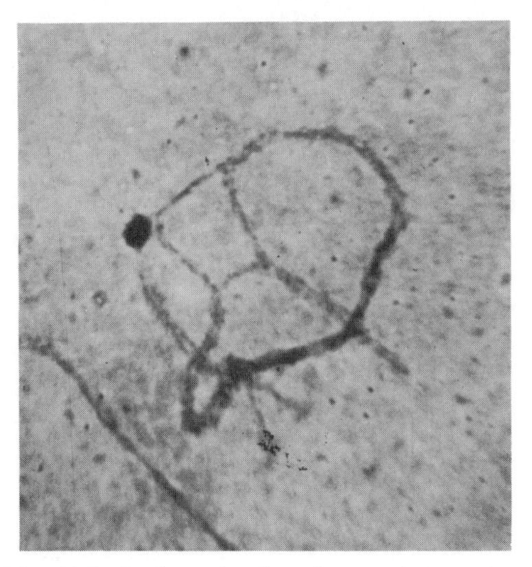

Fig. 19-3. An inversion loop in a pachytene chromosome of *Zea mays* (corn). (From McClintock, B. 1931. Univ. Mo. Agric. Exp. Station Res. Bull. No. 163, pp. 1-30.)

chromosomes. Deletions may be terminal or interstitial. Actually, the location where an interstitial deletion was "extracted" is not represented by a gap in the chromosome; rather, the two broken ends come together and heal. A chromosome is thus shortened by the length of the deletion. When a normal chromosome pairs with a chromosome having an interstitial deletion, the normal chromosome is longer, by the length of the deletion, than the deleted chromosome, and the segment of the normal chromosome that is equivalent to the deletion has no homologous segment to pair with. Often this "extra" segment of the normal chromosome buckles outward as a loop, and sometimes the nonhomologous genes on the opposite sides of this loop pair (nonhomologously) with each other. In other cases the portion of the deleted chromosome may "stretch" across the unbuckled part of the normal chromosome, possibly with some nonhomologous pairing. Long deletions, however, ones more than about one tenth of the length of a chromosome, are usually lost from one generation to the next because they are likely to contain some genes necessary during the haploid phase of the life cycle. The lack of genes in a deletion is genetically equivalent to the simultaneous mutation of all of them to a recessive condition.

Inversions

Inversions (Fig. 19-3) are segments of chromosomes (rarely terminal) that have become reversed in the sequence of genes. An inversion in a chromosome *abcdefghij* might produce a chromosome *abchgfedij,* the segment *defgh* being inverted. Actually, this piece of the chromosome has indeed been turned around. When the two homologous chromosomes synapse in an organism heterozygous for such an inversion, one of three conditions may be observed (Fig. 19-4), according to Maguire (1966) in her studies of a certain strain of corn.

1. A loop is formed at the inversion so that the *chromosomes* run in opposite directions, thereby having the *gene sequence* running in the same direction (Fig. 19-4, *A* and *B*). This condition is called "rêverse synapsis," and Maguire detected it in about 33% of cases.
2. No loop is formed, and yet the segments seem to be synapsed or at least closely paired throughout (Fig. 19-4, *C*). This condition was observed in about 45% of cases; it is called "rod pairing" and obviously consists of nonhomologous genes being paired, if not synapsed.
3. There is no pairing at all of the two segments—they lie remote from each other (Fig. 19-4, *D*). This condition was reported in about 20% of cases. Because crossing-over within a loop, as in condition 1, generally produces a bridge and acentric fragment at anaphase I (Fig. 19-5, *D*), and because Maguire found almost identical percentages of pachytene loops and bridge-fragment anaphase configura-

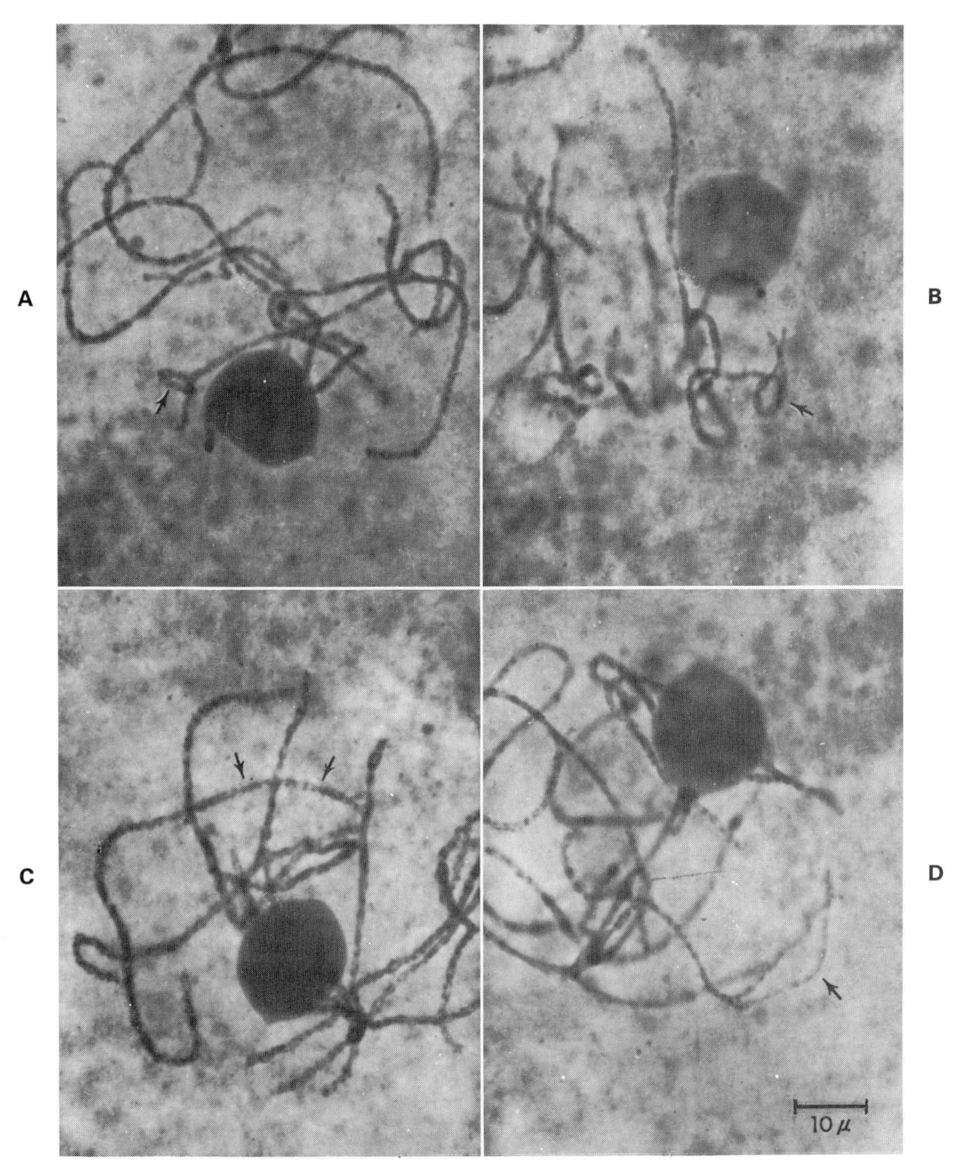

Fig. 19-4. Squashes of microsporocytes (PMCs) of *Zea mays,* all of which are heterozygous for the same short paracentric inversion. In **A** and **B** a typical loop is formed, called "homologous reverse synapsis." This configuration occurred in about one third of the cells studied. In **C** the heterozygous segments (between arrows) are paired nonhomologously, called "rod pairing." This condition was found in about half of the cells examined. In **D** the heterozygous segments are not synapsed (at arrow). Unpaired segments were found in 15% to 20% of cells. (From Maguire, M. P. 1966. Genetics **53:**1071-1077.)

tions, it appears that crossing-over does not occur in conditions 2 and 3, that there probably is no true synapsis in condition 2, and that when there is synapsis (condition 1), even in as short a segment as she was considering, there is also crossing-over.

The model proposed to explain the

bridge-acentric fragment at anaphase I after one or two crossovers within an inversion loop that does not contain the centromere, a *paracentric loop,* is clear if one follows individual chromosome strands from end to end (Fig. 19-5). When such strands separate at anaphase I, centromeres going to opposite poles, some strands will be connected to one, some to two, and some to no centromeres. A strand of the two-stranded anaphase chromosome attached to two centromeres that move to opposite poles will produce a *chromatid bridge* between the two anaphase groups of chromosomes. A strand (actually a piece of a strand) having no centromere will be left at the metaphase

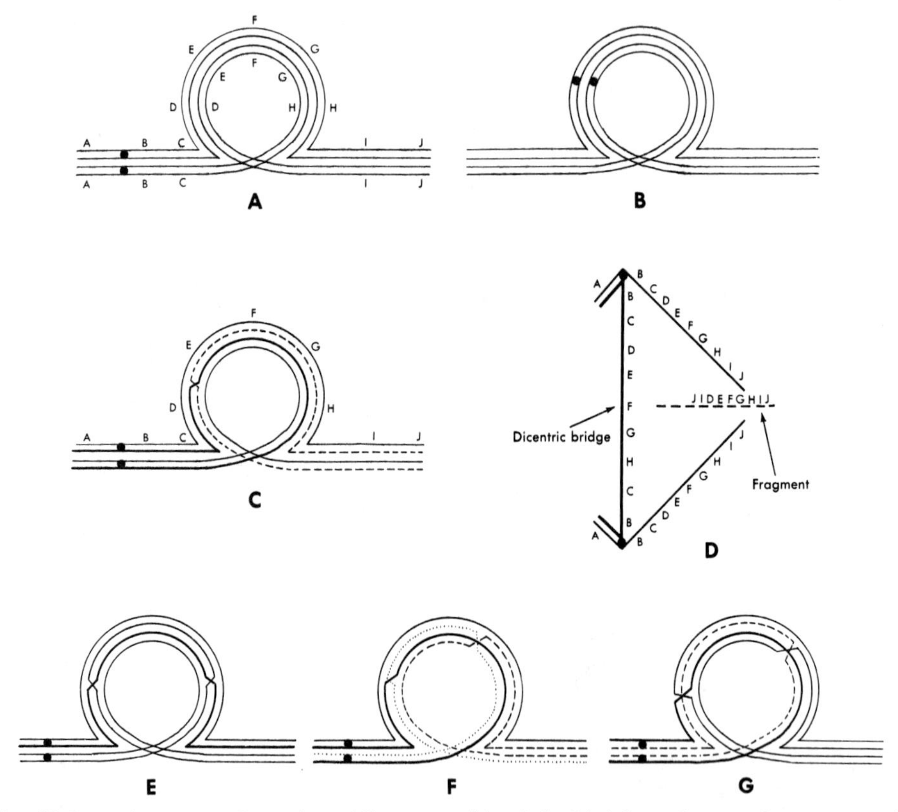

Fig. 19-5. Pachytene configurations (diagrammatic) of doubled homologous chromosomes in a cell heterozygous for inversion. Centromeres are represented by solid dots on each pair of sister strands, crossovers by Xs between two nonsister strands. **A,** Paracentric loop in which the centromeres are outside the loop, **B** and **C** lying in the "proximal" region, **I** and **J** in the "distal" region of the bivalent. **B,** Pericentric inversion loop in which the centromeres are within the loop. **C,** Paracentric inversion loop with a single crossover between two nonsister strands. At anaphase I (**D**) the heavy line indicates the dicentric chromatid; the dashed line represents the acentric fragment. **D,** Diagrammatic representation of anaphase I with a dicentric bridge (heavy line) and an acentric fragment (dashed line). **E,** Two-strand double crossover within an inversion loop. No aberrations are produced. **F,** Three-strand double crossover within a loop. One strand is involved with two others. It produces a dicentric bridge chromatid (heavy line) and an acentric fragment (dashed line). **G,** Four-strand double crossover. Two different strands are involved in each of the crossovers. A double bridge (heavy line forms one and dashed line forms the other) and two acentric fragments are present at anaphase I.

plate as an *acentric fragment* at anaphase (Fig. 19-5, *D*). Additional crossovers within the loop, such as three-strand or four-strand doubles, also produce detectable bridges and acentric fragments at anaphase I.

It is evident from Fig. 19-5, *C*, that when the two centromeres separate at anaphase I, one of the recombination chromatids, the one having two ends at Fig. 19-5, *A*, will be connected to both centromeres and will form a chromatid bridge or connection between anaphase groups (Fig. 19-5, *D*). At late anaphase the bridge breaks somewhere, more or less randomly, along its length. The other recombination chromatid in Fig. 19-5, *C*, has two ends at point *J* and is connected to no centromere. At anaphase (Fig. 19-5, *D*) it just lies on the metaphase plate unable to move or be moved because it is an acentric fragment. Two-strand double crossovers merely restore the original connections, and no bridge-fragment configuration is observed at anaphase I. If three strands are involved in two crossovers within the loop (Fig. 19-5, *F*), again a dicentric bridge and acentric fragment configuration are produced at anaphase I. Two crossovers within the loop, each involving two different nonsister chromatids (Fig. 19-5, *G*), produce two chromatid bridges and two fragments at anaphase I. These and various other anaphase configurations result from combinations of crossovers within the loop and others in the *proximal region* (which is that extent of the bivalent chromosome between the centromeres and the loop) and/or the *distal region* (the extent of the tetrad from the inversion loop to the end of the chromosome arm).

The anaphase bridge-fragment configuration has now been correlated to heterozygosity for an inversion so adequately that the presence of one is accepted as proof of the other. Therefore if bridge-fragment configurations are abundant in a hybrid organism, it is accepted that the two parents differ for numerous inversions.

Pericentric inversions. Pericentric inversions are produced when the centromere is included within the inverted segment. Loops are again formed, but crossing-over within the loop does not produce bridges and fragments at first anaphase as occur with paracentric inversion. This form of chromosomal aberration is responsible for changing chromosome form, such as changing a long arm to a short one.

Translocations

Translocations are produced when pieces of two nonhomologous chromosomes are exchanged (a *reciprocal translocation* or *segmental interchange*) or when a piece of one chromosome is added to a nonhomologous chromosome after a break in each. Because it is believed that most translocations are reciprocal, the term "translocation" usually implies that particular type. They are fairly common among isolated populations within species and even more common when distinct species or genera are compared, as in a hybrid. They are also readily produced by x rays and other radiations such as neutrons. It is gen-

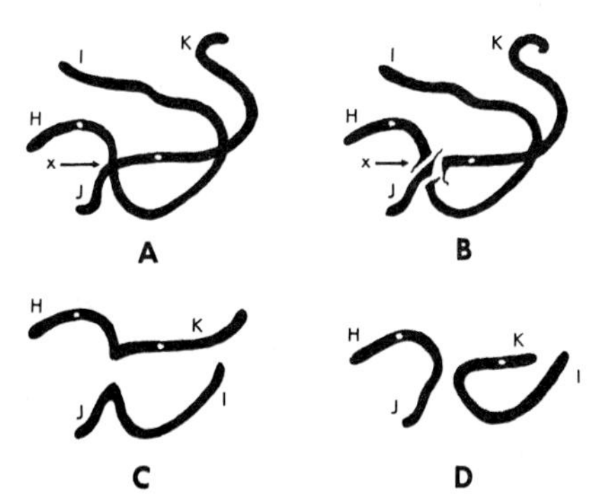

Fig. 19-6. A, Two chromosomes, **H-I** and **J-K,** lie close together. **B,** At point **x** both are broken. They may then rejoin, **C,** as **H-K** and **J-I** or, **D,** as **H-J** and **K-I.** The combination **H-K** would produce a dicentric chromosome and **J-I** an acentric chromosome, neither of which would persist. **H-J** and **I-K,** however, would be two new monocentric chromosomes, unlike the "homologues" **H-I** and **J-K,** which would be within the same nucleus.

erally believed that translocations are formed when two interphase chromosomes lie close together and are both broken at the same time, as by an ionizing radiation event. The result is the production of four broken ends that might rejoin in any combination (Fig. 19-6).

Such exchange between two homologous chromosomes would produce a variety of chromosomal changes, depending on what particular parts of which arms were exchanged.

The result of translocation is the production of new chromosomes, new in structure and linked genes. For example, in Fig. 19-6 the new chromosome K-I would be a much longer chromosome and H-J would be a much shorter chromosome than either of the original H-I or J-K chromosomes. Subsequent translocation between the same two chromosomes could further modify their structures and genetic compositions. Further translocations between one of them and a third nonhomologous chromosome would further mix them up. Repeated translocations may continue, in fact, until all of the chromosomes of one set are transformed, as in many of the permanent hybrid species of *Oenothera* (Cleland, 1936, 1950) and the monotypic *Rhoeo discolor* (Fig. 19-7).

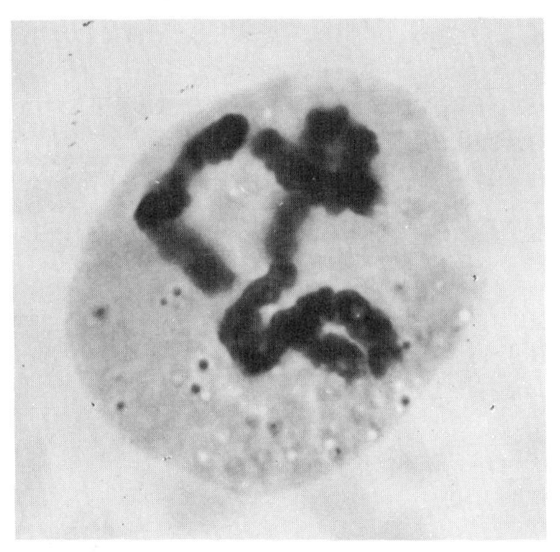

Fig. 19-7. Meiocyte of *Rhoeo discolor* at metaphase I showing the twelve chromosomes attached end to end in a ring. This configuration is produced because the species is completely heterozygous for end arrangements of all chromosomes as a result of translocations.

During the first meiotic division in an organism heterozygous for a translocation, the pairing of homologous genes results in the pairing of four chromosomes, called a *quadrivalent chromosome.* If a species originally contained the chromosomes A-B, A-B, C-D, and C-D and a translocation occurred, the heterozygote would perhaps contain A-B, A-C, C-D, and B-D. In this diagrammatic representation the letters A, B, C, and D represent arms or terminal segments of arms or ends of chromosomes. When such different end-arrangement chromosomes pair, the two A ends pair, as do the two Bs, Cs, and Ds, to produce diagrammatically a cross-shaped configuration (Fig. 19-8, *A*) of four chromosomes, and at metaphase I a circle of four (⊙4) is formed (Fig. 19-8, *B*). If a third chromosome, E-F, is involved in a translocation

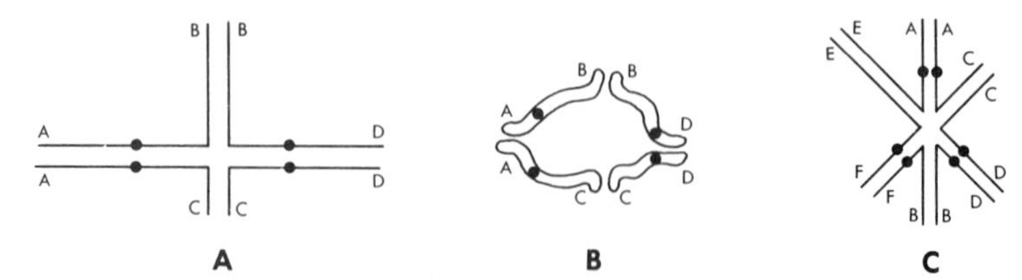

Fig. 19-8. A represents the four chromosomes as they would be paired at pachytene in an organism heterozygous for a translocation between chromosome **A-B** and **C-D. B,** Configuration at diakinesis or metaphase I. **C,** Pachytene pairing in a heterozygote for two translocations involving three nonhomologous chromosomes.

with, for example, A-B, the heterozygote would then be A-E, A-C, C-D, D-B, B-F, and E-F (Fig. 19-8, *C*). At pachytene a chromosome of six parts would be formed, a *hexavalent.* Any meiotic chromosome consisting of three or more chromosomes is called a *multivalent chromosome.*

The commonly cultivated plant *Rhoeo discolor* is permanently heterozygous for six translocations involving all six chromosomes of one haploid set. The result at metaphase I is usually a ring of twelve chromosomes (ʘ12) (Fig. 19-7). In the permanent hybrid species of *Oenothera* a ʘ14 is typical, generation after generation.

Oenothera, the American genus of evening primrose, is nearly unique in that it has evolved among some of its species a balanced genetic and cytological system that permits hybrids to breed true sexually (Cleland, 1936, 1950). As mentioned previously, such species have no homologous chromosomes, only homologous ends. If one haploid set of ends (n = 7) is represented as 1-2, 3-4, 5-6, 7-8, 9-10, 11-12, and 13-14, the other might be 1-3, 4-5, 6-7, 8-9, 10-11, 12-13, and 14-2. When synapsed end for end, a ring of fourteen chromosomes is produced (1-2:2-14:14-13: 13-12:12-11:11-10:10-9:9-8:8-7:7-6:6-5:5-4:4-3:3-1:). At that point in the reproductive system a genetic factor becomes important.

It is evident that if the species is to remain permanently heterozygous, the haploid sets of end arrangements (just listed) must

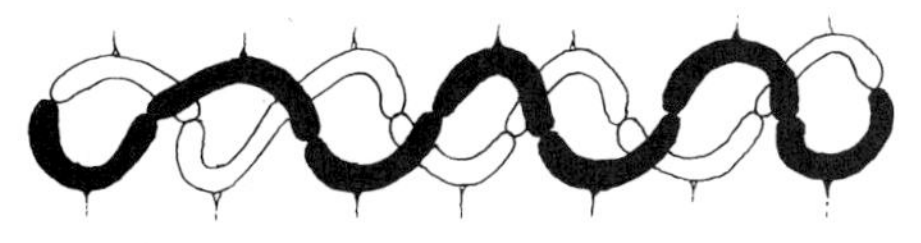

Fig. 19-9. Diagrammatic representation of the fourteen chromosomes of a complex heterozygote of *Oenothera* at metaphase I. Alternate chromosomes are so oriented that alternate disjunction occurs, and all chromosomes of each complex move at anaphase to the same pole.

remain together, and they do. Thus each set of end arrangements and the contained genes function genetically as one "linkage group," although on seven distinct chromosomes. Each such set of end arrangements, and there are many different ones known, is called a *complex,* and the species, race, or population forming a ʘ14 at metaphase I is called a *complex heterozygote;* it is heterozygous for two complexes, and all individuals of that species are heterozygous for the same two complexes (with some exceptions, of course).

A genetic factor that in part ensures the true breeding of the hybrid becomes important at metaphase I; it functions to orient the ring of fourteen chromosomes so that every second chromosome goes to the same pole at anaphase I. That type of separation, called *alternate disjunction,* results in all of the chromosomes of each complex going to the same spindle pole, and so they and their contained genomes remain together as one "linkage group" (Fig. 19-9).

In the previous example, chromosomes 1-2, 14-13, 12-11, 10-9, 8-7, 6-5, and 4-3 would go to one pole as a complete complex. The alternate chromosomes would go to the other pole as a second distinct and complete complex.

The mechanism so far described is not adequate alone to perpetuate the heterozygous condition, since half of the zygotes produced would be homozygous for one complex or the other, if not prevented. It has been found that one of two types of genetic lethality operates in each of these races or species, either *gamete lethality* or *zygote lethality.* In gamete lethality one complex is lethal in the pollen (microspore), whereas the other complex is lethal in the megaspore, which produces the embryo sac and egg. This genetic system produces all male gametes of one complex (the *beta complex*) and all eggs of the other (the *alpha complex*) so that all zygotes and the subsequent generation are again heterozygous for the same two complexes. For example, in the "species" *Chicaginensis* there are the two complexes *excellens* and *punctulans.* Since microspores containing the *excellens* complex and the megaspores containing the *punctulans* complex die, all male gametes must contain the *punctulans* complex (called the beta complex) and all eggs must contain the *excellens* complex (called the alpha complex); therefore all zygotes produced are again *excellens punctulans,* that is, *Chicaginensis.* It is evident that reciprocal crosses between gamete lethal species produce different progeny. *Chicaginensis* crossed to *Cockerelli* (alpha complex = *curtans* and beta complex = *elongans*) produces progeny *excellens elongans* or *curtans punctulans,* depending on the direction of the cross.

The zygote lethal system operates differently but just as effectively—all homozygous zygotes or embryos die. For example, the species *Lamarckiana* contains the complexes *velans* and *gaudens.* All *velans velans* and *gaudens gaudens* zygotes or embryos die. Thus all surviving plants are again the complex heterozygotes *velans gaudens,* that is, *Lamarckiana.* Actually, however, most of these "species" of *Oenothera* are subdivisible into a large number of races that vary among themselves in the complexes they contain. Purity of races is maintained by almost unavoidable self-pollination.

When two complex heterozygous "species" or races are crossed, a wide variety of circles (multivalents) and bivalents may result at meiosis in the hybrid. If the end arrangements of the four complexes of the two parental types are known, the number and composition of the multivalents (ʘs) and bivalents can be predicted. For example, if the gamete lethal "species" *Muricata* (alpha complex = *rigens* [1.2, 3.4, 5.6, 7.11, 9.10, 8.14, and 13.12] and beta complex = *curvans* [1.14, 3.2, 5.13, 7.12, 9.8, 11.10, and 4.6]) is crossed as pistillate parent to the gamete lethal "species" *Cockerelli* (beta complex = *elongans* [1.4, 3.2, 5.10, 6.7, 9.14, 11.12, and 13.8] and alpha complex = *curtans* [1.7, 3.4, 5.8, 2.10, 9.11, 6.12, and 13.14]), all eggs will be *rigens* (from *Muricata*) and all male gametes will be *elongans* from *Cockerelli,* since there is gamete lethality in this cross. Therefore the hybrid will be *rigens elongans,* and its end arrangements will be as they appear at the bottom of the page.

The end arrangement of 1.2-2.3-3.4-4.1 would form a ʘ4. The remainder would form ʘ10. Such predictions work out remarkably well when hybrids are made and meiosis studied.

Translocations are often responsible for change in chromosome number within species and genera, in a downward direction. Within the genus *Crepis* and related genera there seems to have been a gradual reduction from about n = 6 to a minimum of n = 3. In *Haplopappus* it has been established by Jackson (1962) that there has been a reduction from n = 4, as in *H. ravenii,* to n = 3 in *H. gracilis* "tribivalens," to n = 2 in *H. gracilis* *"dibivalens."* The last is typical *gracilis.* The tribivalens has so far been found in only two or three different localities. When dibivalens was crossed to tribivalents, it was found that the B chromosomes of both parents pair as a normal bivalent, but the large A chromosome of *gracilis* (dibivalens) pairs with the other two smaller chromosomes (C and D) of tribivalens. Evidently, a large translocation between the tribivalens C and D chromosomes produced the large A chromosome of *gracilis,* followed by loss of the remaining nearly isolated centromere of the other (either the C or D chromosome), which had lost essentially all of

rigens	1.2	3.4	5.6	7.11	9.10	8.14	13.12
elongans	1.4	3.2	5.10	6.7	9.14	11.12	13.8

itself by translocation. Perhaps all individuals of *gracilis* have not lost their "centromere," since some plants do have a supernumerary chromosome, which *may* be the genetically unimportant remains of either the C or D chromosome of tribivalens. Of course, there is always the option of reading these data the other way—that the A chromosome of dibivalens has broken into the two C and D chromosomes of tribivalens, one part being translocated to the previously inert supernumerary chromosomes as the source of the added centromere.

The same type of analysis (Tobgy, 1943) has "proved" that the 6-chromosome species *Crepis fuliginosa* was produced by a large and small reciprocal translocation between two of the nonhomologous chromosomes of the 8-chromosome species *C. neglecta.*

Similar cases of intrageneric chromosome reduction have been recorded in both the animal and plant kingdoms so that it is now generally accepted that a change downward of one pair of chromosomes is the result of one or more unequal translocations between nonhomologous chromosomes, followed by establishment of homozygosity for the translocation and with the resulting loss of the genetically denuded centromere. Thus translocations have been very important to the evolution of species and genera by the change within an isolated population of one species into another. By this means new chromosomes and new genetic linkage groups are formed. There is likely to be the loss of a few unessential genes and some heterochromatin along with the extra centromere. When the translocation becomes homozygous, it cannot be detected because pairing at meiosis is normal. It remains cytologically evident within the breeding population until it becomes homozygous throughout the population or is eliminated from the population by natural selection or until an individual from a population homozygous for the translocation is crossed with an individual from another population that is homozygous for the original or some other condition.

Duplications

Duplications are generally not detectable cytologically, since they often consist of small segments of chromosome, of a few genes only, that have somehow been repeated, perhaps by an error in duplication. Genetically, however, such small duplications, often adjacent to one another (in tandem), are known.

Cytological duplications are usually of whole chromosome arms or of a large segment of an arm, often accompanied by an increase in chromosome number. One mechanism is by the formation of two *isochromosomes.* Normally, a centromere splits longitudinally at mitosis so that the sister chromatids separate at anaphase. However, if a centromere splits crosswise (or is split, as by a quantum of radiation), it may produce two chromosomes, each of which has two identical arms, called isochromosomes (Fig. 16-15).

Another form of duplication has been recorded in *Drosophila.* Somehow part of an X chromosome containing a centromere was formed and appeared at mitotic metaphase as an extra small chromosome.

Duplicate whole chromosomes occasionally appear in cells, individuals, or populations as a result of *nondisjunction* at anaphase; that is, both chromatids of a metaphase I chromosome go to the same pole. Thus one of the nuclei produced is deficient for one whole chromosome, a condition that is lethal if haploid. The other nucleus and resulting gamete has one extra chromosome that is duplicated for one whole linkage group, and if a diploid organism is produced, it is said to be *trisomic.* Trisomic individuals can be produced and persist in a population, and individuals homozygous for two of the extra chromosomes would be called *tetrasomic.* Such isochromosomes and extra normal chromosomes may occasionally be the first steps in producing an intraspecific increase in chromosome number.

Ploidy

"Ploidy" is a term that refers to the number of chromosomes relative to the standard, actual, or hypothetical basic number of chromosomes or number of sets. The actual hypothetical *basic number* of a species, genus, tribe, or family is often symbolized by x, which would be the haploid or gametic number of chromosomes in a basic, very common, or hypothetical diploid. Thus the basic number (x) for the grass subfamily Festucoideae and for most of its tribes is x = 7. For the subfamily Panicoideae the basic number is x = 9 and/or 10. Such a condition, two or more basic numbers, is called *dibasic, tribasic, multibasic,* etc. Actually, 10 may be the hypothetical single basic number for the subfamily Panicoideae, 9 having been possibly derived from 10 during evolution of the group, as in the tribe Andropogoneae (Fig. 19-10).

The *haploid* condition is the gametic chromosome number of a species and is symbolized by n (n often equals x). A diploid has the zygotic number of twice the haploid number if n = x and is represented by 2n.

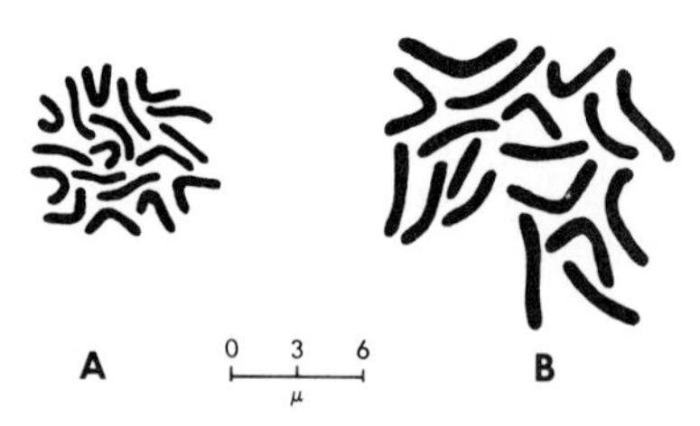

Fig. 19-10. Chromosome basic numbers and sizes in the grass tribe Andropogoneae. **A,** *Manisuris cylindrica* (2n = 18) mitotic metaphase (root tip) chromosomes with size typical of the tribe but an unusual basic number (x = 9). **B,** *Elyonurus tripsacoides* (2n = 20) mitotic metaphase (root tip) chromosomes with size much larger than in the related genus *Manisuris* and in the tribe generally. (From Brown, W. V. 1951. Bull. Torrey Bot. Club **78:**292-299.)

The *diploid* condition, then, is basic for the taxon. Among animals there are few species that are not diploid, although diploid numbers often vary considerably within a genus so that basic numbers are often difficult to determine and are likely to be hypothetical. Cleveland (1947) has reported polyploidy in some termite-inhabiting flagellates such as *Spirotrichosoma,* with n = 12, 24, 48, and 60 chromosomes.

Polyploid animals. One of the most striking examples of polyploidy in animals occurs in the parthenogenetic weevils of the beetle subfamilies Oliorrhynchinae and Brachyderinae. Of those studied cytologically, nearly all are polyploid (euploid). Of the forty-five species from Europe, Asia, and North America examined, one is diploid (2n = 22), thirty are triploid (33 chromosomes), ten are tetraploid (44 chromosomes), and four are pentaploid (55 chromosomes). It is assumed that polyploidy is permitted in this group because they are both asexual and there is no meiosis. This case supports the conclusion that polyploidy and sexuality, in which sex is determined by sex chromosomes, have great difficulty in existing together in a species and that few sexually reproducing animals are polyploid.

It seems that polyploidy among animals is not correlated with hermaphroditism but with parthenogenesis, as in the flatworm races of *Dugesia benazzii* and *Polycelis nigra;* several earthworms (not of the diploid sexual genus *Lumbricus*); the isopod *Trichoniscus* with a triploid race; the freshwater mollusc *Paludestrina jenkinsi* with a tetraploid race; some species of Lepidoptera of the parthenogenetic Psychidae; and the classical case of polyploid parthenogenetic races of the small crustacean *Artemia salina.*

There seems to be good evidence for polyploidy in some Protozoa, including *Paramecium.* Natural and experimental euploid salamanders have been detected. Some of the experimental conditions producing the conditions are low (0 to 4° C) and high (over 40° C) temperature treatments of eggs, conditions that are perhaps experienced in nature. Of about 7,240 individuals examined, most were diploid, but there were 121 haploids, 347 triploids, eight tetraploids, and ten pentaploids. About ten aneuploids were also detected. In all probability, however, all of these nondiploids would be sterile. On the other hand, natural, autotetraploid, sexual frogs have been detected that contain four sets of essentially identical chromosomes. Bogart (cited in Brown, 1972) has stated that there are at least nine species of such tetraploid frogs known.

Aneuploidy. Aneuploidy is the condition resulting from the loss or gain of one or a few typical chromosomes but not of a whole set. A *trisomic,* for example, which has one extra chromosome (2n + 1), is said to be aneuploid. Other aneuploid conditions are *monosomic,* having one chromosome lacking from the diploid condition (2n − 1); *tetrasomic,* having two extra homologous chromosomes so that there are four of that kind of chromosome (2n + 2); *doubly trisomic,* having two extra nonhomologous chromosomes so that there are three of two kinds of chromosomes (2n + 1 + 1); and *nullisomic,* lacking both homologous chromosomes of a diploid set (2n − 2). Nullisomics are rare or impossible in true diploids because the complete loss of so many genes is almost certain to be lethal. Nullisomics do occur in polyploids such as common hexaploid (6n) wheat because the genes lost in a nullisomic are located on other chromosomes of the multiple set. Probably the extreme case of aneuploidy exists in the polyploid grass species *Poa pratensis,* Kentucky bluegrass

Table 19-1. Some human chromosomal aberrations

Chromosomes*	Sex	Result
44A + X	Female	Turner's syndrome
44A + XXY	Male	Klinefelter's syndrome
44A + XXXY	Male	Mentally deficient
44A + XXXXY	Male	Mentally deficient
44A + XXX	Female	Slight mental deficiency
44A + XXXX	Female	Mentally retarded
44A + 21 + XXY	Male	Mongolism and Klinefelter's syndrome
44A + 21 (21 trisomic)	Either	Mongolism (Down's syndrome)
44A + 16, 17, or 18	Either	Mental retardation, head abnormality
44A + 13, 14, or 15	Either	Mental retardation, head and heart abnormalities
44A + 17	Either	Sturge-Weber syndrome
21 monosomic	Either	"Antimongolism," mental retardation
Deficiencies / Duplication	Either	Marfan's syndrome / Chronic myeloid leukemia

Turner's syndrome: female appearance; short, webbed neck; infantile internal sex organs; no secondary sex characters; sterile.

Klinefelter's syndrome: nearly normal male; small testes; tendency toward femalelike breasts; sterile.

Marfan's syndrome: multiple body deformities, especially of the heart.

Sturge-Weber syndrome: abnormal tissue growth on certain nerves and pia; glaucoma.

*A = autosomes = nonsex chromosomes; X and Y = sex chromosomes (Y makes a male regardless of number of Xs, although one X is absolutely necessary); 21, 16, 13, 17, etc., refer to an extra chromosome of that number so that instead of 44 autosomes there are 45 and normal sex chromosomes.

(x = 7), in which all chromosome numbers between about 40 and 150 have been reported.

Aneuploidy is usually an unstable condition, since it is genetically unbalanced and cells or organisms of that sort are selected against and gradually eliminated from a population (Table 19-1). In general, the more the chromosome number differs from an exact multiple of the basic number the more unbalanced and less likely it is to be found in nature. In *Poa pratensis* (x = 7) the most commonly found plants have multiples of 7, next most common are multiples of 7 ± 1, much less common are plants with multiples of 7 ± 2, etc.

Euploidy. Euploidy refers to individuals, populations, or species that have one or more complete sets of chromosomes; they are 1n, 2n, 3n, 4n, 5n, etc. (Fig. 19-11).

Fig. 19-11. Camera lucida drawing of metaphase I in PMC from a spontaneous allododecaploid of *Hibiscus raditus* × *H. diversifolius* (2n = 216). (From Menzel, M. Y., and F. D. Wilson. 1963. J. Hered. **54:**55-60.)

Euploidy, in plants at least, is far more common than aneuploidy or agmatoploidy. Euploidy is generally assumed by the use of the term "polyploidy" and is a highly significant factor in intrageneric evolution. Possibly 30% of plant species are euploid polyploids. The lowest euploid condition is the haploid (1n).

Haploidy. Haploid organisms, the condition of haploidy, is fairly common among organisms as a whole, although diploidy is far more typical. The condition of Haploidy can be divided into the normal condition and the abnormal condition.

Normal haploidy is typical of all plants; that is, at least one part of the life cycle consists of the development by mitotic divisions of an organized body of haploid cells (Fig. 19-15). This haploid body is described as the *gametophyte* (gamete-producing "plant"). Since it is haploid, meiosis cannot take place; *gametes are produced by mitotic divisions* of the haploid organism of the life cycle. That is true with essentially no exceptions in plants (including also the fungi) and, along with the fact that meiosis in plants and fungi typically results in spores, is a significant general difference between plants and animals. The gametophytes of many algae, fungi, all of the mosses, and most of the cryptogamic vascular plants (ferns, horsetails, lycopods, etc.) are independent, free-living, haploid organisms. Among the gymnosperms (conifers, cycads, *Ginkgo*), Gnetales, and angiosperms the male gametophyte (if it really exists as an organism) is the pollen grain–pollen tube; the female gametophyte is parasitic within the ovule, reduced to an embryo sac in the angiosperms. In many algae and fungi nearly the whole life cycle is haploid; the only diploid condition is the zygote, which, when it divides, does so by a meiotic division called *zygotic meiosis.* In contrast, the condition in animals, wherein meiosis immediately precedes gamete formation, is called *gametic meiosis.* Among land plants and some algae and fungi, gametes and zygotes are separated from meiosis by both the gametophytic (or haploid generation) on one side and the sporophytic (or diploid generation) on the other.

Among animals a normal haploid condition, other than gametes, is less common than among plants and fungi. The best known case is the insect group of bees, wasps, ants, etc. (Hymenoptera) in which the males are regularly haploid. In them meiosis cannot occur as a prelude to spermatogenesis. Males arise from unfertilized eggs, which, nevertheless, develop into embryos and adults—a process called *haploid parthenogenesis.*

Haploid parthenogenesis occurs occasionally and *abnormally* in many normally diploid plant species, thereby producing haploid sporophytes. Kimber and Riley (1963) discussed haploids in seventy-one species of flowering plants. They seem to occur in low numbers, of about one in 1,000 to one in 50,000 individuals. Such haploids are rarely found in populations growing in the wild because such plants are almost always small and weak. In populations of cultivated species, however, they can be found, as in tomatoes, wheat, peppers, rye, cultivated jimsonweed, corn, etc. If the species is truly diploid (and not an allopolyploid), at meiosis I there are no homologous chromosomes and little or no pairing occurs, as in tomato (but see Fig. 18-28), corn, etc. In common wheat, on the other hand, which is an allohexaploid, at meiosis I in the haploid there are a few bivalents formed by synapsis between homeologous chromosomes as well as loose associations (not involving synapsis or formation of bivalents) of chromosomes derived from different ancestral species that are, nevertheless, somewhat homeologous, called *secondary association.*

Sadasivaiah and Kasha (1971) have reported good meiotic pairing in a haploid *Hordeum* (n = 7) hybrid, up to three bivalents, whereas in haploid *Nicotiana* (n = 12) there was almost no pairing at all (Collins and Sadasivaiah, 1972). In neither haploid was there assumed to be any true chiasmata.

• • •

Obviously, at meiosis in a triploid (3n), pentaploid (5n), etc., irregularity will exist in pairing and anaphase separation, since there are uneven numbers of each kind of chromosome. Bivalent, trivalent, univalent, etc., chromosomes are formed randomly and are variously oriented toward the two poles at metaphase I. Anaphase distribution in a triploid will range from the haploid to the triploid number of chromosomes, and even higher numbers of chromosomes may occur after fertilization. Generally, however, the unbalanced nuclei, those between the diploid and haploid numbers (and they are the most abundant) fail to persist to fertilization; consequently, triploids are highly sterile. These same conditions also occur in other euploid conditions consisting of odd-numbered multiples of x, such as pentaploids (5x or 5n).

On the other hand, euploids having even-numbered multiples of x, such as *tetraploids* (4n), *hexaploids* (6n), *octoploids* (8n), *10-ploids, 12-ploids,* etc., may have regular segregation of chromosomes and breed as true as diploids (Fig. 19-11). That is especially true of allopolyploids (see later) but is not true of autopolyploids.

Polyploidy. Even-numbered euploid species (called merely polyploid species) are common among most nonwoody plants. Perhaps one half of all grass species, for example, are polyploid. Of the various polyploid conditions in plants the tetraploid is by far the most common although the hexaploid is not rare. Octoploid species are less common than hexaploid, 10-ploid rarer than octoploid, and so on. The wheats and related species represent a polyploid series including diploids, tetraploids, and hexaploids, the last including the common wheats.

Even-numbered euploids are of two sorts,

one of which, the autoploid, is clear-cut; the other, the allopolploid, is obviously to some extent also autoploid.

Autopolyploidy. Autopolyploidy results when the sets of chromosomes of a diploid, triploid, tetraploid, etc., are duplicated so that there are then twice as many of each chromosome, more than two identical sets. For example, when a diploid tomato plant (2n = 24) stem is cut and callus forms on the cut surface, plantlets form in and grow out of the callus. About 10% of such plantlets have double the original chromosome number (2n = 48) and are *autotetraploid.* It is evident that in mature cells of diploid plant stems some cells already contain tetraploid and octoploid numbers of chromosomes. This becomes evident when such mature cells are induced to divide again by 2-4D, auxin, or other plant hormones. In tomato stems, for example, all collenchyma cells are tetraploid or octoploid. Cells of the pericycle, endodermis, and cortical parenchyma are diploid and tetraploid. It is such cells that produce polyploid plantlets after decapitation.

Meiosis in autopolyploids is, of course, irregular, since there are three (in an autotriploid) or more homologues of each chromosome. As stated earlier, only two homologues can pair at any one locus, but different homologues may pair at different loci. Thus during meiosis in an autotetraploid, associations of 2, 3, or 4 chromosomes are typically formed. As one would expect for each chromosome type, either two bivalents, a trivalent and a univalent, or one quadrivalent is found. Since these alternatives seem to be random for each chromosome type in each meiotic cell, the metaphase is complex and highly irregular.

At anaphase the various constituents of each multivalent and the univalents move randomly to one or the other spindle pole. Thus for each chromosome type the telophase I nuclei vary greatly in chromosomal content. Many of the chromosomally most unbalanced nuclei may not survive, but after syngamy a variety of chromosomal types of zygotes are produced, as is evident from observation. Many of such embryos die; only the euploids and the more nearly diploid, triploid, or tetraploid aneuploid forms generally survive, such as 2n + 1, 2n + 2, 3n − 1, 3n + 2, 4n − 2, 4n + 1, etc. Thus autopolyploids, whether autotetraploid, autohexaploid, or auto-octoploid, are generally highly sterile.

Allopolyploidy. The other type of euploid is the allopolyploid, which results from the chromosome doubling (natural or induced) of an interspecific hybrid, generally a rather sterile hybrid. It is obvious that the autopolyploid is in no sense an allopolyploid. On the other hand, it is equally obvious that every allopolyploid is, at least genetically, a sort of autopolyploid, since only closely related species, species having most genes in common, can be crossed. It is impossible to state exactly just how much difference must exist between the parental forms and the genetic content of the various chromosomes to produce, after hybridization and chromosomal doubling, an allopolyploid rather than an autopolyploid. A reasonable generalization, with exceptions of course, is that the parents must be from two different species, whatever species really are! It is also possible to define an allopolyploid as that type of polyploid derived from a fairly or completely sterile interspecific hybrid. Thus the distinction between some autoploids and some alloploids is vague. For example, meiosis in the diploid hybrid between tomato *(Lycopersicon esculentum)* and the wild *L. peruvianum* is regular; synapsis between chromosomes of the two species forms twelve bivalents and synaptinemal complexes. When the chromosome number is doubled, twelve quadrivalents are formed at meiosis. That tetraploid hybrid could be called equally well an autoploid or alloploid, depending on definitions and assumptions.

It is generally accepted at this time that essentially all naturally occurring polyploid species are allopolyploid and not autopolyploid. One reason for this conclusion is that meiosis in autoploids is so irregular that they soon disappear from a population. Meiosis in alloploids, on the other hand, is likely to be more or less regular. In fact, the more sterile, the less synapsis, the less homology there is between chromosomes of the two parents in the hybrid, the more regular the pairing and the higher the fertility in the alloploid. Such meiotically regular alloploids are usually considered to be new and distinct species. This type of sudden formation of a new species is in marked contrast to the slow evolution of new species at the diploid level, depending, as the latter process does, on chance mutations and the action of natural selection during many generations. Allopolyploids, like the diploid *Oenothera* complex heterozygotes, are permanent, true-breeding sexual hybrids possessing characters of both parents as well as new characteristics of their own. An outstanding "natural" example of a newly formed allopolyploid species is the grass *Spartina townsendii* (2n = 120, 122, and 124) by Huskins (1931) and Marchant (1966). Apparently a cross between the hexaploid European species *S. stricta* (n = 30, x = 10) and the aneuploid American species *S. alterniflora* (n = 31) produced a sterile hybrid aneuploid hexaploid (2n = 61) near Townsend, England, about a hundred years ago. A few years later the chromosome number doubled to about 122 and the plant was a fertile, aggressive, 18-ploid new species, *S. townsendii,* which is continuing to occupy saltwater mud flats of the English Channel that were never occupied by either parent.

It is obvious that no new genetic combinations are produced in an autoploid; the existing genotype is merely doubled. In contrast, the bringing together of genomes of two distinct species into one hybrid does produce a distinctly new genome. An autotetraploid differs quantitatively from the one diploid species from which it was derived, but an alloploid differs quantitatively and qualitatively from both of its ancestral species; it is a combination of both, a unique type, a new species, if the parents were distinct species themselves.

Diploidization. There is some evidence that polyploids, even autoploids, can in time and through many generations become more and more like diploids with respect to regularity of bivalent pairing, regularity of meiosis, and high fertility. That process is called diploidization. Probably most newly formed alloploids have some multivalent and univalent chromosomes at metaphase I, and certainly all autoploids do. Yet even in autotetraploid (2n = 40) corn that is normally diploid (2n = 20), during ten generations of selection for vigor, fertility, and disease resistance (natural selection would do the same) the average number of quadrivalents was reduced from 8.7 to 7.4 per cell, and bivalents increased proportionally (Gilles and Randolph, 1951). In autotetraploid rye after six generations there was more regular meiosis, and the frequency of aneuploids in the population decreased. This process, by which polyploids become meiotically like diploids, gives rise to the term *"amphidiploid,"* used to describe a polyploid with regular bivalent pairing and high fertility.

Meiosis in polyploids

It is evident from the previous discussion that meiosis is often irregular (as indicated by other than regular bivalent pairing) in haploids, many polyploids, and diploid hybrids. On the other hand, regular bivalent pairing has been observed in an unexpectedly large number of sterile diploid (including amphidiploid) hybrids. It is obvious in most cases, since the parents are distinct species, that the parental species must have distinctive genotypes and probably differ somewhat chromosomally to produce the observed sterility. Stebbins (1950) has called such sterile hybrids that possess good bivalent pairing *cryptic struc-*

tural hybrids; that is, the parental species differ for numerous structural differences (inversions, duplications, and translocations) that are too small to produce the configurations known to be produced by larger structural changes of the same kinds. Occasional cells in such hybrids may produce rather rare configurations indicative of the hidden small structural changes such as translocation quadrivalents, bridge-fragment anaphases, a few univalents, and multipolar spindles (Fig. 19-12).

Usually, however, meiosis in interspecific hybrids is irregular. If the two parents are diploid at the basic number for the family, there may be no pairing of chromosomes because none of one parent is homologous with any of the other parent. Occasional pairing reported in a diploid hybrid of two diploid parents has been proposed as resulting from an increased basic number. If the original basic number of rice, for example, had been x = 7 but had later increased to 12, so that the present basic number in the genus of rice is now 12, then there would be some homology between certain chromosomes of the haploid set of 12. Therefore if the two n = 12 species were crossed, there could be some pairing among the 12 chromosomes derived from *one* parent and/or the other. Such pairing among chromosomes from one parent is called *autosyndesis,* and it is common in hybrids of polyploids. Pairing of chromosomes derived from *two* parents, the usual sort of pairing, is called *allosyndesis.* It is usually impossible to tell from cytological study which it is, except in haploids (if there is any pairing and there may be some) or in a hybrid possessing at least some chromosomes that are different in the two parents. In a haploid of *Hordeum* (n = 7) many meiocytes at pachytene had up to three bivalents, and some bivalents persisted to diakinesis (Sadasivaiah and Kasha, 1971). In the hybrid of two species of ragweed *(Ambrosia)* the chromosome are of different sizes, and so it could be determined that allosyndesis occurred (Jones, 1943). In the 2n = 5 hybrid of *Haplopappus gracilis* derived from 2n = 4 and 2n = 6 parents, the small C and D chromosomes of the n = 3 gamete paired with the large chromosome A derived from the n = 2 gamete, again proving allosyndesis.

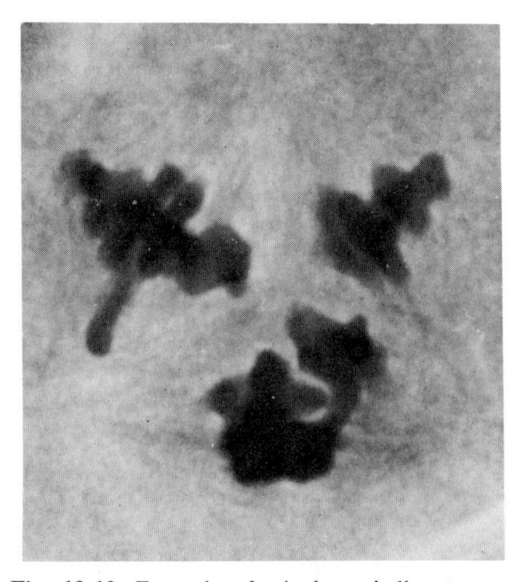

Fig. 19-12. Example of tripolar spindle at metaphase I in an interspecific cryptic structural hybrid of *Elymus canadensis* and *E. virginicus.* The chromosomes are on three distinct metaphase plates.

Meiosis in a hybrid derived from at least one polyploid parent will often include multivalent chromosomes. If the two sets of chromosomes introduced by a diploid gamete from a tetraploid parent are more closely related than either is to the set brought to the zygote by a haploid gamete, autosyndesis may occur. On the other hand, if one of the sets of the diploid gamete has more affinity to the haploid set than to the other set of the diploid gamete, some or all of the sets with the greater homology may pair allosyndetically as bivalents. If all three sets have about the same affinity, some trivalents may be formed unless genes for bivalent pairing only are present. Such genes have been reported.

When synapsis does not occur at meiosis, as in some hybrids or in strains homozygous for an asynaptic mutation, the univalents generally are included on the plate at metaphase I. At anaphase I they usually divide into two chromatids as at a mitotic anaphase, the chromatids going to the two poles. Such chromosomes cannot again divide at anaphase II and generally pass randomly to the two poles to produce genetically unbalanced nuclei. Sometimes, however, the two-chromatid metaphase I univalents pass randomly without separation of chromatids to the spindle poles and separate into chromatids at anaphase II. Occasionally, one or a few univalents neither divide into chromatids nor separate at anaphase I but remain (lag) on or near the metaphase plate, are not included in either telophase I nucleus, and often form one or more tiny *micronuclei* in one or other of the two resulting cells. In plant anthers, at least, micronuclei (which may also result from acentric fragments produced by crossing-over within a paracentric inversion followed by an anaphase bridge-fragment configuration) can be used as a quickly and easily determined indication of a plant with irregular meiosis of some sort. In male flies and some other insects that are normally asynaptic the chromosomes at "meiosis" undergo only one division, thereby producing genetically balanced haploid secondary spermatocyte nuclei.

Chromosomal evolution

An example of intraspecific chromosomal (and morphological) evolution in progress has been reported from the Aegean Islands (Heneen and Runemark, 1962). A species of littoral, tetraploid grass, *Elymus rechingeri,* exists as a few small populations scattered widely among the islands. There is probably little or no interpopulation crossing of these wind-pollinated plants so that each small population is completely inbred and ideally suited to show random fixation. This seems to be true morphologically, genetically, and chromosomally. Fig. 19-13 illustrates chromosomal variations from five randomly picked populations of the recognizable satellited chromosomes from root tip mitoses. These three pairs of chromosomes are 5 to 8 μm in length, with a median or submedian centromere and a fairly long subterminal nucleolus-organizing constriction, terminal to which is a satellite of variable length.

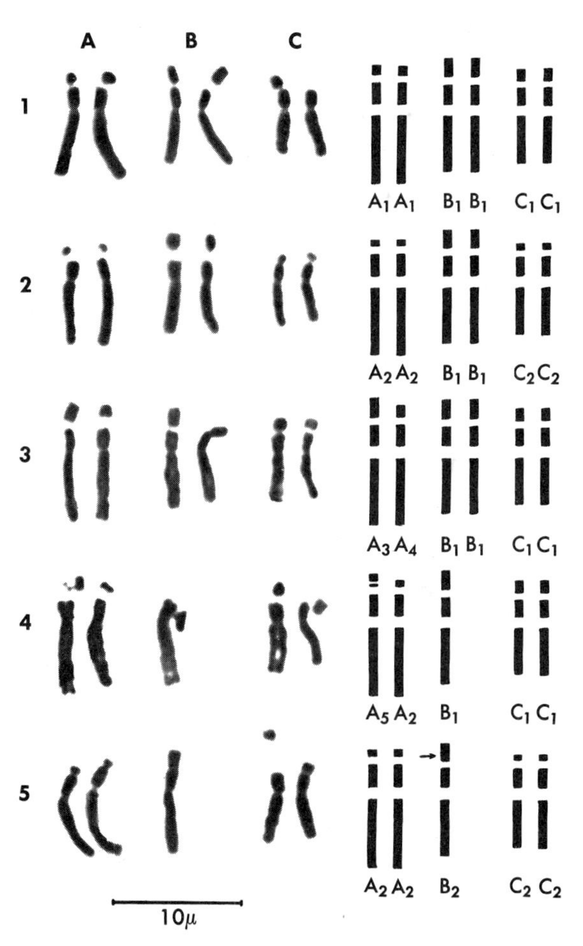

Fig. 19-13. Satellited chromosomes **A, B,** and **C** and interpretive diagrams of plants from five different Greek islands of the grass *Elymus rechingeri* showing morphological differences. These differences illustrate an example of chromosomal evolution in a species consisting of many small, isolated populations. (From Heneen, W. K., and H. Runemark. 1962. Hereditas **48:**545-564.)

In most populations the individual satellited chromosomes are homozygous (C_1C_1, B_1B_1,A_1A_1, for example), but different combinations occur in different populations. Some heterozygosity is present: the A_3A_4 of population 3, A_2A_5 and only one satellited B in population 4, and a single but different B in population 5. Since these plants of populations 4 and 5 had the full chromosome number of 2n = 28, it is assumed that the other Bs have lost the nucleolus organizer and become nonsatellited chromosomes. The chromosome differences among these satellited chromosomes are obvious, and it is likely that similar changes of arm lengths are present among the 22 nonsatellited chromosomes of the set. These changes represent inversions, as indicated by some anaphase I bridges and fragments in about 33% of meiotic anaphase divisions studied, and translocations, as indicated by occasional quadrivalents in some cells of all individuals examined. Such aberrations occur within a largely homozygous population. Hybrids between individuals from different populations would doubtless be highly irregular at meiosis—as irregular as many species hybrids. In fact, this species represents a model case of how one species may, given isolation of populations, give rise to several new species.

CYTOTAXONOMY

The correlation of cytology (chromosomes mostly) with taxonomy began late in the nineteenth century when it was occasionally reported that a certain species of plant or animal was characterized by a particular number of chromosomes. As more and more chromosome numbers of species became known, it was noted that different reports for the same species often varied. It is now known that there were different reasons for such uncertainty, in addition to miscounting, such as variation in number of sex chromosomes, sporadic occurrence of supernumerary chromosomes, abnormal (aneuploid) material such as human inmates of insane asylums, inadequate techniques, intraspecific polyploidy, taxonomic misidentification of materials studied, and others. Thus the true chromosome number of corn was not established until 1928 because of supernumerary chromosomes, and the typical number for normal human beings was not established until the late 1950s because of aneuploidy and inadequate technique.

The actual use of chromosome numbers as characters useful in taxonomy began when chromosome numbers of enough species of a genus had accumulated for comparison or when cytologists deliberately began to compare species and genera on the basis of chromosome number and form. Around 1920, for example, it was noted that among the various cultivated species of wheat, some had 2n = 14, some 2n = 28, and some 2n = 42. Subsequently, the parental species and the evolution of the tetraploid and hexaploid wheats have been satisfactorily determined.

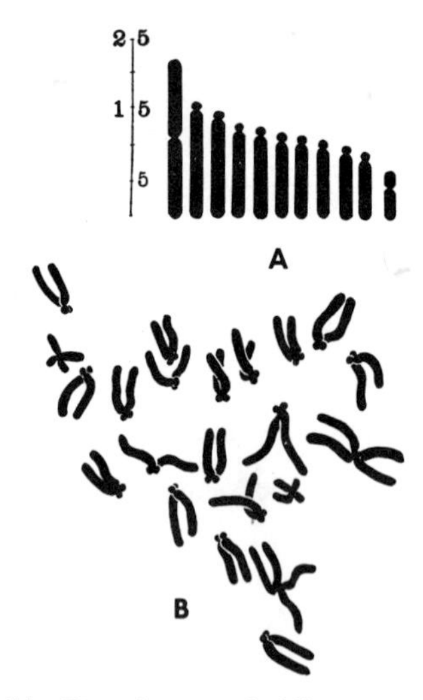

Fig. 19-14. Drawings and idiogram of mitotic metaphase chromosomes of a species of *Sagittaria.* All species so far studied are diploid, 2n = 22, **B,** and all have the same idiogram, **A.** The longest chromosome is metacentric, the shortest is submetacentric, and the other nine are of various lengths and all are subacrocentric. (From Brown, W. V. 1946. Bot. Gaz. **108:**262-267.)

There are, of course, genera in which the cytology is of no value in distinguishing among species of a genus. Thus all species of *Sagittaria* have 2n = 22 (Fig. 19-14), and all species of the grass genus *Melica* have 2n = 18. On the other hand, chromosome numbers may vary significantly within a species. In *Claytonia virginica* at least 40 chromosome numbers are known, ranging from 2n = 12 to 2n = approximately 190 between Texas and New York (Rothwell, 1959; Rothwell and Kump, 1965). Chromosome numbers in this species vary among plants of one population and even within one plant. In general, genera of trees and shrubs tend to be all diploid, grasses tend to have constant basic numbers but a great deal of polyploidy, and the genera of Compositae tend to have rather less polyploidy but considerable evolutionary changes in basic numbers, usually downward.

Some plant cytotaxonomists have expressed the belief that if certain populations within a classical "species" are diploid and others are tetraploid, or some tetraploid and others hexaploid, really two "species" are present. There are many cases in which this proves to be true, but there are other cases, no matter how the species concept is manipulated, that still must be resolved in favor of one species consisting of individuals at two levels of ploidy. A clear example of one such species having both diploid and tetraploid (probably true-breeding autotetraploid) "races" is a monotypic plants species of the eastern United States, *Galax aphylla* (Baldwin, 1941). Both races occupy the same geographical range and differ only slightly—the tetraploid is somewhat sturdier and has somewhat thicker leaves. There are many cases of this sort in which decision as to one or two (or more) species depends entirely on the concept of what a species is in that particular group. Thus knowledge of ploidy may or may not provide useful data to the plant taxonomist and evolutionist.

Karyotype

The karyotype, that is, the number and form of the chromosomes of a set (Fig. 19-14, 16-13, and 16-16), may be of value in deciding taxonomic problems.

Karyotype analysis in vertebrates is now generally done with blood and bone marrow smears to give photographic results similar to those shown in Fig. 16-10. The double metaphase chromosomes are then cut out of the print and arranged in pairs as nearly as possible or at least in groups (Fig. 16-10). Such karyotypes can then be used for comparison within or among species, genera, subfamilies, etc. (Hsu and Arrighi, 1966; Baker and Patton, 1967; Patton, 1967a,b; Baker, 1967). Data acquired from such comparisons include (1) the *fundamental number,* which is the total number of arms of the autosome chromosomes of the 2n set (Matthey, 1951); (2) 2n chromosome number; (3) size groups; (4) lengths; (5) sex chromosome system (XO, XY, XY_1Y_2, etc.); and (6) sex chromosome morphology.

Such data are useful to taxonomists and evolutionists to indicate (sometimes) closeness of relationships and the direction of evolution within a group. This method has also revealed cases of unexpectedly high interpopulation variation within species, although most species vary little if at all from one range extreme to another. Karyotype analysis has been of value in the study of animals, especially insects, bats, rodents, and lizards, and of plants. Changes in basic number within genera, as in *Drosophila* (Patterson and Stone, 1952) and numerous other insect genera (White, 1954), especially grasshoppers, as well as in such plants as *Crepis* and *Haplopappus* have already been discussed.

Changes of chromosome form within a genus by translocations, wherein one large chromosome may be formed out of two smaller ones; by separations, one large metacentric chromosome forming two smaller acrocentric chromosomes by transverse division; and by an unequal pericentric inversion that may change a metacentric into an acrocentric chromosome or vice versa are known. This sort of analysis has been applied to groups and species of *Drosophila,* and concepts of evolutionary changes have been proposed.

In *Drosophila* the assumption is that the original evolutionary basic number was x = 6 and that increases (one species only) up to n = 7 and decreases as far as to n = 3 have taken place during the evolution of the genus. This cytological knowledge, added to concepts derived from morphology, chromosomal rearrangements, and hybridization have permitted the construction of an evolutionary model of the major groups of the genus.

Another outstanding contribution of cytology to taxonomy was the new concept of the close relationship between the plant genera *Yucca, Agave,* and other obviously related genera. Until about 1930 *Yucca,* which has a superior ovary, was included in the family Liliaceae, whereas *Agave* was included in the family Amaryllidaceae, which is typified by an inferior ovary. Cytological study of mitotic and meiotic metaphase chromosomes revealed that *Yucca, Agave,* and related genera had the same sort of chromosome set (karyotype), which was unique and so different from any other Liliaceae or Amaryllidaceae (or any other plant genus for that matter) that it seemed best to treat these xerophytes as one family, the Agavaceae (Whitaker, 1934; Granick, 1944). The new family Agavaceae is characterized by a haploid karyotype consisting at the diploid level of 25 small chromosomes and 5 much larger chromosomes (Fig. 16-11).

Idiogram

On the other hand, karyotype analysis alone may be of no value to taxonomy. This is true of most species with only tiny chromosomes. Additionally, in some genera all species may have the same karyotype. An outstanding example is the plant genus *Sagittaria.* Not only do all species studied have the same number (n = 11) but all have the same karyotype. When scale drawings of the chromosomes of the karyotype are arranged, usually according to length, an idiogram is produced (Figs. 16-10 and 16-13). All species of *Sagittaria* have the same idiogram (Fig. 19-14), but its haploid number and idiogram do differ from those of other genera in the family (Brown, 1946).

NUCLEIC ACID HYBRIDIZATION

Nucleic acid hybridization is a recent biochemical technique for determining the quantitative amount of similarity between two sources of DNA or between a DNA and a RNA. It is determined by the amount of one DNA or RNA (as rather small fragments) base-pairing to the long single strands of DNA (McCarthy and Bolton, 1963). The technique consists of separating the double DNA strand by heat (about 100° C), cooling quickly (well below 60° C) to keep the separated strands apart, and then spreading them on a membrane or embedding them in agar. Meanwhile, other DNA or RNA has been produced with radioactivity (phosphorus or appropriate nucleotide base). This DNA would be separated and fragmented (sheared) or RNA used as it occurs. It is added in solution to the bound, long, single-strand DNA. The evidence indicates that a sequence of about thirty base pairings (identical sequence) will hold a fragment to the anchored long DNA. Any of the unpaired radioactive fragments of DNA or RNA can subsequently be washed away; the amounts washed away and that held to (trapped by) the DNA are determined by the radioactivity in the two portions. DNA or RNA from the same organism is used as the standard, and the amounts trapped by the two different runs are compared.

This system of analyses can compare mRNA of one tissue to DNA of another or mRNA at one time to mRNA produced by the same tissue at another time. It has been used especially to compare DNA of one species to that of another in both animals (Hoyer et al., 1964) and plants (Arnold and Bolton, 1967). This measures the DNA relatedness or genetic similarity between closely or distantly related species such as man to monkey, mouse, or fish as a percentage of the amount of human sheared DNA trapped by human DNA single long strands.

GAMETOGENESIS

The formation of gametes is more widespread than even sexuality, since parthenogenetic animal and most apomictic plant species produce at least eggs. Gametes themselves range from almost completely undifferentiated cells such as sexual unicellular algae, slime molds, some Protozoa, and other lower groups to what is probably the most highly specialized and differentiated cell known, the sperm of metazoan animals and many plants. The ova of most Metazoa, and plants too, seem rather unspecialized, but evidently they do contain, even before meiosis and fertilization, elaborated materials and regional differentiation that is revealed during embryogeny and by embryological experimentation.

Gametes

A gamete is a cell that unites or might unite with another cell in the sexual act. Typically, the gametes that unite are somewhat different from one another. This difference may range from a minimal chemical or antigenic difference, as in plus and minus strains of some algae, fungi, and Protozoa, through only slightly observable morphological differences of isogametes (Fig. 19-23), to the extreme contrast of sperm and ova. The angiosperms, the most highly specialized group of plants, however, have simple gametes. The egg is little different from a typical meristematic cell except that it has no wall, only middle lamella (Fig. 19-16), and the male gamete seems to be merely a haploid interphase nucleus surrounded by a thin layer of protoplasm and a plasma membrane (Fig. 19-17).

The subject matter of gametogenesis in all living organisms is extensive, with a wealth of variations and observations. Here only a few common and general types can be described. Furthermore, it is essential to realize that a single generalized description of a "typical sperm" is impossible. They vary greatly, both morphologically and anatomically. In length they range from 6 to 12,000 μm, a ratio of 2,000:1 (see later in this chapter). Some do not have tails. Nuclei range from spherical to very long and filamentous. Acrosomes range from a few millimicrons to 2.5 mm. Mitochondria vary from a mere ring to a long helical spiral to very long straight filaments. Acronemes are not only of the 9 + 2 composition, but 9 + 9 + 2 and 9 + 9 + 1 are also known. Mammalian sperm have a neck, an annulus, and a fibrous sheath in the main piece, all of which are lacking in insect sperm. As Breland et al. (1966) have demonstrated, the neck, middle piece, and main piece of mammalian sperm cannot be correlated with parts of the insect sperm tail. Furthermore, most of what is known of the act of syngamy comes from study of vertebrate and echinoderm eggs. Certainly, the penetration into a frog egg must be quite different from the arthropodan sperm entering its egg through a micropyle or syngamy in a flowering plant. Biologists have often wondered why many small animals should have sperm from 2 to 12 mm long—up to seven times the length of the animal's body!

Reproductive cells

Among sexual Metozoa, with few exceptions, gametogenesis is immediately preceded or accompanied by meiosis (Fig. 19-15). Among plants and fungi, meiosis does not immediately precede the formation of gametes. Meiosis in plants and fungi gives rise, not to gametes, but generally to haploid cells called *spores;* few or many haploid mitotic divisions derived from them produce, eventually, the cells that differentiate into gametes. The formation of spores and the meiosis that immediately precedes it is called *sporogenesis.*

Meiosis in most higher animals occurs in stem cells of the *germ line* that were set aside early in embryogenesis for no other purpose, except that "nurse" cells are germ line derivatives also (Fig. 18-15). There is no such germ line in plants or fungi. These germ line stem cells are contained within the gonads and usually undergo occasional mitotic divisions. When sexual maturity is reached or before, these germ line cells are called *gonia* and divide rather rapidly. Eventually, division stops in some of them and they are called *primary gametocytes* or *meiocytes,* in which meiosis occurs to form two *secondary gametocytes (spermatocytes)* in testes or one secondary gametocyte (*oocyte*) and a *polar body* in ovaries (Fig. 18-15). The second division produces four *spermatids* in the male and one *ootid* in the female.

Sporogenesis. In anthers of flowering plants, certain cells eventually become *sporogenous cells* (comparable to gonia of animals), which generally divide a few times

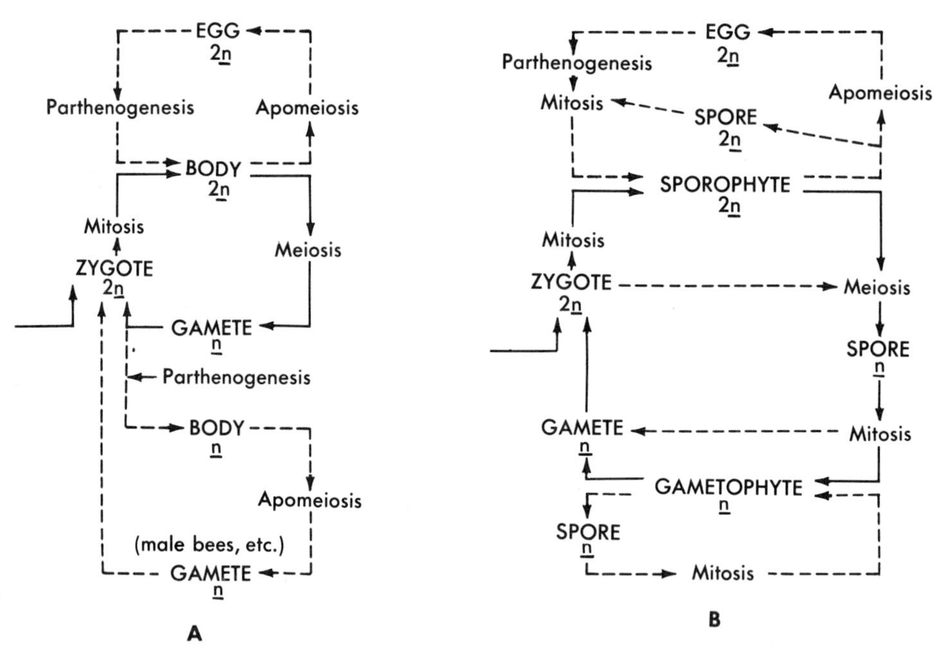

Fig. 19-15. A, Typical life cycle in animals is represented by solid center lines. Thelytoky is diagrammed above and arrhenotoky below, as indicated by dashed lines. In cyclic parthenogenesis all individuals would be parthenogenetic females "going around" the upper cycle for a number of generations and then, under proper stimulation, producing sexual males and females "going around" the central cycle. In Hymenoptera the females follow the central cycle except that some haploid eggs would develop parthenogenetically into haploid males, described by the lower loop. **B,** Typical life cycle of many plants (especially land plants) that have a regular alternation of sporophyte and gametophyte generations is represented by solid lines at center. Various modifications are indicated by dashed lines, such as meiosis in the zygote, gamete production very soon after meiosis, diploid apomixis and diploid sporophyte-spore-sporophyte repetition above, and haploid gametophyte-spore-gametophyte repetition below. Some of these may be variously mixed during a yearly cycle within a single species, especially among algae.

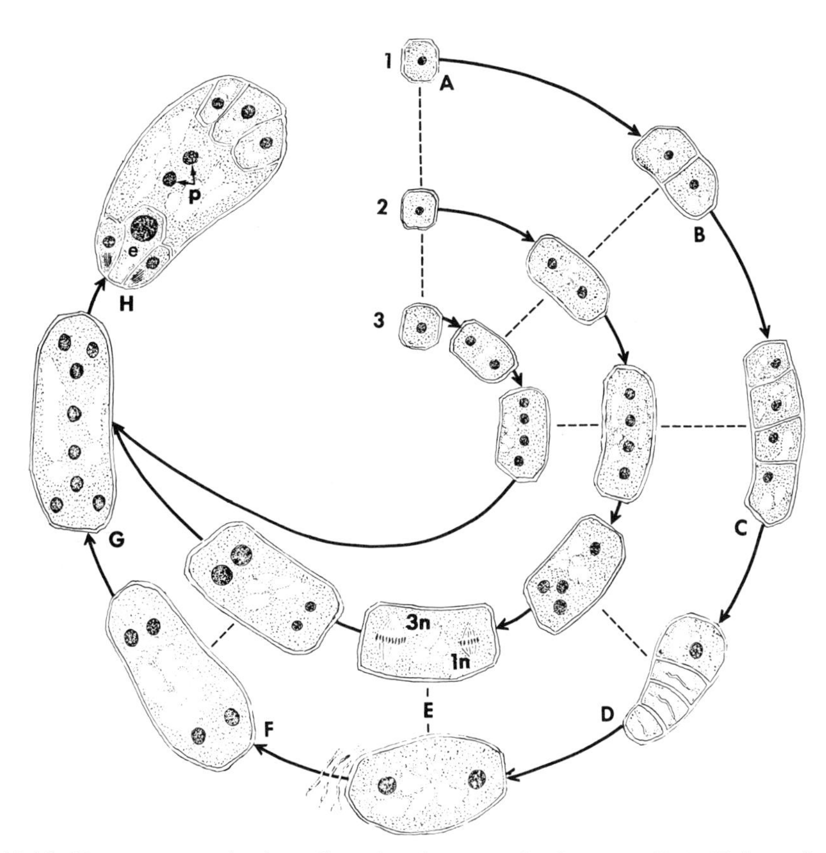

Fig. 19-16. Megasporogenesis, **A** to **C,** and embryo sac development, **D** to **H,** in angiosperm ovules. The outer row, **1,** is the commonest, undistorted sequence, the "polygonum type": meiosis I occurring in **A,** the megasporocyte, meiosis II in **B,** four distinct cellular spores in **C,** growth of one spore and degeneration of three in **D,** three successive haploid mitotic divisions without cytokinesis in **D** to **F** to produce the eight-nucleate condition in **G,** cell membranes forming around six nuclei and some cytoplasm to form the eight-nucleate, seven-celled mature embryo sac (**e** = egg; **p** = polar nuclei). The innermost sequence, **3,** diagrams a common modification, the "adoxa type," a combining of sporogenesis, **A** to **C,** with the first three stages of embryo sac development, **D** to **F.** That is, **A** is equivalent (uninucleate) to **D, B** is also **E** (binucleate), and **C** is also **F** (four-nucleate); **G** and **H** follow. The central sequence, **2,** diagrams megasporogenesis as it occurs in the lily, the "Fritillaria type," which is a modification of **3.** Following **C** (the simultaneous four-megaspore and four-nucleate gametophyte) three of the haploid nuclei aggregate at the end away from the micropyle, **D,** and simultaneously divide so that the three haploid spindles unite into one triploid spindle, **E.** The haploid micropylar nucleus divides at the same time. Thus the first four-nucleate stage (haploid) produces the second four-nucleate stage, the latter having two (micropylar) haploid nuclei and two (chalazal) triploid nuclei, **F.** Therefore the egg is haploid but one polar nucleus is haploid and one is triploid, **G.** After fusion with one of the male nuclei the endosperm nuclei are pentaploid. Numerous other types are known, and many modifications of embryo sacs, its various cells, the endosperm, and embryo produced have been recorded (Maheshwari, 1950.)

by mitosis (Maheshwari, 1950). Eventually, they enter the premeiotic interphase, and the cells are called *microsporocytes,* or *pollen mother cells* (PMCs), in which meiosis occurs. The number of sporogenous cells varies in ovules of angiosperms, but usually only one becomes the *megasporocyte,* or *egg mother cell* (EMC). In many more than half of angiosperm species the two meiotic divisions produce four haploid cells, called *megaspores* (Fig. 19-16). Generally, only one megaspore grows into the *embryo sac,* a structure that can somewhat questionably be equated with a *female gametophyte* (Fig. 19-16, *1*). In other species all four nuclei resulting from meiosis are contained within one cell, which is also at the same time the four-nucleate embryo sac (Fig. 19-16, *3*). Thus one female gametophyte is formed from four genetically different spores—certainly an odd sort of "gametophyte"! Other types of embryo sac development are known (Fig. 19-16, *2*), as in *Lilium,* for example.

Somewhat the same sort of telescoping and combination has evolved in the conversion of the immediate product of meiosis, the *microspore,* into a three-celled pollen grain (Fig. 19-17), which may be considered to be the *male gametophyte.* After the four uninucleate, haploid microspores have formed and the pollen grain shape has been assumed by the microspores, the spore nucleus of each divides to produce two rather different nuclei; one is the *tube nucleus,* the other is the *generative nucleus* (Fig. 19-17). The latter becomes included in a small cell with a thin cell wall, the *generative cell,* which is embedded in the larger *tube cell* that fills the pollen grain. At a later time, either within the pollen grain or within the *pollen tube,* the generative cell divides once to form two *male cells.* Thus the tube nucleus and two male cells are moved down through the stigma and pistil to the embryo sac within the tip of the growing pollen tube. The two male cells (or at least the nuclei) are discharged from the burst tip of the pollen tube into the embryo sac. One male nucleus enters the egg as the male *pronucleus;* the other unites with two embryo sac polar nuclei to form the *primary endosperm nucleus.*

Animal oogenesis. The formation of ova (the female gametes) varies considerably, especially in growth, size, time of meiosis, and length of meiotic stage. Ova typically acquire some sort of covering. In the arthropods the covering is chitinous like the exoskeleton of the organisms themselves. Fish and amphibian eggs are covered with a thick gelatinous covering outside a *chorion.* Everyone is familiar with the membranous covering of reptile eggs and the shelled eggs of birds.

Internal to such coverings there is the typical 75 Å plasma membrane, and just

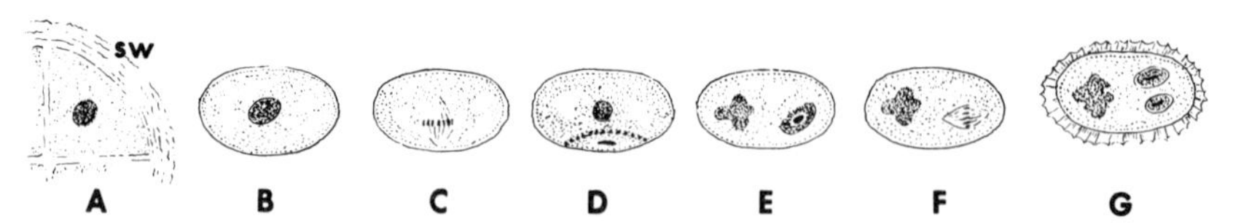

Fig. 19-17. Gametogenesis (pollen grain development) in angiosperms. **A,** One of the four haploid microspores produced by the two meiotic divisions from a microsporocyte (PMC) in an anther. **B,** Rounded-up microspore. **C,** First (asymmetric) pollen grain (haploid) division. **D,** Telophase of the first division; the generative cell forms against the wall, and the tube nucleus occupies the center of the pollen grain. **E,** The tube nucleus becomes polymorphic. Many pollen grains are shed in this condition, **F** and **G,** nuclear events occurring in the pollen tube. **F,** Second pollen grain or generative cell division. **G,** Two male cells have been produced, one to unite with the egg, the other with the two polar nuclei of the embryo sac. During these events the thick *special wall,* **sw,** which is still present at **A,** breaks down and the complex pollen grain wall forms, **G.**

outside it in some eggs is the thicker *vitelline membrane,* peculiar to many eggs that are fertilized outside the female.

Meiotic prophase usually continues for a long time as the oocyte grows in volume. In many kinds of animals, especially the lower vertebrates, it is the diplotene phase that is extensive, bivalents being in the form of lampbrush chromosomes (Figs. 18-16 and 18-19). When there is a nucleus in the oocyte, it is large and called the *germinal vesicle.*

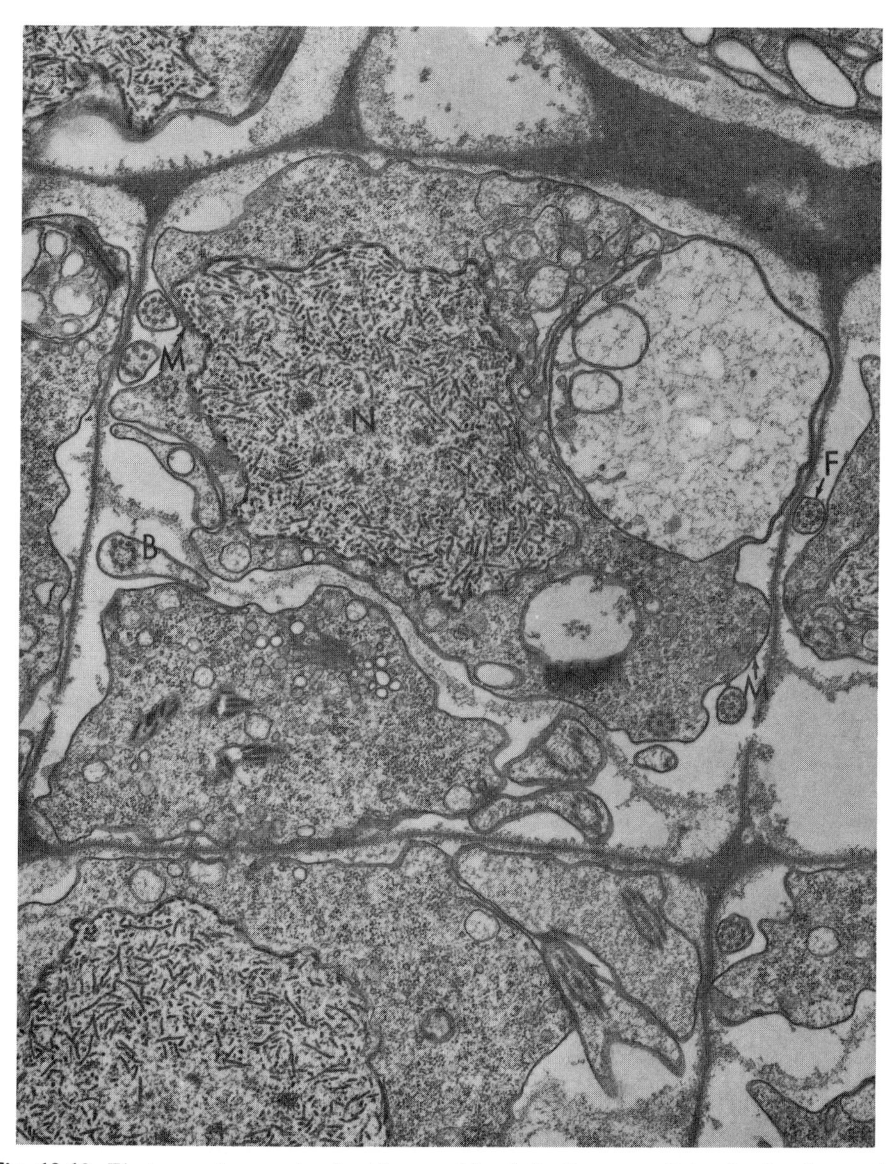

Fig. 19-18. Electron micrograph of midspermatids of the liverwort *Reboulia* showing sections of basal bodies, flagella, microtubular supports, and the filamentous substructure of the nucleus common in gamete (midspermatid) development. **B,** Basal body; **F,** flagellar cross section; **M,** microtubular supports; **N,** nucleus. (Courtesy Dr. F. R. Turner, University of Texas Cell Research Institute, Austin, Texas.)

In general, the accumulation of food reserves both precedes and follows meiosis. The two meiotic divisions are usually not completed until after entrance of the sperm nucleus, called the male *pronucleus*. Meiosis in the oocyte is halted often at completion of the first division. However, the stage of meiosis at which a halt occurs varies from before meiosis begins to no halt at all. In the clam it halts at metaphase I, a condition in which spawning occurs. If fertilization does not occur within 1 hour, the ova begin to degenerate, and metaphase chromosomes can be recognized for up to 20 hours. If the eggs are fertilized immediately on spawning, the first polar body appears in 10 minutes, metaphase II in 15 minutes, and first cleavage division in 20 to 30 minutes.

One of the two haploid nuclei resulting from meiosis I in oocytes forms a *polar body,* which is extruded from the oocyte (see Fig. 18-15). On completion of the second division a second polar body is usually extruded. The remaining nucleus of the ovum, the *pronucleus,* then unites in the interphasic or prophasic condition with the sperm pronucleus to form the zygote nucleus of the fertilized egg; or probably more commonly, union of chromosome sets occurs only as the first or later cleavage mitotic division progresses, called *gonomery*. Subsequent embryogenetic development is the subject matter of the fascinating study of embryology, which is partly cytology but beyond the scope of this text.

Spermatogenesis

Spermatogenesis, spermiogenesis, or *spermateliosis,* the conversion of an essentially typical cell, the spermatid, into a sperm (Fig. 19-19), which is one of the most complex cells known, is a process typical of most multicellular animals and most lower plants. Sperm are not produced by most unicellular organisms, by most seed plants, by the higher fungi, or by the red algae. Sperm therefore constitute that class of male gametes which are highly specialized, almost always motile cells, moving by means of cilia, flagella, or tails and rarely by pseudopodia. They all contain a nucleus, some differentiated cytoplasm, mitochondria or mitochondrial derivatives, one or more basal bodies, and from one to a few thousand flagella, except that sperm cells of many Crustacea, roundworms, and the Mesozoa have no flagellum and are motionless or ameboid, often with spines (Fig. 19-19). The sperm of most animals have one modified flagellum, called the *sperm tail.* Algal sperm generally have two flagella, whereas those of most nonflowering vascular plants, including the gymnospermous *Ginkgo* and the cycads, have from a few, as in ferns, to thousands, as in the cycads (Fig. 19-20).

Nearly all motile sperm, as they differentiate from the spermatid in animals, form a special cytoplasmic structure that generally comes to lie at the anterior end of the sperm cell in front of the nucleus. Various names have been applied to such structures in plant sperm, but in animals it is called the *acrosome,* which is formed by a Golgi apparatus (Fig. 19-19) as the spermatid differentiates into a sperm. The acrosome, or its plant equivalent if such exists, has the important functions of recognizing and of aiding the penetration into the egg through the plasma membrane.

Animal spermatogenesis. Whereas oogenesis is rather unspectacular, the differentiation of sperm consists of a series of unique and extreme cytological changes. At some stage certain testicular cells of the germ line can be called *primary spermatogonia.* These, lying in tubules or cysts, divide by a few mitotic (gonial) divisions, grow between spermatogonial divisions, and produce cells in which meiosis will occur, called *spermatocytes,* or *primary spermatocytes.* There is accumulating evidence that even during the spermatogonial divisions all parts of the cell—cytoplasm, nucleus, and chromosomes—are actually changing in preparation for meiosis and spermatogenesis, for example,

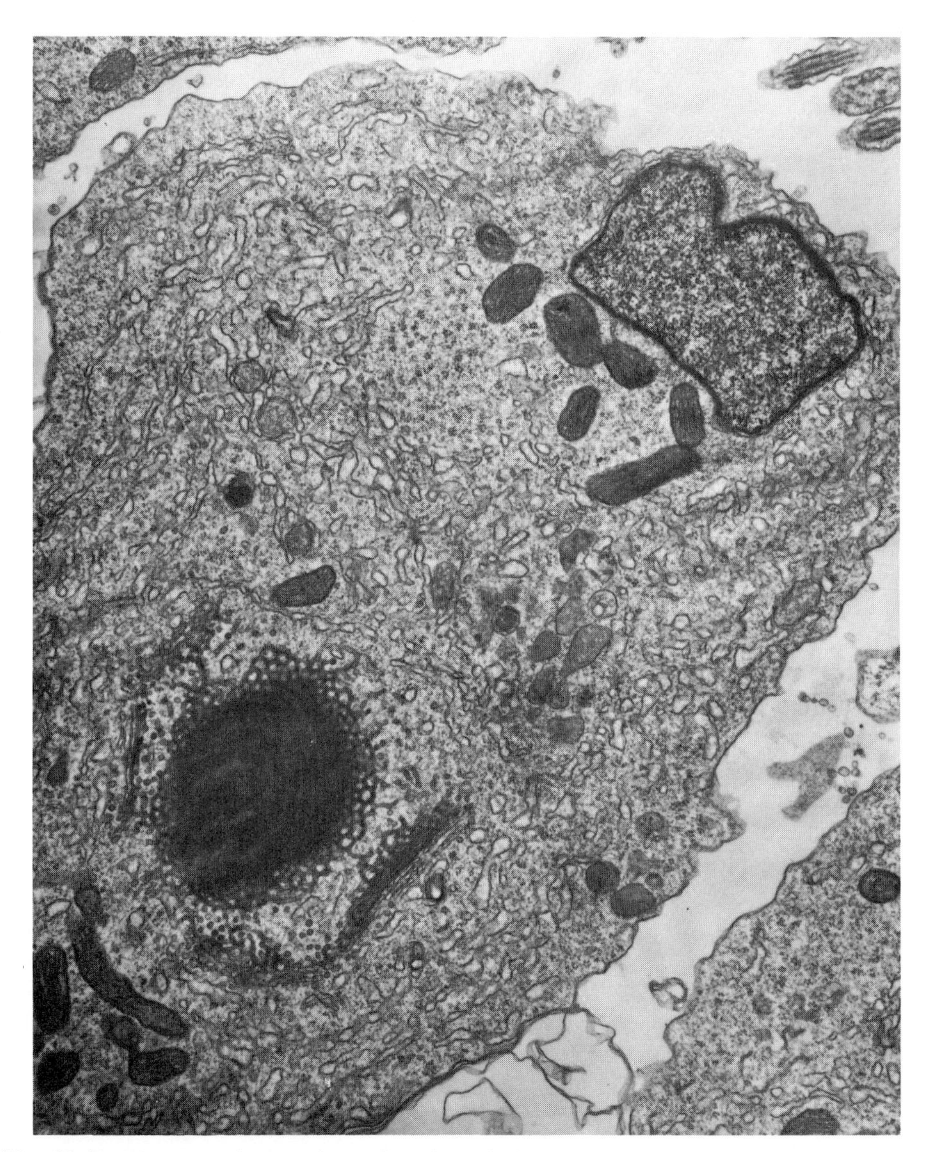

Fig. 19-19. Electron microscopic section through (lower left) an acroblast (Golgi apparatus of a developing animal sperm). One dictyosome is cut nearly parallel with the cisternae; about four other nearby dictyosomes of the acroblast are cut perpendicular to the cisternae. The tubular nature of the peripheral regions of cisternae is evident (compare with Figs. 8-4 and 8-5). Numerous mitochondria surround the Golgi apparatus and functionally compose part of the acrosome. A large amount of ER is also present. The elongating and angular nucleus (upper right) is well along in its change to the sperm condition, and it too is associated with mitochondria. (Courtesy Dr. M. Dauwalder, University of Texas Cell Research Institute, Austin, Texas.)

premeiotic pairing of homologous chromosomes (Chapters 17 and 18). By about 1930 the general details of spermatogenesis had been worked out by light microscopy.

Frequently an abundance of mitochondria and dictyosomes develop in the primary spermatocyte, which as meiotic prophase progresses, arrange themselves around and close to the nucleus so that at telophase I they are about equally distributed in the two resulting cells, the two *secondary spermatocytes.* The second meiotic division follows so that four equal haploid *spermatids* have been producing from each primary spermatocyte. The differentiation of the spermatid into a sperm is part of spermatogenesis, but preparations for that process actually began in the spermatogonia.

At the end of telophase II each centriole of each spermatid divides into two. The mitochondria of some animals such as insects fuse into a large cytoplasmic body called the *nebenkern* or *mitochondrial derivative.* The condensed Golgi apparatus, formerly the "acroblast," becomes very prominent close to the nucleus. All of these structures move around close to the nucleus, but eventually an apical-posterior axis is established. The centrioles (one in insects) and mitochondrial derivatives establish the posterior region, and the acrosome establishes the anterior region. As the concentrated *Golgi complex* (the former "acroblast") (Fig. 19-19) moves toward the apical region, it produces a clear vesicle adjacent to itself, formerly called the acrosome but now called the *acrosome vesicle.* As the acrosome vesicle grows in size, the "acroblast" (the Golgi apparatus) declines in size and eventually separates. The acrosome vesicle remains in the apical region, but the "acroblast" moves toward the posterior region and may even be cast out of the cell. Meanwhile, a granule called the *acrosome granule* has been forming within the acrosome vesicle; it grows in size close to or in contact with the apical region of the nucleus. Eventually, the acrosome granule becomes large and by that time is called the *acrosome.* In the final elongation stage of spermateliosis the acrosome vesicle collapses over the apical region of the nucleus as the *head cap,* and the acrosome forms a sizeable structure, formerly called the "perforatorium," at the anterior end of the sperm head. It contains material for the formation of the *acrosome filament,* which functions in fertilization.

Meanwhile, one of the centrioles has been producing the 9 + 2, 9 + 9 + 2, or 9 + 9 + 1 axoneme (also called the "flagellum," or axial filament) of the sperm tail, which is really a specialized flagellum. As the tail elongates, the two mitochondrial derivatives of insects or the many separate or fused mitochondria of mammals pass into the proximal region of the tail, called the *middle piece.* In insects and molluscs the two mitochondrial derivatives, which are essentially large mitochondria, become very long and lie parallel to the axoneme. In mammals the mitochondria form the long, tight, helical spiral around the axoneme of the middle piece. In echinoderms, annelids, and some molluscs the mitochondria form merely a ring around the basal body of the axoneme adjacent to the posterior surface of the nucleus (Fig. 19-20).

The tails of sperm vary greatly among groups of animals, from none at all in many Crustacea; to those with a long *middle piece* and short or no *principal piece,* as in most insects; to those with a very short middle piece and long principal piece, as in echinoderms, annelids, and some molluscs; to those having medium length of both principal and middle pieces, as in mammals; to those having a lateral undulating membrane and two separate axonemes, as in salamanders. The tails of most sperm terminate in an *endpiece* that is little more than the membrane and axoneme in which the 9 + 2 arrangement breaks down as filaments irregularly terminate.

The most important content of the sperm, of course, is the nucleus, and it varies widely in shape, from essentially spherical to as long as the sperm itself. This elongation of the nucleus takes place late in spermateliosis and is accompanied by chemical and structural changes of the chromosomes and of the nucleus as a whole. Most of the nucleoplasm disappears, and the basic proteins (the histones) often change from lysine rich to arginine rich; in some, such as salmon sperm, protamine finally replaces the his-

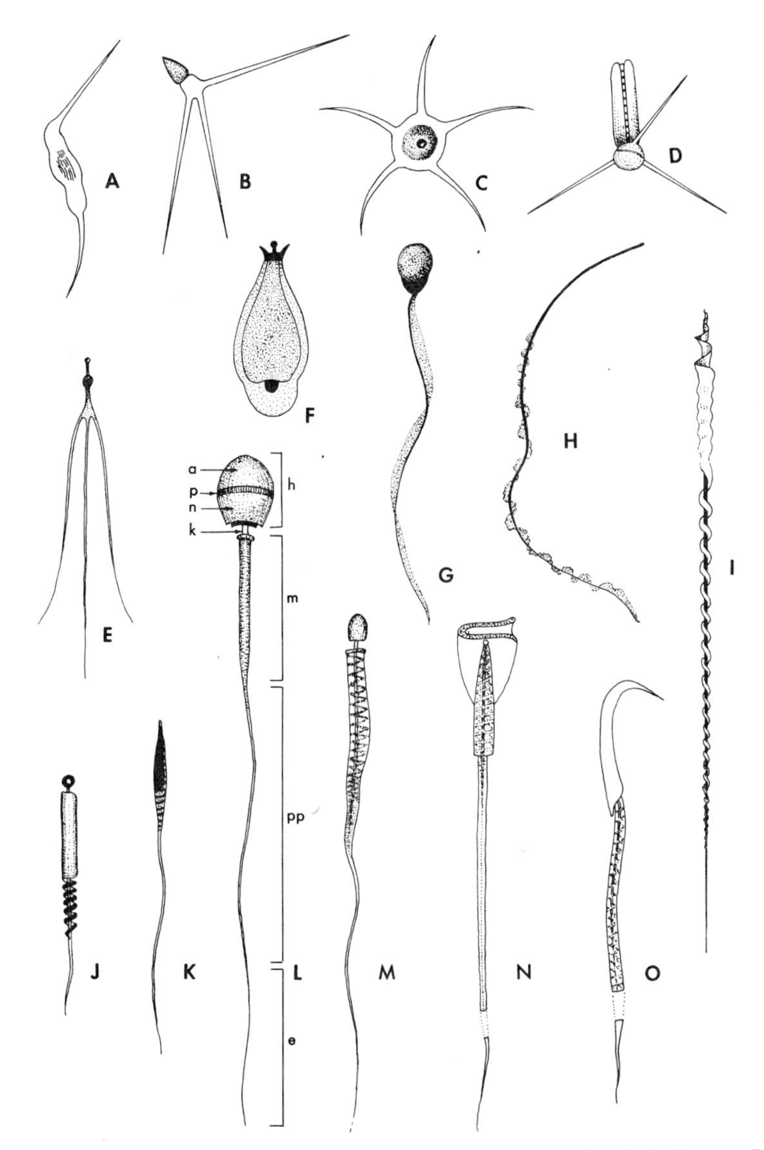

Fig. 19-20. Sperm of various types of animals. **A** to **E,** Crustacea (**A,** *Polyphemus;* **B,** *Ethusa;* **C,** *Maja;* **D,** lobster; **E,** crab). **F,** The nematode, *Ascaris.* **G,** The fish pike. **H,** The amphibian *Triton.* **I,** The bird *Phyllopneuste.* **J,** The bird *Larus* (gull). **K,** The snake *Coluber.* **L** to **O,** Various mammals (**L,** badger; **M,** bat; **N,** opossum; **O,** rat). The mammalian sperm, **L,** has been labeled: **a** = acrosome; **p** = perforatorium; **n** = nucleus; **h** = head; **k** = neck; **m** = middle piece; **pp** = principal piece; **e** = endpiece; **m** + **pp** + **e** = sperm tail. (Redrawn from various nineteenth century zoologists.)

tone. Even the internal fibrillar structure of the nucleus seems to be altered, and some sort of thick fibrils are easily revealed (Fig. 19-18).

Plant spermatogenesis. In contrast to that of animals, spermatogenesis in plants is not associated with meiosis. Haploid cells, usually within special haploid gametophyte structures, form into the motile male gametes. Among many algae and fungi of the Phycomycetes a single cell either forms a single male gamete or, by a series of mitotic divisions within the old cell wall, forms a large number of small, biflagellate sperm. Among the Characeae, bryophytes, and cryptogamic vascular plants the sperm are formed within a multicellular structure of the gametophyte called the *antheridium.* The sperm of the bryophytes and Characeae are biflagellate, but sperm of cryptogamic vascular plants have from a few to many flagella (Fig. 19-21). In this latter group there are no flagella on any other cells of the whole life cycle, and no cells have centrioles. Therefore to have flagella, basal bodies are produced de novo during the last one or two interphases and mitotic divisions before the spermatid is formed. This involves the origin and development of a unique structure called the *blepharoplast* (Fig. 19-22).

Angiosperms and other plants. Since the male gametes of conifers, Gnetales, and angiosperms are not self-propelled by cilia or flagella but are transported probably passively within the tip of an elongating tube of the male gametophyte, the *pollen*

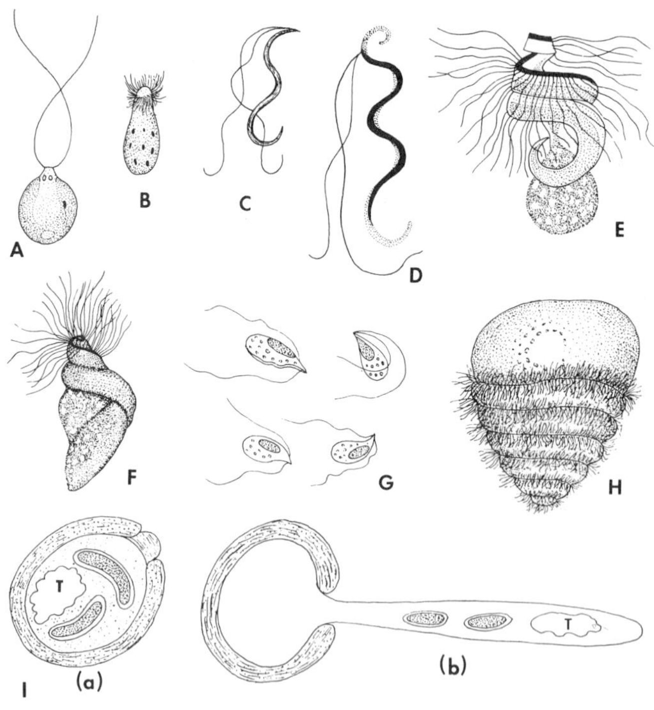

Fig. 19-21. Sperm of various types of plants and also the nonmotile male cells of angiosperms. **A,** Isogamete of the alga *Tetraspora.* **B,** Multiciliate sperm of the alga *Oedogonium.* **C,** Biflagellate sperm of the moss *Sphagnum.* **D,** Biflagellate sperm of *Chara.* **E,** Multiflagellate sperm of fern. **F,** Sperm of *Equisetum.* **G,** Biflagellate sperm of *Lycopodium.* **H,** Sperm of cycad *(Zamia).* **I,** Male cells of angiosperms formed by mitosis either within the pollen grain, **a,** or within the pollen tube, **b.** The tube nucleus is designated by **T.** (Redrawn from various nineteenth century botanists.)

tube, they are not even called sperm but, rather, *male cells* or *male nuclei.* In angiosperms each pollen tube brings two male nuclei to the embryo sac, where the so-called *double fertilization* occurs. One nucleus enters the egg cell and the other unites with the polar nuclei, usually two, to accomplish the unique *triple fusion* of angio-

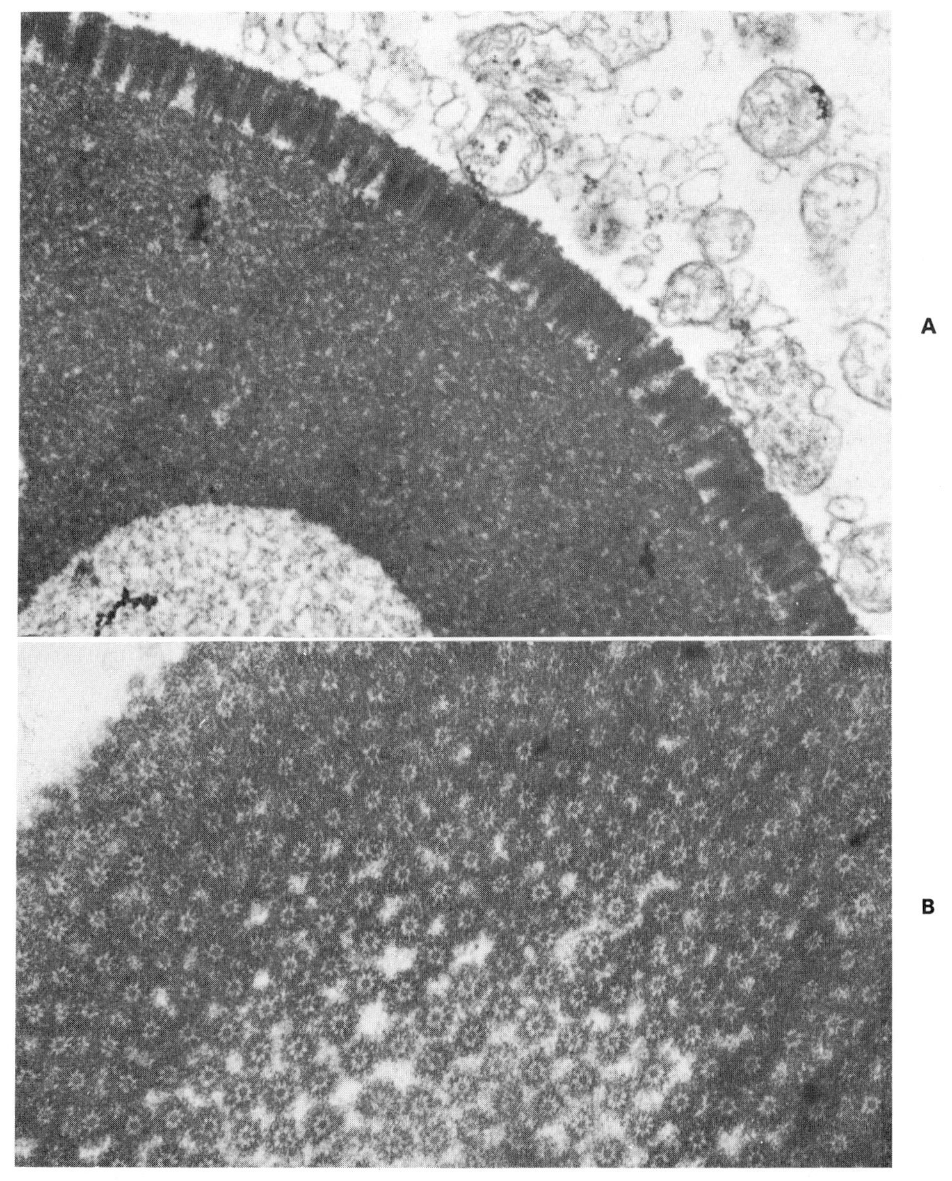

Fig. 19-22. A, Electron micrograph of the part of a circumference of a blepharoplast of *Zamia* showing that the surface consists of a layer of thousands of procentrioles. **B,** Tangential section of procentriole layer. Each procentriole is well developed as a cartwheel around the central microtubule, but the nine triple tubules are not clearly formed. (Courtesy Dr. F. R. Turner, University of Texas Cell Research Institute, Austin, Texas.)

sperms. Thus the endosperm nuclei that develop from this *primary endosperm nucleus* are triploid in most species of angiosperms.

• • •

Thus male gametes range among plants, fungi, and animals from nearly bare nuclei or nonmotile cells of angiosperms and conifers, red algae, Ascomycetes, and Basidiomycetes; to spiny or ameboid sperm of some animals; to the more typical animal sperm with one tail; to biflagellate sperm of numerous algae and fungi; to the multiciliate or flagellate sperm of some algae and lower vascular plants such as ferns, Characeae, and cycads. Most extreme is the complete elimination of sperm in some insects in which the haploid egg nucleus is "fertilized" by one of its polar nuclei, or two haploid cells of the embryo unite to from the diploid condition. In most species there is the union of two cells (gametes), called *fertilization, syngamy,* or *plasmogamy,* followed by the union of the nuclei of the two gametes, called *karyogamy.* Mere union of gametes is only the first phase of fertilization; it is the fusion of nuclei that restores the diploid condition.

Variations in animal sperm. Animal sperm vary considerably in form (Fig. 19-19) and in length. Some are essentially spherical, but most are elongate, in general from about 50 to 300 μm long. Some

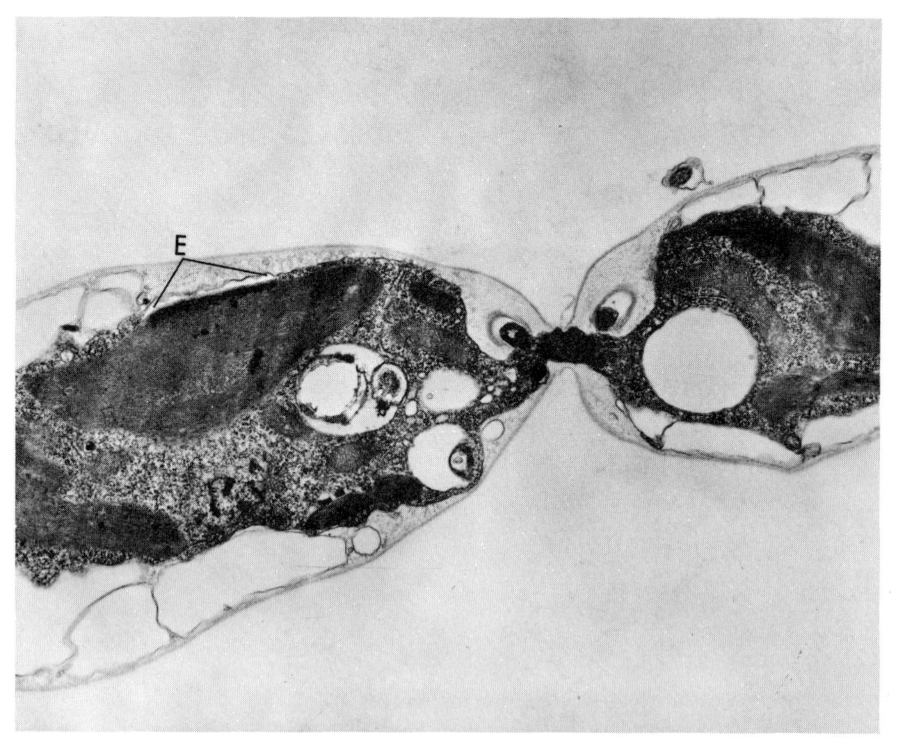

Fig. 19-23. Midstage in the union of isogametes (syngamy) of the unicellular alga *Chlamydomonas moewusii.* A cytoplasmic bridge between protoplasts has been formed near the two "eyelike" basal bodies. The large clear spaces closest to the bridge are the contractile vacuoles. The plate of dark spheres on the surface of one chloroplast, **E,** just below a clear flat vesicle is the eyespot. Eventually, the cytoplasmic bridge becomes much larger, and the two protoplasts fuse into one zygote cell. This is a later stage than that shown in Fig. 13-2. (Courtesy R. M. Brown, Sr., Clement Johnson, and H. C. Bold, University of Texas Cell Research Institute, Austin, Texas.)

exemplary lengths are a sea urchin, 45 μm; man, 56 to 81 μm; rabbit, 60 to 70 μm; cat, 70μm; dog, 70 μm; bull, 80 μm; guinea pig, 130 μm; rat, 140 μm; bandicoot, 200 μm; Chinese hamster, 250 μm; *Sciara* sp., 400 μm; and the anuran *Discoglossus,* 2,000 μm. Many insects, however, have much longer sperm. A species of *Panorpa,* for example, has sperm about 1,300 μm long. Among the longest sperm are those of the tiny ostracod Crustacea of the family Cypridae, which includes freshwater forms. One of the authors (W. V. Brown) has seen an unidentified freshwater species 2 mm in length in which the sperm were 6 mm long. Dozens of these are confined in each testis, which is no more than a third of a millimeter in length. It is recorded that the ostracod species *Pontocypris monstrosa,* itself 1 mm long, has sperm as long as 7 mm. Such sperm are about fifty times the diameter of a mature egg and about ten times the distance from the testis to the eggs during copulation. Sperm transfer and especially gametic union must be unusual processes, especially in the insect *Notonecta,* which has sperm (the longest known) 1.2 cm long. In the ostracods the female does have a complicated system, including a pair of long coiled tubes, to accomplish fertilization.

It would be anticipated that sperm length might be rather uniform within a genus, but that is not necessarily so. In *Drosophila,* sperm length ranges from 280 μm. in *D. persimilis,* to 1,800 μm (1.8 mm) in *D. melanogaster,* to 6.6 mm in *D. hydei.* In *D. hydei* the sperm of normal XY males are 6.6 mm long, whereas sperm of XYY males are twice as long, 13 to 14 mm. Similarly, XO males of *D. melanogaster* are 1.2 mm long, sperm of normal XY males are 1.8 mm long, and those of XYY males are up to 3.5 mm long. There is something about the Y chromosome that affects chromosome length (Hess and Meyer, 1968). In two species of water strider, *Gerris marginatus* has sperm 3.2 mm long and *G. remigis* has sperm more than 5 mm long.

Variations in sperm length and structure do not seem to be correlated to any other factor. Apparently any sort of sperm can work, and almost all conceivable sorts have evolved.

FERTILIZATION

Fertilization (Austin, 1965; Monroy, 1965) includes (1) the penetration of membranes by the sperm, (2) fusion of the two gamete cytoplasms *(plasmogamy)* (Fig. 19-23) in most animals and lower forms (algae and *Paramecium*), and (3) fusion of the two pronuclei. The latter process, called *karyogamy,* completes the process.

LITERATURE CITED

Cytogenetics

Arnold, J. B., and E. T. Bolton. 1967. Relatedness among plants as measured by the DNA-agar technique. Plant Physiol. **42:**959-967.

Baker, R. J. 1967. Karyotypes of bats of the family Phyllostomidae and their taxonomic implications. Southwest. Nat. **12:**407-428.

Baker, R. J., and J. L. Patton. 1967. Karyotypes and karyotypic variation in vespertilionid bats. J. Mammal. **48:**270-286.

Baldwin, J. T. 1941. Galax: the genus and its chromosomes. J. Hered. **32:**249-254.

Brown, W. V. 1946. Cytological studies in the Alismaceae. Bot. Gaz. **108:**262-267.

Brown, W. V. 1972. Textbook of cytogenetics. The C. V. Mosby Co., St. Louis.

Cleland, R. E. 1936. Some aspects of the cytogenetics of Oenothera. Bot. Rev. **2:**316-348.

Cleland, R. E. (editor). 1950. Studies in Oenothera cytogenetics and phylogeny. Indiana Univ. Publ. Sci. Ser. No. 16.

Cleveland, L. R. 1947. The origin and evolution of meiosis. Science **105:**287-289.

Collins, G. B., and R. S. Sadasivaiah. 1972. Meiotic analysis of haploid and doubled haploid forms of Nicotiana octophora and N. tabacum. Chromosoma **38:**387-404.

Gilles, A., and L. F. Randolph. 1951. Reduction of quadrivalent frequency in autotetraploid maize during a period of 10 years. Amer. J. Bot. **38:**12-17.

Granick, E. B. 1944. A karyosystematic study of the genus Agave. Amer. J. Bot. **31:**283-289.

Heneen, W. K., and H. Runemark. 1962. Chromosome polymorphism and morphological diversity in Elymus rechingeri. Hereditas **48:**545-564.

Hess, O., and G. Meyer. 1968. Genetic activities of the Y chromosome in Drosophila during spermatogenesis. Adv. Genet. **14:**171-223.

Hoyer, B. H., B. J. McCarthy, and E. T. Bolton. 1964. A molecular approach in the systematics of higher organisms. Science **144:**959-967.

Hsu, T. C., and F. E. Arrighi. 1966. Chromosomal evolution in the genus Peromyscus (Cricetidae, Rodentia). Cytogenetics **5:**355-359.

Huskins, C. L. 1931. The origin of Spartina townsendii. Genetica **12:**531-538.

Jackson, R. C. 1962. Interspecific hybridization in Haplopappus and its bearing on chromosome evolution in the Blepharodon section. Amer. J. Bot. **49:**119-132.

Jones, K. L. 1943. III. Studies on Ambrosia. Bot. Gaz. **105:**226-232.

Kimber, G., and R. Riley. 1963. Haploid angiosperms. Bot. Rev. **29:**480-531.

Lima-de-Faria, A., and H. Jaworska. 1964. Haplo-diploid chimaeras in Haplopappus gracilis. Hereditas **52:**119-122.

Maguire, M. P. 1966. The relationship of crossing over to chromosome synapsis in a short paracentric inversion. Genetics **53:**1071-1077.

Marchant, C. J. 1966. The cytology of Spartina and the origin of S. × townsendii. In C. D. Darlington, and K. R. Lewis (editors). Chromosomes today. Vol. 1. Plenum Press, Inc., New York.

Matthey, R. 1951. The chromosomes of the vertebrates. Adv. Genet. **4:**159-180.

McCarthy, B. J., and E. T. Bolton. 1963. An approach to the measurement of genetic relatedness among organisms. Proc. Nat. Acad. Sci. U.S.A. **50:**156-164.

Muller, H. J. 1927. Artificial transmutation of the gene. Science **66:**84-87.

Painter, T. S. 1933. A new method for the study of chromosome rearrangements and the plotting of chromosome maps. Science **78:**585-586.

Patterson, J. T., and W. S. Stone. 1952. Evolution in the genus Drosophila. Chap. 4. The Macmillan Co., New York.

Patton, J. L. 1967a. Chromosome studies of certain pocket mice, genus Perognathus (Rodentia: Heteromyidae). J. Mammal. **48:**27-37.

Patton, J. L. 1967b. Chromosomes and evolutionary trends in the pocket mouse subgenus Perognathus (Rodentia: Heteromyidae). Southwest. Nat. **12:**429-438.

Rhoades, M. M. 1955. The cytogenetics of maize. In G. F. Sprague (editor). Corn and corn improvement. Academic Press, Inc., New York.

Rothwell, N. V. 1959. Aneuploidy in Claytonia virginica. Amer. J. Bot. **46:**353-360.

Rothwell, N. V., and J. G. Kump. 1965. Chromosome number in populations of Claytonia virginica from the New York metropolitan area. Amer. J. Bot. **52:**403-407.

Sadasivaiah, R. S., and K. J. Kasha. 1971. Meiosis in haploid barley—an interpretation of non-homologous chromosome associations. Chromosoma **35:**247-263.

Schwartz, D. 1953. Evidence for sister-strand crossing over in maize. Genetics **38:**251-260.

Stadler, L. J. 1928. Genetic effects of X-rays in maize. Proc. Nat. Acad. Sci. U.S.A. **14:**69.

Stebbins, G. L. 1950. Variation and evolution in plants. Columbia University Press, New York.

Swanson, C. P. 1957. Cytology and cytogenetics. Prentice-Hall, Inc., Englewood Cliffs, N. J.

Swanson, C. P., T. Merz, and W. J. Young. 1967. Cytogenetics. Foundations of Modern Genetics Series. Prentice-Hall, Inc., Englewood Cliffs, N. J.

Tobgy, H. A. 1943. A cytological study of Crepis fulginosa, C. neglecta, and their F_1 hybrid, and its bearing on the mechanism of phylogenetic reduction in chromosome number. J. Genet. **45:**67-111.

White, M. J. D. 1954. Animal cytology and evolution. Cambridge University Press, New York.

Whitaker, T. W. 1934. Chromosome constitution in certain monocotyledons. J. Arnold Arb. **15:**135-143.

Reproductive cells

Austin, C. R. 1965. Fertilization. Foundations of Developmental Biology Series. Prentice-Hall, Inc., Englewood Cliffs, N. J.

Breland, O. P., et al. 1966. Certain aspects of the centriole adjunct, spermiogenesis, and the mature sperm of insects. Canad. J. Genet. Cytol. **8:**759-773.

Maheshwari, P. 1950. An introduction to the embryology of angiosperms. McGraw-Hill Book Co., New York.

Monroy, A. 1965. Chemistry and physiology of fertilization. Biology Studies Series. Holt, Rinehart & Winston, Inc., New York.

Stewart, K. D., and E. M. Gifford. 1967. Ultrastructure of the developing megaspore mother cell of Ginko biloba. Amer. J. Bot. **54:**375-383.

Index

D

T

U